ANALYSIS
OF
DECISIONS
UNDER
UNCERTAINTY

ANALYSIS OF DECISIONS UNDER UNCERTAINTY

ROBERT SCHLAIFER

Professor of Business Administration
Harvard University

McGraw-Hill Book Company

New York   St. Louis   San Francisco   London   Sydney   Toronto

Mexico   Panama

ANALYSIS
OF
DECISIONS
UNDER
UNCERTAINTY

Library of Congress Catalog Card Number 69–19203

55300

1 2 3 4 5 6 7 8 9 0   HDBP   7 6 5 4 3 2 1 0 6 9

PREFACE

This book is an introduction to logical analysis of the problems of decision under uncertainty that arise in the practice of business administration. The book is intended for readers who actually have, or expect to have, such decisions to make, not for readers who are primarily interested in mathematics or computation; and accordingly the emphasis is on logical principles rather than efficient computational techniques. Specifically, the emphasis is on (1) correct formulation of a decision problem, with special attention to correct accounting for interactions between an individual problem and the context in which it is situated, (2) understanding of the meaning of the objective and subjective inputs that are required for logical analysis of the problem, (3) understanding of the meaning of the outputs that can be obtained from such analysis, and (4) methods by which the person who is responsible for a decision can most effectively supply those inputs that can only be supplied by him or by experts to whom he delegates his responsibility. Because the decision is made under uncertainty, it must necessarily depend on the decision maker's own preferences for the possible consequences of the various courses of action he is considering, and it must necessarily depend on his own judgments, or those of his expert delegates, concerning the chances of those consequences. These preferences and judgments need not and should not be arbitrary, however—they should be based on careful consideration of all available evidence, and they should be carefully checked for internal consistency. Accordingly, particular attention is paid to methods for exploiting the available evidence and checking for consistency.

Although the present book rests on the same logical foundations as the author's earlier *Probability and Statistics for Business Decisions*,[1] the two books are almost wholly different in subject matter and approach. Whereas the earlier book was primarily concerned with decision problems in which the stakes were so small that each problem could be considered in isolation and solved by maximization of expected monetary value, the present book is primarily concerned with large-scale problems in which risk aversion must be taken into account and which cannot therefore be analyzed in isolation from other risks to which the decision maker may be exposed. Whereas the earlier book devoted very considerable attention to special methods for solving special classes of problems by use of closed formulas or published tables and charts, the present book emphasizes the use of digital computers to solve wide varieties of problems by general-purpose methods based on simple arithmetic. A number of special computer programs have been written to facilitate analysis of problems of the kind dealt with in the present book; these programs are described, listed, and documented in *Computer Programs for a First Course in Decision under Uncertainty*.[2]

Part 1 of the present book is entirely devoted to basic principles. The first three chapters show how a decision problem and its interactions with the context in which it is situated can be clearly described by a diagram or "tree", how monetary or nonmonetary values which take proper account of the interactions can usually be assigned to the possible consequences of the various courses of action that are under consideration, and how the problem can then be "decomposed" into a number of very much simpler, hypothetical decision problems that can be analyzed one at a time. The fourth chapter then shows that even these simpler problems can be still further decomposed, so that all that the decision maker really has to do is give suitable quantitative expression to (1) his preferences for the possible consequences of the courses of action he is considering, and (2) his judgments concerning the chances of the various unpredictable events that will determine what consequence he actually enjoys. By so doing, he reduces his problem to a form in which it can be analyzed by a routine application of arithmetic.

Part 2 deals with the basic methods by which a decision maker can practically arrive at quantitative expressions of his preferences for consequences and his judgments about chances with only a reasonable expenditure of time and effort, while making sure at the same time that these expressions correctly reflect not only his own most deeply held attitudes and beliefs but also all available objective evidence and expert opinion. Chapter 5 deals with assessment of preferences for consequences; Chapters 6 to 9 deal with assessment of judgments about chances and with the systematic processing of evidence and expert opinion bearing on these chances.

[1] McGraw-Hill Book Company, New York, 1959.
[2] Published by the Division of Research, Harvard Business School, Boston, Massachusetts, 02163.

Part 3 is quite different in character from Parts 1 and 2. It is devoted, not to general principles that underlie the logical analysis of any problem of decision under uncertainty, but to some special problems that may be of interest even to a businessman with no interest in technical problems as such.

All of the problems discussed in Part 3 involve the acquisition and use of information obtained by sampling or experimentation. Chapters 10 to 12 and 14 to 15, which deal with sampling and experimentation in the usual sense, are aimed primarily at showing that sampling problems are simply special cases of the general problem of decision under uncertainty; but they also contain enough information about general-purpose computer programs and tables to allow a businessman to evaluate the reliability of sample information in very simple situations without having to call in an expert. Chapter 13 deals with an analytical technique known as "simulation" which is currently of great interest to many businessmen. The main purpose of the chapter is to show that, contrary to what seems to be widespread belief, simulation does not in any sense either facilitate the formulation of a decision problem or reduce the amount of input data required for analysis of the problem. More specifically, the chapter shows that simulation is merely a way of using sampling to reduce the amount of arithmetic required to analyze a problem *after* it has been completely formulated and all necessary input data have been supplied.

The methods of analysis developed in the present book are formally applicable only to "short-term" decision problems in which the passage of time plays no essential role. But even though logically sound methods for analysis of most problems in which time does play an essential role are a subject more for research than for an elementary or even an advanced text, there is one special class of problems involving the passage of time to which the methods developed in the present text can easily be extended. The problems in question are those in which (1) there is no material interaction between the decision problem immediately at hand and the context in which it is situated, and (2) expected monetary value is an acceptable guide to action. When both these conditions are satisfied, it seems usually legitimate to reduce future cash flows to present equivalents by discounting at a rate which does not depend on the amount discounted; and when such a reduction is legitimate, the problem can be analyzed as if all consequences were immediate.

To facilitate study of problems of the kind just described, some supplementary "technical notes" and special tables of compound interest were prepared at the same time that the present text was being developed. All these materials can be obtained from the Intercollegiate Case Clearing House;[3] the titles and stock numbers are as follows:

Compound Interest, ICH 13C1.

Tables of Compound Interest, ICH 13C2.

[3] Boston, Massachusetts, 02163.

Effect of Depreciation Allowances on Cash Flows Associated with Income Taxes, ICH 13C3.

Some Problems in Inventory Control, ICH 13C4.

Taken by themselves, the text and exercises of the present book would be seriously inadequate as even a first introduction to the analysis of decisions under uncertainty. No matter how well a person has learned basic principles and their use in solving clearly structured exercises, he will usually be unable to structure even a quite simple real-world problem until he has had experience with a number of realistic cases. The present text was, in fact, developed primarily as an aid to the teaching of a number of cases written specially for a first course in decision under uncertainty at the Harvard Business School. All these cases can be obtained from the Intercollegiate Case Clearing House; their names, authors, and stock numbers are as follows:

Rositex Company, by A. S. Kahr and S. I. Buchin, ICH 12C19.

The Davison Press, Inc., by A. S. Kahr, ICH 12C20.

Art and Science of Competitive Bidding, abridged from an article by Franz Edelman, ICH 12C21.

Caroline Development Corporation, by A. Schleifer, ICH 12C22 and 12C23.

AFG Textile Corporation (A) and (B), by A. S. Kahr, ICH 12C24 and 12C25.

Gray Cap and Closure Company (A) and (B), by S. I. Buchin, A. Schleifer, and R. Glauber, ICH 12C26 and 12C27.

Hooker Grinding Wheel Company and *Supplement*, by S. I. Buchin, ICH 10C57R and 10C57RS.

Two further pieces of supplementary material are available to teachers only. The *Teacher's Manual* contains detailed solutions of all the exercises that appear in the present book together with some suggestions concerning the handling of the text and exercises in the classroom. The *Manual of Cases on Decision under Uncertainty* contains a copy of each of the longer cases listed above together with a detailed analysis of the case and a teaching note with suggestions concerning the amount of class time required to discuss the case and assignments to guide the students' preparation of the case. Both these manuals are published by the publisher of the present book.[4]

---

[4] Qualified persons should order these manuals, not through ordinary commercial channels, but by writing to the Business and Economics Editor, College Division, McGraw-Hill Book Company, 330 West 42nd Street, New York 10036.

The contents and organization of this book reflect experience gained by the author and many of his colleagues in teaching four successive classes of 700 first-year students at the Harvard Business School. Whether or not the conclusions reached by the author as a result of this experience are correct, the reasons for some of the resulting peculiarities may be of interest to a teacher who considers using the book as a classroom text.

The discussion of formulation of decision problems in the first three chapters is entirely in terms of the general case, where it is not assumed either that expected monetary value is a valid guide to action or that the problem at hand can be analyzed in isolation from the context in which it is situated. The subject could obviously be made to seem much easier if one began with problems in which both these assumptions are made, but one year's experience with this approach seems to the author to have made it clear that in the long run it does not pay. It is true that students who have started by learning to compute expected monetary value mechanically can be taught easily enough to compute expected preference mechanically when they are given someone else's preference function, but it is much harder to teach them always to ask whether the decision maker's—or even their own—preferences would really be linear in any given situation. And what is even more serious, students who start by accepting without question the very simple problem formulations that are valid when preference is linear almost never really learn that these simple formulations are valid only in very special circumstances. In the long run, it is easier to exclude the special case until the students have become thoroughly familiar with the general case; and accordingly the simplified formulations and analyses that are possible when expected monetary value is relevant and there is no interaction between a problem and its context are not introduced until the end of Chapter 5.

For essentially the same reason, the method of analysis that is described in the first three chapters is based on directly assessed certainty equivalents for uncertain values of a *numéraire*; the two standard tools of decision analysis, probability and preference (or "utility"), are not introduced until Chapter 4, after the basic principles of problem formulation have been completely discussed. It would of course be much easier to impress the students with the power of decision theory if probability and preference were introduced almost at the start, but what would be gained would be bought at too high a price. The important thing to teach is not the mechanics of the calculations by which a problem is solved but the nature and meaning of the assessments that are the inputs to these calculations; and the author for one believes that these essentials can be taught most effectively by insisting for some time on the meaning and relevance of directly assessed certainty equivalents.

When probability and preference are finally introduced in Chapter 4, they are presented as a way of decomposing the assessment of certainty equivalents; the fact that expected preference can be used directly as a criterion for choice among courses of action is left to the students to discover for themselves. In principle, this approach entails a substantial loss of generality, since it does not bring out the fact that preferences can be assessed and problems can be analyzed by computation of expected preference even when consequences have not been valued in terms of a monetary or other *numéraire*. In practice, however, there are certainly very few if any real decision problems in which it would be feasible to assess preferences for consequences without first valuing the consequences in terms of a *numéraire*, and pedagogically it seems much better to emphasize the basic similarity rather than the apparent difference between analysis based on probability and preference and analysis based on directly assessed certainty equivalents.

Perhaps this is the place to explain why the word "preference" is used throughout instead of "utility". The reason is simply that if the word "utility" is used, a very great deal of time must be devoted to explaining what the word does *not* mean. The word "preference", on the contrary, seems to have almost no false connotations for the student, so that the only problem is to explain what the word does mean. The term "uncertain quantity" is used instead of "random variable" for a similar reason.

The discussion in Chapter 5 of methods for assessing preferences for values of a *numéraire* does not, of course, pretend to be anything like complete. The objective of the discussion is rather simply to show that a businessman *can* assess a reasonable set of preferences with a reasonable amount of effort and that he can detect and reconcile many inconsistencies in his own attitudes in the process of doing so. The demonstration that this can be done when the businessman's preference function is everywhere decreasingly risk averse should suffice to convince a reasonable person that it can also be done when the function has other well defined overall properties.

The one purely technical chapter in Parts 1 and 2 is the long discussion in Chapter 7 of probability distributions, functions, and expectations. It would be nice if much of this material could be eliminated, since much of it is of no direct interest to the readers for whom this book is intended, but again the gain would seem to come at too high a price. Much of the material on description of probability distributions is essential to the discussion in Chapter 8 of the assessment of distributions, a subject that *is* of importance to the businessman. The material on "grouped approximations" to distributions—i.e., on simple numerical integration—is of no interest in itself, but if this material were omitted, it would be very difficult even to explain to students how problems involving uncertain quantities with quasi-continuous distributions can be analyzed, let alone give students any direct experience with the analysis of such problems. Finally, the subject of linear functions usually gives trouble in class, but to the author at least it seems absolutely essential. The real objective of this section is not to teach students to use the shortcuts that are permissible when functions are linear; it is to teach them not to use shortcuts that are not permissible when functions are not linear. If the minds of arriving students were *tabulae rasae*, this material could and should be omitted from a book of this sort. They are not, however, and consequently avoiding discussion of linear versus nonlinear functions amounts to burying one's head in the sand.

The last peculiarity of organization worth mentioning is the placement of the discussion of independence in Chapter 9. The distinction between the two "obviously" quite different concepts of dependence and conditionality is not at all obvious to the majority of the students with whom the author and his colleagues have had experience, and it is in the hope of getting these two concepts straight that as much space as possible has been left between the introduction of the distinction between conditional and unconditional distributions and the distinction between dependent and independent uncertain quantities.

As has already been said, the topics in sampling and simulation which make up Part 3 of the book are nothing but a set of special applications of the basic methods for assessment of probabilities that are developed in Part 2, and for this reason it can be and has been argued that the subject is of interest only to the specialist, not to the businessman. A good deal of experience shows, however, that this argument is unsound. No matter how well he has understood the principles of conditional and joint probabilities as presented in Chapter 9, it ordinarily simply does not occur to a person who wishes to know what "inferences" he can draw from a sample that his problem can be solved by a routine application of these principles. And even after he has learned that this is true when the sampling process is unbiassed, it ordinarily does not occur to him that he can allow for his doubts about unbiassedness by another routine application of these same general principles.

A reader who is interested in sampling but not in simulation can read Chapters 14 and 15 without reading Chapter 13, and Chapter 15 can be read without previously reading Chapter 14. A reader who wishes only an introduction to the basic principles involved in the interpretation of sample evidence can stop with Chapter 12, or even with Chapter 10.

At the same time that the author must take responsibility for the many serious imperfections this book contains, he must recognize that much of what is good in the book is due to others. The present version of the book incorporates innumerable improvements in organization and presentation that were first suggested by other members of the faculty of the Harvard Business School who have taught from earlier versions during the past four years. The contributions of Professors Charles Christenson, Alfred Conrad, Robert Glauber, Richard Meyer, and Arthur Schleifer were especially important.

Most of the short cases and exercises that appear in the book are due to persons other than the author of the book. The cases *Waggoner Engineering Corporation* and *National Grain Corporation* were written by Professor Andrew

Kahr, *Morgan Metal Products, Inc.* by Professor Robert Hayes, *Science Books, Inc.* by Professor Gordon Kaufman, now of the Massachusetts Institute of Technology. More than half of the exercises are due to Professor Glauber, many others to Professor Kahr, one of the best to Dr. Rex Brown. Table T1 of the binomial mass function was computed and edited by Professor Stanley Buchin, Table T3 of the fractiles of the beta distribution by Professor Schleifer with the assistance of Mr. James Dolben.

Finally, the author must mention particularly his debt to Professor Andrew Kahr, whose penetrating criticisms of each of the first three versions of the book led not merely to major changes in its contents and organization but to major changes in the author's own views on the subject matter, particularly as regards questions of problem formulation.

Robert Schlaifer

CONTENTS

PART
1

FOUNDATIONS

CHAPTER

1

SYSTEMATIC ANALYSIS OF DECISIONS UNDER UNCERTAINTY: AN EXAMPLE

Virtually all important business decisions are made under uncertainty. The responsible executive must choose one definite course of action among all those open to him, even though the consequences of some if not all of the possible courses of action will depend on events that cannot be predicted with certainty. The desirability of each possible course of action usually depends on a great variety of factors, some bearing on the chances that various possible events will occur, others on the consequences that will result if certain events do occur, and still others on the desirability or undesirability of these consequences. Because it is almost impossible to take reasoned account of all these factors simultaneously, the businessman would like to be able to *decompose* his decision problem and think through the implications of one set of factors at a time.

Decomposition of a decision problem is easy and common in situations where no material uncertainties are present. A businessman will, for example, figure out separately the cost of tooling up to produce a special item, the "incremental" cost per unit produced, the number of units that can be sold, and the sales revenue that will result; and he will then combine the results of these partial analyses in order to decide whether he should market the product or not. It is, of course, much harder to decompose a decision problem and recombine the results of the partial analyses when every part of the problem is surrounded by material uncertainty; but it is nevertheless possible and useful to do so. The objective of this book is to show how.

In the first four chapters we shall be concerned only with expounding the basic principles of the method of analysis with which the book is concerned, paying almost no attention to the practical difficulties that may arise in applying these basic principles to the complex decision problems that are actually encountered in business. Ways of surmounting these practical difficulties will constitute the subject of the remainder of the book.

This organization should be kept constantly in mind while reading the first four chapters. On the one hand, the fact that in them we illustrate logical principles by painstaking analysis of "decision problems" which are so simple as to require no analysis at all does not mean that the book will be devoted to trivialities. When the reader has become sufficiently familiar with the basic principles through applying them to extremely simple examples, we shall show by text and cases how to apply them to real decision problems. On the other hand, when we say or imply that a businessman should give carefully thought-out answers to hundreds or thousands of separate questions, the reader should not assume that we are really asking the impossible. Later in the book we shall describe methods by which the businessman can arrive at reasonable answers to all these questions with only a reasonable expenditure of effort.

In the present Chapter 1, we shall merely suggest by way of an example how a businessman faced with a problem of decision under uncertainty can:

1 Describe the problem in a way which puts immediately before him all the possible courses of action, all the possible events which may affect the consequences of these courses of action, and all the relevant factual data required to evaluate each possible consequence.

2 Decompose the problem into a number of separate subproblems, analyze these subproblems separately, and then infer from the results of these partial analyses what course of action he should choose in his main problem.

The basic principles of analysis that are suggested by this example will then be stated and discussed systematically in Chapter 2.

A general orientation to the main ideas in this chapter can be obtained by reading rapidly as far as the end of Section 1.2.4, omitting the remainder of the chapter. The text and exercises can then be studied in detail in the following order:

1 Sections 1.1.1–1.1.2 and Exercises 1.1–1.2.

2 Sections 1.1.3–1.1.6 and Exercises 1.3–1.4.

3 Section 1.2.1 and Exercises 1.5–1.10.

4 Sections 1.2.2–1.2.6 and Exercise 1.11.

5 Sections 1.3.1–1.3.4 and Exercise 1.12.

CONTENTS OF CHAPTER 1

1.1
DESCRIPTION OF A SIMPLE PROBLEM
OF DECISION UNDER UNCERTAINTY

1.1.1
Statement of the Problem

On September 18, 1968, Mr. A. H. Mallon, the president of ABC Controls, Inc., was informed by his sales manager that if he will build a prototype control unit of a special type at ABC's expense and submit it for test by the XYZ Chemical Corporation, he may succeed in getting the quantity order for 5,000 units that XYZ will place with some supplier on November 1 for delivery and payment in full on December 31. The XYZ company needs these 5,000 units for use in a new plant that is nearing completion. XYZ had originally intended to purchase units of the kind used in its existing plant, for which it would pay $25 each in a quantity of 5,000; but following a presentation by a sales engineer from ABC, XYZ has agreed that if ABC will supply one prototype unit as a sample, XYZ will test this unit in competition with a unit of the type currently in use and will buy the entire quantity of 5,000 units from ABC at $25 each if the ABC prototype proves better on test. ABC will of course have to guarantee that the production units will meet the performance standards set by the prototype.

On being informed of these facts by his sales manager, Mr. Mallon immediately consulted his chief design engineer and was told that there is a fair chance, although by no means a certainty, that ABC can actually design and produce a unit which will outperform a control of the type currently used by XYZ. Design of the proposed unit will cost about $2,500, and production of a single prototype without production jigs and fixtures will cost another $2,500.

Mallon next asked his chief production engineer what it would cost to manufacture the 5,000 production units if the order was actually received from XYZ. Using the design engineer's preliminary sketches as a basis for his calculations, the production engineer replied that if the 5,000 production units are manufactured using machined parts throughout, as in the prototype, tooling will cost about $10,000 and the incremental cost of each unit produced will be about $19 for material, labor, and variable overhead. There is no doubt that units produced in this way will perform at least as well as the handmade prototype. By substituting stampings for some of the machined parts in the unit, incremental production costs can be lowered to about $16.40 per unit, but an attempt to use stampings will require an investment of about $6,000 in dies and will reduce the cost of other tooling by only some $2,000, making a net additional investment of $4,000; and only after this additional investment has been made will it be possible to determine whether units with stamped parts can in fact match the performance of the prototype. As of now, the production engineer can say only that stamped parts have succeeded in some designs but failed in others, although he does feel sure that if stampings are tried and fail on this occasion, there will be plenty of time left to switch over and meet the December 31 deadline with units built with all machined parts.

Having thus determined the possible direct effects of the XYZ proposition on his profits, Mallon next called in his production manager and his treasurer and asked them to evaluate the possible effects of the proposition on ABC's other business. After a careful study of schedules and shop capacity, the treasurer reported that while building the prototype will have no unfavorable side effects, filling a quantity order with either machined or stamped parts will make it necessary to refuse a certain amount of subcontract business that would otherwise be scheduled for November and December. If this happens, the total net contribution to overhead and profit that ABC realizes between now and December 31 on business with customers other than XYZ will be reduced from about $10,000 to about $5,000.

To summarize, ABC will have to lay out $5,000 cash between September 18 and November 1 to produce a prototype for which XYZ will pay nothing. If this prototype leads to a production order, XYZ will pay ABC 5,000 × $25 = $125,000 cash on December 31, but against this ABC will have to set its cash outlays for tooling and direct production costs. If ABC chooses to produce with all machined parts, tooling will require a cash outlay of $10,000, and incremental production costs will lead to laying out another 5,000 × $19.00 = $95,000. If ABC chooses to try stampings, the initial tooling will require a cash outlay of $14,000; if the stampings work, the only further outlay will be 5,000 × $16.40 = $82,000 for direct production costs; but if the stampings fail, ABC will have to lay out $2,000 for the additional tooling required to produce with all machined parts plus $95,000 for direct production costs. Besides entailing these direct costs, production of a quantity order for XYZ will reduce the cash contribution realized by ABC between now and December 31 on business with other customers from about $10,000 to about $5,000.

1.1.2
The Logical Structure of the Problem

Even this very simple decision problem suffices to illustrate a complexity that is characteristic of the majority of decision problems actually encountered in business, namely: it is usually impossible to think through a decision that must be made now without at the same time thinking through some decision or decisions that may have to be made at some time in the future. In our example, Mallon's only immediate problem is to decide whether or not to spend $5,000 on building a prototype; but since his only incentive for building a prototype is the fact that it may lead to a profitable production order, he cannot think through his immediate problem without evaluating the profit that will result from a production order. And since the profit that will result from a production order will depend on whether or not he decides to try to use stampings in filling this order, he cannot think through his immediate problem without also thinking through the problem concerning stampings that he may face later on.

What this means, of course, is that if Mallon tries to make a *direct* attack on his immediate problem of deciding whether or not to spend $5,000 on a prototype, he will have to keep in mind simultaneously all the factors involved in *both* decision problems, namely the chance that the prototype will not lead to a production order, the $5,000 loss that he will suffer if it does not, the chance that the prototype will on the contrary actually lead to a production order, the profit that he will make if he then decides not to try stampings, the chance that stampings will work if he tries them, the profit he will make if he tries them and they do work, the chance that they will not work, and the profit he will make if he tries them and they do not work.

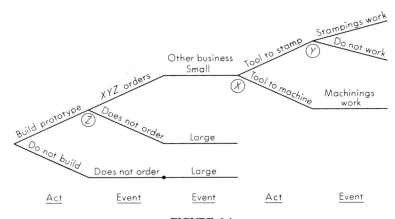

FIGURE 1.1
Possible Acts and Events

The logical structure of Mallon's complete problem can be represented diagrammatically in the way shown in Figure 1.1.   As of now, Mallon stands at the ≪origin≫[1] of the diagram—i.e., at the base of the ≪fork≫ at the extreme left of the diagram—and must decide whether to proceed along the upper ≪branch≫ emanating from this ≪position≫ (i.e., to choose the ≪act≫ "build prototype") or along the lower branch (i.e., to choose the act "do not build").

If Mallon chooses the lower branch, the decision problem ends, but if he chooses the upper branch and goes to position Z, he must next wait to see whether "chance" takes him on along the branch representing the ≪event≫ "XYZ orders" (5,000 production units) or along the branch representing the event "XYZ does not order".

If the event that occurs is "XYZ does not order", the decision problem ends, but if the event that occurs is "XYZ orders", Mallon will arrive at position X in the diagram with a choice to make between the act represented by the lower branch emanating from X (tool for production with all machined parts) and the act represented by the upper branch emanating from X (tool for production using stampings).

If Mallon chooses the lower branch at X, the decision problem ends because the production units are sure to be satisfactory, as is indicated by the fact that a single branch labelled "machinings work" emanates from the end of the branch "tool to machine".   If, however, Mallon chooses the upper branch at X and goes to position Y, then it is an uncertain event that will determine how the decision problem ends.   Either the stampings will work, or they will fail and Mallon will have to produce with all machined parts.

---

[1] The special brackets surrounding certain words in this paragraph and later in the text indicate that these words are important technical terms to whose meaning the reader should pay careful attention whether or not a formal definition is given.

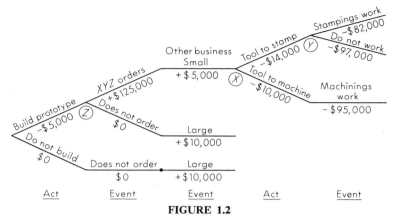

FIGURE 1.2

Partial Cash Flows due to Individual Acts and Events

1.1.3
Cash Flows due to Individual
Acts and Events

Although Figure 1.1 is of some use as it stands in helping Mallon to keep in mind the logical structure of his decision problem, it can be made much more useful by simply writing down on each branch the cash outflow or inflow that will result from the act or event represented by that branch. This is done in Figure 1.2, where all the numerical values are taken from the summary at the end of Section 1.1.1 above. The cash flows on the branches of a figure like this one will be called ≪partial cash flows≫ in order to distinguish them from the "total" cash flows that will be discussed in the next section.

Three points should be noticed particularly in Figure 1.2.

1. The figure − $95,000 on the branch for "machinings work" represents the cash outlay for only the "variable" part of the cost of production with machined parts, the cash outlay for tooling having been shown on the preceding branch; and similarly for the − $82,000 on the branch for "stampings work". The figure − $97,000 on the branch for "stampings do not work" must, on the contrary, include not only − $95,000 for direct production costs but also − $2,000 for the additional tooling that will be required because the event "stampings do not work" occurs; the only tooling outlays that can be shown on the branch for the act "tool to stamp" are those that are *sure* to result from this act.

2. Because Mallon feels sure that if he receives a quantity order he will succeed in filling it in one way or another, he can write down the $125,000 sales revenue that will result from filling the order as soon as he gets to the branch "XYZ orders". Similarly, he can write down the $5,000 or $10,000 net contribution from "other" business immediately after any branch representing either "XYZ orders" or "XYZ does not order", since even though this contribution

will not be completely realized until December 31, he knows how much it will be as soon as he knows whether or not XYZ orders. *Partial cash flows appear on a decision diagram in the order in which they become known to the decision maker, not necessarily in the order in which they will actually occur.*

 3. This last statement does not imply, however, that the dates at which cash flows will actually occur are necessarily of no importance. Because Mallon cannot actually collect $125,000 from XYZ until after he has built a prototype and filled a quantity order, it may be that he will have to resort to bank loans to cover some or all of the cash outlays required to produce the prototype and/or to fill a quantity order; and if this is true, the amount of interest that will be paid should have been added to the corresponding direct costs in Figure 1.2. It is really only in order to keep the example as simple as possible that we shall assume in what follows that Mallon is willing to disregard these interest costs as being too small to be of any practical importance in the problem he is facing.

1.1.4
Cash Flows due to Act-event Sequences

Figure 1.2 shows all the data that are essential to Mallon's decision problem, but it shows these data in a form which is awkward to use. When Mallon considers, for example, that building a prototype may lead to a quantity order which he may fill by tooling to produce with all machined parts, he will certaintly want to know the financial implications of this ≪act-event sequence≫; but once the details of these financial implications have been correctly figured out, Mallon will no longer be interested in the details as such. All that he will really want to know is that the *net* amount of the positive and negative partial cash flows resulting from the sequence is +$20,000.

 More generally, Mallon will want to know the net ≪total cash flow≫ that will result from every possible act-event sequence in his decision problem, and this information can easily be added to a diagram like Figure 1.2. Because every possible act-event sequence is represented by a ≪path≫ from the origin of the diagram to an ≪end position≫, all that Mallon has to do is take every end position in turn, compute the algebraic sum of the cash flows on the branches that make up the path from the origin to the end position in question, and write down this sum opposite the end position.

 This has been done in Figure 1.3, where the total cash flow corresponding to each end position is circled. Because these total cash flows contain all the *relevant* information that was provided by the partial cash flows on the individual branches of Figure 1.2, the partial cash flows are not shown in Figure 1.3.

1.1.5
Final Valuation of Consequences

Although the total cash flows in Figure 1.3 completely describe the financial consequences that will result from every possible act-event sequence in Mallon's

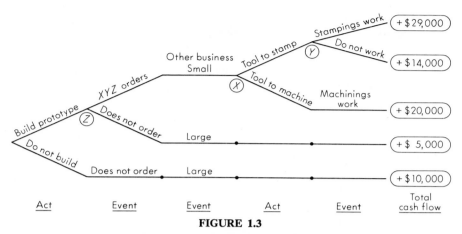

FIGURE 1.3

Total Cash Flows due to Act-event Sequences

decision problem, Mallon will very probably do well to replace even these figures by others before he sets out actually to analyze his problem.

To see why, let us simplify the problem for a moment by assuming contrary to fact that Mallon feels sure that stampings will work and therefore does not want even to consider either the alternative of producing with all machined parts or the possibility that stampings will fail. In this hypothetical case, a diagram of his problem would have the very simple form shown in Figure 1.4, where a total cash flow of +$29,000 can be shown immediately at the end of the branch for "XYZ orders" because everything beyond that point is certain; and looking at the diagram, Mallon would see immediately that his choice was between (1) a certainty of a +$10,000 total cash flow, and (2) a ≪gamble≫ which would result in a total cash flow of either +$5,000 or +$29,000.

Before making a choice, Mallon would of course ask his engineers for their opinions and for all available data bearing on the chance that the prototype will be successful enough to lead to a quantity order; but this is not the only factor that Mallon would want to consider. For suppose by way of example that Mallon decides that there is about an even chance that ABC will get the

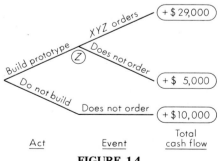

FIGURE 1.4

Problem if Mallon Were Sure that Stampings Will Work

quantity order if the prototype is built. If ABC has a large amount of idle cash in the bank, Mallon might well decide to take the gamble (build a prototype), arguing that an even chance of earning $29,000 cash instead of $10,000 more than outweighs an equal chance of earning only $5,000 instead of $10,000. If, on the contrary, ABC is desperately short of cash and has a sizable bank loan that will fall due very shortly, Mallon might well decide to refuse the gamble, arguing that he could not afford to take even a small chance, let alone an even chance, of reducing his cash earnings from $10,000 to $5,000 in order to have a chance of increasing them from $10,000 to $29,000.

Generalizing from this example, we see that Mallon's decisions in any problem involving uncertainty will really depend, not on the possible total cash *flows* as such, but on the possible financial *positions* in which he may find himself as a result of these total cash flows. And even though Mallon can analyze his real decision problem by mentally translating each total cash flow in Figure 1.3 into a description of the financial position that will result from that total cash flow, his analysis will be facilitated if the diagram is altered to show at each end position, not the corresponding total cash flow as such, but some direct measure of the financial position that will result from that flow.

Suppose, then, that Mallon feels that to him the most salient or meaningful measure or «criterion» of his financial position is the amount of his «net liquid assets», defined as his cash on hand plus all financial claims that he will collect in the short run (e.g., receivables) minus all financial claims that he will have to pay in the short run (e.g., payables and short-term bank loans); and suppose further that as of now Mallon is in fact in a very tight financial position with net liquid assets of $-\$4,000$—his short-term debts exceed the sum of his cash and receivables by $4,000. By simply adding $-\$4,000$ to every total cash flow in Figure 1.3 we can make the diagram show directly the net liquid assets that Mallon will have on December 31 as a result of any possible act-event sequence in the decision problem before him. The result is the diagram shown as Figure 1.5.

1.1.6
Synchronization of the Values
of the End Positions

The reader will have remarked that all the total cash flows in Figure 1.3 and all the criterion values in Figure 1.5 appear at the same horizontal distance from the origin of the diagram, some meaningless or "dummy" branches having been included in the diagram to make this possible. This is done to symbolize the fact that all these values are evaluated as of the same point in time, namely December 31, 1968; and it is worth emphasizing that the values attached to the end positions of a decision diagram *must* be synchronized if they are to be useful parts of the description of a decision problem. It would be extremely difficult, if not impossible, for any businessman to make a *direct* comparison between,

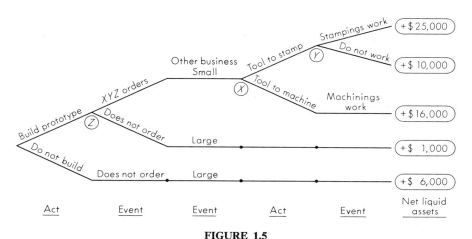

FIGURE 1.5

Final Description of A. H. Mallon's Decision Problem

say, one alternative which will leave him with net liquid assets of $17,000 two years hence and another which will leave him with either $12,000 now or $22,000 five years hence.

The common date (December 31, 1968) as of which Mallon evaluates his criterion (net liquid assets) at every end position of his decision diagram will be called his ≪evaluation date≫ for description of his decision problem. The amount of his net liquid assets at any end position will be called the ≪terminal value≫ of his criterion at that end position.

1.2
ANALYSIS OF THE PROBLEM

If Mallon puts himself at the origin of Figure 1.5 and looks at the possible consequences of the two acts between which he must choose now, "build prototype" and "do not build", he will see that although the act "do not build" is sure to result in a terminal value of +$6,000, the consequence of the act "build" is uncertain because he does not know (1) whether XYZ will or will not give ABC the quantity order, (2) whether if XYZ does give ABC the quantity order he will or will not try to use stampings in filling it, and (3) whether if he does try to use stampings, the stampings will or will not prove satisfactory. What we shall now show is that:

■ If Mallon will consider these three sources of uncertainty in reverse order and make one simple decision concerning each of them separately, he will be able to infer from these decisions whether he should find the complex gamble that results from the act "build prototype" more or less attractive than the known consequence of the act "do not build".

1.2.1
A Hypothetical Insurance Contract

To explain the nature of the first of the simple decisions that we shall ask Mallon to make, let us suppose that, *before* knowing whether or not he will actually build the prototype, let alone whether he will receive a quantity order from XYZ or try to fill it by use of stampings, Mallon is approached by an insurer named Jones with an offer of an insurance contract the terms of which are as follows:

1 Jones agrees that if as a result of an unsuccessful attempt to use stampings Mallon's net liquid assets on December 31 are less than $+\$20,000$, Jones will hand over to Mallon enough cash to raise them to exactly $+\$20,000$.

2 Mallon agrees that if as a result of a successful attempt to use stampings his net liquid assets on December 31 are greater than $+\$20,000$, he will hand over to Jones the entire excess above $+\$20,000$.

3 If Mallon never tries to use stampings, neither Jones nor Mallon will pay the other anything.

Observe that, from Mallon's point of view, signing this insurance contract is equivalent to agreeing now that if and when he reaches position Y in Figure 1.5 he will exchange his rights to the uncertain terminal value that will actually result from the gamble on stampings for a guaranteed terminal value of $+\$20,000$,

Now Mallon can presumably decide whether or not he would be willing to sign this proposed contract, just as he can decide whether or not to sign any more usual form of insurance contract. But if Mallon can decide whether or not he would be willing to agree to exchange the uncertain terminal value he will face at Y for a guaranteed $+\$20,000$, then he can also decide whether or not he would be willing to agree to exchange that uncertain value for any other guaranteed value that might be named. And if Mallon can make a decision of this sort concerning any particular guaranteed terminal value, then he can also decide what is the *smallest* guaranteed terminal value that he would be willing to agree to accept upon reaching position Y. He can decide, in other words, what guaranteed terminal value he would be ≪just willing≫ to agree to accept upon reaching position Y; and because he is *just* willing to accept this guaranteed value in lieu of the uncertain value he will actually face at position Y, we may assume that this guaranteed value is *exactly as attractive to him* as the uncertain value he will actually face.

1.2.2
The First Simple Decision

We can now describe the first of the simple decisions that Mallon must make if he wishes to solve the prototype problem by decomposition. To set the stage

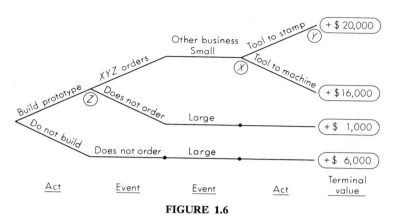

FIGURE 1.6

First Simplification of A. H. Mallon's Decision Problem

for the decision, we ask Mallon to imagine that Jones approaches him at this very moment with an offer to negotiate an insurance contract that will amount to replacing the uncertain terminal value at position Y in Figure 1.5 by a guaranteed terminal value, the actual amount of this guaranteed value being still open to bargaining between Mallon and Jones. Then after reminding Mallon that such a contract will be desirable if the guaranteed terminal value is close enough to the $+\$25,000$ which is the best he can do if he refuses the contract, and that it will be undesirable if the guaranteed terminal value is too close to the $+\$10,000$ which is the worst he can do if he refuses the contract, we ask Mallon to decide what guaranteed terminal value would leave him completely indifferent between accepting and refusing the contract. More briefly, we say that:

■ Mallon should decide what guaranteed terminal value he would be just willing to agree now to accept if and when he reaches position Y in lieu of the uncertain terminal value that he will actually face in that position.

To see how this decision will contribute to a solution of the prototype problem, suppose that Mallon's answer is $+\$20,000$—he decides that this is the borderline between the guaranteed terminal values that he would refuse and the guaranteed terminal values that he would really want to accept if he could not persuade Jones to go any higher. We can then argue that since the gamble Mallon will actually face if he reaches position Y in Figure 1.5 is exactly as attractive to him as a guaranteed terminal value of $+\$20,000$, we will in no way alter the attractiveness to Mallon of any act that will or may lead to position Y if we simply replace the gamble at this position by a terminal value of $+\$20,000$, as we have done in Figure 1.6. *Mallon can properly decide what acts to choose in the real decision problem of Figure 1.5 by deciding what acts he would prefer in the simpler substitute problem of Figure 1.6.*

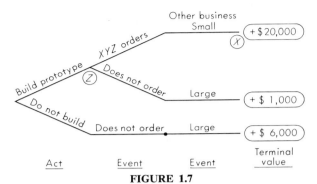

FIGURE 1.7
Second Simplification of A. H. Mallon's Decision Problem

1.2.3
The Second Simple Decision

The advantage of working with Figure 1.6 instead of Figure 1.5 is even greater than it appears at first glance. Because both the available acts at position X in the substitute problem of Figure 1.6 will result in known terminal values, we do not have to ask Mallon what act he would be willing to agree now to choose if and when he reaches position X in that figure. He would agree to choose the act resulting in the greater terminal value, $+\$20,000$, and therefore the problem of deciding on the prototype can be reduced to the still simpler form shown in Figure 1.7.

1.2.4
The Third Simple Decision

The third simple decision that Mallon must make in order to solve his prototype problem is of exactly the same type as the first.

■ Mallon must decide what guaranteed terminal value he would be just willing to agree now to accept if and when he reaches position Z in Figure 1.7 in lieu of the uncertain terminal value that he will actually face in that position, i.e., if and when he has already committed himself to build a prototype but does not yet know whether XYZ will order.

If now Mallon decides, for example, that he would not care whether or not he negotiated a deal that replaced the gamble at Z in Figure 1.7 by a guaranteed terminal value of $+\$9,000$, then the act "build prototype" must be exactly as attractive to Mallon as it would be if it were sure to result in a terminal value of $+\$9,000$; and therefore Mallon can solve the decision problem of Figure 1.7 by solving the still simpler decision problem of Figure 1.8.

The hypothetical decision problem of Figure 1.8 can of course be solved by merely observing that an act which results in a terminal value of $+\$9,000$ is obviously preferable to an act which results in a terminal value of only $+\$6,000$. And since Mallon's three previous hypothetical decisions imply that the con-

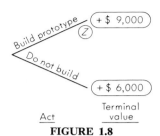

FIGURE 1.8
Third Simplification of A. H. Mallon's Decision Problem

sequences of the acts in Figure 1.8 are exactly as attractive to him as the consequences of those same acts in his real decision problem, we conclude that *the decisions which Mallon has reached in his four simple, hypothetical decision problems imply that he should build the prototype in his real decision problem.*

1.2.5
Certainty Equivalents

Although Mallon had to make four decisions in all in order to solve his prototype decision problem, two of these decisions—the two choices between acts—were completely "automatic". The two decisions that required real thought on Mallon's part were the decisions concerning insurance contracts by means of which he reduced Figure 1.5 to Figure 1.6 and reduced Figure 1.7 to Figure 1.8, and therefore we shall now go back and look at the way in which Mallon might have reasoned in reaching these two latter decisions.

When Mallon sets out to decide what guaranteed terminal value is exactly as attractive to him as the uncertain terminal value that will result from the gamble on stampings at position Y in Figure 1.5, he will probably start by taking some one, specific terminal value, say $+\$18,000$, and asking himself whether he prefers that terminal value to the gamble or vice versa.

In making this decision, Mallon will want to take two quite different kinds of considerations into account: (1) the chances of the two possible events, "stampings work" and "do not work", one of which will determine his terminal value if he does not choose the guaranteed $+\$18,000$, and (2) his own degree of liking for a $+\$18,000$ terminal value relative to the two terminal values, $+\$25,000$ and $+\$10,000$, that may result from the gamble.

As regards the chances of the events, he will as we said earlier consider all available data bearing on the suitability of stampings for the purpose at hand, and he will consult his engineers for their opinions on the way in which the peculiarities of this particular design affect the question. As regards his degree of liking for each of the possible terminal values, he will certainly consider the probable effects of each of them on the future operations of his business, and he may want to reflect on other kinds of effects as well.

If after duly reflecting on all these factors Mallon decides that he definitely prefers the uncertain terminal value that will result from the gamble to a guaranteed terminal value of only $+\$18,000$, he can repeat the procedure for some larger guaranteed terminal value, say $+\$22,000$. If this time he decides that he definitely prefers the certainty to the uncertain terminal value, he can try again with some guaranteed terminal value between $+\$22,000$ and $+\$18,000$; and by repeatedly narrowing the range in this way he can ultimately arrive at a guaranteed terminal value that he would be "just" willing to accept because it seems to him neither more nor less attractive than the uncertain terminal value that will result from the gamble. We have supposed that the figure he finally arrives at is $+\$20,000$; henceforth we shall refer to this equally attractive guaranteed terminal value as Mallon's ≪certainty equivalent≫ for the uncertain terminal value that will result from the stampings gamble.

Very probably Mallon will not find it at all easy to decide on his certainty equivalent for either the uncertain terminal value that will result from the stampings gamble at position Y in Figure 1.5 or the uncertain terminal value that will result from the gamble on "XYZ orders" at position Z in Figure 1.7; and even after he has decided on his certainty equivalents for these two uncertain terminal values, he may very well feel very unsure that he has made the "right" decisions. But if Mallon really wants to make a *reasoned* decision concerning the prototype, he *must* take account in some way or another of (1) all the factors that he would want to consider before deciding on his certainty equivalent for the uncertain terminal value that will result from the stampings gamble, and (2) all the factors that he would want to consider before deciding on his certainty equivalent for the uncertain terminal value that will result from the gamble on "XYZ orders"; and it should be much easier for him to take account of these two sets of factors separately, by deciding separately on his two certainty equivalents, than to take account of both sets of factors simultaneously, as he would have to do if he tried to reach a decision concerning the prototype without first deciding on the two certainty equivalents.[2] It follows that even though he is not at all sure that his two decisions on certainty equivalents are "right", he should nevertheless feel more confidence in the "rightness" of his prototype decision if he bases it on these certainty equivalents than if he arrives at it directly, without decomposing the problem into separable subproblems.

1.2.6
Analysis by Evaluation
of Individual Acts

The form of analysis that we have just applied to Mallon's XYZ decision problem is one form of what is known as analysis by ≪backward induction≫. The name comes from the fact that the analysis is conducted by starting at the end

---

[2] Mallon did not of course really have to decide on his exact certainty equivalent for the uncertain terminal value that would result from the gamble on "XYZ orders"—all that he had to decide was whether it was greater or less than $+\$6,000$, as can readily be seen from Figure 1.7.

of the decision diagram and working back toward the origin, successively reducing forks to definite values by either ≪assessing≫ (i.e., deciding on) a certainty equivalent for an uncertain terminal value or selecting the act with the
greatest certainty-equivalent terminal value, whichever is appropriate. Any
decision problem, no matter how complex, can be thus decomposed into a series
of subproblems each of which consists in the evaluation of a single fork.

The particular form of backward induction that we have used here will
be called analysis by ≪evaluation of individual acts≫ because it results in
assigning a definite terminal value of the decision maker's criterion to every act
on every act fork on the decision diagram. Another form of analysis by backward induction will be examined in a later chapter.

1.3
SUMMARY

1.3.1
Description of the Decision Problem

In order to describe his decision problem as meaningfully as possible, Mr. A. H.
Mallon first selected December 31 as the ≪evaluation date≫ for his description
and then constructed a ≪decision diagram≫ which showed all the acts that he
wished to consider and all the events that in his judgment could affect his choices
among those acts, laying out these acts and events *in the order in which they
would be chosen by or become known to him.*

Next, having decided that the most meaningful single measure or ≪cri-
terion≫ of the consequence of any act-event sequence was the value of his net
liquid assets on December 31, Mallon proceeded to calculate the value corresponding to each act-event sequence on the diagram.

1. He made memoranda on the branches of the diagram of the ≪partial
cash flows≫ that would become known as soon as a given act was chosen or a
given event was learned to have occurred, *including not only the cash flows that
would result from the XYZ deal but also the cash flows that would result from all
his other business.*

2. He summed these partial cash flows along each path in the diagram
to obtain the ≪total cash flow≫ corresponding to each end position.

3. Finally, he found the ≪terminal value≫ of his criterion at each end
position by adding the total cash flow at that position to the current value of his
criterion, which was − $4,000. He could then think of his problem exclusively
in terms of these terminal criterion values, forgetting all about the current value
of his criterion and the partial and total cash flows.

The possible acts, events, and terminal criterion values in Mallon's
problem were fully described by Figure 1.5, which is reproduced as Figure 1.9A
below.

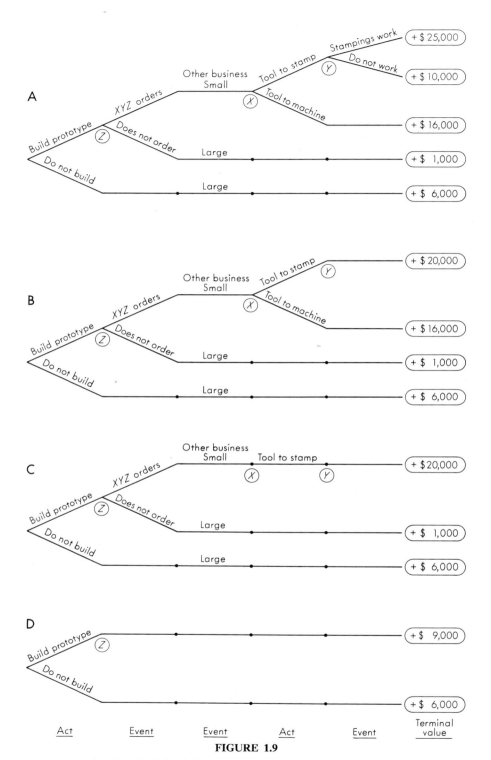

FIGURE 1.9

Analysis of A. H. Mallon's Decision Problem by Evaluation of Individual Acts

1.3.2
Analysis by Evaluation
of Individual Acts

In order to analyze the decision problem thus described, Mallon decomposed it into four simpler problems by working backward on the diagram and reaching four successive decisions, only two of which required thought, the other two being completely "automatic".

1. Starting with the complete diagram in Figure 1.9A, Mallon first went to the last event fork in the diagram, the one at position Y, and ≪assessed≫, i.e., decided on, his ≪certainty equivalent≫ for the uncertain terminal value that would result from the gamble represented by that fork. He decided, in other words, what guaranteed terminal value he would be just willing to agree now to accept in lieu of the uncertain terminal value if and when he should actually arrive at position Y. After he decided that his certainty equivalent for this uncertain terminal value was +$20,000, Figure 1.9A could be immediately reduced to Figure 1.9B, which shows that Mallon's first decision means that the act "tool to stamp" is exactly as attractive to him as it would be if it would yield a terminal value of +$20,000 for certain.

2. This being so, Mallon knew at once what act he would be willing to agree now to choose if and when he should ever reach position X in Figure 1.9B. He would agree to choose the act with the greater terminal value; and therefore he could reduce Figure 1.9B to Figure 1.9C, which shows that Mallon finds position X exactly as attractive to him as it would be if it would yield a terminal value of +$20,000 for certain.

3. Mallon next went to position Z in Figure 1.9C and decided what certainty equivalent or guaranteed terminal value he would be just willing to agree now to accept in lieu of the uncertain terminal value represented by the fork at Z if and when he should actually arrive at position Z. His certainty equivalent was +$9,000, and therefore Figure 1.9C could be immediately reduced to Figure 1.9D, which shows that Mallon's successive partial analyses have led him to decide that the act "build prototype" is exactly as attractive to him as it would be if it would yield a terminal value of +$9,000 for certain.

4. This being so, Mallon knew at once what act he preferred at the origin of Figure 1.9D and therefore at the origin of Figure 1.9A. He preferred the act with the greater terminal value, namely, to build the prototype.

1.3.3
Reservations

The conclusions Mallon reached by analyzing the diagram of his problem in Figure 1.9A are valid and logically compelling provided that his decision problem is correctly described by that diagram. We call the reader's attention to the fact that Figure 1.9A implies, among other things, that:

1. The only acts that Mallon thinks it worth his while to consider are those shown in Figure 1.9A.

2. The only uncertain events that Mallon thinks it worth his while to consider are those shown in the figure. In particular, he does not think it worth his while to consider the possibility that (*a*) his actual choice between stampings and machinings may be influenced by any information he does not already have, or (*b*) the cost of building a prototype or filling a quantity order may be materially different from his engineers' estimates of those costs, or (*c*) the net contribution from "other" business may be materially different from his treasurer's estimate of that contribution.

3. Mallon does not believe that the decision he makes regarding the XYZ deal will have any long-run effects on his fortunes other than those due to the net liquid assets that he possesses on December 31 as a result of that decision. He does not believe, for example, that getting this order from XYZ will have any direct effect on his chances of getting future orders from XYZ or anyone else.

Even if one or more of these assumptions were false, however, it would not mean that Mallon could not apply the general method of description and analysis that is suggested by our example. It would mean only that a correct description of the problem would have to be more complex than Figure 1.9A; the same basic method of description and analysis could still be applied, as we shall see in detail in later chapters.

1.3.4
The Meaning of the Results

We have said that the results of Mallon's analysis via certainty equivalents are "valid and logically compelling" provided that this analysis was based on a correct description of his problem, but before concluding this chapter we must look more closely at the exact meaning of this assertion.

1. What we have actually shown is that Mallon's two decisions on certainty equivalents logically imply that he should find the act "build prototype" more attractive than the act "do not build". We have not shown or tried to show that these two decisions were "correct" in any objective sense, and it would be impossible to show any such thing. Mallon's decisions on certainty equivalents depend on Mallon's evaluations of the chances of the possible events and Mallon's attitudes toward the possible consequences. Another decision maker in exactly the same situation and possessing exactly the same information might decide on very different certainty equivalents.

2. Despite the fact that Mallon's decisions on certainty equivalents imply that he "should" build the prototype, Mallon may nevertheless feel, after looking at his real decision problem as a whole, that he does not want to build the prototype; and we have not shown in any absolute sense that it would be "wrong" for Mallon not to build the prototype. All that we have shown is that

a decision not to build the prototype would be logically *inconsistent* with Mallon's two decisions on certainty equivalents; and therefore all we can say is that if Mallon does find himself face to face with such a logical contradiction, he will almost certainly do well to think hard about it before he finally acts. He will do well, in other words, to try to convince himself either (*a*) that a decision not to build the prototype really disagrees with his best judgments about chances and true attitudes toward consequences and should therefore be revised, or (*b*) that one or both of his two decisions on certainty equivalents really disagree with his best judgments about chances and true attitudes toward consequences and should therefore be revised.

Observe, moreover, that even though analysis by decomposition and assessment of certainty equivalents may lead to a result inconsistent with the result of a direct, intuitive analysis, this is not a reason for avoiding either kind of analysis. On the contrary, it is a reason for making *both* kinds of analysis wherever this is possible, since only in this way will the decision maker be able to detect and correct inconsistencies in his thinking before they have led to action which is inconsistent with his own best judgments about chances and true attitudes toward consequences.

EXERCISES

Many of the exercises in this and later chapters call for construction of decision diagrams which you will be called on to analyze or reanalyze when new methods of analysis are developed in later chapters. After each of these exercises has been discussed in class, make any needed corrections in your diagrams and analysis and save them for later use.

In order to allow you to gain some real feeling for what is involved in evaluation of risky ventures, we shall ask you to consider a number of problems involving lotteries. You should try to think of these admittedly artificial problems as you would think about real risky ventures in real life. To facilitate analysis and discussion of these exercises, assume that gambling contracts are legally binding and that there are no taxes on gambling gains and losses.

A. DECISION DIAGRAMS

1.1 Imagine that you are offered the following deal by a person named Smith, who is a representative of a foundation established to assist in teaching managerial economics to students of business; you have one hour in which to decide whether you will refuse or accept. If you accept, you will hand Smith $200 in cash or Smith will take your IOU for $200 payable in a week. Smith will then toss a penny fairly. If the penny comes up heads, Smith will hand you $250; if not, he will hand you $150; but in either case he will also give you your choice between the option "Stop", in which case your dealings with Smith are over, and the option "Continue", in which case Smith will go on to toss a dime fairly. If the dime comes up heads, Smith will hand you $250; if it comes up tails, you will hand Smith $100; in either case, these payments are over and above any payments previously made by Smith to you or you to Smith.

Diagram your decision problem, but do not describe the consequences.

1.2   Imagine that instead of offering you the deal described in Exercise 1.1, Smith offers you the following deal. You have one hour to decide whether you will accept this deal, but you are not allowed to go in search of useful information before giving your answer to Smith. If you accept the deal, you will hand Smith $250 in cash or Smith will take your IOU for $250 payable in a week. The two of you will then proceed to the front door of your school library, where you will stop the first student to emerge and inquire whether he has bought any cigarettes in the past 24 hours. *After* this student answers "yes" or "no", you will choose between two options, "Stop" and "Continue". If you choose "Stop", Smith will hand you $225 and your dealings with Smith are then over. If you choose "Continue", Smith will hand you nothing for the moment; instead, you will ask the student whether he has smoked a cigarette within the past hour, and after he has answered, Smith will hand you $450 if the answer was "yes", $150 if it was "no".

Diagram your decision problem, but do not describe the consequences.

B. VALUATION OF CONSEQUENCES

In answering all exercises in this chapter which ask you to consider a risky venture or gamble in which you yourself might become engaged, take as your evaluation date the date at which the last payment described in the exercise will be made, assume that the foundation referred to in Exercise 1.1 is willing to lend you up to $1,000 payable without interest one year after graduation, and take as your criterion your cash on hand and in the bank plus all marketable securities that you own minus all debts that you will have to pay within one year after graduation.

1.3   Show appropriate partial cash flows on the branches of the diagram you prepared in answer to Exercise 1.1 and compute the total cash flow corresponding to each end position of the diagram. Then after calculating the current value of your criterion, compute the terminal value of your criterion at each end position of the diagram.

1.4   Value the end positions of the diagram you prepared in answer to Exercise 1.2.

C. VALUATION OF GAMBLES

1.5   Imagine that earlier today you were given a lottery ticket that entitles the bearer to receive $10,000 if a fairly tossed coin comes up heads, nothing if it comes up tails; the coin will be tossed and the prize will be paid exactly one hour from now. Imagine further that you are not allowed to sell this ticket to anyone except a certain Richard Roe; you may refuse to sell to Roe if you like. Whether or not you sell to Roe, you will never have any dealings with him again.

   a Suppose that Roe offers you $4,999 spot cash for your ticket and tells you to take it or leave it; Roe is *not* willing to bargain with you. After thinking about what you would do with the $4,999 if you sold the ticket and also about what you would do with the $10,000 if you kept the ticket and were lucky enough to win, decide whether *you* would or would not sell the ticket. (Observe that you are *not* being asked whether $4,999 is a "fair" price for the ticket, or whether you "ought" to be willing to sell the ticket for $4,999, or whether you would sell the ticket for that price if you were richer than you actually are. You are being asked purely and simply whether you would *in fact* take $4,999 for the ticket if you actually had the ticket *now*, if Roe actually made you the offer *now*, and if you knew that you could not sell the ticket to anyone for any price other than the one named by Roe.)

   b Same as (*a*) except that Roe offers only $4,500 for the ticket rather than $4,999.

   c What would you decide if the offer were $4,000? $3,000? $2,000? $1,000? $100?

   d What is the *lowest* price for which you would be willing to sell the ticket? Can you decide on this price without knowing what price Roe will actually offer for the ticket?

   e Would you do better to decide on your minimum selling price before learning how much Roe will actually offer or should you wait until you have heard Roe's offer and then decide whether or not you want to sell? (If you do decide on your minimum before Roe makes his offer, you will of course keep the figure to yourself. Your decision cannot therefore in any way affect the amount that Roe offers; and as was stated before, Roe will make his offer on a take-it-or-leave-it basis—he is not willing to bargain.)

1.6   Suppose that you still have the lottery ticket described in Exercise 1.5 and suppose as before that you can sell the ticket only to Richard Roe. Instead of making you an offer outright, however, Roe lays on the table before you a sealed envelope containing cash in an amount which is known to him but not to you and then offers you the following deal. You are to write on a piece of paper the *minimum* amount of cash that you will accept in trade

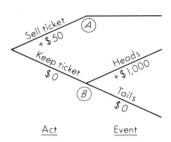

FIGURE 1.10
The Decision Problem of Exercise 1.7

for your ticket, after which Roe will open the envelope and you will both count the cash it contains. If the amount of cash in the envelope is at least as great as the minimum you wrote down, you will take the cash and Roe will take your ticket; if the amount of cash in the envelope is less than the minimum amount you wrote down, Roe will keep his cash and you will keep your ticket.

a What minimum amount will you write down?

b Is your answer to (*a*) the same as your answer to Exercise 1.5*d*? Why?

c Does the amount you write down depend in any way on the amount of cash Roe seals in the envelope? On how much you think he seals in the envelope? On your beliefs about his motives in offering you this deal?

1.7   Suppose that you are given a lottery ticket entitling the bearer to receive $1,000 (not $10,000) if a fairly tossed coin comes up heads, nothing if it comes up tails; the coin will be tossed and the prize will be paid exactly one hour from now. You cannot sell this ticket to anyone except John Doe, but you can refuse to sell to Doe if you choose. Doe offers you $50 spot cash for your ticket, so that your decision problem can be described by the diagram in Figure 1.10.

a Using the criterion and evaluation date prescribed in the paragraph preceding Exercise 1.3, value the end positions of Figure 1.10.

b Suppose that, before you have decided whether or not to accept Doe's offer, Mr. Jones of Section 1.2.1 appears and offers to write an insurance contract that will eliminate all uncertainty about the value of your criterion on your evaluation date if you refuse to sell your ticket to Doe and go to position *B* in Figure 1.10. The policy will specify some definite guaranty value for your criterion on your evaluation date and will provide that if you keep your ticket and the coin then comes up tails, Jones will pay you an amount sufficient to bring the terminal value of your criterion *up* to the specified guaranty value, but if the coin comes up heads, you will have to pay Jones an amount sufficient to bring the terminal value of your criterion *down* to the specified guaranty value. If you sell your ticket to Doe, the contract will be null and void.

For what range of guaranty values would you be willing to sign such a contract with Jones? For what range of guaranty values would you be unwilling to sign?

c Suppose that Jones has already written out a contract containing a guaranty value that is known to him but not to you and offers you the following deal. He will lay the contract in a sealed envelope on the table before you, and you will write down on a piece of paper the minimum guaranty value that you are willing to accept. The envelope will then be opened and if the guaranty value in the contract is at least as great as the value you wrote down, you will both sign the contract; otherwise you will not sign. What minimum guaranty value would you write down?

d What is the smallest *cash payment* for which you would be willing to sell your ticket to Doe?

e If you do sell your ticket for that amount of cash, what will be the terminal value of your criterion? Is your answer to (*d*) consistent with your answer to (*c*)?

1.8 a Same as Exercise 1.7 except that just before receiving the lottery ticket you are informed that you have inherited $3,000 from a long-forgotten uncle.

b Same as Exercise 1.7 except that just before receiving the lottery ticket you are notified that the settlement of a lawsuit arising out of an automobile accident in which you were recently involved requires immediate payment by you of $1,000 in excess of your insurance coverage. (Remember the availability of the $1,000 interest-free loan mentioned just before Exercise 1.3.)

c Same as (*b*) just above except that the prizes in the lottery are $2,000 for heads, $1,000 for tails, and the partial cash flows in Figure 1.10 are modified accordingly.

1.9 Suppose that you have for some reason or another signed a contract which obliges you to *pay* one James Clark $1,000 in cash tomorrow if a fairly tossed coin comes up tails; if the coin comes up heads, you will pay nothing.

a What will be the terminal value of your criterion if the coin comes up heads? If it comes up tails?

b What guaranteed terminal value of your criterion would you find exactly as attractive as the gamble on terminal values to which you are exposed as a result of your contract with Clark? (Remember the availability of the $1,000 interest-free loan mentioned just before Exercise 1.3.)

c What is the greatest amount of cash that you would be willing to pay Clark for a release from your contract?

d If you do pay Clark that amount of cash, what will be the terminal value of your criterion?

e Are your answers to (*b*) and (*c*) consistent?

1.10 When a gamble offers *even* chances at two or more terminal values, the arithmetic average of the possible values is called the "expected" terminal value, whereas the definite terminal value that is exactly as attractive as the gamble to some particular person is called that person's "certainty-equivalent" terminal value. The difference

(expected terminal value) − (certainty-equivalent terminal value)

is called a "risk premium".

a What were your risk premiums for the gambles described in Exercises 1.5, 1.7, 1.8*a*, 1.8*b*, 1.8*c*, and 1.9?

b Why *should* your risk premiums be exactly the same in Exercises 1.7 and 1.8*c*? In Exercises 1.8*b* and 1.9?

c If your risk premiums for the gambles described in Exercises 1.5 and 1.7 were not the same, why were they not the same?

d If your risk premiums for the gambles described in Exercises 1.7, 1.8*a*, and 1.8*b* were not all the same, why were they not all the same?

D. ANALYSIS OF DECISION PROBLEMS

1.11 Analyze the two separate decision problems described in Exercises 1.1 and 1.2, assuming as regards Exercise 1.2 that smoking is permitted in the library. (Remember the availability of the $1,000 interest-free loan mentioned just before Exercise 1.3.)

E. REVIEW EXERCISE

1.12 Suppose that after telling Mr. A. H. Mallon that a prototype which may be acceptable to XYZ can be designed along conventional lines and built for a total cost of $5,000, as stated in the text, ABC's chief design engineer goes on to say that he has an alternative idea for a radically new type of control, using transistors and printed circuits. He is not sure whether a control of this kind can be made to work at all with the components currently available, but he is sure that if it actually can be made to work, its performance will be so superior in every respect to the units currently in use by XYZ that XYZ cannot fail to prefer it. It will cost $10,000 to build a prototype along these radically different lines, but the radical design will cost much less to produce in quantity than a conventional control; Mallon's chief production engineer tells him that the out-of-pocket cost would be only about $7,000 for production tooling plus $12.60 per unit. Building a radical prototype will have no effect on ABC's "other business", but manufacture of a production quantity according to the radical design will reduce the net contribution realized on other business from +$10,000 to +$8,000.

The engineers agree that the time available before a prototype must be submitted to XYZ is sufficient to let ABC build and test a radical prototype and still be able to build a conventional prototype if the radical design fails. Since XYZ is willing to consider at most one prototype from ABC and since Mallon believes that nothing could be gained by postponing the decision to build the radical design until after the conventional prototype has been constructed and tested, Mallon has decided that if the radical prototype is tried at all it should be built and tested *before* the conventional design is begun.

a Diagram Mr. Mallon's decision problem and value the end positions.

b Placing yourself in the role of a consultant to Mallon, decide what questions you would have to ask Mallon in order to analyze his problem. Your instructor will assume the role of Mallon in class and respond to your questions with answers that Mallon might reasonably give.

CHAPTER
2

SYSTEMATIC ANALYSIS
OF DECISIONS
UNDER UNCERTAINTY:
BASIC PRINCIPLES

In Chapter 1 we merely suggested by means of a simple example how a problem of decision under uncertainty can be systematically described and then analyzed. In the present chapter we shall first consider carefully the basic principles that must be followed in describing the logical structure of a decision problem and the possible consequences of the available acts. Next, we shall reexamine the concept of a certainty equivalent, which lies at the heart of any method of decomposition and systematic analysis. Next, we shall state general rules for the method of analysis by evaluation of individual acts that we applied in Chapter 1; and finally, we shall describe an alternative method of analysis which often leads to a clearer understanding of certain aspects of decision under uncertainty than can be gained by thinking exclusively in terms of individual acts.

The text and exercises of the present chapter are designed to be studied in the following order:

1 Section 2.1.1 and Exercise 2.1.

2 Section 2.1.2 and Exercise 2.2.

3 Section 2.1.3 and Exercise 2.3.

4 Section 2.1.4 and Exercises 2.4–2.5.

5 Sections 2.1.5–2.1.6 and Exercises 2.6–2.7.

6 Sections 2.2.1–2.2.4 and Exercises 2.8–2.10.

CONTENTS OF CHAPTER 2

1.

Decision Problems and Decision Diagrams

2.

Valuation of Consequences

3.

Certainty Equivalents

4.
Analysis by Evaluation
of Individual Acts

1 Reduction of Terminal Event Forks
2 Reduction of Terminal Act Forks
3 Analysis by Evaluation of Individual Acts

5.
Analysis by Evaluation
of Complete Strategies

1 Definition of Strategy
2 Strategies Implicit in a Decision Diagram
3 Analysis by Evaluation of Complete Strategies
4 Equivalence of the Two Methods of Analysis
5 Completeness of a Decision Diagram

6.
Summary

1 Delimitation of a Decision Problem
2 Decision Diagrams
3 Valuation of Consequences
4 Certainty Equivalents and Equivalent Decision Problems
5 Analysis by Evaluation of Individual Acts
6 Analysis by Evaluation of Complete Strategies

2.1
DECISION PROBLEMS AND DECISION DIAGRAMS

2.1.1
Delimitation of a Decision Problem

When a decision maker tries to choose one among a number of possible immediate acts, he only rarely finds that he can foresee the ultimate consequences of all of these acts with certainty or even near certainty. Usually, the consequences of some if not all of the acts will depend on uncertain events, and often they will also depend on the decision maker's own future acts; and therefore the decision maker usually cannot make a reasoned choice among the various immediate acts that he is considering without systematically evaluating the possible effects of future acts and uncertain events on the consequences of the immediate acts.

On the other hand, it is never possible to take *explicit* account of *all* the future acts and uncertain events that may affect the ultimate consequences of an immediate act, since to do so the decision maker would have to look indefinitely far into the future. The decision maker must necessarily delimit his decision problem by selecting some definite future ≪evaluation date≫ beyond which it is not worthwhile in his judgment to try to take account of specific acts and events. In formally describing his problem, he will consider only acts and events that may be chosen by or become known to him before this date; and instead of trying to consider the possible ultimate consequences of his immediate acts, he will describe and evaluate the consequence of each possible sequence of explicitly considered acts and events as it will appear to him on his evaluation date.

After the decision maker has delimited his decision problem by choice of an appropriate evaluation date, he can describe the problem by means of a ≪decision diagram≫. The general nature of such a diagram is suggested by the example in Figure 1.5 (page 13), but before giving general rules for diagramming decision problems we shall do well to look at certain complexities that appear in many problems even though they did not appear in that very simple example.

2.1.2
Informational Events

The only events that appeared in the decision diagrams in Chapter 1 were events which would have a direct effect on the consequence of an immediate act, but in many decision problems the decision maker will wish also to take account of various events which will not have any direct effect on the consequence of any immediate act but will provide information that may affect his future acts and thus have an indirect effect on the consequences of the immediate acts.

For example, suppose that Mr. A. H. Mallon of ABC Controls had believed that a competitor was experimenting with the use of stamped parts in control units similar to those Mallon would build for XYZ, and suppose that Mallon thought he might learn whether the results of this experiment were "favorable" or "unfavorable" to the suitability of stampings in the XYZ application before he would actually be obliged to choose between stampings and machinings. In these circumstances the subdiagram emanating from position *X* in Figure 1.5 would have had to be replaced by the more complex subdiagram shown in Figure 2.1 below.

Using Figure 2.1, Mallon might very well have decided, for example, that if and when he reached position *A* or *C*, he would use stampings, whereas if he reached position *B*, he would use machinings. He might have decided, in other words, to ≪condition≫ his choice between stampings and machinings on the new information. Because the diagram in Figure 1.5 does not show the possibility of such conditioning, it would under our present assumptions be an incorrect description of Mallon's decision problem; and it goes without saying that a correct analysis cannot be based on an incorrect description.

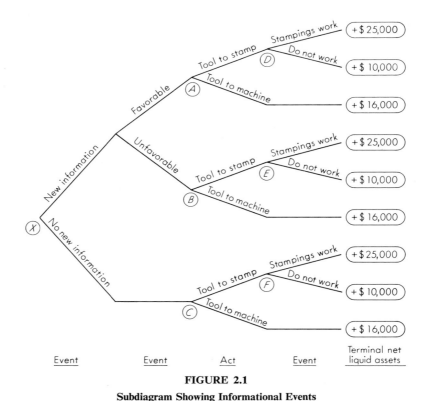

				Terminal net
Event	Event	Act	Event	liquid assets

FIGURE 2.1
Subdiagram Showing Informational Events

2.1.3
Act and Event Forks with Many Branches

Although none of the act and event forks in Figure 1.5 (page 13) had more than two branches, forks with more than two branches appear frequently in decision diagrams, and some forks will have so many branches that it is impractical to show them all explicitly on the decision diagram.

For example, suppose that, instead of feeling sure that the cost of production with all machined parts would amount to exactly $95,000 exclusive of tooling costs, as shown on the branch labelled "machinings work" in Figure 1.2 (page 9), Mr. A. H. Mallon had felt that this cost might be anywhere between say, $76,000 and $114,000. Since each possible value of the uncertain cost is a possible event, this additional uncertainty would have had to be represented in Mallon's decision diagram by putting an event fork with one branch for each possible cost in place of the single branch labelled "machinings work" with its associated − $95,000 cash flow. This fork would have had thousands of branches, however, and it is neither necessary nor feasible actually to draw each individual branch on such a fork. The uncertainty can be adequately represented by a schematic fork or ≪fan≫ of the sort shown in Figure 2.2.

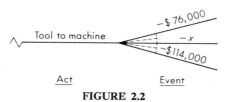

FIGURE 2.2

Event Fan Representing an Uncertain Cost

The event fan in Figure 2.2 is to be understood as having one branch for each possible event or possible value of the uncertain cost that the fan represents. The symbol x on the ≪typical branch≫ stands for the ≪typical value≫ —i.e., for *any possible* value—of the uncertain cost, $-x$ being the resulting cash flow.

Fans will often be needed to represent choices among acts as well as uncertainties concerning events. For example, suppose that a businessman must decide what price to bid in competing for a certain contract. Each possible bid price is a possible act, and the acts which the businessman wishes to consider may well be so numerous that they must be represented schematically by a fan rather than literally by a fork.

When a fan occurs in the "interior" of a diagram rather than at the end, the entire diagram beyond the fan becomes schematic rather than literal. If, for example, the only events concerning which the businessman of our last example is uncertain are the events "win contract" and "lose contract", his entire decision problem might be represented by the diagram in Figure 2.3, which is to be interpreted not only as if the act fan had one branch for every possible act or bid price x but also as if every one of these act branches were followed by an event fork exactly like the event fork that is actually drawn after the typical act branch.

2.1.4
Successive Act or Event Forks

The set of acts or events represented by any fork that has more than two branches can be equally well represented by a sequence of forks each of which has a smaller number of branches. For example, suppose that, instead of believing

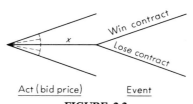

FIGURE 2.3

Decision Diagram with an Interior Fan

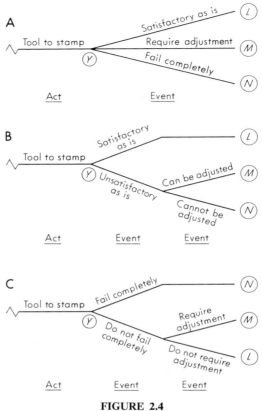

FIGURE 2.4

Alternate Representations of an Uncertainty

that controls with stamped parts would either give complete satisfaction or fail completely and have to be replaced by controls with all machined parts, Mr. A. H. Mallon had felt that there was an intermediate possibility, namely that controls with stamped parts would have to be adjusted by hand at considerable cost. To show this additional possibility on his decision diagram, Mallon could have replaced the two-branched fork at *Y* in Figure 1.5 (page 13) by the three-branched fork in Figure 2.4A above, but he could equally well have replaced it by either of the *sequences* of event forks shown in parts B and C of that same figure.

All three representations of possible events in Figure 2.4 are logically equivalent because they all lead from position *Y* to three positions, *L*, *M*, and *N*, each of which has exactly the same meaning in any one representation as in any other. We leave it to the reader to invent examples of different logically equivalent representations of choices among three or more acts.

Which of the various possible representations of a set of possible acts should be used in a decision diagram is purely a matter of convenience. As regards representation of events, on the contrary, we shall see later on how choice of one representation rather than another may enable the decision maker to exercise his judgment more effectively when he comes to the actual analysis of his decision problem.

2.1.5
General Principles of Diagramming

The examples of decision diagrams and subdiagrams that we have now examined should suffice to make clear the meaning of the general principles that must be followed in describing any decision problem by a diagram.

Even though the decision maker's only immediate problem is to choose an immediate act, the decision diagram must show not only

1 All *immediate acts* among which the decision maker wishes to choose,

but also

2 All uncertain events and future acts that the decision maker wishes to consider because they may *directly affect the consequences* of the immediate acts,

and

3 All uncertain events that the decision maker wishes to consider because they may *provide information that can affect his future choices among acts* and hence indirectly affect the consequences of immediate acts.

Events may of course have *both* direct and indirect effects on the consequences of immediate acts.

An individual act or event is represented in the diagram by a branch; either end of any branch is called a position. A ≪choice≫ among possible acts is represented by an act fork consisting of a number of act branches all of which emanate from a single position called the base of the fork; an ≪uncertainty≫ regarding events is represented by an event fork consisting of a number of event branches all of which emanate from a single position, again called the base of the fork.

■ The events on any event fork or the acts on any act fork must be (1) ≪mutually exclusive≫ in the sense that no more than one of them can possibly occur or be chosen, and (2) ≪collectively exhaustive≫ in the sense that in the decision maker's judgment some one of them must occur or be chosen.

Observe that this definition of "collectively exhaustive" leaves the decision maker free to exclude from the diagram acts which *he* does not wish to consider and events which *he* believes to be practically certain not to occur.

The complete decision diagram takes the form of a "tree" with successive branchings; a very simple example was shown in Figure 1.5 on page 13.

At the origin of the diagram there is a single act fork representing the decision maker's choice among the immediate acts that he wishes to consider. Each branch of this initial fork may lead either (*a*) to an end position of the diagram, indicating that choice of the corresponding act puts an end to the decision problem, or (*b*) to another fork representing either another choice by the decision maker or the decision maker's uncertainty concerning a set of mutually exclusive and collectively exhaustive events. On the initial fork in Figure 1.5, the branch representing the act "do not build prototype" led to an end position; the branch representing the act "build prototype" led to another fork representing the decision maker's uncertainty about the mutually exclusive events "XYZ orders" and "XYZ does not order".

Like the branches of the initial fork, the branches of subsequent forks may lead either to end positions or to still other forks; and so forth until finally all branches have led to end positions.

The order in which particular act and event forks appear in the decision diagram must agree with the following:

- ■ *Basic Ordering Principle* The acts and events along the path from the origin of a decision diagram to the base of any *act* fork must give a correct representation of the *information* that will and will not be available to the decision maker when he actually has to make the choice represented by the act fork in question.

This principle is of such crucial importance that we shall devote the next section to a detailed examination of its implications.

2.1.6
Ordering of Forks in a Diagram

The basic ordering principle which was stated at the end of the last section is a consequence of two more basic propositions about the analysis of decisions under uncertainty.

1 If the decision maker will not have to make an irrevocable choice among a number of mutually exclusive acts until *after* he has learned which of a number of mutually exclusive events actually occurred or will occur, then as we saw in Section 2.1.2 he may wish to *condition* his choice— i.e., make it depend—on the event that actually occurs. To show the possibility of such conditioning diagrammatically, a fork representing the decision maker's choice among acts must *follow* each branch representing an event which might occur.

2 If on the contrary the decision maker will have to make an irrevocable choice among a number of mutually exclusive acts *before* he has learned which of a number of mutually exclusive events has occurred or will occur, then he *cannot condition* his choice on the event that actually occurs. To show the impossibility of such conditioning diagrammatically, the fork representing the choice among acts must *precede* all branches representing the possible events.

Chronological Ordering   A decision diagram will necessarily represent possible conditionings correctly if the order in which act and event forks appear in the diagram agrees with the chronological order in which the decision maker's choices will have to be irrevocably made and his uncertainties will be resolved. In Figure 1.5, the act fork representing A. H. Mallon's choice between "build prototype" and "do not build" appeared before the event fork representing his uncertainty about the events "XYZ orders" and "XYZ does not order" because the choice in question had to be made before the uncertainty in question could possibly be resolved. Observe that:

1 As regards choices, what counts in determinining chronological order is the date at which one of the acts on an act fork will have to be chosen *irrevocably*. A choice which can be revoked later at no cost is not a choice; a choice which can be revoked later at a cost is really a sequence of two choices at different dates and must be diagrammed as such.

2 As regards uncertainties, what counts in determining chronological order is not the date at which one of the events on an event fork actually occurs but the date at which the decision maker's uncertainty about the events is *resolved*.

If A. H. Mallon would like to base his choice between stampings and the machinings on the outcome of a competitor's experiment with stampings, the date that is relevant to Mallon's decision problem is not the date at which the experiment will be conducted and its outcome or event will be determined; it is the date at which *Mallon's uncertainty* about the experiment will be resolved through *his learning* what event occurred.

If the decision maker does not know whether his uncertainty about a particular set of mutually exclusive events will or will not be resolved before he has to make a particular choice among acts, *this uncertainty about chronological order must also be represented in the decision diagram*. Figure 2.1 (page 34) shows how Mallon could have represented his XYZ decision problem if he had (*a*) believed that a competitor's experiment with stampings would yield information bearing on the suitability of stampings for Mallon's own purpose, but (*b*) been uncertain whether he would learn the outcome of this experiment before or after the date at which he would have to make his final decision about the use of stampings.

Permissible Departures from Chronological Ordering   Although possible conditionings of acts can always be correctly represented by constructing a diagram which is in strict agreement with chronological order as defined above, certain departures from strict chronological order are permissible and often facilitate diagramming considerably. Specifically:

1. Two or more *choices* may be diagrammed in an order different from that in which they will actually be made if the decision maker will *learn of no event* between the earliest and latest dates at which the various choices must be made.

2. Two or more *uncertainties* may be diagrammed in an order different from that in which they will actually be resolved if the decision maker will *choose no act* between the earliest and latest dates at which the various uncertainties will be resolved.

The fact that uncertainties can under appropriate conditions be diagrammed in an order different from that in which they will actually be resolved can be of considerable practical importance in either of two ways. (1) It follows from this fact that it is not *always* necessary to show on the diagram all possible orders in which a number of uncertainties may be resolved. (2) Diagramming uncertainties in an order other than that in which they will actually be resolved may, for reasons which we shall be able to explain later on, enable the decision maker to exercise his judgment more effectively when he comes to the actual analysis of his decision problem.

2.2
VALUATION OF CONSEQUENCES

2.2.1
Detailed Descriptions of Consequences

After the decision maker has constructed a diagram of his decision problem, he must next consider in turn each possible act-event sequence that is shown on the diagram and write down an adequate description of the consequence of that sequence. By "adequate" we mean, of course, adequate in the *decision maker's* judgment for the purpose at hand. The description must reflect every aspect of the consequence that the decision maker wishes to consider in arriving at his final decision.

An adequate description of the consequence of an act-event sequence may be very complex, including not only statements concerning the financial effects of the sequence but also statements concerning the effects of the sequence on the physical assets, technological know-how, and business reputation of the decision maker's company, statements concerning its effects on the behavior of various people, and possibly also a statement concerning its effects on the decision maker's own personal position and reputation and psychological well-being. What is more, the date at which each of these effects occurs will in general be of importance to the decision maker and will therefore have to be included in the description.

2.2.2
Restriction to Short-term Decision Problems

Systematic analysis of a decision problem along the lines suggested in Chapter 1 would, of course, be exceedingly difficult if all or many of the possible consequences in the problem had very complex descriptions, but fortunately such detailed descriptions can often be replaced by much simpler descriptions which are nevertheless equally adequate in the sense of the previous section. Specifically, the decision maker can often reduce the detailed description of each consequence in a decision problem to a single number which in a suitable sense represents the "value" of that consequence and which therefore constitutes an adequate even though condensed description of the consequence.

Because finding appropriate values for the consequences in a given decision problem is usually relatively easy when all the dates that are involved in the detailed descriptions of the consequences are virtually the same but is often extremely difficult when these dates are widely spaced out in time, the discussion in this book will be restricted to ≪short-term≫ decision problems in which consequences can be adequately described without use of dates.

This restriction does not mean that we are excluding from consideration all problems in which the dates at which various acts and events actually occur lead to payments of interest by or to the decision maker's company; but it does mean that we are excluding all problems in which the importance of dates cannot be completely allowed for by simply including the *amount* of interest paid or received in the description of a consequence. In particular, all problems involving changes in long-term debt are excluded from the discussion in this book.

In most decision problems of the sort to which we have restricted our discussion, the easiest way to attach an appropriate value to each consequence is to start by attaching a monetary value to the purely financial or monetary effects of each act-event sequence and then to adjust this monetary value to allow for the nonmonetary effects of the sequence. After we have discussed the two steps in this procedure in some detail, we shall suggest how it may be possible to find nonmonetary values for consequences in situations where our procedure for assigning monetary values is hard to apply.

2.2.3
Valuation of Monetary Consequences

Although the consequences of the various act-event sequences in A. H. Mallon's XYZ decision problem were completely described by the total cash flows shown at the end positions of Figure 1.3 (page 11), Mallon did not wish to base his analysis of the problem on these descriptions. He felt that he could not properly evaluate the various possible consequences unless he viewed them *in their business context;* and to do so in the way that was most meaningful to him, he first selected his net liquid assets as the ≪criterion≫ by which he would evaluate the consequences and he then proceeded as shown in Figure 1.5 (page 13) to replace each total cash flow on his decision diagram by the resulting ≪terminal value≫ of his criterion—i.e., the value of his net liquid assets on his chosen evaluation date.

The implications of this example are quite general. A decision maker will usually be much better able to evaluate the monetary consequences of the various possible act-event sequences in a decision problem if he looks, not at the cash flow or *change* in his financial position which will result from each sequence, but at the resulting terminal value of some suitably chosen measure or criterion of the actual financial *position* in which he will find himself on his evaluation date as a result of the act-event sequence.

Very frequently—although by no means always—the best criterion of financial position in a short-term decision problem is what we have called

- ≪Net liquid assets≫: cash on hand, plus all claims to receive cash which will or could be realized in the near future, minus all obligations to pay cash which will or could be enforced in the near future.

What is to be considered the "near" future in any particular situation is up to the decision maker—a transfer of cash is in the "near" future if the only importance which the decision maker attaches to the difference between his evaluation date and the date at which the transfer of cash will actually take place is due to the effect of this difference on the amount of interest paid or earned.

2.2.4
Computation of Monetary Values

In order to compute the terminal value of his criterion that will result from any particular act-event sequence in a decision problem, the decision maker will ordinarily start from the value of his criterion at the time of the analysis of the problem and then add to and subtract from this ≪initial value≫ the changes that will occur because of the various acts and events in the sequence.

When the decision maker's criterion is net liquid assets as defined in Section 2.2.3, some of the changes in the value of the criterion will be due to cash flows in the ordinary sense of the word—i.e., to actual receipts or payments of cash—but others will be due to changes in short-term financial claims—e.g., to purchases or sales of goods or services on open account. In future discussion we shall have need of a single term that can denote either kind of change in net liquid assets, and since there is no generally accepted term with this meaning, we shall simply make the term "cash flow" serve both purposes.[1] In other words, we shall henceforth use the expression "cash flow" as a technical term defined as follows:

---

[1] The term "funds flow" includes changes in long-term financial claims as well as changes in short-term claims and actual transfers of cash.

■ Any change in net liquid assets will be called a ≪cash flow≫. An increase in net liquid assets will be called a cash inflow and will be treated as algebraically positive; a decrease in net liquid assets will be called a cash outflow and will be treated as algebraically negative.

Partial and Total Cash Flows   The various acts and events that make up any one act-event sequence in a decision problem will in general give rise to a great number of individual cash flows representing individual items of cost, expense, and revenue. Although all that the decision maker needs to know about these flows in order to compute the terminal value of his criterion is their aggregate or net amount, it is easy to overlook some of the individual flows in computing the aggregate, and therefore it will often be advisable to carry out this computation by a systematic two-stage procedure of the sort that we applied to A. H. Mallon's decision problem in Sections 1.1.3 and 1.1.4.

1 The decision maker first writes down on each branch of the decision diagram the ≪partial≫ net cash flow he attributes to the individual act or event represented by the branch in question, using a plus sign to designate a net inflow, a minus sign to designate a net outflow.

The partial cash flows in Mallon's problem were shown in Figure 1.2 (page 9).

2 The decision maker then computes the ≪total≫ net cash flow that will result from each act-event sequence by simply following the corresponding path through the diagram and computing the algebraic sum of the partial flows that he has written down on the branches that make up this path; after which he erases the partial cash flows from the diagram and never refers to them again.

The total cash flows in Mallon's problem were shown in Figure 1.3 (page 11).

A great deal of latitude is permissible in deciding just which individual cash flows are to be included in the partial net cash flow that is attributed to any one individual act or event. Consider, for example, the portion of Figure 1.2 which is reproduced as Figure 2.5A below. The partial flows shown in this figure were arrived at by attributing to the act "tool to stamp" only the minimum tooling cost to which that act would lead, all subsequent production costs being attributed to one or the other of the two events "stampings work" and "stampings do not work", but we could have argued equally well that the act "tool to stamp" would necessarily lead to total production costs amouting to at least $14,000 + $82,000 = $96,000, which would be augmented by $15,000 if stampings failed to work. This latter line of argument would have led to the partial cash flows shown in Figure 2.5B rather than the quite different flows shown in Figure 2.5A, but because the *total* cash flow assigned to any act-event *sequence* will have exactly the same value if it is computed from the partial flows in Figure

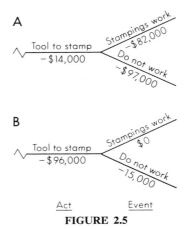

Act   Event

FIGURE 2.5

Alternate Values for Partial Cash Flows

2.5B as it will if it is computed from the partial flows in Figure 2.5A, either *set* of partial flows is as correct as the other.

What is suggested by this example is true in general. The analyst is free to define the partial cash flow attributable to any one act or event in any way that he finds convenient, but he must make all of his partial flows *consistent* in the sense that the total flows to which they lead are correct. He must take care that (1) every individual cash flow that will actually occur as a result of any given act-event sequence is attributed to some act or event along the path representing the sequence, and (2) no individual cash flow is attributed to more than one act or event.

Timing of Cash Flows; Interest Payments and Infeasible Acts   Even in short-term decision problems, the dates at which certain cash flows will actually occur are often of very real importance. The interest payments to which a given act-event sequence gives rise will in general depend on the dates at which the other cash flows associated with that sequence occur; and it may even happen that certain acts which would otherwise be feasible are infeasible because they call for excessively large cash outlays to be made before the covering inflows are received.

In most situations where the timing of cash flows is important, for either of the reasons just mentioned, the timing of the flows and its implications will have to be analyzed on a work sheet separate from the decision diagram. The relevant timing information cannot in general be shown on the diagram because the cash flow or flows to which a given act or event gives rise do not in general take place at the same time at which the decision maker chooses the act or learns of the event, and it is this latter time that determines the position of the branch in the decision diagram.

Contextual Cash Flows   We call the reader's particular attention to the very important fact that the terminal values of the decision maker's criterion cannot be computed unless he has shown on his decision diagram not only the cash flows that are directly associated with the decision problem at hand but also all cash flows that will result from his "other" business. Even if these "other" flows will be completely unaffected by any of the possible acts or events in the decision diagram, they must be included in order to enable the decision maker to view the consequences of these acts and events in their business context; and if there is any uncertainty about the other flows, this uncertainty must be explicitly represented in the decision diagram.

In what follows, we shall use the term ≪contextual cash flow≫ to denote a cash flow which is not directly associated with the decision problem at hand but will nevertheless affect the value of the decision maker's criterion on his evaluation date.

2.2.5
Description of Nonmonetary Consequences

Having seen how the decision maker can evaluate the purely monetary consequences of the possible act-event sequences in a decision problem, we next ask how he can evaluate the nonmonetary consequences, and as a starting point, we remind the reader that our essential conclusion concerning the evaluation of monetary consequences was that these consequences should be viewed in their business context. To make sure that they were in fact viewed in this way, we recommended that the decision maker should in general base his analysis, not on the cash flows or changes in financial position that would result from the various act-event sequences in his decision problem, but on some criterion or measure of the resulting financial position itself—e.g., his net liquid assets.

The same reasoning that led to this conclusion regarding the evaluation of monetary consequences leads to a similar conclusion regarding nonmonetary consequences. Whether or not the decision maker starts by writing down a description of the nonmonetary changes in his general business position that will result from each possible act-event sequence, his actual analysis of the problem should be based, not on descriptions of changes, but on descriptions of the actual business positions in which he may find himself on his evaluation date as a result of these changes.

In what follows, we shall refer to the nonmonetary aspects of the decision maker's general business position as his ≪nonmonetary assets≫. Notice, however, that the word "asset" is here to be interpreted, not in the accounting sense, but as meaning anything to which the decision maker attaches value. The decision maker's business reputation or psychological well-being is as much an asset in the sense in which we shall use the word as his plant and equipment; and from our point of view, a debt is a negative asset rather than a separate kind of entity called a liability.

The principle of evaluation by assets rather than changes in assets cannot, however, be usefully applied to nonmonetary assets until we have found a way of circumventing a difficulty that does not arise when the principle is applied to short-term monetary assets. The decision maker's net liquid assets at any end position of his decision diagram can be completely described by a single number, but a description of his total tangible and intangible nonmonetary assets at any end position would virtually always constitute so large a document that it would be completely useless as a basis for analysis.

A way out of this difficulty can be found as soon as we stop to think that most of the decision maker's tangible and intangible nonmonetary assets will be exactly the same at any one end position of his decision diagram as they are at any other, and the decision maker will almost certainly already have in mind a very good idea of this common asset base when he sets out to analyze his decision problem. Only the *differences* between his nonmonetary assets at various end positions require *explicit* description, and the decision maker can describe these differences systematically by proceeding as follows:

1 The decision maker first selects some one end position as a ≪base end position≫ and thinks of his *total* nonmonetary assets at this end position as constituting his ≪base nonmonetary assets≫.

2 He then writes down opposite each *other* end position a careful statement of all the *differences* between his base nonmonetary assets and the nonmonetary assets he will have at that end position.

For example, let us now be a little more realistic about A. H. Mallon's XYZ decision problem and admit that Mallon would have wanted to take account, not only of the purely monetary consequences of the various act-event sequences in Figure 1.5 (page 13), but also of the fact that one of these sequences would leave him in possession of the tooling required to produce control units using all machined parts, another with the tooling required to produce them using some stamped parts, and another (the sequence involving the event "stampings do not work") with the tooling required to produce them in either one of these two ways. If Mallon chooses as his base end position the position following the act "do not build prototype", he can describe the difference between his base nonmonetary assets and the nonmonetary assets he will have at each other end position by simply mentioning the special tooling (if any) that will be present at that end position.

2.2.6
Monetary Valuation
of Nonmonetary Consequences

Now that we have shown how the decision maker can systematically describe the assets—monetary and nonmonetary, tangible and intangible—that he will have at any end position of his decision diagram, we are ready to show how he can reduce each of these descriptions to a single number that in a suitable sense expresses the value of the end position to him.

To start with an example, suppose that A. H. Mallon takes as his base end position the end position following "do not build prototype", and suppose that he feels that the only significant nonmonetary difference between his base end position and the end position following "tool to machine" is the presence at the latter of the tooling acquired to produce with all machined parts. Mallon can assign an appropriate monetary value to this leftover tooling by simply deciding for exactly how much cash he would be just willing to agree now to sell the tooling if and when he arrives at the end position following "tool to machine". For if he decides, say, that he would be just willing to agree to sell the tooling for $2,000, then the total assets at the end position following "tool to machine" must be exactly as attractive to him as they would be if the leftover tooling at that position were in fact replaced by an extra $2,000 of cash; and therefore he will make no error in the analysis of his decision problem if he (1) adds $2,000 to the net liquid assets that he will actually have at the end position following "tool to machine", and then (2) erases the mention of special tooling from his description of his assets at that end position and forgets all about it in analyzing his decision problem.

If Mallon believes that one of the end positions in his decision diagram is significantly superior to the base end position in respect to some intangible and nonsaleable asset (such as general business reputation) rather than a tangible and saleable asset (such as tooling), he may find it hard to assign a monetary value to the "additional" reputation he will have at the end position in question by thinking about selling this additional reputation as such, but he can accomplish the same purpose by deciding for how much cash received on his evaluation date he would be just willing to agree now to divest himself of all benefits that he might derive from this additional reputation after his evaluation date. For the sake of brevity, however, we shall in what follows talk simply about the price for which the decision maker would be just willing to agree now to "sell" an asset or an additional amount of an asset if and when he arrives at a particular end position, leaving it to the reader to decide exactly how the decision maker should interpret the word "sell" in any particular case.

In the two examples just discussed we considered the case where at a given end position the decision maker either possesses an asset (tooling) which he does not possess at the base end position or possesses "more" of an asset (general business reputation) than he does at the base end position. The opposite relation can of course also occur—at a given end position the decision maker may either not possess an asset which he possesses at the base end position or possess "less" of the asset than he does at the base end position.

In order to assign a monetary value to such a "negative" asset difference, the decision maker must decide on the cash price for which he would be just willing to agree now to *buy* the missing asset if and when he arrives at the end position in question. He can then *subtract* this price from the actual value of his monetary criterion at the end position in question and proceed to analyze his decision problem as if this adjusted value were the true value of his monetary criterion and the difference in nonmonetary assets did not exist.

Generalizing from what we have said thus far, we conclude that the decision maker can reduce the detailed description of his assets at any end position to a single monetary value by the following procedure:

1 After the decision maker has determined the value of his monetary criterion at a given end position, he selects some one *difference* between the nonmonetary assets he will have at the given end position and the base nonmonetary assets he will have at his base end position, and he decides for how much cash he would be just willing to agree now to buy or sell that difference if and when he arrives at the given end position.

This purchase or sale is of course to be thought of as being made in such a way that it will have no effect on the price at which the decision maker will be able to buy or sell *other* assets on or after his evaluation date.

2 The decision maker then ≪adjusts≫ the value of his monetary criterion at the given end position by either subtracting from it the cash price that he would be just willing to agree now to pay for the difference in nonmonetary assets or adding to it the cash price for which he would be just willing to agree now to sell the difference in nonmonetary assets.

3 The decision maker then selects another difference in nonmonetary assets between the given end position and the base end position and repeats steps 1 and 2; and he continues in this way until the value of his criterion at the given end position has been adjusted to reflect *all* differences in nonmonetary assets between that position and the base end position.

After this procedure has been carried out at every end position in a decision problem,

4 The decision maker can proceed to analyze his decision problem as if (*a*) his monetary assets at each end position would in fact be equal to the adjusted value of his criterion at that end position, and (*b*) his nonmonetary assets at every end position would in fact be identical to the base nonmonetary assets that he will actually have at his base end position.

What this really means is that, instead of analyzing his real decision problem, the decision maker may solve that problem by analyzing a *substitute decision problem* in which (1) the *actual* value of his monetary criterion at each end position is equal to the "adjusted" value of the criterion at the corresponding end position in the real decision problem, and (2) his *actual* nonmonetary assets are the same at every end position as they are at the base end position in the real decision problem. Because the total assets at each end position in the substitute problem are exactly as attractive to the decision maker as the total assets at the corresponding end position in the real problem, the two problems are ≪equivalent≫ in the sense that the decision maker should prefer the same acts in his real problem that analysis leads him to prefer in the substitute problem.

2.2.7
Salvage Value and Replacement Cost

In some situations, the cash price for which the decision maker would be just willing to agree now to buy or sell a nonmonetary asset if and when he arrives at a given end position on his evaluation date will be simply the price at which he will in fact buy or sell that asset or a similar asset shortly after his evaluation date. When the value of an asset at an end position is determined by the price for which that asset or a similar asset will actually be *sold*, we shall say that the value of the asset is equal to its ≪salvage value≫. When the value is determined by the price at which the asset or a similar asset will actually be bought, we shall say that the value of the asset is equal to its ≪replacement cost≫.

Salvage Value   As an example of a situation where the value of an asset at an end position is determined by its salvage value, suppose that any special tooling acquired by A. H. Mallon to fill a quantity order from XYZ will be scrapped as soon as the order has been filled. If Mallon believes that the scrap value of tooling for production with all machined parts will be $2,000 net of removal costs, then $2,000 must be the net price for which Mallon would be just willing to agree to sell that tooling on his evaluation date. Because he can actually get $2,000 for the tooling a little after his evaluation date, he would be unwilling to agree to sell it on his evaluation date for appreciably less than $2,000; because $2,000 is all he can actually get for the tooling, he would be happy rather than "just willing" to agree to sell it for more than $2,000; his indifference point is therefore exactly $2,000.

Replacement Cost   As an example of a situation in which the value of an asset at an end position is determined by its replacement cost, suppose that a retailer regularly stocks a nonperishable item which he buys from a wholesaler for $2 per unit and sells to his customers for $5 per unit; suppose that the retailer places an order with the wholesaler at the close of each business week and receives delivery before the beginning of the next business week; suppose that the moment has now arrived when the retailer must decide how many units he should order to meet the coming week's uncertain customer demand; suppose that in analyzing this decision problem he takes as his evaluation date the moment at which he will place his *next* weekly order and chooses as his base end position the end position following the act-event sequence "buy 0 units from wholesaler, sell 0 units to customers"; and consider the end position following the sequence "buy 15 units from wholesaler, sell 14 units to customers".

At this end position the retailer will have one more leftover unit than he will have at his base end position, and since the unit is not perishable, we may assume that it will in fact ultimately be sold for $5 to some real customer in the regular course of the retailer's business. It would nevertheless be incorrect to conclude that $5 is the value of this leftover unit to the retailer on his evaluation date, since if the unit were suddenly to disappear on that date he could replace it at a cost of only $2 by simply adding one more unit to the next order that he places with the wholesaler. Because the retailer is thus exactly $2 better off on his evaluation date with the leftover unit than he would be without it, $2 is the proper value to assign to the leftover unit in valuing the retailer's total assets at the end position at which the leftover unit appears.

Observe that $2 *is* the value that the retailer will assign to the unit if he decides for how much cash he would be just willing to agree to sell the leftover unit *on* his evaluation date on the assumption that the sale will have no effect on the price at which he will be able to sell other assets *after* his evaluation date. Because the retailer could and would replace the leftover unit for $2 if he did sell it on his evaluation date, and because selling it on his evaluation date would not affect his ability to sell other units for a profit in the regular course of business, $2 is the price at which he would be just willing to agree now to sell the leftover unit on his evaluation date.

2.2.8
Dependence of Asset Value
on Other Assets

Although it very frequently happens that the value of an asset at an end position is equal either to its salvage value or to its replacement cost, it must not be assumed that asset value will always be equal to one or the other of these two market values. All that can be said in general is that salvage value establishes a floor under asset value and replacement cost establishes a ceiling. *The actual end-position value of an asset must in general be established judgmentally, and in general the value of an asset at any given end position may depend very substantially on the decision maker's other assets at that end position.*

Consider, for example, the leftover special tooling that Mallon will have at the end position following "stampings do not work", and suppose that although this tooling would cost $16,000 to replace, its net scrap value is only $2,500. Although these two market prices establish a ceiling over and a floor under the price for which Mallon would be just willing to agree now to sell the tooling if and when he actually arrives at the end position in question, they do not tell him where he should set his indifference price between these two limits. If he will be desperately short of cash at the end position following "stampings do not work", he may decide that he would in fact sell all of the tooling for scrap as soon as the XYZ order had been filled, in which case the price for which he would be just willing to agree now to sell it on his evaluation date would be exactly equal to its $2,500 value as scrap. If on the contrary he will have a large amount of idle cash in the bank at the end position following "stampings do not work", he may decide that he would retain the tooling for future use in his business rather than sell it for a mere $2,500 cash, in which case the price for which he *would* be just willing to agree to sell it might be, say, $7,500. If, as we assumed in Chapter 1, his cash position at the end position following "stampings do not work" will be neither desperate nor really comfortable, he may decide that although he would keep the tooling rather than sell it for $2,500, he would be ready to agree to sell it for as little as $5,000.

    Besides depending on the amount of cash that he will have on his evaluation date, the value that Mallon assigns to leftover tooling at any end position will depend on what he will be able to do with the tooling and thus on the whole complex of tangible and intangible nonmonetary assets which he will have at that end position. We conclude that:

> ■ In assigning monetary values to differences between his nonmonetary assets at any given end position and his nonmonetary assets at his base end position, the decision maker should imagine that he is already at the given end position and is really in the process of buying and selling asset differences for cash; and as he decides on his buying or selling price for each successive difference he must be careful to keep in mind both (1) the value of his monetary criterion as adjusted to reflect any "purchases" or "sales" already made, and (2) his total nonmonetary assets, again as adjusted to reflect any "purchases" or "sales" that have already been made.

2.2.9
Share of Market and Reported Income[2]

Our recommendation that the decision maker should value the end positions of his decision diagram by first describing and then assigning monetary values to the "assets" that he will have at these positions may seem at first glance to overlook the fact that in many decision problems a businessman will feel that one of the most important aspects of the consequence of any act-event sequence is its effect on the share of market that he will have on his evaluation date and/or the net income that he will report for some particular accounting period.[3] But while it is true that share of market and net income are not assets in the accounting sense, they are very definitely assets in the sense in which we have used the word throughout our previous discussion. As we said at the outset, anything to which the decision maker attaches value is to be counted as an asset in describing and valuing end positions.

---

[2] This section should be omitted on a first reading.
[3] We assume that the reader is familiar with at least some of the many reasons why the amount by which an act-event sequence affects net income may be quite different from the amount of the net cash flow to which the sequence gives rise.

What is more, no special problems arise when a decision maker sets out to take account of "assets" like share of market or reported income by the procedure we have described in previous sections. If, for example, a company's reported income at a given end position will be less than it is at the base end position, the decision maker can value this difference by deciding how much cash he would be just willing to agree now to pay for the advantage to be gained from reporting the same income at the given end position that he would report at the base end position. In so doing he must, however, remember that what he is buying for this price is only the advantage that he would gain from the *report*, since the difference between the actual *cash flows* that result from going to the two end positions is already reflected in the difference between the unadjusted values of his monetary criterion at the two positions.

2.2.10
Nonmonetary Criteria[4]

We have for some time now been occupied with various problems that can arise when a decision maker tries to value the end positions of a decision diagram by first calculating the actual value of some monetary criterion at each end position of his diagram and then "adjusting" these values to take account of nonmonetary consequences. We must remember, however, that there is no reason why the values assigned to the end positions of a decision diagram must be monetary. All that is really required is to find *some* way of replacing detailed descriptions of consequences by meaningful numerical values, and in some problems the most suitable values may well be nonmonetary.

Valuation of end positions by use of a monetary criterion will usually work well when the monetary aspect is the most important aspect of most if not all of the possible consequences in the decision problem at hand, and this will be true of most of the problems that we shall encounter in the course of our study. In some problems, however, the decision maker may feel that the most important aspect of the consequence of each act-event sequence is some nonmonetary aspect—e.g., the number of barrels of proved oil reserves that he will own as a result of the sequence; and when this is true, he may find it extremely hard to decide for how much cash he would be just willing to agree now to buy or sell very large differences between his nonmonetary assets at various end positions.

In such problems, the decision maker will usually do much better to base his entire valuation procedure on the use of a nonmonetary criterion. In the example just mentioned, the decision maker could select as his criterion the total number of barrels of proved oil reserves that he owns. The first step in the valuation procedure will then be to calculate the actual value of this nonmonetary criterion at each end position of the decision diagram; the second step will be to adjust the value of the criterion for all differences in other assets, in-

---

[4] This section should be omitted on a first reading.

cluding monetary assets, between the base end position and each other end position of the decision diagram.

2.3

CERTAINTY EQUIVALENTS

Assume now that a decision maker has chosen a monetary criterion for valuation of the end positions of his decision diagram, and assume that after calculating the actual terminal value of this criterion at each end position of the diagram he has chosen a base end position and adjusted the terminal value of his criterion at each other end position to allow for all differences between the nonmonetary assets he will have at that end position and the "base" nonmonetary assets he will have at his base end position. As we said in Section 2.2.6, he is now ready to solve his real decision problem by actually analyzing an equivalent substitute decision problem in which (1) his monetary assets at each end position are *in fact* equal to the "adjusted" value of his criterion at the corresponding end position of his real problem, and (2) his nonmonetary assets at each end position are *in fact* equal to the base nonmonetary assets that he will actually have at the base end position of his real problem.

We have already suggested via the example of Chapter 1 how the decision maker can decompose this equivalent substitute problem and analyze it systematically by assessing certainty equivalents for uncertain terminal values. We shall now examine the concept of a certainty equivalent more closely, calling attention to certain misunderstandings that frequently arise.

2.3.1

Definition of Certainty Equivalent

In order to define the expression "certainty equivalent" carefully, let us first agree to use the expression ≪terminal fork≫ to denote a fork all of whose branches lead directly to end positions of a decision diagram, and let us recall once more that although a different terminal value of the decision maker's criterion may be attached to each different end position of a terminal fork, his nonmonetary assets at every end position of a diagram that is ready for analysis will be exactly the same base nonmonetary assets that appear at the base end position. We can then say that:

■ A decision maker's ≪certainty equivalent≫ for the uncertain terminal value that will result from the gamble represented by a particular terminal event fork is the guaranteed terminal value that he would be just willing to agree now to accept in lieu of the uncertain value if and when he actually arrives at the base of the fork in question, it being understood that this guaranteed terminal value of his monetary criterion will be accompanied by *exactly the same base nonmonetary assets* that accompany the terminal criterion value associated to every end position of the decision diagram.

2.3.2
Certainty Equivalents and Nonmonetary Assets

In assessing a certainty equivalent for the uncertain terminal monetary value that will result from a gamble, it is absolutely essential to keep in mind the base nonmonetary assets that accompany all the monetary values being compared— the guaranteed value which is the certainty equivalent as well as the various possible monetary values that may result from the gamble. It may seem at first glance that because the nonmonetary assets that accompany any one of the monetary values are exactly the same as those that accompany any other, these nonmonetary assets could perfectly well be completely forgotten, but a simple example will suffice to show that this is by no means true.

Consider a decision maker named Dupont, whose decision diagram contains a terminal event fork with two branches, one leading to terminal net liquid assets of $+$100,000$ while the other leads to terminal net liquid assets of $+$300,000$; assume that Dupont feels that the two events represented by these branches are equally likely; and consider two different suppositions concerning the base nonmonetary assets that will accompany either the net liquid assets that result from the gamble or the guaranteed net liquid assets that Dupont might agree to accept as a certainty equivalent for the gamble.

1. If Dupont's nonmonetary assets are thoroughly adequate for the continuing conduct of his business, he may well argue that he would not be in a very difficult position even if he emerged from the gamble with net liquid assets of only $+$100,000$ rather than $+$300,000$; and accordingly he may well decide that he would insist on net liquid assets of at least $199,000 in exchange for the gamble.

2. If on the contrary Dupont's uninsured plant has just burned down and Dupont is desperately in need of $150,000 to rebuild it, he may well decide that he would be ready to accept guaranteed net liquid assets of $150,000 or possibly even a little less rather than run the risk of ending up with too little cash to rebuild his plant.

2.3.3
Certainty Equivalents vs. Market Values

In some decision problems, it is possible actually to obtain some definite terminal value in lieu of the uncertain terminal value that will result from a gamble, and at first glance it might seem that this "market value" for the gamble should affect the decision maker's certainty equivalent. Actually, however, this notion represents a complete misunderstanding of the meaning of a certainty equivalent, as can be shown by another very simple example.

Consider a Mr. Durand, whose only possession is a lottery ticket which will leave him with net liquid assets of $+$20 if a coin comes up heads when it is tossed tomorrow, otherwise $0; and suppose that if he makes up his mind to

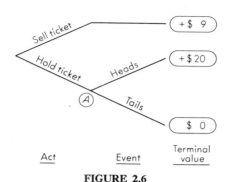

FIGURE 2.6

Mr. Durand's Decision Problem

do so within the next hour, Durand can sell this ticket for a price which will leave him with net liquid assets of $+\$9$, so that he faces the decision problem diagrammed in Figure 2.6. It is perfectly true that *in his present position*, at the origin of Figure 2.6, Durand would be unwilling to sell his ticket for any price that would leave him with less than the $+\$9$ of net liquid assets that he can have by accepting the offer for the ticket that he has actually received; but this by no means implies that his certainty equivalent for the uncertain terminal value that will result from the gamble at position A in Figure 2.6 cannot be less than $+\$9$. This certainty equivalent is by definition the guaranteed terminal value he would be just willing to agree now to accept *if and when he actually arrives at position A*, where the existing offer is no longer available; and it is quite conceivable that Durand would be quite willing to accept only $+\$5$, say, in lieu of the gamble, if by inadvertence he should allow the existing offer to expire and thus did in fact arrive at position A.

In other words, whether or not Durand actually wants to choose the act "hold ticket" and go to position A as a result is not a factor to be considered when he assesses his certainty equivalent for the uncertain terminal value that he will face *if* he goes to position A. On the contrary, his choice of act is a *consequence* of his assessment in the sense that he will actually go to position A only if his assessed certainty equivalent for the uncertain terminal value that he will face there is at least as great as the definite terminal value he will obtain by choosing the act "sell ticket".

Assessment of Certainty Equivalents vs. Valuation of Assets at End Positions   The fact that a decision maker's certainty equivalent for the uncertain terminal value represented by an event fork should not be affected by any definite terminal value he can actually obtain in place of the uncertain value may seem inconsistent with the assertion in Section 2.2.7 that the value a decision maker should assign to an asset at an end position will often depend on the price for which he can actually buy or sell that asset. In fact, however, these two assessment problems are quite different, and no inconsistency exists.

Real opportunities for purchase or sale of an asset at an *end position* must be considered in valuing such an asset because these opportunities will actually be available to the decision maker when he reaches the end position in question. Real opportunities to obtain a definite terminal value in lieu of the uncertain terminal value represented by an *event fork* must be explicitly repreresented by an act fork on the decision diagram and therefore must not be considered in assessing a certainty equivalent for the event fork because they will no longer be available when the decision maker reaches the base of the event fork.

2.3.4
Likings for Consequences
and Judgments about Chances

We have already pointed out in Chapter 1 that there are two quite different kinds of consideration to which a decision maker should pay attention in assessing his certainty equivalent for the uncertain terminal value represented by any given terminal event fork. They are:

1 His relative degree of *liking* for each of the possible *consequences* described by the various terminal values associated to the various branches of the fork.

2 The *chance* (as he sees it) of each of the possible *events* represented by the various branches of the fork, some one of which will determine the consequence that the decision maker actually enjoys.

In a later chapter we shall see how a decision maker can decompose a problem of assessing a certainty equivalent and take account of each of these two kinds of considerations separately. For the time being, however, we argue only that even a decision maker who does not know how to decompose such an assessment problem can reach a *decision* on a certainty equivalent that takes account of both kinds of consideration simultaneously. Because he can decide whether or not he prefers the uncertain terminal value represented by any particular terminal event fork to any given guaranteed terminal value, he can decide what is the smallest guaranteed terminal value that he would be willing to agree now to accept if and when he actually faces the uncertain terminal value in question.

2.3.5
"Estimates" vs. Decisions

Although a decision maker can always decide on some one, definite value as his certainty equivalent for the uncertain terminal value represented by a given terminal event fork, he will often find it difficult to do so. Often he will feel that he might just as well select any one value in some fairly wide range as any other;

and for this reason the reader may be tempted to think of the certainty equivalent actually assessed by the decision maker as being a kind of "estimate" of his "true" certainty equivalent and as being therefore subject to some kind of "range of error".

Notions of this sort amount, however, to a complete misunderstanding of the meaning of a certainty equivalent.

■ There exists no such thing as a "true though unknown" certainty equivalent, and therefore there exists no such thing as an "estimate" of a true certainty equivalent. A certainty equivalent is purely and simply a *decision;* and it follows that no matter how hard it may be for a decision maker to decide on one particular value among all possible values for a given certainty equivalent, the value he decides on is to be thought of as exact and accurate to an infinite number of decimal places.

A decision maker who must assess a certainty equivalent is really in exactly the same kind of situation as a purchasing agent who must place an order for a certain number of units of part XB–411 even though he does not know exactly how many units he "should" order at this time. The purchasing agent cannot conveniently get out of his difficulties by placing an order for "somewhere between 200 and 300" units. If he does not *decide* that he will order exactly 250 units, say, he will have to decide that he will order exactly some other number of units; and whatever number of units he decides to order, however unhappily, that is the number his company will have to pay for and will have available for use.

2.4
ANALYSIS BY EVALUATION
OF INDIVIDUAL ACTS

Now that we have carefully examined the concept of a certainty equivalent for an uncertain terminal value, which lies at the heart of any method of decomposition and systematic analysis of a problem of decision under uncertainty, we are ready to state the general rules for the method of analysis by ≪evaluation of individual acts≫ that we applied to an example in Chapter 1.

2.4.1
Reduction of Terminal Event Forks

The definition in Section 2.3.1 of a certainty equivalent for the uncertain terminal value represented by a terminal event fork implies that the position at the base of any terminal event fork is exactly as attractive to the decision maker as it would be if upon arriving at this position he would in fact obtain a definite terminal value equal to his certainty equivalent for the uncertain terminal value represented by the fork. Accordingly:

■ After the decision maker has assessed his certainty equivalent for the uncertain terminal value represented by a terminal event fork, he may analyze his decision problem as if the position at the base of the fork were an *end* position with a definite terminal value equal to his assessed certainty equivalent and with the same base nonmonetary assets that appear at all the other end positions of his diagram.

What this really means is that instead of analyzing his real decision problem, the decision maker may solve that problem by analyzing a *substitute decision problem* in which the terminal event fork of the real problem is replaced by an end position with definite, well defined total assets. Because these definite total assets are exactly as attractive to the decision maker as the gamble represented by the original terminal event fork, the two problems are equivalent in the sense that the decision maker should prefer the same acts in his real problem that analysis leads him to prefer in the substitute problem.

What we have hitherto described at length as "the decision maker's certainty equivalent for the uncertain terminal value represented by a terminal event fork" can therefore be referred to more simply as the (definite) terminal value that the decision maker "assigns" to the position at the base of the fork. Although we shall sometimes refer to such a terminal value as a "certainty-equivalent terminal value", we shall do so merely in order to remind the reader of the process by which the decision maker decided on the value. After the value has once been decided on, the decision maker should think of it as a perfectly ordinary terminal value at a perfectly ordinary end position in a substitute decision problem.

2.4.2
Reduction of Terminal Act Forks

When the decision maker has replaced all the terminal event forks on the original diagram of his real decision problem by definite terminal values, he will find that the resulting ≪reduced diagram≫ of an equivalent substitute decision problem contains terminal act forks with definite terminal values attached to the ends of their branches. In the analysis of A. H. Mallon's XYZ decision problem, such an act fork first appeared at position X in Figure 1.6 (page 15).

If the decision maker ever actually-arrives at the base of any given act fork in his decision diagram, he will of course select the act on that fork to which he assigned the greatest terminal value in the course of his analysis. Accordingly:

■ The decision maker may analyze his decision problem as if the position at the base of any terminal act fork were actually an *end* position with a definite terminal value equal to the greatest of the terminal values assigned to the various branches of the fork and with the same base nonmonetary assets that appear at all the other end positions of his diagram.

In other words, the decision maker can solve the decision problem in which the terminal act fork appears by analyzing a simpler equivalent problem in which the act fork is replaced by an end position with definite, well defined total assets.

2.4.3
Analysis by Evaluation
of Individual Acts

From what we have said in Sections 2.4.1 and 2.4.2, it follows that a decision maker can analyze a problem by working backward on the decision diagram in the way illustrated in Figure 1.9 on page 20.

1. The decision maker first selects some one terminal *event* fork on the diagram, assigns a definite terminal value to the position at its base by assessing his *certainty equivalent* for the uncertain terminal value represented by the fork, eliminates the fork from the diagram, and then repeats this procedure for other terminal event forks until there are no terminal event forks left on the diagram.

2. If step 1 does not yield a definite terminal value for every immediate act, the decision maker next selects some one of the terminal *act* forks that now appear on his diagram, assigns to the position at its base the *greatest* terminal value that appears at the end of any of its branches, eliminates the fork from the diagram, and then repeats the procedure for other terminal act forks until there are no terminal act forks left on the diagram.

3. The decision maker then returns to step 1 and repeats the entire procedure until it has resulted in assigning a definite terminal value to every immediate act, after which he has only to select the immediate act with the greatest terminal value.

As we said in Chapter 1, this method of analysis is called analysis by "evaluation of individual acts" because it leads to assignment of a definite value to every act on every act fork in the decision diagram.

2.5
ANALYSIS BY EVALUATION
OF COMPLETE STRATEGIES

When Mr. A. H. Mallon analyzed his problem of deciding whether or not to build a prototype for XYZ, the conclusion that the immediate act "build prototype" was preferable to the immediate act "do not build" was not the only conclusion to which his analysis led. His analysis led also to the conclusion that if his chosen immediate act were to be followed by the event "XYZ orders", then the act "tool to stamp" should be chosen in preference to the act "tool to machine". In other words, Mallon's analysis led, not merely to choice of an immediate act, but to choice of a *complete course of action* or "strategy" for dealing with the complete decision problem at hand.

We shall now show how a decision problem can be analyzed, not by systematically assigning values to individual acts on individual act forks, but by first describing all the complete strategies that the decision maker wishes to consider and then systematically assigning a value to each such strategy. We do so, not because this new form of analysis is actually more convenient in certain special circumstances, as we shall see much later on, but because a decision maker can often gain a clearer understanding of certain aspects of a problem of decision under uncertainty by thinking in terms of strategies even though he will actually analyze his problem by evaluation of individual acts.

2.5.1
Definition of Strategy

As we suggested above, a complete course of action for dealing with a problem of decision under uncertainty is called a strategy. More specifically:

- A ≪strategy≫ is a rule which prescribes exactly what act shall be chosen in every situation in which a choice may have to be made before the evaluation date is reached.

The strategy that A. H. Mallon decided to adopt as a result of the analysis described in Chapter 1 is defined by the rule:

- Choose the act "build prototype", then if the event "XYZ orders" occurs, choose the act "tool to stamp".

In more complex decision problems, a rule defining a strategy might consist of a very long list of instructions specifying the act to be chosen if and when each possible successive event becomes known to the decision maker.

2.5.2
Strategies Implicit
in a Decision Diagram

After a decision maker has constructed a diagram of his decision problem and evaluated the consequence at each end position of his diagram, he can systematically extract from his diagram descriptions of all the possible strategies implicit therein. The procedure by which he can do so can best be suggested by showing how we could have described all the strategies implicit in the decision diagram in Figure 1.5 (page 13) of Mr. A. H. Mallon's XYZ decision problem.

Starting with the act fork at the origin of Figure 1.5, we see that any strategy must start by telling Mallon whether to choose the act "build prototype" or the act "do not build". If the strategy prescribes the latter act, it carries Mallon down a path which leads to an end position of the diagram without requiring any further choice of act, and therefore we have already defined one complete strategy, namely:

STRATEGY I: Do not build prototype.

If, on the contrary, a strategy tells Mallon to start by choosing the act "build prototype" on the initial act fork in Figure 1.5, then the event "XYZ orders" may occur and carry him to a position where he must make a second choice, between stampings and machinings; and therefore "build prototype" does not by itself describe a well defined strategy or complete course of action. There are in fact two different strategies both of which begin with this same act, namely:

> STRATEGY II: Build prototype and then:
> > if XYZ orders, tool to machine;
> > if XYZ does not order, stop.

> STRATEGY III: Build prototype and then:
> > if XYZ orders, tool to stamp;
> > if XYZ does not order, stop.

Each of these two rules does define a complete strategy, because each of them does prescribe all the choices that Mallon may have to make before reaching an end position of Figure 1.5.

Generalizing from this example, we see that one of the strategies implicit in any decision diagram can be defined by selecting one branch on the initial or "first-level" act fork at the origin of the diagram, then selecting a branch on each "second-level" act fork that can be reached from the selected branch on the first-level fork, and continuing in this way until the decision maker can have no further choices to make before reaching an end position of the diagram. *All* the strategies that are implicit in the diagram can be defined by making all possible sequences of choices on the act forks in the diagram.

Diagrams of Individual Strategies   At the same time that the strategies implicit in the decision diagram are being identified, a separate diagram of each individual strategy can be constructed. Separate diagrams of the three strategies implicit in Figure 1.5 are shown in Figure 2.7A; the reader should observe that:

- ■ Although the diagram of an individual strategy must contain event forks showing all the events that may occur if the strategy in question is followed, it must not contain any act forks—instead, it must contain single act branches showing what particular act is prescribed by the strategy initially and as each successive event occurs.

2.5.3
Analysis by Evaluation of Complete Strategies

Once a strategy has been diagrammed, the decision maker can evaluate it by a form of backward induction which is identical to the backward induction used to analyze a complete decision diagram except that no choices of acts have to be made.

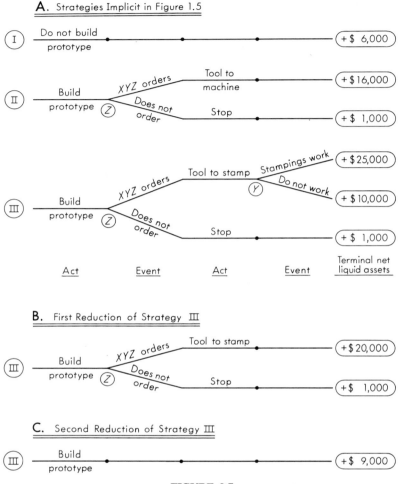

FIGURE 2.7
Strategies in A. H. Mallon's Decision Problem

Taking strategy III in Figure 2.7A as our first example, we start with the terminal event fork at position Y in its diagram and ask Mallon to assess his certainty equivalent for the uncertain terminal value represented by that fork. Assuming as we did in Section 1.2.2 that Mallon's certainty equivalent is $+\$20,000$, we can reduce the diagram of strategy III in Figure 2.7A to the simpler form in Figure 2.7B, which shows that Mallon's assessment means that strategy III is exactly as attractive to him as it would be if the act "tool to stamp" were sure to lead to a terminal value of $+\$20,000$.

Next, we go to the terminal event fork at position Z in this simplified diagram and ask Mallon to assess his certainty equivalent for the uncertain terminal value represented by this fork. Assuming as we did in Section 1.2.4 that Mallon's certainty equivalent is $+\$9,000$, we can reduce Figure 2.7B to

Figure 2.7C; and we see that Mallon's two assessments have implied that strategy III is exactly as attractive to him as it would be if it were sure to lead to a +$9,000 terminal value. We can say that Mallon's certainty-equivalent terminal value for strategy III is +$9,000.

Having obtained Mallon's certainty equivalent for the uncertain terminal value that will result from strategy III in Figure 2.7, we next take strategy II and ask Mallon to assess his certainty equivalent for the uncertain terminal value represented by the terminal event fork at position Z in the diagram of that strategy. This terminal event fork was not evaluated by Mallon in his earlier analysis; we shall assume by way of example that Mallon now assigns it a certainty-equivalent value of +$7,000.

The remainder of the analysis of Mallon's problem by «evaluation of complete strategies» is purely mechanical. By Figure 2.7, strategy I is sure to yield a terminal value of +$6,000; Mallon's assessments imply that strategies II and III are exactly as attractive to him as they would be if they were sure to yield terminal values of +$7,000 and +$9,000 respectively; and therefore strategy III is the strategy that he should choose.

2.5.4
Equivalence of the Two Methods of Analysis

Most of the results of the analysis by evaluation of complete strategies that we have just described agree exactly with the results of Mallon's earlier analysis by evaluation of individual acts, which is summarized in Figure 1.9 on page 20. Specifically, both analyses assigned the same +$6,000 value to strategy I, "do not build prototype", and both analyses assigned the same +$9,000 value to strategy III, "build prototype and then tool to stamp if XYZ orders". (Formally, this latter value was assigned to the individual act "built prototype" in the earlier analysis, but because it was not assigned until after Mallon had decided that he would tool to stamp if XYZ ordered, we can equally well think of it as the value assigned by that analysis to the complete strategy "build prototype and then tool to stamp if XYZ orders".)

Nor is this agreement between the results of the two analyses a mere coincidence or a consequence of arbitrary assumptions. The values assigned by the two analyses to strategies I and III *had* to agree because they were derived in both cases from Mallon's evaluations of exactly the same end positions and Mallon's certainty equivalents for exactly the same uncertain terminal values, namely (1) the uncertain terminal value that he will face at position Y in Figure 1.9A and Figure 2.7A, and (2) the uncertain terminal value that he will face at position Z in Figure 1.9C and Figure 2.7B.

The one and only difference between the results of the two analyses regards strategy II, which was assigned a value of +$7,000 when Mallon analyzed his problem by evaluation of complete strategies but which was not evaluated at all when he analyzed his problem by evaluation of individual acts.

This does not mean, however, that when Mallon analyzed his problem by evaluation of complete strategies he was free to assign a higher value to strategy II than he assigned to strategy III and thus to reach a different conclusion by evaluation of complete strategies than he had reached by evaluation of individual acts. If we compare the gamble involved in strategy II in Figure 2.7A with the gamble involved in strategy III in Figure 2.7B, we see that whereas both gambles will yield the same terminal value if XYZ does not order, the gamble in strategy III will yield a higher terminal value if XYZ does order. It follows that Mallon's assessments would have been logically *inconsistent* if in analyzing his problem by evaluation of complete strategies he had assigned a greater terminal value to strategy II than he assigned to strategy III.

Returning now to Figure 1.9, let us observe why it was that strategy II was never assigned a definite terminal value when Mallon analyzed his problem by evaluation of individual acts. The reason was simply that this complete strategy, which calls for "tool to machine" if XYZ orders, was eliminated from the decision diagram as soon as Mallon assigned a higher value to the individual act "tool to stamp" than he had assigned to the act "tool to machine". As a result of this same valuation, however, Mallon became logically obliged to assign a lower value to strategy II than he assigned to strategy III when he analyzed his problem by evaluation of complete strategies, and what is true in this example is true in general.

■ If all the certainty equivalents assessed by a decision maker in an analysis by evaluation of complete strategies are logically consistent with the certainty equivalents he would assess in an analysis by evaluation of individual acts, the two methods of analysis will necessarily lead to choice of exactly the same strategy and hence to choice of exactly the same immediate act.

In a later chapter we shall describe indirect methods for assessing certainty equivalents which ensure that all of a decision maker's certainty equivalents will in fact be logically consistent and at the same time greatly reduce the time and effort required to assess them. When certainty equivalents are assessed by these indirect methods, analysis by evaluation of complete strategies and analysis by evaluation of individual acts are not only logically equivalent in principle but certain in fact to yield exactly the same results in any decision problem. Which method should be used in any particular decision problem then becomes a purely technical question of computational convenience that the decision maker can delegate to a technical assistant.

2.5.5
Completeness of a Decision Diagram

When we stated the general rules for diagramming decision problems in Section 2.1.5, we said that a decision diagram must show, not only all the immediate acts

among which the decision maker actually wishes to choose now, but also all uncertain events and future acts that he wishes to consider because they may
directly or indirectly affect the consequences of his immediate act. Using the
concept of strategies, we can reexpress this "completeness" requirement somewhat more clearly.

1 The decision diagram must show all *strategies* which the decision maker
wishes to consider. If it fails to do so, it may be said to be ≪structurally
incomplete≫.

2 The decision diagram must show all events which could materially affect
the *value* of the decision maker's criterion on his evaluation date. If it
fails to do so, it may be said to be ≪valuationally incomplete≫.

2.6
SUMMARY

2.6.1
Delimitation of a Decision Problem

When a decision maker must choose one among a number of possible immediate
acts, the ultimate consequences of some if not all of these acts will in general
depend on uncertain events and future acts extending indefinitely far into the
future. In principle, the decision maker would like to take systematic account
of the effects of all these uncertain events and possible future acts, but since this
is impossible,

■ The decision maker must delimit his decision problem by selecting some
definite ≪evaluation date≫ beyond which it is not worthwhile in his
judgment to try to take account of the effects of specific acts and events.
He will describe his problem in terms of only those acts and events that
may be chosen by or become known to him before he reaches his evaluation date, and he will evaluate the consequences of these acts and events
as they will appear to him directly upon reaching his evaluation date.

2.6.2
Decision Diagrams

After a decision problem has been delimited by a definite evaluation date, it can
be described by a ≪decision diagram≫.

1 A decision diagram consists of interconnected branches each of which
represents either an act which the decision maker may choose or an
event of which the decision maker may learn.

2 A choice among acts is represented by an act fork; an uncertainty about
events is represented by an event fork. The events or acts on any one

fork must be (1) mutually exclusive in the sense that no more than one of them can possibly occur or be chosen, and (2) collectively exhaustive in the sense that some one of them must occur or be chosen.

3 The order in which act and event forks appear in a decision diagram must be such that the path from the origin of the diagram to the base of any act fork gives a correct representation of the information that will and will not be available to the decision maker when he actually has to make the choice represented by the act fork in question.

4 To be complete, a decision diagram must show (1) all the immediate acts among which the decision maker wishes to choose, (2) all future acts and uncertain events he wishes to consider because they may directly affect the consequences of the immediate acts, and (3) all uncertain events that he wishes to consider because they may affect his future choices among acts and thus indirectly affect the consequences of the immediate acts.

For an alternative definition of completeness in terms of strategies, see paragraph 3 in Section 2.6.6 below.

2.6.3
Valuation of Consequences

After a decision diagram has been constructed, the decision maker must describe the consequence of every act-event sequence in the diagram, but before proceeding to the actual analysis of his problem he will usually do well to replace each such description by a numerical value. In this book, the discussion of assigning such values will be restricted to ≪short-term≫ decision problems where dates are relevant only insofar as they affect the *amount* of interest actually paid or received.

When consequences are wholly or primarily of a financial or monetary nature, a decision maker can frequently assign values to them by proceeding as follows:

1 The decision maker first selects that single measure of *monetary* assets whose value best describes his general business position. This quantity will be called his ≪criterion≫ for valuation of consequences and its value on his evaluation date will be called its ≪terminal value≫.

Very frequently, a good choice for the criterion will be ≪net liquid assets≫, defined as cash on hand, plus all claims to receive cash which will or could be realized in the near future, minus all obligations to pay cash which will or could be enforced in the near future.

2 The decision maker next calculates the actual terminal value of his criterion that will result from each act-event sequence on his decision diagram and records this value at the corresponding end position.

These terminal values will depend, not only on the cash flows associated with acts and events that are directly connected with the decision problem at hand, but also on the net ≪contextual≫ cash flow resulting from the decision maker's "other business". Consequently any uncertainty that the decision maker may have concerning the contextual flow must be explicitly represented in the decision diagram.

3 After selecting a ≪base end position≫, the decision maker next writes down opposite each other end position all *differences* between his *non-monetary* assets at that position and the ≪base nonmonetary assets≫ that he will have at the base end position.

4 Finally, the decision maker ≪adjusts≫ the value of his criterion at each end position to reflect the value of these differences in nonmonetary assets by deciding for how much cash he would be just willing to agree now to buy or sell the differences if and when he arrives at the end position in question.

5 The decision maker can now solve his real decision problem by analyzing an equivalent *substitute decision problem* in which (1) the actual value of his criterion at each end position is equal to its adjusted value at the corresponding end position of his real problem, and (2) his nonmonetary assets are identical at every end position to those he will actually have at the base end position of his real problem.

When consequences are wholly or primarily of a nonmonetary nature, it may be better to use a measure of some nonmonetary asset as a criterion. See Section 2.2.10.

2.6.4
Certainty Equivalents
and Equivalent Decision Problems

If the term ≪terminal fork≫ is used to denote any fork all of whose branches terminate in end positions, then:

1 A decision maker's ≪certainty equivalent≫ for the uncertain terminal value represented by a particular terminal event fork is the guaranteed terminal value that he would be just willing to agree now to accept in lieu of the uncertain terminal value if and when he arrives at the base of the fork in question, it being understood that this guaranteed value of the decision maker's criterion asset will be accompanied by exactly the same base nonmonetary assets that are present at all end positions of his decision diagram.

2 Because the position at the base of a terminal event fork is exactly as attractive to the decision maker as it would be if it would actually yield a definite terminal value equal to his assessed certainty equivalent, he can solve the decision problem in which the fork appears by analyzing a simpler substitute decision problem in which the position at the base of the fork is treated as an end position with a definite terminal value equal to his certainty equivalent.

Because every consequence in the substitute problem is exactly as attractive to the decision maker as the corresponding consequence in the original problem, the two problems are equivalent in the sense that the decision maker should prefer the same acts in the original problem that analysis leads him to prefer in the substitute problem.

    3 Because on a terminal act fork the decision maker will choose the act with the greatest terminal value, he can solve the decision problem in which the fork appears by analyzing a simpler substitute decision problem in which the position at the base of the fork is treated as an end position with a definite terminal value equal to the greatest terminal value associated to any branch of the original fork.

Again, the original and the substitute problems are equivalent in the sense that the decision maker should prefer the same acts in the original problem that analysis leads him to prefer in the substitute problem.

2.6.5
Analysis by Evaluation of Individual Acts

    ■ To analyze a decision problem by ≪evaluation of individual acts≫, the decision maker works backward on the diagram of his decision problem, alternately replacing terminal event forks and terminal act forks by definite terminal values until all event forks have been eliminated and he has assigned a definite terminal value to every act on the act fork at the origin of the diagram.

2.6.6
Analysis by Evaluation
of Complete Strategies

    1 A ≪strategy≫ is a rule which prescribes exactly what act shall be chosen in every situation in which a choice may have to be made before the evaluation date is reached.

    2 One of the strategies implicit in a decision diagram may be defined by selecting a branch on the initial or first-level act fork at the origin of a decision diagram, then selecting a branch on each second-level act fork that can be reached from the selected branch on the first-level act fork, and continuing in this way until the decision maker can have no further choices to make before reaching an end position of the diagram. All the strategies that are implicit in a decision diagram can be defined by making all possible sequences of choices on the act forks in the complete decision diagram.

3 To be complete, a decision diagram must show (1) all the strategies the decision maker wishes to consider, and (2) all the events the decision maker wishes to consider because they may affect the terminal value of his criterion.

4 An individual strategy can be described by a diagram which resembles a complete decision diagram except for the fact that it contains no act forks. Instead, it contains single act branches representing the acts prescribed by the strategy.

5 To analyze a decision problem by ≪evaluation of complete strategies≫, the decision maker first constructs a separate diagram of each strategy. He then evaluates each strategy by working backward on its diagram, replacing terminal event forks by definite certainty-equivalent terminal values until all forks have been eliminated and he has assigned a definite terminal value to the strategy as a whole.

6 Provided that all the decision maker's certainty equivalents are logically consistent, analysis by evaluation of complete strategies must lead to choice of exactly the same strategy and hence the same immediate act that would be chosen as a result of analysis by evaluation of individual acts.

EXERCISES

A. DECISION PROBLEMS AND DECISION DIAGRAMS

2.1   In analyzing an investment opportunity he has recently been offered, Mr. Robert Kent takes July 17, 1969, as his evaluation date and selects as his criterion the sum of his cash and the market value of his securities. One of the terminal event forks in his decision diagram is reproduced as Figure 2.8, which shows that if Kent reaches position A and event X then occurs, the terminal value of his criterion will be $+\$100,000$, whereas if event Y occurs, the terminal value of his criterion will be only $+\$10,000$.

As Kent tries to assess his certainty equivalent for the uncertain terminal value at position A in Figure 2.8, he is unsure how to take account

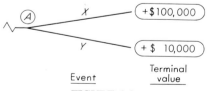

FIGURE 2.8
Robert Kent's Decision Problem

of what he feels to be a substantial chance that sometime in fall of 1969 he will be offered an opportunity to participate in a venture which he thinks very likely to prove extremely lucrative. He is not sure how much capital he will have to put up to enter into this venture, but he thinks it not unlikely that the minimum might be as high as $50,000; he does not believe that he could borrow any substantial part of this amount.

a If you were in Kent's position, would you allow an opportunity which cannot materialize until after your evaluation date to affect your certainty equivalent for the uncertain value of your criterion on your evaluation date?

b If your answer to (*a*) is no, why? If your answer to (*a*) is yes, why, and in what way?

c Whether your answer to (*a*) is yes or no, is there any other way of bringing the deal that may materialize in the fall into the analysis of the deal that Kent is currently considering? If there is, should it be so brought in?

2.2 Although the terms of the deal with Mr. Smith that was described in Exercise 1.2 do not allow you to ask to see the hands of the student you question on the steps of your school library, you may nevertheless be able to see whether his fingers have tobacco stains before you tell Smith whether you wish to "Stop" or to "Continue".

Draw a diagram of your decision problem that takes account of this possibility.

2.3 A manufacturer must decide whether or not to accept a special order at a fixed price of $100,000; he believes that the out-of-pocket cost of filling the order may be anywhere between $50,000 and $125,000. His evaluation date for analysis of this problem is the end of his fiscal year; as his criterion, he has chosen his net liquid assets, which currently amount to $+$50,000. He feels sure that he will receive no more special orders during the period between now and his evaluation date, but he is very uncertain about sales of his regular products during that period and hence about the net cash flow that will result from these sales. All that he feels sure of is that this net cash flow will be somewhere between $-$20,000 and $+$100,000.

Letting x denote the cost of filling the special order and y denote the net contextual cash flow that will result from sales of the manufacturer's regular products, diagram his decision problem schematically but do not value the end positions.

2.4 A manufacturer has an immediate requirement for 10,000 connector pins and an equal number of bushings for use in filling an order for a special product, but he is uncertain whether he should buy them from a vendor or make them in his own shop. It is clearly uneconomical either to buy or to make less than 10,000 pins or 10,000 bushings in one lot, but it may be economical to make the pins and buy the bushings or vice versa. The costs of purchasing and/or manufacturing the pins and the bushings will not depend on the order in which they are purchased and/or manufactured; and no information about the costs pertaining to either item will be gained by purchasing or manufacturing the other.

Construct three different subdiagrams representing the set of acts (not complete act-event sequences) among which the manufacturer must choose.

2.5   The PQR Company has received an order from the LMN Company for a batch of a certain chemical, but management is uncertain whether or not to accept the order. The chemical is so unstable that the reaction used to produce it may get out of control and cause an explosion completely destroying the production facilities, and even if no explosion occurs, the finished batch of chemical may fail to meet specifications and have to be scrapped. If the order is accepted, the required labor and raw material will cost $20,000 out of pocket, all of which will be lost if an explosion occurs or if the product is unsatisfactory. If a satisfactory product is delivered, LMN will pay $50,000. The damage done to the plant by an explosion would cost $75,000 to repair.

Construct three different subdiagrams representing the events which may occur if PQR accepts the LMN order.

2.6   The Brown Chemical Company has just completed production of a batch of RB–73, a chemical reagent used by the Smith Manufacturing Corporation in the final stage of the production of a resinated polymer. Just as Brown's production manager is about to ship the batch of RB–73, he learns that one of its constituent chemicals may have come from a batch containing impurities and therefore the batch of RB–73 may not perform satisfactorily for Smith. If the batch is shipped to Smith and does not perform satisfactorily, the other components of the polymer will be ruined and Brown will be obliged not only to supply another batch of RB–73 free of charge but also to reimburse Smith for the production cost of the ruined polymer.

Rather than decide immediately whether to ship this batch or to scrap it and manufacture another batch which he can be sure will be good, the production manager can first subject this batch to a test which will give either a favorable or an unfavorable indication concerning the batch's quality, although neither indication can be accepted as definite assurance of the performance of the batch if it is used by Smith Manufacturing.

To help him decide what to do about the batch which has just been produced, the production manager calls in a young member of Brown

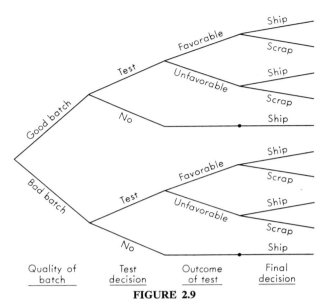

FIGURE 2.9

Analyst's Diagram of Brown Chemical's Decision Problem

Chemical's operations analysis staff and explains the problem to him. After several hours the operations analyst returns with the diagram shown in Figure 2.9 and tells the production manager: "I've represented the things that can happen in the order in which they occur. The batch is either good or bad as soon as it's been manufactured; testing can't change its nature. Of course, the test is not infallible, so it still isn't perfectly certain whether or not we should ship the batch, regardless of the outcome of the test."

Does this diagram correctly represent the logical structure of the production manager's decision problem?

2.7 Mr. Horace Black, an oil wildcatter, holds an option to drill for oil on a certain plot of land and must choose very shortly among three possible alternatives:

1 Have a well drilled on a fixed-price contract for a cost of $100,000.

2 Abandon his rights.

3 Have a seismic survey made on a fixed-price contract at a cost of $25,000 in order to learn more about the chance of striking oil and *then* decide whether to drill or abandon his rights.

Black has already signed a firm contract with the holder of a lease on a neighboring property to sell out immediately for $400,000 *if* he drills and strikes oil, the purchaser to take his chances on the amount of oil that will actually be recovered. Black's rights are worthless if he does not drill or if he drills and fails to strike oil.

Black has chosen his net liquid assets, which currently amount to +$250,000, as his criterion for analyzing this problem; he has selected an evaluation date just far enough in the future to include any cash flows that may result from drilling, from a seismic survey, or from the sale of a successful well; and he believes that these are the only cash flows that can occur before this evaluation date.

If a seismic survey is made, the information it yields will be reported simply as "favorable" or "unfavorable" to the existence of oil beneath the surface and will not be infallible; that is, there is a chance of finding oil even though the seismic indication is "unfavorable" and a chance of drilling a dry hole even though the seismic indication is "favorable".

Diagram Mr. Black's decision problem but do not describe the consequences.

B. VALUATION OF MONETARY CONSEQUENCES

2.8   Value the end positions of the diagram you drew in answer to Exercise 2.7.

2.9   The Toscanini Harmonica & Kazoo Co. presently has net liquid assets of $5,000. The President of Toscanini, Mr. Fazulli, faces the problem of deciding whether to travel to Sheboygan for three days to try to sell the Nivel Novelty Co. a shipment of kazoos for use as a promotion premium. Fazulli already has the kazoos in stock and he is fairly confident but by no means sure that if he makes the trip Nivel will buy them for $2,000; he is certain that if he does not make the trip, he will not get the order. If the kazoos are not sold to Nivel Novelty, Fazulli will unload them on the Musical Distress Company, whose president has agreed to purchase them for $1,500 cash on November 5.

Fazulli is not particularly worried about the expenses of the trip to Sheboygan, which would amount to only $300. His main concern is that his absence from the plant, even for only three days, might lead to production inefficiencies which would cause Toscanini to miss the contract deadline for delivery of 750 harmonicas to the Harmonica Corp. of America. Harmonica Corp. will pay Toscanini $3,000 on November 1 if the harmonicas are delivered on or before that date, but any lateness will result in a penalty reducing the on-time delivery price by $800. Whether or not the harmonica order is completed on time, Fazulli feels completely sure that his absence will result in wastage of materials which will increase the total cash cost of production of the harmonica order to $2,500; if he does not go to Sheboygan, the total cost of harmonica production will be only $2,100.

Mr. Fazulli plans to begin production of the harmonica order tomorrow, and he is sure that it will be delivered no later than November 3 even if he goes to Sheboygan, no later than October 31 if he does not make the trip. Excluding the production cost and revenue associated with the harmonica order and the revenue that will be received through sale of the

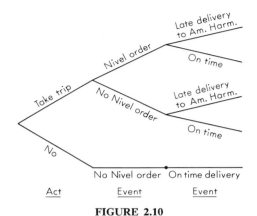

FIGURE 2.10

Mr. Fazulli's Decision Problem

kazoos, Toscanini will incur a net cash outflow of $1,000 through its other operations during the period from now through November 5. With these facts in mind, Fazulli has chosen November 5 as his evaluation date and net liquid assets as his criterion for analysis of his problem of deciding whether or not to go to Sheboygan, and he has drawn the decision diagram shown in Figure 2.10.

a Value the end positions of Figure 2.10.

b Without any further information or assessments, can Fazulli decide whether or not to take the trip to Sheboygan? If he can decide, what should he do?

C. VALUATION BY FORMULA

2.10 a Write down the dollar value of the manufacturer's criterion at every end position of your diagram for Exercise 2.3 at which the actual dollar value can be computed.

    b Give a formula in terms of x and/or y for the value of the manufacturer's criterion at every end position at which the value depends on x and/or y.

D. VALUATION OF NONMONETARY CONSEQUENCES

2.11 Mrs. I. J. Kresge, sole proprietor of Kresge Home Comforts, Inc., the holder of an exclusive franchise for operating a lunch counter at an elite midwestern trade school, must decide how many of her renowned *soufflés maison* to prepare for her 20 customers at lunch today. Because the soufflés are finished by a secret aging process, they must all be prepared well before the customers arrive for lunch. The out-of-pocket cost of producing each soufflé is $.30; its price to a customer is $.90. Members of the Kresge staff with sturdy household pets are always happy to pay $.10 each for any soufflés left over after lunch.

In order to keep expenses down, Mrs. Kresge has an established policy of offering a limited menu of only two luncheon selections, but since Kresge Home Comforts has the exclusive noontime meal concession, none of the 20 customers ever refuses the alternate selection when his preferred selection runs out. Today Mrs. Kresge's customers are indeed fortunate, for she is offering as the alternate selection her *paté froid*, a staple item which finds its way onto the menu with striking regularity. Experience has shown that the paté can be stored almost indefinitely without any noticeable deterioration in taste, a fact which has led to a policy of producing it in batches of 50 servings; there is presently nearly a full batch on hand. A serving of paté is, unfortunately, a low-profit item, having an out-of-pocket cost of \$.40 and selling for only \$.50.

After some thought, Mrs. Kresge has decided to measure the result of today's operations by the amount of cash she has in the till at the end of the day. At the present moment, the till contains \$500, since Mrs. Kresge likes to operate her business with working capital more than adequate for any possible combination of circumstances.

a Letting Q denote the number of soufflés produced and letting d denote the number of soufflés demanded by customers, verify that the schematic diagram in Figure 2.11 below correctly describes the logical structure of Mrs. Kresge's decision problem. Notice, for example, that end position E corresponds to the case where 4 soufflés are produced and 5 are demanded, while end position C represents the general case where Q soufflés are produced and d are demanded.

It is now necessary to calculate the value of Mrs. Kresge's criterion, duly adjusted for nonmonetary consequences, at every end position of Figure 2.11. Parts (*b*) to (*e*) of this exercise will ask you to calculate the *actual* value of her criterion by calculating successively her cash outlay for soufflé production, her cash inflow from sale of soufflés, and her cash inflow from sale of paté. Parts (*f*) to (*h*) will then ask you to calculate the *adjustment* that should be made in the value of her criterion to allow for differences in the amount of paté left over at the end of the day.

b Suppose that as your first step in valuing the end positions of this diagram you wish to compute the cash outflow due to soufflé production corresponding to each end position. Assuming that the only appreciable cost of soufflé production is the cost of the raw materials, which are bought fresh each day for cash in a quantity just sufficient for that day's production, and letting c denote the cost of these materials, verify that:

at end position D, $\quad c = 4 \times \$.30 = \$1.20$,

$\qquad\qquad A, \qquad 0 \times \$.30 = \$0$,

$\qquad\qquad C, \qquad Q \times \$.30 = \$.30Q$.

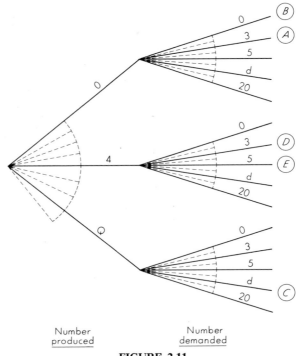

Number   Number
produced   demanded

FIGURE 2.11

Mrs. Kresge's Decision Problem

c Suppose that you next compute at each end position the revenue that
Mrs. Kresge will realize from the sale of soufflés either to customers or to
staff members. Denoting this revenue by *s*, verify that:

at end position D, $s = (3 \times \$.90) + (1 \times \$.10) = \$2.80$,

$\qquad\qquad$ E, $4 \times \$.90$ $\qquad\qquad = \$3.60$,

and that at end position C,

$$s = \begin{cases} \$.90d + \$.10(Q - d) & \text{if } d \leqslant Q, \\ \$.90Q & \text{if } d > Q. \end{cases}$$

d Next consider the revenue at each end position that results from the sale
of paté. Denoting this revenue by *p*, compute the value of *p* at end positions *D*, *E*, and *C*. (In the case of end position *C*, the value of *p* must of
course be expressed by a formula or formulas containing *Q* and *d* rather
than as a definite number of dollars.)

e The amount of cash that will be in the till at each end position can now
be computed by adding to the initial cash in the till the revenue from sale
of soufflés and paté and subtracting the cost of soufflé production. De-

noting the amount of cash in the till by t, write formulas in terms of Q and d for the value of t at end position C.

f Suppose that Mrs. Kresge selects B as her base end position. Letting n denote the amount by which the number of servings of paté that will be left over at any given end position exceeds the number that will be left over at the base end position, verify that:

at end position D, $n = 3$,

$\qquad\qquad\quad E$,   4,

$\qquad\qquad\quad A$,   0.

Write formulas in terms of Q and d for n at end position C.

g What will be the value to Mrs. Kresge of a serving of paté left over at the end of the day? May it depend on the amount of cash she has in the till? On the number of servings she has left?

h Letting v denote the terminal value of Mrs. Kresge's criterion as adjusted for differences in nonmonetary assets, use your answers to (*e*), (*f*), and (*g*) to write formulas in terms of Q and d for v at end position C.

2.12 Osgood Vischer owns and operates a quaint old shop in which he sells slegums and vorpids, among a great many other things, to a select clientele. Osgood purchases his slegums from an accommodating man who works nearby; whenever his stock of slegums is running low, Osgood calls this man and arranges to have a few more delivered. Slegums cost Osgood 25 cents each and he sells them at 40 cents, unless it is raining, in which case he charges 50 cents. He has found that about half of his slegum sales occur when it is raining.

Osgood's trade in vorpids is quite a different matter. He is able to buy them (at a cost of $1 each) only under certain very special astrological conditions, and so they are usually out of stock; when he has them to sell, he charges $3 each.

Osgood pays rent of $200 a month but otherwise incurs no expenses other than the cost of the items he sells. His entire stock in trade, slegums and vorpids included, is available in nearby shops, to which his customers are referred whenever Osgood is out of stock. All his customers are loyal, however, and invariably return to Osgood for subsequent purchases.

Osgood currently faces a decision problem which involves slegums and vorpids but no other nonmonetary assets. He has already chosen October 31, 1969, as his evaluation date, diagrammed his problem, chosen net liquid assets as his monetary criterion, and calculated the actual terminal value of his criterion at every end position. As his base end position for evaluation of nonmonetary consequences, he has chosen an end position at which he will have no vorpids and no slegums in stock; he is presently engaged in assessing his adjusted terminal value for an end position at which his actual net liquid assets will amount to $+\$1,000$ and his nonmonetary assets will include 100 slegums and 200 vorpids. This end position is labelled X on Osgood's diagram.

At this moment Mr. Horace Throckmorton, a private collector of slegums and vorpids who has never traded with Osgood in the past and will never trade with him again in the future, approaches Osgood with the intention of negotiating contracts for the purchase of the 100 slegums and the 200 vorpids that Osgood will have left over on October 31 if he reaches end position X. The contracts provide that if Osgood is at end position X on October 31, Throckmorton will immediately pay Osgood in cash and permanently remove the slegums and vorpids from the market. If Osgood does not reach end position X, the contracts will be null and void.

Osgood is entirely certain that ordinary demand during November will exceed 100 slegums and 200 vorpids. He can obtain more slegums on demand, but the astrological conditions under which he can replenish his stock of vorpids will not recur until some time in 1970.

a For what amount of cash should Osgood be just willing to agree now to sell the 100 slegums if and when he reaches end position X?

b For what amount of cash should Osgood be just willing to agree now to sell the 200 vorpids if and when he reaches end position X?

c What should be Osgood's adjusted terminal value for end position X?

2.13 Comment on the following letter, which a student sent to his instructor after studying Section 2.2.6 of the text.

I wish to point out that under certain circumstances the introduction of monetary valuations of nonmonetary consequences can either lead one to the wrong decision or cause one to consider an action that is not feasible. Consider the case of a company that has just received a special rush order. Due to overtime and other factors, the company cannot make an actual *cash* profit on the order. However, the company believes that its goodwill in the industry will be materially enhanced by the acceptance and completion of the order. The company's criterion is its cash on hand, which at the origin of the decision diagram is $\$1,000$. But suppose that the company has some short-term bank loans, say $\$800$, which it must soon repay. Thus, at the evaluation date, the company must have cash on hand of at least $\$800$. Any course of action that leads to a terminal value below $\$800$ cannot be considered. Suppose that

1. The rush order will result in a cash outflow of $\$300$.
2. The company decides that it would just exchange the goodwill gained for $\$500$ in cash.

Then the terminal value of the decision "take order" will be $1,200 and the terminal value of the decision "refuse order" will be $1,000. Clearly, the company should accept the rush order. But the actual cash on hand at the evaluation date is $700. Since the bank will not accept any of the 500 intangible dollars, you have come to the wrong decision. The company needed $800 in cash and by valuing the gain in the nonmonetary asset, goodwill, you are led to violate one of the constraints of the problem.

Clearly, my argument does not invalidate the general principle of monetary valuation of nonmonetary assets. However, one should be made aware of the above possibility and told that the constraints of the problem may invalidate the use of certain tools.

E. ANALYSIS BY EVALUATION OF COMPLETE STRATEGIES

2.14 Diagram all the strategies that are implicit in your diagram of the decision problem that was described in Exercise 1.1, analyze the problem by evaluation of complete strategies, and compare the results of this analysis with the results of the analysis by evaluation of individual acts that you carried out in answer to Exercise 1.11.

2.15 Again playing the role of a consultant to Mr. A. H. Mallon, diagram the various strategies available to Mallon in the decision problem of Exercise 1.12 and decide what questions you would have to ask Mallon in order to analyze the problem by evaluation of complete strategies. As before, your instructor will play the role of Mallon in class and respond with answers Mallon might reasonably give.

F. STRUCTURAL COMPLETENESS

2.16 Mr. O. N. Manning presents you with two box tops and says that he will redeem either or both of them within the next hour on the following terms. If at any time during the hour you give him box top *A* together with $100 cash, he will immediately toss a penny fairly and pay you $250 if it comes up heads, otherwise nothing. If at any time during the hour you give him box top *B* together with $25 cash, he will immediately toss a nickel fairly and pay you $400 if it comes up heads, but you will have to pay Manning $10 if the coin comes up tails.

Using the evaluation date and criterion specified in the paragraph preceding Exercise 1.3, diagram your decision problem, value the end positions, and decide what strategy you will adopt.

G. REVIEW EXERCISES

2.17 Mr. A. L. Hartley owns a plot of land on one of the only two possible routes for a new highway. He bought the land a year ago for $3,000, solely as a speculation on the highway route. The highway department's choice of route will be announced within the next thirty days.

In the past several days Hartley has been offered several deals in connection with his land, but he has not yet reached a decision about any of them. Two days ago Mr. T. Jones offered Hartley $1,000 in cash in return for an option to buy the land for an additional $9,000 within two days after the highway department's announcement. Mr. Gerald Smith, the owner of a property very similar to Hartley's but situated on the alternate route for the highway, has offered to make an even trade of his property for Hartley's. Finally, Hartley has been approached with a different kind of proposition by Mr. G. Ravenel, who has made a small fortune operating a numbers racket and now wishes to switch to more respectable forms of speculation. Ravenel's proposition is that in exchange for a deed to Hartley's land he will allow Hartley to flip a coin and will pay him $10,000 spot cash if the coin comes up heads, otherwise nothing. Although Hartley was at first somewhat offended because Ravenel added the stipulation that Hartley would have to let him inspect the coin before it was tossed, Hartley has nevertheless decided to consider the Ravenel offer.

Each of the following parts of this exercise presents different assumptions about the conditions under which Mr. Hartley will dispose of any land he still owns when the highway department announces its decision. In addition to these assumptions, you may assume that (1) Hartley has selected as his criterion his net liquid assets, which presently are $5,000, and (2) there will be no changes in his net liquid assets over the next two months other than those arising from transactions involving his plot of land. In answering each part, first choose a suitable evaluation date and diagram Hartley's decision problem. Then putting yourself in the position of a consultant to Hartley, decide exactly what questions you would ask Hartley in order to value the end positions of the diagram and to analyze the decision problem. So that you can complete the valuation of the end positions of your diagram and perform your analysis of the decision problem, your instructor will play the role of Mr. Hartley in class and reply to your questions with answers Hartley might reasonably give.

a Hartley feels sure that immediately after the highway department's decision is announced he will be able to, and will in fact, sell the land for $10,000 if the highway is routed past the land, $2,000 if it is not.

b Within one month after the decision has been announced, Hartley will hold an auction at which he will sell the land to the highest bidder.

c Hartley has stated that he doesn't want to think about what he will do with the land after the decision is announced. He might actively seek a buyer, and then again he might not; and in either case, he has no clear idea how long it will take to close a satisfactory deal or what price he will actually get for the land.

2.18 *Waggoner Engineering Corporation (A)*

On August 14, 1969, Mr. L. E. Waggoner had only a few more days in which to make up his mind whether or not to sign a proposed contract with a syndicate of businessmen in the city of Norwood. The contract provided that the Waggoner Engineering Corporation, of which Mr. Waggoner was president, should build a community television antenna according to certain specifications on a site some distance from the city and link it to a distributing point near the center of the city; the local syndicate would then pay Waggoner in cash for the complete system and take over its operation.

The Waggoner Engineering Corporation's sole business was the design and construction of community antenna systems to service towns and small cities beyond the reach of existing television broadcast facilities. The company had been founded by Mr. L. E. Waggoner in 1965, after he had received a master's degree in civil and electrical engineering from Georgia Tech in June, 1963, and then spent two years working in the Broadcasting Facilities Department of a major television network. Its initial capital had consisted of $15,000 paid in by Mr. Waggoner's father, a successful construction contractor. Since the founding of the company, all of its stock has been held by members of the Waggoner family. The company's assets on August 14, 1969, amounted to $75,000, of which $40,000 represented cash while the remainder represented the net book value of construction and office equipment.

In order to conserve working capital,[5] Waggoner had a firm policy of avoiding involvement in the ownership and operation of any antenna system once it had been completed and tested. In developing a new location, the company obtained a franchise from the city government and then, before committing any resources to actual construction, tried to interest local businessmen and investors in forming a local company to purchase and operate the system as soon as it was completed and proved out. When Waggoner failed to organize a local group which would contract for purchase of the system on satisfactory terms, he invariably preferred to forfeit the franchise rather than tie up his capital for an indefinite period of time. On August 14, 1969, Waggoner held only one franchise, the one in the city of Norwood, and saw no prospect of getting another one within the next several months. The Norwood franchise would become invalid unless

[5] Working capital, also called net current assets, is equal to net liquid assets as defined in Section 2.2.3 plus inventories at the lower of cost or market.

construction "begins not later than September 1 and continues thereafter with no unnecessary or undue delays."

The only suitable location for the antenna at Norwood was at a very substantial distance from the city, and therefore it would be more economical to transmit the television signals from the antenna to the distributing point in the center of Norwood by microwave relay than by coaxial cable. Such microwave transmission required a license from the Federal Communications Commission, however, and because there was a local television station in Norwood, it was not at all certain what action the FCC would take concerning Waggoner's application for a license. The license might be granted without restrictions, but in similar circumstances in the recent past the FCC had sometimes restricted the license to prohibit transmission of programs that the local station wished to rebroadcast by use of kinescope recordings and sometimes refused to grant any license at all. The examiner's report on the Waggoner case was not to be rendered until December 15, and Waggoner knew of no way of getting any advance indication of the examiner's conclusion; he felt sure, however, that the commission would accept the examiner's recommendation in this case whichever way he ruled.

The granting of a restricted license would be disadvantageous to Waggoner because the proposed contract with the Norwood syndicate specified a price of only $120,000 for a system with a microwave connection and a restricted license, whereas it specified a price of $150,000 for a system with a microwave connection and unrestricted license. The syndicate would also pay $150,000 for a system with connection by coaxial cable, over which the FCC would have no control, but whereas construction of the system would cost only about $110,000 if a microwave link was used, it would cost about $180,000 if a cable connection was necessary. Although no money would have to be spent on equipment for either type of connection until after the examiner's report was received on December 15, the terms of the franchise meant that the antenna itself, which accounted for about $80,000 of the total cost, would have to be nearly if not quite completed before that date.

Diagram the decision problem that Waggoner faced on August 14, 1969, and value the end positions of the diagram in the way that you believe would be most helpful to Waggoner, but do not try to decide what Waggoner should do.

2.19 Waggoner Engineering Corporation (B)

On August 15, 1969, before he had made up his mind whether or not to sign the contract with the local group in Norwood that was described in *Waggoner Engineering Corporation (A)*, Mr. L. E. Waggoner learned quite unexpectedly that a competitor, the Electronics Service Corporation, was willing to sell him a franchise and contract held by Electronics in the city of Prescott; the price would be $10,000 cash. Waggoner had offered to buy the franchise and contract at that price some months before, but at that time Electronics had flatly refused to sell. Electronics now indicated that they had another offer for the franchise and contract, in the amount of $9,000, which they would accept if Waggoner did not close the deal within one week. Although the Prescott franchise had come along unexpectedly, Waggoner felt quite sure that the chance of his being offered still another franchise within the next several months was virtually nil.

The contract with the local operating group at Prescott called for an antenna to be erected on a hill just outside the city and to be connected by cable with a distributing point in the city. The price to be paid by the group for the completed system was $140,000, and from the investigation he had conducted before making his original offer, Waggoner had concluded that he could build the complete system for about $90,000 provided that he could get by with an antenna 100 feet high, as he hoped he could. There was some risk, however, that an antenna only 100 feet high would not receive a signal of the strength and clarity required by the contract, since a mountain range partially obstructed the antenna's reception. If the 100-foot antenna did prove insufficient, Waggoner was certain he could increase its height to a point where the signal was not obstructed for an additional cost of $70,000; virtually none of this extra cost could be saved by building the higher antenna to begin with.

The local group and the city government had agreed to allow Electronics to sell the franchise and contract to Waggoner. The franchise was valid provided that the system was in operation on April 1, 1970, and Waggoner felt absolutely sure that construction would take less than three months even if he had to work on the Norwood job at the same time and even if the height of the antenna at Prescott had to be increased. Waggoner would, however, have to deposit $5,000 with the operating group within one week of taking over the contract, and he would have to agree that if he should fail to complete the system, the deposit would be forfeited in lieu of any suit the operating group might have brought.

Diagram the decision problem that Waggoner faced on August 15, 1969, and value the end positions of the diagram in the way that you believe would be most helpful to Waggoner, but do not try to decide what Waggoner should do.

CHAPTER
3
SPECIAL TOPICS
IN DIAGRAMMING
AND ANALYSIS

Having already laid down in Chapter 2 all of the basic principles underlying the description and analysis of problems of decision under uncertainty, we shall in the present chapter discuss some special problems that frequently arise and some errors that are frequently made in trying to apply the basic principles. In Section 3.1, we discuss errors that are frequently made in dealing with uncertain costs and other cash flows. In Section 3.2, we recognize that most if not all real decision problems are far too complex to be analyzed by brute-force application of the principles laid down in Chapter 2 and try to suggest various devices that may be of help in the practical analysis of such problems.

Because of the necessarily unsystematic character of the present chapter, an instructor using this book as a text may well prefer to go directly from Chapter 2 to Chapter 4 and only subsequently assign individual sections of Chapter 3 when they seem most likely to be useful in the light of class discussion of exercises or as preparation for particular cases. A person reading the book without the guidance of an instructor will probably do well to go through the chapter quite rapidly on a first reading and then return to the discussion of individual problems when these problems really bother him later on.

The exercises at the end of the chapter are all designed to be studied immediately after Section 3.1. Cases rather than exercises are required to illustrate the topics discussed in Section 3.2.

CONTENTS OF CHAPTER 3

1.
Uncertain Partial Cash Flows

1 Estimates of Uncertain Partial Cash Flows
2 An Example
3 Certainty Equivalents for Uncertain Partial Cash Flows
4 Conditioning of Acts on Partial Cash Flows

2.
Simplification of Decision Diagrams

1 Summary Description of Acts and Events
2 Elimination of Obviously Nonoptimal Strategies
3 Elimination of Inessential Acts and Events
4 Successive Approximations

3.
Summary

1 Uncertain Partial Cash Flows
2 Simplification of Decision Diagrams

3.1
UNCERTAIN PARTIAL CASH FLOWS

There is no difference in principle between uncertainty about the amount of a cash flow and any other uncertainty, and we have already seen in Section 2.1.3 that an uncertain cash flow can be represented on a decision diagram by an event fork or fan in exactly the same way that any other uncertainty is represented. Nevertheless, certain types of errors are made much more frequently in dealing with uncertain cash flows than in dealing with other uncertainties, and therefore we shall point out two kinds of errors that are typically made and emphasize the importance of avoiding them. In Sections 3.1.1 through 3.1.3 we shall discuss errors resulting from the use of "estimates" of uncertain cash flows; in Section 3.1.4 we shall discuss errors resulting from failure to represent correctly the date at which an uncertainty about a cash flow will be resolved.

3.1.1
Estimates of Uncertain
Partial Cash Flows

One of the most common practices in the analysis of business decision problems in which one or more individual or partial cash flows are uncertain is to make or obtain "estimates" of these uncertain flows and then to carry out the analysis as if the flows were certain to be equal to the estimates. Such a procedure is perfectly justifiable when the degree of uncertainty about each of the estimated cash flows is clearly so small as to be negligible for practical purposes, but when it is not, an analysis based on estimates can produce results which are seriously in error.

It is frequently argued that the trouble arises not from the use of estimates as such but from the use of improper estimates—i.e., estimates which are not made in a way that is appropriate to the purpose to which they will be put. More specifically, it is argued that just as the decision maker can assess a certainty equivalent for any uncertain terminal value, he can assess a certainty equivalent for any uncertain partial cash flow; and from this it would seem to follow that if the decision maker is properly careful in assessing his certainty equivalent for an uncertain partial cash flow, then an analysis which treats the uncertain flow as if it were certain to be equal to the assessed certainty equivalent must lead to perfectly valid results.

In a sense, this argument is correct; but the sense in which it is correct is by no means the obvious one. We shall now show by an example that although uncertain cash flows can in principle be legitimately replaced by definite cash flows in describing a decision problem, a single uncertain cash flow must in general be replaced by a *different* definite cash flow at each different place that the uncertain flow would appear in a complete decision diagram.

3.1.2
An Example

Consider a businessman named Olsen, who is already involved in an existing deal in which he will either gain $140,000 or lose $60,000 cash, and who must decide before he learns how this deal will come out whether or not he wishes to enter into a proposed deal in which he will either gain $90,000 or lose $50,000 cash. His criterion for judging the proposed deal is his net liquid assets, which at the moment amount to $+\$60,000$, and the only cash flows that can affect his criterion before his evaluation date are those resulting from the two deals we have described. A diagram of his decision problem is shown in Figure 3.1A.[1]

As a basis for discussion of the use of certainty equivalents for uncertain partial cash flows in this problem, let us first assume that Olsen's basic attitudes toward consequences are those of a typical, reasonably conservative businessman and see what values he may assign to positions X, Y, and Z in Figure 3.1A if he analyzes his problem by assessing certainty equivalents for uncertain criterion values. To keep the example as simple as possible, we shall suppose that

---

[1] Observe that this diagram is valid regardless of the order in which the two deals will pay off, since (as we pointed out in Section 2.1.6) uncertainties can be diagrammed in an order opposite to that in which they will actually be resolved provided that no choice of act will intervene.

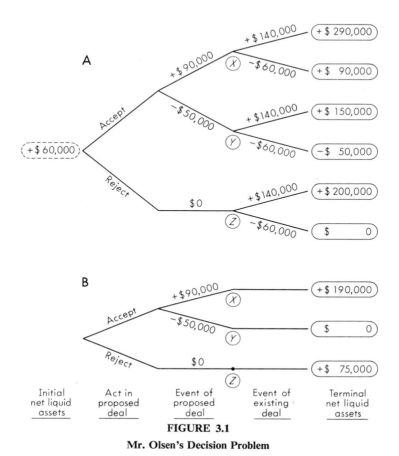

FIGURE 3.1

Mr. Olsen's Decision Problem

Olsen feels that the chances of the two possible events on the forks at these positions are about equal.

At position X in Figure 3.1A, Olsen will observe that the average of the two equally likely terminal values that he faces is $+\$190,000$; and since the worst that can happen to him is to end up with net liquid assets of $+\$90,000$, he may decide that he would not be willing to agree now to exchange the uncertain terminal value at X for a guaranteed terminal value one cent less than $+\$190,000$. At position Y, on the contrary, he may decide that even though the average of the two equally likely terminal values is $+\$50,000$, ending up with net liquid assets of $-\$50,000$ would put him in so embarrassing a financial position that he would be willing to agree now to accept a guaranteed terminal value of $\$0$ rather than run this risk. Finally, at position Z he may take an intermediate attitude and decide that he would be just willing to agree now to exchange the uncertain terminal value for $+\$75,000$ rather than insist on the $+\$100,000$ average of the two possible terminal values. The results of these three assessments are shown in Figure 3.1B.

3.1.3

**Certainty Equivalents
for Uncertain Partial Cash Flows**

Observe now that by assessing his certainty equivalents for the uncertain terminal values that he would face in positions *X*, *Y*, and *Z* in Figure 3.1A, Olsen also decided implicitly on the value to him of the uncertain partial cash flow that he would face in each of these positions.

If Olsen reaches position *X*, for example, his net liquid assets will already amount to +$150,000: the sum of the +$60,000 he had at the start plus $90,000 gained in the new deal; and therefore his decision that he would be just willing to agree now to take guaranteed net liquid assets of +$190,000 in exchange for the uncertain net liquid assets he will face at position *X* is equivalent to a decision that he would be just willing to agree now that if and when he reaches position *X*, he will exchange the still uncertain partial cash flow from the existing deal for a guaranteed cash flow of

$$+\$190{,}000 - (\$60{,}000 + \$90{,}000) = \$40{,}000.$$

By similar reasoning we can see that Olsen implicitly decided that he would be just willing to agree now that if and when he reaches position *Y*, he will exchange this *same* uncertain partial cash flow for a guaranteed flow of

$$\$0 - (\$60{,}000 - \$50{,}000) = -\$10{,}000$$

and that he would be just willing to agree now that if and when he reaches position *Z*, he will exchange this same uncertain partial cash flow for a guaranteed flow of

$$+\$75{,}000 - (\$60{,}000 + \$0) = \$15{,}000.$$

This means that if Olsen wishes to substitute a certainty-equivalent flow for the uncertain cash flow from the existing deal before he analyzes his decision problem, then as shown in Figure 3.2 his certainty-equivalent cash flow must have a different value at each of the three different positions at which the uncertain cash flow would appear in a complete decision diagram. No further argument is required to show that if Olsen replaces the uncertain cash flow by the *same* definite cash flow at every one of these positions, then no matter what value he chooses for this flow, his subsequent analysis will be based on a seriously incorrect description of the possible consequences of his immediate acts and can lead to correct results only by chance.

The general principle that is illustrated by this example is the following:

■ There is no such thing as a certainty equivalent for an uncertain partial cash flow considered in isolation. A decision maker's certainty equivalent for an uncertain partial cash flow depends on the complete context in which the flow occurs—i.e., on everything which would precede or

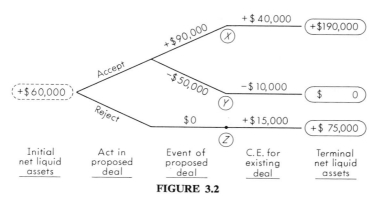

FIGURE 3.2

Certainty Equivalents for an Uncertain Partial Cash Flow

follow a fan representing the flow in a diagram of his complete decision problem.

From this it follows immediately that in general, all material uncertainties about partial cash flows must be shown explicitly on the decision diagram. Serious errors can result from "estimating" the amount of a partial cash flow and then treating the flow as if it were certain to be equal to the estimate.

3.1.4
Conditioning of Acts
on Partial Cash Flows

Even when a decision maker remembers that all uncertain partial cash flows in his decision problem must be explicitly represented by event forks in the decision diagram and thus avoids the serious errors that can result from replacing uncertain flows by "estimates" or improperly assessed certainty equivalents, he sometimes falls into other serious errors by failing to remember that the positions at which event forks appear in the diagram must agree with the dates at which the corresponding uncertainties will be resolved.

For an example, let us return to A. H. Mallon's XYZ decision problem and reconsider the cost of building the prototype. When Mallon asked his chief design engineer about the cost of building a prototype, the latter quoted a definite figure of $5,000; but although we treated that figure as a certainty in our original analysis of Mallon's problem, it is perfectly clear that in reality the cost would be subject to very substantial uncertainty. We shall now suppose, therefore, that in response to further questioning by Mallon the engineer says that while $5,000 is his "best estimate" of the cost of building a prototype, the true cost can easily be as low as $2,000 or as high as $8,000 or $9,000 and may possibly run as high as $15,000 if a certain critical aspect of the performance specifications proves very hard to meet and requires a great deal of expensive experimentation.

Knowing that serious errors can result from treating this uncertain cost as if it were certain to be equal to the engineer's "best estimate", Mallon will presumably refuse to base his analysis on the partial cash flows shown originally in Figure 1.2 and again here in Figure 3.3A; but he may be tempted to try to represent his uncertainty about the cost of the prototype by simply adding a fan representing it to each end position as shown in Figure 3.3B, arguing that such a diagram allows him to compute correctly the total cash flow that will result from any act-event sequence in the decision problem and therefore constitutes a valid basis for analysis.

Actually, however, the diagram in Figure 3.3B is nearly as incorrect a description of Mallon's decision problem as the diagram in Figure 3.3A because it does not correctly represent the fact that Mallon will learn the cost of the prototype before he can be obliged to choose between stampings and machinings. A correct diagram of the problem is shown in Figure 3.4, where the fan at Z represents the uncertain cost of the prototype and a complex of branches or sub-diagrams such as emanates from positions B, C, and D is to be understood as emanating from every branch, expressed or unexpressed, of this fan.

It is not for the sake of logical nicety that we insist on correct diagrammatic representation of the dates at which uncertainties about cash flows will be resolved. We do so because an incorrect diagram can easily lead to a wrong decision. If in our example Mallon believes that there is a good chance but by no means a certainty that stampings will work, and if he feels that he would be seriously embarrassed if he were to end up with very small net liquid assets on his evaluation date, then it is quite possible that the decision he would reach concerning the prototype by analyzing the incorrect diagram in Figure 3.3B would be the opposite of the decision he would reach by analyzing the correct diagram in Figure 3.4.

To see why, observe that if Mallon bases his analysis on the incorrect diagram in Figure 3.3B, he will be forced in the course of his analysis to make one definite choice between stampings and machinings at position X; whereas if he bases his analysis on the correct diagram in Figure 3.4, he may condition his choice between stampings and machinings on the actual cost of the prototype. He may, in other words, decide that (*a*) if the cost of the prototype turns out to be small and he then reaches a position like E, he will gamble on stampings because even if he is unlucky in this gamble he will still be in a strong financial position on his evaluation date, whereas (*b*) if the cost of the prototype turns out to be large and he then reaches a position like F, he will play it safe with machinings because an unsuccessful attempt to use stampings would leave him in a very weak financial position on his evaluation date.

This ability to "adjust" his choice between stampings and machinings to the actual cost of the prototype will almost certainly make the act "build prototype" more attractive to Mallon than it would be if he had to decide definitely *now* whether he would use stampings or machinings; and the difference

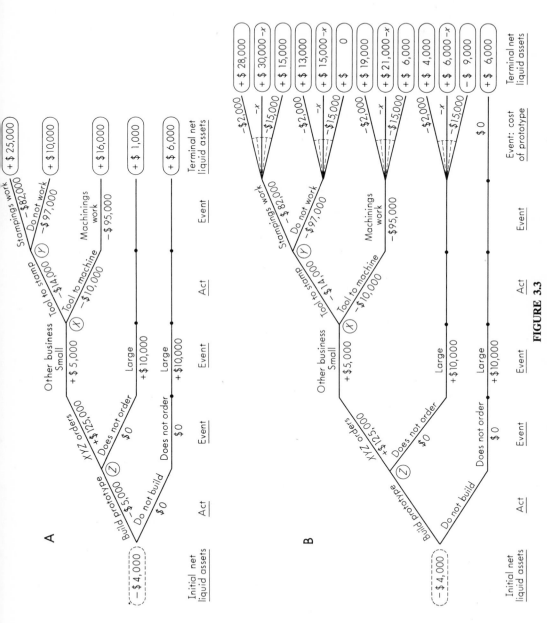

FIGURE 3.3

Incorrect Representations of Uncertainty about the Cost of the Prototype

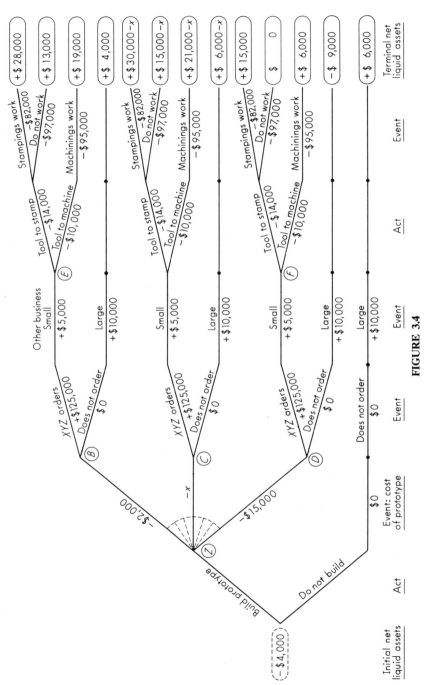

FIGURE 3.4

Correct Representation of Uncertainty about the Cost of the Prototype

could easily be great enough to swing Mallon's decision concerning the prototype from "do not build" to "build".

3.2
SIMPLIFICATION OF DECISION DIAGRAMS

While it is just possible that an extremely simple decision problem like the one faced by A. H. Mallon of ABC Controls could be diagrammed in strict accordance with the basic principles set forth in Chapter 2, an attempt to diagram a decision problem of any real complexity by brute-force application of the principles would be sure to result in failure.   With only a little effort, anyone could think up endless acts that might be chosen and endless events that might affect the values of the end positions or supply information that would affect the decision maker's certainty equivalents even though they did not affect the values of the end positions.   As one example, virtually every cost that enters into any business decision problem is more or less uncertain, so that strict adherence to the principles would require as many event fans as there are different cost elements involved in each total cash flow.   As another example, it is virtually always possible that some piece of new information relevant to a future choice among acts will be received before the choice has actually to be made, so that in principle every act fork except the one at the origin would have to be preceded by an event fork representing all the kinds of relevant information that might be received.

In short, an exact description of any real business decision problem would be so complex that it could not be written down and could not be analyzed even if it could be written down.   Whether or not he uses the methods of analysis described in this book, a businessman who wishes to reach a decision in a real-world decision problem must simplify the problem before he can think it through.

Simplification of a decision problem calls for both common sense and sophistication on the part of the person who diagrams the problem.   The really essential elements of the problem must be retained at the same time that inessential elements are eliminated, and this must be done without the aid of clear-cut rules.   But even though we cannot give definite rules for selecting the elements of a decision problem that are to be included in the formal statement or diagram of the problem, we shall in the present section make a few suggestions that the reader may find helpful.

3.2.1
Summary Description of Acts and Events

One very important thing to remember in trying to avoid undue complexity in a decision diagram is that the decision maker is free to decide what he will consider to be an act and what he will consider to be an event.   The point can best be explained by means of an example.

Suppose as we did in Section 2.1.3 that when A. H. Mallon asks his chief production engineer about the variable production cost of 5,000 control units with all machined parts, the engineer replies that although $95,000 is his best guess, the actual cost might be anywhere between $76,000 and $114,000; but now suppose in addition that the engineer is a talkative person and goes on to describe to Mallon in detail all the various factors that can affect the production cost—all the things (events) that can happen in the shop and all the things (acts) that may have to be done as a result. Although all of these "detailed" acts and events could be individually represented in Mallon's decision diagram by adding a long sequence of act and event forks to the branch for "tool to machine" in Figure 1.5 (page 13), Mallon may very well feel that so much detail would simply confuse him when he came to assign a definite certainty-equivalent terminal value to the position at the end of the branch for "tool to machine".

Mallon may feel, in other words, that he will be able to make a more satisfactory analysis of his decision problem if he does not try to think separately about every individual factor that can affect the cost of production; and it may be that he will decide that his diagram will be most helpful to him if his "total" uncertainty about this cost is represented by a single fan like the one in Figure 2.2 (page 35), where each branch represents an event of the form "cost actually amounts to $97,000".

If now we observe that the event represented by each branch of a fan like the one in Figure 2.2 is in effect an expression of the net result of a large number of more detailed events and acts which Mallon might have considered explicitly but preferred not to consider explicitly, we see that we can generalize from this example to the following conclusion:

■ In defining the acts and events that are to be represented in the diagram of a decision problem, the decision maker may go into whatever degree of detail he thinks will be most helpful to him when he comes to the actual analysis of the problem. In particular, a single event fan representing an uncertain net cash flow may be used to express the net effect of a large number of more detailed acts and events.

Event fans representing uncertain "contextual" cash flows (cf. Section 2.2.4) are another example of summary description of the net effect of a large number of acts and events which could have been, but do not have to be, described in detail.

3.2.2
Elimination of Obviously
Nonoptimal Strategies

It clearly makes no sense to pay money for information that will never be used, and this fact can sometimes be exploited to simplify the diagram of a decision problem. Specifically, it can be so exploited when (1) it is possible to purchase information whose *only* possible use is in choosing between two and only two

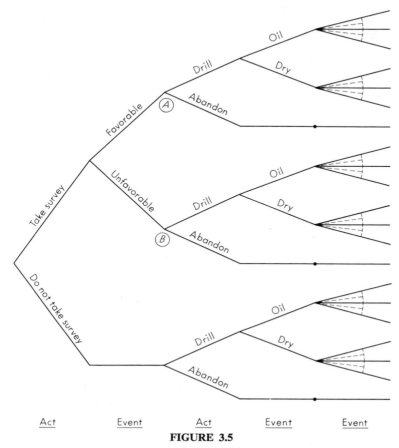

FIGURE 3.5

Complete Description of Mr. Black's Decision Problem

acts, and (2) the information when received will be of one or the other of two and
only two types: favorable to act 1, or favorable to act 2.

For example, consider the decision problem faced by a Mr. Black, who
holds an option to drill for oil on a certain plot of land and must choose very
shortly among three possible alternatives:

1 Drill.

2 Abandon his rights.

3 Have a seismic survey made (at a cost) in order to learn more about the
   subsurface structure and only then decide whether to drill or abandon
   his rights.

Assume that if Black does drill and strikes oil, he will sell out at once for the best
price he can get; and assume that if a seismic survey is made, its results will be
reported as simply "favorable" or "unfavorable" (not as more or less favorable)
to the existence of oil beneath the surface. On these assumptions, we can represent Mr. Black's decision problem by the diagram in Figure 3.5, where the

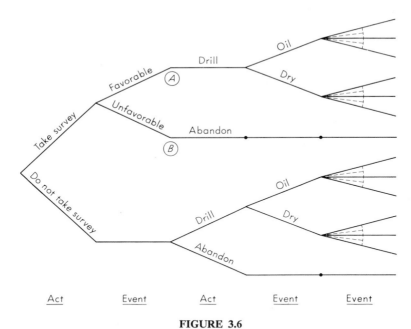

FIGURE 3.6
Simplified Description of Mr. Black's Decision Problem

fans following branches labelled "dry" represent the uncertain cost of drilling
while the fans following branches labelled "oil" represent the net difference
between the uncertain amount for which the well will be sold and the uncertain
cost of drilling.

The complete diagram of Mr. Black's decision problem in Figure 3.5
shows that he is still free to abandon his rights after getting "favorable" information from a seismic survey and that he is still free to drill after getting "unfavorable" information from a seismic survey. Common sense tells us, however,
that it makes no sense for Black to pay money for the survey unless he intends
to act in accordance with the information he obtains from it; and from this we
may conclude that the complete diagram of Mr. Black's problem in Figure 3.5
can be replaced by the simplified diagram in Figure 3,6, which implies that if
Black decides to have a seismic survey made at his expense, then he will definitely
drill if he receives favorable seismic information and will definitely abandon his
rights if he receives unfavorable seismic information.

One warning must be given before we leave the present topic. We did
not assert, and it would be incorrect to assert, that it would necessarily be wrong
for Mr. Black to abandon his rights after receiving favorable seismic information
or to drill after receiving unfavorable seismic information. Seismic surveys are
by no means infallible predictors of the presence or absence of oil beneath the
surface, and therefore (a) if other geological and geophysical evidence is very
favorable to the presence of oil, Mr. Black might be very well advised to drill

despite an unfavorable seismic, whereas (*b*) if the other evidence is very unfavorable to the presence of oil, he might do better not to drill despite a favorable seismic.

In other words, we did not assert and we could not legitimately assert that "drill" was necessarily the optimal individual act at position *A* in Figure 3.5 or that "abandon" was necessarily the optimal individual act at position *B*. It is only by actually assessing his certainty equivalents for the event forks beyond these two positions that Black can decide what act he should choose if he actually arrives at either of these two positions.

What we could and did assert was that it would be foolish for Mr. Black to spend money for the seismic survey unless he intended to act in accordance with the information it provided. We asserted, in other words, that no complete *strategy* which called for taking the seismic and then acting otherwise than in accordance with the information it provided could possibly be optimal. The complete diagram in Figure 3.5 contains six strategies in all, namely:

1 Do not take survey; drill.

2 Do not take survey; abandon.

3 Take survey and then: drill if favorable, abandon if unfavorable.

4 Take survey and then: drill if favorable, drill if unfavorable.

5 Take survey and then: abandon if favorable, abandon if unfavorable.

6 Take survey and then: abandon if favorable, drill if unfavorable.

Because the last three strategies in this list are in fact obviously nonoptimal,[2] a diagram which excludes these strategies but no others is a valid basis for analysis of Mr. Black's decision problem; and the reader can verify that the simplified decision diagram in Figure 3.6 does in fact exclude the three obviously nonoptimal strategies but no others.

To sum up, it is legitimate to eliminate obviously nonoptimal strategies from a decision diagram by eliminating acts which are not in themselves obviously nonoptimal, but before doing so the decision maker must make sure that elimination of the acts will not also eliminate one or more strategies that are *not* obviously nonoptimal. In case of doubt, the acts should be left in the decision diagram even though the task of analysis will be slightly greater as a result.

---

[2] We know in advance that if Black did analyze the complete decision diagram in Figure 3.5, his analysis could not lead him to select either strategy 4 or strategy 5 because these two strategies incur the cost of the seismic survey to no purpose. We know in advance that he cannot prefer strategy 6 because even though other geological and geophysical information might lead Black to decide *either* that he should abandon despite favorable seismic information *or* that he should drill despite unfavorable seismic information, it cannot lead him to *both* these conclusions.

3.2.3
Elimination of Inessential
Acts and Events

Another very important fact to remember in diagramming any decision problem is that although the decision maker must choose a complete strategy in order to make a reasoned choice of an immediate act, he will actually be bound only by his choice of an immediate act. The future choices that are prescribed by the strategy can be revised before they become irrevocable. It follows that though the decision maker's formal objective is to choose an optimal complete strategy, his real objective is merely to choose a strategy which begins with the optimal immediate act; and this fact permits very considerable simplification of the decision diagram.

First of all, a future choice among acts does not have to be represented on the diagram simply because the choice will in fact have to be made. It has to be represented only if the decision maker not only is uncertain about the act he will ultimately choose but also feels that his freedom to postpone this choice may have a material effect on the *ranking* of the certainty-equivalent terminal values that he assigns to his available immediate acts (cf. Section 3.1.4). If he feels fairly sure that he would select the same immediate act no matter what act he decided to choose in the future, he can suppress the fork representing the future choice and base his valuation of end positions on a more or less arbitrary assumption about his future act.

Even when a future choice among acts does have to be shown on the diagram because the decision maker feels that his freedom to postpone this choice may have an important effect on his choice of an immediate act, it is usually unnecessary to show all the possible informational events that might affect that future choice. The possibility of new information has to be considered only if the decision maker believes that there is a *material* chance that new information will make a *material* change in the relative attractiveness of the acts among which he will have to choose in the future, since only if both these conditions are met can the possibility of receiving new information have any material effect on the relative attractiveness of the immediate acts among which he actually has to choose now.

3.2.4
Successive Approximations

Even if every element that can be definitely eliminated from a complete description of a decision problem is in fact eliminated, the elements that remain will still be so numerous and so complex that they cannot all be represented on a single diagram and taken account of in a "one-pass" analysis. Instead, the decision maker must almost always find his way to a solution of his decision problem by a process of successive approximations.

The first step in the practical analysis of a real business decision problem is to size up the problem and try to identify (1) the main lines of the courses of action that need to be considered—what we might call the "basic" strategies that should be compared—and (2) the principal uncertainties concerning the consequences of these "basic" strategies.

The next step is to get a grasp on the way in which the principal uncertainties affect the consequences of the basic strategies by carefully diagramming the simplified problem that results when all seemingly less important choices and uncertainties are simply neglected. Where an act fork could be introduced representing a choice among minor variants of a basic strategy, the decision maker will make a temporary guess at the best act on that potential fork and show only this act in his diagram. Where a cost is subject to relatively minor uncertainty, the decision maker will select some "representative" value for the cost and proceed as if the cost were known to have this value instead of introducing another event fan into the diagram.

The decision maker will then analyze the simplified problem represented by this diagram, taking as much care and only as much care as is needed to make sure he understands its main implications. For example, suppose that all the branches of a particular act fork are followed by terminal event forks representing uncertain terminal values. If it is obvious to the decision maker that his certainty-equivalent terminal value for branch 3 is greater than his value for any other branch, he will immediately eliminate all branches except branch 3 and thus have only one certainty equivalent to assess exactly.

The analysis of the simplified problem will usually suffice to show that some of the basic strategies originally under consideration will prove to be inferior to others no matter how they are refined in detail and no matter how the assumptions of the simplified problem are changed. The decision maker is then ready to start on his second round of analysis—his second "successive approximation". Having eliminated some of the original basic strategies, he will be able to analyze the remaining contenders in more detail. His new decision diagram can contain some act forks where previously an act was chosen by guessing, and it can contain event forks or cost fans where previously one event was assumed "almost certain" to occur or one cost was selected as "representative". In introducing these additional complexities the decision maker will, however, be guided by what he has already learned from his previous analysis. He will not, for example, introduce any event fork where it is clear that the corresponding uncertainty cannot affect his choice of an immediate act, although he will introduce the fork if he is not sure whether doing so will affect the choice.

Repeating this process a number of times, the decision maker will ultimately reach a point where he feels reasonably sure that further repetition cannot alter his choice of an immediate act. More accurately, he will reach a point where he feels that the chance that further analysis will lead to a substantially better choice is too small to justify the expenditure of time and effort that further analysis would require. It is when this point is reached that his analysis may be said to be complete.

3.3
SUMMARY

3.3.1
Uncertain Partial Cash Flows

1 There is no such thing as a certainty equivalent for an uncertain partial cash flow considered in isolation. A decision maker's certainty equivalent for an uncertain partial cash flow depends on the complete context in which the flow occurs—i.e., on everything which would precede or follow a fan representing the flow in a diagram of his complete decision problem.

2 The decision diagram must correctly represent the date at which uncertainty about a partial cash flow will be resolved because the decision maker may wish to condition a choice among acts on the actual amount of the cash flow.

This last remark applies just as much to "contextual" cash flows that arise from the decision maker's "other" business as to cash flows that are directly connected with the decision problem immediately at hand.

3.3.2
Simplification of Decision Diagrams

1 In defining the acts and events which are to be represented in the diagram of a decision problem, the decision maker may go into whatever degree of detail he thinks will be most helpful to him when he comes to the actual analysis of the problem. In particular, a single event fan representing an uncertain cash flow may be used to express the net effect of a large number of more detailed acts and events.

Fans representing uncertain costs or net contextual cash flows are examples of summary descriptions of the net effect of a large number of acts and events which could have been, but do not have to be, described in detail.

2 In decision problems where (1) it is possible to purchase information whose *only* possible use is in choosing between two and only two acts, and (2) the information when received will be of one or the other of two and only two types, it is sometimes legitimate to simplify the decision diagram by assuming that if the information is purchased, the decision maker will act in accordance with its indications. To prove that such simplification is legitimate, the analyst must prove that *every* complete strategy that calls for acting contrary to the information received is in fact obviously nonoptimal.

3 Future choices among acts and uncertainties about purely informational events may be omitted from a decision diagram if the decision maker feels sure that the best strategy implicit in the simplified diagram begins with the same immediate act as the best strategy in a complete diagram.

Virtually all real decision problems are far too complex to be described "exactly" and analyzed in a single pass even if advantage is taken of all simplifications that can be shown to be legitimate before analysis begins, and therefore:

4 In general, a decision maker must begin by analyzing a relatively crude decision diagram which shows only the most important choices among acts and uncertainties about events. After this analysis has shown that certain strategies can be rejected as almost certainly inferior to others, he can introduce variants of the strategies that seem to be real contenders and consider additional events that may affect their consequences.

EXERCISES

3.1 Imagine that after having received the offer from Smith that was described in Exercise 1.1 but before having given Smith an answer, you are given a free ticket in a lottery to be conducted tomorrow. The lottery will be conducted by fairly tossing a quarter. If the quarter comes up heads, you will receive $500, but if it comes up tails, you will receive nothing.

a Taking the time at which you will learn the outcome of this lottery as a new evaluation date for analysis of the decision problem of Exercise 1.1, modify your original diagram of that problem accordingly by adding to each original end position a terminal event fork representing the possible results of the lottery.

b Value the end positions of your modified diagram using the criterion specified in the paragraph just preceding Exercise 1.3.

c Assess your certainty-equivalent terminal value for (1) the position at the base of the terminal event fork following the sequence "accept, penny comes up heads, continue, dime comes up heads", and (2) the position at the base of the terminal event fork following the sequence "accept, penny comes up tails, continue, dime comes up tails".

d For how much cash would you be just willing to agree now to sell the lottery ticket if and when you arrive at the first of the two positions described just above? if and when you arrive at the second?

3.2 Suppose that Mr. A. H. Mallon has constructed a graph which shows, for every possible cost x of building a prototype, his certainty-equivalent terminal value for the position at the end of the corresponding branch of the fan at position Z in Figure 3.4 (page 92); suppose that these certainty-equivalent terminal values range from $+\$14,000$ at the end of the branch for $x = \$2,000$, through $+\$7,000$ at the end of the branch for $x = \$6,000$, down to $-\$8,000$ at the end of the branch for $x = \$15,000$; and suppose that after assigning these values to the ends of the individual branches of the fan at Z, Mr. Mallon has gone on to assign a certainty-equivalent terminal value of $+\$7,000$ to position Z itself.

a What should be Mallon's certainty equivalent for the uncertain *partial cash flow* represented by the fan at Z? (In other words, how much cash should Mallon be just willing to agree now to lay out for a prototype if and when he actually reaches position Z in lieu of having to lay out whatever the prototype actually costs?)

b Has the certainty equivalent which you have just calculated been determined wholly by Mallon's judgments concerning the cost of building the prototype or has it been affected by other factors? Specifically, has it been affected by his judgments concerning the costs of production with stamped and machined parts? by his judgment concerning the chance that stampings will work? by his judgment concerning the chance that XYZ will order? by the fact that his net liquid assets currently amount to $-\$4,000$?

3.3 "Well, Max, it looks like we can bargain with Perlman," Irving Levy, President of Frolic Frocks, said with a sigh of relief as he put down the phone. "I think we can settle the suit out of court. He'll be out of town for the next two weeks, but we'll sit down with him and his lawyers as soon as he comes back."

"Thank God we don't have to worry about Perlman until after our show next week," his brother-in-law and partner, Max Turner, replied. "Everything really depends on that show; if it's a success, our spring line is off and rolling and we're out of the woods again. But if the buyers don't like it—and you sure can tell all there is to know as soon as the last model is back in the dressing room—well, all I can say is, one more bad line after this one and we can add our name to the illustrious list of bankruptcies."

About one year earlier Frolic Frocks, one of the many small manufacturers of a line of inexpensive cotton casual dresses, had been sued for breach of contract by Perlman and Company after Frolic had refused a shipment of cloth from Perlman on the grounds that the cloth did not meet contract specifications. Like many of its competitors, Frolic operated on very limited capital. Several seasons' unsuccessful lines had pushed the company toward financial disaster, and as Mr. Turner indicated, two more bad seasons would almost surely wipe Frolic out. It was because of Frolic's precarious financial position that the determination of the Perlman suit assumed such importance. A successful spring line would put Frolic back in a position where even a most adverse judgment would cause little financial stress, but if the spring line proved to be a failure, an adverse judgment would place the company on the verge of bankruptcy.

"Let's talk about what amount we'll settle for," Levy said as he resumed the conversation. "I know we don't have to make up our minds for almost two weeks, but waiting until after the show's over won't help us. After all, the chance of that jury ruling against us doesn't depend on whether our show's a success."

After a lengthy and at times heated discussion, Levy and Turner agreed on the maximum amount they would be willing to pay in settlement of the lawsuit. "I'm glad we came up with a firm figure. With that off our minds, we can concentrate on the show, although I'll be darned if I know what we can do for the next week except sit tight and hope the buyers will like the line," Levy said.

Comment on the way in which Messrs. Levy and Turner decided on the greatest amount for which they would settle with Perlman.

CHAPTER
4

CHANCES OF EVENTS
AND LIKINGS
FOR CONSEQUENCES

In the previous three chapters we saw how a person responsible for reaching a decision in a complex problem can apply his judgment more effectively by making a series of much simpler decisions. More specifically, we saw that the decision maker could solve any decision problem, however complex, by deciding on his certainty equivalents for uncertain terminal values taken one at a time. Often, however, the responsible person finds it very hard to reach a satisfactory decision even in one of these relatively simple problems where all he has to do is decide on his certainty equivalent for a single uncertain terminal value; and therefore our next task is to show how these problems can be broken down into still simpler problems.

One important reason why a decision maker finds it hard to decide on his certainty equivalent for the uncertain terminal value represented by a given terminal event fork is that to do so he must simultaneously take into account considerations of two totally different sorts. He must consider both (1) his judgments concerning the chances of all the events on the fork and (2) his likings for all the terminal values that either appear on the fork or might be selected as his certainty equivalent for the fork.

In this and the next several chapters we shall show how the decision maker can take judgments and likings into account separately rather than simultaneously. More specifically, we shall show how the decision maker can "quantify" his judgments about the chances of all the events in his decision problem without thinking about terminal values; we shall show how he can quantify his likings for all the (known or certainty-equivalent) terminal values that may be involved in his problem without thinking about the events; and we shall show how any certainty equivalent that may be required for analysis of the decision problem can be computed by simple arithmetic from these quantified judgments and likings.

It is only the basic logic of this procedure for "indirect" assessment of certainty equivalents that will concern us in the present chapter. We shall show how the decision maker can in principle quantify his judgments and likings, and we shall show that it is easy to compute his certainty equivalents after he has done so, but we shall not even try to suggest practical methods by which the decision maker can in reality quantify his judgments concerning thousands of events and quantify his likings for thousands of terminal values with only a reasonable expenditure of time and effort. Practical methods of quantification will be developed in subsequent chapters.

The text and exercises of the present chapter are designed to be studied in the following order:

1 Sections 4.1–4.2 and Exercises 4.1–4.2.

2 Section 4.3 and Exercises 4.3–4.4.

3 Section 4.4 and Exercise 4.5.

4 Section 4.5 and Exercises 4.6–4.9.

5 Section 4.6 and Exercise 4.10.

CONTENTS OF CHAPTER 4

1.
Standard Drawings and Standard Chances

2.
Quantification of
Judgments about Chances

1 Intuitive Quantification of Judgments about Chances
2 Unique vs. Repetitive Trials
3 Measurement of Strength of Conviction
4 Contamination of Judgments about Chances by Likings for Terminal Values
5 Event Forks with More than Two Branches
6 Equivalent Urns

3.
Quantification of
Likings for Consequences

1 An Example
2 Generalization

4.
Computation of Certainty Equivalents
for Real Gambles

1 Substitution of an Equivalent Urn for a Real-world Event Fork
2 Substitution of Reference Gambles for Terminal Values
3 Computation of the Chances of the Reference Terminal Values
4 Determination of the Certainty Equivalent
5 Generalization
6 Practical Computation

5.
Probability and Preference

1 Probabilities for Events
2 Preferences for Terminal Values or Consequences
3 Preferences for Gambles, Terminal Event Forks, or Positions
4 Computation of Preference for a Terminal Event Fork
5 "Estimates" vs. Decisions

6.
Summary

1 Standard Drawings
2 Quantification of Judgments Concerning Chances of Events
3 Quantification of Likings for Terminal Values
4 Computation of Certainty Equivalents for Terminal Event Forks

4.1
STANDARD DRAWINGS AND STANDARD CHANCES

In order to create a scale by use of which a decision maker can quantify both his judgments concerning chances and his likings for terminal values, we shall ask him to imagine an urn containing a known number of serially numbered balls, one of which is to be drawn in such a manner that he would be completely indifferent between (*a*) the right to receive a valuable prize if ball number 317 is drawn from the urn, and (*b*) the right to receive that same prize if ball number 526 is drawn from the urn, and similarly for any two specified balls.

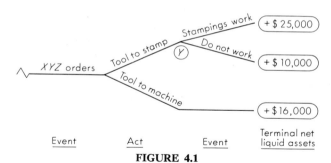

Event   Act   Event   Terminal net
                                                  liquid assets

FIGURE 4.1

Choice between Stampings and Machinings

Any drawing toward which a particular decision maker has this attitude of indifference will be said to be ≪standard≫ for that decision maker, and any gamble in which the payoff depends on the outcome of one or more standard drawings will be called a ≪standard gamble≫.

If a standard drawing is to be made from an urn containing 1,000 balls, we shall say that any one individual ball has a 1/1,000 ≪standard chance≫ of being drawn; and if 267 of the balls are colored red, we shall say that there is a 267/1,000 standard chance that a red ball will be drawn. We leave it to the reader to define standard chances by generalizing these examples.

In reading the present chapter, it is essential to observe that none of our arguments depend on the "true" chance—whatever that may mean—of any event in any drawing from an urn. The arguments will depend only on the fact that the *decision maker* holds the *attitude of indifference* which defines a standard drawing.

4.2

QUANTIFICATION OF JUDGMENTS
ABOUT CHANCES

As we have already said, "standard" chances will serve as a scale by use of which the decision maker can quantify both his judgments concerning the chances of events and his likings for terminal values. In the present section we shall deal with quantification of judgments concerning the chances of events.

4.2.1

Intuitive Quantification
of Judgments about Chances

Quantified judgments about chances often play an essential role in a businessman's analysis of a decision problem even when his analysis is completely informal, as we can see by considering afresh the decision that A. H. Mallon of ABC Controls will have to make if he builds a prototype and gets a quantity order from XYZ Chemical. As shown in Figure 4.1, he will then have to choose between an act "tool to stamp" that may result in either of two possible terminal values, + $25,000 or + $10,000, and an act "tool to machine" that is certain to result in a terminal value of + $16,000.

In this situation, it is immediately clear that Mallon's choice *must* depend on his judgment concerning what are commonly called the chances of the events "stampings work" and "do not work". Even though Mallon cannot know for sure which of these two events will occur, and even though he cannot determine objectively whether in some sense or another it would really be better for him to gamble on stampings or play it safe with machinings, he will not flip a coin or tell his secretary to decide which of the two acts he should choose. If *in his judgment* the chance that stampings will work is good enough, he will tool to stamp; otherwise, he will tool to machine.

What is more, many businessmen would naturally give quantitative expression to their judgments about the chances in a problem of this kind. It would be perfectly natural, for example, for Mallon to say, after due reflection on the available evidence, "Everything considered, I'd guess the chances are about four out of five that stampings will work."

Finally, it is also perfectly natural for such quantified judgments to be taken as a basis for decision. If Mallon made the statement just quoted, he might quite naturally go on to say, "And as far as I'm concerned, you'd have to bring my net liquid assets up to a good deal more than the + $16,000 I'll get with machinings before you could persuade me to give up a gamble on stampings that gives me a 4/5 chance of + $25,000 and only a 1/5 chance of + $10,000.

4.2.2
Unique vs. Repetitive Trials

Although businessmen often find it completely natural thus to assign a numerical value to the chance of an event like "stampings work", other people—statisticians more often than businessmen—will say that such numerical values are meaningless. They will argue that while it makes sense to say that the chance of rolling an ace with a fair die is 1/6 because a fair die will come up ace 1/6 of the time in a very large number of trials, Mallon will try stampings only once at most and on that one trial they will either work or not work—it is nonsense to say or imply that they will work 4/5 of the time. A slight variant of this argument would say that if Mallon were foolish enough to make repeated tests of stampings of this particular design in this particular application, he would find either that they always worked or else that they always failed; and accordingly the chance that they will work is either 0 or 1, not some number in between.

These arguments are completely irrelevant to Mallon's decision problem, however, because what must determine Mallon's decision is not the true frequency with which stampings would actually work in repeated trials but what we might call the strength of his personal conviction that stampings will or will not work on the one trial that may actually be made. We repeat that Mallon, or any other businessman, will choose stampings if and only if in his best judgment the chance that they will work on this one trial is good enough.

4.2.3
Measurement of Strength of Conviction

As regards numerical values for chances, the relevant question is thus not whether Mallon knows the frequency with which stampings would work on repeated trials but whether he can find a useful measure of the strength of his conviction that stampings will or will not work on this one trial; and whether or not Mallon finds it "natural" to assign a numerical value to the chance of an event such as "stampings work", he can find a useful measure of the strength of his conviction that this event will occur by making a simple decision.

To set the stage for the decision by which Mallon can usefully measure the strength of his conviction that stampings will or will not work, we first ask him to imagine that at this moment he is approached by a gambler named Tupolov who offers to negotiate a contract on the following terms. If and when Mallon has actually received a quantity order from XYZ, tried to fill it using stampings, and met with either success or failure in the attempt, a standard drawing will be made from an urn in which some definite fraction P of the balls are red while the remainder are black. If the ball which is drawn is red, Tupolov will hand Mallon any cash that may be needed to raise Mallon's net liquid assets to $+\$25,000$; if the ball is black, Mallon will hand Tupolov any cash that may be needed to reduce Mallon's net liquid assets to $+\$10,000$. The only part of the deal left open for negotiation is the fraction P of red balls to be placed in the urn.

If Mallon were to sign this contract, an attempt to use stampings would still give rise to a gamble from which Mallon would emerge with terminal net liquid assets of either $+\$25,000$ or $+\$10,000$, exactly as if he had not agreed to the deal, but which one of these two terminal values Mallon would have would depend on whether or not the ball drawn from the urn was red instead of depending on whether or not the stampings actually worked. Consequently (*a*) if Mallon thinks that there is a good chance that stampings will work, he would refuse the contract unless Tupolov agreed to put a fairly large fraction P of red balls in the urn, whereas (*b*) if Mallon thinks that there is a poor chance that stampings will work, a rather small fraction P of red balls would suffice to induce him to accept the contract; and therefore it would seem that Mallon can measure the strength of his conviction that stampings will work by simply deciding what fraction P of red balls would have to be placed in the urn in order to make him *just willing* to accept Tupolov's contract.

After carefully considering the available data and his engineer's opinions concerning the suitability of stampings for the purpose at hand, Mallon may decide, for example, that he would want to accept the contract if more than 4/5 of the balls in the urn were red, that he would refuse the contract if less than 4/5 of the balls were red, and that he would be indifferent between accepting and refusing if exactly 4/5 of the balls in the urn were red. And if Mallon does thus decide that he would be just willing to sign the contract if $P = 4/5$ of the balls were red, we would seem to be entitled to say that 4/5 is a measure of the strength of Mallon's conviction that stampings will work, or alternatively that 4/5 is a quantified expression of Mallon's judgment concerning the chance of the event "stampings work".

4.2.4
Contamination of Judgments about Chances
by Likings for Terminal Values

Before we make these statements, however, we must make sure that Mallon has avoided a certain very common kind of confusion in his thinking.

When one of the possible consequences of a gamble is either extremely desirable or extremely undesirable, a decision maker is very likely to give undue weight to this consequence when he makes a decision concerning the gamble. After consciously taking full account of the desirability or undesirability of the consequence, he unconsciously behaves as if it were more likely to occur than his best judgment would tell him it really is.

This same kind of unconscious double counting can easily occur even if the decision maker makes a separate assessment of the chances of the events in a gamble before deciding whether to accept or reject the gamble. When an extremely desirable or undesirable consequence is associated to a particular event, the decision maker is very likely to assign a higher value to the chance of that event than he would if the consequence were less extreme; and since the consequence obviously has no effect on the chance, one or both of the two different values he would assign to the chance must reflect confused thinking rather than careful judgment.

Accordingly we cannot be sure that Mallon gave expression to an uncontaminated judgment about the chance of the event "stampings work" when he decided what mix of balls would have to be placed in an urn in order to make him indifferent between (*a*) the gamble in Figure 4.1 which associated two *particular* consequences to the events "stampings work" and "do not work", and (*b*) a gamble which associated those same two particular consequences to the two possible events of a standard drawing from the urn. To make sure that his decision reflects *only* his judgments about the chances of the events and not his likings for particular consequences, Mallon should ask himself what mix of balls in an urn would make him indifferent between (*a*) a gamble which associates *any* set of consequences to the events "stampings work" and "do not work", and (*b*) a gamble which associates those same consequences to the corresponding events of a standard drawing from the urn.

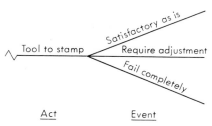

FIGURE 4.2
Event Fork with Three Possible Events

If Mallon decides that he would be indifferent between *any* two gambles of this sort if 4/5 of the balls in the urn corresponded to the event "stampings work" and 1/5 to the event "do not work", then we will really be entitled to say that the proportion of each kind of ball in the urn represents Mallon's best judgment concerning the chance of the corresponding event, uncontaminated by any liking or dislike that Mallon feels for any particular consequence.

4.2.5
Event Forks with More than Two Branches

The method of quantifying judgments concerning chances that we have applied to an event fork with only two branches can of course be applied to event forks with any finite number of branches. If Mallon believes that there are three rather than just two possibilities concerning stampings, as shown in Figure 4.2, he can quantify his judgments concerning the chances of the three possible events by considering an urn containing three different kinds of balls and deciding what proportional mix of balls would leave him indifferent between (*a*) a gamble which associated *any* definite set of consequences to the real-world events, and (*b*) a gamble which associated the same set of consequences to the corresponding events of a standard drawing from the urn. After due reflection he might decide, for example, that he would be indifferent if 3/5 of the balls would yield the same consequence as the event "satisfactory as is", 1/5 of the balls would yield the same consequence as the event "require adjustment", and 1/5 of the balls would yield the same consequence as the event "fail completely".

Mallon would, of course, find it harder to decide on the proper proportions for three kinds of balls to represent three different possible events than it was to decide on the proper proportions for just two kinds of balls to represent just two possible events, and if we asked him to quantify his judgments concerning any really large number of mutually exclusive events without showing him how to do so in some simple and systematic manner, he might very well answer that we were asking the impossible and that he would much prefer to dispense with our services and analyze his decision problem in the good old-fashioned way. But even though we fully recognize the validity of such an objection, and even though there do exist simple methods by which a decision maker can quite easily quantify his judgments concerning very large numbers of mutually exclusive events, we must postpone discussion of these methods to later chapters. Our immediate purpose is only to show, first, how a decision maker can in principle quantify his judgments concerning the chances of events, and second, how these quantified judgments can be used to compute the decision maker's certainty equivalents for uncertain terminal values.

4.2.6
Equivalent Urns

In order to generalize the preceding discussion of chances of events, we first define "equivalent" standard drawings as follows:

1 Consider any event fork, terminal or not, which appears in the diagram of a real decision problem; and imagine a standard drawing of one ball from an urn in which each ball is labelled with the name of one of the events on the event fork. If the mix of balls in the urn is such that, upon arriving at the base of the fork in question, a particular decision maker would be indifferent between (*a*) a gamble which associates any definite set of consequences to the events on the fork, and (*b*) a gamble which associates those same consequences to the corresponding events of the standard drawing, then the standard drawing from the urn may be said to be ≪equivalent≫ to the event fork for that decision maker.

For brevity, we shall sometimes refer to the urn itself as equivalent to the event fork, but when we do, the reader must remember that it is really a standard drawing from the urn that is involved.

All our discussion of chances up to this point can now be generalized by saying that:

2 A decision maker can quantify his judgments concerning the chances of the events on any event fork in a real decision problem by (1) thinking of an urn in which each ball is labelled with the name of one of the events on the event fork, and (2) deciding what proportional mix of balls bearing the various labels will make the urn equivalent to the event fork for him.

4.3
QUANTIFICATION OF LIKINGS
FOR CONSEQUENCES

Having shown how a decision maker can quantify his judgments concerning the chances of the events in a decision problem, we shall next show how he can quantify his likings for all the terminal values of his criterion that either appear on his original diagram of the problem or might be selected as certainty equivalents during the analysis of the problem.

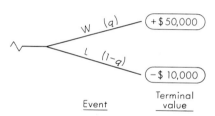

FIGURE 4.3
A. H. Mallon's Reference Gamble

4.3.1
An Example

The method by which a decision maker can quantify his likings for terminal values can be explained by returning once more to Mr. A. H. Mallon's XYZ decision problem. We assume that Mallon has already diagrammed his problem, computed the actual value of his criterion at every end position, selected a base end position, and adjusted the value of his criterion at each other end position to take account of all differences between the nonmonetary assets he will have at that end position and the base nonmonetary assets he will have at his base end position; and for definiteness we further assume that the greatest of these adjusted terminal values is no greater than +$50,000 while the least is no less than −$10,000. We also remind the reader that the problem that Mallon will actually analyze is not his real decision problem but an equivalent substitute problem in which (1) the actual value of his criterion at each end position is equal to the adjusted value of his criterion at the corresponding end position of his real problem, while (2) his nonmonetary assets at every end position are identical to the base nonmonetary assets that he will actually have only at the base end position of his real problem. Accordingly,

- ■ All terminal values mentioned in the discussion to follow, including all terminal values appearing in hypothetical gambles, are to be understood as being accompanied by Mallon's base nonmonetary assets.

To show Mallon how he can usefully quantify his likings for all terminal values now on his decision diagram and all terminal values that he might select as certainty equivalents in analyzing this diagram, we first ask him momentarily to forget all about the problem actually before him and to imagine that he faces instead a problem whose diagram contains the terminal event fork shown in Figure 4.3. This fork represents the two possible outcomes of a ≪reference gamble≫ which will be conducted by making a standard drawing of one ball from an urn in which a fraction q of the balls are labelled W(in) while the remaining fraction $(1 − q)$ are labelled L(ose). If the event W occurs, Mallon will end up with terminal net liquid assets of $50,000 on his evaluation date for analysis of his real problem; if the event L occurs, he will end up with −$10,000; in either

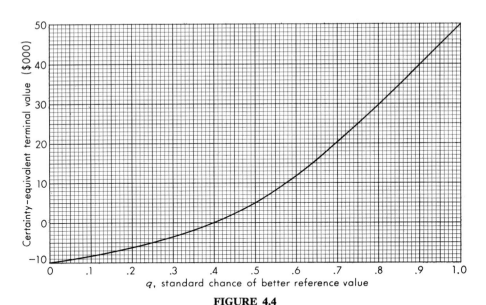

FIGURE 4.4

A. H. Mallon's Certainty Equivalents for Reference Gambles

Between Terminal Values $+$ \$50,000 and $-$ \$10,000

case, his nonmonetary assets will be identical to those he will actually have at the base end position in his real problem. The two terminal values that can result from this "reference gamble" will be called «reference terminal values» or simply "reference values" for short.

If Mallon knew the actual numerical value of the fraction q of W balls in the urn, he could without undue difficulty assess his certainty equivalent for the reference gamble of Figure 4.3; but instead of telling him the value of q and asking him to assess one certainty equivalent, we ask him to assess his certainty equivalent for the gamble given every possible value of q, from 0 to 1 inclusive. The task is admittedly one which may seem extremely difficult at first glance, but we must nevertheless postpone discussion of practical methods by which it can be accomplished until the next chapter. For the moment, we shall merely assume that Mallon can and does make all the required assessments by constructing the graph in Figure 4.4 and telling us that we can read from it his certainty equivalent for a reference gamble which gives him *any* definite standard chance q at a terminal value of $+$ \$50,000 and a complementary chance at $-$ \$10,000. The graph tells us, for example, that if the reference gamble gives a standard chance $q = .75$ at $+$ \$50,000 and a complementary chance $(1 - q) = .25$ at $-$ \$10,000, then Mallon's certainty equivalent for the gamble is $+$ \$25,000; and so forth.

We now assert that by assessing his certainty equivalents for all reference gambles that will result in a terminal value of either $-$ \$10,000 or $+$ \$50,000, Mallon has in effect quantified his likings for all terminal values between $-$ \$10,-000 and $+$ \$50,000.

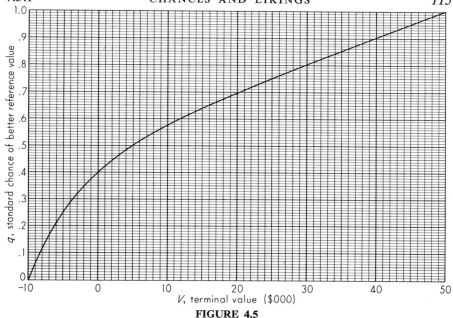

FIGURE 4.5

A. H. Mallon's Likings for Terminal Values Relative to +\$50,000 and −\$10,000

To show that this is so, we first proceed in Figure 4.5 to redraw Mallon's graph in such a way that the standard chances q appear on the vertical axis while Mallon's certainty equivalents appear on the horizontal axis. Then recalling that any decision maker's certainty equivalent for any gamble is by definition the definite terminal value that is exactly as attractive to him as the gamble, we see that we can read from Figure 4.5 the value of q which makes a reference gamble exactly as attractive to Mallon as any given terminal value between −\$10,000 and +\$50,000. We can read, for example, that Mallon would be just willing to exchange the definite terminal value +\$10,000 for a reference gamble which gives him a $q = .58$ chance at +\$50,000 with a complementary chance at −\$10,000; he would be just willing to exchange the definite terminal value +\$20,000 for a reference gamble in which $q = .70$; he would be just willing to exchange a definite +\$25,000 for a reference gamble in which $q = .75$; and so forth.

Suppose now that we let V denote any particular terminal value and let q_V denote the q which makes a reference gamble exactly as attractive to Mallon as V for certain. Because q_V increases as V increases, as shown by Figure 4.5, we can think of q_V as a quantitative measure of Mallon's liking for any given terminal value V. More precisely, we can say that q_V measures his liking for the terminal value in question *relative* to the two reference terminal values which can result from the gamble, *it being understood that any terminal value will be accompanied by Mallon's base nonmonetary assets.*

Because the greatest terminal value in Mallon's XYZ decision problem is no greater than +\$50,000 and the least is no less than −\$10,000, the terminal values for which Mallon has quantified his likings obviously include all the terminal values that actually appear in the problem. Because a decision maker's certainty equivalent for a terminal event fork can never be greater than the greatest terminal value on the fork or less than the least, the values for which Mallon has quantified his likings also include all values that Mallon might select as certainty equivalents for the terminal event forks on the original diagram of his problem. We leave it to the reader to convince himself that they also include all values that Mallon might select as certainty equivalents for any terminal event fork on any reduced diagram of his problem, no matter what the structure of his original diagram may be.

4.3.2
Generalization

Generalizing from the example just discussed, we reach the following conclusion:

■ Consider a context in which every terminal value under discussion will be accompanied by exactly the same base nonmonetary assets; suppose that in this context the decision maker wishes to quantify his liking for every terminal value between two ≪reference values≫ that he has chosen; and let the expression ≪reference gamble≫ denote a gamble that gives the decision maker a standard chance q at his better reference value with a complementary chance $(1 - q)$ at his worse reference value. The decision maker can accomplish his objective by constructing a graph which shows his certainty equivalent for every possible reference gamble with q between 0 and 1.

From this graph, he can read the q which makes a reference gamble exactly as attractive to him as any given terminal value V that lies between the two reference values, and this q can be taken as a measure of his liking for that V relative to his chosen reference values.

If the greater of the decision maker's two reference values is at least as great as the greatest terminal value on his diagram, and if the lesser reference value is at least as small as the smallest terminal value on his diagram, the terminal values for which he quantifies his likings by the procedure just described will include not only all terminal values that appear on his diagram but also all terminal values that he might select as certainty equivalents in the course of his analysis of the problem.

4.4
COMPUTATION OF CERTAINTY
EQUIVALENTS FOR REAL GAMBLES

Our next task is to show how, after a decision maker has suitably quantified his judgments concerning chances and his likings for terminal values, it is possible for anyone to compute the certainty-equivalent terminal value that he should assign to any real gamble or terminal event fork that appears in the course of analysis of his decision problem. Both the method and the underlying logic of the computation can be explained by showing how we can compute the certainty-equivalent terminal value that Mr. A. H. Mallon should assign to the terminal event fork in Figure 4.6A, which might appear on either the original or a reduced diagram of his XYZ decision problem.

4.4.1
Substitution of an Equivalent Urn
for a Real-world Event Fork

As regards the chances of the events on the fork in Figure 4.6A, we assume that Mallon has already quantified his judgments by deciding on his equivalent urn for the fork. Specifically, we assume that Mallon has decided that if an urn contains 600 balls labelled *S* for "satisfactory as is", 200 labelled *R* for "require adjustment", and 200 labelled *F* for "fail completely", then upon arriving at the base of the event fork in Figure 4.6A he would be indifferent between (*a*) a gamble which associates any set of consequences to the events on the fork, and (*b*) a gamble which associates those same consequences to the corresponding events of a standard drawing from the urn.

    This decision or "assessment" by Mallon implies that he is indifferent between the real-world gamble of Figure 4.6A and the ≪standard gamble≫ of Figure 4.6B, where the consequences are the same as in Figure 4.6A but the events are the possible outcomes of a standard drawing from Mallon's equivalent urn. And since a decision maker who is indifferent between two gambles must assign the same certainty-equivalent value to either one that he assigns to the other, we conclude that we can compute the certainty-equivalent value that Mallon should assign to the real-world gamble of Figure 4.6A by computing the certainty-equivalent value that he should assign to the standard gamble of Figure 4.6B.

4.4.2
Substitution of Reference Gambles
for Terminal Values

In order to compute Mallon's certainty equivalent for the standard gamble in Figure 4.6B, we make use of the information about his likings for the possible consequences of that gamble that is provided by Figure 4.5.

    First taking the terminal value +$25,000 which is associated to the top end position in Figure 4.6B, we read from Figure 4.5 that Mallon is indifferent between this definite terminal value and a reference gamble which gives him a .75 standard chance at +$50,000 together with a complementary chance at −$10,-000, and we record this fact in the first row of Table 4.1. In the same way, we

A   Real-World Gamble on Stampings

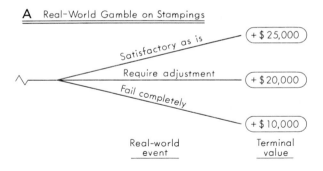

Satisfactory as is   (+ $ 25,000)

Require adjustment   (+ $ 20,000)

Fail completely   (+ $ 10,000)

Real-world   Terminal
event   value

B   Equivalent Standard Gamble

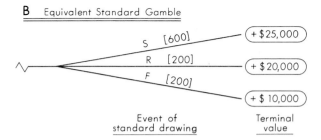

S   [600]   (+ $25,000)

R   [200]   (+ $ 20,000)

F   [200]   (+ $ 10,000)

Event of   Terminal
standard drawing   value

C   Equivalent Two-Stage Standard Gamble

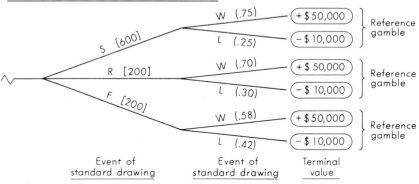

W   (.75)   (+ $ 50,000) } Reference gamble

L   (.25)   (− $ 10,000)

S   [600]

R   [200]   W   (.70)   (+ $ 50,000) } Reference gamble

L   (.30)   (− $ 10,000)

F   [200]

W   (.58)   (+ $ 50,000) } Reference gamble

L   (.42)   (− $ 10,000)

Event of   Event of   Terminal
standard drawing   standard drawing   value

D   Equivalent Reference Gamble

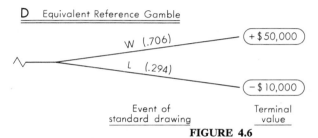

W   (.706)   (+ $ 50,000)

L   (.294)   (− $ 10,000)

Event of   Terminal
standard drawing   value

FIGURE 4.6

Reduction of a Real-world Gamble to an Equivalent Reference Gamble

find from Figure 4.5 and record in Table 4.1 that a reference gamble with $q = .70$ is as attractive to Mallon as the terminal value $+\$20,000$ which appears in Figure 4.6B, and a reference gamble with $q = .58$ is as attractive as the $+\$10,000$ in Figure 4.6B.

TABLE 4.1
Selected Terminal Values and Equivalent Reference Gambles

Definite Terminal Value	Chances of Terminal Values in Equivalent Reference Gamble	
	$+\$50,000$	$-\$10,000$
$+\$25,000$	.75	.25
$+\$20,000$	.70	.30
$+\$10,000$	.58	.42

Now consider the two-stage standard gamble of Figure 4.6C, where the event fork at the origin is identical to the event fork at the origin of Figure 4.6B but each terminal value in Figure 4.6B has been replaced by a terminal event fork representing a second-stage reference gamble that will result in one or the other of Mallon's two reference terminal values. The standard chances in these reference gambles are shown in parentheses on the branches of the forks which represent them, and referring to Table 4.1 the reader will see that these chances are such that *each second-stage reference gamble in Figure 4.6C is exactly as attractive to Mallon as the corresponding terminal value in Figure 4.6B.*

Because (1) the chance of each of the events S, R, and F is exactly the same in Figure 4.6C as it is in Figure 4.6B, and (2) the position to which each of these events leads in Figure 4.6C is exactly as attractive to Mallon as the position to which it leads in Figure 4.6B, we may conclude that the entire gamble of Figure 4.6C must be exactly as attractive to Mallon as the entire gamble of Figure 4.6B. To say the same thing in different words, the gamble of Figure 4.6B must be exactly as attractive to Mallon as the gamble of Figure 4.6C because Figure 4.6B could be derived from Figure 4.6C by simply replacing each terminal event fork in Figure 4.6C by Mallon's certainty equivalent for that fork as read from Figure 4.4 or 4.5.

It follows that we can compute the certainty-equivalent terminal value that Mallon should assign to the gamble of Figure 4.6B, and hence to the gamble of Figure 4.6A, by computing the terminal value he should assign to the gamble of Figure 4.6C.

4.4.3

Computation of the Chances
of the Reference Terminal Values

Observing that the two-stage gamble of Figure 4.6C must result in one or the other of Mallon's two reference terminal values, our next step is to compute the "overall" chance which the gamble gives at each of these two terminal values. We do so by reasoning as follows.

If one of the 600 *S* balls is drawn in the first-stage drawing, then as shown by Figure 4.6C there is a .75 standard chance that a *W* ball will be drawn in the second stage, leading Mallon to a terminal value of + $50,000, and a .25 chance that an *L* ball will be drawn, leading to − $10,000. Mallon's chances at the two terminal values will not be altered if we put a supplementary label *W* on .75 × 600 = 450 of the 600 *S* balls in the first-stage urn, put a supplementary label *L* on the remaining 150, and agree that if an *S* ball is drawn in the first stage, Mallon's terminal value will be determined by the supplementary label on this ball, without recourse to any second-stage drawing.

By similar reasoning, Mallon's chances at the two terminal values will not be altered if we put a supplementary label *W* on .70 × 200 = 140 of the 200 *R* balls in the first-stage urn, put a supplementary label *L* on the remaining 60, and use these labels instead of a second-stage drawing to determine the terminal value that will result if an *R* ball is drawn in the first stage. Finally, there will be no need for a second-stage drawing after an *F* ball has been drawn in the first stage if we put a supplementary label *W* on .58 × 200 = 116 of the *F* balls in the first-stage urn and put a supplementary label *L* on the remaining 84.

We can now count up the results of our supplementary labelling in the way shown in Table 4.2 and find that the label *W* has been put on 706 of all the 1,000 balls in the first-stage urn while the label *L* has been put on the remaining 294. The overall chances which the two-stage gamble of Figure 4.6C gives at the better and worse reference terminal values are thus 706/1,000 = .706 and 294/1,000 = .294; and it follows that this gamble must be exactly as attractive to Mallon as the reference gamble of Figure 4.6D, which gives these same chances at the two reference values.

TABLE 4.2
Results of Supplementary Labelling

1	2	3	4
Original Label	*Number of Balls*	*Number with Supplementary Label* W	*L*
S	600	.75 × 600 = 450	150
R	200	.70 × 200 = 140	60
F	200	.58 × 200 = 116	84
	1000	706	294

4.4.4
Determination of the Certainty Equivalent

Because every one of the gambles in Figure 4.6 should be exactly as attractive to Mallon as every other, we can now determine the certainty-equivalent terminal value that Mallon should assign to the real-world gamble of Figure 4.6A by simply reading from Figure 4.5 or Figure 4.4 the certainty-equivalent terminal value that he has already assigned to the reference gamble of Figure 4.6D. Either figure shows that his certainty equivalent should be very close to + $21,000.

4.4.5
Generalization

Using the word "equivalent" to mean "equally attractive to Mallon", we can say that the procedure by which we arrived at Mallon's certainty equivalent for the real-world gamble represented by the terminal event fork of Figure 4.6A consisted of the following steps:

1 We replaced each *real-world event* on the fork by the corresponding event of a standard drawing from Mallon's *equivalent urn*, thus converting Mallon's real-world gamble into an equivalent single-stage standard gamble.

2 We replaced each *terminal value* on the fork by an equivalent *reference gamble*, thus converting the single-stage standard gamble into an equivalent two-stage standard gamble that could lead only to one or the other of Mallon's two reference terminal values.

3 We computed the overall chances of the two reference terminal values in this two-stage standard gamble and then replaced that gamble by an equivalent single-stage reference gamble which offered these same chances at the two reference consequences.

4 Finally, we argued that Mallon should assign to his real-world gamble the same certainty-equivalent terminal value that he had already assigned to this equivalent reference gamble.

By "should" we mean, of course, should if Mallon wants his certainty equivalent to be logically consistent with his quantified judgments concerning events, as expressed by his equivalent urn, and with his quantified likings for terminal values, as expressed by his certainty equivalents for reference gambles.

Exactly this same procedure could clearly be used to find the certainty-equivalent terminal value that Mallon should assign to any terminal event fork that emerges in the course of the analysis of his XYZ decision problem; and more generally, a similar procedure can be used to compute all the certainty equivalents that are required for the analysis of any decision problem. Analysis is thus reduced to a routine application of arithmetic that can be carried out by anyone as soon as the decision maker has (1) quantified his judgments concerning the chances of all the events in his problem, and (2) quantified his likings for all known or certainty-equivalent terminal values that may be involved in the analysis of his problem.

4.4.6
Practical Computation

The series of diagrams in Figure 4.6 and the ball-counting argument summarized in Table 4.2 were needed to make clear the basic logic underlying the procedure by which we reduced A. H. Mallon's real-world gamble to a reference gamble for

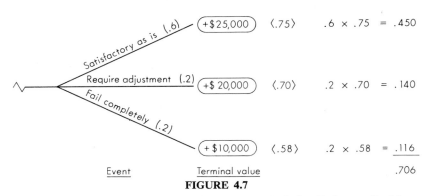

FIGURE 4.7

Practical Reduction of a Real-world Gamble to an Equivalent Reference Gamble

which he had already assessed his certainty equivalent, but all the really essential elements in the procedure can be presented in the much more compact form shown in Figure 4.7. The figure is to be interpreted as follows:

1. The number in parentheses which follows the name of the real-world event on each branch of the fork is the fraction of balls labelled to correspond with that event in Mallon's *equivalent urn* for the event fork.

2. The number in angular brackets which follows each terminal value on the fork is the standard chance of the better reference value ($+\$50,000$) that would make a *reference gamble* exactly as attractive to Mallon as the terminal value on the fork. We remind the reader that these standard chances can be read from Figure 4.4 or 4.5.

3. Since the chance of the worse reference value in a reference gamble is necessarily 1 minus the chance of the better reference value, the numbers in parentheses and the numbers in angular brackets in Figure 4.7 contain all the information about chances that is contained in the diagram in Figure 4.6C of Mallon's two-stage standard gamble.

4. The overall chance of the better terminal value in the equivalent two-stage standard gamble—the fraction of all balls in Mallon's urn that receive the supplementary label *W*—is computed in the right-hand margin of Figure 4.7 by multiplying the fraction of balls on each branch of the fork by the standard chance at the end of each branch and then adding the products. This method of computation differs from the method of Table 4.2 only by starting from the fraction rather than the number of balls bearing each label in the decision maker's equivalent urn; we leave it to the reader to convince himself that the two methods must lead to the same overall chance of the better terminal value not only in this example but in any problem.

5. Knowing that the overall chance of the better terminal value in Mallon's equivalent two-stage standard gamble is .706, and knowing that the two possible terminal values in this gamble are Mallon's reference values, we conclude that the two-stage standard gamble, and hence Mallon's real-world

gamble, is equivalent to a reference gamble in which the chance of the better reference value is .706.

Mallon's certainty equivalent for his real gamble can now be determined by simply reading from Figure 4.4 or 4.5 his certainty equivalent for a reference gamble in which the chance of the better reference value is .706.

4.5
PROBABILITY AND PREFERENCE

4.5.1
Probabilities for Events

It will be convenient in future discussion to have a short, agreed name for the fraction of balls corresponding to a particular real-world event in a decision maker's equivalent urn, and the name that we shall use is "probability". More specifically, we now define the technical term "probability" as follows:

■ Consider a particular decision maker's equivalent urn for a particular event fork in a particular decision diagram. The fraction of balls in the urn corresponding to any specific event on the fork may be called the ≪ probability≫ which that decision maker assigns to that event on that fork in that diagram.

The reason for defining probability in terms of a particular event fork in a particular decision diagram can easily be seen by referring back to Figure 2.1 on page 34 and remembering that a decision maker's equivalent urn for any event fork is defined in terms of the attitude he will hold toward certain pairs of gambles *upon arriving at the base of the fork in question*. If Mallon receives new information which is favorable to the success of stampings, the chance of success will certainly seem greater to him than if he receives no new information; and accordingly the fraction of balls labelled "stampings work" will be greater in Mallon's equivalent urn for the event fork at *D* in Figure 2.1 than in his equivalent urn for the event fork at *F*. By a similar argument, the fraction of balls labelled "stampings work" will be smaller in Mallon's equivalent urn for the event fork at *E* in Figure 2.1 than it is in his equivalent urn for the event fork at *F*; and much more generally:

■ Any decision maker's probability for any event on any event fork may depend on the decision diagram in which the fork is found and on the position of the fork in the diagram—i.e., on the acts and events on the path which leads to the fork from the origin of the diagram.

As for the fact that we have defined probability in terms of a decision (on an equivalent urn) made by a particular decision maker, it is true that a quite different definition is often given, identifying "the" probability (not a particular decision maker's probability) of an event with the relative frequency with which the event would in fact occur in a very large or infinite number of "identical trials". But while we do not assert that our definition is the only correct definition of probability, we do assert that our definition is the one that is relevant to decision under uncertainty. The use of equivalent urns facilitates the analysis of decision problems in which events will occur only once if at all; relative frequencies as such have nothing directly to do with such decision problems.[1]

4.5.2
Preferences for Terminal
Values or Consequences

It will also be convenient in future discussion to have a short, agreed name for the standard chance of the better reference value that makes a reference gamble exactly as attractive to the decision maker as a particular terminal value, and the name that we shall use is "preference". More specifically, we now define the technical term "preference" as follows:

■ Consider (*a*) a reference gamble which gives a standard chance *q* at a better reference terminal value V_1 and a complementary chance at a worse reference terminal value V_0, and (*b*) any definite terminal value *V* which lies between the two reference values inclusive; and let it be understood that any one of the three terminal values in question will be accompanied by the same nonmonetary assets. The standard chance q_v which would make the reference gamble exactly as attractive to the decision maker as the definite terminal value *V* will be called the decision maker's ≪preference≫ for *V relative* to V_1 and V_0 *in the presence* of the specified nonmonetary assets.

We can also say that q_v is the decision maker's preference for the *consequence* consisting of *V* plus the specified nonmonetary assets relative to the consequences consisting of V_1 or V_0 plus the specified nonmonetary assets.

Any statement about a decision maker's preferences can be interpreted as a statement about his certainty equivalents for reference gambles and vice versa.

■ If a decision maker is indifferent between (*a*) a definite terminal value *V*, and (*b*) a gamble which gives a standard chance q_v at a better terminal

---

[1] This is not to say, however, that a decision maker should not consider relative frequencies in *assessing* probabilities—i.e., in deciding on the mix of balls that will make an urn equivalent for him to a particular event fork. We shall see in Chapter 6 that he should do so wherever possible. What the decision maker and the reader must not do is confuse the *meaning* of the term "probability" as we shall use it with the meaning of the term "relative frequency".

value V_1 with a complementary chance at a worse terminal value V_0, we can say *either* (*a*) that q_V is his preference for V relative to V_1 and V_0, or (*b*) that V is his certainty equivalent for the gamble.

4.5.3
Preferences for Gambles,
Terminal Event Forks, or Positions

The word "preference" will also be used to denote the chance of the better reference value that makes a reference gamble exactly as attractive to a decision maker as the real-world gamble represented by some particular terminal event fork.

■ The standard chance q which would make a reference gamble exactly as attractive to a decision maker as the real-world gamble represented by a particular terminal event fork in an original or reduced decision diagram may be called that decision maker's preference for the real-world gamble. It may also be called his preference for the terminal event fork or his preference for the position at the base of the terminal event fork.

4.5.4
Computation of Preference
for a Terminal Event Fork

In the terminology we have just defined, the numbers in parentheses on the branches of the terminal event fork in Figure 4.7 (page 122) are A. H. Mallon's probabilities for the real-world events that are named on the branches; the numbers in angular brackets beside the terminal values on the fork are his preferences for those terminal values; the computation in the right-hand margin consists in multiplying each preference by the corresponding probability and adding the products; and because the result of this computation is the chance of the better reference value in an equivalent reference gamble, it is Mallon's preference for the terminal event fork. Generalizing from this example, we arrive at the following rule for computing a decision maker's preference for a terminal event fork:

■ A decision maker's preference for a terminal event fork is computed by multiplying his preference for each terminal value on the fork by his probability for the corresponding event and then adding the products.

Because the probabilities that are used as multipliers in this computation add to 1, the result of the computation—the decision maker's preference for the gamble represented by the fork—can be called a *probability-weighted average* of his preferences for the terminal values to which the gamble can lead.

4.5.5

"Estimates" vs. Decisions

Although a preference can be regarded as a quantitative expression of a decision maker's liking for a consequence and a probability can be regarded as a quantitative expression of his judgment concerning the chance of an event, the reader will completely misunderstand the true nature of an analysis based on probability and preference if he forgets that these "expressions" are actually decisions in the full sense of the word. In assessing any one of the certainty equivalents for reference gambles which determine his preferences for terminal values, the decision maker *decides* how he would actually behave if he were given a choice between a definite consequence and a particular reference gamble. In assessing a probability, the decision maker *decides* how he would actually behave if he were given a choice between a gamble based on certain real-world events and a lottery based on a standard drawing from an urn containing a particular mix of balls. In other words:

■ Neither probabilities nor preferences should be thought of as possibly erroneous "estimates" of "true values" that exist even though they may be unknown. Probabilities and preferences are *decisions*, and it follows that no matter how hard it may be for the decision maker to decide on one value among many possible values for a particular probability or preference, the value he finally decides on is to be treated as exact and accurate to an infinite number of decimal places.

As we said in Section 2.3.5 concerning certainty equivalents, a decision maker who must assess a preference or a probability is really in exactly the same kind of situation as a purchasing agent who must place an order for a certain number of units of part XB–411 even though he does not know exactly how many units he "should" order at this time. The purchasing agent cannot conveniently get out of his difficulties by placing an order for "somewhere between 200 and 300" units. If he does not decide that he will order exactly 250 units, say, he will have to decide that he will order exactly some other number of units; and whatever number of units he *decides* to order, however unhappily, that is the number his company will have to pay for and will have available for use.

Since confusion concerning the real meaning of probabilities is more common than confusion over the real meaning of preferences, we shall close this chapter by examining once more the nature and implications of one particular, very simple probability assessment—namely, A. H. Mallon's assessment of his probabilities for the events involved in the stampings gamble described by Figure 4.6A (page 118).

1. When Mallon decided that his probabilities for "satisfactory as is", "require adjustment", and "fail completely" were respectively .6, .2, and .2, he thought about just one trial of stampings and just one standard drawing from

an urn. He did not have to think about what would happen in repeated trials of stampings or repeated drawings from the urn.

2. Mallon did not "estimate" the "true" chances of the three possible events, whatever the expression "true chances" may mean. He *decided* that *he would be indifferent* between a gamble based on those events and a gamble based on a standard drawing from an urn in which a fraction .6 of the balls were labelled "satisfactory as is", .2 were labelled "require adjustment", and .2 were labelled "fail completely".

3. Even if Mallon feels that he knows what he means by the "true" chance that stampings will be satisfactory as is and feels unhappy because he is not certain that this chance is really .6, he must not conclude that he might therefore do better to make a different decision concerning the real gamble on stampings in Figure 4.6A than he would make concerning the gamble with the same consequences in Figure 4.6B, where the chance of the event *S* is "known" to be .6. Such an attitude would be in direct contradiction to his decision that he is *indifferent* between the gamble on stampings in Figure 4.6A and the corresponding gamble in Figure 4.6B.

4.6
SUMMARY

4.6.1
Standard Drawings

1 If a drawing of one ball from an urn is to be made in such a way that, for any specified pair of balls in the urn, a particular decision maker is indifferent between (*a*) the right to receive a prize if a particular one of the two balls is drawn, and (*b*) the right to receive the same prize if the other one of the two balls is drawn, then the drawing will be called «standard» for that decision maker.

2 If a standard drawing is to be made from an urn containing N balls, then by definition:
  a There is a $1/N$ «standard chance» that any one, particular ball will be drawn, and
  b There is an n/N standard chance that some one of the balls on any list of n particular balls will be drawn.

4.6.2
Quantification of Judgments Concerning Chances of Events

A decision maker can quantify his judgments concerning the chances of the events on any event fork by deciding what mix of balls in an urn would make a standard drawing from the urn equivalent to the event fork in the sense of the following definition:

1 Consider any event fork, terminal or not, which appears in the diagram of a real decision problem; and consider a standard drawing of one ball from an urn in which each ball is labelled with the name of one of the events on the event fork. If the mix of balls in the urn is such that, upon arriving at the base of the event fork in question, a particular decision maker would be indifferent between (*a*) a gamble which associates *any* definite set of consequences to the events on the real event fork, and (*b*) a gamble which associates those same consequences to the corresponding events of the standard drawing, then the standard drawing from the urn will be called ≪equivalent≫ to the event fork for that decision maker.

For brevity, we shall sometimes say that (the mix of balls in) the urn itself is equivalent to the event fork.

2 After a particular decision maker has decided on the composition of an equivalent urn for a particular event fork in a particular decision diagram, the fraction of balls corresponding to any particular real-world event on the fork may be called that decision maker's ≪probability≫ for that event on that fork in that diagram.

3 When the same set of events is represented by more than one fork in a decision diagram, the decision maker's probabilities for the events may vary from one fork to another because the information available to the decision maker at the base of the fork varies from one fork to another.

A. H. Mallon would almost certainly assess a different probability for the event "stampings work" on each of the three forks where that event appears in Figure 2.1 (page 34), and similarly for the event "stampings do not work".

4.6.3
Quantification of Likings
for Terminal Values

1 In everything that follows, all terminal values are to be understood as being accompanied by the base nonmonetary assets that the decision maker will actually have at the base end position of his decision diagram.

2 If a decision maker is indifferent between (*a*) some definite terminal value V, and (*b*) a reference gamble which gives a definite standard chance q at a better reference value V_1 and a complementary chance at a worse reference value V_0, we may say either (a) that V is his certainty equivalent for the gamble, or (b) that q is his ≪preference≫ for the terminal value V *relative* to V_1 and V_0 *in the presence* of his base nonmonetary assets.

3 If a decision maker selects reference values V_1 and V_0 and then constructs a graph which shows his certainty equivalent for a reference gamble with any q between 0 and 1, he can read from this graph his preference q for any terminal value between V_0 and V_1.

4.6.4
Computation of Certainty Equivalents
for Terminal Event Forks

1 A decision maker should be indifferent between (*a*) the gamble represented by any particular terminal event fork that appears on either the original or a reduced diagram of his decision problem, and (*b*) a two-stage standard gamble in which (1) the event fork is replaced by a fork representing a standard drawing from his equivalent urn, and (2) each terminal value is replaced by an equivalent reference gamble.

2 This equivalent two-stage standard gamble may be described by simply writing the decision maker's probability for each real-world event on the corresponding branch of the fork and writing his preference beside each terminal value on the fork.

The probabilities describe the fractions of balls bearing various labels in the equivalent urn used in the first stage of the gamble; the preferences describe the chances of obtaining the better reference value in the various second-stage reference gambles.

3 The overall chance of obtaining the better reference value in the two-stage standard gamble can be computed by multiplying the decision maker's preference for each terminal value by the probability of the corresponding event and adding the products.

4 The two-stage standard gamble is equivalent to a single-stage reference gamble which gives this same chance at the better reference value, and therefore:

    a The computed chance may be called the decision maker's preference for the terminal event fork or the position at its base;

    b The certainty-equivalent terminal value which the decision maker assigns to this fork or position should be equal to his certainty equivalent for the equivalent reference gamble.

EXERCISES

A. QUANTIFICATION OF JUDGMENTS CONCERNING CHANCES

4.1   The decision diagram in Figure 4.8 shows the structure and partial cash flows of the decision problem described in Exercise 1.2.

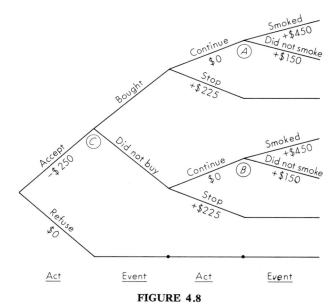

FIGURE 4.8
The Decision Problem of Exercises 1.2 and 4.1

a Value the end positions of this diagram using the evaluation date and criterion prescribed in the paragraph preceding Exercise 1.3.

b Suppose that you do accept Smith's deal and that Smith then offers to modify its terms as follows. If you reach position *A* in the diagram, then instead of asking the student whether he has smoked, Smith will make a standard drawing from an urn in which a fraction *P* of the balls are labelled *S*(moked), the remainder *D*(id not smoke). If an *S* ball is drawn, Smith will pay you $450; if a *D* ball is drawn, he will pay you $150.

    Would you allow Smith to make this change in the terms of the deal if *P* = .99? .90? .50? .05? What is the smallest value of *P* that would induce you to allow Smith to make the change?

c Same as (*b*) except that the drawing will be substituted for the question if and when you reach position *B* in the diagram.

d Would your answers to (*b*) and (*c*) be the same if the $450 payment were changed to $4,500 and the $150 payment were changed to $0? If the $450 payment were changed to $0 and the $150 payment were changed to $10,000?

e Would your answers to (*b*) and (*c*) be the same if you had just been given $10,000 cash, so that all your terminal values at the end positions of the diagram were increased by $10,000? If you had just lost all the cash you own?

4.2   Suppose that you and Smith do agree that if you reach either position *A* or position *B*, the amount Smith pays you next will be determined by a drawing from an urn rather than by asking the student whether he has smoked. Suppose further that Smith now proposes that, instead of going to the library and questioning the first student to emerge, the two of you will make a standard drawing from an urn in which some of the balls are labelled *B*(ought), the remainder *D*(id not buy). If a *B* ball is drawn, you will have the same options and rights that you would have if a student said he had bought, and similarly for a *D* ball.

What is the smallest fraction of balls labelled *B* that would induce you to allow Smith to make the change in the terms of the deal? Does your answer depend on the fraction of balls labelled *S* in the urn to be used if you reach position *A*?

B. QUANTIFICATION OF LIKINGS FOR TERMINAL VALUES

4.3 Figure 4.4 shows that + $30,000 is A. H. Mallon's certainty equivalent for a reference gamble that gives a .8 chance at a + $50,000 terminal value and a .2 chance at − $10,000, it being understood that any one of these three terminal values will be accompanied by Mallon's base nonmonetary assets. Exactly how could you obtain this same information from Figure 4.5?

4.4 Figure 4.5 shows that .9 is the standard chance of the better reference value which would make a reference gamble neither more nor less attractive to Mallon than a definite + $40,000 terminal value. Exactly how could you obtain this same information from Figure 4.4?

C. COMPUTATION OF CERTAINTY EQUIVALENTS

4.5 Suppose that, contrary to the text of this chapter, Mr. A. H. Mallon believes that the diagram in Figure 1.5 (page 13) is a correct representation of his XYZ decision problem. He believes, in other words, that stampings will either work as is or fail completely; there is no chance that they will require adjustment. Suppose further that Mallon decides (1) that .8 of the balls in his equivalent urn for the event fork at position *Y* in Figure 1.5 would be labelled to correspond to the event "stampings work", and (2) that .5 of the balls in his equivalent urn for the event fork at position *Z* would be labelled to correspond to the event "XYZ orders". His certainty equivalents for reference gambles are given by Figures 4.4 and 4.5 on pages 114 and 115.

a Diagram a two-stage standard gamble of the general sort typified by Figure 4.6C (page 118) which should be exactly as attractive to Mallon as the real gamble represented by the terminal event fork at position *Y* in Figure 1.5.

b What is the overall chance that this two-stage gamble will yield a + $50,-000 terminal value? That it will yield a − $10,000 terminal value?

c What should be Mallon's certainty equivalent for the two-stage gamble? For the terminal event fork in Figure 1.5?

d Using your answer to (*c*), reduce the diagram of Mallon's decision problem to a stage where the event fork at position *Z* in Figure 1.5 appears as a terminal event fork.

e What should be Mallon's certainty equivalent for this new terminal event fork?

D. PROBABILITY AND PREFERENCE

4.6 Given your answers to Exercises 4.1 and 4.2, what are your probabilities for the events on the forks at positions *A*, *B*, and *C* in Figure 4.8 (page 130)? Is your probability for the event "smoked" the same on the fork at position *A* as on the fork at position *B*?

4.7 *a* Taking each terminal value in Figure 1.5 (page 13) in turn, read from Figure 4.4 *and* from Figure 4.5 (page 115) Mr. A. H. Mallon's preference for this terminal value relative to +$50,000 and −$10,000 in the presence of his base nonmonetary assets.

b Using Mallon's probabilities as given in Exercise 4.5, compute his preferences for positions *Y*, *X*, and *Z* in Figure 1.5.

4.8 Harold Haskins, who holds a lottery ticket that gives him a .75 standard chance of ending up with net liquid assets of +$100,000 and a .25 standard chance of ending up with net liquid assets of $0, decides that he would trade the ticket for guaranteed net liquid assets of +$50,000 but not a cent less. In any case, Haskins will end up with the same nonmonetary assets that he now has.

a What is Haskins' certainty equivalent for the uncertain terminal value that he will face if he keeps the lottery ticket?

b What is Haskins' preference for a terminal value of +$50,000 relative to terminal values of +$100,000 and $0 in the presence of his existing nonmonetary assets?

c If Haskins' uninsured house were to burn down, might this affect his certainty equivalent for the gamble he will face if he keeps the lottery ticket? How?

d Might Haskins' preference for +$50,000 relative to +$100,000 and $0 in the presence of the nonmonetary assets he would have after his uninsured house burned down differ from his preference in the presence of his existing nonmonetary assets? How?

4.9 In response to a request from Amalgamated Aviation, prime contractor for the Hercules missile, Trontech, Inc., has submitted a design proposal for the stabilization mechanism of the missile's guidance system. Within a week from today, Amalgamated will award the subcontract either to

Trontech or to General Gyroscope, the only other company which submitted a proposal. If Trontech's proposal is chosen, sales revenue will exceed out-of-pocket production costs by $500,000; if Trontech's proposal is not chosen, Trontech will realize nothing in cash, although the knowledge gained in working on the mechanism up to the design stage will undoubtedly be of value later on.

Several days ago Mr. D. G. Bell, Trontech's Executive Vice-president, was talking with Mr. G. W. Larson, the President, about the company's chances of getting the contract. Bell, being somewhat pessimistic about Trontech's chances of winning the award, stated that he would give a "pretty penny" to trade proposals with General Gyroscope. "Ridiculous," retorted Larson, "our chances are a darn sight better than theirs and the margin we'd realize if we used their design would be just about the same as the $500,000 we'll make on ours. I wouldn't trade even if they threw in some cash besides."

Today, the President of United Guidance Corporation, a small, aggressive competitor with peculiar business ideas, approached Larson with the following proposition. In return for rights to Trontech's design proposal, he will allow Larson to flip a coin and will pay Trontech $500,000 one week from today if the coin comes up heads. After some consideration Larson has just about decided to accept United Guidance's proposition, arguing that a known 50% chance at $500,000 is better than gambling on something as vague as the factors which will ultimately determine Amalgamated Aviation's final choice.

What do you think of Larson's tentative decision?

E. REVIEW PROBLEM

4.10 Analyze the modified version of Mr. A. H. Mallon's decision problem that was described in Exercise 1.12, assuming that Mallon's preferences are as shown in Figure 4.5 (page 115) and that his probabilities are as follows:

Radical prototype:

Works:	.25
Does not work:	.75
	1.00

Result of submitting conventional prototype:

XYZ orders:	.50
Does not order:	.50
	1.00

Performance of stampings in conventional production units:

Satisfactory as is:	.80
Fail completely:	.20
	1.00

PART
2

ASSESSMENT
OF
PREFERENCES
AND
PROBABILITIES

CHAPTER
5

PREFERENCE AND MATHEMATICAL EXPECTATION

In Chapter 4 we saw that the actual analysis of a decision problem becomes a routine application of arithmetic if the decision maker first decides on his probability for every event branch and his preference for every terminal value in his decision diagram. In the present chapter we shall examine in detail certain problems concerning the practical assessment and use of preferences that were passed over in Chapter 4; in Chapters 6 through 9 we shall deal with the many problems that can arise in the practical assessment and use of probabilities.

The main topics treated in the present chapter are taken up in the following order:

1. In Sections 5.1 through 5.3 we show how a decision maker can, with only a reasonable expenditure of time and effort, assess his preferences for all terminal values of his criterion that lie between any two reference values he chooses.

2. In Section 5.4 we discuss certain problems involving choice of reference values, the "permanence" of assessed preferences, and preferences for total cash flows.

3. Finally, we take up the very important special case where the decision maker's preference curve for terminal values is nearly a straight line. We first show in Section 5.5 that in this special case certainty equivalents can be computed directly from probabilities and monetary values, without any explicit use of preferences; and we then show in Section 5.6 that in this same special case it is often legitimate to simplify the decision diagram itself very substantially.

The text and exercises of this chapter can be studied in the following order:

1 Sections 5.1.1–5.1.3 and Exercises 5.1–5.3.

2 Section 5.1.4 and Exercise 5.4.

3 Section 5.2.1 and Exercises 5.5–5.6.

4 Exercise 5.7.

5 Section 5.2.2 and Exercise 5.8.

6 Sections 5.2.3–5.2.4 and Exercise 5.9.

7 Sections 5.2.5–5.2.6 and Exercise 5.10.

8 Sections 5.3.1–5.3.2 and Exercises 5.11–5.12.

9 Section 5.3.3.

10 Section 5.4 and Exercise 5.13.

11 Section 5.5.1 and Exercises 5.14–5.15.

12 Sections 5.5.2–5.5.6 and Exercises 5.16–5.17.

13 Section 5.6 and Exercise 5.18.

14 Section 5.7 and Exercises 5.19–5.22.

CONTENTS OF CHAPTER 5

1.
Shapes of Preference Curves
and General Attitudes toward Risk

1 Notation for Two-valued Standard Gambles
2 Continuously Increasing Certainty Equivalents for Reference Gambles
3 Risk Aversion as Regards 50–50 Gambles
4 Decreasing Risk Aversion

2.
Assessment of Points
on a Preference Curve

1 Certainty Equivalents for Reference Gambles
2 Certainty Equivalents for 50–50 Gambles
3 Inconsistencies between the Two Sets of Assessments
4 Reconciliation of the Assessments
5 A Final Test of Consistency
6 Summary

3.
Fitting a Preference Curve
to the Decision Maker's Assessments

1 Determination of a Curve by Selected Points and General Properties
2 Graphical Construction of Preference Curves
3 Mathematical Formulas for Preference Curves

4.
Some Comments on Preference Curves

1 Choice of Reference Values
2 Certainty Equivalents for Small Gambles
3 Permanence of Preferences
4 Preferences for Total Cash Flows

5.
Linear Preference
and Mathematical Expectation

1 Mathematical Expectations for Uncertain Terminal Values
2 Notation
3 Certainty Equivalents Which Imply Linear Preference
4 Implications of Linear Preference for Certainty Equivalents
5 Approximation of Certainty Equivalents by Mathematical Expectations
6 Backward Induction on Mathematical Expectations

6.
Description of Decision Problems
When Preference Is Linear

1 Mathematical Expectations for Uncertain Monetary Values
2 Mathematical Expectations for Sums of Monetary Values
3 Adjustment of Partial Cash Flows for Nonmonetary Consequences
4 Replacement of Terminal Event Forks by Single Branches
5 Replacement of Internal Event Forks by Single Branches
6 Addition of a Constant to All Terminal Values
7 Disregard of Contextual Cash Flows
8 Opportunity Costs
9 Relative vs. Absolute Terminal Values
10 Test for Legitimacy of Simplifications

7.
Summary

1 Shapes of Preference Curves and General Attitudes toward Risk
2 Assessment of Points on a Preference Curve
3 Fitting the Preference Curve to the Assessments
4 Preferences for Total Cash Flows
5 Mathematical Expectations for Uncertain Monetary Values
6 Simplification of Decision Diagrams

5.1
SHAPES OF PREFERENCE CURVES
AND GENERAL ATTITUDES TOWARD RISK

We saw in Section 4.3 that if a decision maker wishes to assess his preference for every terminal value V between two chosen reference values V_0 and V_1, he can do so by assessing his certainty equivalent for every "reference gamble" that gives a standard chance q at the better reference value V_1 and a complementary chance at V_0. We remind the reader that this is true because:

■ If a decision maker is indifferent between (*a*) a definite terminal value V, and (*b*) a gamble which gives a standard chance q at a better value V_1 and a complementary chance at a worse value V_0, then we can say either (*a*) that V is the decision maker's certainty equivalent for the gamble, or (*b*) that q is the decision maker's preference for V relative to V_1 and V_0.

We also remind the reader that in any discussion of certainty equivalents and/or preferences, all terminal values are to be understood as being accompanied by the decision maker's *base* nonmonetary assets.

Assessment of a certainty equivalent for every possible reference gamble or value of q would, of course, be an impossible task if the decision maker had to assess his certainty equivalent for each gamble separately. We shall show in this chapter, however, that if the decision maker shares certain very commonly held general attitudes toward *all* reference gambles and *all* 50–50 gambles, he can make all the required assessments with only a reasonable expenditure of time and effort. After he has made carefully thought-out assessments of his certainty equivalents for only a very few reference gambles, he can assess his certainty equivalents for all other reference gambles by a procedure which is almost purely mechanical.

Specifically, we shall first show that certain commonly held general attitudes toward reference gambles and 50–50 gambles imply that a ≪preference curve≫ like the one in Figure 4.5 (page 115) must have a certain general shape. Certainty equivalents read or computed from a curve that is not of this shape will disagree with these general attitudes. We shall then be able to show that if a decision maker who holds these general attitudes makes "direct" assessments of his certainty equivalents for a few suitably chosen reference gambles and plots these assessments as points on a graph, these few points together with his general attitudes will almost completely determine his entire preference curve. Any curve that (1) passes through the plotted points, and (2) has a general shape that agrees with the decision maker's general attitudes, will be practically the same as any other curve that has these two properties; and therefore the decision maker can assess his certainty equivalents for all possible reference gambles by simply constructing one such curve. Even more than this, we shall be able to show that if the decision maker checks certain implications of his direct assessments and revises them where necessary before plotting his points and constructing his curve, he will actually be entitled to place greater confidence in certainty equivalents read or computed from the curve than he would be entitled to place in his directly assessed certainty equivalent for any individual gamble considered by itself.

5.1.1
Notation for Two-valued Standard Gambles

In the discussion to follow, we shall have to discuss certainty equivalents for a large number of different standard gambles, each of which gives some specified standard chance at some one specified terminal value with a complementary chance at another specified terminal value; and to make it easy to describe any such "two-valued" standard gamble, we now introduce special notation.

The symbol $\langle q, V'; V'' \rangle$ will denote a gamble which gives a standard chance q at the terminal value V' with a complementary chance $(1 - q)$ at V''. The symbol $\langle \frac{1}{4}, +\$50,000; -\$10,000 \rangle$ will denote a gamble which gives a $1/4$ standard chance at $+\$50,000$ with a complementary $3/4$ chance at $-\$10,000$; and so forth. Observe that the standard chance which appears explicitly within the brackets is the chance of the *first* of the two terminal values that appear within the brackets.

5.1.2
Continuously Increasing Certainty
Equivalents for Reference Gambles

Let V_1 and V_0 respectively denote a decision maker's better and worse reference values, so that $\langle q, V_1; V_0 \rangle$ denotes a reference gamble in which the chance of the better reference value is q; and recall that:

1 If $q = 0$, any decision maker's certainty equivalent for $\langle q, V_1; V_0 \rangle$ must be V_0 because the gamble is sure to result in V_0.

2 If $q = 1$, any decision maker's certainty equivalent for $\langle q, V_1; V_0 \rangle$ must be V_1 because the gamble is sure to result in V_1.

Now let V denote the decision maker's certainty equivalent for $\langle q, V_1; V_0 \rangle$ and consider how V will vary as q increases continuously—i.e., without jumps. Without making any specific, numerical assessments of V for specific values of q, almost any reasonable decision maker will feel that his certainty equivalent V should increase continuously from V_0 to V_1 as q increases continuously from 0 to 1. This "general attitude" toward reference gambles is so nearly universal that in this book we shall restrict the discussion to cases where it is in fact held by the decision maker.

As regards preference curves like Figure 4.5 (page 115), where it is the standard chance q of the better reference value that is plotted on the vertical axis while the decision maker's certainty equivalent V is plotted on the horizontal axis, what we want to know is how q behaves as V increases rather than the reverse. But if V increases continuously with q, then q increases continuously with V, and it follows that:

■ If the decision maker's certainty equivalent for $\langle q, V_1; V_0 \rangle$ increases continuously from V_0 to V_1 as q increases continuously from 0 to 1, then the ordinate q of his preference curve must rise continuously from 0 to 1 as the abscissa V increases from V_0 to V_1.

5.1.3
Risk Aversion as Regards 50–50 Gambles

Turning now from reference gambles to 50–50 gambles, let $\langle \frac{1}{2}, V'; V'' \rangle$ denote a gamble that gives equal chances at two specified terminal values V' and V'' which may or may not be equal to the decision maker's reference values V_0 and V_1; and let us agree to say that a decision maker is:

1 ≪Risk averse≫ as regards any particular gamble of the form $\langle \frac{1}{2}, V'; V'' \rangle$ if his certainty equivalent for the gamble is *less* than the average $\frac{1}{2}(V' + V'')$ of the two terminal values that can result from the gamble;

2 ≪Risk seeking≫ if his certainty equivalent is *greater* than $\frac{1}{2}(V' + V'')$;

3 ≪Risk neutral≫ if his certainty equivalent is *equal* to $\frac{1}{2}(V' + V'')$.

Without assessing specific, numerical certainty equivalents for any particular gambles of the form $\langle \frac{1}{2}, V'; V'' \rangle$, very many decision makers will decide that they are risk averse as regards *all* gambles of this form. No matter what particular values V' and V'' might be involved in a particular gamble, their certainty equivalent for the gamble would be less than $\frac{1}{2}(V' + V'')$. Decision makers who are not risk averse toward absolutely all gambles of the form $\langle \frac{1}{2}, V'; V'' \rangle$ often decide that they are risk averse whenever both V' and V'' lie within some interval that may or may not extend all the way from V_0 to V_1. These same or other decision makers may decide that they are risk neutral or

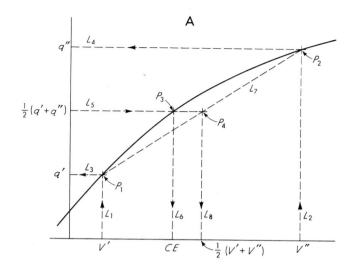

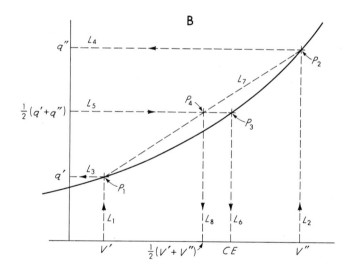

FIGURE 5.1

Computation of Certainty Equivalents for 50–50 Gambles

even risk seeking whenever both V' and V'' lie within some other specified interval; and so forth.

Any general attitude of the sort just described has definite implications for the general shape of the decision maker's preference curve. What these implications are can be seen by examination of Figures 5.1A and B, which show the computation of a certainty equivalent for the gamble $\langle \frac{1}{2}, V'; V'' \rangle$ from each of two different preference curves. Observing that the decision maker's preferences for V' and V'' are called respectively q' and q'' in both cases, the reader should prove for himself that in both cases:

1. The decision maker's preferences for V' and V'' can be found by constructing vertical lines L_1 and L_2 through V' and V'' on the horizontal axis, finding the points P_1 and P_2 where these lines intersect the preference curve, and then constructing horizontal lines L_3 and L_4 through these points.

2. The decision maker's preference for the gamble $\langle \frac{1}{2},\ V';\ V'' \rangle$ is $\frac{1}{2}(q' + q'')$ by the rule in Section 4.5.4 and therefore corresponds to a point half way between q' and q'' on the vertical axis.

3. The decision maker's certainty equivalent for the gamble can be found on the horizontal axis by first constructing a horizontal line L_5 through the point $\frac{1}{2}(q' + q'')$ on the vertical axis, finding the point P_3 where this line intersects the preference curve, and then constructing a vertical line L_6 through this point.

4. The average of V' and V'' is $\frac{1}{2}(V' + V'')$ and therefore corresponds to a point half way between V' and V'' on the horizontal axis.

5. The average can also be found by first constructing a line L_7 joining P_1 and P_2, finding the point P_4 where this line intersects L_5, and then constructing a vertical line L_8 through this point.

From this geometry the reader should be able to convince himself of the truth of the following propositions.

1. Whenever V' and V'' lie within an interval over which the decision maker's preference curve is ≪concave≫ when viewed from below, like the curve in Figure 5.1A, his certainty equivalent for $\langle \frac{1}{2},\ V';\ V'' \rangle$ as computed from the curve will be less than $\frac{1}{2}(V' + V'')$, implying that he is risk averse as regards the gamble.

2. Whenever V' and V'' lie within an interval over which the decision maker's preference curve is ≪convex≫ when viewed from below, like the curve in Figure 5.1B, his certainty equivalent for $\langle \frac{1}{2},\ V';\ V'' \rangle$ as computed from the curve will be greater than $\frac{1}{2}(V' + V'')$, implying that he is risk seeking as regards the gamble.

3. Whenever V' and V'' lie within an interval over which the decision maker's preference curve is a straight line, his certainty equivalent for $\langle \frac{1}{2},\ V';\ V'' \rangle$ as computed from the curve will be equal to $\frac{1}{2}(V' + V'')$, implying that he is risk neutral as regards the gamble.

The relations that help the decision maker to construct a preference curve that agrees with his general attitudes toward 50–50 gambles are, of course, the inverse of those just stated.

■ If the decision maker is risk averse to $\langle \frac{1}{2},\ V';\ V'' \rangle$ whenever V' and V'' are within some specified interval, his preference curve must be concave over that interval; if he is risk seeking, it must be convex; if he is risk neutral, it must be a straight line.

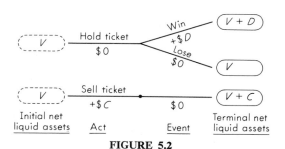

FIGURE 5.2

Description of a Gamble and an Equivalent Certainty

5.1.4
Decreasing Risk Aversion

To bring out some further relations between a decision maker's general attitudes toward risk and the general shape of his preference curve, we first introduce the concept of a risk premium.

■ When a gamble gives *equal* chances at a number of terminal values, the amount by which a decision maker's certainty-equivalent terminal value falls short of the simple arithmetic average of the equally likely terminal values will be called his ≪risk premium≫ for the gamble:

$$\text{risk premium} = \text{average} - \text{certainty equivalent.}$$

Notice that the decision maker's risk premium for a 50–50 gamble will be

positive if he is risk averse,

zero if he is risk neutral,

negative if he is risk seeking

as regards the gamble in question.

Suppose now that a decision maker holds a lottery ticket which gives even chances at a cash prize of D dollars or nothing; let C denote the cash price for which he would be just willing to sell this ticket; let V denote the current value of his criterion, which is net liquid assets; suppose that the terminal value of his criterion will be

V if he holds the ticket and loses,

$V + D$ if he holds the ticket and wins,

$V + C$ if he sells the ticket for C;

and observe that, as shown in Figure 5.2:

1. The lesser of the two terminal values that can result from the gamble is V regardless of D;

2. The ≪spread≫ between the two possible terminal values is D regardless of V;

3. The average of the two possible terminal values is

$$\tfrac{1}{2}V + \tfrac{1}{2}(V + D) = V + \tfrac{1}{2}D;$$

4. The decision maker's certainty equivalent for the uncertain terminal value that will result from the gamble is $V + C$;

5. Consequently his risk premium for the gamble is

$$(V + \tfrac{1}{2}D) - (V + C) = \tfrac{1}{2}D - C.$$

In general, the cash price C for which a decision maker would be just willing to sell a lottery ticket in a situation like the one we have just described will depend not only on the amount of the prize D but also on the current level V of the decision maker's net liquid assets or other criterion; and very often C depends on V in a very special way. Many decision makers feels that (*a*) if V were very small or negative, they would be willing to sell a ticket giving a $1/2$ chance at a substantial prize D for a very small fraction of D, whereas (*b*) if V were large, they would not be willing to sell unless they could get virtually $\tfrac{1}{2}D$ for the ticket. More generally, many decision makers feel that as V increases continuously from their lower reference value V_0 toward their upper reference value V_1, the price C for which they would be just willing to sell the ticket would increase continuously from some relatively small amount toward $\tfrac{1}{2}D$.

Now recall (1) that V can also be interpreted as the lower of the two terminal values that can result from the gamble, (2) that D is the spread between the two possible terminal values, and (3) that the difference $(\tfrac{1}{2}D - C)$ is the decision maker's risk premium for the gamble. This being so, the kind of general attitude we have just described can also be described as follows:

■ Many decision makers feel that their risk premium for a gamble of the form $\langle \tfrac{1}{2}, V + D; V \rangle$ would (1) always be positive, but (2) would decrease continuously toward 0 as (*a*) the lesser of the two possible terminal values that can result from the gamble increases while (*b*) the spread between the two terminal values remains fixed.

We shall refer to this general attitude as one of ≪positive but decreasing risk aversion≫.

Turning now to the implications of this attitude for the general shape of a preference curve, we already know that if a decision maker would assess a positive risk premium for any 50–50 gamble—if his certainty equivalent for any such gamble would be less than the average of the two possible terminal values—then his preference curve must be everywhere concave. What remains to be investigated is the implications for the preference curve of the fact that the decision maker's risk premium for a 50–50 gamble with any given spread becomes smaller as the lesser of the two terminal values that can result from the gamble becomes larger; and these implications can be seen by reexamining Figure 5.1A.

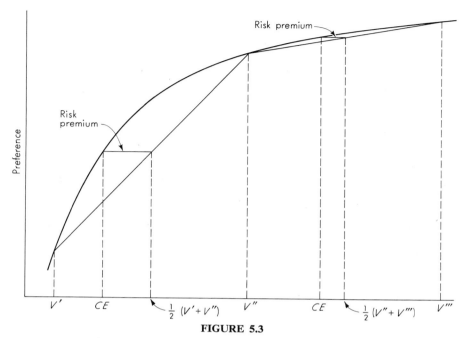

FIGURE 5.3

Preference Curve Implying Positive But Decreasing Risk Aversion

Recalling that a decision maker's risk premium for a gamble is the amount by which his certainty-equivalent terminal value falls short of the average of the possible terminal values, we see that in the case described in Figure 5.1A the risk premium is equal to the distance between the points P_3 and P_4. And having made this observation, it is easy to see that the size of the computed risk premium for any particular 50–50 gamble depends on the degree of concavity of the preference curve. If the curve of Figure 5.1A were more concave than it is, the computed risk premium would be larger than it is; if the curve were less concave, the computed risk premium would be smaller.

It follows that if a decision maker's risk premium for a gamble of fixed spread becomes smaller as the lesser terminal value that can result from the gamble becomes larger, the concavity of his preference curve must decrease from left to right. A portion of a curve with this property is illustrated in Figure 5.3, which shows computed risk premiums for two 50–50 gambles both of which have the same spread; one of them gives even chances at V' and V'', while the other gives even chances at V'' and V'''.

Before closing this discussion of the relation between concavity and risk aversion, we urge the reader to remember that the only measure of concavity that is relevant to risk aversion is the *horizontal* measure illustrated in Figures 5.1A and 5.2. *A curve may "look" as if its concavity decreases from left to right when in fact its concavity as measured in the way relevant to risk aversion actually increases from left to right.*

5.2

ASSESSMENT OF POINTS
ON A PREFERENCE CURVE

When the general shape of a decision maker's preference curve is determined by general attitudes toward risk of the kind we have just discussed, the curve can be completely determined for practical purposes by specifying only a very few points through which it must pass. In the present section we shall describe two different procedures by which the decision maker can assess the required points, show that the points assessed by one procedure may be logically inconsistent with the points assessed by the other, and argue that a decision maker should assess points by both procedures and then reconcile the inconsistencies if he wants a really solid foundation for a preference curve.

5.2.1

Certainty Equivalents
for Reference Gambles

Since any preference curve is also a statement of certainty equivalents for reference gambles, as we saw in Section 4.3, points through which a preference curve must pass can be assessed by assessing certainty equivalents for reference gambles.

For example, suppose that Mr. A. H. Mallon wishes to assess his preferences for all terminal values between the reference values $V_0 = -\$10,000$ and $V_1 = +\$50,000$. He can assess five points on his preference curve by directly assessing his certainty equivalents for reference gambles $\langle q, V_1; V_0 \rangle$ with the five different values of q that are shown in the first column of Table 5.1. The first and last values of these values of q are chosen because the corresponding certainty equivalents can be "automatically" assessed at $V_0 = -\$10,000$ and $V_1 = +\$50,000$ respectively. The reason for selecting the other three values of q will appear later on; for the moment, we simply remind the reader that Mallon's certainty equivalents for reference gambles with these q's will depend on *his* likings for consequences. The certainty equivalents in the second column of the table are merely values on which Mallon *might* decide if he feels that $-\$10,000$ represents so unpleasant a consequence that even $-\$2,000$ is substantially better.

TABLE 5.1
A. H. Mallon's Certainty Equivalents
for Selected Reference Gambles

$V_1 = +\$50,000; V_0 = -\$10,000$

Standard Chance of Better Terminal Value q	Certainty-equivalent Terminal Value V
0	$-\$10,000$
1/4	$-\ \ 2,000$
1/2	$+\ \ 5,000$
3/4	$+\ 25,000$
1	$+\ 50,000$

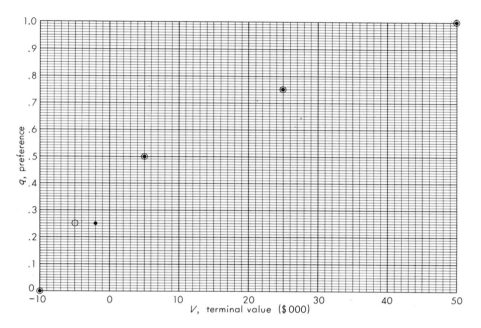

FIGURE 5.4

Points Assessed by Mr. A. H. Mallon

as a Basis for His Preference Curve

Assuming that Mallon does assess the certainty-equivalent terminal values that appear in the second column of Table 5.1, and recalling that any q in the first column of the table can also be interpreted as Mallon's preference for the corresponding terminal value in the second column, we next plot Mallon's assessments as heavy dots in Figure 5.4. Entering this graph at $1/4$ on the *vertical* axis and reading over to the heavy dot and down to the horizontal axis, we would find that $-\$2,000$ was Mallon's certainty equivalent for a reference gamble giving a $1/4$ chance at $+\$50,000$ and a complementary chance at $-\$10,000$. What interests us here, however, is the fact that by entering the graph at $-\$2,000$ on the *horizontal* axis, we would find that $1/4$ is Mallon's preference for $-\$2,000$ relative to $+\$50,000$ and $-\$10,000$; and similarly for the other four points. If Mallon makes no changes in these basic assessments, his preference curve must pass through the five points indicated by heavy dots.

5.2.2

Certainty Equivalents for 50–50 Gambles

Points through which a preference curve should pass can also be assessed by assessing certainty equivalents for a number of properly selected 50–50 gambles only one of which is a reference gamble. The procedure is based on the fact that, by the rule in Section 4.5.4,

■ If q' and q'' are respectively the decision maker's preferences for terminal values V' and V'', then his preference for a gamble giving even chances at V' and V'' is $\frac{1}{2}q' + \frac{1}{2}q''$.

To show Mr. A. H. Mallon how he can apply this alternative assessment procedure, we first ask him to forget for the moment that he ever assessed his certainty equivalents for the three intermediate reference gambles in Table 5.1. He should carry over from the preceding argument only the fact that his preferences for $V_0 = -\$10,000$ and $V_1 = +\$50,000$ are necessarily 0 and 1.

We then ask Mallon to begin his new set of assessments by assessing his certainty equivalent for a gamble that gives even chances at the only two terminal values for which his preferences are known at this point, namely $-\$10,000$ and $+\$50,000$. Assuming by way of example that Mallon answers $+\$5,000$, we next argue as follows. Since Mallon's preferences for the two terminal values that can result from the gamble are 0 and 1, his preference for the gamble must be

$$(\frac{1}{2} \times 0) + (\frac{1}{2} \times 1) = 1/2;$$

and since Mallon is indifferent between the gamble and $+\$5,000$ for certain, his preference for $+\$5,000$ must be $1/2$. The argument and the conclusion are summarized in the first row of Table 5.2.

TABLE 5.2
A. H. Mallon's Preferences and Certainty Equivalents for Selected 50–50 Gambles

Description of 50–50 Gamble Terminal Values		Preferences for Terminal Values		Computed Preference for Gamble	Certainty Equivalent for Gamble
$+\$50,000$	$-\$10,000$	1	0	$(\frac{1}{2} \times 1) + (\frac{1}{2} \times 0) = 1/2$	$+\$\ 5,000$
$+\ 5,000$	$-\ 10,000$	$1/2$	0	$(\frac{1}{2} \times 1/2) + (\frac{1}{2} \times 0) = 1/4$	$-\ 5,000$
$+\ 50,000$	$+\ 5,000$	1	$1/2$	$(\frac{1}{2} \times 1) + (\frac{1}{2} \times 1/2) = 3/4$	$+\ 25,000$

The fact that Mallon's preference for $+\$5,000$ is now known enables us to construct two more 50–50 gambles involving terminal values for which his preferences are known, namely, a gamble which gives even chances at $+\$5,000$ and $-\$10,000$, and another which gives even chances at $+\$5,000$ and $+\$50,000$. Assuming that Mallon tells us that his certainty equivalent for $\langle \frac{1}{2}, +\$5,000; -\$10,000 \rangle$ is $-\$5,000$ and that his certainty equivalent for $\langle \frac{1}{2}, +\$50,000; +\$5,000 \rangle$ is $+\$25,000$, we next argue as follows.

1. Since Mallon's preferences for $+\$5,000$ and $-\$10,000$ are respectively $1/2$ and 0, his preference for $\langle \frac{1}{2}, +\$5,000; -\$10,000 \rangle$ must be

$$(\frac{1}{2} \times 1/2) + (\frac{1}{2} \times 0) = 1/4;$$

and since he has just said that he is indifferent between this gamble and $-\$5,000$ for certain, his preference for $-\$5,000$ must be $1/4$. The argument and conclusion are summarized in the second row of Table 5.2.

2. Similarly, Mallon's preference for the gamble $\langle \frac{1}{2}, +\$50,000; +\$5,000 \rangle$ must be

$$(\frac{1}{2} \times 1) + (\frac{1}{2} \times 1/2) = 3/4;$$

and since he has just said that $+\$25,000$ is his certainty equivalent for this gamble, his preference for $+\$25,000$ must be $3/4$. The argument and conclusion are summarized in the third row of Table 5.2.

Summing up, we see that this second assessment procedure has led Mallon to assess the five preferences shown in Table 5.3. The points corresponding to these five assessments are surrounded by circles in Figure 5.4, and if Mallon adheres to this new set of assessments, his preference curve must pass through these five circled points.

TABLE 5.3
A. H. Mallon's Preferences
for Selected Terminal Values
as Assessed via 50–50 Gambles

Terminal Value	Preference
−$10,000	0
− 5,000	1/4
+ 5,000	1/2
+ 25,000	3/4
+ 50,000	1

5.2.3

Inconsistencies between
the Two Sets of Assessments

Comparing the set of points designated by circles in Figure 5.4 with the set of points designated by heavy dots, we see that Mallon's two sets of assessments are mutually inconsistent. Whereas the second heavy dot from the left shows that his directly assessed certainty equivalent for the reference gamble $\langle \frac{1}{4}, +\$50,000; -\$10,000 \rangle$ was $-\$2,000$, the second circle from the left shows that his directly assessed certainty equivalents for 50–50 gambles imply that his certainty equivalent for $\langle \frac{1}{4}, +\$50,000; -\$10,000 \rangle$ should be $-\$5,000$. Alternatively, we can say that whereas the circle shows that his directly assessed certainty equivalent for the 50–50 gamble $\langle \frac{1}{2}, +\$5,000; -\$10,000 \rangle$ was $-\$5,000$, the heavy dot shows that his directly assessed certainty equivalents for reference gambles imply that his certainty equivalent for $\langle \frac{1}{2}, +\$5,000; -\$10,000 \rangle$ should be $-\$2,000$.

Until this logical inconsistency has been eliminated, none of Mallon's direct assessments can be accepted as an expression of really carefully thought-out likings for consequences. Mallon must revise one or more of the assessments in one or both of his two sets of assessments in such a way that both sets of revised assessments lead to the same five points in Figure 5.4.

Our reason for choosing the three particular intermediate q's that we did choose in Table 5.1 on page 148 should now be apparent. Assessing points by "chaining" 50–50 gambles in the way illustrated in Table 5.2 necessarily leads the decision maker to assess the terminal values for which his preferences are $1/2$, $1/4$, and $3/4$. We asked Mallon to make direct assessments of his certainty equivalents for reference gambles with $q = 1/2$, $1/4$, and $3/4$ so that if any inconsistencies in this thinking existed, they would appear when we compared the two complete sets of assessments.

5.2.4

Reconciliation of the Assessments

In general, it is up to the decision maker and the decision maker alone to decide which and how many of his direct assessments he will alter by how much in order to arrive at logical consistency. Because every individual assessment in Tables 5.1 and 5.2 depends entirely on Mallon's own likings for consequences and attitudes toward risk, an outsider has in general no reason to question the "rightness" of any one assessment any more than another.

In this particular example, however, only one pair of points shows a direct contradiction, and therefore Mallon would probably do well to start by observing that each of these points can be moved in the direction of the other by changing only one direct assessment. Reducing his certainty equivalent for the reference gamble $\langle \frac{1}{4}, +\$50,000; -\$10,000 \rangle$ will move the second heavy dot to the left without affecting any of the other heavy dots. Increasing his certainty equivalent for the 50–50 gamble $\langle \frac{1}{2}, +\$5,000; -\$10,000 \rangle$ will (as shown by the second row of Table 5.2) move the second circle to the right without affecting any of the other circles.

If after careful reflection Mallon decides that these two gambles are really equally attractive to him and therefore assigns to them the same certainty-equivalent value, the points designated by the circle and the heavy dot will coincide and he will have completely reconciled his two sets of direct assessments. If on the contrary he decides that his certainty equivalent for $\langle \frac{1}{4}, +\$50,000; -\$10,000 \rangle$ is definitely *not* equal to his certainty equivalent for $\langle \frac{1}{2}, +\$5,000; -\$10,000 \rangle$, then he will have to consider changing more of his assessments. He might, for example, move the middle heavy dot and middle circle to the right by increasing his certainty equivalent for $\langle \frac{1}{2}, +\$50,000; -\$10,000 \rangle$ from $+\$5,000$ to, say, $+\$7,500$, after which he would have to substitute $+\$7,500$ for $+\$5,000$ in the descriptions of the second and third gambles in Table 5.2, assess certainty equivalents for these new 50–50 gambles, and replace the second and fourth circles in Figure 5.4 by new circles representing these two new certainty equivalents. If these revisions resulted in general consistency, he would be through; if they did not, he would have to make still further revisions.

In what follows, we shall assume that Mallon succeeds in reconciling his inconsistencies in the simplest possible way. After reflecting again on the very difficult position he would be in if he ended up with a terminal value of $-\$10,-000$, he decides that the reference gamble $\langle\frac{1}{4}, +\$50,000; -\$10,000\rangle$, which gives him 3 chances in 4 of ending up with $-\$10,000$, is really not so attractive to him as $-\$2,000$ for certain. He decides that his certainty equivalent for this gamble is really $-\$5,000$ rather than $-\$2,000$ and thus moves the second heavy dot in Figure 5.4 over to the point designated by the second circle.

5.2.5
A Final Test of Consistency

After a decision maker has assessed five points on his preference curve by the two procedures described above and has reconciled all inconsistencies that have appeared, he should make one further test of the implications of his assessments before he accepts them as a valid foundation for a preference curve. The nature and logic of the test can be explained by showing how it could be made by Mr. A. H. Mallon.

Recalling that Mallon has already tentatively decided that his preferences for $-\$5,000$ and $+\$25,000$ are respectively $1/4$ and $3/4$, suppose that Mallon considers a gamble giving even chances at these two terminal values and decides that his certainty equivalent for this gamble is, say, $+\$7,500$. Since Mallon's preference for the gamble must be

$$(\frac{1}{2} \times 1/4) + (\frac{1}{2} \times 3/4) = 1/2,$$

the fact that $+\$7,500$ is as attractive to him as the gamble implies that his preference for $+\$7,500$ must be $1/2$. Mallon's previous assessments, however, led to the conclusion that $1/2$ was his preference for $+\$5,000$ rather than $+\$7,500$; and hence Mallon has discovered another inconsistency in his basic attitudes which must be reconciled before any of his assessments can be accepted as a valid basis for a preference curve.

Which and how many of his direct assessments Mallon should alter in order to remove this new inconsistency is again a matter which he alone can decide. Purely for the sake of simplicity, we shall assume that after further reflection he finally decides that his certainty equivalent for $\langle\frac{1}{2}, +\$25,000; -\$5,-000\rangle$ is really $+\$5,000$ rather than $+\$7,500$, so that all of his direct assessments now agree with the preferences shown in Table 5.4 below.

TABLE 5.4
A. H. Mallon's Final Preferences
for Selected Terminal Values

Terminal Value V	Preference q
$-\$10,000$	0
$-\ \ \ 5,000$	1/4
$+\ \ \ 5,000$	1/2
$+\ \ 25,000$	3/4
$+\ \ 50,000$	1

5.2.6

Summary

We remind the reader that Mallon has now decided that (1) each terminal value in the first column of Table 5.4 is in fact his certainty equivalent for a reference gamble with the q shown in the second column, and (2) his certainty equivalents for various 50–50 gambles are in fact as shown in Table 5.5. Each set of assessments corroborates the other because the computed preferences in the next to the last column of Table 5.5 for the terminal values in the last column of that table agree with the directly assessed preferences for those same terminal values that appear in Table 5.4.

TABLE 5.5

A. H. Mallon's Final Certainty Equivalents For Selected 50–50 Gambles

Description of 50–50 Gamble				Computed Preference for Gamble	Certainty Equivalent for Gamble
Terminal Values		Preferences for Terminal Values			
−$10,000	+$ 5,000	0	1/2	1/4	−$ 5,000
−$ 5,000	+ 25,000	1/4	3/4	1/2	+ 5,000
+ 5,000	+ 50,000	1/2	1	3/4	+ 25,000

The procedure of assessment and reconciliation that we have discussed at length above can be summarized very briefly. To do so, we shall denote by V_q the terminal value for which the decision maker's preference is q; in Mallon's case, $V_{.25} = -\$5,000$, and so forth.

1. Start from the fact that V_0 and V_1 are necessarily certainty equivalents for $\langle 0, V_1; V_0 \rangle$ and $\langle 1, V_1; V_0 \rangle$ respectively.

2. Assess $V_{.25}$, $V_{.5}$, and $V_{.75}$ by assessing certainty equivalents for $\langle .25, V_1; V_0 \rangle$, $\langle .5, V_1; V_0 \rangle$, and $\langle .75, V_1; V_0 \rangle$.

3. Reassess $V_{.25}$ and $V_{.75}$ by assessing certainty equivalents for $\langle \frac{1}{2}, V_{.5}; V_0 \rangle$ and $\langle \frac{1}{2}, V_1; V_{.5} \rangle$, and reconcile assessments if necessary until the results of (2) and (3) agree.

4. Reassess $V_{.5}$ by assessing the certainty equivalent for $\langle \frac{1}{2}, V_{.75}; V_{.25} \rangle$, and reconcile assessments if necessary until the results of (2), (3), and (4) all agree.

5.3

FITTING A PREFERENCE CURVE
TO THE DECISION MAKER'S ASSESSMENTS

5.3.1

Determination of a Curve by
Selected Points and General Properties

Suppose now that Mr. A. H. Mallon has not only assessed the five points on his preference curve that are listed in Table 5.4 (page 153) and designated by circles in Figure 5.4 (page 149) but has also decided that (1) his preference q increases

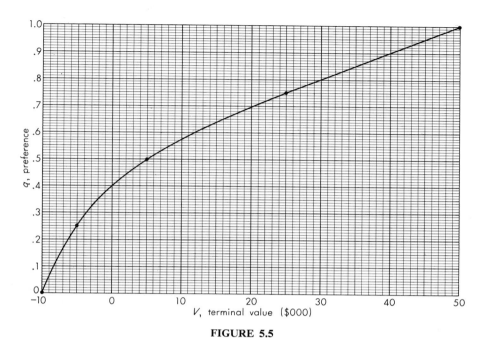

FIGURE 5.5

A. H. Mallon's Preferences for Terminal Values
Relative to $V_1 = +\$50,000$ and $V_0 = -\$10,000$
in the Presence of His Base Nonmonetary Assets

continuously with terminal value V, and (2) he is at least somewhat risk averse as regards all 50–50 gambles, but (3) his risk aversion decreases as V increases.

These specifications mean that, in addition to passing through his five directly assessed points, Mallon's preference curve must also be (1) continuous and (2) everywhere concave, but (3) with concavity which decreases from left to right. A curve which meets all these specifications is shown in Figure 5.5,[1] where Mallon's final direct assessments appear as heavy dots, and the reader can quickly convince himself by experimentation that it is impossible to draw a curve which differs substantially from this curve and still agrees with all of Mallon's specifications. He can further convince himself that even if Mallon does not assert that his risk aversion decreases continuously as V increases, it would still be impossible to draw a concave curve which differs by any really large amount from the one in Figure 5.5 without introducing one or two sharp bends that would imply extremely high risk aversion for gambles with terminal values in the corresponding intervals on the horizontal axis.

We conclude that Mallon can almost certainly accept the curve shown in Figure 5.5 as a basis for decisions that agree essentially with his likings for

---

[1] The same curve was also shown as Figure 4.5 (page 114), and Figure 4.4 is the same curve with the axes reversed.

the possible consequences. In fact, we are entitled to go even further and say that, because this curve is based on the very carefully reconciled assessments that were described in Section 5.2, Mallon should actually place greater confidence in preferences read from this curve and in certainty equivalents computed from them than he should place in his directly assessed certainty equivalent for any one gamble considered by itself.

5.3.2
Graphical Construction of Preference Curves

A preference curve accurate enough for practical purposes can usually be constructed graphically, by simply fairing a curve which passes through the points assessed by the decision maker and has a general shape which agrees with the decision maker's general attitudes toward risk. Great care must be taken, however, not merely to make sure that the curve is concave or convex where it should be, but also to make sure that the degree of concavity or convexity changes from left to right in the way specified by the decision maker.

We warn the reader that the way in which the degree of concavity or convexity changes cannot be effectively checked except by actually computing risk premiums for various 50–50 gambles all of which have the same spread between the two possible terminal values. As we said in Section 5.1.4, the right-hand portion of a preference curve can easily imply larger risk premiums than the left-hand portion even though the right-hand portion looks much straighter.

5.3.3
Mathematical Formulas
for Preference Curves

Even though a graphically fitted preference curve may be accurate enough for practical purposes, such a curve is tedious to construct and even more tedious to use. This unpleasant labor can often be avoided by finding and working with a mathematically defined preference function that agrees with the decision maker's specifications.

In principle, it is possible to find functions of many different types that agree with any set of specifications the decision maker might provide. As of now, however, it is only for the special case of positive but decreasing risk aversion that the mathematical problem of actually finding a suitable function has been solved and the necessary computer program written.

For this special but very important case of positive but decreasing risk aversion, two different types of function have been investigated, and of these two types, called piecex and sumex functions, it seems that the latter will in most cases provide a thoroughly satisfactory fit to the decision maker's specifications.[2]

The actual fitting of a sumex preference function to a particular set of specifications is very easily carried out by use of a general-purpose computer program called *Expref*.[3] As inputs to the program, the decision maker merely supplies the terminal values V_0, $V_{.25}$, $V_{.5}$, $V_{.75}$, and V_1 for which he has decided by direct assessment that his preferences are respectively 0, .25, .5, .75, and 1. The computer then tries to fit a sumex function to these data and then, if it succeeds, tells the decision maker whether or not the fitted function agrees with his specification of positive risk aversion. (A sumex function always implies decreasing risk aversion, but it sometimes implies that risk aversion decreases so far as to become negative somewhere between $V_{.75}$ and V_1.)[4]

After a preference function has been fitted, the computer will go on at the user's request to compute the decision maker's preferences for any terminal values he cares to specify, to compute the terminal values corresponding to any preferences he cares to specify, or to compute his certainty equivalent for any gamble he cares to describe by listing the possible terminal values together with their probabilities.[5] The program can also be used as a subroutine in connection with a main program that has been written to analyze a complete decision problem. In this case, the main program carries out the backward induction, calling on the subroutine to compute the decision maker's preferences and / or certainty-equivalent terminal values as they are required in the course of the analysis.

[2] For definitions of piecex and sumex functions, see the description of the computer program *Expref* cited in the next footnote. A piecex function is capable of fitting the decision maker's specifications in absolutely all cases where his five directly assessed points are logically consistent with positive but decreasing risk aversion; but the fitted function usually implies abrupt decreases in risk aversion at a few points on the horizontal axis and therefore is usually not entirely satisfactory even though the abrupt decreases could never be detected on a graph of the function. A sumex function is superior in that it always implies smoothly decreasing risk aversion; but it is sometimes impossible to fit the five directly assessed points with a sumex function even though the points are consistent with positive but decreasing risk aversion, and when a sumex function can be fitted, it sometimes implies that the decision maker's risk aversion decreases so far as to become negative somewhere between $V_{.75}$ and V_1. Accordingly the best procedure is usually to try a sumex function first and then try a piecex function only if the sumex function fails to give a satisfactory fit.

[3] For a description of this program, see the publication mentioned on page vi of the Preface.

[4] Program *Expref* is also capable of fitting a piecex function to the decision maker's five directly assessed points. When asked to do so, it first determines whether the points are logically consistent with positive but decreasing risk aversion and then, if they are, actually fits a piecex function passing through the points.

[5] When the user asks the program to evaluate a gamble, the program can not only state the exact certainty equivalent implied by either a sumex or a piecex preference function but can also state two limits between which the certainty equivalent would certainly lie if it were computed from *any* preference function consistent with the decision maker's original specifications concerning his preferences.

```
>DO PART 1

V(0)   = -10
V(.25) = -5
V(.5)  = 5
V(.75) = 25
V(1)   = 50


FUNCTION FITTED
EVERYWHERE RISK AVERSE
>

>DO PART 2 FOR V = -10 BY 5 TO 50

        VALUE    PREFERENCE
       -10.000    0.0000
        -5.000    0.2500
         0.000    0.3997
         5.000    0.5000
        10.000    0.5757
        15.000    0.6391
        20.000    0.6962
        25.000    0.7500
        30.000    0.8018
        35.000    0.8525
        40.000    0.9023
        45.000    0.9514
        50.000    1.0000
>

>DO PART 3 FOR Q = .1, .5, .9

PREFERENCE          VALUE
   0.1000          -8.321
   0.5000           5.000
   0.9000          39.768
>

>DO PART 4

V = 25   P = .6
V = 20   P = .2
V = 10   P = .2
PREF =          0.7044
CE   =         20.742
```

FIGURE 5.6

Use of Program *Expref*

Use of this program to fit a sumex function on a time-sharing computer is illustrated in Figure 5.6, where the underlined material was typed by the user and everything else was typed by the computer. After the user started the program running by typing "Do part 1," the computer asked successively for V_0, $V_{.25}$, . . ., V_1, and the user answered each request by typing in the value that had been assessed by Mr. A. H. Mallon (cf. Table 5.4 on page 153). As soon as the last of these values, V_1, had been supplied, the computer sought for a function that would agree with these specifications, found one, tested it to find that it implied positive risk aversion over the whole interval from V_0 to V_1, and reported

"Function fitted; everywhere risk averse." The user then obtained a number of points on Mallon's preference curve—i.e., on the graph of the function found by the computer—by typing "Do part 2 for $V = -10$ by 5 to 50"; he next obtained the terminal values for which Mallon's preferences were .1, .5, and .9 by typing "Do part 3 for $Q = .1, .5, .9$"; and finally he calculated Mallon's certainty equivalent for the gamble of Figure 4.7 (page 122) by first typing "Do part 4" and then typing the payoffs and probabilities as they were requested by the machine.[6]

The reader should verify that the preferences and terminal values printed out in Figure 5.6 agree with Mr. A. H. Mallon's preference curve in Figure 5.5. That curve is, in fact, a graph of the preference function fitted in the way just described.

5.4
SOME COMMENTS ON PREFERENCE CURVES

5.4.1
Choice of Reference Values

For reasons already explained in Section 4.3, the reference terminal values V_1 and V_0 relative to which a preference curve is assessed must encompass all the possible terminal values in the decision problem that is to be analyzed by use of the curve, but they can lie as far outside the possible terminal values as the decision maker likes. It may therefore naturally occur to the reader to ask whether the choice of reference values V_1 and V_0 can affect the conclusions of an analysis based on the resulting preference curve; and the answer is that they can.

It is easy to prove that choice of reference values would *not* have any effect on an analysis based on a preference curve if all of the decision maker's intuitive assessments of preferences or certainty equivalents were logically consistent. We shall not bother with the proof, however, because the proposition is one of purely theoretical interest. The fact is that intuitive assessments of preferences and certainty equivalents are virtually always highly inconsistent, and therefore the real problem is not one of showing that reference values do not matter but one of choosing the best possible reference values.

By "best possible" reference values we mean, of course, reference values that will lead to a preference curve in which the decision maker is entitled to place the greatest possible confidence—a curve which he can feel sure expresses really meaningful likings for consequences. And if a preference curve is to express really meaningful likings for consequences, the gambles for which the de-

---

[6] In response to further instructions not shown in Figure 5.6, the computer informed the user (1) that a piecex function fitted to Mallon's preference specifications implied a certainty equivalent of $+\$20,759$ for the gamble of Figure 4.7, and (2) that the certainty equivalent would not be higher than $+\$21,000$ or lower than $+\$20,195$ if it were computed from *any* preference function consistent with Mallon's specifications.

cision maker assesses certainty equivalents in order to assess points on the curve must involve consequences with two properties.

1. The possible consequences of the gambles for which the decision maker directly assesses his certainty equivalents must be consequences that are psychologically real to him. They must *not* be effectively inconceivable. A businessman who has never thought seriously about what it would really be like to have net liquid assets in excess of $100,000 simply has no feeling for the question whether he would or would not prefer $24 million for certain to a gamble giving even chances at $20 million or $30 million. To give a meaningful answer to the question, he would first have to take off a few months to reflect about running a business with assets of this new order of magnitude; and the same thing would be true if a businessman who had never contemplated the possibility of negative net liquid assets were asked to decide whether he would or would not prefer $-\$600,000$ for certain to a gamble giving even chances at $-\$1$ million or $0.

Our first conclusion, therefore, is that a decision maker who wishes to assess his preference curve should choose reference values that are psychologically real to him. They should not be unrealistically high or low.

2. On the other hand, the *difference* between the consequences of any gamble for which the decision maker assesses his certainty equivalent must also be psychologically real. If a businessman with net liquid assets of $1 million is asked whether he prefers $1,000,049 for certain to a gamble giving even chances at $1,000,000 or $1,000,100, the only true answer he could give would be that he simply does not care. The psychological stimulus provided by any one of these three terminal values is indistinguishable from the stimulus provided by any other; the differences between the terminal values are below the threshhold of perception.

Our second conclusion, therefore, is that a decision maker who wishes to assess his preference curve should choose reference values that are far enough apart to let him really *feel* the differences between consequences, not only when he assesses $V_{.5}$ by assessing his certainty equivalent for $\langle \frac{1}{2}, V_1; V_0 \rangle$, but also when he assesses his certainty equivalents for "narrower" gambles such as $\langle \frac{1}{2}, V_{.5}; V_0 \rangle$, $\langle \frac{1}{2}, V_1; V_{.5} \rangle$, and $\langle \frac{1}{2}, V_{.75}; V_{.25} \rangle$.

5.4.2
Certainty Equivalents for Small Gambles

A person who has based a preference curve on directly assessed certainty equivalents for gambles with really substantial spread is often surprised by the results when he uses this curve to compute his certainty equivalents for gambles with small spreads. Specifically, the risk premiums implied by the computed certainty equivalents are often much smaller than those the person in question would have assessed directly.

For example, suppose that someone with $3,000 cash in the bank says that (1) he would be just willing to exchange this amount for a gamble giving even chances at $10,000 or $0, and (2) his risk aversion is essentially constant over the range from $0 to $10,000 in the sense that his risk premium for any 50–50 gamble involving terminal values within this range depends only on the spread between the two possible terminal values and not on the actual amount of either one. His risk premium for $\langle \frac{1}{2}, +\$1000; \$0 \rangle$ is exactly the same as his risk premium for $\langle \frac{1}{2}, +\$10,000; +\$9,000 \rangle$, and so forth.

It can be shown mathematically that there exists one and only one preference function or preference curve that agrees with these attitudes, and it can further be shown that this function implies the risk premiums for various 50–50 gambles that appear in Table 5.6, where the "proportional" risk premiums in the last column are calculated by dividing the dollar risk premiums by the spreads of the gambles.   The thing to observe in this table is the way in which the proportional risk premium behaves as the spread of a gamble decreases.   Even though the person we are discussing has assessed a substantial 20% premium on a gamble with a spread of $10,000, consistency with this assessment and with constant risk aversion requires him to assess a premium of only 2% or about $20 on a gamble with a $1,000 spread, and he must assess a premium of only 2/10 of one percent or about 20 cents on a gamble with a $100 spread.

TABLE 5.6
A Set of Mutually Consistent Risk Premiums

Equally Likely Balances		Spread	Average Balance	Certainty Equivalent	Risk Premium	Proportional Premium
$10,000	$ 0	$10,000	$5,000	$3,000	$2,000	20 %
7,000	2,000	5,000	4,500	3,955	545	11
4,500	2,500	2,000	3,500	3,410	90	5
3,800	2,800	1,000	3,300	3,277	22	2
3,400	2,900	500	3,150	3,144	6	1
3,150	2,950	200	3,050	3,049	1	.5
3,070	2,970	100	3,020.00	3,019.77	.23	.2
3,030	2,980	50	3,005.00	3,004.94	.06	.1
3,007	2,997	10	3,002.00	3,002.00	.00	.0

Many people who would agree with this person that a $2,000 risk premium was large enough for a gamble with a $10,000 spread, and who would also agree that their risk aversion was essentially constant over a $10,000 range, would nevertheless want to assess very much larger risk premiums than are shown in Table 5.6 for the smaller gambles in that table.   There is a seeming logical inconsistency in this attitude which may or may not be real.

Taking a gamble may involve bothersome nonmonetary consequences for the person involved, particularly if he loses, and these nonmonetary consequences may be more important relative to purely monetary consequences in small gambles than they are in large gambles.   It may be, in other words, that if the possible terminal values in each of the later rows of Table 5.6 above were appropriately adjusted for nonmonetary consequences, the average of the two possible values would be substantially reduced and would come close to the certainty equivalent that the people we are discussing would feel naturally inclined to assess.

In most cases, however, there is probably a real logical inconsistency between the risk premiums that a person assesses on large gambles and those that he assesses on small gambles. The reader should test this out by assessing his own preference curve by the method we described in Sections 5.2 and 5.3, using this curve to compute the risk premiums he "should" assess on a few gambles with relatively small spreads, comparing these computed premiums with those he would have assessed directly, and finally making up his mind which set of premiums really expresses his own carefully thought-out likings for consequences.

5.4.3
Permanence of Preferences

When a decision maker assesses his preferences for values of his criterion on a particular evaluation date, he must take into account the way in which each possible value of the criterion will affect what happens to him *after* this date, but if he wishes to avoid double counting he must not think about the way in which the criterion will come to have any particular value *on* this date. The whole point of assessing preferences is to separate the evaluation of possible consequences from the evaluation of the chances of actually enjoying those consequences.

This implies that the decision maker does not necessarily have to assess a new preference curve for each new decision problem that he analyzes. For example, suppose that on January 1 a decision maker selects December 31 as his evaluation date for analysis of a decision problem he currently faces, selects a definite base end position in that problem, and then assesses his preference curve for net liquid assets as of December 31 in the presence of the nonmonetary assets he will have at his base end position. If on July 1 he wishes to analyze another decision problem using a December 31 evaluation date, and if in this new problem he selects a base end position at which his nonmonetary assets are the same as they were at the base end position of his original problem, he can use his original preference curve to analyze his new problem. His *current* net liquid assets may be quite different on July 1 from what they were on January 31, but this fact should have no effect on his preference curve, which expresses his likings for various amounts of net liquid assets *as of December 31*. The only factors that *should* change his original preferences for net liquid assets as of December 31 are (1) changes in the base nonmonetary assets that are assumed to accompany the monetary assets, and (2) changes in his own basic likings for consequences as described by total assets.

On the other hand, likings for assets as of a given date are not likings for assets in the abstract, and there is therefore no reason why a decision maker should necessarily have the same preferences for assets as of December 31, next year, that he has for assets as of December 31, this year. If the decision maker's business is a stable one operating in a stable environment, his preferences for year-end assets *may* remain almost unchanged from year to year; but in a rapidly changing environment with rapidly changing opportunities, his preferences for assets as of one date are very likely to differ substantially from his preferences for assets as of another date.

5.4.4
Preferences for Total Cash Flows

When A. H. Mallon first described the possible consequences in his XYZ decision problem in Figure 1.3 (page 11), he wrote down the total cash flow that would occur between "now" and his evaluation date as a result of each possible act-event sequence; but before he actually began to analyze his problem by assessing his certainty equivalents for gambles, he replaced these descriptions of consequences in terms of total cash flows by descriptions in terms of the resulting terminal values of his net liquid assets. Substitution of net liquid assets for total cash flows enabled him better to evaluate his liking for each of the possible consequences of a gamble and for the consequence that he finally selected as his certainty equivalent for the gamble.

This same reason for thinking in terms of net liquid assets rather than total cash flows will apply if, instead of analyzing his problem by the method described in Chapter 1, Mallon now proposes to analyze it by assessing probabilities for events and preferences for consequences. Although he could in principle select a pair of total cash flows to describe reference consequences and then assess his preferences for the total cash flows in Figure 1.3 relative to these reference flows, he will be much better able to evaluate his liking for each of the possible consequences in his problem if he first expresses the consequences in terms of terminal net liquid assets and then assesses his preferences for terminal net liquid assets. In general:

■ Although a decision maker can in principle directly assess his preferences for consequences described by total cash flows, he will usually be much better able to evaluate his likings for consequences if he describes the consequences by terminal values of a suitably chosen criterion before assessing his preferences.

It is well worth remarking, however, that even though a decision maker will usually find it difficult to make good direct assessments of his preferences for total cash flows, he can very easily *infer* his preferences for total cash flows from his directly assessed preferences for terminal values of a criterion such as net liquid assets.

For example, suppose as we did in Chapter 1 that when A. H. Mallon sets out to analyze the XYZ deal the current value of his net liquid assets is

— $4,000; and suppose that on his evaluation date the terminal value of his net liquid assets will be simply this — $4,000 plus whatever total cash flow occurs between "now" and the evaluation date (implying that the terminal value will not have to be adjusted for nonmonetary consequences). Then saying that net liquid assets have any particular terminal value V and saying that the total cash flow between now and his evaluation date has the value ($V +$ $4,000) are just two different ways of describing the same consequence; and even though the way in which consequences are described may affect the decision maker's ability to *assess* his preferences for consequences "correctly", a change in description clearly should not affect his preferences after he has assessed them as well as he can. It follows that:

■ If Mallon has decided that q is his preference for terminal net liquid assets of amount V relative to V_1 and V_0, then q is also his preference for a total cash flow of ($V +$ $4,000) relative to ($V_1 +$ $4,000) and ($V_0 +$ $4,000).

In other words, we can convert the graph in Figure 5.5 (page 155) of Mallon's preferences for net liquid assets into a graph of his preferences for total cash flows between "now" and his evaluation date by simply adding $4,000 to every figure on the horizontal scale of that graph.

The conclusion just reached has some practical value because it allows the analyst to work directly with a diagram on which the end positions are valued with total cash flows and thus to avoid the extra step of replacing each total cash flow by the corresponding criterion value. A person who wishes to analyze a decision problem using preferences for total cash flows must, however, watch out for three points that can easily be overlooked.

1. The decision maker's preferences for total cash flows occurring between "now" and a fixed evaluation date do not remain constant as he approaches the evaluation date in the way that his preferences for terminal values of his criterion remain constant. If his evaluation date is December 31, his preferences for total cash flows between July 1 and December 31 will not in general be the same as his preferences for total cash flows between January 1 and December 31 unless the current value of his criterion is the same on July 1 as it was on January 1.

2. The total cash flows at the end positions of any decision diagram must be truly total—they must include all contextual cash flows that will take place between "now" and the evaluation date as well as all cash flows resulting from the acts and events directly related to the decision problem at hand.

3. If some of the act-event sequences in a decision problem have nonmonetary as well as monetary consequences, the actual total cash flow resulting from each such sequence must be adjusted to reflect the monetary value of the nonmonetary consequences in the same way that the actual terminal value of the decision maker's criterion would be adjusted for this purpose. And since

the monetary value of nonmonetary consequences often depends on the actual terminal value of the decision maker's criterion, as we saw in Section 2.2.8, it may be very difficult to make the required adjustments without first writing down the actual value of the criterion at each end position of the decision diagram.

5.5
LINEAR PREFERENCE AND
MATHEMATICAL EXPECTATION

When the less good of the two terminal values that can result from a 50–50 gamble is not "too" bad and the spread between the two values is not "too" great, a businessman's certainty equivalent for the gamble may be practically if not strictly equal to the average of the two possible terminal values; and more than this, a businessman can often specify a fairly wide range of terminal values such that his certainty equivalent for a 50–50 gamble between any two terminal values within this range would be practically if not strictly equal to the average of those two values.

In the present section we shall show that if a businessman says that all the terminal values in a particular decision problem lie within a range of this sort, the problem can be analyzed without asking the businessman any further questions about either certainty equivalents or preferences.

5.5.1
Mathematical Expectations for
Uncertain Terminal Values

Before we can begin the main line of our argument, we must introduce the concept of a decision maker's "mathematical expectation" for the uncertain terminal value that will result from a gamble.

■ A decision maker's ≪mathematical expectation≫ for the uncertain terminal value that will result from any gamble is the number obtained by (1) multiplying each possible terminal value that may result from the gamble by the decision maker's probability for that value, and (2) adding these products.

As a first example, consider the uncertain terminal value that will result from the gamble represented by the terminal event fork in Figure 5.7, where the number at the end of each branch is a possible terminal value of the decision maker's criterion and the number in parentheses on each branch is the decision maker's probability for that branch or possible value. The decision maker's mathematical expectation for the uncertain terminal value represented by the fork is

$$.2(+\$12,000) + .5(\$0) + .3(-\$5,000) = +\$900.$$

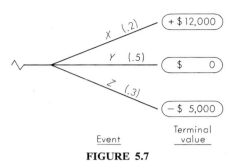

FIGURE 5.7
An Uncertain Terminal Value

As a second example, consider the uncertain terminal value that will re-sult from a gamble which gives a standard chance p at a terminal value of $+\$300$ and a standard chance $(1 - p)$ at a terminal value of $+\$100$. The decision maker's mathematical expectation for this uncertain terminal value is

$$+\$300p + \$100(1 - p).$$

Since the probabilities or standard chances that are used as multipliers in computing a mathematical expectation add to 1, we may also say that:

■ A decision maker's mathematical expectation for any uncertain terminal value is a *weighted average* of the possible terminal values, the weights being the probabilities or standard chances of those values.

In one respect this definition of a decision maker's mathematical expec-tation for an uncertain terminal value is very similar to the rule in Section 4.5.4 for computing his preference for such a quantity, but in another respect the definitions are totally different. Both quantities are weighted averages in which probabilities or standard chances are the weights; but whereas the decision maker's preference for the uncertain terminal value is a weighted average of his *preferences* for the possible terminal values, his mathematical expectation for the uncertain terminal value is a weighted average of the possible *terminal values themselves*.

It is absolutely essential to observe that there is *no* relation between the definition of the decision maker's mathematical expectation for an uncertain terminal value and the definition of his certainty equivalent for an uncertain terminal value that was given in Section 2.3.1; and therefore there is in general absolutely no reason why the decision maker's certainty equivalent for an uncer-tain terminal value should necessarily be equal, or even anywhere near equal, to his mathematical expectation for that uncertain value. The point will be obvious enough if the reader asks himself whether he would really be willing to exchange a certainty of $1 billion in the bank tomorrow for a gamble which gives him even chances at ending up with either $2 billion or $0 in the bank.

On the other hand, there is also no reason why in any particular case a particular decision maker's certainty equivalent for an uncertain terminal value should *not* be equal or nearly equal to his mathematical expectation for that uncertain value; and in the remainder of this chapter we shall be concerned with those special situations in which such a near equality holds for all the certainty equivalents required for analysis of a particular decision problem.

5.5.2

Notation

As another necessary preliminary to our main line of discussion, let us agree on some useful notational conventions.

The letter V will be used as before to denote a *definite* although unspecified terminal value. Thus V may be used to denote the terminal value that is associated to the typical branch of a terminal event fork; or V may stand for any particular one of the possible terminal values that may result from a gamble that has or has not been diagrammed.

The same letter with a tilde (til ' deh) over it, $\tilde{V}$, will be used to denote an *uncertain* terminal value. The symbol $\tilde{V}$ should be read "V tilde".

Finally, the same letter with a bar over it, $\bar{V}$, will be used to denote the decision maker's *mathematical expectation* for $\tilde{V}$—i.e., the probability-weighted average of all the possible V's or definite terminal values which are associated to the individual branches of a terminal event fork or which may result from a gamble. The symbol $\bar{V}$ should be read "V bar".

As an example of the use of this notation, we can say that the decision maker's mathematical expectation $\bar{V}$ for the uncertain terminal value $\tilde{V}$ represented by the complete terminal event fork in Figure 5.7 is a weighted average of the three possible V's or definite terminal values that appear at the ends of the individual branches of the fork; or we can say that the decision maker's certainty equivalent for $\tilde{V}$ will be some definite terminal value V that lies between the least and the greatest of the three possible V's.

5.5.3

Certainty Equivalents Which
Imply Linear Preference

All the results that we shall obtain in the remainder of this chapter will be derived from two fundamental propositions about relations between certainty equivalents and the shape of a preference curve. The first of them is as follows:

■ Let V' and V'' be any two specified terminal values, and consider the class of gambles which consists of every gamble giving even chances at just two terminal values both of which lie within the interval from V' to V'' inclusive. If a decision maker's certainty equivalent for the uncertain terminal value $\tilde{V}$ that will result from *any* gamble in this class is equal to his mathematical expectation for $\tilde{V}$, then the following two equivalent statements are true:

1 The decision maker's preference curve for terminal values in the interval from V' to V'' is a *straight line*.

2 If we let π (pi) denote the preference function which relates the decision maker's preference q to any terminal value V in the interval from V' to V'', then π is a *linear* function and we can write

$$q = \pi(V) = a + bV$$

where a and b are constants.

The truth of this proposition follows directly from the discussion in Section 5.1.3 of the implications of concavity or convexity of a preference curve.

5.5.4
Implications of Linear Preference
for Certainty Equivalents

The second fundamental proposition from which the results in the remainder of this chapter will be derived is the following:

■ Let $\tilde{V}$ denote the uncertain terminal value represented by a particular terminal event fork with any number of branches and with any set of probabilities assigned to the branches. If all the possible terminal values associated to the individual branches of the fork lie within an interval over which the decision maker's preference function π is linear, then the decision maker's certainty equivalent for $\tilde{V}$ should be equal to his mathematical expectation $\bar{V}$.

If the reader is willing to accept this proposition on faith, he may omit the proof which follows.

Proof To prove the above proposition we must show that a definite terminal value numerically equal to $\bar{V}$ should be exactly as attractive to the decision maker as the uncertain terminal value $\tilde{V}$; we can show this by showing that the decision maker's preference for a definite terminal value numerically equal to $\bar{V}$ should be equal to his preference for the uncertain terminal value $\tilde{V}$; and since the decision maker's preference for a definite terminal value numerically equal to $\bar{V}$ is simply $\pi(\bar{V})$, all that we really have to prove is that his preference for the uncertain terminal value $\tilde{V}$ is equal to $\pi(\bar{V})$. We prove this as follows.

Let V denote the terminal value associated to any particular branch of the fork, let $q = \pi(V)$ denote the decision maker's preference for V, let $\bar{q}$ denote his preference for the uncertain terminal value $\tilde{V}$ represented by the fork as a whole, and recall that $\bar{V}$ denotes his mathematical expectation for $\tilde{V}$. By the rule in Section 4.5.4, $\bar{q}$ is simply a probability-weighted average of all possible *values*

$q = \pi(V)$ of the function π; by the definition of mathematical expectation in Section 5.5.1, $\bar{V}$ is simply a probability-weighted average of all possible *arguments* V of the function π; and therefore the rule in Section A.5.4 of the Appendix tells us that because π is a *linear* function, $\bar{q} = \pi(\bar{V})$, as was to be proved.

5.5.5
Approximation of Certainty Equivalents
by Mathematical Expectations

In practical applications, the exact result derived in the previous section is less useful than the following approximate version:

■ A decision maker's preference function may be so *nearly* linear over a given interval that if all the terminal values on any terminal event fork are within this interval, his certainty equivalent for the uncertain terminal value $\tilde{V}$ that is represented by the fork as a whole can be *approximated* by his mathematical expectation for $\tilde{V}$ with accuracy that is sufficient for the practical purpose at hand.

To decide whether his preference function is "practically" linear in this sense over the interval between any given pair of terminal values V' and V'', the decision maker has only to assess his certainty equivalents for a few suitably chosen 50–50 gambles with terminal values in this interval and decide whether there is a really material difference in any case between his certainty equivalent and the simple average of the two possible terminal values. The 50–50 gambles selected for this test should of course be gambles in which there is a substantial spread between the two possible terminal values, and one of them should be a gamble giving even chances at the values V' and V'' themselves.

5.5.6
Backward Induction on
Mathematical Expectations

Suppose that we compare the range of possible terminal values at the end positions of some decision diagram with the range of possible terminal values that appear after all the terminal event forks in that diagram have been replaced by definite certainty-equivalent terminal values. Because the decision maker's certainty equivalent for the uncertain terminal value represented by any terminal event fork must lie between the best and worst terminal values on the fork, all the terminal values on the reduced decision diagram must lie between the best and worst terminal values on the original diagram.

It follows that if the decision maker's preference function is "practically" linear in the sense of Section 5.5.5 over an interval extending from the worst to the best of the terminal values on the original diagram of any decision problem, then it is practically linear over the terminal values on any terminal event fork that can emerge in the course of an analysis of the problem by backward induction. But this means that the decision maker's certainty equivalent for the uncertain terminal value represented by any terminal event fork is practically equal to his mathematical expectation for that uncertain terminal value; and therefore the entire decision problem can be analyzed by a backward induction in which mathematical expectations are treated as certainty equivalents. There is no need to ask the decision maker for further direct assessments of either his preferences for definite terminal values or his certainty equivalents for uncertain terminal values.

Even when the range of terminal values on the original diagram of a decision problem is so great that it is not possible to analyze the *entire* decision problem by treating mathematical expectations as if they were certainty equivalents, it may still be true that, of all the terminal event forks that will appear in the course of the analysis, there are only a very few where the approximation cannot be used. If in addition these "exceptional" forks have only two or three branches each, it may be easier for the decision maker to make direct assessments of his certainty equivalents for the uncertain terminal values represented by the exceptional forks and then use mathematical expectations in the remainder of the analysis than it would be to assess a complete preference curve for terminal values and then use the curve to compute his certainty equivalent for the uncertain terminal value represented by every terminal event fork that emerges in the course of the complete analysis by backward induction.

5.6
DESCRIPTION OF DECISION PROBLEMS
WHEN PREFERENCE IS LINEAR

Given that a decision problem is to be *analyzed* by treating the decision maker's mathematical expectations for uncertain terminal values as if they were certainty equivalents, it is usually possible to *describe* the problem by a very much simpler diagram than would otherwise be required. In particular, contextual uncertainties can often be completely omitted from a diagram that will be analyzed by use of mathematical expectations, and an uncertain cost can usually be represented by a single, separately calculated number instead of an event fan.

After we have laid some essential groundwork in Sections 5.6.1 to 5.6.3, we shall show in Sections 5.6.4 to 5.6.10 exactly what simplifications are legitimate under exactly what conditions. Because the simplifications themselves will seem completely natural to the reader, he may feel that our very careful examination of the conditions for the legitimacy of these simplifications is unnecessary, but we warn him that this is not so. The very fact that the simplifications we shall discuss *are* so natural often leads to their use in situations where they are not legitimate; and the results of an analysis based on an oversimplified description of a decision problem may be very seriously in error.

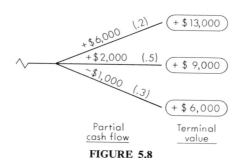

FIGURE 5.8

Uncertain Monetary Values Differing by a Constant

5.6.1
Mathematical Expectations for
Uncertain Monetary Values

Just as we may talk about the uncertain terminal value represented by a terminal event fork to whose branches definite terminal values have been associated, so we may talk about the uncertain total cash flow represented by a terminal event fork to whose branches definite total cash flows have been associated; and similarly we may talk about the uncertain partial cash flow represented by any event fork, terminal or not, to whose branches definite partial cash flows have been associated. Terminal values, total cash flows, and partial cash flows can be thought of as three different species of the genus monetary values; and we now define a decision maker's mathematical expectation for an uncertain monetary value of any species:

- A decision maker's mathematical expectation for any uncertain monetary value which is represented by an event fork is the number obtained by (1) multiplying the possible monetary value associated to each branch of the fork by the decision maker's probability for that branch, and (2) adding these products.

This definition implies, of course, that:

- A decision maker's mathematical expectation for an uncertain monetary value is a *weighted average* of the possible monetary values, the weights being the decision maker's probabilities for the possible values.

5.6.2
Mathematical Expectations for
Sums of Monetary Values

Consider the terminal event fork in Figure 5.8, where probabilities and partial cash flows are shown on the branches and terminal values are shown at the ends of the branches; and observe that the terminal value on any branch differs from the partial cash flow on that branch by a constant $7,000, the same for all branches. The decision maker's mathematical expectations for the uncertain terminal value and the uncertain partial cash flow represented by the fork are respectively +$8,900 and +$1,900, as the reader should verify; and we observe that there is the same $7,000 difference between the two expectations that there is between the two definite monetary values associated to any one branch.

More generally, consider any terminal event fork; let f and V respectively denote the partial cash flow and terminal value associated to any particular branch of the fork; suppose that on every branch of the fork the difference $(V - f)$ has the same value c; denote by $\tilde{f}$ and $\tilde{V}$ respectively the uncertain partial cash flow and the uncertain terminal value represented by the fork as a whole; and denote by $\bar{f}$ and $\bar{V}$ the decision maker's mathematical expectations for $\tilde{f}$ and $\tilde{V}$ respectively. Because V is related to f by the formula

$$V = c + f$$

where c is a constant, V is a *linear* function of f; and because $\bar{f}$ and $\bar{V}$ are by definition probability-weighted averages of the individual f's and V's on the various branches of the fork, the proposition about weighted averages of linear functions in Section A.5.4 of the Appendix tells us that the expectations $\bar{V}$ and $\bar{f}$ are similarly related:

$$\bar{V} = c + \bar{f}.$$

Still more generally, suppose that to each branch of a terminal event fork there is associated a monetary value x of *any* kind and another monetary value y of *any* kind; let $\tilde{x}$ and $\tilde{y}$ denote the corresponding uncertain monetary values represented by the fork as a whole; and let $\bar{x}$ and $\bar{y}$ be the decision maker's mathematical expectations for $\tilde{x}$ and $\tilde{y}$ respectively. If on every individual branch of the fork

$$y = c + x$$

where c is a constant, then y is a linear function of x and therefore

$$\bar{y} = c + \bar{x}.$$

Or we can say more briefly that:

■ A decision maker's mathematical expectation for the sum $c + \tilde{x}$ of a constant monetary value c plus an uncertain monetary value $\tilde{x}$ is the sum of the constant c plus his mathematical expectation for $\tilde{x}$.

This proposition will be the basis for all the results we shall derive in the remainder of this chapter.

5.6.3
Adjustment of Partial Cash Flows
for Nonmonetary Consequences

It will become clear in the discussion to follow that we cannot simplify a complete decision diagram by use of the basic principle stated just above unless we can assume that the terminal value at each end position of the complete diagram is (or would be) exactly equal to the initial value of the decision maker's criterion plus the sum of the partial cash flows along the path from the origin of the diagram to the end position in question. This is automatically true, of course, in problems where none of the terminal values have to be adjusted for nonmonetary consequences, but the applicability of our results will by no means be restricted to such problems.

■ The results to be obtained below will be valid in any decision problem whatever provided only that the necessary adjustments for nonmonetary consequences are applied, not only to the terminal values at the end positions of the complete diagram of the problem, but also to the partial cash flows on appropriate branches of the diagram.

For example, consider a decision problem in which the act "buy machine *A*" appears; suppose that this machine will cost $10,000; and suppose that it will still be worth $3,000 to the decision maker on his evaluation date. In our earlier discussion of valuation of consequences, we have assumed that the decision maker would assign a partial cash flow of $-\$10,000$ to the branch representing the act "buy machine *A*" and then make a $+\$3,000$ adjustment for the value of the left-over machine in the terminal value at every end position following this act in the decision diagram. He can achieve exactly the same result, however, by assigning a partial cash flow of $-\$10,000 + \$3,000 = -\$7,000$ to the branch representing the act "buy machine *A*" and then making *no* adjustment for the value of the left-over machine at any end position; and in what follows we assume that *all adjustments for nonmonetary consequences have been thus reflected in the partial cash flows we are discussing.*

5.6.4
Replacement of Terminal Event Forks
by Single Branches

We now begin our examination of the various ways in which the basic proposition stated in Section 5.6.2 allows a decision maker to simplify the diagram of a decision problem which is to be analyzed by treating mathematical expectations as certainty equivalents. As a source of examples, we shall reconsider A. H. Mallon's XYZ decision problem and show how various aspects of this problem would have been changed if, contrary to our original assumption, Mallon had decided that his certainty equivalent for any uncertain terminal value that might

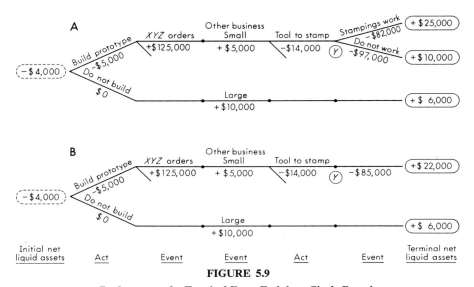

FIGURE 5.9

Replacement of a Terminal Event Fork by a Single Branch

be involved in the problem would be equal to his mathematical expectation for that uncertain value.

The first important result that we shall derive from the proposition at the end of Section 5.6.2 is the following:

■ Given that a decision problem is to be analyzed by treating mathematical expectations as certainty equivalents, and given that all adjustments for nonmonetary consequences have been reflected in the partial cash flows, any *terminal* event fork in the diagram of the problem may be replaced by a single branch to which is associated a partial cash flow equal to the decision maker's mathematical expectation for the uncertain partial cash flow represented by the fork.

To see this result illustrated before it is proved, consider the partial diagram of A. H. Mallon's decision problem in Figure 5.9A, which shows both the partial cash flows originally shown in Figure 1.2 (page 9) and the resulting terminal values originally shown in Figure 1.5 (page 13); suppose that Mallon's probabilities for the events "stampings work" and "do not work" are respectively 4/5 and 1/5; and observe first of all that (1) Mallon's mathematical expectation for the uncertain *terminal value* represented by the fork at position Y in Figure 5.9A is

$$\tfrac{4}{5}(+\$25,000) + \tfrac{1}{5}(+\$10,000) = +\$22,000,$$

and (2) his mathematical expectation for the uncertain *partial cash flow* represented by that same fork is

$$\tfrac{4}{5}(-\$82,000) + \tfrac{1}{5}(-\$97,000) = -\$85,000.$$

Now suppose that, instead of constructing a complete diagram of his decision problem, Mallon had constructed a diagram in which the terminal event fork at Y in Figure 5.9A was replaced by the single branch at Y in Figure 5.9B; and suppose that Mallon had assigned to this branch a definite partial cash flow equal to his mathematical expectation for the uncertain partial cash flow represented by the fork it replaced, viz. $-\$85,000$. If Mallon had then treated this definite partial cash flow exactly like a known partial cash flow in computing the terminal value of his criterion at the end position beyond Y in Figure 5.9B, he would have obtained the value

$$-\$4,000 - \$5,000 + \$125,000 + \$5,000 - \$14,000 - \$85,000 = +\$22,000;$$

and this is exactly the same value that he would have obtained by computing his mathematical expectation for the uncertain terminal value represented by the terminal event fork at Y in Figure 5.9A.

If now we observe that the terminal value at the end of either branch of the fork at position Y in Figure 5.9A is equal to the partial cash flow on that branch plus a constant $\$107,000$, we see that the result just obtained for a particular example follows directly from the basic proposition about expected monetary values that appears at the end of Section 5.6.2; and if we further observe that the terminal value at the end of every branch of *any* terminal event fork will be equal to the partial cash flow on the branch plus a constant if all adjustments for nonmonetary consequences have been reflected in the partial cash flows as well as the terminal values, we see that the general result stated at the beginning of this section follows directly from that same basic proposition.

<h3 style="text-align:center">5.6.5</h3>

<h3 style="text-align:center">Replacement of Internal Event Forks
by Single Branches</h3>

We shall next show that a nonterminal or ≪internal≫ event fork in a decision diagram can *under certain conditions* be replaced by a single branch when the diagram is to be analyzed by use of mathematical expectations.

Suppose as we did in Section 3.1.4 that Mallon is uncertain about the cost of the prototype, so that a complete diagram of his decision problem would have to look like Figure 3.4 (page 92), a part of which is reproduced here as Figure 5.10A; and suppose that, on *every one* of the subdiagrams like those emanating from B, C, and D in Figure 3.4, Mallon assesses his probabilities as shown in Table 5.7, so that the subdiagram emanating from position C in Figure

TABLE 5.7

A. H. Mallon's Probabilities for Selected Events

Event	Probability
XYZ:	
Orders	1/2
Does not order	1/2
Stampings:	
Work	4/5
Do not work	1/5

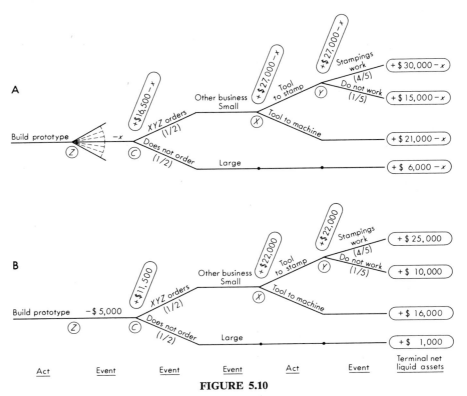

FIGURE 5.10

Replacement of an Internal Event Fork by a Single Branch

5.10A can be taken as representing *any* of the subdiagrams following the fork at *Z*. Recalling the basic proposition concerning mathematical expectations for sums of monetary values that was stated at the end of Section 5.6.2 we can argue as follows:

1. Mallon's mathematical expectation for the uncertain terminal value at position *Y* on *any one* of the subdiagrams implicit in Figure 5.10A is

$$\tfrac{4}{5}(+\$30{,}000 - x) + \tfrac{1}{5}(+\$15{,}000 - x) = +\$27{,}000 - x;$$

only the cost *x* of the prototype varies from one subdiagram to another.

2. Since the value of "tool to machine" on any subdiagram is only $+\$21{,}000 - x$, Mallon will choose "tool to stamp" on *every* subdiagram if he bases his choice on mathematical expectation; and if this is true, then his mathematical expectation for the uncertain terminal value at position *X* will be $+\$27{,}000 - x$ on every subdiagram.

3. Therefore Mallon's mathematical expectation for the uncertain terminal value at position *C* on every subdiagram is

$$\tfrac{1}{2}(+\$27{,}000 - x) + \tfrac{1}{2}(+\$6{,}000 - x = +\$16{,}500 - x;$$

again, only the value of *x* varies from one subdiagram to another.

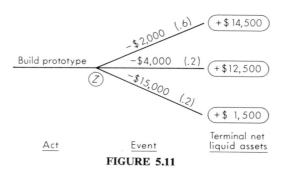

FIGURE 5.11

Reduction of Figure 5.10A in a Special Case

4. Therefore, by the basic proposition at the end of Section 5.6.2, Mallon's mathematical expectation for the uncertain terminal value at position Z is $+\$16,500$ minus his mathematical expectation for the uncertain partial cash outflow $\tilde{x}$ represented by the fork at Z as a whole. If, for example, the fork at Z in Figure 5.10A had only the three branches shown in Figure 5.11, and if Mallon assigned to these branches the probabilities shown in parentheses, then Mallon's mathematical expectation for the uncertain terminal value at position Z could be calculated as $11,500 either by working directly with the terminal values at the ends of the branches, in which case he would compute

$$.6(+\$14,500) + .2(+\$12,500) + .2(+\$1,500) = +\$11,500,$$

or by first computing his mathematical expectations for the uncertain partial cash outflow $\tilde{x}$,

$$.6(\$2,000) + .2(\$4,000) + .2(\$15,000) = \$5,000,$$

and then subtracting this result from $+\$16,500$ to obtain $+\$11,500$.

From this result it follows that if Mallon's certainty equivalents would in fact have been equal to his mathematical expectations, then he could have replaced the event fork at Z in Figure 5.10A by the single branch at Z in Figure 5.10B and analyzed his problem as if the partial cash outflow that would result from building the prototype were certain to be $5,000, even though this was in fact only his mathematical expectation for that cash flow.

Observe, however, that in order to justify this simplification we had to make use of the fact that the subdiagrams emanating from *all* the implicit branches of the fork at Z in Figure 5.10A were identical in *all* the following respects:

1 They all showed the same structure of possible acts and events.

2 The terminal value at any end position of any subdiagram differed from the terminal value at the corresponding end position of any other subdiagram *only* because of the difference in prototype costs. This was true, of course, because (1) differences in partial cash flows were the only

cause of differences in terminal values in the entire diagram, and (2) the partial cash flows beyond the fork at Z were the same on every subdiagram.

3 Mallon's probability for each possible event was the same on every subdiagram.

Generalizing from this example we now state the second important result that can be derived from the basic proposition concerning expectations for sums of monetary values that was stated at the end of Section 5.6.2.

■ If (1) a decision problem is to be analyzed by treating mathematical expectations as certainty equivalents, (2) all adjustments for nonmonetary consequences have been reflected in the partial cash flows, and (3) all the branches of a particular internal event fork in the diagram of the problem are followed by subdiagrams which are identical as regards (*a*) structure, (*b*) adjusted partial cash flows, and (*c*) probabilities, then that event fork can be replaced by a single branch to which is associated a partial cash flow equal to the decision maker's mathematical expectation for the uncertain partial cash flow represented by the fork.

5.6.6
Addition of a Constant to All Terminal Values

The third important result to be derived from the basic proposition in Section 5.6.2 concerning mathematical expectations for sums of monetary values is the following:

■ Given that a decision problem is to be analyzed by treating mathematical expectations as certainty equivalents, addition of any fixed positive or negative amount to *every* terminal value on the diagram of the problem will result in adding that same amount to the value of every act and every strategy and will therefore have no effect on the *ranking* of the various possible acts and strategies.

This result follows directly from the fact that (1) addition of a fixed amount c to the terminal value on every branch of a terminal *event* fork simply adds c to the decision maker's mathematical expectation for the uncertain terminal value represented by the event fork as a whole; and (2) addition of a fixed amount c to the terminal value of every branch on a terminal *act* fork has no effect on the decision maker's choice of act and therefore simply adds c to his value for the position at the base of the fork.

There would of course be no sense in making a totally arbitrary change in all the terminal values on a decision diagram *after* these values have been correctly determined. The reason why the result stated just above is of very real practical importance will appear in the next two sections, where we shall see that it makes it possible to use "relative" rather than "absolute" terminal values of

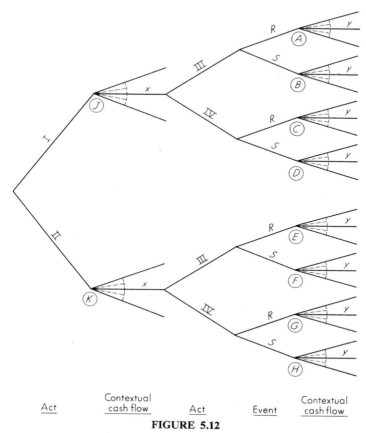

| Act | Contextual cash flow | Act | Event | Contextual cash flow |

FIGURE 5.12

A Decision Problem Involving Uncertain Contextual Cash Flows

the decision maker's criterion and thereby often spares the analyst a very great deal of labor.

5.6.7
Disregard of Contextual Cash Flows

In Sections 5.6.4 and 5.6.5 we saw how it is sometimes possible to replace an event fork by a single branch when a decision problem is to be analyzed by treating mathematical expectations as certainty equivalents, but in the examples we considered in those sections it was still necessary to compute the decision maker's mathematical expectation for the uncertain partial cash flow represented by the suppressed fork and show this on the branch which replaced the fork. Such a computation will always be necessary when the suppressed fork represents a cash flow that arises directly from the decision problem at hand, but when the fork represents a "contextual" cash flow it will *sometimes* be possible simply to suppress the fork and disregard the cash flow completely.

For example, suppose that a decision maker faces a problem of the sort diagrammed in Figure 5.12. He must choose now between acts I and II, and at

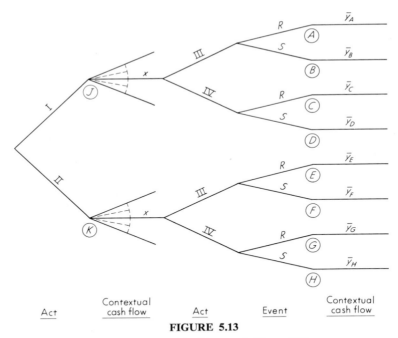

FIGURE 5.13

Simplification of the Diagram in Figure 5.12

some future date he will have to choose between acts III and IV, after which either event R or event S will occur. The terminal value of his criterion will depend, not only on the partial cash flows resulting directly from these acts and events, but also on various contextual cash flows resulting from acts and events which do not appear explicitly in the diagram. Because the decision maker may wish to condition his choice between acts III and IV on the amount of contextual cash flow that is realized before he has to make this choice, the total contextual cash flow is divided into two parts and represented by two sets of fans in the diagram. The fans at positions J and K represent the aggregate contextual flow $\bar{x}$ which will be realized *before* the decision maker actually has to choose between acts III and IV. The fans at positions A, B, . . ., H represent the aggregate contextual flow $\bar{y}$ which will be realized *after* he has had to choose between acts III and IV but before his evaluation date.

We shall now state and prove several propositions about the extent to which it is legitimate to simplify the decision diagram of Figure 5.12 when various conditions are met. In so doing, we shall use the symbol $\bar{y}_A$ to denote the decision maker's mathematical expectation for the uncertain partial cash flow represented by the fan at position A, and $\bar{y}_B$, . . ., $\bar{y}_H$ and $\bar{x}_J$ and $\bar{x}_K$ will have corresponding meanings.

Condition 1: Mathematical expectations will be treated as certainty equivalents, and all adjustments for nonmonetary consequences have been reflected in the partial cash flows. When this one condition is met, we know by the

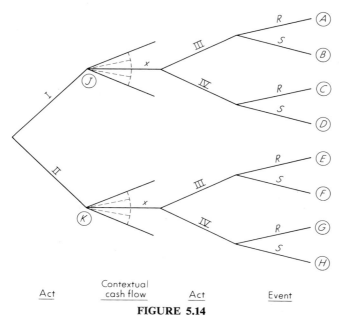

FIGURE 5.14

Simplification of the Diagram in Figure 5.13

result of Section 5.6.4 that we may replace the terminal event fan at position A in Figure 5.12 by a single branch to which a definite partial cash flow equal to $\bar{y}_A$ is associated, and similarly for all the other *terminal* event fans in the figure. Condition 1 alone thus allows us to replace Figure 5.12 by the simpler diagram in Figure 5.13.

Condition 2: The decision maker's mathematical expectations $\bar{y}_A, \bar{y}_B, \ldots,$ $\bar{y}_H$ are all equal. When this condition is satisfied in addition to Condition 1, we know by the result of Section 5.6.6 that we may suppress the four terminal branches in Figure 5.13 and the associated partial cash flows because doing so merely alters the terminal value at every end position by the same amount. Conditions 1 and 2 together thus allow us to replace Figure 5.13 by the still simpler Figure 5.14.

Condition 3: All the implicit subdiagrams which follow the implicit branches of the fan at position J in Figure 5.14 are identical as regards structure, partial cash flows, and probabilities; and similarly for the fan at position K. When this condition is satisfied in addition to Conditions 1 and 2, we know by the result of Section 5.6.5 above that we may replace the internal event fan at J in Figure 5.14 by a single branch to which a definite partial cash flow equal to $\bar{x}_J$ is associated, and similarly for the other internal event fan at K. Conditions 1, 2, and 3 together thus allow us to replace Figure 5.14 by the still simpler Figure 5.15.

Condition 4: The decision maker's mathematical expectations $\bar{x}_J$ and $\bar{x}_K$ are equal. When this condition is satisfied in addition to Conditions 1, 2, and 3, we know by the result of Section 5.6.6 that we may suppress the branches at J

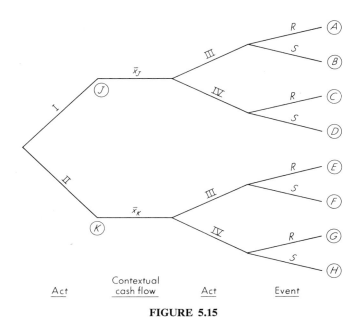

Act | Contextual cash flow | Act | Event

FIGURE 5.15
Simplification of the Diagram in Figure 5.14

and K in Figure 5.15 because doing so merely alters the terminal value at every end position by the same amount. Conditions 1, 2, 3, and 4 together thus allow us to replace Figure 5.15 by the still simpler Figure 5.16, in which contextual cash flows are completely disregarded.

Generalizing from this example, we reach the following conclusion:

■ A contextual cash flow may be disregarded in analyzing a decision problem if (1) the decision maker is willing to treat mathematical expectations as certainty equivalents, (2) all adjustments for nonmonetary consequences have been reflected in the partial cash flows, and (3) there is no "interaction" between the contextual flow and the acts and events that are directly connected with the decision problem at hand. There will be interaction, and it will not be legitimate to disregard the contextual flow, unless all of the following statements are true:

1 The acts open to the decision maker in the decision problem at hand do not depend on the contextual flow.

2 The contextual flow cannot either affect or provide information about and act or event in the decision problem at hand.

3 No act or event in the decision problem at hand can either affect or provide information about the contextual flow.

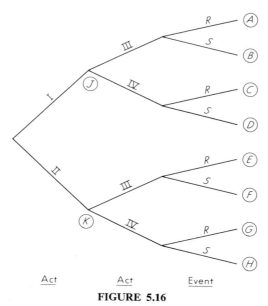

FIGURE 5.16

Simplification of the Diagram in Figure 5.15

5.6.8

Opportunity Costs

The importance of checking for interaction before concluding that contextual cash flows may be disregarded would be hard to overemphasize. In particular, contextual acts and therefore contextual cash flows may be affected by the acts that actually appear in a decision diagram because these latter acts require the use of limited resources that would otherwise be devoted to profitable contextual acts. We have already seen that if A. H. Mallon ties up some of his capital, equipment, and manpower in producing a quantity order for XYZ, he will be forced to forego the opportunity of devoting these resources to other uses (contextual acts) and enjoying the (contextual) net cash inflow that would result from these other uses.

    Any reduction in net contextual cash flow that is caused by diversion of limited resources from contextual acts to an act on the decision diagram can be thought of as a "cost" of the act on the diagram. Such costs should, however, be distinguished from costs associated with the use of resources that are available in unlimited quantities at a price—e.g., materials and supplies in most situations—and therefore they are usually given the special name of "opportunity" costs:

■ Any reduction in net contextual cash flow that is caused by diversion of limited resources from a contextual act or acts to an act which appears explicitly on a decision diagram may be called an ≪opportunity cost≫ of the act which appears explicitly on the decision diagram.

In principle, any decision problem can be analyzed correctly without making any use of the concept of opportunity cost. We have already emphasized that contextual cash flows must in general be represented in a decision diagram; and since the total opportunity cost of the acts preceding any contextual cash flow in the diagram is simply the amount by which those acts reduce the contextual cash flow in question, all that is required in principle is that the decision maker keep these reductions in mind when he evaluates the contextual cash flow.

If, however, opportunity costs are the *only* interaction between contextual cash flows and the decision problem at hand, then a shortcut may be used. Instead of taking explicit account of the *total* contextual cash flow, the decision maker may take explicit account of only the *reductions* in contextual cash flow or "opportunity costs" that will result from the acts on the diagram. If the opportunity cost of an act is known, it can be simply netted out of the partial cash flow attributed to that act on the corresponding branch of the decision diagram; and when the decision maker is willing to treat mathematical expectations as certainty equivalents, even an uncertain opportunity cost can be treated in essentially this same way. The decision maker simply computes his expectation for the uncertain cost and then nets this expectation out of the partial cash flow attributed to the act on the decision diagram.

5.6.9
Relative vs. Absolute Terminal Values

If contextual uncertainties are eliminated from a decision diagram, the value of the decision maker's criterion will be uncertain at every end position of the simplified diagram, but this creates no difficulty when the decision problem is to be analyzed by treating mathematical expectations as certainty equivalents.

We already know from Section 5.6.6 that even if we do assign definite criterion values to all end positions, these values can all be altered by any fixed amount without affecting the results of an analysis based on mathematical expectations. The *differences* between terminal values at end positions are all that really count when the analysis is based on expectations; and the end positions of a diagram can be valued in such a way that these differences are correct even when the actual criterion values cannot be determined because the contextual cash flow has been omitted from the diagram.

Specifically, the differences between end position values will be correct if each end position is valued simply by the total cash flow resulting from the acts and events on the path leading to that end position. This total cash flow must, of course, take account of any opportunity costs associated to the acts on the path; and it must be correctly adjusted for any nonmonetary consequences of the acts and events along the path. Otherwise stated, the total-cash-flow value assigned to any end position must differ from the value of the decision maker's criterion at that position *only* by the sum of (1) the initial value of the decision maker's criterion, and (2) the (unknown) amount of the contextual cash flow.

Total cash flows duly adjusted for opportunity costs and nonmonetary consequences can thus take the place of terminal values of a true criterion in any situation where the decision maker is willing to treat mathematical expectations as certainty equivalents.

5.6.10
Test for Legitimacy of Simplifications

If a decision maker has already constructed a valuationally complete diagram of his decision problem and calculated the terminal value of his true criterion at every end position, he can easily enough decide whether or not his preference is linear over the whole range of terminal values that appear; but if he does determine in this way that his preference is linear, and hence that the problem can be analyzed by treating mathematical expectations as certainty equivalents, it is too late to gain any advantage from the fact that a much simpler diagram might have been constructed.

In order to take advantage of the simplifications in diagramming which linear preference permits, the decision maker must start with an informal "size-up" of his decision problem in which he determines *roughly* what range of values of his criterion would appear if he did construct a complete decision diagram. If as a result of this sizeup he feels reasonably sure that the results of an analysis in which mathematical expectations are treated as certainty equivalents will give an adequate approximation to the results of an exact analysis based on preferences or directly assessed certainty equivalents, then he can construct a diagram that takes advantage of the simplifications that are permitted when the analysis is to be based on mathematical expectations.

Even when the range of terminal values on a valuationally complete diagram of a decision problem would be so large that the decision maker's preferences would be far from linear, it is still possible in some circumstances to analyze the problem by treating mathematical expectations as certainty equivalents and to make the corresponding simplifications in the diagram of the problem. Very loosely speaking, this can be done when the decision problem at hand accounts for only a very small part of the decision maker's total uncertainty about the value of his criterion on his evaluation date, most of his uncertainty being due to uncertainty about contextual cash flows.

More precisely, a decision problem may be isolated from its context and analyzed by treating mathematical expectations as certainty equivalents when *both* of the following conditions are satisfied:

1 There is *no interaction* between acts and events in the decision problem at hand and the contextual cash flows that would appear in a valuationally complete diagram of the problem.

The reader should review the definition of "no interaction" that was given at the end of Section 5.6.7.

2 If the decision maker could learn the actual amounts of the contextual flows in advance, so that he could represent them by single branches rather than fans in a valuationally complete diagram of the problem at hand, the range of terminal values on the diagram would be so small that his preference would in fact be practically linear over that range.

5.7
SUMMARY

5.7.1
Shapes of Preference Curves and
General Attitudes toward Risk

1 A decision maker's ≪risk premium≫ for a 50–50 gamble is the amount by which his certainty-equivalent terminal value falls short of the average of the two equally likely terminal values. The risk premium is negative if the certainty equivalent is greater than the average.

2 If a decision maker's risk premium for a particular 50–50 gamble is positive, he is said to be ≪risk averse≫ as regards the gamble; if it is 0, he is ≪risk neutral≫; if it is negative, he is ≪risk seeking≫.

3 If a decision maker is risk averse as regards all 50–50 gambles whose possible terminal values lie within some specified interval on the horizontal axis of his preference curve, the curve must be concave over that interval when viewed from below. If he is risk seeking, the curve must be convex; if he is risk neutral, it must be a straight line.

4 If the decision maker's risk premium for a 50–50 gamble decreases as the two possible terminal values increase while the spread between them remains constant, he is said to have ≪decreasing risk aversion≫, and the concavity of his preference curve as measured in the way shown in Figure 5.3 (page 113) must decrease from left to right.

5.7.2
Assessment of Points
on a Preference Curve

In what follows, the symbol $\langle q, V'; V'' \rangle$ will denote a gamble which gives a standard chance q at a terminal value V' with a complementary chance $(1 - q)$ at V'', and the symbol V_q will denote the terminal value for which a decision maker's preference relative to some specified reference values is q.

1 Because a decision maker's preferences for his better and worse reference values are necessarily 1 and 0, these values may be respectively called V_1 and V_0.

2 The decision maker can assess $V_{.25}$, $V_{.5}$, and $V_{.75}$ by assessing his certainty equivalents for the reference gambles $\langle \frac{1}{4}, V_1; V_0 \rangle$, $\langle \frac{1}{2}, V_1; V_0 \rangle$, and $\langle \frac{3}{4}, V_1; V_0 \rangle$.

3 The decision maker can also assess $V_{.5}$, $V_{.25}$, and $V_{.75}$ by successively assessing his certainty equivalents for the 50–50 gambles $\langle \frac{1}{2}, V_1; V_0 \rangle$, $\langle \frac{1}{2}, V_{.5}; V_0 \rangle$, and $\langle \frac{1}{2}, V_1; V_{.5} \rangle$.

4 If these two sets of assessments lead to different values for $V_{.25}$, $V_{.5}$, and/or $V_{.75}$, some or all of the assessments must be revised until the inconsistency is eliminated.

5 After $V_{.25}$ and $V_{.75}$ have been assessed, $V_{.5}$ can be reassessed by assessing a certainty equivalent for $\langle \frac{1}{2}, V_{.75}; V_{.25} \rangle$, and this assessment can be used as a final check on consistency.

5.7.3

Fitting the Preference Curve
to the Assessments

■ Although a few directly assessed points by no means suffice in themselves to determine a preference curve, a few points in conjunction with general specifications regarding risk aversion and the way in which risk aversion varies as assets increase will often almost completely determine a preference curve.

5.7.4

Preferences for Total Cash Flows

Because preferences for consequences should not depend on the way in which consequences are described,

1 A preference curve for terminal values of a monetary criterion can be converted into a preference curve for total cash flows by simply subtracting the current value of the criterion from every terminal value on the horizontal axis.

It must be remembered, however, that:

2 If a decision problem is to be analyzed by use of preferences for total cash flows, each total cash flow must be adjusted for nonmonetary consequences in exactly the same way that the terminal value of the decision maker's criterion would be adjusted.

5.7.5
Mathematical Expectations for
Uncertain Monetary Values

1*a* Let $\tilde{x}$ denote an uncertain monetary value. The decision maker's ≪mathematical expectation≫ for $\tilde{x}$ is by definition the number $\bar{x}$ obtained by (1) multiplying every possible monetary value x by the decision maker's probability for that value, and (2) adding these products over all values.

b In other words, the decision maker's mathematical expectation for an uncertain monetary value is a probability-weighted average of the possible monetary values.

2 If a decision maker's certainty equivalent for even chances at any two terminal values which lie between specified limits V' and V'' is equal to the average of those two values, then his preference is a *linear* function of terminal value over the interval from V' to V''.

3 Let $\tilde{V}$ denote any uncertain terminal value which must be between two specified limits V' and V''. If the decision maker's preference is a linear function of terminal value over the interval from V' to V'', then his certainty equivalent for $\tilde{V}$ should be equal to his mathematical expectation for $\tilde{V}$.

4 If the decision maker's preference is a linear function of terminal value over an interval extending from the worst to the best terminal value in a given decision problem, then that problem can be analyzed by backward induction on mathematical expectations treated as certainty equivalents.

5.7.6
Simplification of Decision Diagrams

1 If (1) a decision problem is to be analyzed by treating mathematical expectations as certainty equivalents, and (2) all adjustments for nonmonetary consequences have been reflected in the partial cash flows, then any *terminal* event fork in the diagram of the problem may be replaced by a single branch to which is associated a partial cash flow equal to the decision maker's mathematical expectation for the uncertain partial cash flow represented by the fork.

2 If (1) a decision problem is to be analyzed by treating mathematical expectations as certainty equivalents, (2) all adjustments for nonmonetary consequences have been reflected in the partial cash flows, and (3) all the branches of a particular *internal* event fork in the diagram of the problem are followed by subdiagrams which are identical as regards (*a*) structure, (*b*) partial cash flows, and (*c*) probabilities, then that event fork can

be replaced by a single branch to which is associated a partial cash flow equal to the decision maker's mathematical expectation for the uncertain partial cash flow represented by the fork.

3 A contextual cash flow may be disregarded in analyzing a decision problem if (1) the decision maker is willing to treat mathematical expectations as certainty equivalents, and (2) there is no "interaction" between the contextual flow and the cash flows that are directly connected with the decision problem at hand. There will be interaction, and it will not be legitimate to disregard the contextual flow, unless all of the following statements are true:

a The acts open to the decision maker in the decision problem at hand do not depend on the contextual flow.

b The contextual flow cannot either affect or provide information about any act or event in the decision problem at hand.

c No act or event in the decision problem at hand can either affect or provide information about the contextual flow.

4 If all the conditions for disregarding contextual flows are satisfied except for the fact that acts in the decision problem at hand reduce those flows by diverting scarce resources, it is legitimate to omit the contextual flows as such from the diagram and show instead these reductions or "opportunity costs".

EXERCISES

A. ASSESSMENT OF PREFERENCES

In answering Exercises 5.1 to 5.11, imagine that *you* are about to decide whether or not to enter into a risky venture in the following circumstances. In order to participate, you must invest $1,000. If you like, you can borrow the $1,000 from an educational foundation and repay it without interest within one year after graduation. The venture may pay out anything between $0 and $4,000, so that the net result of participation can be anywhere between a loss of $1,000 and a gain of $3,000. The payout will be known within a week or less, and you have chosen a week hence as the evaluation date for your analysis. Your criterion is your cash on hand and in the bank, plus all marketable securities you own, minus all debts that you will have to repay within one year after graduation. You have diagrammed the problem and written down the total cash flow at each end position, but you have not yet calculated the terminal values of your criterion, which you will do by adding the current value of your criterion to each total cash flow. There will be no adjustments for nonmonetary consequences.

5.1 Suppose that, in order to analyze your decision problem, you wish to construct a preference curve covering the range of terminal values involved in the problem. To do so, you must of course first select a pair of reference terminal values, and assessment will be easier if both these values are integral numbers of thousands of dollars.

  a Calculate the current value of your criterion, and then choose reference values V_0 and V_1 which "encompass" all terminal values of your criterion that can result from the venture you are analyzing.

  b On a suitable piece of graph paper, construct and label a horizontal axis to show all terminal values V from V_0 to V_1, and construct and label a vertical axis to show all preferences q from 0 to 1.

  c Letting V^* denote the current value of your criterion, calculate and record the following possible terminal values:

$$V^1 = V^* - \$1,000$$
$$V^2 = V^*$$
$$V^3 = V^* + \$1,000$$
$$V^4 = V^* + \$2,000$$
$$V^5 = V^* + \$3,000$$

5.2 *a* Consider a gamble giving you even chances at terminal values V^2 and V^3, compute the average of these two equally likely terminal values, and then decide whether your certainty equivalent for the gamble would be less than, equal to, or greater than the average.

  b Same as (*a*) except that the gamble gives even chances at V^3 and V^4.

  c Same as (*a*) except that the gamble gives even chances at V^4 and V^5.

  d Same as (*a*) except that the gamble gives even chances at V^0 and V^1.

5.3 In view of your answers to Exercise 5.2, over what parts of the horizontal axis should your preference curve be concave when viewed from below? Over what parts should it be linear? Convex?

5.4 *a* Assess your exact certainty-equivalent terminal values for the various gambles described in Exercise 5.2 and compute your risk premium for each gamble.

  b Over what parts of the horizontal axis should your preference curve imply decreasing risk aversion? Constant risk aversion? Increasing risk aversion?

5.5 *a* Letting $\langle q, V_1; V_0 \rangle$ denote a gamble that gives you a standard chance q at V_1 and a complementary chance at V_0, assess your certainty equivalents for $\langle 0, V_1; V_0 \rangle$, $\langle \frac{1}{4}, V_1; V_0 \rangle$, $\langle \frac{1}{2}, V_1; V_0 \rangle$, $\langle \frac{3}{4}, V_1; V_0 \rangle$, and $\langle 1, V_1; V_0 \rangle$.

  b Plot each of your assessments as a point on your graph.

5.6 *a* Sketching lightly with a pencil, try to put through your five points a curve which has the properties you said your preference curve should have when you answered Exercises 5.3 and 5.4*b*.

  b If no such curve can be drawn, your answers to Exercises 5.3 and 5.4*b* are logically inconsistent with your answers to Exercise 5.5*a*. Make up your mind which of your answers you wish to change in order to remove this inconsistency and keep trying until you have sketched a curve which seems to express your true preferences for terminal values of your criterion.

c Record your present assessments of $V_{.25}$, $V_{.5}$, and $V_{.75}$—i.e., the assessments that agree with the curve you have just drawn.

5.7 Table 5.8 shows the certainty equivalents which Mr. J. B. Jenkins has assessed for a number of gambles each of which gives him even chances at two possible terminal values of his criterion. The two terminal values which may result from each gamble are shown in the first column of the table; Jenkins' certainty-equivalent terminal value for the gamble is shown in the second column.

TABLE 5.8

Equally Likely Terminal Values		Certainty-equivalent Terminal Value
+$25,000	−$5,000	$ 0
+ 25,000	0	+ 10,000
0	− 5,000	− 3,000
+ 10,000	− 3,000	+ 1,000

a Relative to terminal values of +$25,000 and −$5,000, Jenkins' preferences for +$25,000 and −$5,000 are of course 1 and 0 respectively. Plot these two preferences as points on a piece of graph paper.

b Show that .5 should be Jenkins' preference for a gamble which gives him a .5 chance at +$25,000 and a .5 chance at −$5,000.

c Since Jenkins' certainty equivalent for the gamble of (*b*) is $0 by Table 5.8, Jenkins finds a terminal value of $0 exactly as attractive as that gamble. Show that Jenkins' preference for a terminal value of $0 should be .5, and plot this preference as a point.

d Show that .75 should be Jenkins' preference for a gamble which gives him a .5 chance at +$25,000 and a .5 chance at $0; then show by use of Table 5.8 that .75 should be his preference for a terminal value of +$10,000 and plot this preference.

e What should be Jenkins' preference for a gamble which gives him a .5 chance at $0 and a .5 chance at −$5,000? Using the information in Table 5.8, determine his preference for a terminal value of −$3,000 and plot this preference.

f What should be Jenkins' preference for a gamble which gives him a .5 chance at +$10,000 and a .5 chance at −$3,000? According to Table 5.8, what should be his preference for +$1,000?

g Are the assessments in Table 5.8 mutually consistent? [Hint: compare your answers to (*c*) and (*f*).]

5.8 Returning now to your own preferences and your own reference values V_1 and V_0:

    a Assess $V_{.5}$ by assessing your certainty equivalent for a gamble $\langle \frac{1}{2}, V_1; V_0 \rangle$ which gives you even chances at V_1 and V_0.

    b Assess $V_{.25}$ by assessing your certainty equivalent for $\langle \frac{1}{2}, V_{.5}; V_0 \rangle$ and assess $V_{.75}$ by assessing your certainty equivalent for $\langle \frac{1}{2}, V_1; V_{.5} \rangle$.

5.9 Do your answers to Exercise 5.8 agree with your answers to Exercise 5.6*c*?

    a If they do not, your assessments are logically inconsistent. Revise some or all of them until you feel that you have at last determined your true certainty equivalents for the gambles $\langle \frac{1}{4}, V_1; V_0 \rangle$, $\langle \frac{1}{2}, V_1; V_0 \rangle$, $\langle \frac{3}{4}, V_1; V_0 \rangle$, $\langle \frac{1}{2}, V_{.5}; V_0 \rangle$, and $\langle \frac{1}{2}, V_1; V_{.5} \rangle$.

    b Plot your revised values for $V_{.25}$, $V_{.5}$, and $V_{.75}$ and repeat Exercise 5.6.

5.10 Reassess $V_{.5}$ by taking your revised values for $V_{.25}$ and $V_{.75}$ and assessing your certainty equivalent for $\langle \frac{1}{2}, V_{.75}; V_{.25} \rangle$. If your assessment is inconsistent with your previous assessment of $V_{.5}$, revise one or more of all the assessments you have made thus far until your certainty equivalents for the five gambles listed in Exercise 5.5*a* and your certainty equivalent for $\langle \frac{1}{2}, V_{.75}; V_{.25} \rangle$ are not only consistent with each other but acceptable to you as bases for real decisions involving your own real money.

5.11 *a* Plot your final values for $V_{.25}$, $V_{.5}$, and $V_{.75}$ and repeat Exercise 5.6.

    b Recalling the values $V^1, \ldots, V^5$ that you computed in Exercise 5.1*c*, use your preference curve to compute your certainty equivalents and risk premiums for $\langle \frac{1}{2}, V^1; V^2 \rangle$, $\langle \frac{1}{2}, V^2; V^3 \rangle$, $\langle \frac{1}{2}, V^3; V^4 \rangle$, and $\langle \frac{1}{2}, V^4; V^5 \rangle$.

    c Do your answers to (*b*) agree with your answers to Exercises 5.3 and 5.4*b*? If they do not, make such changes as are needed to reconcile all of your decisions concerning gambles and revise your preference curve accordingly.

5.12 It has frequently been argued that instead of going to all the trouble of assessing a preference curve, a decision maker could just as well assess his certainty equivalents for 50–50 gambles by first calculating the average of the two possible terminal values and then deducting a risk premium equal to some fixed percentage of the spread or difference between the two terminal values, the percentage in question being a kind of measure of the decision maker's risk aversion. If, for example, a decision maker felt that 10% of the spread of a 50–50 gamble was the right amount to assess as a risk premium, his risk premium for $\langle \frac{1}{2}, +\$70,000; +\$30,000 \rangle$ would be $.1(\$70,000 - \$30,000) = \$4,000$ and his certainty equivalent for this same gamble would be $\frac{1}{2}(\$70,000 + \$30,000) - \$4,000 = \$46,000$.

    a Suppose that a Mr. Wilson, whose reference values are $V_0 = 0$ and $V_1 = +\$100,000$, does in fact feel that his risk premium for any 50–50 gamble should be 10% of the spread of the gamble. What will be his certainty equivalent $V_{.5}$ for $\langle \frac{1}{2}, V_1; V_0 \rangle$?

b Using your answer to (*a*), compute Mr. Wilson's certainty equivalent $V_{.25}$ for $\langle \frac{1}{2}, V_{.5}; V_0 \rangle$ and his certainty equivalent $V_{.75}$ for $\langle \frac{1}{2}, V_1; V_{.5} \rangle$.

c Using your answers to (*b*), reevaluate $V_{.5}$ by computing Mr. Wilson's certainty equivalent for $\langle \frac{1}{2}, V_{.75}; V_{.25} \rangle$.

d Is it rational (i.e., logically self-consistent) to assess certainty equivalents for all 50–50 gambles by deducting a fixed percentage of the spread from the average of the two possible terminal values?

B. PREFERENCES FOR TOTAL CASH FLOWS

5.13 Add a second scale to the monetary-value axis of your own preference curve so that it will show directly your preferences for total cash flows as well as your preferences for terminal values of your criterion, and be prepared to explain in class exactly how you calculated the new labels.

C. MATHEMATICAL EXPECTATIONS

5.14 An event fork has four branches, representing events *A*, *B*, *C*, and *D*. The terminal values associated to the events are respectively $+\$100$, $+\$50$, $\$0$, and $-\$100$; the probabilities assigned to the events by the decision maker are respectively .1, .2, .3, and .4. Show that the decision maker's mathematical expectation for the uncertain terminal value represented by the fork is $-\$20$.

5.15 An act fork has only two branches, *A* and *B*. Certainty equivalents, preferences, and mathematical expectations have been determined for the end positions of each branch. Determine whether (1) act *A* should be chosen, (2) act *B* should be chosen, or (3) at least one of the various values assigned to the acts must be recalculated or reassessed, if:

a Act *A* has the higher preference but act *B* has the higher certainty equivalent.

b Act *A* has the higher preference but act *B* has the higher mathematical expectation.

c Act *A* has the higher mathematical expectation but act *B* has the higher certainty equivalent.

D. LINEAR PREFERENCE

5.16 a Reanalyze the decision problem that was presented to you in Exercise 1.1 by carrying out a backward induction in which your mathematical expectation for each gamble that has to be evaluated is treated as if it were your certainty equivalent for that gamble.

b Would you be willing to accept the results of this analysis as a basis for action?

5.17 Suppose that you are in Mallon's position as president of ABC Controls, faced with the XYZ decision problem described in Chapter 1, and decide whether you would analyze the problem by treating mathematical expectations as certainty equivalents if, instead of currently having net liquid assets of − $4,000:

a ABC Controls had $500,000 on hand and in the bank, had earned $5 million on sales of $120 million last year, and expected earnings to improve by 20% to 25% this year.

b ABC Controls had $50,000 on hand and in the bank, had no debt outstanding, had earned $175,000 last year, expected to earn between $150,- 000 and $200,000 this year, and was wholly owned by you.

c ABC Controls had working capital of $45,000, had earned $75,000 in 1965, − $30,000 in 1966, and $10,000 in 1967, expected to earn somewhere between − $10,000 and + $20,000 in 1968, and was traded over the counter.

5.18 A manufacturer must decide how many units of Product A23Z to produce in the next scheduled production run. The product is produced once a quarter at an out-of-pocket cost of $3,000 for setup plus $.20 per unit produced; rental of warehouse space for a quarter costs $.01 for each unit on hand immediately after a production run is completed. The product is sold for $.40 per unit; orders that cannot be filled the day they are received are lost. Currently there are 4,000 units on hand.

a Assuming that the manufacturer will analyze this decision problem by treating mathematical expectations as certainty equivalents, diagram his decision problem schematically, labelling typical branches with Q for number produced and d for number demanded during the coming quarter.

b Select the end position following $Q = 0, d = 4,000$ as your base end position and value it.

c Referring to the quarter which is about to begin as "this" quarter and to the following quarter as "next" quarter, and assuming that (1) the manufacturer will want to make a production run next quarter no matter how many units are left over from this quarter's run, and (2) all production costs will be the same at the beginning of next quarter as they are at the beginning of this quarter, give a formula or formulas for the value of each end position of your diagram other than the base end position.

d Why is each of the assumptions in (*c*) crucial?

e Exactly how would a correct diagram of this problem have to differ from the one you drew in answer to (*a*) if the manufacturer were *not* willing to treat mathematical expectations as certainty equivalents?

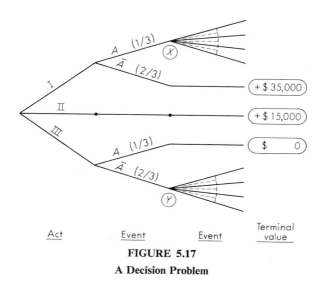

FIGURE 5.17

A Decision Problem

E. REVIEW EXERCISES

5.19 Figure 5.17 shows the structure of a decision problem together with incomplete information about probabilities and consequences. In addition to the information on the diagram, you are told that the decision maker's mathematical expectation for the uncertain terminal value he faces at position Y is $+\$45,000$ and that his certainty equivalent for the uncertain terminal value he faces at position X is $-\$10,000$. The symbol $\bar{A}$ in Figure 5.17 denotes the nonoccurence of the event A.

a To what extent is it possible to rank the three acts in order of attractiveness to the decision maker using only the information available and making no assumptions of any sort whatever?

b To what extent is it possible to rank the acts if you are also told that the decision maker's preferences for selected terminal values relative to some pair of reference terminal values are as shown in the following table?

Terminal Value	Preference
$-\$10,000$	.21
0	.40
$+\ 15,000$	.59
$+\ 35,000$	.72
$+\ 45,000$	.75

5.20 *American Rubber Products Company (A)*

Part XZ714 is sold by the American Rubber Products Company for \$31. It is produced in a large run once every six months, extra runs being impossible because of the scheduling difficulties they would create in the shop. Production costs amount to \$2,500 for setup plus \$14 per part produced.

To avoid loss of goodwill, American Rubber supplies a part of superior quality at no extra charge to the customer whenever an order is received for part XZ714 and there is no stock on hand. This superior part is produced by hand as required at a total cost of $23 per unit; there is no setup cost.

If any units of part XZ714 are left over from an old run at the time a new production run is due, they are thoroughly reconditioned in a completely separate operation at a total cost of $4 per part; there is no setup cost for this operation. Storage costs and the cost of capital tied up in inventory are negligible in comparison with this cost of deterioration.

a Assuming that the responsible executive of the American Rubber Products Company will treat mathematical expectations as certainty equivalents when he analyzes the problem of deciding how many units of part XZ714 to produce, diagram his problem schematically, labelling typical branches with Q for number produced and d for number demanded during the next six-month period.

b Assuming (1) that there are 1,000 units of part XZ714 currently on hand, (2) that all these units will be reconditioned concurrently with the production run which is about to be made, (3) that all units left on hand six months from now will be reconditioned at that time, and (4) that the cost of reconditioning will be the same six months from now as it is now, select a base end position and value it.

c Assuming further that (5) American Rubber will want to make a production run six months from now no matter how many units are left over at that time, and (6) all production costs will be the same six months from now as they are now, give a formula or formulas for the value of each end position of your diagram other than the base end position.

5.21 Waggoner Engineering Corporation (C)

On August 16, 1969, Mr. L. E. Waggoner decided to make a systematic analysis of the decision problem he faced regarding a proposed contract with a syndicate of local businessmen in the city of Norwood and an offer he had received from the Electronics Service Corporation.[3] To do so, he first assessed the following probabilities:

License for Microwave Connection at Norwood:

Granted without restrictions	.5
Granted with restrictions	.2
Refused	.3
	1.0

Increase in Height of Antenna at Prescott:

Necessary	.3
Unnecessary	.7
	1.0

[3] See Exercises 2.18 and 2.19: *Waggoner Engineering Corporation* (A) and (B).

Assuming that Mr. Waggoner is willing to treat mathematical expectations as certainty equivalents in analyzing his decision problem:

a Determine Mr. Waggoner's optimal strategy and his certainty-equivalent terminal value for that strategy.

b Determine Mr. Waggoner's certainty-equivalent terminal values for each of the following strategies:

1 Accept and complete both Norwood and Prescott.

2 Accept Norwood but refuse Prescott.

3 Refuse Norwood but accept and complete Prescott.

c Using your answers to (*b*), compute Mr. Waggoner's certainty equivalent for the uncertain total cash flow that will result from each of the three strategies defined in (*b*), and then compare your result for strategy *1* with the sum of your results for strategies *2* and *3*.

5.22 *Waggoner Engineering Corporation* (D)

After thinking more carefully about the possible consequences of his possible courses of action, Mr. Waggoner decided that his certainty equivalents for some of the gambles he might face would not be at all close to his corresponding mathematical expectations. After some further thought he decided to base his analysis on his preferences for net liquid assets on April 1, 1970, and selecting +$150,000 and −$20,000 as his reference terminal values, he assessed a preference curve of which two portions are shown in Figure 5.18. In doing so, he took his current nonmonetary assets as his base, assuming that none of the acts or events in the decision problem he was facing would in any way alter this base.

a Determine Mr. Waggoner's optimal strategy and his certainty-equivalent terminal value for that strategy.

b Determine Mr. Waggoner's certainty-equivalent terminal values for each of the following strategies:

1 Accept and complete both Norwood and Prescott.

2 Accept Norwood but refuse Prescott.

3 Refuse Norwood but accept and complete Prescott.

c Using your answers to (*b*), compute Mr. Waggoner's certainty equivalent for the uncertain total cash flow that will result from each of the three strategies defined in (*b*), and then compare your result for strategy *1* with the sum of your results for strategies *2* and *3*.

d Compute Mr. Waggoner's certainty equivalents for even chances at each of the following pairs of terminal values of his criterion and be prepared to discuss what *your* certainty equivalents for these gambles would be if you were in Mr. Waggoner's position.

1 −$20,000 and $0,

2 $0 and +$20,000,

3 $0 and +$50,000,

4 +$50,000 and +$100,000.

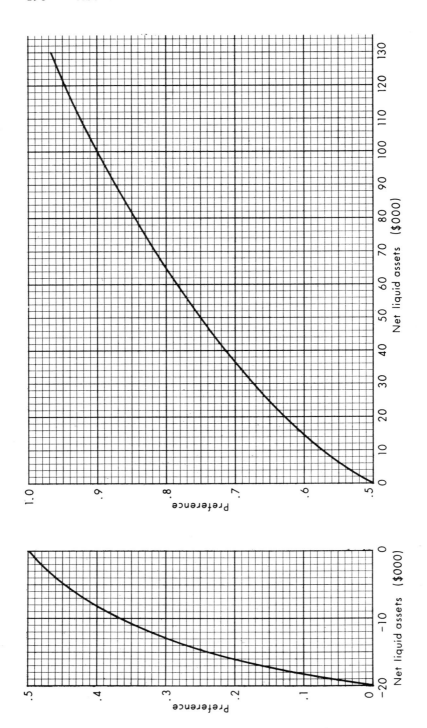

FIGURE 5.18

L. E. Waggoner's Preferences for Net Liquid Assets Relative to +$150,000 and −$20,000 in the Presence of His Base Nonmonetary Assets

CHAPTER

6

PROBABILITY AND
RELATIVE FREQUENCY

We saw in Chapter 4 that the actual analysis of any decision problem becomes a matter of routine arithmetic once the decision maker has assessed his preferences for all the consequences and his probabilities for all the events that are involved in the problem. In Chapter 5 we went somewhat more deeply into the assessment of preferences, and we now enter into a sequence of several chapters dealing with the assessment and use of probabilities. The present chapter will deal with the basic principles that must be observed in assessing probabilities; subsequent chapters will deal with techniques by which these principles can be implemented in practice. The topics treated in the present chapter are organized as follows:

1. In Section 6.1 we review the definition of probability and show that this definition implies that the numerical values of the probabilities assigned to the events on any event fork must obey certain rules of consistency.

2. In Section 6.2 we discuss various ways in which the decision maker's probabilities for the events on any event fork should be influenced by acts or events on the path leading to that event fork in the decision diagram.

3. In Section 6.3 we discuss the way in which a decision maker's probability for a given event should be influenced by what he knows or believes about either (1) the long-run relative frequency with which that event would occur in repeated trials, or (2) the long-run relative frequency with which he would be right in predicting the occurrence of events that seem to him as likely to occur as the given event; and we then go on to show how the results of our discussion can be applied in making use of an expert's estimate of the chance of some event.

4. Finally, we take account of the fact that a decision maker can rarely if ever take the time to make careful assessments of all the probabilities required for analysis of a complex decision problem. In Section 6.4 we point out that very quick, tentative assessments are often good enough for many of the required probabilities, and in Section 6.5 we point out that the decision maker can usually quite legitimately delegate to subordinates the assessment of most of the required probabilities.

The text and exercises of this chapter can be studied in the following order:

1 Section 6.1 and Exercise 6.1.

2 Section 6.2.

3 Sections 6.3.1–6.3.5 and Exercise 6.2.

4 Sections 6.3.6–6.3.8 and Exercise 6.3.

5 Sections 6.3.9–6.3.11 and Exercise 6.4.

6 Sections 6.4–6.5 and Exercise 6.5.

CONTENTS OF CHAPTER 6

1.
Consistency of Judgments

1 Review of Definitions
2 Rules of Consistency for Assessed Probabilities
3 Multiple Assessment and Reconciliation of Inconsistencies

2.
Dependence of Probabilities
on Acts and Events

1 Dependence of Probabilities on Acts
2 Dependence of Probabilities on Events

3.
Probability and Relative Frequency

1 Probability and Experience
2 Overwhelming Common Experience
3 Limited Experience
4 Learning from Additional Experience
5 Application to Business Problems
6 Indistinguishable Conditions
7 Assertion under Indistinguishable Conditions

4.

Tentative Assessment and Sensitivity Analysis

5.

Delegation of the Authority to Decide

6.

Summary

6.1

CONSISTENCY OF JUDGMENTS

6.1.1

Review of Definitions

Let us begin by reviewing the basic definitions that underlie the concept of probability as that word will be used in this book.

1. The most basic idea is that of a standard drawing, introduced in Section 4.1. We say that a drawing of one ball from an urn is standard for a particular decision maker when that decision maker would be indifferent between (*a*) the right to receive a valuable prize if any one, particular ball is drawn, and (*b*) the right to receive that same prize if any other one, particular ball is drawn.

2. We next introduced the concept of an equivalent urn in Section 4.2. If every ball in an urn is labelled with the name of one and only one of the events on some event fork, and if upon arriving at the base of the fork the decision maker would be indifferent between (*a*) a gamble that associates any particular set of consequences to the events on the event fork, and (*b*) a gamble that associates those same consequences to the corresponding events of a standard drawing from the urn, then we say that the urn is equivalent to the event fork for that decision maker. The decision maker *decides* on the mix of balls that makes an urn equivalent to a particular event fork as far as *he* is concerned.

3. Finally, we said in Section 4.5.1 that, given an event fork and an urn that is equivalent to that event fork for a particular decision maker, the proportion of balls corresponding to any one event on the event fork will be called that decision maker's "probability" for that event on that fork.

We do not insist that the decision maker should actually think in terms of equivalent urns when he assigns numerical values to the "chances" of the events on any event fork, but we do insist that these numerical values cannot logically be used as bases for decisions, and we therefore refuse to call them probabilities, unless (1) they *could* be represented by proportions of balls in an urn, and (2) that urn *would* be equivalent to the event fork for that decision maker.

6.1.2
Rules of Consistency for Assessed Probabilities

The fact that probabilities can by definition be represented by proportions of balls in an urn means that a decision maker's probabilities for the events on any event fork must obey any rules that proportions obey. In particular, probabilities must obey the three following rules of logical consistency:

1 A probability must be a number between 0 and 1 inclusive.

2 Given any list of mutually exclusive events, the probability that some one or another of the events on the list will occur must be equal to the sum of the probabilities of the individual events on the list.

3 The sum of the probabilities of a set of mutually exclusive and collectively exhaustive events must be 1.

6.1.3
Multiple Assessment and Reconciliation of Inconsistencies

We saw in Section 5.2 that because intuitive evaluations of gambles are often mutually inconsistent, a decision maker who wishes to assess preferences that express really carefully thought-out likings for consequences will usually do well to assess a set of points on his preference curve in more than one way and then reconcile any inconsistencies that appear. In much the same way, intuitive evaluations of the chances of events are often mutually inconsistent, and therefore a decision maker who wishes to assess probabilities that represent really carefully thought-out judgments concerning the chances of a number of mutually exclusive events will often do well to assess these probabilities in more than one way and then reconcile any inconsistencies that appear.

For example, suppose that Mr. A. H. Mallon believes that an attempt to use stampings will be followed by one or the other of just two possible events, namely "stampings work" or "do not work". He can if he likes assess his probabilities for both events by directly assessing the chance of only one of them and then using the last of the three rules in the previous section to calculate the chance of the other, but he may very well do much better to make direct assessments of the chances of both events and then check these assessments for consistency. Proceeding in this latter way he might quite conceivably find that although he assessed the chance of "stampings work" at 3/4 when he thought about that event directly, he assessed the chance of "do not work" at 1/5 when he focussed his attention on this alternate event. The inconsistency in these two assessments would be revealed when Mallon checked to see whether they added to 1, and he would be able to rethink and reconcile his assessments before he tried to use them in the actual analysis of his decision problem.

When there are more than two events on an event fork, a decision maker's original evaluations of the chances of these events are still more likely to be inconsistent, either with each other (in which case they will not add to 1) or with other evaluations which the decision maker might make if he thought about the chance that some one out of several events on the fork might occur.

For example, suppose that a retailer who is deciding how many units to stock of a certain commodity wishes to assess his probabilities for all possible values of customer demand, and suppose that after reflection he assesses them as shown in Table 6.1. These probabilities add to 1 and are thus consistent with

TABLE 6.1
Initial Probability Assessments for Customer Demand

Number of Units Demanded	Probability as Initially Assessed
0	.0
1	.1
2	.2
3	.4
4	.2
5	.1
6 or more	.0
	1.0

each other, but if the retailer thinks about the chance of some ≪compound event≫ such as "*2 or less* units demanded", an inconsistency may still appear. By the second rule in Section 6.1.2, the probabilities in Table 6.1 imply that the retailer should assign probability .0 + .1 + .2 = .3 to demand for 2 or less units; but if the retailer thinks directly about this compound event, he may feel that its chance has some value other than .3. If so, there is an inconsistency in his thinking that he must eliminate before analysis of his decision problem can proceed.

Observe that the possibility that quantitative evaluations of chances will be mutually inconsistent and have to be revised before being used as probabilities is not a reason for avoiding the use of judgmental probabilities in analyzing a decision problem. Quite the contrary:

■ The fact that a decision maker's initial judgments about chances are frequently inconsistent is one of the strongest reasons for assessing explicit probabilities, since this is the only way in which the decision maker can make sure that his inconsistencies will be detected and corrected before they have had a chance to lead to a defective analysis of his decision problem.

6.2
DEPENDENCE OF PROBABILITIES
ON ACTS AND EVENTS

When we first defined probability, in Section 4.5.1, we pointed out that because a decision maker's judgment about the chance of an event necessarily depends on the information available to him at the time he forms the judgment, his probability for any event on any particular event fork in a decision diagram may depend on the acts and events which precede that fork in the diagram. Because an analysis based on probability assessments which fail to take account of such dependencies can lead to very seriously wrong conclusions, we shall in the present section call the reader's attention to some of the various ways in which preceding acts and events can or should affect the decision maker's judgments and hence his assessed probabilities.

6.2.1
Dependence of Probabilities on Acts

That previous acts can affect the probabilities that it is reasonable to assign to subsequent events is so obvious that the point scarcely needs illustration. The reader has only to think of the fact that the kind of presentation put on by an advertising agency will have a large effect on its chances of getting an account. We therefore merely remind the reader that when the decision maker sets out to assess his probabilities for the events on any event fork, he should not forget to look back and see what acts actually precede that particular fork.

6.2.2
Dependence of Probabilities on Events

Although it is almost always very easy to see whether a preceding act should affect the probability that a decision maker assigns to an event, it is not always so easy to see whether a preceding event should affect the probability that a decision maker assigns to a following event. The three examples which follow may help to alert the reader to the many different ways in which such dependence can arise.

1. As an example of the most obvious way in which a preceding event

can affect the probability assigned to a following event, consider a manufacturer who is thinking of trying to sell a new product to two potential customers one after the other. This manufacturer may very possibly feel that purchase of the product by the first customer will help to persuade the second customer to buy; and hence he may assign a much higher probability to the event "second customer purchases" on a fork following the event "first customer purchases" than he assigns on a fork following "first customer does not purchase".

In cases like this one, we may say that the probability assigned to one event depends on a preceding event because in the decision maker's opinion the preceding event has a direct "causal" effect on the following event, exactly as an act may be said to have a direct "causal" effect on a following event.

2. As an example of a slightly less obvious kind of reason for dependence of probabilities on preceding events, consider again a manufacturer who is thinking of trying to sell a new product to two potential customers successively, but this time suppose that the manufacturer believes that the second customer's decision will not be influenced in any way by the first customer's decision. If nevertheless the manufacturer believes that the two customers' needs are very similar, he may assign a higher probability to the event "second customer purchases" on a fork following "first customer purchases" than he assigns on a fork following "first customer does not purchase" because he believes that the fact that the first customer purchases constitutes favorable evidence concerning the attractiveness of the product to both customers.

In cases like this one we may say that the probability assigned to one event depends on a preceding event because, even though the preceding event as such has no causal effect on the subsequent event, it provides information about an underlying "factor" which has a causal effect on both events.

3. As an example of a still more subtle way in which probabilities for events on a given event fork may depend on events which precede that event in the decision diagram, suppose that a businessman who knows that a competitor has been experimenting with two new products receives information which suggests that the competitor intends to market only one of the two products. If in analyzing some decision problem of his own this businessman wishes to consider the events "competitor markets product *A*" and "competitor markets product *B*", the probability he assigns to "markets *B*" should clearly be lower on a fork following "markets *A*" than on a fork following "does not market *A*", even though the event "markets *A*" cannot be said either to have a direct causal effect on the event "markets *B*" or to provide information about a common factor which has a causal effect on both these events.

In cases like this one we may say that the probability assigned to one event depends on another event because the decision maker has information which bears on the chance that *both* of the two events will occur even though it does not bear on the chance of either one of the two events considered by itself.

6.3
PROBABILITY AND RELATIVE FREQUENCY

6.3.1
Probability and Experience

In our original discussion of the meaning of probabilities, we emphasized that any probability is necessarily an expression of a personal judgment and is therefore necessarily "subjective" in the sense that two reasonable men may assign different probabilities to the same event. This by no means implies, however, that a reasonable man will assign probabilities *arbitrarily*. Reasonable men base the probabilities which they assign to events in the real world on their experience with events in the real world, and when two reasonable men have had roughly the same experience with a certain kind of event they assign it roughly the same probability.

6.3.2
Overwhelming Common Experience

As an extreme example of this principle, consider the assessment of the probability of heads on the toss of a coin which has been very carefully inspected and found to be perfectly symmetric and which is to be tossed in such a way that it will spin a very large number of times before it falls. Although we may or may not have had direct experience with this particular coin and this particular tossing procedure, almost everyone has observed that other coins tossed in more or less this same way seem to turn up heads roughly half of the time. We have further observed that although the ratio of heads to tosses is often very far from 1/2 in short sequences of tosses, it is usually much closer to 1/2 in long sequences. Still further, we have observed that heads occur about as frequently on tosses which follow heads as on tosses which follow tails, and more generally that heads occur about half the time whatever the pattern of heads and tails on previous tosses. Finally, all this experience with coins agrees with our experience with other symmetric objects—all the above statements apply to the event "ace" on the roll of a perfectly symmetric die if 1/6 is substituted for 1/2, and so forth.

On the basis of all this experience we proceed to construct a "model" of the long-run behavior of a tossed coin. This model asserts that the fraction of tosses resulting in heads is almost certain to be almost exactly 1/2 if the coin is tossed indefinitely, and it asserts further that in a very long run half the heads will be followed by heads, half the runs of two heads will be followed by third heads, and so forth. We expect, furthermore, that any reasonable man either will adopt this same model on the basis of his own experience or will adopt it as soon as he is informed of the very great amount of experience which other people have had on the point.

Now such a model of the long-run behavior of a tossed coin says nothing directly about the probability of heads on any particular toss. It predicts what would happen in a very large number of tosses and says nothing whatever about any individual toss. Such a prediction is exactly analogous to a prediction that the average diameter of parts produced by a certain machine will be 1.037 inches, and it is obvious that a predicted average diameter and a probability are not the same thing.

On the other hand, a reasonable man will clearly take account of long-run behavior in assigning probabilities. If he believes that a certain coin would fall heads half the time when tossed repeatedly under a certain set of conditions, and if he has no way of predicting which particular tosses will be heads, he will assign probability 1/2 to the event "heads" on any one toss—he will pay neither more nor less for the right to receive a prize conditional on heads on a particular toss than he will pay for the right to receive the same prize conditional on tails. In general, we shall assume it to be a characteristic of reasonable behavior that:

■ If a person assessing the probability of a given event on one trial under a given set of conditions feels virtually sure that the event would occur with *relative frequency p* in a very great number of trials made under conditions indistinguishable from the given conditions, he will assign *probability p* to the event on the one trial in which he is interested.

6.3.3
Limited Experience

It is only rarely that experience with a given kind of event will be as overwhelming as it is for "heads" on the toss of a coin, but even when experience is limited it is still a guide to reasonable assessment of probabilities. Suppose, for example, that we wish to assess the probability of ace on the next roll of a die which has been deformed in such a way that it is no longer symmetric. General experience with rolled objects will lead us to adopt a model of die behavior which is like the coin model except that the fraction of aces is unknown. Our experience is sufficient to lead us to predict that in the long run the relative frequency of ace would become and remain nearly equal to *some* fraction *p*, that ace would be followed by ace with this *same* relative frequency, and so forth, even though our experience is not adequate for a prediction of the exact value of this frequency.

Obviously such an "incomplete" model does not tell us exactly what probability to assign to ace. We can say that *if* we had had enough experience with the die to feel sure that the long-run relative frequency of ace would be .15, *then* we would assign probability .15 to ace on any one roll, and so forth; but our problem is not to make statements of this sort, If the consequences of a decision depend on the occurrence of ace on the next roll of the die, we must assess a definite probability for this event in the light of whatever experience we actually have. We must make the most reasonable estimate that we can of the true long-run relative frequency p and then assess a probability which is equal or nearly equal to the estimated frequency.[1]

Two reasonable people may well disagree concerning the probability to be assigned to ace in a situation like this, since neither of them will have had much if any experience with the behavior of a die deformed in exactly the way this one is. Observe, however, that this does not mean that there is *no* relevant experience: if the deformation of the die is slight, we will not consider a person reasonable who assigns probability .01 or .99 to ace.

6.3.4
Learning from Additional Experience

The case of the perfectly symmetric coin and the case of the deformed die differ not only in the amount of agreement to be expected in the initial assessment of the probabilities of heads or ace but also in the way in which further experience affects any one individual's assessments of these same probabilities on subsequent trials. In the case of the perfectly symmetric coin, we might still assess the probability of heads on the next toss at 1/2 even though we had just observed a large number of consecutive heads or tails; our model of the long-run behavior of the coin rests on an extremely great amount of evidence and we may consider this new evidence negligible in comparison. In the case of the asymmetric die, on the contrary, we will use any experience we gather by rolling the die to modify the probability we originally assigned to ace.

Notice, however, that we usually will *not* simply equate the probability of ace on the next roll to the fraction of aces observed in a limited number of rolls. If we roll the die once and it comes up ace, we will not assign probability 1 to ace on the next roll; if we roll it six times and get no ace, we will not assign probability 0 to ace on the next roll. Our assessment of the probability of ace on the next roll will continue to be substantially influenced by our observation of the shape of the die, and the relative importance we attach to the observed shape of the die in comparison with the importance we attach to the observed frequencies is necessarily a matter of subjective judgment.[2]

6.3.5
Application to Business Problems

In exceptional circumstances the probabilities involved in a business problem can be simply equated to "known" relative frequencies in the way probability 1/2 is assigned to heads on the toss of a symmetric coin. If 5% of the last 100,000

---

[1] In Chapter 11 we shall be able to describe a systematic procedure by which a decision maker can fully exploit his experience in making the required estimate; and we shall further be able to show that if the decision maker uses this procedure, then his probability for the event on the next trial should be exactly equal to his estimate of the relative frequency with which it would occur in the long run. See Section 11.4.

[2] See the preceding note.

parts produced by some machine have been defective, if we have no reason either in theory or in observation to believe that defectives occur in "streaks", and if a new production run is to be made under conditions indistinguishable from those under which all these past runs were made, we will be strongly tempted to adopt a model of the behavior of the machine which is exactly like the model of coin behavior discussed above. We will be willing to predict that 5% of all future parts will be defective, that 5% of the defectives will be followed by defectives, etc., and we will not change these predictions whatever the pattern of quality in the next ten or twenty pieces produced.

In the majority of cases, however, the problem will not be so simple. If the machine is new or has just been repaired, or if the tooling is becoming worn, or if a new operator is employed, or if a slightly off-standard batch of raw material is received, we will be in the same position that we are when we assess our probability for ace on a roll of a slightly deformed die. The probability assigned to defective on the first piece will depend on "judgment" in the sense that two reasonable men may well assign different values. This probability will be revised as more experience is gained, and again judgment will determine the relative weights given to the observed frequencies on the one hand and to other kinds of evidence on the other.

6.3.6
Indistinguishable Conditions

Now that we have looked at some examples of the use of long-run relative frequencies as a basis for the assessment of probabilities, it is time to take a closer look at the set of trials over which the relative frequency of an event is to be measured.

Observe first of all that we have talked about the relative frequency with which an event would occur in a long series of trials made under "*indistinguishable*" conditions, not about relative frequency on trials made under the "same" or "identical" conditions. If the expression "identical conditions" means anything at all, it presumably means conditions such that if a particular event occurs on one trial, that same event will occur on all trials; whereas trials may be said to be made under "indistinguishable" conditions if just before any one trial is made the prevailing conditions do not *seem to the decision maker* to be either more or less favorable to the occurrence of any particular event than they seem just before any other trial is made. More concretely:

- ■ The conditions under which various trials are made may be said to be ≪indistinguishable≫ for a particular decision maker if that decision maker would be neither more nor less willing to bet on a particular event of any one trial just before that trial is made than he would be to bet on that same event of any other trial just before that other trial is made.

Trials which are indistinguishable to one person may be distinguishable to a better informed person, but this is just the usual state of affairs when decisions are made under uncertainty. Each individual decision maker must base his decision exclusively on what he himself knows or believes, not on what truly is or on what some better informed person knows or believes.

6.3.7
Assertion under
Indistinguishable Conditions

Now consider a decision maker who makes, or is capable of making, a series of "assertions", each of which concerns a different physical phenomenon. For example, the decision maker may first assert that it will rain on June 30; he may next assert that at least 20,000 units of Product X will be sold before the end of the current fiscal year; he may next assert that his company will win a certain contract if it submits a proposal; and so forth. Even though each assertion concerns a different physical phenomenon, we can still think of the whole series of assertions as a series of "trials" all of which are alike in the sense that each one either will or will not result in the event "the assertion is correct".

What is more, it may perfectly well be true of some particular series of assertions that the decision maker who makes them regards them all as "equally likely" to be correct. He would be neither more nor less willing to bet on the correctness of any one of the assertions in the series at the moment he makes it than he would be to bet on the correctness of any other assertion in the series at the moment he makes that other assertion. If the decision maker does in fact hold this attitude of indifference toward the assertions in any particular series, then we may say that these "assertion trials" are made under conditions which are indistinguishable in the sense defined in the previous section, despite the fact that the various assertions do not involve the same physical phenomenon.

6.3.8
Relative Frequency of Correct Assertion

When a particular series of assertions is or might be made under indistinguishable conditions, the implications for the assessment of probabilities are exactly the same as when any other series of trials is made under indistinguishable conditions. Specifically: (1) if the decision maker knows for certain what fraction p of all these assertions are or would be correct, he should assign probability p to the correctness of any one assertion in the series, and (2) even if he does not know the fraction p for certain, he will be guided by whatever he does know or believe about this fraction when he assesses his probability for the correctness of any one assertion.

It is, of course, only rarely that a decision maker has occasion to assess his probability for the correctness of an assertion as such, but the fact that such probabilities can sometimes be based on beliefs about the long-run "relative frequency of correct assertion" is of very considerable practical importance because it can be of great help in assessing probabilities for the events that are actually involved in a practical decision problem. We shall give an example of a practical application as soon as we have made the logic clear by a very simple artificial example.

Consider a person who, after inspecting two stones labelled respectively *A* and *B*, has guessed that *A* is heavier than *B* but also wishes to assign a definite numerical probability to the event "*A* is heavier than *B*"; the fact of the matter will ultimately be settled by carefully weighing the two stones. Clearly this person cannot find a useful frequency basis for his probability assessment by imagining a long series of pairs of stones labelled *A* and *B* and trying to estimate the relative frequency with which the stone labelled *A* would in fact be the heavier one; nor can he find a useful frequency basis by thinking about the frequency with which this particular stone labelled *A* would turn out to be heavier than this particular stone labelled *B* in a long series of weighings. He can, however, find a frequency basis by thinking about the long-run frequency with which *he* could *guess* which stone was heavier if he were to be presented with long series of pairs of stones such that the two stones in every pair *seemed to him* to be just about as much alike as the two stones in the pair with which he is actually confronted.

If he has been allowed to pick up the two stones and has observed that *A* feels quite definitely heavier than *B*, he may conclude that he would go wrong concerning so large an apparent difference only about one time in a thousand, say. If so, he will assess at .999 the probability that his guess concerning the relative weights is correct on this one occasion; and therefore he will assign probability .999 to the event "*A* is heavier than *B*". If he has not been allowed to pick up the stone and has merely observed that *A* looks somewhat bigger than *B*, he may decide that if he guessed on the basis of only this much evidence which stone was heavier in a long series of pairs, he would guess right only about 2/3 of the time. If so, he will assess at 2/3 the probability that his guess is correct on this one occasion; and therefore he will assign probability 2/3 to the event "*A* is heavier than *B*". If he has not even seen the two stones and knows nothing at all about them, he may conclude that in a completely blind choice he would in the long run identify the heavier stone correctly on only 1/2 of all occasions. If so, he will assign probability 1/2 to the event "*A* is heavier than *B*".

As an example of the practical application of the principle just illustrated, consider a marketing manager who believes that a certain new product will "probably" succeed if placed on the market but who also wishes to quantify this judgment by assessing a definite numerical probability of success. He cannot usefully think about the long-run relative frequency with which this product would succeed if it were placed on the market repeatedly; but he can get a frequency basis for his assessment by first mentally summarizing the available evidence bearing on the success or failure of this product and then guessing how often he would go wrong in predicting success if he were to predict success for many different products concerning each of which the evidence seemed to favor success just about as strongly as it favors the success of the present product.

The true long-run frequency of correct prediction will of course almost never be known with certainty in situations like the one just described, but it is important to observe that neither will the decision maker often be forced to make a completely blind guess at the frequency with which he could predict correctly. A person does not in general get to be a marketing manager before he has had considerable experience in marketing, and in the course of this experience he will ordinarily have had many occasions to predict success for new products manufactured by his own company or its competitors. By thinking back to those earlier predictions which have been proved either correct or false, he is likely to find a fairly solid basis for his guess at the relative frequency with which he would now go wrong in such predictions.

6.3.9
The True Chance of an Event

Although we have insisted from the outset that a decision maker's probability for an event is necessarily a personal decision on the fraction of balls which must correspond to this event in that decision maker's equivalent urn, we have also frequently said that this decision should reflect or quantify the decision maker's judgment about the chance that the event in question will in fact occur (or has already occurred). Such language implies, of course, that something that can be called "the", or "the true", chance of an event actually exists, distinct from the decision maker's evaluation thereof; and we can now define the expression "true chance" as simply a shorter way of saying "relative frequency in a sequence of indistinguishable trials".

Our earlier discussion of the meaning of indistinguishable trials should make it clear, however, that we cannot know what is meant by the true chance of any particular event in any particular situation unless we know exactly what trials the decision maker would consider indistinguishable from the present trial. In this sense, even the "true" chance of an event is a subjective quantity, since it is always an individual decision maker who decides what trials are indistinguishable to him.

In a few particularly simple kinds of situations, we may feel sure that all reasonable decision makers would define the true chance of an event with respect to the same sequence of indistinguishable trials. If, for example, someone speaks of the true chance that a certain coin will come up heads if it is tossed in a certain way, we can be quite sure that what he means is the relative frequency with which heads would come up in a series of trials each of which consists of tossing that particular coin in that particular manner.

In most situations, however, the identity of the trials with respect to which a true chance is defined will not be at all obvious and will have to be carefully specified before we can know what is meant by the chance in question. For example, suppose that an engineer asserts that there is a 1/10 chance that a certain pressure vessel will burst if it is put to a certain abnormal use. On the one hand, he may mean that if a very large number of such vessels were put to this use, 1/10 of all the vessels would burst. On the other hand, he may think that if a large number of such vessels were all put to this use, either all or none of them would burst; and if so, then what he means by saying that there is a 1/10 chance that this vessel will burst is that if he were to consider a long series of physically quite different trials on each of which some one event seemed to him as likely to occur as the event "burst" on the present trial, then 1/10 of all these seemingly equally likely events would in fact occur.

6.3.10
Use of Experts' Opinions about Chances

In many situations a decision maker who wishes to assess his probability for some event will feel that there is some "expert" who knows far more than he does about the objective facts that should be considered in making the assessment. In such a situation the decision maker can if he likes ask the expert to describe and explain all the relevant facts, after which the decision maker can try to weigh all these facts properly in assessing his probability, but usually a much simpler procedure will lead to a much better result. The decision maker can ask his expert simply to give him an estimate of the chance that the event will actually occur (or has actually occurred), and he can then base his own probability for the event on this estimate.

For example, consider Mr. A. H. Mallon's problem of assessing his probability for the event "stampings work". We have previously suggested that before assessing this probability Mallon would ask his engineers for all relevant facts about the suitability of stampings for the purpose at hand, but unless Mallon is himself an expert in production engineering, this is probably not the way in which he really should or would proceed. He will probably take much more correct account of the relevant technical facts if he asks his chief production engineer to estimate the chance that stampings will work and then bases his own probability for this event on his engineer's estimate.

The fact that a decision maker should often ask an expert to estimate the chance of an event does not imply, however, that the decision maker should then assess his probability for the event by simply *equating* it to the chance quoted by the expert. For example, suppose that Mallon asks an expert to estimate the chance of the event "stampings work", and suppose that the expert answers that it is about 4/5. Before Mallon assesses any probability at all for the event, he may do well to imagine that use of stampings in the present context is just one of a great number of minor technical innovations for each of which this *same expert* has quoted this *same 4/5 chance* of success, and he should then ask himself what fraction of all these hypothetical innovations he, Mallon, thinks would *really* succeed. It is this fraction which is the "true" chance of the event "stampings work" in this example, and all that the expert has given or can give Mallon is his best guess at this true chance.

If now Mallon has no reason to think that his expert would either over-estimate or underestimate the fraction of successes, then Mallon may conclude that his own best guess at the fraction of successes is equal to his expert's, viz. 4/5, and therefore he may reasonably assess his probability for the event "stampings work" at 4/5. If, however, the expert is a person who in Mallon's opinion tends to be either overoptimistic or overpessimistic about the success of minor techni-cal innovations, Mallon may conclude that innovations which look as promising to the expert as stampings do on this occasion would in fact succeed either much less often or much more often than the expert thinks they would. In either case, Mallon's best guess at the fraction of successes in his imaginary sequence of innovations may be quite different from the 4/5 chance quoted by the expert for each innovation, and accordingly his probability for the event "stampings work" may be quite different from 4/5.

6.3.11
Calibration of Experts

A decision maker will of course be in a much better position to revise an ex-pert's estimate of a true chance if he has definite, quantitative data bearing on the expert's ability to estimate chances correctly than he will be if all that he has is qualitative information about the expert's psychological set. As an extreme ex-ample, suppose that, before the XYZ problem ever arose, Mr. A. H. Mallon had asked his chief production engineer to estimate the chance of success of some minor technological innovation on each of a large number of occasions; suppose that on 100 of these occasions the expert had given 4/5 as his estimate; suppose that the innovation in question actually succeeded on only 3/5 of these 100 occa-sions; and suppose that the chief production engineer now gives 4/5 as his esti-mate of the chance of the event "stampings work". Provided that all these 100 "trials" are indistinguishable to Mallon, Mallon will be justified in thinking that 3/5 is a thoroughly reasonable estimate of the true chance of success when his ex-pert quotes a 4/5 chance, and he will therefore be justified in assessing 3/5 as his probability for the event "stampings work".

It is of course very unlikely that a decision maker who wishes to revise an expert's estimate of the chance of some event will have anything like the amount of directly relevant historical data that we supposed Mr. Mallon to have in the extreme example we have just discussed. Even though the expert has esti-mated chances on a number of previous occasions, few if any of these previous estimates will have been exactly equal to the current estimate that the decision maker wishes to revise. In such a situation, the decision maker will be unable to revise the estimate by the very simple logic he could use if on 100 previous occasions the expert had quoted exactly the same chance he now quotes, but the historical record will nevertheless constitute a reasonably solid basis for revision of the expert's current estimate if it is properly exploited by a more complex logic known as regression analysis.

The actual technique of regression analysis is a subject for advanced books on statistics rather than an introductory text, but fortunately the businessman has no need to know anything about the technique as such. All that he needs to know is that by use of this technique, a properly trained statistician can take any new estimate of a true chance that an expert may make and revise this estimate in a way which takes correct logical account, not only of all historical data bearing on the accuracy with which this expert can estimate chances, but also of the businessman's own judgments about his expert's accuracy.

6.4
TENTATIVE ASSESSMENT AND
SENSITIVITY ANALYSIS

It is only rarely that a decision maker will be able to assess probabilities by simply equating them to long-run relative frequencies that he knows for certain. Usually, he will have only incomplete information about relevant long-run frequencies if he has any, and consequently he will usually find it hard to decide on his probabilities for the events on an event fork—to decide, i.e., exactly what fraction of the balls in an urn must be labelled with the name of each event in order to make the urn equivalent to the event fork for him. He can, of course, ultimately reach a definite decision on his probabilities just as he can reach a definite decision on any other matter that confronts him; but obtaining and weighing all the information needed to reach a really careful definite decision may require a very substantial expenditure of time and effort.

It is fortunate, therefore, that it is frequently unnecessary to reach a really definite decision concerning a set of probabilities. Instead of trying to reach such a decision concerning every event fork on his diagram before even beginning the actual analysis of his problem, the decision maker will often do well to make "tentative" assessments of his probabilities, analyze his decision problem on the basis of these tentative assessments, and then carry out a "sensitivity analysis" aimed at determining the effects of changes in these assessments on the values of the available immediate acts. This procedure will often lead to a clear conclusion that no reasonable changes in the probabilities assigned to many of the event forks in the decision diagram could have any material effect on the ranking of the available immediate acts; and if the procedure does lead to such a conclusion, then it is only as regards his probabilities for the remaining event forks that the decision maker will have to go to the trouble of making really careful, final decisions.

6.5
DELEGATION OF THE AUTHORITY TO DECIDE

In all of our previous discussion of probabilities, we have assumed that the decision maker himself will assess all the probabilities required for the analysis of his problem, even though some of these assessments may be based on the opinions of experts concerning the true chances of various events. It is, however, only in the simplest decision problems and the smallest business organizations that this can actually happen. In even an only moderately complex problem in an only moderately large organization, the executive ultimately responsible for the final decision would clearly be unable to participate directly in more than a tiny fraction of all the probability assessments required. The great majority of the assessments will have to be made by appropriate subordinates and accepted by the ultimate decision maker without review.

It may seem at first glance that an executive who bases an important decision in whole or in part on probabilities that he has not personally assessed is in effect failing to act in accordance with his responsibility for the final decision itself, but in reality he is simply doing what executives in all but the smallest organizations must always do in exercising their responsibilities. If we recall that the assessment of a probability is a decision, neither more nor less, we see that an executive who relies on probabilities assessed by subordinates is simply delegating to these subordinates his authority to make decisions on various detailed aspects of a larger decision problem, and such delegation is an essential part of almost all decision making. Just as an executive who is ultimately responsible for all aspects of the construction and equipment of a new plant will normally delegate virtually all the detailed decisions on specific pieces of equipment to appropriately qualified subordinates, so an executive who is ultimately responsible for the final decision in a complex decision problem can delegate virtually all the detailed decisions on equivalent urns for specific event forks to appropriately qualified subordinates. In both cases, the executive takes full responsibility for all the decisions made by his subordinates even though he does not personally review the reasoning behind more than a very few of these decisions. In both cases the executive delegates, not in order to avoid his responsibility, but in order better to carry out his responsibility.

In many situations, systematic analysis of decision problems by use of probabilities and preferences can actually permit a top executive to play a much more direct role in reaching a final decision than he can play when decision problems are analyzed by less systematic methods. Traditionally, complete real-world decision problems are often delegated to subordinates because the top executive simply cannot be familiar enough with the facts of the situation to reach a responsible decision himself, but this kind of delegation is attended by an extremely serious difficulty. The subordinate's real-world decision will depend, not only on probabilities which he is better qualified to assess than the top executive, but also on his own descriptions of consequences and his own likings for consequences as thus described, and these descriptions and likings may be greatly different from the top executive's. In particular, the subordinate may take a much shorter-run view of consequences than the top executive, and he may be much more averse to risk. Such conflict of objectives will be avoided if the top executive delegates to the subordinate only the assessment of the probabilities that the subordinate is peculiarly qualified to assess and reserves for himself the description of consequences and the assessment of preferences that express his own likings for consequences and attitudes toward risk.

6.6
SUMMARY

6.6.1
Rules of Consistency

The fact that a decision maker's probability for any event on any event fork is by definition the fraction of balls corresponding to that event in his equivalent urn for that fork implies that probabilities must obey the following rules of consistency:

1 A probability must be a number between 0 and 1.

2 Given any list of mutually exclusive events, the probability that some one or another of the events on the list will occur must be equal to the sum of the probabilities of the individual events on the list.

3 The sum of the probabilities of a set of mutually exclusive and collectively exhaustive events must be 1.

6.6.2
Dependence of Probabilities
on Acts and Events

The probabilities it is reasonable to assign to the events on a given event fork will often depend on acts and/or events on the path from the origin to the base of the event fork in question. As regards dependence on events,

■ The probability that it is reasonable to assign to an event X may depend on another event Y for many different reasons among which are the following: (1) the occurrence of Y has a direct causal effect on the chance that X will occur, (2) the occurrence of Y constitutes evidence concerning a common factor that has a causal effect on the chances of both X and Y, (3) the decision maker has information which bears on the chance that X and Y will occur *together*.

6.6.3
Probability and Relative Frequency

1 Consider a fixed list of possible events and a sequence of trials on each of which some one of the events on the list will occur. If just before each trial is made each event seems to a particular decision maker to be just as likely to occur on that trial as on any other, in the sense that he would be just as ready to bet on that event on any one trial as on any other, the trials may be said to be ≪indistinguishable≫ to that decision maker.

The events may be occurrences of some physical phenomenon (e.g., "heads" on a toss of a coin or "demand for 3 units" on a particular day) which can be defined without reference to the decision maker, but they may equally well be correct assertions by the decision maker concerning phenomena which are physically quite different but which nevertheless seem to the decision maker equally likely to occur (e.g., prediction of the winner in a sequence of unrelated athletic matches).

2 If a decision maker knows for certain the long-run relative frequency with which an event would occur if indistinguishable trials were repeated indefinitely, he should set his probability for the event on any one trial equal to this long-run relative frequency, which may be called the "true chance" of the event.

3 If a decision maker does not know for certain the long-run relative frequency with which an event would occur on indistinguishable trials but does know the relative frequency with which the event occurred on some finite number of trials, he must consider both this historical evidence and any other relevant information he may have when he assesses his probability for the event on the next trial.

4 A decision maker who would predict or assert that a certain event will occur will often do well to assess his probability for the event indirectly, by imagining a long sequence of similar assertions and estimating the fraction that would prove correct.

5 In situations where an expert estimates the chance of some event at some particular value p, the decision maker will often do well to assess his probability for the event by (1) imagining a long sequence of occasions on each of which this same expert gives this same estimate of the chance of some event, and (2) making his own estimate of the fraction of all such occasions on which the event would in fact occur.

6.6.4
Tentative Assessment and Sensitivity Analysis

Instead of reaching a definite decision on his probabilities for a given set of mutually exclusive events, a decision maker will often do well to make tentative assessments very quickly and then test whether any reasonable changes in these tentative assessments could affect his choice of an immediate act.

6.6.5
Delegation of Assessment

Except in very small organizations, the executive who is ultimately responsible for a decision problem will usually be unable personally to assess, or decide on, more than a very few of the probabilities required for analysis of the problem. Decisions on most of the probabilities will have to be delegated to subordinates, in exactly the same way that most other decisions on details are delegated to subordinates.

EXERCISES

6.1 In trying to assess his probability for each possible value of tomorrow's demand for weegie boards, Mr. F. A. Farthing first decided that there was a .2 chance of demand for less than 2, a .5 chance of demand for 2 or 3, and a .3 chance of demand for 4 or 5. He then thought again about the problem, making a different grouping of the possible values of demand, and decided that there was a .3 chance of demand for 1 or 2, a .4 chance of demand for 3 or 4, and a .3 chance of demand for either 0 or more than 4. Finally, he decided that the most likely thing was a demand for somewhere between 2 and 4 inclusive, and that the chance of this event was .6.

   a Are Farthing's decisions mutually consistent?

   b Do they logically determine Farthing's probability for each possible value of demand?

6.2 Suppose that you are offered a gamble in which you will win $1.50 if a silver dollar comes up heads when tossed by a certain machine but will lose $1.00 if the dollar does not come up heads. To allay any misgivings you have about its honesty, the house gives you as much time as you need to inspect the machine and to run any test you care to run before you announce your decision to accept or reject the gamble.

   a Suppose that you visually inspect the machine, decide that so far as you can tell it is perfectly "fair", and therefore assess at 1/2 your probability for the event "heads" on the next toss of the dollar. If you had to make your decision at this point, would you accept the gamble?

   b Suppose that after making the assessment in (*a*) but before announcing any decision concerning the gamble you let the machine toss the dollar 10 times and heads occurs on 4 of these tosses. If at this point you had to make your decision, would you accept the gamble?

   c Same as (*b*) except that heads occurs on 40 out of 100 tosses.

   d Same as (*b*) except that heads occurs on 400 out of 1,000 tosses.

   e Same as (*b*) except that heads occurs on 4,000 out of 10,000 tosses.

6.3 Assess your probability for the event that Harvard will win the Harvard-Yale football game this fall. What relative frequencies, if any, seem relevant to you in making your assessment?

6.4 A manufacturer asks his chief engineer what the chances are that a certain pressure vessel will burst if it is used for a particular purpose for which it was not designed. The chief engineer answers 1 chance in 10.

    a If you were in the manufacturer's position and felt that the engineer knew incomparably more than you did about stresses and bursts, how would you go about assessing your probability for the event that the tank will burst if you use it for the purpose in question?

    b Same as (*a*) except that since the chief engineer first gave you his opinion you have already succeeded in using the tank for the purpose in question nine times and are now proposing to use it a tenth time. You and the engineer agree that the tank has not been weakened in the least by being used nine times previously; the engineer insists that the chance of a burst is therefore still 1 in 10.

6.5 National Grain Corporation

In early 1969, Peter Reynolds, President of the National Grain Corporation, met with Richard McIlvaine, a management consultant, to discuss an administrative problem which had troubled Mr. Reynolds for some time. This problem concerned the extent to which authority was to be delegated to the chief officers of National's operating subsidiaries and the means to be taken to ensure that decentralized decision making would lead to results consistent with the corporation's objectives. The importance of these questions had become increasingly clear as National proceeded, during the late 1960's, to implement an aggressive program of expansion by merger with companies operating in diverse fields largely unrelated to National's traditional and primary focus of activity—the purchase, storage, processing, and domestic and export sale of food and feed grains.

    Reynolds was aware that in many instances neither he nor any other executive at corporate headquarters was equipped to judge the crucial uncertainties on which the major strategic decisions of the subsidiary companies hinged. On the other hand, it seemed unmistakably evident that managers of subsidiaries could not be allowed to "go on making their moves as if they were still playing for peanuts—forgetting that we've got tens of millions ready to back them up and that we're willing to take some risks to get the growth we need." Reynolds explained to McIlvaine that in assessing a proposed merger with a company they placed the strength and quality of the management of the company at the very top of the list. "That is because we know we have to delegate, and I do it with great confidence," he explained. "These men have proved they know how to run their businesses. Trouble is, there *is* a difference between how to run a small, independent company and how to run a National subsidiary, and I'm lecturing them on it all the time. But somehow they always go back to thinking small."

In the course of his study, McIlvaine learned that National's traditional lines of business offered low return on investment and limited opportunities for growth. Profits from these lines fluctuated substantially and seemingly uncontrollably with changes in commodity prices, export demand, and governmental agricultural policy. A substantial fraction of the stock was controlled by descendants of the founder, and these stockholders frequently admonished management that the company's prime goal should be long-run growth; year-to-year profit fluctuations, though of some concern, were of secondary importance. As a result, top corporate management showed very little aversion to risk in normal years over the range of financial results that were thought to be reasonably likely, although with respect to great uncertainties involving possibly large swings in their financial results they tended to be rather more risk averse, especially in years in which the economic environment was unfavorable for their commodity trade.

In talking to the top managers of several National Grain subsidiaries, McIlvaine found that these companies typically manufactured products of great technological sophistication sold in rapidly growing and highly competitive markets, in which success was largely dependent on direction and speed of new-product development efforts. Officers of these subsidiaries tended to feel that ignorance of their problems and of their realistic prospects at the headquarters level was more of a threat than an opportunity for them. "One or two bad years and they'd have me either looking for another job or riding a grain elevator in Kansas City," the president of a New England subsidiary claimed. "After all, they'd never understand my explanations and they'd have no basis for judging whether I'd done a lousy job under good conditions or a superb job under stinking conditions. Give them an excuse —one or two bad profit years—and they'll pull the rug right out from under us. They keep egging me on to take what I regard as huge risks—Reynolds particularly wants me to do things that just don't make sense for a company as small as we are. Sure they have the money to bail us out, and Reynolds is well aware that it'd be my neck rather than his if that should happen. Besides, even if I were working only for myself there are plenty of chances I just wouldn't want to take no matter how good the odds were in my favor. In any event, as good as their management is, I just don't see how they can tell me whether a risk is worth taking or not."

If you were in Mr. McIlvaine's position, what advice would you give Mr. Reynolds as regards the way in which important decisions concerning the operations of National's subsidiaries should be reached and the way in which the managers of the subsidiaries should be judged? What problems are likely to arise if your advice is adopted, and how should Mr. Reynolds try to deal with these problems?

CHAPTER

7

UNCERTAIN QUANTITIES, PROBABILITY DISTRIBUTIONS, AND EXPECTATIONS

The diagrams of many business decision problems contain event forks representing the possible values of an uncertain quantity such as the amount of some product that could be sold during the next year or the number of defectives that will be produced in the next run of some machine. Since there is a possible event corresponding to every possible value of the uncertain quantity, such forks often have a very large number of branches, and when they do, they give rise to some problems that we must now examine.

First of all, the mere description of such a fork presents a problem. A fan like the one in Figure 2.2 (page 35) will serve to show the place of the fork in the diagram of the decision problem, but it offers no place to record the probabilities assigned to its branches. In principle this problem can be solved by listing the branches rather than diagramming them, but frequently the number of branches is so great that even this device becomes very awkward. An even more serious problem arises when we come to assessment of the probabilities for all the branches on the fork, since no decision maker can possibly sit down and think out separately the probability he wants to assign to each of a thousand or ten thousand possible values of the uncertain quantity. And finally, supposing that the assessment problem has somehow been solved, a serious computational problem arises when we try to evaluate the decision maker's preference or mathematical expectation for the uncertain monetary value represented by an event fork with thousands of branches.

All these problems will be dealt with in this chapter and the next, but not exactly in the order we have listed them. Postponing the problem of assessment until the next chapter, we shall deal with purely mechanical problems in the present chapter.

1. In Section 7.1 we define certain terms that are needed for discussion of uncertain quantities and show how a whole set of probabilities assigned to the possible values of an uncertain quantity can be described by a graph.

2. In Section 7.2 we define various "summary measures" which describe particular aspects of such a set of probabilities and which are frequently useful either in assessing the probabilities or in using them after they have been assessed.

3. In Section 7.3 we discuss certain problems that arise when the decision maker has assigned probabilities to the possible values of some "underlying" uncertain quantity such as customer demand but is really interested in some function of this uncertain quantity such as contribution to overhead and profit.

4. In Section 7.4 we face the computational problems that arise when nonzero probability has been assigned to so many possible values of an uncertain quantity that it is not practical to take account of each of these probabilities individually, and we show how adequate approximations to exact results can be obtained either by hand or with the aid of a digital computer.

5. Finally, in Section 7.5 we discuss a short-cut method for computing expectations of functions which are of a certain special but very common type.

The present chapter consists almost entirely of definitions and rules, with almost no examples of their use in analyzing decision problems. For this reason it may appear to the reader that we are introducing more new concepts than can possibly be really needed, but in actual fact every one of these concepts will prove essential to the analysis of practical decision problems.

The text and exercises of this chapter are designed to be studied in the following order:

1 Section 7.1.1 and Exercise 7.1.

2 Sections 7.1.2–7.1.3 and 7.1.5 and Exercise 7.2.

3 Section 7.1.4 and Exercises 7.3–7.4.

4 Section 7.2.1 and Exercise 7.5.

5 Sections 7.2.2–7.2.4 and Exercise 7.6.

6 Sections 7.2.5–7.2.6 and Exercise 7.7.

7 Sections 7.3.1–7.3.2 and Exercise 7.8*a* and *b*.

8 Sections 7.3.3–7.3.5 and Exercises 7.8*c*–7.10.

9 Sections 7.4.1–7.4.3 and Exercise 7.11.

10 Sections 7.4.4–7.4.6 and Exercise 7.12.

CONTENTS OF CHAPTER 7

1.
Probability Distributions, Mass Functions, and Cumulative Functions

1 Definitions
2 Exact Graphs of Mass and Cumulative Functions
3 Smooth Graphs of Mass and Cumulative Functions
4 Relations between the Shapes of Mass and Cumulative Functions
5 Notation

2.
Summary Measures of a Probability Distribution

1 Modes of a Distribution
2 Median of a Distribution
3 Fractiles of a Distribution
4 Identification of Fractiles by Use of a Smooth Graph
5 Mean of a Distribution or Expectation of an Uncertain Quantity
6 Relations among Mean, Median, and Mode
7 Variance and Standard Deviation of a Distribution

3.
Functions of an Uncertain Quantity

1 An Example
2 Definition of a Function of a UQ
3 Distribution of a Function of a Discrete UQ
4 Expectation of a Function of a Discrete UQ
5 Summary

4.
Approximation of an Expectation

1 An Example of Approximate Computation
2 Alternative Description of the Method of Computation
3 Grouped Approximations to Probability Distributions

4 Equiprobable Groups
5 Bracket Medians
6 Construction of Grouped Approximations Using Bracket Medians
7 Size of Groups and Accuracy of Approximation
8 Use of a Digital Computer

5.
Expectations of Linear Functions

1 A Common Error
2 Expectation of a Linear Function
3 Functions Linear over the Range of a UQ
4 A Common Variant of the Common Error
5 Use of Expectations in the Analysis of Decision Problems

6.
Summary

1 Definitions and Notation
2 Graphs
3 Summary Measures of a Distribution
4 Functions of a UQ
5 Grouped Approximations
6 Linear Functions

Appendix

Description of Computer Program *Smooth*

7.1
PROBABILITY DISTRIBUTIONS,
MASS FUNCTIONS, AND CUMULATIVE FUNCTIONS

7.1.1
Definitions

The reader will find it essential to keep the following definitions of technical terms absolutely clear in his mind. We first distinguish between what we shall call possible and impossible values of an ≪uncertain quantity≫, or UQ for short.

- ■ Any value which an uncertain quantity cannot have because of the way in which its value will be measured will be called an ≪impossible value≫ of the UQ and will be automatically assumed to have zero probability. Any value that is not excluded for this reason will be called a ≪possible value≫ of the UQ, whether or not it has zero probability in the decision maker's judgment.

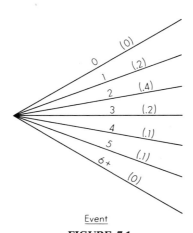

Event

FIGURE 7.1

Event Fork Representing the UQ "Number of Units Demanded Tomorrow"

If a retailer is analyzing a decision problem in which profit depends on demand for a prepackaged product, and if the retailer would force anyone demanding a fraction of one unit to convert his demand into a demand for either no unit or one unit, then we shall say that 2.7, for example, is an impossible value of the UQ "number of units demanded tomorrow"; but we shall say that 1 million is a possible value of this UQ even if the decision maker feels absolutely sure that demand cannot exceed 5. If a production manager has instructed an operator to measure the diameter of pieces turned out on a certain lathe to the nearest hundredth (of an inch), then we shall say that 1/3 and .237 are impossible values of the UQ "diameter of the next piece turned out"; but we shall say that 15.00 is a possible value of this UQ even if the blueprint calls for 25.50 and the production manager feels sure this operator would never deviate from specifications by more than .03.

With this distinction between possible and impossible values of a UQ in mind, we can proceed to our next definition.

■ An uncertain quantity will be called ≪discrete≫ if its possible values can be listed.

The UQ "number of units demanded tomorrow" in the example described above is discrete because its possible values can be listed as 0, 1, 2, etc. The UQ "diameter of next piece produced" is discrete because its possible values are .00, .01, .02, etc.[1]

Suppose now that a retailer has assigned the probabilities shown on the event fork in Figure 7.1 and in Column 2 of Table 7.1 to the possible values of the

[1] Discrete UQ's are the only UQ's that we shall study in this introductory text. We shall encounter some decision problems that involve UQ's which are not discrete—e.g., the fraction defective that a machine would generate in an "infinite number" of trials—but we shall find that in all such problems we can get excellent approximations to exact answers by treating the UQ *as if* it were discrete.

TABLE 7.1
Probability Distribution of the UQ
"Number of Units Demanded Tomorrow"

1	2	3
Number Demanded	*Probability of Demand for:*	
d	*d*	*d or less*
0	0	0
1	.2	.2
2	.4	.6
3	.2	.8
4	.1	.9
5	.1	1.0
6 and up	0	1.0
	1.0	

discrete UQ "number of units demanded tomorrow". In order to have a convenient name for a complete list of probabilities like the one in Column 2 of Table 7.1, we next agree that:

■ A list showing for each possible value of a discrete UQ the probability that the UQ will have exactly that value will be said to define the ≪mass function≫ of the UQ.

(When we refer to "the" probability of an event as we do in this definition, we mean, of course, the probability as assessed by some particular decision maker. The shorter phrase is always to be taken as an abbreviation, not as a suggestion that an event can have an inherent probability which is something other than the result of some particular person's decision.)

In some situations we will be interested in the probabilities, not of events such as "demand for exactly 3 units", but of events such as "demand for 3 units or less", and the probabilities of all possible events of this sort are shown for our example in Column 3 of Table 7.1. These probabilities were computed from the entries in Column 2 by using a rule first stated in Section 6.1.2: the probability that some one or another of a set of mutually exclusive events will occur is the sum of the probabilities of the individual events. Thus the probability of "1 or less" is the sum of the probabilities of "exactly 0" and "exactly 1", and so forth. Probabilities of events like "demand for 1 or less" are known as ≪cumulative≫ probabilities because they *can* be computed by cumulating the probabilities of events like "demand for 1", whether or not they are in fact so computed in a particular problem.

It is also possible to compute the probabilities of the individual values of a UQ from a complete set of cumulative probabilities. If, for example, we had been given the probabilities in Column 3 of Table 7.1 rather than those in Column 2, we could have computed the probabilities in Column 2 by making use of the fact that the probability of "demand for 3" is the difference between the probability of "demand for 3 or less" and the probability of "demand for 2 or less", and so forth.

We shall use the term ≪probability distribution≫ to denote a complete set of consistent probability assignments in either the form of a mass function or any other form which makes it possible to compute the mass function.

One technical point about cumulative probabilities deserves a remark. Even if an event such as "demand for 2.7 units" is impossible, an event such as "demand for 2.7 units or less" is not impossible, nor will its probability ordinarily be zero—its probability will be equal to the probability of "demand for 2 units or less". With this observation in mind, we give the following definition:

■ A list from which it is possible to read the probability that a discrete UQ will be less than or equal to any given number, positive or negative, will be said to define the ≪cumulative function≫ of the UQ.

The list actually needs to contain only as many entries as there are values of the UQ with nonzero individual probability, since it is only at these values of the UQ that the value of the cumulative function actually changes. In the example of Table 7.1, the entries in Column 3 suffice to show that the probability assigned to "demand for 3½ or less" is .8.

7.1.2
Exact Graphs of Mass and Cumulative Functions

A mass or cumulative function can be much more readily apprehended intuitively if it is presented in the form of a graph rather than a list, and we shall see later that graphs are often also very useful in the actual assessment of mass or cumulative functions.

Graphing a mass function presents no real problems at all, as can be seen by looking at the graph in Figure 7.2A of the mass function in Column 2 of Table 7.1. The horizontal axis shows the possible values of the UQ "number of units demanded"; the height of the bar above each value, when referred to the vertical axis, shows the probability that the UQ is equal to that value.

In graphing a cumulative function, we must remember that such a function has a meaningful value in between as well as at the possible values of the UQ; with this fact in mind it is easy to see that Figure 7.2B is a correct representation of the cumulative function defined by Column 3 of Table 7.1. The height of the graph above any value on the horizontal axis, possible or impossible, shows the probability that the UQ is equal to that value or less; at the points where there is a vertical jump in the graph, a heavy dot indicates where the graph is to be read. The reader should notice, and explain to himself why:

1 There is a jump in the cumulative function at each value of the UQ for which the mass function shows nonzero probability.

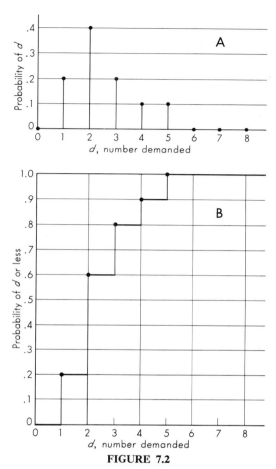

FIGURE 7.2

Probability Distribution of the UQ "Number of Units Demanded Tomorrow"

2 The height of each jump in the cumulative function is equal to the height of the corresponding bar in the mass function.

7.1.3
Smooth Graphs of Mass and
Cumulative Functions

Graphs like those in Figure 7.2 become very tedious to draw when nonzero probability has been assigned to a large number of values of the UQ, and therefore we shall in all such cases use "smooth" graphs that are easier to draw even though they cannot be read correctly without first remembering which are the possible values of the UQ.

Taking another hypothetical probability distribution of demand for some commodity as our example, we show exact graphs of its mass and cumulative functions in Figure 7.3 with smooth graphs of these same functions super-

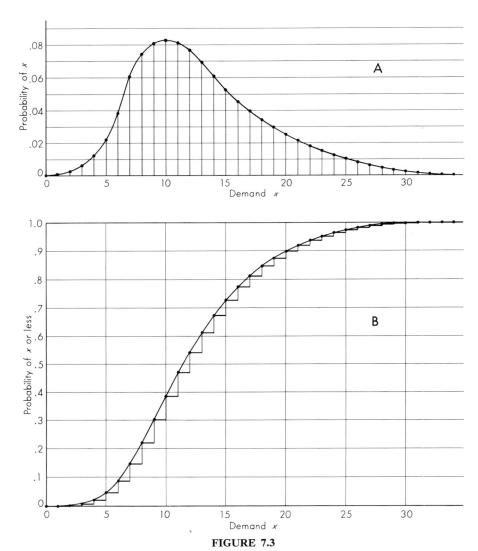

FIGURE 7.3

Exact and Smooth Graphs of a Distribution

posed.[2] Comparing the two graphs of the mass function, the reader will see that the smooth graph (*a*) gives exactly the same probability as the exact graph at any possible value of the UQ, but (*b*) is meaningless at any impossible value. Then comparing the two graphs of the cumulative function, the reader will see that the smooth graph (*a*) again gives exactly the same probability as the exact graph at

[2] Because the vertical scales for the mass functions in these two graphs are not the same as the vertical scales for the cumulative functions, the jumps in the exact graph of the cumulative function are proportional rather than equal to the heights of the corresponding bars in the exact graph of the mass function.

every possible value of the UQ, but (*b*) overstates the probability at any impossible value between the two ends of the curve.

7.1.4
Relations between the Shapes of
Mass and Cumulative Functions

By comparing the two smooth graphs in Figure 7.3, the reader can readily observe that the upward *slope* of the *cumulative* function is great at those values of the UQ at which the *height* of the *mass* function is great, that the slope of the cumulative function is small where the height of the mass function is small, and that the slope of the cumulative function is 0 (the graph is flat) where the height of the mass function is 0.   Then by thinking about the implications of the two remarks at the end of Section 7.1.2, the reader can convince himself that these same relations must hold in any case where (1) the possible values of a UQ are evenly spaced out on the horizontal axis, and (2) the probabilities of these values are all very small and change gradually from one value to the next.   And with a little more thought, the reader can convince himself that the relation can actually be stated in the following stronger form:

■ If (1) the possible values of a UQ are evenly spaced out, and (2) the probabilities of these values are all very small and change gradually from one value to the next, then the *slope* of a smooth graph of the *cumulative* function at any particular value of the UQ will be almost exactly proportional to the *height* of the *mass* function at that value.

Smooth graphs are useful and will be used only when the two conditions of this basic proposition are satisfied; and the reader should convince himself that under these conditions the basic proposition implies the following particular conclusions concerning smooth graphs:

1 A smooth graph of the cumulative function of a UQ will never slope downward.

2 If a smooth graph of the mass function of a UQ has only one peak or ≪local maximum≫ like the curve in Figure 7.3A, a smooth graph of its cumulative function will be S-shaped like the curve in Figure 7.3B—i.e., the direction in which it curves will reverse once and only once.   A cumulative function with many reversals of curvature corresponds to a mass function with many local maxima and minima.

3 If the left end of a smooth graph of the mass function of a UQ rises gradually from 0, the slope of a smooth graph of the cumulative function will be 0 at the outset and increase gradually; and similarly for the right ends.   A cumulative function whose smooth graph runs into the horizontal axis at a sharp angle corresponds to a mass function whose smooth graph has a large jump at the left end, and similarly for the right ends.

7.1.5
Notation

Subsequent discussion of probability distributions of uncertain quantities will be very greatly facilitated by the use of some shorthand notation.

1. Any probability will be denoted by a capital P followed by parentheses enclosing the name of the event whose probability is in question. Thus $P(\text{red})$ will denote the probability that a ball is red, $P(\text{defective})$ will denote the probability that a manufactured part is defective, and so forth.

2. Any uncertain quantity will be denoted by a letter with a tilde (pronounce til'deh) over it; thus we may use $\tilde{d}$ to denote the UQ "tomorrow's demand" or $\tilde{r}$ to denote the UQ "number of defectives in this uninspected lot".

3. We have already seen that to each possible value of a UQ there corresponds a possible event; thus if $\tilde{x}$ denotes demand, $\tilde{x} = 4$ denotes the event "demand for 4". Consequently we may write

$P(\tilde{x} = 4)$: the probability that the UQ $\tilde{x}$ has the value 4.

The symbol $<$ means "less than", $>$ means "greater than", $\leqslant$ and $\geqslant$ mean respectively "less than or equal to" and "greater than or equal to". Thus,

$P(\tilde{x} \leqslant 4)$: the probability that the UQ $\tilde{x}$ has a value less than or
equal to 4, or more briefly, the probability that $\tilde{x}$ has
a value equal to 4 or less.

The following relations between the "tails" of a distribution will give an example of the use of this notation.

$$P(\tilde{x} < 4) + P(\tilde{x} = 4) + P(\tilde{x} > 4) = 1.$$

$$P(\tilde{x} \leqslant 4) = 1 - P(\tilde{x} > 4).$$

$$P(\tilde{x} < 4) = 1 - P(\tilde{x} \geqslant 4).$$

4. We shall often need a symbol which denotes an individual but unspecified *value* of a UQ, and for this purpose we shall use the same letter we use to denote the UQ itself but without the tilde. Thus the horizontal axis of a graph of the cumulative function of the UQ $\tilde{x}$ may be labelled simply x while the vertical axis is labelled $P(\tilde{x} \leqslant x)$. We can write

$$P(\tilde{x} \leqslant x) = 1 - P(\tilde{x} > x)$$

because this relation between the tails of the distribution holds for any particular value x and not just for the value 4 used in our previous illustration.

7.2
SUMMARY MEASURES OF A
PROBABILITY DISTRIBUTION

7.2.1
Modes of a Distribution

When greater probability is assigned to some one value of a discrete UQ than to the values just to either side of it, the value with the greater probability is called a ≪mode≫ of the distribution. If there is only one such value, it is called "the" mode of the distribution. The mode of the distribution in Figure 7.2 is 2.

A smooth graph of the *mass* function of a discrete UQ will have a *local maximum* at each mode, and if the possible values of the UQ are evenly spaced, the *cumulative* function will have *greater slope* at a mode than at neighboring values of the UQ—there will be a reversal of curvature at each mode. The distribution graphed in Figure 7.3 has only one mode, namely the value 10.

Most distributions encountered in business decision problems have only one mode and are called ≪unimodal≫. Distributions with two modes are sometimes of considerable interest; they are called ≪bimodal≫.

7.2.2
Median of a Distribution

Roughly speaking, the ≪median≫ of a distribution is the value of the UQ which "cuts the distribution in half" in the sense that the probability that the UQ will have a value less than the median and the probability that the UQ will have a value greater than the median are both approximately 1/2. The median is precisely defined by the following procedure for identifying it on an exact graph of the cumulative function of the UQ.

  ■ To identify the median of the distribution of a UQ, enter an exact graph of the cumulative function of the UQ at .5 on the vertical axis, read over to the graph, and then read down to find the median on the horizontal axis.[3]

As shown in Figure 7.4, the median of the distribution of Figure 7.3 is 12.

7.2.3
Fractiles of a Distribution

Let k denote any fraction between 0 and 1. Roughly speaking, the ≪k fractile≫ of a distribution is the value of the UQ which divides the distribution in such a

---

[3]This rule differs from the standard definition of medians by identifying one value of the UQ as "the" median of a distribution in some special cases where by the standard definition the distribution would have many other medians in addition to the one singled out by the rule.

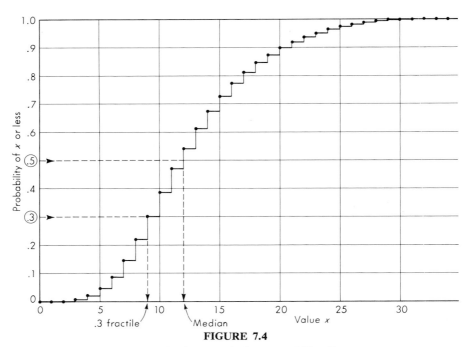

FIGURE 7.4

Determination of a Median and a .3 Fractile

way that the probability that the UQ will have a value less than the k fractile is approximately equal to k and the probability that the UQ will have a value greater than the k fractile is approximately equal to $(1 - k)$. The k fractile is precisely defined by the following procedure for identifying it on an exact graph of the cumulative function of the UQ:

■ To identify the k fractile of the distribution of a UQ, enter an exact graph of the cumulative function of the UQ at k on the vertical axis, read over to the graph, and then read down to find the k fractile on the horizontal axis.

As shown in Figure 7.4, the .3 fractile (read: point three fractile) of the distribution of Figure 7.3 is 9.

Notation If a UQ is called $\tilde{x}$, the k fractile of its distribution will be called x_k, and similarly for other UQ's.

Special Fractiles Certain fractiles are commonly given special names. Our definitions have already shown that the .5 fractile is also called the median of a distribution. We shall frequently refer to the .25 and .75 fractiles respectively as the lower and upper ≪quartiles≫ of a distribution.

7.2.4
Identification of Fractiles
by Use of a Smooth Graph

We have defined the fractiles of a distribution with respect to an exact graph of the cumulative function, but in most of our work we shall be using smooth graphs and therefore the following rule will be useful.

■ To identify the k fractile of a distribution by use of a smooth rather than an exact graph of the cumulative function, proceed as with the exact graph except that if the value found on the horizontal axis is an impossible value for the UQ, the k fractile is the first possible value to the right.

By superposing a smooth graph on the exact graph in Figure 7.4, the reader can verify for himself that this rule necessarily leads to the same value that would be obtained by use of an exact graph.

7.2.5
Mean of a Distribution or Expectation
of an Uncertain Quantity

The ≪mean≫ of a probability distribution is defined by the following rule for computation:

■ To compute the mean of the probability distribution of any discrete UQ, (1) multiply each possible value of the UQ by the probability that the UQ has that value, and (2) add these products.

In Table 7.2 we show that the mean of the distribution in Table 7.1 of the UQ "demand" is 2.5.

TABLE 7.2
Computation of the Mean of a Distribution

d	$P(\tilde{d} = d)$	$d \times P(\tilde{d} = d)$
0	0	0
1	.2	.2
2	.4	.8
3	.2	.6
4	.1	.4
5	.1	.5
6 and up	0	0
	1.0	2.5

The mean of a decision maker's probability distribution for an uncertain quantity is also called his ≪mathematical expectation≫ for the uncertain quantity itself. If the UQ "demand" is assigned the probability distribution shown in Table 7.2, the decision maker's mathematical expectation for demand is 2.5. Observe that, by its definition,

■ A decision maker's mathematical expectation for an uncertain quantity is a *weighted average* of the possible values of the UQ, the weights being the probabilities assigned by the decision maker to the possible values.

An uncertain monetary value is of course just one special kind of uncertain quantity; and the definition in Section 5.6.1 of a decision maker's mathematical expectation for an uncertain monetary value is accordingly just a special case of the definition we have now given of a decision maker's mathematical expectation for any uncertain quantity.

Abbreviated Terminology   Henceforth we shall drop the adjective "mathematical" from the expression "mathematical expectation" and refer simply to the decision maker's "expectation" for an uncertain quantity.

Sometimes we shall abbreviate even more and refer simply to "the" expectation of an uncertain quantity. The reader must always remember, however, that this is in fact only an abbreviation and does not imply that a UQ can have either a probability distribution or an expectation that has not been assigned to it by some particular decision maker.

We shall also sometimes follow common practice and refer to a decision maker's expectation for the UQ "demand" as the decision maker's "expected demand", and similarly for UQ's with other names. It must be remembered, however, that "expected" demand is a weighted average of the possible values of demand and therefore need not be equal to any *possible* value of demand. Thus in the example of Table 7.2, expected demand is 2.5 units despite the fact that a demand for 2.5 units cannot possibly occur.

Notation   The expectation of the UQ $\tilde{x}$ will be denoted by either $E\tilde{x}$ or $\bar{x}$ (read: *x* bar), and similarly for other UQ's. Observe that the E in $E\tilde{x}$ does not represent a number by which $\tilde{x}$ is multiplied; E is an "operator", operating on the UQ $\tilde{x}$.

7.2.6
Relations among Mean, Median, and Mode

The definitions of the mean, median, and mode of a distribution are totally different one from the other, and in general these three ≪summary measures≫ will have distinct numerical values. In the distribution of Figure 7.3, the reader can verify that the mode is 10 while the median is 12; the mean can be shown by computation to be 13.6. More generally, if we consider *any* unimodal distribution one of whose "tails" is longer than the other, and if we take the median as a point of reference, we can see that:

1 Because the mean is an average and the median is not, the mean will be pulled away from the median toward the longer tail.

2 Because the probability is more "concentrated" on the side of the shorter tail, the mode will usually lie on that side of the median.

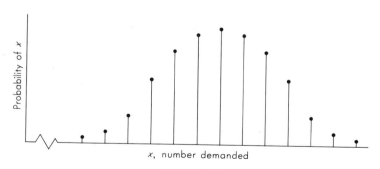

FIGURE 7.5

A Symmetric Unimodal Probability Distribution

Symmetric Distributions   There is, however, one special case where the mean, median, and mode of a distribution *are* necessarily equal. This is the case where the mass function of the distribution is (1) unimodal, and (2) ≪symmetric≫ in the sense that its right half looks exactly like its left half folded over, as in Figure 7.5.

7.2.7

**Variance and Standard Deviation
of a Distribution[4]**

In some problems we need a measure of the extent to which the mass function of a UQ "spreads out" or "scatters" to both sides of the mean, and for reasons that will be explained in a later chapter the particular measure that we usually need is one which may seem very peculiar at first glance. The measure in question is called the ≪variance≫ of the distribution and is defined by the following rule for computation:

- ■ To compute the variance of the probability distribution of a discrete UQ, (1) compute the square of the difference between each possible value of the UQ and the mean of its probability distribution, (2) multiply each of these squares by the probability of the corresponding value of the UQ, and (3) add these products.

In Table 7.3 we show that the variance of the distribution in Table 7.2 of the UQ "demand" is 1.450; the values in Column 3 of Table 7.3 rest on the fact that the mean of this distribution was shown to be 2.5 in Table 7.2. Observe that:

- ■ The variance of (the distribution of) a discrete UQ is a weighted average of the squares of the differences between the possible values of the UQ and the expectation of the UQ, the weights being the probabilities assigned to the possible values.

---

[4] To be omitted until assigned in a later chapter.

TABLE 7.3
Computation of the Variance of a Distribution

1	2	3	4	5
d	$P(\tilde{d} = d)$	$d - E\tilde{d}$	$(d - E\tilde{d})^2$	2×4
0	0	-2.5	6.25	0
1	.2	-1.5	2.25	.450
2	.4	$- .5$	.25	.100
3	.2	$+ .5$	.25	.050
4	.1	$+1.5$	2.25	.225
5	.1	$+2.5$	6.25	.625
6+	0	—	—	—
	1.0			1.450

Standard Deviation   The variance of a UQ measures the spread or scatter of its distribution in very peculiar units—in our example, the variance is 1.450 "units squared"—and in many situations it is more convenient to use a measure which is expressed in the same units in which the UQ itself is measured.   We therefore define:

■ The ≪standard deviation≫ of (the distribution of) any UQ is the square root of its variance.

In our example, the standard deviation of "demand" was $\sqrt{1.450} = 1.204$ units. Observe that:

■ The standard deviation of a distribution cannot be computed without first computing the variance.

Some feeling for the meaning of the numerical value of a standard deviation can be given by the following *very* rough and approximate empirical generalization.   In many, but by no means all, of the probability distributions encountered in practice,

1. The total probability assigned to values of the UQ which differ from the mean by more than the standard deviation is very roughly $1/3$;

2. The total probability assigned to values of the UQ which differ from the mean by more than 3 times the standard deviation is extremely small if not 0.

7.3
FUNCTIONS OF AN UNCERTAIN QUANTITY [5]

7.3.1
An Example

Suppose that a retailer wishes to decide how many units to stock of a prepackaged commodity which spoils and becomes a total loss if it is not sold on the day that it is stocked; suppose that he pays $2 for each unit he buys and collects $5

---

[5] The reader should make himself thoroughly familiar with all of the Appendix on Sets, Functions, and Weighted Averages before even beginning to read this section.

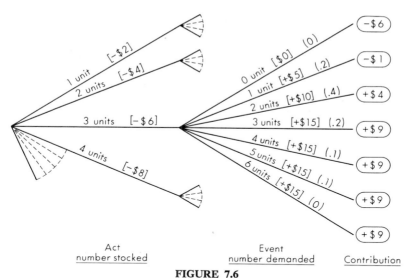

FIGURE 7.6

Portion of a Retailer's Decision Diagram

for each unit he sells; and suppose that he assigns the distribution of Figure 7.1 and Table 7.1 to the UQ "number of units demanded tomorrow." Assuming that the retailer takes the end of the day as his evaluation date and decides to treat expected monetary values as certainty equivalents, we show a portion of his decision diagram in Figure 7.6. Each possible act is a particular number of units stocked, each possible event is a particular number of units demanded, probabilities are shown in parentheses, partial cash flows are shown in square brackets, and the values at end positions are total cash flows or "contributions to overhead and profit". Because the retailer cannot sell more than he stocks, the partial cash flows or sales revenues on the branches of the event fork shown in Figure 7.6 cannot exceed $3 \times \$5 = \$15$, and hence the contributions at the end positions of the fork cannot exceed $\$15 - \$6 = \$9$.

We already know that if the retailer wishes to compute his expectation for the uncertain contribution that will result from the gamble of Figure 7.6, he should multiply each possible contribution or total cash flow by the corresponding probability and add the products; and similarly if he wishes to compute his expectation for the uncertain partial cash flow or sales revenue that will result from the gamble. We shall now show that these expectations are simply special cases of what we shall call expectations of ≪functions≫ of the UQ "demand".

7.3.2

Definition of a Function of a UQ

For use in further discussion of the example just described, let us define

d: units demanded,

s: units sold,

r: sales revenue,

c: contribution,

Q: number of units stocked.

If demand does not exceed stock on hand, unit sales will equal demand; if demand does exceed stock on hand, unit sales will equal the stock. Symbolically,

$$s = \begin{cases} d & \text{if} & d \leqslant Q, \\ Q & \text{if} & d > Q. \end{cases}$$

(This formula would be neither more nor less correct if $\leqslant$ and $>$ were replaced by $<$ and $\geqslant$ respectively.)

The sales revenue will be simply \$5 times the number of units sold, so that we can write

$$r = \$5s;$$

and we can then substitute herein the formulas for s given just above, thus obtaining

$$r = \begin{cases} \$5d & \text{if} & d \leqslant Q, \\ \$5Q & \text{if} & d > Q. \end{cases}$$

Finally, contribution will equal sales revenue less cost of stock, and stock will cost \$2Q, so that

$$c = r - \$2Q;$$

and substituting herein the formulas derived above for r, we get

$$c = \begin{cases} \$5d - \$2Q & \text{if} & d \leqslant Q, \\ \$5Q - \$2Q = \$3Q & \text{if} & d > Q. \end{cases}$$

Before proceeding further, the reader should verify that the contributions in Figure 7.6 agree with this last result when 3 is substituted for Q.

Now given any particular stock such as $Q = 3$, the value of the uncertain quantity $\tilde{c}$ is determined by the value of the UQ $\tilde{d}$ via the last formula above, and therefore the UQ $\tilde{c}$ is said to be a function of the UQ $\tilde{d}$ given any particular stock Q. If we use the symbol f_3 to denote the function which relates c to d when $Q = 3$, we can write

$$\tilde{c} = f_3(\tilde{d}) = \begin{cases} \$5\tilde{d} - \$6 & \text{if} & \tilde{d} \leqslant 3, \\ \$9 & \text{if} & \tilde{d} > 3. \end{cases}$$

Similarly, given any particular stock, the UQ $\tilde{s}$ (unit sales) is a function of the UQ $\tilde{d}$ (demand), and if we use the symbol g_3 to denote the function which relates $\tilde{s}$ to $\tilde{d}$ when $Q = 3$, we can write

$$\tilde{s} = g_3(\tilde{d}) = \begin{cases} \tilde{d} & \text{if} & \tilde{d} \leqslant 3, \\ 3 & \text{if} & \tilde{d} > 3. \end{cases}$$

More generally,

■ Any uncertain quantity $\tilde{y}$ whose value is determined by (can be computed from) the value of another uncertain quantity $\tilde{x}$ is said to be a *function* of $\tilde{x}$.

We warn the reader concerning two points that are likely to cause confusion.

1. Although a symbol such as $f(2)$ or $f(x)$ is to be understood as representing a *number*, a symbol such as $f(\tilde{x})$ represents an *uncertain quantity*.

2. The meaning of the words "function of $\tilde{x}$" in the expression "$\tilde{y}$ is a function of $\tilde{x}$" is quite different from the meaning of those same words in the expression "mass function of $\tilde{x}$" or "cumulative function of $\tilde{x}$".

7.3.3
Distribution of a Function
of a Discrete UQ

Recall now that our retailer has assigned to the UQ $\tilde{d}$ the probability distribution originally shown in Table 7.1 and shown again in the first two columns of Table 7.4. The values of $\tilde{s}$ and $\tilde{c}$ which correspond to each value of $\tilde{d}$ when $Q = 3$ have

TABLE 7.4
Data for Computing Distributions of Functions

Value of UQ d	Probability $P(\tilde{d} = d)$	Function Values	
		$s = g_3(d)$	$c = f_3(d)$
0	0	0	$-\$6$
1	.2	1	$-\ 1$
2	.4	2	$+\ 4$
3	.2	3	$+\ 9$
4	.1	3	$+\ 9$
5	.1	3	$+\ 9$
6+	0	—	—
	1.0		

been computed from the formulas in the previous section and are shown in the last two columns of the table; and from these values and the probabilities in the second column we compute in Table 7.5 the probability distributions that the retailer should assign to the UQ's $\tilde{s}$ and $\tilde{c}$ when $Q = 3$.

TABLE 7.5
Computed Distributions of Functions

Function Values		Probability
s	c	
0	$-\$6$	0
1	$-\ 1$	.2
2	$+\ 4$	.4
3	$+\ 9$	$.2 + .1 + .1 = \ .4$
		1.0

Generalizing from this example, we give the following rule for computing the distribution of a UQ which is a function of a discrete UQ to which a probability distribution has already been assigned.

■ If $\tilde{y}$ is a function of a discrete UQ $\tilde{x}$, the probability of any particular value of $\tilde{y}$ is the sum of the probabilities of all values of $\tilde{x}$ that give rise to that value of $\tilde{y}$.

7.3.4
Expectation of a Function
of a Discrete UQ

By the definition of the expectation of a UQ that was given in Section 7.2.5, the expectation of the UQ $\tilde{s}$ (unit sales) whose distribution was computed in Table 7.5 is

$$(0 \times 0) + (.2 \times 1) + (.4 \times 2) + (.4 \times 3) = 2.2.$$

This same value could have been computed as shown in Table 7.6 by applying the following rule for computing the expectation of a function of a discrete UQ.

■ The expectation of a function of a discrete UQ can be computed by multiplying the *probability* of each possible value of the *uncertain quantity* by the corresponding *value* of the *function* of the UQ and adding these products.

We leave it to the reader to satisfy himself that these two methods for computing the expectation of a function of a discrete UQ will always lead to exactly the same result. The method of Table 7.6 is ordinarily the more useful in practice.

TABLE 7.6
Computation of the Expectation of a Function

1	2	3	4
Value of UQ d	Probability $P(\tilde{d} = d)$	Value of Function $s = g_3(d)$	Product $g_3(d) \times P(\tilde{d} = d)$
0	0	0	0
1	.2	1	.2
2	.4	2	.8
3	.2	3	.6
4	.1	3	.3
5	.1	3	.3
6+	0	3	0
	1.0		2.2

Notation   If $\tilde{y}$ is a function of $\tilde{x}$, so that we can write $\tilde{y} = f(\tilde{x})$, then the expectation of $\tilde{y}$ may be denoted by $Ef(\tilde{x})$ as well as by $E\tilde{y}$ or $\bar{y}$.

Expected Monetary Value   In Table 7.7 we compute the expectation of the contribution function

$$\tilde{c} = f_3(\tilde{d}) = \begin{cases} \$5\tilde{d} - \$6 & \text{if} & \tilde{d} \leqslant 3, \\ \$9 & \text{if} & \tilde{d} > 3, \end{cases}$$

using exactly the same method that we used in Table 7.6 to compute the expectation of the unit-sales function $\tilde{s} = g_3(\tilde{d})$. The reader should observe that this

TABLE 7.7

Computation of Expected Contribution

1	2	3	4
Value of UQ *d*	*Probability* $P(\tilde{d} = d)$	*Value of Function* $c = f_3(d)$	*Product* $f_3(d) \times P(\tilde{d} = d)$
0	0	$-\$6$	$\$0.0$
1	.2	$-\ 1$	$-\ \ .2$
2	.4	$+\ 4$	$+\ 1.6$
3	.2	$+\ 9$	$+\ 1.8$
4	.1	$+\ 9$	$+\ \ .9$
5	.1	$+\ 9$	$+\ \ .9$
6+	0	$+\ 9$	0.0
	1.0		$+\$5.0$

computation is exactly the one that we would have carried out in order to compute the retailer's expectation for the uncertain contribution that would result from the gamble in Figure 7.6 (page 239); as we said before, the expectation of an uncertain monetary value is simply a special case of the expectation of a function.

"Expected Preference" In problems where the decision maker's preferences for terminal criterion values are not linear and expected monetary values are therefore irrelevant, we can find the decision maker's certainty equivalent for the uncertain terminal value represented by a terminal event fork by use of his preference curve. To do so, we first read his preference for each terminal value on the fork from the preference curve; we then compute his preference for the fork by multiplying his preference for each terminal value by the probability of that terminal value and adding the products; and finally we again use his preference curve to find the terminal value for which his preference is equal to his preference for the fork.

We now observe that (1) because terminal value determines preference, preference can be thought of as a function of terminal value; and (2) because preference for an event fork is a probability-weighted average of preferences for terminal values, preference for an event fork can be thought of as an expectation of the function defined by the preference curve.

7.3.5
Summary

The essential points to remember concerning functions of UQ's are the following.

    1. When the value of a UQ $\tilde{y}$ is determined by the value of some other

UQ $\bar{x}$, $\bar{y}$ is said to be a function of $\bar{x}$. Thus the UQ "contribution" may be a function of the UQ "demand".

2. If $\bar{y}$ (e.g., contribution) is a function of $\bar{x}$ (e.g., demand) and we wish to compute the expectation of $\bar{y}$ that is implied by a probability distribution that the decision maker has already assigned to $\bar{x}$, there are two different ways in which we can proceed.

    a We can *compute the distribution of the function $\bar{y}$* from the distribution of $\bar{x}$ according to the rule in Section 7.3.3 and then compute the expectation of $\bar{y}$ by multiplying each possible value of $\bar{y}$ by the probability of that value of $\bar{y}$ and adding the products.

    b We can *work directly from the distribution of $\bar{x}$*, multiplying the value of $\bar{y}$ which corresponds to each possible value of $\bar{x}$ by the probability of that value of $\bar{x}$ and adding the products.

7.4

APPROXIMATION OF AN EXPECTATION

As we saw in the previous section, computation of the expectation of a UQ or of a function thereof requires in principle that we multiply the probability assigned to each possible value of the UQ by that value itself or by the corresponding value of the function, as the case may be, and then add all the resulting products. When the UQ has only a small number of values with nonzero probability, this is easy to do, but when the UQ has thousands of possible values with non-zero probability, such computations may be completely infeasible. We shall see in the next chapter that when a decision maker decides that he should assign non-zero probability to thousands of possible values of some UQ $\bar{x}$ such as "demand" or "production cost", he can usually best assess his distribution of $\bar{x}$ by drawing a smooth graph of its cumulative function. In order to determine from such a graph his probability for every possible individual value x of the UQ $\bar{x}$, he would first have to read $P(\bar{x} \leqslant x)$ from the graph for every x and then compute

$$P(\bar{x} = x) = P(\bar{x} \leqslant x) - P(\bar{x} < x)$$

for every x; and even though the subtractions could be done quickly enough, either by hand or on a digital computer, the task of reading $P(\bar{x} \leqslant x)$ from the graph for thousands of x's would be enormous.

    In such circumstances the decision maker would usually be willing to settle for a good approximation to the expectation he seeks if such an approximation could be obtained with only a small part of the chart reading that would be required to compute the exact value of the expectation. In the remainder of this chapter we shall first show how we could in principle calculate by hand an approximation to the expectation of any UQ or function thereof that would be satisfactory in any practical decision problem, and we shall then go on to show how these same calculations can be carried out on a digital computer with any required degree of accuracy and with almost no effort.

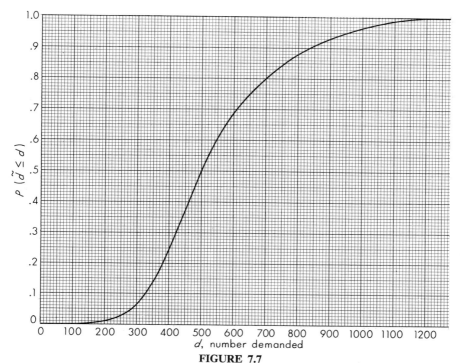

FIGURE 7.7

The Retailer's Probability Distribution of Demand

7.4.1

An Example of Approximate Computation

As a concrete example to illustrate the problem we are discussing, let us suppose that the retailer of the example introduced in Section 7.3.1 has sold his small shop and bought a large supermarket, with the result that he feels that he might sell over a thousand units of the prepackaged commodity in one day; his probability distribution for the number d that will be demanded tomorrow is shown in Figure 7.7. Despite this increase in the scale of his operations, the retailer still pays $2 for each unit he buys and collects $5 for each unit he sells; and therefore his problem of deciding how many units to stock can be diagrammed schematically as shown in Figure 7.8, where Q stands for any particular number stocked, d stands for any particular number demanded, and c stands for any particular value of the contribution function

$$\tilde{c} = f_Q(d) = \begin{cases} \$5d - \$2Q & \text{if} & d \leqslant Q, \\ \$3Q & \text{if} & d > Q. \end{cases}$$

As the first step in the analysis of this decision problem, the retailer asks us to compute his expected contribution with a stock of $Q = 500$ units—i.e., his expectation of the function

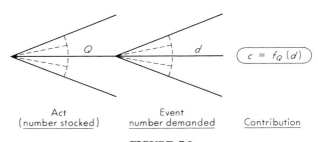

Act
(number stocked)

Event
number demanded

Contribution

FIGURE 7.8

The Retailer's Decision Problem

$$f_{500}(d) = \begin{cases} \$5d - \$1,000 & \text{if} & d \leqslant 500, \\ \$1,500 & \text{if} & d > 500. \end{cases}$$

If we wished to compute the exact value of the required expectation, we would have to use a worksheet of the form shown in Table 7.8, which is identical in principle to Table 7.7 in the original example but would contain a very much larger number of rows if completely filled out. Specifically, we would have to start by listing all the individual values d of the UQ $\tilde{d}$ to which Figure 7.7 implicitly assigns nonzero probability; we would then have to read from Figure 7.7 all the cumulative probabilities that are required to compute the actual probabilities of the individual d's by use of the relation

$$P(\tilde{d} = d) = P(\tilde{d} \leqslant d) - P(\tilde{d} \leqslant d - 1);$$

and we would then have to compute for each d the function value $f_{500}(d)$, multiply each function value by the corresponding probability, and add these products over all the d's that would appear in the complete table. Since Figure 7.7 implicitly assigns nonzero probability to about 1,100 possible d's, from about $d = 100$ to about $d = 1,200$, the operation would be extremely laborious.

To see how this labor could be cut in five with almost no loss of accuracy, consider the entries that actually appear in Table 7.8 for the group of five d's from 401 to 405 inclusive and make the two following observations.

1. If we were to substitute the "intermediate" function value $1,015 for each of the four other function values that actually appear in Columns 3 and 4 of Table 7.8, thus converting that table into Table 7.9, the resulting increase in the values of the first two products in Column 4 would be just about offset by the resulting decrease in the values of the last two products; the *sum* of the five products would be scarcely affected at all.

2. The sum of the five products in the modified table, Table 7.9, can be calculated without having to determine the five individual probabilities that appear in that table. Because the first factor in each of the five products is a constant, the same in all five cases, the sum of products can be calculated by multiplying the constant function value $1,015 by the sum of the five probabilities.

TABLE 7.8
Exact Computation of Expected Contribution

1	**2**	**3**	**4**
Value of UQ	*Probability*	*Value of Function*	*Product*
d	$P(\tilde{d} = d)$	$c = f_{500}(d)$	$f_{500}(d) \times P(\tilde{d} = d)$
. . .	. . .	. . .	. . .
. . .	. . .	. . .	. . .
401	$P(\tilde{d} = 401)$	\$1,005	\$1,005 $P(\tilde{d} = 401)$
402	$P(\tilde{d} = 402)$	1,010	1,010 $P(\tilde{d} = 402)$
403	$P(\tilde{d} = 403)$	1,015	1,015 $P(\tilde{d} = 403)$
404	$P(\tilde{d} = 404)$	1,020	1,020 $P(\tilde{d} = 404)$
405	$P(\tilde{d} = 405)$	1,025	1,025 $P(\tilde{d} = 405)$
. . .	. . .	. . .	. . .
. . .	. . .	. . .	. . .

TABLE 7.9
Approximate Computation of Expected Contribution

1	**2**	**3**	**4**
		Intermediate	
Value of UQ	*Probability*	*Value of Function*	*Product*
d	$P(\tilde{d} = d)$	$c = f_{500}(403)$	$f_{500}(403) \times P(\tilde{d} = d)$
. . .	. . .	. . .	. . .
. . .	. . .	. . .	. . .
401	$P(\tilde{d} = 401)$	\$1,015	\$1,015 $P(\tilde{d} = 401)$
402	$P(\tilde{d} = 402)$	1,015	1,015 $P(\tilde{d} = 402)$
403	$P(\tilde{d} = 403)$	1,015	1,015 $P(\tilde{d} = 403)$
404	$P(\tilde{d} = 404)$	1,015	1,015 $P(\tilde{d} = 404)$
405	$P(\tilde{d} = 405)$	1,015	1,015 $P(\tilde{d} = 405)$
. . .	. . .	. . .	. . .
. . .	. . .	. . .	. . .

This latter sum, however, is simply the probability that the UQ *d* has some value between 401 and 405 inclusive; and this probability can be directly obtained from Figure 7.7 by use of the relation

$$P(401 \leqslant \tilde{d} \leqslant 405) = P(\tilde{d} \leqslant 405) - P(\tilde{d} \leqslant 400).$$

Now this method of approximating the sum of products for a group of five *d*'s clearly could be applied to any other group just as well as it can be applied to the group including *d*'s from 401 to 405 inclusive; and thus it appears that we could get a very close approximation to the retailer's expected contribution—i.e., to the sum of products for *all d*'s—by (1) forming all the *d*'s with non-zero probability into groups of five, e.g., 101–105, 106–110, 111–151, etc., (2) approximating the sum of products for each group in the way just explained for the group 401–405, and finally (3) adding these approximate group sums over all groups.

7.4.2
Alternative Description of the
Method of Computation

The method for approximating the retailer's expected contribution that we have just described can also be described in a different way which will be more convenient in future discussion.

We said in the previous section that the sum of products for the group of d's from 401 to 405 inclusive could be approximated by multiplying the intermediate function value $1,015 by the probability of the entire group. This intermediate function value, however, was simply the value of the function for the intermediate value $d = 403$ of the UQ $\tilde{d}$; and therefore we could just as well have said that the sum of products for the group of d's from 401 to 405 inclusive can be approximated by proceeding as if the entire probability of the group had been assigned to the intermediate value $d = 403$ of the UQ $\tilde{d}$ and zero probability had been assigned to all other d's in the group. Since this proposition is the key to everything that follows, the reader should make sure that he understands it before proceeding further.

More generally, we could have described the whole procedure by which we could approximate the retailer's expected contribution—the sum of products for all d's—by saying that we could (1) form all the d's into groups, (2) select within each group an intermediate d to "represent" the group, and then (3) compute the expectation as if the entire probability of each group had been assigned to the representative d of the group.

7.4.3
Grouped Approximations
to Probability Distributions

In order to have a still briefer way of describing this method of approximate computation of expectations, we first introduce the concept of a ≪grouped approximation≫ to a probability distribution.

1 Let $\tilde{x}$ denote any UQ, and suppose that a decision maker has assigned some particular "exact" probability distribution to $\tilde{x}$. To construct a grouped approximation to the decision maker's exact probability distribution:

   1 Form into groups all possible values x which have nonzero probability.

   2 Select within each group an intermediate x to represent the group.

   3 Assign to the representative x of each group the probability that the exact distribution assigns to the entire group.

We can now state the following general rule for approximating the expectation of any UQ or of any function of any UQ:

2 Let $\tilde{x}$ denote any UQ to which a decision maker has assigned a probability distribution. To approximate either the implied expectation of $\tilde{x}$ or the implied expectation of any function of $\tilde{x}$:

    1 Construct a grouped approximation to the probability distribution of $\tilde{x}$.

    2 Compute the required expectation by proceeding exactly as if this grouped approximation were the true probability distribution of $\tilde{x}$.

To illustrate this method of computation, we show in Tables 7.10 and 7.11 how we can compute the retailer's expected contribution using groups each of which contains 100 possible values of the UQ "demand"; the accuracy of results based on groups of so large a size will be discussed later on.

Table 7.10 shows the construction of our grouped approximation to the retailer's exact probability distribution of the UQ $\tilde{d}$ that was shown in Figure 7.7. Column 1 shows the groups of values of $\tilde{d}$ that we have chosen to use. Column 2 shows for each group the exact probability as read from Figure 7.7 that demand will have a value equal to or less than the greatest value in the group; thus

TABLE 7.10
Construction of a Grouped Approximation
to the Retailer's Distribution of $\tilde{d}$

1	2	3	4
Group of Values of $\tilde{d}$	*Cumulative Probability*	*Probability of Group*	*Representative Value of $\tilde{d}$*
0– 100	.000	.000	—
101– 200	.011	.011	150
201– 300	.065	.054	250
301– 400	.246	.181	350
401– 500	.500	.254	450
501– 600	.687	.187	550
601– 700	.800	.113	650
701– 800	.880	.080	750
801– 900	.930	.050	850
901–1,000	.965	.035	950
1,001–1,100	.990	.025	1,050
1,101–1,200	1.000	.010	1,150
		1.000	

$P(\tilde{d} \leqslant 100) = .000$, $P(\tilde{d} \leqslant 200) = .011$, $P(\tilde{d} \leqslant 300) = .065$, and so forth. Column 3 shows for each group the probability of that group as calculated from the appropriate entries in Column 2; thus $P(201 \leqslant \tilde{d} \leqslant 300) = .065 - .011 = .054$, and so forth. Finally, Column 4 shows for each group an intermediate value of $\tilde{d}$ which will "represent" the entire group in subsequent calculations.

Table 7.11 shows the computation of our approximation to the retailer's expected contribution with a stock of 500—i.e., the expectation of the function $f_{500}(\tilde{d})$. Columns 1 and 2 of the table, which are identical to Columns 4 and 3

TABLE 7.11
Computation of an Approximation to the Expectation
of the Function $f_{500}(\tilde{d})$

1	2	3	4
Representative *d*	*Probability* *Assigned to d*	*Function Value* $f_{500}(d)$	*Product* **2 × 3**
150	.011	−$ 250	−$ 2.75
250	.054	+ 250	+ 13.50
350	.181	750	135.75
450	.254	1,250	317.50
550	.187	1,500	280.50
650	.113	1,500	169.50
750	.080	1,500	120.00
850	.050	1,500	75.00
950	.035	1,500	52.50
1,050	.025	1,500	37.50
1,150	.010	1,500	15.00
	1.000		+$1,214.00
			$= Ef_{500}(\tilde{d})$

respectively of Table 7.10, show our grouped approximation to the retailer's exact distribution of demand. The expectation of $f_{500}(\tilde{d})$ is then computed in Columns 3 and 4 of the table by proceeding as if this grouped approximation were the retailer's true distribution of $\tilde{d}$; the computational procedure is therefore identical to that used in Table 7.7 on page 243.

The essential nature of this method of approximate computation is shown diagrammatically in Figure 7.9. Instead of finding the retailer's probability $P(\tilde{d} = d)$ and the function value $f_{500}(d)$ for every one of the 1,100 branches on the event fan in Figure 7.8 on page 246, we proceeded as shown in Figure 7.9A to form the branches of this fan into groups and determined the retailer's probability for each group. We next proceeded as shown in Figure 7.9B to select an intermediate branch in each group to represent the entire group and assigned the entire probability of the group to that one representative branch. We could then compute our approximation to the required expectation by proceeding in Table 7.11 as if the retailer's decision diagram actually contained the event fork of Figure 7.9B rather than the event fan of Figure 7.8.

7.4.4
Equiprobable Groups

In order to simplify our exposition of the basic logic of approximation by grouping, we assumed that the values of the UQ would be formed into groups each of which contained the same number of values, but in practice it is much more convenient and just as accurate to use groups each of which has the same probability.

The procedure by which such ≪equiprobable groups≫ of values of a

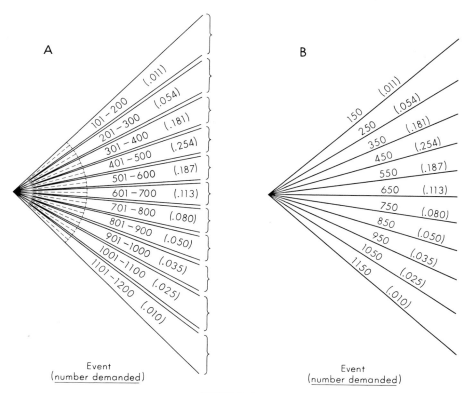

FIGURE 7.9
Grouping of Branches of an Event Fan

UQ are formed is illustrated in Figure 7.10 and Table 7.12, where we form 10 equiprobable groups of values of the UQ "demand" whose exact distribution was shown in Figure 7.7 on page 245.

    1. As shown by the horizontal solid lines in Figure 7.10, we first divide the *vertical* axis of Figure 7.7 into 10 equal intervals or «brackets» of cumulative probability, and we then enter the cumulative probabilities corresponding to the edges of these brackets in Column 1 of Table 7.12.

    2. As shown by the vertical solid lines in Figure 7.10, we next locate on the *horizontal* axis of Figure 7.7 the values of the UQ which correspond to the edges of the vertical brackets and use these readings to establish the groups or brackets of values of the UQ that are shown in Column 2 of Table 7.12. (Since the exact locations of the edges of the horizontal brackets will prove to be of no practical importance, we simply make an arbitrary decision whenever it is hard to tell from the chart in which of two brackets a given value of d belongs.)

    3. We then infer from Column 1 of Table 7.12 that each of our 10 groups or brackets of values of the UQ has probability 1/10, as shown in Column 3 of Table 7.12.

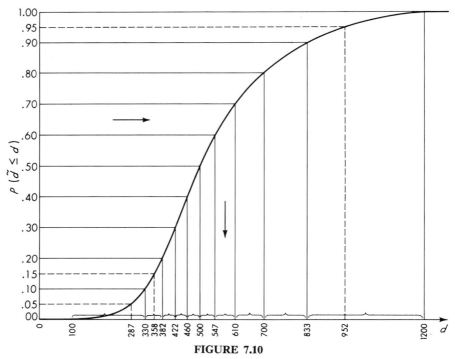

FIGURE 7.10

Formation of Equiprobable Groups of Values

7.4.5

Bracket Medians

Just as we used groups containing equal numbers of values of the UQ in order to simplify our exposition of the basic logic of grouping, so we selected the middle value in each group as the value which would represent the group in sub-

TABLE 7.12

Grouped Approximation with Equiprobable Groups

1	2	3	4
Vertical Bracket	*Horizontal Bracket*	*Probability of Bracket*	*Bracket Median*
.0– .1	100– 330	.1	287
.1– .2	331– 382	.1	358
.2– .3	383– 422	.1	402
.3– .4	423– 460	.1	441
.4– .5	461– 500	.1	480
.5– .6	501– 547	.1	522
.6– .7	548– 610	.1	576
.7– .8	611– 700	.1	650
.8– .9	701– 833	.1	757
.9–1.0	834–1,200	.1	952
		$\overline{}$	
		1.0	

sequent computations; but again there is an alternative procedure which is just as accurate and much more convenient in practice. This alternative is to choose as the representative value for each group or bracket the value which divides the probability of the bracket approximately in half—i.e., the value such that about half of the total probability of the bracket belongs to lower values of the UQ and about half to higher values. This value of the UQ will be called the «bracket median».

The bracket median of any group or horizontal bracket of values of the UQ is found by entering the graph of the cumulative function of the UQ at the midpoint of the corresponding *vertical* bracket and reading over to the curve and down; because we are aiming at approximations rather than exact results, it does not matter whether the value found on the horizontal axis is a possible or an impossible value of the UQ.

The determination of the bracket medians of three of the brackets in Table 7.12 is illustrated graphically by the dotted lines in Figure 7.10, and the bracket medians of all ten brackets are shown in Column 4 of Table 7.12. Columns 3 and 4 of Table 7.12 define a new grouped approximation to the retailer's exact distribution of demand which was shown in Figure 7.7 on page 245; the use of this approximation to compute a new approximation to the retailer's expected contribution is shown in Table 7.13.

TABLE 7.13
Computation of an Expectation Using Equiprobable Brackets

1	2	3	4
Bracket Median d	*Probability of Bracket*	*Function Value* $f_{500}(d)$	*Product* 3×2
287	.1	+$ 435	+$ 43.5
358	.1	790	79.0
402	.1	1,010	101.0
441	.1	1,205	120.5
480	.1	1,400	140.0
522	.1	1,500	150.0
576	.1	1,500	150.0
650	.1	1,500	150.0
757	.1	1,500	150.0
952	.1	1,500	150.0
	1.0		+$1,234.0 ≐ $Ef_{500}(d)$

7.4.6
Construction of Grouped Approximations Using Bracket Medians

If now the reader will look back at the computation in Table 7.13, he will see that we made absolutely no use of the information about the edges of the horizontal brackets of values of the UQ that is contained in Column 2 of Table 7.12.   All that we needed to know was (1) the probability, and (2) the bracket median of each horizontal bracket, and both these quantities could be determined without determining the edges.   Generalizing from this example, we see that:

> ■ To construct a grouped approximation to the probability distribution of a UQ by use of a graph of its cumulative function, decide on the vertical or probability brackets that are to be used and then:
>
> > *1* Calculate the *probability* of each horizontal bracket of values of the UQ by measuring the height of the corresponding vertical bracket;
> >
> > *2* Determine the *bracket median* of each horizontal bracket by entering the graph at the midpoint of the corresponding vertical bracket and reading over to the curve and down.

When the brackets of values of the UQ are equiprobable in addition to being represented by their bracket medians, another shortcut can be taken when we come to the actual use of the grouped approximation as the basis for computing the expectation of the UQ or of a function thereof.   We leave it to the reader to discover this shortcut for himself by examining the computations in Table 7.13.

7.4.7
Size of Groups and Accuracy of Approximation

The accuracy with which an expectation can be approximated by use of a grouped approximation to the underlying probability distribution depends upon both the widths and the probabilities of the brackets into which the values of the UQ are grouped.

If a bracket is very narrow, every value of the UQ within the bracket will be nearly equal to the representative value and very little relative error will be introduced into the group sum of products when we approximate it by substituting the representative value for the actual values, as we did when we went from Table 7.8 to Table 7.9 on page 247.   If, on the contrary, a horizontal bracket is very wide, the value of the UQ will vary substantially across the bracket and substitution of the representative value for the actual values of the UQ may introduce a substantial error into the group sum of products.

If a bracket has only a small probability, the group sum of products will be only a small part of the total sum of products—i.e., of the expectation that is being computed—and therefore even a fairly large relative error in the group sum of products will give rise to only a small relative error in the total sum of products.   If, on the contrary, the probability of a bracket is large, the group sum of products will be a large part of the total sum of products and therefore an error in the group sum of products can give rise to a large relative error in the total sum of products.

Use of fairly wide brackets with fairly large probabilities is not so dangerous as it might seem at first glance, however, because the contributions of the individual brackets to the total error will usually offset each other to a considerable extent. Some brackets will make positive contributions to the total error while others will make negative contributions, with the result that the total error will usually be far smaller in percentage terms than many of the contributions of the individual brackets.

As a rule of thumb, expectations can be calculated with an accuracy which is adequate for most practical business decision problems by grouping the value of the UQ into 100 equiprobable brackets; and although computations using this large a number of brackets would be very laborious if carried out by hand, we shall see in a moment that it takes very little effort to have them carried out on a digital computer.

The only reason for manual computing in the text and exercises of this book is to make clear to the reader the nature and logic of the computations that would in actual practice be performed by a computer. Since accuracy quite sufficient for this illustrative purpose can be obtained by using only ten equiprobable brackets, we shall use ten equiprobable brackets in all examples in the text, and the reader should use ten equiprobable brackets in all exercises in which a probability distribution must be grouped.

7.4.8
Use of a Digital Computer

That a digital computer can carry out arithmetical computations like those in Table 7.13 is too obvious to require comment and is of relatively little interest in any case, since the hard part of the work required to compute an expectation based on a grouped approximation is not the arithmetic but the chart reading required to derive the grouped approximation from the exact probability distribution. What is really interesting, therefore, is the fact that with very little handwork the computer can be made to carry out the actual derivation of the grouped approximation as well as the subsequent arithmetical computations.

To see how a digital computer can be made to construct a grouped approximation to a probability distribution, suppose that we read from the graph in Figure 7.7 the coordinates (abscissas and ordinates) of a number of roughly equally spaced-out points on the curve and plot just these points on another piece of graph paper; the result might be as shown in the first two columns of Table 7.14 and in Figure 7.11. It is apparent from the figure that these points serve to define the cumulative function almost exactly, in the sense that if we were to fair a *smooth* curve through the points in Figure 7.11, the result could scarcely differ from the original curve in Figure 7.7 by enough to matter for practical purposes, particularly since we have taken care to include among our selected points the points at which the curve of Figure 7.7 begins and ends and the

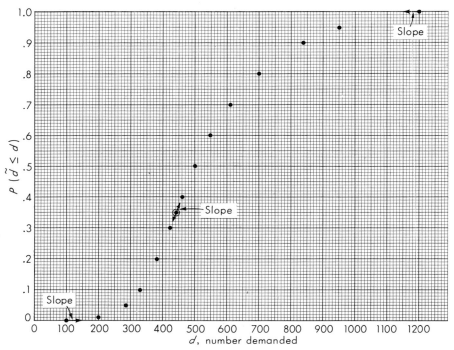

FIGURE 7.11

Selected Points and Slopes on a Cumulative Function

TABLE 7.14

Selected Points on a Cumulative Function

Abscissa d	Ordinate $P(\tilde{d} \leqslant d)$	Slope
100	.00	0
287	.05	
330	.10	
382	.20	
422	.30	
450	.374	.00265
460	.40	
500	.50	
547	.60	
610	.70	
700	.80	
833	.90	
952	.95	
1,200	1.00	0

point (circled in Figure 7.11) at which its curvature reverses. We can, however, guarantee a still better reproduction of the original curve if, as shown in Column 3 of Table 7.11, we also measure the *slope* of the curve in Figure 7.7 at the three

NUMBER DEMANDED

INPUT DATA

VALUE	CUM PROB	SLOPE
100.	0.	0.
287.	0.050	
330.	0.100	
382.	0.200	
422.	0.300	
450.	0.374	0.002650
460.	0.400	
500.	0.500	
547.	0.600	
610.	0.700	
700.	0.800	
833.	0.900	
952.	0.950	
1200.	1.000	0.

SUMMARY STATISTICS

MEAN	543.
STD DEV	202.

BRACKET MEDIANS

VALUE	CUM PROB	VALUE	CUM PROB	VALUE	CUM PROB	VALUE	CUM PROB
145.	0.005	404.	0.255	502.	0.505	655.	0.755
189.	0.015	408.	0.265	507.	0.515	664.	0.765
220.	0.025	412.	0.275	511.	0.525	674.	0.775
249.	0.035	416.	0.285	515.	0.535	684.	0.785
275.	0.045	420.	0.295	520.	0.545	694.	0.795
294.	0.055	424.	0.305	524.	0.555	706.	0.805
302.	0.065	428.	0.315	529.	0.565	717.	0.815
311.	0.075	431.	0.325	534.	0.575	729.	0.825
319.	0.085	435.	0.335	539.	0.585	740.	0.835
326.	0.095	439.	0.345	544.	0.595	752.	0.845
334.	0.105	443.	0.355	550.	0.605	765.	0.855
340.	0.115	447.	0.365	555.	0.615	777.	0.865
346.	0.125	450.	0.375	561.	0.625	790.	0.875
351.	0.135	454.	0.385	567.	0.635	805.	0.885
356.	0.145	458.	0.395	573.	0.645	823.	0.895
361.	0.155	462.	0.405	579.	0.655	843.	0.905
366.	0.165	466.	0.415	585.	0.665	864.	0.915
370.	0.175	470.	0.425	592.	0.675	886.	0.925
375.	0.185	474.	0.435	599.	0.685	908.	0.935
380.	0.195	478.	0.445	606.	0.695	935.	0.945
384.	0.205	482.	0.455	614.	0.705	971.	0.955
389.	0.215	485.	0.465	622.	0.715	1010.	0.965
393.	0.225	489.	0.475	630.	0.725	1052.	0.975
397.	0.235	494.	0.485	638.	0.735	1096.	0.985
400.	0.245	498.	0.495	646.	0.745	1152.	0.995

FIGURE 7.12

Bracket Medians of a Cumulative Function Fitted by Computer

most critical points and specify that the curve fitted to the points in Figure 7.11 shall have exactly these slopes at these points.

Instead of graphically fairing a smooth curve that goes through the points and has the slopes specified in Figure 7.11, we could get the same effect by finding a mathematical formula for a smooth curve that has the required properties. In particular, we could compute the bracket medians of any number of brackets from this formula instead of having to read them from the graph in Figure 7.7. And while it would be more laborious to carry out these calcula-

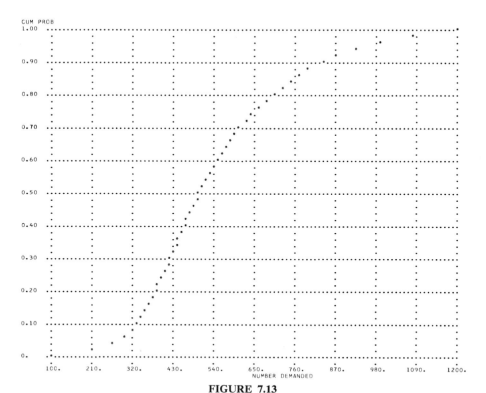

FIGURE 7.13

Sketch of a Cumulative Function Fitted by Computer

tions by hand than to read 100 bracket medians from the graph in Figure 7.7, the calculations can be performed in a few seconds by a digital computer.

A general-purpose computer program called *Smooth* is available for performing these computations; a brief description of it is appended to this chapter (pages 268ff.).[6] As an example of its use, we show in Figure 7.12 the output it produces when supplied with the data of Table 7.14 as inputs; this output consists of the bracket medians of 100 equiprobable brackets, as computed from the formula for the cumulative function, together with the approximate mean and standard deviation of the distribution as computed from the 100 bracket medians by exactly the same method that we have explained in previous sections using only 10 bracket medians. The program also enables the computer to prepare and print out a rough-sketch graph of the mathematical cumulative function, to be used in making a quick check on the reasonableness of that function rather than as a basis for computations; the graph for our example is shown in Figure 7.13.[7]

[6] A complete description of both the batch-processing version of *Smooth* described in the appendix to this chapter and a time-sharing version of the same program can be found in the publication mentioned on page vi of the Preface.

[7] The slight irregularities in Figure 7.13 do not result from real irregularities in the mathematical cumulative function fitted by the computer and used as the basis for its computations. They result from the fact that the graph is printed out on an ordinary printer and therefore there are only 130 possible positions for a symbol on any line.

Although we could use the computer only as an easy way of getting the bracket medians shown in Figure 7.12 and then carry out by hand all the subsequent computations required to analyze any decision problem in which the original distribution of Figure 7.7 was involved, this would of course be wasteful of the computer's capacity. In actual practice, the complete analysis of the particular decision problem being analyzed would be programmed for the computer, and the computer would proceed to carry out the analysis as soon as it had computed the required bracket medians. There would be no intermediate delay and no need for the user even to know what the numerical values of the bracket medians actually were.

7.5
EXPECTATIONS OF LINEAR FUNCTIONS

7.5.1
A Common Error

In Section 7.3.4 we showed how to compute the expectations of certain functions that were of interest to a retailer who could not sell more units than he stocked. If, for example, he stocked $Q = 3$ units and then experienced a demand for d units, his actual unit sales would be

$$s = \begin{cases} d & \text{if} & d \leqslant 3, \\ Q & \text{if} & d > 3. \end{cases}$$

From the fact that *actual* unit sales in this situation will be equal to *actual* demand if actual demand does not exceed 3 units, it is a very common error to infer that *expected* unit sales will be equal to *expected* demand if expected demand does not exceed 3 units. Actually, however, this inference is erroneous, as has already been shown numerically for our example. Expected demand is 2.5 units by Table 7.2 (page 235), but expected unit sales are only 2.2 units by Table 7.6 (page 242). The expectations of the two UQ's are not in fact related in the same way that the actual values of the two UQ's are related, and this example is typical:

■ In general, it is not true that the expectation of a function of a UQ is related to the expectation of the UQ itself in the same way that the actual value of the function is related to the actual value of the UQ.

The proposition just stated in terms of relations can also be stated in terms of formulas, as follows:

■ If we have a formula for $\tilde{y}$ in terms of $\tilde{x}$, we cannot in general find $E\tilde{y}$ by substituting $E\tilde{x}$ for $\tilde{x}$ in the formula.

Finally, the proposition can be most neatly stated as follows:

■ $Ef(\tilde{x})$ is not in general equal to $f(E\tilde{x})$.

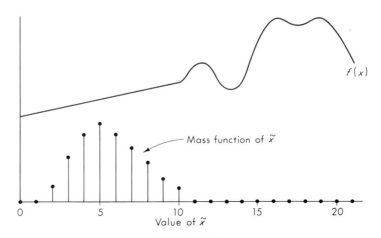

FIGURE 7.14

A Function Linear over the Range of a UQ

7.5.2
Expectation of a Linear Function

Although it is not true *in general* that $Ef(\tilde{x}) = f(E\tilde{x})$, there is a very important special case in which this relation does hold true:

- If $\tilde{y} = f(\tilde{x})$ is a *linear* function of $\tilde{x}$, i.e., if $\tilde{y}$ can be expressed in terms of $\tilde{x}$ by a formula of the type

$$\tilde{y} = a + b\tilde{x}$$

where a and b are constants, *then*

$$Ef(\tilde{x}) = f(E\tilde{x}), \qquad \text{i.e.,} \qquad E\tilde{y} = a + b\ E\tilde{x}.$$

If, for example, $\tilde{y} = 3 + 2\tilde{x}$ and the expectation of $\tilde{x}$ is 7, then the expectation of $\tilde{y}$ is $3 + (2 \times 7) = 17$. The assertion follows directly from the proposition about weighted averages of linear functions that is found in Section A.5.4 of the Appendix on Sets, Functions, and Weighted Averages.

7.5.3
Functions Linear over the Range of a UQ

Suppose now that a function $\tilde{y}$ of a UQ $\tilde{x}$ is related to $\tilde{x}$ in the way shown in Figure 7.14: if the value of $\tilde{x}$ is between 0 and 10, $\tilde{y}$ is related to $\tilde{x}$ by the linear formula

$$\tilde{y} = f(\tilde{x}) = a + b\tilde{x},$$

but if the value of $\tilde{x}$ is greater than 10, $\tilde{y}$ has some other relation to $\tilde{x}$. Then $\tilde{y}$ is not a linear function of $\tilde{x}$ and it will not be true in general that $E\tilde{y} = f(E\tilde{x})$.

    Suppose, however, that as shown in Figure 7.14 the decision maker assigns *zero probability* to all possible values of $\tilde{x}$ to which the linear formula does not apply. Since values with zero probability contribute nothing to the computation of any expectation, $E\tilde{y}$ will have exactly the same value that it would have if the linear formula applied everywhere, and therefore it *will* be true that $E\tilde{y} = f(E\tilde{x})$.

The general principle illustrated by this example is of very great importance in practical analysis of decision problems. In order to state it concisely, we first agree that:

- The set of all possible values of a discrete UQ to which nonzero probability is assigned will be called the ≪range≫ of the UQ;[8]

and we next agree to say that:

- A function $\tilde{y} = f(\tilde{x})$ is ≪linear over the range≫ of $\tilde{x}$ if a *single* formula of the type

$$\tilde{y} = a + b\tilde{x}$$

applies for *all* values of $\tilde{x}$ to which nonzero probability is assigned.

The general principle in which we are interested can then be stated as follows:

1 If a function $\tilde{y} = f(\tilde{x})$ is linear over the range of $\tilde{x}$, then necessarily $E\tilde{y} = f(E\tilde{x})$.

2 If $\tilde{y} = f(\tilde{x})$ is not linear over the range of $\tilde{x}$, then for practical purposes it should be assumed that $E\tilde{y}$ is *not* equal to $f(E\tilde{x})$.

Even when a function $\tilde{y} = f(\tilde{x})$ is not linear over the range of $\tilde{x}$, it may still happen accidentally that $E\tilde{y} = f(E\tilde{x})$, but such accidents are extremely rare and the only way of being sure that we have met one in any particular situation is actually to compute both $E\tilde{y}$ and $f(E\tilde{x})$ directly and then test whether they are equal.

7.5.4
A Common Variant of the Common Error

We call particular attention to a type of error that is very frequently made even by persons who think they have the principle just stated clearly in mind. The error in question consists in failing to remember that a function whose graph is a *broken* line is *not* a linear function.

In Figure 7.15 we graph the function

$$s = g_3(d) = \begin{cases} d & \text{if} & d \leqslant 3, \\ 3 & \text{if} & d > 3, \end{cases}$$

that we defined on page 240, and we also graph the mass function of the distribu-

---

[8] This definition of the range of a UQ is not the standard one, which makes the range identical to what we have called the set of all "possible" values of the UQ.

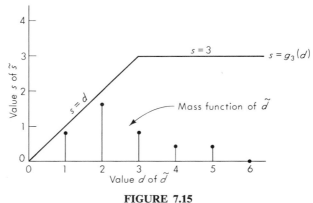

FIGURE 7.15

A Nonlinear Function

tion of $\tilde{d}$. The UQ $\tilde{s} = g_3(\tilde{d})$ is not a linear function of $\tilde{d}$ even though it is "piece-wise linear", and it is not true that $E\tilde{s}$, i.e., $Eg_3(\tilde{d})$, is equal to $g_3(E\tilde{d})$. We saw in Section 7.3.4 that $Eg_3(\tilde{d}) = 2.2$, whereas $g_3(E\tilde{d}) = g_3(2.5) = 2.5$ as can be seen from the formulas just above.

7.5.5

Use of Expectations in the
Analysis of Decision Problems

We saw in Section 5.6 that when the decision maker's preference is a linear function of the terminal value of his criterion, he can under certain conditions omit event forks representing uncertain partial cash flows from his decision diagram and treat the uncertain partial cash flows as if they were certain to be equal to their expectations. We are now in a position to show by an example that under certain conditions a decision maker can omit event forks representing other uncertain quantities from his decision diagram and treat the UQ's as if they were certain to be equal to their expectations.

Suppose that a particular terminal event fork in an original or reduced decision diagram represents the UQ "hours worked", which we shall denote by $\tilde{h}$; let $\tilde{v}$ denote the terminal value that will be determined by $\tilde{h}$; and let $\bar{h}$ and $\bar{v}$ respectively denote the decision maker's expectations of $\tilde{h}$ and $\tilde{v}$ as calculated by use of the distribution he assigns to $\tilde{h}$ on this particular fork.

1. If the decision maker's preference is a linear function of terminal value $\tilde{v}$, then as we saw in Section 5.5.4 his certainty equivalent for $\tilde{v}$ is equal to his expectation $\bar{v}$.

2. If terminal value $\tilde{v}$ is a linear function of $\tilde{h}$ over the range of $\tilde{h}$, then as we saw in Section 7.5.3 the decision maker's expectation $\bar{v}$ is equal to the value that $\tilde{v}$ would actually have if $\tilde{h}$ were actually equal to $\bar{h}$.

3. It follows that if both the above conditions are met, the event fork

under consideration may be replaced by a single branch to which is associated a definite value of $\bar{h}$ equal to the decision maker's expectation $\bar{h}$.

The reader should pay particular attention to the fact that there are *two* conditions that must be satisfied before any one event fork representing a UQ may be replaced by a branch representing the decision maker's expectation for the UQ on that fork. What must be found in order to reduce the fork correctly is the decision maker's *certainty equivalent* for the associated uncertain terminal value $\tilde{v}$; his certainty equivalent will not be equal to his expectation $\bar{v}$ unless his preference is linear in $\tilde{v}$; and treating the UQ represented by the fork as if it were certain to be equal to its expectation will not even lead to a correct value for $\bar{v}$ unless $\tilde{v}$ is linear in the UQ.

When the same uncertain quantity is represented by more than one event fork in a decision diagram, the reader must also remember that the decision maker may assign a different distribution to the UQ on each of these forks. If he does, his expectation of the UQ will in general be different on each fork; and therefore even if each individual fork can be replaced by the appropriate expectation, there will in general be no one expectation that can replace the complete distribution of the UQ throughout the entire description and analysis of the decision problem.

In order to summarize the discussion above, let $\tilde{x}$ stand for any one UQ involved in a decision problem.

■ If (1) a decision maker's preference is a linear function of the terminal value of his criterion, (2) his terminal value is a linear function of $\tilde{x}$ on every event fork that would represent $\tilde{x}$ in a complete diagram of his decision problem, and (3) his distribution of $\tilde{x}$ would be the same on every such event fork, *then* he may omit all event forks representing $\tilde{x}$ from his decision diagram and treat $\tilde{x}$ as if it were certain to be equal to his expectation $\bar{x}$ when he computes values for the end positions of his simplified diagram.

7.6
SUMMARY

7.6.1
Definitions and Notation

1 *a* An ≪uncertain quantity≫ (UQ) will be denoted by a letter with a tilde over it, e.g., $\tilde{x}$.

b The same letter without the tilde will stand for any one, particular value of the UQ.

2 An uncertain quantity is called ≪discrete≫ if its possible values can be listed.

3 A list which for each possible value x of a discrete UQ $\tilde{x}$ shows the probability $P(\tilde{x} = x)$ that the UQ will have exactly that value defines the ≪mass function≫ of $\tilde{x}$.

4 A list which for each possible value x of a discrete UQ $\tilde{x}$ shows the probability $P(\tilde{x} \leqslant x)$ that the UQ will have that value or less defines the ≪cumulative function≫ of $\tilde{x}$.

7.6.2
Graphs

"Exact" and "smooth" graphs of the mass and cumulative functions of a UQ are illustrated in Figure 7.3 (page 230).

1 Smooth graphs are useful only when (1) the possible values of the UQ are evenly spaced out, and (2) the probabilities of these values are all very small and change gradually from one value to the next.

2 When these two conditions are met, the *slope* of a smooth graph of the cumulative function of a UQ at any possible value of the UQ will be almost exactly proportional to the *height* of a smooth graph of the mass function at that value. It follows that:

a Each reversal of curvature in the graph of the cumulative function corresponds to a local maximum or minimum in the graph of the mass function;

b A cumulative function whose left end meets the horizontal axis at a sharp angle corresponds to a mass function with a large jump at the left end, and similarly for the right ends.

7.6.3
Summary Measures of a Distribution

1 If greater probability is assigned to some particular value of a discrete UQ than to the immediately adjacent possible values, this value is called a ≪mode≫ of the probability distribution of the UQ.

2 *a* To find the ≪k fractile≫ x_k of the distribution of a UQ $\tilde{x}$, enter a smooth graph of its cumulative function at k on the vertical axis and read across to the curve and down to the horizontal axis. If the value encountered on the horizontal axis is a possible value of the UQ, it is the k fractile of the UQ; if the value encountered on the horizontal axis is an impossible value, the k fractile is the first possible value to the right.

b If the probability $P(\tilde{x} = x_k)$ that a UQ $\tilde{x}$ will be exactly equal to its k fractile x_k is very small, then $P(\tilde{x} < x_k)$ is approximately equal to k and $P(\tilde{x} > x_k)$ is approximately equal to $(1 - k)$.

c The .5 fractile of a distribution is called the ≪median≫; the .25 and .75 fractiles are called the lower and upper ≪quartiles≫.

3 a The ≪mean≫ of the distribution of a UQ is computed by (1) multiplying each possible value of the UQ by the probability of that value, and (2) adding these products.

  b The mean of the distribution of $\bar{x}$ is also called the ≪expectation≫ of $\bar{x}$ and is denoted by $\bar{x}$ or $E\bar{x}$.

The expectation of a UQ is thus by definition the probability-weighted average of the possible values of the UQ.

4 The mean, median, and mode of a distribution are in general unequal unless the distribution is unimodal and symmetric.

5 a The ≪variance≫ of (the distribution of) a UQ is computed by (1) computing the square of the difference between each possible value of the UQ and the expectation of the UQ, (2) multiplying each squared difference by the probability of the corresponding value of the UQ, and (3) adding these products.

  b The ≪standard deviation≫ is the square root of the variance.

The variance of a UQ is thus by definition the probability-weighted average of the *squares* of the *differences* between the possible values of the UQ and the expectation of the UQ.

7.6.4
Functions of a UQ

1 A UQ $\bar{y}$ is said to be a ≪function≫ of another UQ $\bar{x}$ if the value of $\bar{x}$ determines the value of $\bar{y}$.

2 If $\bar{y}$ is a function of a discrete UQ $\bar{x}$, the probability of any possible value of $\bar{y}$ is the sum of the probabilities of all values of $\bar{x}$ that give rise to that value of $\bar{y}$.

3 If $\bar{y}$ is a function of a discrete UQ $\bar{x}$, the expectation of $\bar{y}$ can be computed by (1) multiplying the probability of each possible value of $\bar{x}$ by the corresponding value of the function $\bar{y}$, and (2) adding these products.

7.6.5
Grouped Approximations

1 To construct a ≪grouped approximation≫ to a distribution that has been specified by a graph of its cumulative function:
  a Divide the *vertical* axis into brackets,
  b Assign the entire probability in each vertical bracket to the value of the UQ found by entering the graph at the midpoint of the vertical bracket and reading over to the curve and down to the horizontal axis.

The edges of each vertical bracket implicitly define the edges of a horizontal bracket of values of the UQ; cf. Figure 7.10 on page 252. The value of the UQ within each horizontal bracket that corresponds to the midpoint of the vertical bracket is called the ≪bracket median≫ of the horizontal bracket.

2 To compute a grouped approximation to the expectation of a UQ or any function thereof, first construct a grouped approximation to the distribution of the UQ and then proceed as if this were the true distribution of the UQ.

7.6.6
Linear Functions

1 A function $\tilde{y}$ of a discrete UQ $\tilde{x}$ is ≪linear over the range≫ of $\tilde{x}$ if a *single* formula of the type

$$\tilde{y} = a + b\tilde{x}$$

holds for all values of $\tilde{x}$ to which nonzero probability is assigned.

2 If, and for practical purposes only if, $\tilde{y} = f(\tilde{x})$ is linear over the range of $\tilde{x}$,

$$Ef(\tilde{x}) = f(E\tilde{x}),$$

or in other words,

$$E\tilde{y} = a + b \ E\tilde{x}.$$

A very important special case of the last proposition above is the one where the role of $\tilde{y}$ is played by the terminal value $\tilde{V}$ of the decision maker's criterion.

3 If terminal value $\tilde{V}$ is a linear function of some UQ $\tilde{x}$, then expected terminal value can be correctly calculated by treating $\tilde{x}$ as if it were certain to be equal to the decision maker's expectation of $\tilde{x}$.

Recall, however, that (1) expected terminal values are relevant to the analysis of a decision problem *only* when the decision maker is willing to treat such expectations as certainty equivalents—i.e., when his preference is (practically) a linear function of terminal value, and (2) the decision maker's expectation of a UQ will have different values on different event forks representing the UQ unless he assigns exactly the same distribution to the UQ on every event fork in his decision diagram. It follows that:

4 A UQ $\tilde{x}$ which affects terminal value in a decision problem may be treated as if it were certain to be equal to the decision maker's expectation $E\tilde{x}$ if and only if (1) terminal value is a linear function of $\tilde{x}$, (2) preference is a linear function of terminal value, and (3) the decision maker assigns the same distribution to $\tilde{x}$ on every event fork in his decision diagram.

If either of the first two conditions is not satisfied, uncertainty about $\tilde{x}$ must be explicitly represented by an appropriate event fan or fans on the decision diagram and these fans must be reduced by computing the decision maker's (expected) preference for each fan. If the first two conditions are satisfied but the third is not, each $\tilde{x}$ fan may be replaced by a single branch to which is associated a definite value of $\tilde{x}$ equal to the decision maker's expectation of $\tilde{x}$ on that particular fan, but these expectations will differ from one such branch to another.

Harvard Business School
Computer Programs for Managerial Economics
MEPD–15
Stanley I. Buchin, 5/21/65

SMOOTHING A CUMULATIVE DISTRIBUTION FUNCTION THROUGH A SET OF SPECIFIED POINTS

PREFACE

Program package *Smooth* is designed to facilitate numerical analysis of problems involving quasi-continuous probability distributions that have been specified empirically rather than analytically. The units in the package can process a distribution of any shape provided only that its cumulative distribution function (CDF) is defined over a finite range and has at most one point of inflection, corresponding to a density function that is unimodal, possibly J-shaped.

For each distribution to be processed, the user must specify a number of points on the CDF and the slope of the CDF at certain of these points. A subroutine *Smooth*, which is the essential part of the package, then fits a smooth analytic CDF to the specified points and slopes and computes and makes available the .005, .015, .025, . . ., .995 fractiles of the distribution thus defined. Numerical analysis can be based on the discretized distribution obtained by assigning probability .01 to each of these 100 values of the random variable (RV); the 100 values will be referred to hereafter as the 100 "bracket medians" of the fitted distribution. The mean and standard deviation of this discretized distribution are also computed and made available by *Smooth*.

To permit the user to decide whether he is satisfied with the CDF fitted by *Smooth*, there is provision within this subroutine for printing out either a complete mathematical description of the CDF or a list of the 100 bracket medians together with the mean and standard deviation of the discretized distribution based thereon. Alternatively or in addition, a sketch graph of the fitted CDF can be printed out by a subroutine *Graph* which is also included in the package.

The subroutines *Smooth* and *Graph* can be used in conjunction with any calling program that requires the 100 bracket medians computed by *Smooth* as inputs to analysis, but the package also contains a simple calling program which can be used when all the user wishes is to examine the distribution which *Smooth* will fit to a given set of inputs.

The time required to fit and graph a distribution on an IBM 7094 is less than half a minute.

1
REQUIRED SPECIFICATIONS CONCERNING ANY DISTRIBUTION TO BE FITTED BY SMOOTH

The user must supply the following specifications concerning any distribution that is to be fitted by *Smooth*. He may obtain them by reading a CDF that he has already assessed graphically, by actually computing them from the formula for an analytic distribution that is awkward to process analytically, or in any other way he pleases.

1.1
Formal Requirements

The user must specify *at least 3* but *no more than 26* points through which the fitted CDF is to pass, each point being specified by a statement of its *abscissa* (value of the RV) and its *ordinate* (probability of that value or less—i.e., probability that the RV will be equal to or less than the value in question). The specified points *must* include the points for which the abscissa or value of the RV is:

a The "*0 fractile*" of the distribution—i.e., the greatest value of the RV such that the probability of that value or less is 0.

b The "*1 fractile*" of the distribution—i.e., the least value of the RV such that the probability of that value or less is 1.

c The *mode* of the distribution (the value of the RV at which the slope of the CDF is steepest). It is permissible, however, for the mode to be identical to the 0 or 1 fractile, corresponding to a CDF with no inflection point and a J-shaped density function.

For comments on the additional points which should be specified in order to obtain a good fit, see Section 1.2 below.

The user must also specify the slope of the CDF at the *0 fractile*, the *1 fractile*, and also at the *mode* if the mode differs from both the 0 and 1 fractiles. The slope of the CDF may *not* be specified at any *other* points.

The slope of the CDF at any given point can be measured most easily by first constructing a straight line parallel to, but *not* coincident with, the curve at the point in question, and then reading the abscissa and ordinate of each of two points as far apart as possible on this straight line. If the abscissas (values of the RV) of these two points are denoted by v_1 and v_2 and the corresponding ordinates (cumulative probabilities) by p_1 and p_2, the slope is $(p_2 - p_1)/(v_2 - v_1)$. The slope may be 0 at the 0 and/or the 1 fractile, but it must not of course be 0 at the mode.

1.2
Selection of Points to Ensure a Good Fit

The CDF fitted by *Smooth* will usually be a good approximation to the CDF from which the input data are obtained if the user specifies 10 to 12 points on the CDF in addition to the two or three formally required points (those corresponding to the 0 and 1 fractiles and the mode if it differs from both of these). The best procedure is usually to start by specifying 9 or 10 points on the CDF that are about equally spaced out either horizontally or vertically; the 9 deciles are a choice that facilitates chart reading. A few additional points should then be supplied to improve the definition of the curve in regions where its slope is changing most rapidly.

1.3
Layout of Data

To facilitate correct punching of data cards, the user's specifications of points and slopes should be laid out in the form of a table which contains one *row* for each specified point and which shows in successive *columns:*

  a Value of the RV (abscissa of the point),

  b Probability of that value or less (ordinate of the point),

  c Slope of the CDF at that point *if and only if* the value of the RV (abscissa) is the 0 or 1 fractile or the mode.

The values of the RV should be listed in the table *in order of increasing size.*

1.4
Verification of Data

The fitting procedure used by *Smooth* may give completely nonsensical results unless (1) the specified points from the 0 fractile to the mode inclusive can all be contained in a curve which is everywhere convex from below, and (2) the specified points from the mode to the 1 fractile inclusive can all be contained in a curve which is everywhere concave from below. Since small errors in reading abscissas and ordinates from an assessed graphic CDF can easily lead the user to specify points which fail this test, he may do well to verify that his specified points do not fail.

2
OUTPUTS AVAILABLE FROM SMOOTH AND GRAPH

2.1
Output Available to a Calling Program
for Use in Numerical Analysis

The output which *Smooth* can make available to a calling program for immediate use in numerical analysis consists essentially of:

1 The 100 bracket medians of the fitted distribution;

2 The mean and standard deviation of these bracket medians.

The quartiles and the 0 and 1 fractiles are also available but will usually be of little use in numerical analysis.

2.2
Printed Output Available
for Checking the Operation of Smooth

As regards the printed output available for checking the operation of *Smooth*, a much wider choice is available. The program automatically prints out a proof list of the specifications (points and slopes) for each distribution that is processed; the user can also have any of the following outputs printed if he so desires, although not all of them are available separately:

a Sketch graph of the analytic CDF fitted by *Smooth*.

b List of the 100 bracket medians of the fitted distribution and of its "five quartiles"—i.e., the "0 fractile", the three quartiles in the usual sense of the word, and the "1 fractile".

c Mean and standard deviation of the bracket medians.

d Complete mathematical description of the fitted analytic CDF.

EXERCISES

A. DISTRIBUTIONS AND GRAPHS

7.1 *a* Compute the cumulative function of the uncertain quantity "number of units sold" whose probability distribution is given in Table 7.15 below.

TABLE 7.15

Number Sold	Probability of That Number
0	.07
1	.13
2	.27
3	.31
4	.22
5 and up	.00
	1.00

b Compute the mass function of the uncertain quantity "number of units demanded" whose possible values are 0, 1, 2, . . . and whose probability distribution is given in Table 7.16.

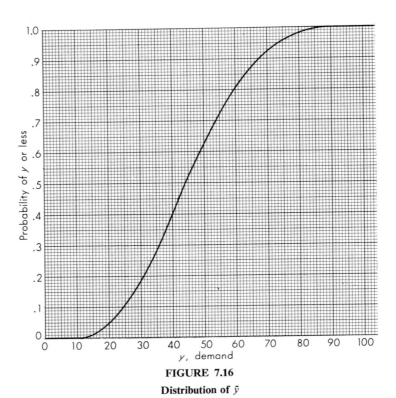

FIGURE 7.16

Distribution of ỹ

TABLE 7.16

Number Demanded	Probability of That Number or Less
0	.20
1	.50
2	.70
3	.85
4	.95
5	1.00

7.2   Consider the uncertain quantity ỹ, number of yo-yo's demanded, and read to two decimal places the following probabilities under the distribution of ỹ defined in Figure 7.16.   The possible values of the UQ are, of course, 0, 1, 2, ...

a. $P(\tilde{y} \leqslant 20)$

b. $P(\tilde{y} < 43)$

c. $P(\tilde{y} > 72)$

d. $P(\tilde{y} \geqslant 63)$

7.3   Each of the smooth graphs in Figure 7.17 represents either the mass function or the cumulative function of a UQ whose possible values are 0, 1, 2, ...   Because there are very many possible values in each case, the probability of any individual value is very small.   For each of these graphs, determine whether the graph is a

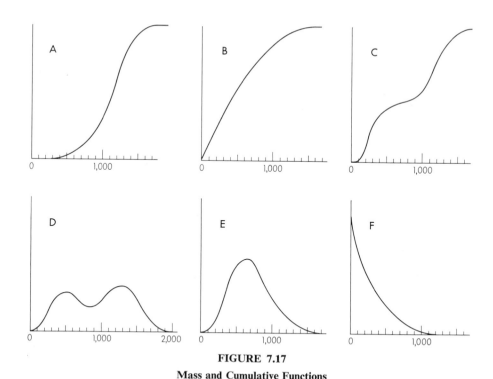

FIGURE 7.17

Mass and Cumulative Functions

mass or a cumulative function; then sketch the general shape of the cumulative function of the UQ if the graph in Figure 7.17 is a mass function, or sketch the general shape of the mass function if the graph in Figure 7.17 is a cumulative function.

7.4 Be prepared to justify the three statements at the end of Section 7.1.4.

B. SUMMARY MEASURES AND EXPECTATIONS

7.5 *a* What is the mode of the distribution of the UQ $\tilde{y}$ described in Exercise 7.2 and graphed in Figure 7.16?

  b What is the probability that $\tilde{y}$ is (1) less than, and (2) greater than, its mode?

7.6 *a* Compute the .40, .60, and .94 fractiles and the median of the distribution of $\tilde{y}$ which is graphed in Figure 7.16.

  b Compute the probability that $\tilde{y}$ will be (1) less than, and (2) greater than, each of the four values specified in (*a*).

7.7 Compute the mean of the distribution defined by Table 7.15 (page 271).

C. EXPECTATIONS OF FUNCTIONS

7.8 As part of his line of specialty furniture items, Mr. P. J. Woodman produces wooden coffee tables with square tops three, four, and five feet on a side. The last step in producing a table is the application of varnish to only the top surface of the table; the process requires .04 pint of varnish per square foot and varnish costs $1.25 per pint.

Woodman would like to compute his mathematical expectation for the uncertain cost of varnish for the table top he is about to finish. The top will be selected at random from the inventory of unfinished tops by Woodman's assistant; Woodman assigns the distribution shown in Table 7.17 below to the size of the table top that will be selected.

TABLE 7.17

Length of Side (Feet)	Probability of That Length
3	.2
4	.5
5	.3
	1.0

a Write a formula relating the cost $\tilde{c}$ of varnish to the area $\tilde{a}$ of the selected table top.

b Write a formula relating $\tilde{a}$ to the length $\tilde{s}$ of one side of the table top selected, and then, using your answer to (*a*), write a formula relating $\tilde{c}$ directly to $\tilde{s}$.

c Compute the expectation $E\tilde{c}$ of the cost of varnish by the method illustrated in Table 7.6 (page 242).

d Compute the expectation $E\tilde{s}$ of the length of one side, substitute the number $E\tilde{s}$ for the symbol $\tilde{s}$ in the formula you wrote relating $\tilde{c}$ to $\tilde{s}$, and compare the result with your answer to (*c*).

7.9 Mr. Hiram Quimby, who operates a small antique factory in a university community, has decided to produce as many Louis XIV tables next Thursday as have been ordered up to Thursday morning. No tables can be produced after Friday morning because a run of Sheraton highboys must be begun at that time, and since only two tables can be produced on regular time on Thursday at a cost of $37 each, any remaining orders will have to be filled on overtime at a cost of $56 each. The tables sell for $375 each. Mr. Quimby assigns the distribution shown in Table 7.18 below to the number of orders received by Thursday morning.

TABLE 7.18
Distribution of Orders
Received by Thursday Morning

Number of Orders	Probability of That Number
0	.05
1	.10
2	.30
3	.35
4	.15
5	.05
6 and up	0
	1.00

a Denoting the number of orders on hand Thursday morning by $\tilde{d}$ and denoting contribution by $\tilde{c}$, write formulas relating $\tilde{c}$ to $\tilde{d}$. [Hint: you may find it easiest to proceed by (1) writing formulas that relate $\tilde{c}$ to sales revenue $\tilde{r}$ and production cost $\tilde{p}$, (2) writing formulas relating $\tilde{r}$ and $\tilde{p}$ to $\tilde{d}$, and then (3) writing formulas relating $\tilde{c}$ to $\tilde{d}$.]

b Compute the expectation $E\tilde{c}$ of contribution by the method illustrated in Table 7.6 (page 242).

c Compute the expectation $E\tilde{d}$ of demand, substitute it for the symbol $\tilde{d}$ in the formulas relating $\tilde{c}$ to $\tilde{d}$, and compare the result with your answer to (*b*).

7.10 Suppose that Mrs. I. J. Kresge of Exercise 2.11 states that she is willing to treat mathematical expectations as certainty equivalents and suppose further that she assigns the probability distribution shown in Table 7.19 to today's demand for soufflés.

TABLE 7.19
Mrs. I. J. Kresge's
Probability Distribution of Demand
for Soufflés Maison

Number Demanded	Probability of That Number
0	.20
1	.30
2	.23
3	.15
4	.10
5	.02
6 and up	0
	———
	1.00

a Compute Mrs. Kresge's expected terminal value if she produces 2 soufflés; if she produces 5 soufflés. (In working this problem, you must carry out all multiplications to the very last figure. All that you will learn with slide-rule accuracy is that because Mrs. Kresge's contribution from today's business will be very small relative to her starting cash in till, she will end up with "about" $500 in the till no matter what she does.)

b What additional calculations would you have to perform in order to determine the optimal number of soufflés for Mrs. Kresge to produce?

c If all that you knew about Mrs. Kresge's probability distribution were its mean, could you compute her expected terminal value given that she produces 2 soufflés? given that she produces 5 soufflés?

D. GROUPED APPROXIMATIONS

7.11 In the course of analyzing a decision problem, Harry Tilden has drawn a diagram that contains a terminal event fan representing the UQ "demand", which he denotes by $\tilde{d}$, and has assigned to $\tilde{d}$ the cumulative function shown in Figure 7.18. In order to compute a grouped approximation to his expectation $E\tilde{d}$ of demand, Tilden has divided the possible values of $\tilde{d}$ that appear on the horizontal axis of

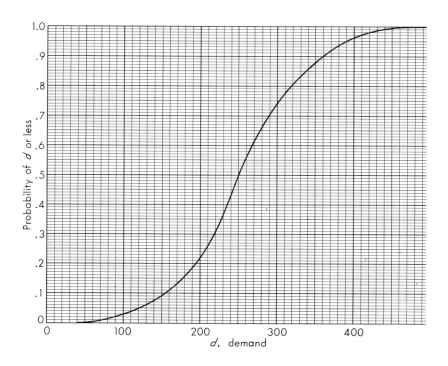

FIGURE 7.18

Mr. Tilden's Original Distribution of Demand

Figure 7.18 into 10 groups or brackets and has selected a representative value for each bracket; the least and greatest values in each bracket and the value which Tilden has chosen to represent each bracket are shown in Table 7.20. (The reason for Tilden's choices of brackets and representative values will appear in a moment.)

TABLE 7.20
Brackets Selected by Tilden

Least Value of Demand	Greatest Value of Demand	Representative Value of Demand
47	154	120
155	194	177
195	219	208
220	234	227
235	250	242
251	268	259
269	289	278
290	318	303
319	360	338
361	470	390

a Read to two decimal places from the graph in Figure 7.18 the probability that d will have a value less than or equal to the greatest value in each of the ten brackets, and then compute the probability that d will have a value *within* each of the brackets.

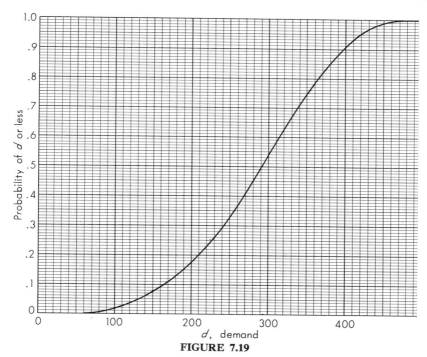

FIGURE 7.19

Mr. Tilden's Revised Distribution of Demand

b Assigning the entire probability of each bracket of values of $\tilde{d}$ to the representative value for that bracket, show by the method illustrated in Table 7.11 (page 250) that $E\tilde{d}$ is approximately 254.3.

c Read to two decimal places from Figure 7.18 the probability that $\tilde{d}$ will have a value less than or equal to the "representative" value for each of the ten brackets.

d On the vertical axis of Figure 7.18, mark off (1) the cumulative probabilities you read in answer to (*a*), and (2) the cumulative probabilities you read in answer to (*c*).

e How did Tilden select his brackets of values of $\tilde{d}$ and his representative values for these brackets?

f What part of the information about Tilden's brackets that was given you in Table 7.20 did you actually use in computing your answer to (*b*)?

g How could Tilden have obtained the useful information in Table 7.20 without obtaining the useless information?

7.12 Suppose that after further reflection Mr. Tilden of Exercise 7.11 decides to assign to $\tilde{d}$ the revised distribution defined by the cumulative function shown in Figure 7.19 instead of the cumulative function shown in Figure 7.18; and suppose further that he now assigns a terminal value v to each branch of the $\tilde{d}$ fan in his diagram via the formulas

$$v = \begin{cases} \$d - \$200 & \text{if} \quad d \leqslant 300, \\ \$3d - \$800 & \text{if} \quad d > 300. \end{cases}$$

a Group the distribution defined by Figure 7.19 into 10 equiprobable brackets of

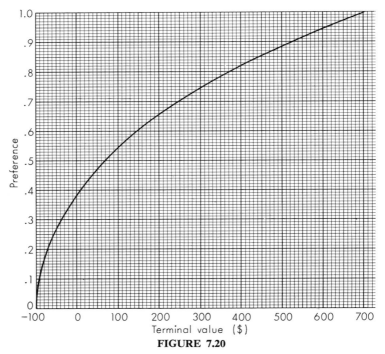

FIGURE 7.20

Mr. Tilden's Preferences for Terminal Values

values of $\tilde{d}$ and let the bracket median of each bracket represent all the values
in that bracket.

b Verify that the value of $\tilde{v}$ which corresponds to the representative value of $\tilde{d}$
is $-\$69$ for the first bracket and $+\$457$ for the tenth bracket.

c Compute an approximation to Tilden's expectation of the uncertain terminal
value $\tilde{v}$ represented by the $\tilde{d}$ fan in his decision diagram.

d Suppose that Tilden's preferences for terminal values between $-\$100$ and
$+\$700$ are those graphed in Figure 7.20. Reading preferences from Figure 7.20
to two decimal places, compute an approximation to his preference for the
position at the base of the $\tilde{d}$ fan in his decision diagram and then compute his
certainty-equivalent terminal value for this position.

7.13 The manufacturer of Exercise 5.18 has been given a forecast that $F = 25{,}000$ units
of Product A23Z will be demanded next quarter. Instead of directly assessing his
distribution of actual demand $\tilde{d}$, he assesses the distribution shown in Figure
7.21 of the *ratio* $\tilde{x} = \tilde{d}/F$ of actual to forecast demand. The figure shows, for
example, that he assigns probability .305 to the event $\tilde{x} \leqslant .95$ and hence to the
event $\tilde{d} \leqslant .95F$; since $F = 25{,}000$, this means that he assesses $P(\tilde{d} \leqslant 23{,}750) =$
.305.

a Modify the diagram of this manufacturer's decision problem that you constructed in answer to Exercise 5.18 by substituting a fan or fans representing
the manufacturer's uncertainty about $\tilde{x}$ for the fan or fans which represented
his uncertainty about $\tilde{d}$ in your original diagram.

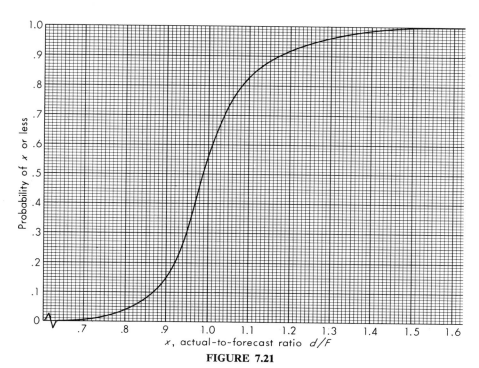

FIGURE 7.21

Manufacturer's Distribution of the Ratio of Actual to Forecast Demand

b Letting x denote the value of $\tilde{x}$ represented by the typical branch on any $\tilde{x}$ fan in your new diagram, write a formula or formulas for the terminal value v at each end position of that diagram. (Remember that since actual demand d no longer appears in the diagram, it cannot appear in any formula. The formulas may only involve Q and/or x.)

c Considering $\tilde{v}$ as an uncertain quantity, approximate the manufacturer's expectation of $\tilde{v}$ given that $Q = 23,000$ units are produced.

d Because the manufacturer intends to treat his mathematical expectations for uncertain monetary values as certainty equivalents, he will wish to produce that number of units which leads him to have the greatest possible expectation of $\tilde{v}$. How could you estimate this number without actually computing his expectations for more than a half dozen different Q's?

e A bright young analyst on the company's staff suggests that the manufacturer will maximize his expectation of $\tilde{v}$ if he chooses Q in such a way that the total number of units on hand after the production run is made is equal to his expectation of this quarter's demand. If, for example, the manufacturer's expectation of demand is 23,000 units, the company should produce $23,000 - 4,000 = 19,000$ units. What do you think of the analyst's method for deciding how many units to produce?

CHAPTER

8

ASSESSMENT OF PROBABILITY DISTRIBUTIONS

When an event fork has only a very few branches, the decision maker can assess his probabilities for the events represented by the branches by thinking about each one individually and assigning it a tentative value, then adjusting these tentative values so that they add to 1, and finally verifying the revised values by computing from them the probability of selected compound events (Section 6.1.3) and seeing if these computed probabilities agree with the probabilities he would assess directly. Such a procedure becomes difficult, however, as soon as there are more than a very few branches on the fork, and it becomes completely infeasible as soon as the number of branches becomes really large. In such cases some other way of assessing the required probabilities must be found, and in this chapter we shall study the two simplest methods by which the decision maker can assess his probabilities for many-branched event forks of the type most commonly encountered in practical business decision problems, namely event forks on which each branch represents a possible value of some uncertain quantity.

    1. In Section 8.1, we take the case where the assessment must be based directly on the decision maker's judgment, unaided by any quantitative evidence that can be processed systematically.

    2. In Section 8.2 we consider situations where the decision maker can usefully think of the value that a UQ (e.g., demand) will actually have as being generated by some kind of physical process that is capable of generating values repeatedly (e.g., on successive days), and we show how values generated by this

process on previous occasions can be systematically processed in assessing a probability distribution for the UQ on "this" occasion.

3. In Section 8.3, we show how these two basic methods of assessment can be applied in the very common kind of situation in which either the decision maker or someone else has made a "point forecast" or "estimate" of an uncertain quantity.

4. Finally, in Section 8.4 we consider decision problems in which the mean of the distribution of a UQ is the only fact about the distribution that is relevant to the problem and examine the conditions under which the decision maker should and should not try to assess this mean directly, without assessing his complete distribution of the UQ.

The text and exercises of this chapter are designed to be studied in the following order:

1 Exercise 8.1.

2 Sections 8.1.1–8.1.4 and Exercise 8.2*a*.

3 Sections 8.1.5–8.1.6 and Exercises 8.2*b* and 8.3.

4 Section 8.1.7 and Exercise 8.4.

5 Sections 8.2.1–8.2.5 and Exercise 8.5.

6 Section 8.2.6 and Exercise 8.6.

7 Sections 8.3.1–8.3.3 and Exercise 8.7.

8 Sections 8.3.4–8.3.7 and Exercise 8.8.

9 Section 8.4 and Exercise 8.9.

10 Section 8.5 and Exercises 8.10–8.11.

11 Exercise 8.12.

CONTENTS OF CHAPTER 8

1.
Direct Judgmental Assessment of Probability Distributions

1 Shape of the Mass Function in the Simplest Case
2 Assessment of Probabilities for Individual Values
3 Assessment of Cumulative Probabilities
4 Assessment of Fractiles
5 Graphical Assessment of the Remaining Probabilities
6 Tentative Assessment and Sensitivity Analysis
7 Decomposition of Assessment Problems

2.
Assessment by Smoothing Historical Data

1 Historical vs. Long-run Relative Frequencies
2 A Model of a Random Process
3 Estimation of Long-run Frequencies
4 Assessment of the Probability Distribution
5 Estimation of Cumulative Long-run Frequencies
6 Distinguishable and Indistinguishable Occasions

3.
Use of Forecasts and Estimates

1 Historical Data on Forecast Errors
2 Distinguishable and Indistinguishable Occasions
3 The Actual/Forecast Ratio
4 Effect of Self-calibration
5 Assessment in the Absence of Historical Data
6 The Meaning of a Forecast
7 Median Forecasts

4.
Assessment of Expectations

1 Estimates vs. Expectations
2 Direct Assessment of Expectations
3 Probability and Expected Long-run Relative Frequency

5.
Summary

1 Direct Judgmental Assessment
2 Smoothing of Historical Frequencies
3 Forecasts and Estimates

8.1
DIRECT JUDGMENTAL ASSESSMENT
OF PROBABILITY DISTRIBUTIONS

A decision maker who wishes to assess his probabilities for 100 or 100,000 possible values of a discrete UQ such as "next year's demand" cannot accomplish this task by considering each possible value separately and reaching a separate decision on the probability he will assign to that value. As we said earlier, he cannot afford the time that would be required; and even if he could, he would be totally dissatisfied with the results. He would find, not only that his assessments were formally inconsistent in the sense that they did not add to 1, but also that many of the individual assessments seemed completely unreasonable relative to other individual assessments.

The problem of assessing probabilities for a very large number of possible values of a UQ is thus very much like the problem of assessing preferences for a very large number of terminal values, and the practical solutions of the two problems are also very much the same. We saw in Chapter 5 that in order to assess his preferences for a very large number of terminal values, the decision maker should first decide how he wants his preferences for individual terminal values to be related to each other. Thus he might decide that he wants his preference to increase continuously as his terminal value increases, that he wants his preferences to reflect the fact that his certainty equivalent for the uncertain terminal value that will result from any gamble is less than his mathematical expectation for that uncertain value, and so forth. Once he has decided on these general relations among individual preferences, he can proceed to decide on his preferences for just a few specific terminal values and then construct a preference curve that agrees both with these specific decisions and with his decisions about the relations among all of his preferences.

To apply this same general approach to the assessment of probabilities for the possible values of a UQ, the decision maker must first decide how he wants his individual probabilities to be related to each other, after which he can carefully assess just a few probabilities and then complete his task by constructing a curve. Exactly what probabilities he should assess individually and how he should assess them will be discussed after we have looked at the kind of general relation among probabilities that he might want to specify in the simplest kind of situation.

8.1.1
Shape of the Mass Function
in the Simplest Case

Suppose that a marketing manager wishes to assess his probability distribution for the first year's demand for a new product which his company is thinking of marketing. He may feel that (1) demand is more likely than not to be between, say, 400 and 700 units, but (2) there is nevertheless a substantial chance that demand will turn out to be outside this range, and (3) there is some small chance that demand will turn out to be *very* far outside this range, particularly on the high side; and if so, he may decide that he wants to assign probabilities to all the individual possible values of demand in such a way that his mass function of demand has the general shape shown in Figure 8.1. He may decide, in other words, that (1) the probabilities of the individual values of the UQ should fall off smoothly to either side of a single mode, and (2) most of the probability should be concentrated within a fairly small interval around the mode, but (3) there should be some probability fairly far out in the "tails", particularly in the right tail.

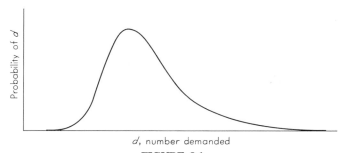

FIGURE 8.1

General Shape of the Marketer's Mass Function

Observe that we have not even suggested that the marketing manager "should" decide that he wants to assess a mass function having the general shape shown in Figure 8.1. All that we assert is that in some situations some business-men do in fact feel that they want to assess mass functions having this general shape.

8.1.2

Assessment of Probabilities
for Individual Values

Having decided on the general shape of the mass function he wants to assess, the marketing manager might try to complete his task by assessing his actual proba-bilities for a few values of the UQ "demand", plotting these assessments as points on a piece of graph paper, and finally fairing through these points a smooth curve with the general shape of Figure 8.1; but if he did try to follow this procedure, he would find the required numerical probabilities extremely hard to assess simply because they would all be extremely small. If he wishes to assign nonzero prob-ability to each of 1,000 possible values of demand, the average probability as-signed to an individual value would be only 1/1,000; and one can readily imagine the difficulty the manager would have in deciding whether, for example, he should assess the probability of demand for 500 units at 1/500, 1/1,000, 1/2,000, or what.

8.1.3

Assessment of Cumulative Probabilities

Although the marketing manager of our example will almost certainly have no intuitive feeling whatever for the chance that demand will be *exactly* equal to any one of its possible values, he can reexpress his problem in such a way that he can solve it by assessing probabilities for events for which he does have a real intuitive feeling. All that he has to do is think in terms of the cumulative func-tion rather than the mass function of his distribution of demand.

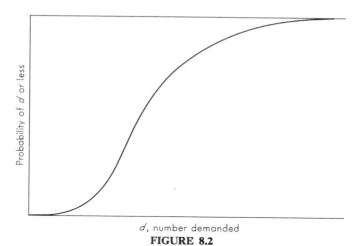

d, number demanded
FIGURE 8.2
General Shape of the Marketer's Cumulative Function

We have already seen in Section 7.1.1 that a probability distribution can be specified by its cumulative function just as well as by its mass function; and we have seen in Section 7.1.4 that if the marketing manager has decided on the general shape that he wants his mass function to have, this decision implies the general shape of his cumulative function. The shape of the mass function in Figure 8.1 implies that, as shown in Figure 8.2, the *slope* of the cumulative function must be 0 at the beginning, become greater and greater until it reaches a maximum at the mode, and then become smaller and smaller until it is 0 at the end. It follows that if the marketing manager can directly assess a few points on his cumulative function—i.e., if he can assess $P(\tilde{d} \leqslant d)$ for a few values of $\tilde{d}$—he can assess his complete probability distribution of $\tilde{d}$ by plotting these numerical assessments as points and then fairing through these points a smooth curve with the general shape of Figure 8.2; and this time the required numerical assessments are of a sort the marketing manager can make without undue difficulty because except for the two ends of the curve he can choose values of $\tilde{d}$ for which $P(\tilde{d} \leqslant d)$ is neither too small nor too large to have a real intuitive meaning.

8.1.4
Assessment of Fractiles

Although the assessment procedure just described is thoroughly feasible, most people find that the numerical assessments required by a slight variant of that procedure are still easier to make. Instead of selecting a number of possible values of the UQ and assessing his cumulative probability for each of them, the decision maker can so to speak make his assessments "in reverse", by assessing fractiles rather than probabilities. A procedure of the following sort will often prove satisfactory.

1. First, the decision maker can divide all the possible values of demand into two equally likely halves. To do so he can look for, and ultimately decide on, some value of demand such that he would be just as ready to bet that demand will be below this value as he would be to bet that demand will be above. By way of example, we shall suppose that our marketing manager decides that he would be just as ready to bet that there will be a demand for less than 500 units as he would be to bet that there will be a demand for more than 500; from which it follows that 500 is the median or .5 fractile of his distribution of demand (cf. Section 7.2.2).

2. Having divided his distribution into halves, the decision maker can go on to subdivide it into quarters by assessing his upper and lower quartiles. To assess his upper quartile (i.e., his .75 fractile), our marketing manager can focus his attention on those values of the UQ that lie above his assessed median and decide on a value that divides them into two equally likely halves, and similarly for the lower quartile. In what follows we shall assume that he decides on 650 as the upper quartile of his distribution and on 400 as his lower quartile.

3. Finally, the decision maker can assess upper and lower limits between which demand will in his opinion almost certainly lie. Our marketing manager might assess an upper limit of this sort by looking, for example, for the value that demand seems 99 times more likely to fall short of than to exceed; and if he decides that demand is about 99 times more likely to fall short of than to exceed 1,100, say, then 1,100 is the .99 fractile of his distribution of demand (cf. Section 7.2.3). Without describing the exactly analogous problem of selecting a lower limit, we shall assume that he decides on 200 as the .01 fractile of his distribution.

Observe that although each of these fractile assessments is made by fixing certain probabilities or ratios of probabilities and then deciding on the corresponding value of the UQ, these decisions have exactly the same kind of meaning as the decisions that are made in assessing probabilities for fixed values of the UQ. When the marketing manager decides on 500 as the median of his distribution, he means (or should mean) that he is indifferent between (1) a gamble that associates any pair of consequences to the events "demand for less than 500" and "demand for more than 500", and (2) a gamble that associates these same consequences to the events "red" and "black" of a standard drawing from an urn in which there are exactly as many red as black balls.

8.1.5
Graphical Assessment of the
Remaining Probabilities

Having divided the range of the UQ "demand" into four equally likely parts by assessing his three quartiles, the decision maker could in principle continue to subdivide the range in this same general way, dividing it next into eight equally likely parts, then into 16, and so forth; but in most cases he will do well to stop

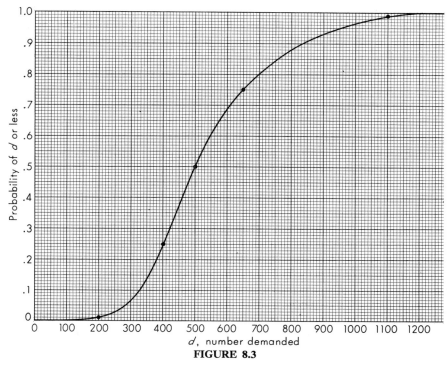

FIGURE 8.3

Cumulative Function Fitted to Assessed Fractiles

making individual numerical assessments at this point and complete his task by curve fairing. In Figure 8.3 the five fractiles which we suppose the marketing manager to have assessed have been plotted as points, and a smooth curve having the general shape of the one in Figure 8.2 has been faired through them.

8.1.6
Tentative Assessment
and Sensitivity Analysis

There is, of course, considerable latitude in fairing a curve like the one in Figure 8.3, especially the parts below the lower quartile and above the upper quartile; and the decision maker may therefore want to read various probabilities from this curve, see whether they agree with his judgment, and change the curve if they do not.

   Experience suggests, however, that when assessed probability distributions are actually used in the analysis of real decision problems, there is usually very little to be lost by use of one generally reasonable curve rather than another if both of them pass through the points representing the decision maker's directly assessed fractiles; and therefore the decision maker should in general avoid taking excessive pains with his first assessment of every probability distribution required for the analysis of the problem.

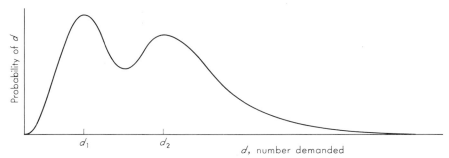

FIGURE 8.4
Bimodal Distribution of Demand

Particularly as regards the difficulties involved in assessing the extreme tails of any distribution, the decision maker should ordinarily start by drawing a curve that is little more than a thoughtful guess at the curve that he would assess if he really took great pains with the assessment.[1] After he has made a preliminary analysis of his actual decision problem based on such tentative assessments of his probabilities, he will be able to carry out a sensitivity analysis of the sort described in Section 6.4 and thus decide which parts of which distributions, if any, are really worth the trouble of more careful assessment.

8.1.7
Decomposition of Assessment Problems

We have already said that the cumulative function of Figure 8.3 is a reasonable one if and only if the decision maker has decided, independently of his specific numerical probability assessments, that he wants his mass and cumulative functions to have the general shapes sketched in Figures 8.1 and 8.2; and we have also already said that while the decision maker may in a particular situation want the assessments to have these general shapes, there is absolutely no reason why he should or must hold this attitude in any particular situation.

To see how a decision maker might very naturally and reasonably want his probability distribution to have a radically different shape, suppose that our marketing manager believes that if his company markets the product whose demand distribution he is assessing, there is a chance that a competitor will immediately follow suit with a very similar product. In such a situation he might say that if he knew for certain that the competitor would not enter the market, he would assess the distribution of demand shown in Figure 8.3, but if on the contrary he knew for certain that the competitor would in fact enter the market, he

---

[1] This is ordinarily a sensible way to proceed because in most decision problems small changes in the small probabilities in the extreme tails of a distribution will have a negligible effect on computed preferences or expectations. It goes without saying that the decision maker must assess the tails of his distributions very carefully in all cases where the tails really matter.

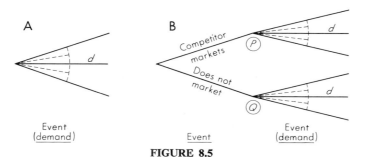

FIGURE 8.5

Decomposition of an Assessment Problem

would assess quite a different distribution of demand. In such a situation, the mass function of the distribution he would assess without knowing whether or not the competitor will enter the market might very well have the general shape illustrated in Figure 8.4, where d_1 is the most probable value of demand if the competitor enters the market while d_2 is the most probable value if he does not.

It is very difficult to make a reasonable direct assessment of a distribution like the one in Figure 8.4, but fortunately it is rarely if ever necessary to assess such a distribution directly. If our marketing manager modifies the decision diagram for which the distribution is required by substituting the sequence of event forks shown in Figure 8.5B for the single fork shown in Figure 8.5A, he can separately assess (1) his probabilities for the events on the first event fork in Figure 8.5B, (2) the distribution he would assign to demand d if he were at position P in Figure 8.5B, and (3) the distribution he would assign to demand if he were at position Q in Figure 8.5B; and very probably he will feel that both these latter distributions should have the relatively simple general shape shown in Figure 8.1 rather than the relatively complex shape shown in Figure 8.4.

This simple example illustrates a very important general principle. It is true in general that:

■ It is very difficult to assess a distribution of a UQ that takes proper account of uncertainty about events which can individually have a substantial effect on the value of the UQ. When such uncertainties are present, it is almost always better to show the events in question explicitly on the decision diagram and then place a fan representing the possible values of the UQ at the end of every possible sequence of individually important events.[2]

The reason is not merely that it is difficult to assess a probability distribution that does not have the relatively simple shape shown in Figures 8.1 and 8.2; the irregular shape is a symptom rather than a cause of the difficulty. The essential reason is that:

---

[2] An alternative method of attaining the same objective will be described in Chapter 9.

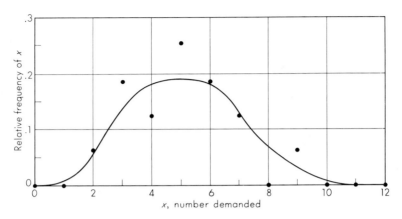

FIGURE 8.6
Demand for Product A

■ Whenever it is possible for a decision maker to decompose his overall uncertainty about any set of events or values of a UQ and express it as the "resultant" of separate uncertainties about separate "components", he should do so, because this permits him to quantify his judgment about one component at a time and thus to bring his experience to bear on the problem more effectively.

8.2
ASSESSMENT BY SMOOTHING HISTORICAL DATA

We saw in Section 6.3 that a person who wishes to assign a reasonable probability to a particular event on a particular occasion must take acount of all available evidence bearing on the long-run relative frequency with which that event would occur on a very great number of occasions all indistinguishable from the present occasion; and we saw that very frequently there will be very important evidence available in the form of historical data on the frequency with which that event has in fact occurred on previous indistinguishable occasions. We are now ready to examine some methods for using such evidence when each possible event is of the form "the UQ $\bar{x}$ has the value x"—i.e., when the problem is to assess the probability distribution of an uncertain quantity.

8.2.1
Historical vs. Long-run
Relative Frequencies

Consider a retailer who wishes to assess his probability distribution of the UQ "tomorrow's demand for Product A", and suppose that this retailer has a record of demand for this product on each of 16 days in the past, all of them indistinguishable from tomorrow in the sense that just *before* any one of these days actually transpired, the retailer had no reason to think that demand would be higher or lower than he now has to think that it will be tomorrow. Suppose further that the historical record of these 16 days can be summarized as shown in Table 8.1, where Column 2 shows, for example, that there was 1 day among the 16 on which 2 units were demanded, 3 days on which 3 units were demanded, and so forth. Column 3 then shows the relative frequency of each of these values of demand, calculated by dividing each number in the second column by the total of that column—thus .063 = 1/16, .187 = 3/16, and so forth.

TABLE 8.1
Historical Record of Demand for Product A

1	2	3
Number Demanded	*Number of Occasions*	*Relative Frequency*
0 or 1	0	0
2	1	.063
3	3	.187
4	2	.125
5	4	.250
6	3	.187
7	2	.125
8	0	.000
9	1	.063
10 or more	0	0
	16	1.000

The same information is presented again in graphical form in Figure 8.6, where the heavy dots show the relative frequencies with which demands for the various possible numbers of units actually occurred. The smooth curve in the figure will be explained later on; for the moment, observe only that it does not go through the heavy dots and therefore is not a graph of the historical frequencies.

Now turn to the retailer's problem of assessing his probability distribution of the UQ "tomorrow's demand for Product *A*". If the retailer were very naive, he might be tempted to assign to each possible value of this UQ a probability equal to the relative frequency with which that value actually occurred in the historical record, but such assignments would almost certainly be unreasonable in the light of the total evidence in Figure 8.6.

Take "demand for 8" as an example, and observe that whereas the figure shows a historical relative frequency of 0 for this event, it shows relative frequencies of .125 for "demand for 7" and .063 for "demand for 9". As we have emphasized repeatedly, it is *long-run* relative frequency that should serve as a guide in the assessment of probability, and therefore the retailer cannot reasonably set the probability of "demand for 8" equal to its historical relative frequency of 0 unless he believes that 0 is a reasonable estimate of the long-run relative frequency of "demand for 8". But since demands for 7 and for 9 are known to have occurred already, it would be very peculiar indeed if "demand for 8" were never to occur in a very long series of days all indistinguishable from the 16 days in the record, and therefore the retailer cannot reasonably take 0 as an estimate of the long-run relative frequency of "demand for 8" unless he knows of some good reason why demand for 8 is impossible.

Next consider the case of "demand for 4", and observe that whereas this event actually occurred with a relative frequency of only .125, demands for 3 and 5 occurred with relative frequencies of .187 and .250 respectively. Although any one of these historical frequencies taken by itself might be a reasonable estimate of the corresponding long-run frequency, the three of them taken together are almost certainly not reasonable estimates of the corresponding long-run frequencies. Unless there is real reason to suppose the contrary, it is reasonable to assume that in the long run "demand for 4" would occur with a relative frequency somewhere near the relative frequencies of "demand for 3" and "demand for 5".

8.2.2
A Model of a Random Process

The intuitive feeling that it is not reasonable in this problem to estimate long-run relative frequencies by simply equating them to the corresponding historical frequencies can be rationalized as follows. Certain known or predictable factors affecting demand on any given day can be identified and their effects can be isolated and measured. Thus we may know that Friday demand tends to be greater than Saturday demand by a certain amount. But after we have identified all the known or predictable factors that would have allowed us to predict a part of the day-to-day variation in historical demand, we are usually left with a part of the historical variation that we could not have predicted in advance. It is because we could not have predicted all the past variation in demand that we are uncertain about tomorrow's demand.[3]

It is often reasonable to think of this unpredictable variation as being the joint effect of a large number of unknown or unpredictable factors each of which individually has only a small effect, since any individual factor which has a large effect usually can and should be identified and predicted. Furthermore we may usually think of these small, residual factors as acting independently of each other, since if several small factors tend to act together, the group as a whole will produce large effects and therefore usually can and should be identified and predicted. Consequently:

■ It is reasonable under most circumstances to think of demand on any one day as being equal to some "basic" amount determined by the known or

---

[3] We can of course explain much more of the variation in historical demand after the fact than we could have predicted before the fact, but our ability to explain after the fact does not reduce our uncertainty about tomorrow's demand.

predictable factors plus or minus a "deviation" which is really the sum of a large number of small, independent deviations due to the unknown or unpredictable factors.

Let us now simplify the problem for a moment by imagining that although some deviations will be positive while others will be negative, all the deviations are of equal absolute size. If this were true, the variation in demand would be something like the variation in the number of heads turning up when 100 coins are tossed repeatedly. Even though some or all of these coins may be badly bent, so that the probability of heads for any one coin may be far from 1/2, intuition tells us immediately that in the long run (1) there will be some one most common number of heads, and (2) the relative frequencies of other numbers of heads will be smaller the farther the numbers are from this most common number.

If, therefore, a very short series of tosses showed, say, that 34 heads had occurred twice, 36 heads once, and 35 heads not at all, we would nevertheless insist that in the long run the relative frequencies of 34, 35, and 36 heads would all be nearly equal. In other words, irregularities in the long-run frequency distribution of number of heads would seem inconsistent with our intuitive ideas concerning the nature of the chance mechanism or «random process» generating this number. We would say that the irregularities in the record are due to the fact that these tosses are only a "sample" of the behavior of the random process and reflect "sampling error" rather than the true long-run behavior of the process.

We do not, of course, really think that the total deviation of demand from its most common value is the sum of deviations which are exactly of equal size, but this part of the analogy is not essential. A closer analogy would be a sequence of rolls of 100 deformed dice, all different, and here again intuition tells us (and it can be proved) that in any really long sequence of rolls of the 100 dice (1) there will be some one most common total number of spots showing, and (2) the relative frequencies of other numbers will be smaller the farther the numbers are from this most common number. This second analogy is close enough to our notions of the mechanism generating demand to justify the proposition that the long-run frequency distribution of demand *on indistinguishable occasions* should fall away smoothly on either side of a single most probable value or mode.

8.2.3
Estimation of Long-run Frequencies

Returning now to our example, where we have already assumed that (1) the retailer did not know in advance of any reason why demand on any one of the days in the historical record should be different from tomorrow's demand, let us now assume further that (2) the retailer does feel that the demand-generating process would in the long run generate a smooth, unimodal distribution of relative frequencies. Given these two assumptions, the long-run frequency distribution that the process would generate can be estimated by applying the following two-stage line of reasoning.

1. Taken by itself, the relative frequency with which one particular event such as "demand for 5" has occurred will in general be a reasonable estimate of the long-run relative frequency of that event. Therefore to start the process of estimating long-run relative frequencies:

■ For every possible number x of units demanded, the retailer can take the historical relative frequency of "demand for x" as a ≪preliminary estimate≫ of the long-run relative frequency of "demand for x".

These preliminary estimates will be easiest to work with if they are represented graphically; they are so represented for our example by the heavy dots in Figure 8.6 on page 290.

2. Taken all together, however, these preliminary estimates disagree with the retailer's general beliefs about the kind of long-run frequency distribution that the demand-generating process would produce; and therefore to complete the process of estimating long-run relative frequencies:

■ The retailer should make ≪revised estimates≫ of the long-run relative frequencies by increasing some of his preliminary estimates and decreasing others in such a way as to reflect his general beliefs about the shape of the long-run distribution of demand, keeping the set of revised estimates as a whole as close to the original estimates as is consistent with the required shape.

The easiest way to make these revised estimates is illustrated for our example in Figure 8.6. The retailer draws a smooth graph showing his revised estimate of the mass function of the long-run frequency distribution of demand, keeping in mind as he does so, not only the historical data or preliminary estimates represented by the heavy dots, but also the general shape that the mass function must have if it is to agree with his general beliefs about the behavior of the demand-generating process. The curve must of course be drawn so that the sum of the long-run relative frequencies it represents is equal to 1.

8.2.4
Assessment of the
Probability Distribution

If the retailer felt absolutely sure that the long-run frequency of demand for any possible number of units would be exactly equal to the value given by the smooth curve in Figure 8.6, his task of assessing his probability distribution for tomorrow's demand would be complete. By the principle stated in Section 6.3.2, he could assess his probability for any event such as "demand for 3" by simply equating it to the long-run relative frequency of that event.

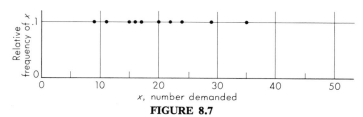

FIGURE 8.7

Historical Record of Demand for Product B

Usually, however, a decision maker will not feel absolutely sure that he has correctly estimated the long-run frequencies, and therefore he must, at least in principle, again exercise his judgment in order to assess his probabilities. For example, the fact that the retailer has estimated that "demand for 3" would occur on .14 of all occasions in the long run does not in itself prove that he should assign probability .14 to the occurrence of this event tomorrow. More specifically, it does not oblige the retailer to be indifferent between the right to receive a valuable prize if this event occurs and the right to receive that same prize if a red ball emerges in a standard drawing from an urn in which .14 of the balls are red; and if the retailer stops to think about it, he may in fact prefer one of these rights to the other.

The retailer may feel, for example, that although .14 is his "best estimate" of the long-run frequency of the event "demand for 3", the true long-run frequency of this event could easily be as high as .18 but almost certainly could not be lower than .12; and if he does, he may prefer the right conditional on "demand for 3" to the right conditional on a drawing from an urn in which .14 of the balls are red. In other words, he may assess his probability for the occurrence of this event tomorrow at a value higher than his "best estimate" of the long-run frequency of the event; and in general,

■ After a decision maker has *estimated* the *relative frequency* with which each possible value of a UQ would occur on repeated trials, he must proceed to *decide* on his *probability* for each possible value of the UQ on the one trial that is actually of interest.

8.2.5
Estimation of Cumulative
Long-run Frequencies

Although the method of assessment described above works very well in situations where there are sufficient historical data, the data in many if not most situations are so sparse that the method either becomes very difficult to apply or cannot be applied at all. As an example, consider the assumed record of demand for Product *B* on ten successive days that is shown in Table 8.2 and Figure 8.7; there is clearly a tendency for demand to "bunch" in the neighborhood of 16 units and to "tail out" farther to the right than to the left, but it would be extremely hard for anyone to draw a smooth curve that reflects these observations.

To put the historical record of Table 8.2 into a form in which we can work with it, we first use the data it contains to compute for every possible value of demand the historical relative frequency of demand for *that value or less;* the results of this computation are shown in Table 8.3.

TABLE 8.2
Historical Record of Demand for Product *B*

Number Demanded	Number of Occasions	Relative Frequency
9	1	.1
11	1	.1
15	1	.1
16	1	.1
17	1	.1
20	1	.1
22	1	.1
24	1	.1
29	1	.1
35	1	.1
	10	1.0

TABLE 8.3
Historical Record of Demand for Product *B*

Demand x	Relative Frequency of x	of x or less	Demand x	Relative Frequency of x	of x or less
0–8	0	0	21	0	.6
9	.1	.1	22	.1	.7
10	0	.1	23	0	.7
11	.1	.2	24	.1	.8
12–14	0	.2	25–28	0	.8
15	.1	.3	29	.1	.9
16	.1	.4	30–34	0	.9
17	.1	.5	35	.1	1.0
18–19	0	.5	36 and up	0	1.0
20	.1	.6		1.0	

If now we assume as we did in our previous example that the retailer (1) did not know in advance of any reason why demand on any one of the days in the historical record should be different from tomorrow's demand, and (2) feels that the long-run distribution of relative frequencies would be unimodal and smooth, then he can proceed to estimate the cumulative function of the long-run frequency distribution of demand by applying to the cumulative historical frequencies in Table 8.3 a two-step procedure which is almost identical to the procedure that he used in Section 8.2.3 to estimate the mass function of a long-run frequency distribution of demand from the individual historical frequencies.

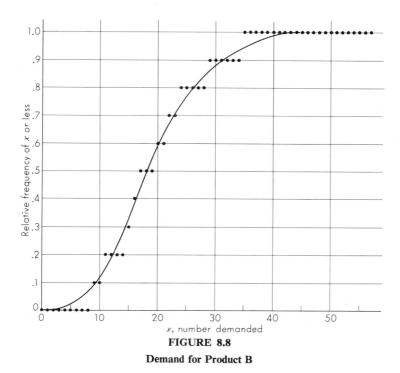

FIGURE 8.8

Demand for Product B

1. Taken by itself, the historical relative frequency of any one particular event such as "demand for 13 units or less" is a reasonable estimate of the long-run relative frequency of that event; and therefore to start the process of estimating long-run frequencies:

■ For every possible number x of units demanded, the retailer can take the historical relative frequency of "demand for x or less" as a preliminary estimate of the long-run relative frequency of "demand for x or less".

These preliminary estimates will be easiest to work with if they are represented graphically; they are so represented for our example by the heavy dots in Figure 8.8. Notice particularly that, exactly as in Figure 8.6 (page 290), *there is a heavy dot for every possible value of demand, not just for the values that actually occurred in the historical record.*

2. Taken all together, however, these preliminary estimates disagree with the retailer's general beliefs about the kind of long-run frequency distribution that the demand-generating process would produce; and therefore to complete the process of estimating long-run relative frequencies:

■ The retailer should make revised estimates of the long-run relative frequencies by increasing some of his preliminary estimates and decreasing others in such a way as to reflect his general beliefs about the shape of the long-run distribution of demand, keeping the set of revised estimates as a whole as close to the original estimates as is consistent with the required shape.

The easiest way to make these revised estimates is illustrated for our example in Figure 8.8. The retailer can draw a smooth graph showing his revised estimate of the cumulative function of the long-run frequency distribution of demand, keeping in mind as he does so, not only the historical data or preliminary estimates represented by the heavy dots, but also the general shape that the cumulative function must have if it is to agree with his general beliefs about the behavior of the demand-generating process. More particularly,

a As regards the general shape of the curve: if the mass function of the long-run frequency distribution would have the same general shape as the curve in Figure 8.6 (page 290), then we know from the discussion in Section 7.1.4 that the slope of the cumulative function should be 0 at the start, increase steadily to a maximum (at the mode), and then decrease steadily to 0 again.

b As regards the details, the heavy dots give very good guidance in drawing the central portion of the curve, but near the ends, particularly the upper end, they give less. The fact that no demand for more than 35 units occurred in the ten days in the record clearly does not constitute strong evidence against the proposition that demands for as many as 50 units or even 500 units might occur occasionally in the long run, and therefore the retailer will be forced to rely entirely on judgment rather than direct evidence when he decides on the highest value of demand to which he will assign nonzero probability and thus determines the point at which the curve should first show a cumulative frequency of 1.

3. The revised estimate of the long-run frequency distribution of demand that is given by the curve in Figure 8.8 can now be used by the retailer as a guide in deciding on his probability distribution for tomorrow's demand. The relation between these two distributions was fully discussed in Section 8.2.4, which the reader should review at this point together with the discussion in Section 8.1.6 of the amount of effort that should be spent in refining the details of a probability distribution.

8.2.6

Distinguishable and Indistinguishable Occasions

Now that we have shown how to estimate long-run relative frequencies and thus to assess probabilities by smoothing out the irregularities in historical relative frequencies, we again caution the reader that this should not be done indiscriminately.

Knowable or predictable causes for irregularities often exist. If a decision maker thinks hard enough, he will often be able to find knowable or predictable reasons for dips in a historical frequency distribution. In the case of daily demand, this means that he can often explain why the frequencies bunch in two or more ranges by looking for known or predictable factors which were present on the days (or months or other periods) showing high demand and which were absent on the days showing low demand or vice versa. We have already said that if the data in the record apply to all days in the week, investigation may show that demand was usually higher on Friday than on other days. Unless general knowledge of consumer behavior leads to a strong belief that there is no real reason for this phenomenon, the decision maker should not reject it as an accident of chance, which is what he is doing implicitly if he assesses a probability distribution by smoothing a frequency distribution containing data on both Fridays and other days. If demand in summer was higher than demand in winter and it is reasonable to believe that there is a real cause for this phenomenon, summer and winter data should not be pooled in arriving at a probability distribution; and so forth.

When a very great deal of historical data is available, it is easy to take account of knowable and predictable factors by the method described in the present section. The decision maker simply excludes all data generated on occasions which were distinguishable from the present occasion and proceeds to smooth the data generated on occasions which were indistinguishable.

In many situations, however, the available data are too scanty to allow him to proceed in this way. There may easily be so many knowable or predictable causes of variation that virtually every historical occasion is distinguishable from every other, with the result that there are no historical data that can legitimately be pooled and smoothed. In such situations, more sophisticated methods such as regression analysis must be used in order to arrive at a reasonable probability distribution for the uncertain quantity of interest; but methods of this sort must be left for advanced books on statistics.

8.3
USE OF FORECASTS AND ESTIMATES

We have already said in effect (Section 6.3.8) that a person who makes predictions, forecasts, or estimates can often usefully be regarded as a random process, in which case the probability that his current forecast will be correct can be based on an estimate of the relative frequency with which similar predictions would be correct in the long run. Our earlier discussion was concerned with situations where there are just two possible events, but we shall now see that essentially this same device will often be helpful when every possible value of a UQ represents a different possible event.

8.3.1
Historical Data on Forecast Errors

Suppose first that regularly each quarter a sales manager makes a forecast of the next quarter's sales, basing these forecasts on his "feel for the market" as obtained from salesmen's reports, articles in newspapers and the trade press, conversations with his opposite numbers in other companies, and perhaps a wide variety of other factors as well; and suppose that the record of both his forecasts and actual sales for the last ten quarters is as shown in Columns 1–3 of Table 8.4. Suppose further that after the sales manager forecasts sales of 165 units for the quarter which is about to begin (the third quarter of year 3), the production manager decides that, because this forecast is not absolutely reliable, he needs to assess his probability distribution of next quarter's actual sales in order to reach a reasonable decision on production scheduling.

TABLE 8.4
Historical Record of Forecasts and Actual Sales

1		2	3	4	5
Year	*Quarter*	*Forecast*	*Actual*	*Error*	*A/F Ratio*
1	1	92	107	−14%	1.16
	2	105	140	−25	1.33
	3	151	156	− 3	1.03
	4	96	110	−13	1.15
2	1	83	90	− 8	1.08
	2	94	93	+ 1	.99
	3	175	156	+12	.89
	4	106	121	−12	1.14
3	1	69	93	−26	1.35
	2	130	152	−14	1.17
	3	165	?	?	?

We observe first of all that in this situation it would certainly not be legitimate for the production manager to assess his probability distribution of the UQ "sales" by smoothing the ten historical values of this UQ shown in Column 3 of Table 8.4. Even if these ten values did not show the strong seasonal pattern that is clearly apparent in the table, the fact that the sales manager's forecasts were not all the same on the one present and ten past occasions means that those occasions are not indistinguishable if forecasts have any relation to sales; and clearly forecasts do have a relation to sales in this example. Since the seasonal pattern in sales means that sales are also related to the factor "quarter", the problem of assessing a probability distribution for the current quarter's sales is in principle a very complex one; but we shall now show that it can be solved by a very simple method provided that certain conditions are satisfied.

Specifically, we shall inquire whether in this situation the production manager can use the historical data on the *errors* in the sales manager's ten previous forecasts to assess a probability distribution of the *error* in his current forecast. If he can do this, then his original problem has been solved, for he will be able to compute the probability distribution that he should assign to next quarter's actual sales by combining the current "point" forecast of those sales with the probability distribution that he has assigned to the error in that forecast.

8.3.2
Distinguishable and
Indistinguishable Occasions

The easiest way for the production manager to assess a probability distribution of the error in the sales manager's current forecast would of course be to compute the ten historical errors and then treat them exactly as we treated the ten historical demands in Section 8.2.5; but before he does so mechanically, he must remember that assessment of any probability distribution by smoothing historical data is legitimate only if the data were generated on occasions that are indistinguishable from the present occasion. He must therefore ask whether any known or predictable factors such as the quarter, the year, the amount of information available to the sales manager, or the mere size of the sales manager's forecast have any appreciable effect on, or any discernible relation to, the errors in the forecasts; for if they do, then these factors will distinguish at least some of the previous occasions from the present occasion and thus render it incorrect to assess a probability distribution for this occasion by simply smoothing the historical data.[4]

The question whether any particular factor does in fact affect, or is in fact related to, the error in the sales manager's forecasts is one to be settled, in part by inspecting the historical data, but in greater part by more general experience and judgment. In problems like the present one, moreover, general experience will lead immediately to one very important conclusion, namely:

■ Except in very special circumstances, the magnitude of the difference between forecast and actual will tend to be larger for large forecasts than for small forecasts;

and this means that the occasions on which forecasts are made will usually not be indistinguishable if the error in each forecast is measured by the difference between forecast and actual. An association between large forecasts and large differences has actually been observed in so many situations that a tendency toward association should ordinarily be presumed in any particular situation even if a short historical record shows no numerical evidence thereof—even, in fact, if it shows weak numerical evidence for an inverse association.

It is much more likely that errors will be independent of size of forecast if we measure errors in percentage terms rather than in terms of differences, and therefore we have computed and shown in Column 4 of Table 8.4 the percent error, i.e., the ratio

$$\frac{\text{Forecast} - \text{Actual}}{\text{Actual}} \times 100,$$

---

[4] Although it is necessary to ask whether forecast errors are related to *forecast* sales, it is not necessary to ask whether forecast errors are related to *actual* sales, since actual sales are not known in advance and therefore cannot serve to distinguish this occasion from previous ones.

in each of our sales manager's ten previous forecasts. There is no apparent tendency for the size of the percent errors in Table 8.4 to increase or decrease with size of forecast; and we shall assume that after considering all the other evidence bearing on this question—i.e., everything known about the way in which the sales manager actually makes his forecasts—the production manager concludes that there is in fact no relation of practical importance between percent error and size of forecast.

The production manager must next ask himself whether any other known or predictable factor has an effect on, or is related to, the errors in the sales manager's forecasts. The easiest question to dispose of will be the amount of information available to the sales manager. If the sales manager has acquired better (or lost good) sources of information over the past ten quarters, then obviously his historical errors are not directly applicable to the problem of assessing a distribution of his current error.

When the production manager comes to the factor "quarter", however, he must be very careful with his reasoning. As we have already remarked, the season or quarter obviously has a large effect on actual sales, and this means that it may have a substantial effect on the forecast error, as the reader can easily see by thinking what the errors would have been if the sales manager had made the same forecast for every quarter in any one year. The errors in the forecasts will not be independent of quarter unless the forecasts take correct account of the effect of quarter on actual sales.

Whether this is in fact true in our example is again a question to be resolved, partly by inspecting the record, and partly by judgment. The record in Table 8.4 shows no substantial relation between quarter and error; and in what follows we shall assume that the production manager's judgment agrees with this finding. We assume, in other words, that the production manager believes that the sales manager knows his business well enough to take account of the seasonality of sales in a way which is correct for all practical purposes.

If now the production manager also concludes that no other known or predictable factor affects or is related to the sales manager's forecast errors, either by affecting the forecast without having a corresponding effect on actual sales, or by affecting sales and not being properly taken account of in the forecast, then he can legitimately proceed to assess a probability distribution of the percent error in the sales manager's current forecast by smoothing the historical percent errors in exactly the same way that the retailer smoothed historical demands in Section 8.2.5.

8.3.3
The Actual/Forecast Ratio

Although it is convenient to think about a forecaster's performance in terms of the percent error in his forecasts, the computations required to analyze a decision problem will be easier if they are based, not on a probability distribution of the percent error in the forecaster's current forecast, but on a probability distribution of the ratio of actual sales to the current forecast. This ratio, which we shall call the ≪actual-to-forecast ratio≫ or A/F ratio for short, is mathematically equivalent to percent error in the sense that we could compute the A/F ratio for any forecast if we knew the percent error in that forecast and nothing else; and hence we could compute the distribution of the A/F ratio from an assessed distribution of the percent error. But if we are actually going to work with the distribution of the A/F ratio and not with the distribution of the percent error, we might better assess the distribution of the A/F ratio directly instead of assessing the distribution of the percent error and then having to compute from it the distribution of the A/F ratio.

Column 5 of Table 8.4 (page 300) shows the A/F ratio for the ten forecasts in the historical record, and if the production manager assesses his probability distribution for the next ratio by smoothing these historical ratios,[5] he can obtain his distribution of next quarter's actual sales from this distribution just as correctly as, and more easily than, he could obtain it from a distribution of percent error. Since the forecast is 165, the probability that actual sales will be 150 or less is simply the probability that the ratio will be 150/165 or less, and so forth.

8.3.4
Effect of Self-calibration

If it had been the sales manager rather than the production manager who had wished to assess a probability distribution of actual sales in our example, the problem would have had one additional degree of complexity. In addition to all the questions about indistinguishable occasions that the production manager had to ask, the sales manager would also have had to ask himself whether he was sure that his own performance as a forecaster would not be materially changed by the very act of "calibrating" that performance.

In our example, the sales manager's forecasts have had a very clear tendency to err on the low side, as shown by Table 8.4; and observation of this fact by the sales manager might easily reduce the tendency in his next forecast. Unless the sales manager can convince himself that the observation would not in fact have this effect, he should not assess his probability distribution of his next error by smoothing the historical data.

8.3.5
Assessment in the Absence
of Historical Data

Let us now return to a problem we have already discussed in Section 8.1, the problem of a marketer who wishes to assess his own probability distribution of

---

[5] Because the A/F ratio is mathematically equivalent to the percent error, it will not be affected by or related to any factors that the percent error is not affected by or related to.

first-year demand for a new product. We saw there how such a person can assess his distributions without reference to long-run relative frequencies, but he will usually have much more confidence in his assessments if he can base them on ideas about frequencies, and he can often find such a "frequency basis" for his assessments by thinking in terms of point forecasts and forecast errors instead of thinking directly about possible values of demand.

Thus even though the marketer of Section 8.1 has not been in the habit of making explicit point forecasts of first-year demand for new products and then recording the actual demand as well as his forecast, he will probably be able to think back in his general experience as a marketer to other introductions of new products by his own company or its competitors, recall as well as he can the extent to which he was surprised by their high or low sales, and thus get some kind of factual basis for estimating the long-run frequency distribution of the errors he would make (or of the A/F ratios that would emerge) if he were *now* to make point forecasts of first-year sales for a very large number of new products. Having done so, he can formalize his conclusions by estimating selected fractiles of this long-run frequency distribution, plotting these estimates as points, and fairing a smooth cumulative function through the points. The process is identical in form to the one described in Section 8.1, even though the immediate objective in the present case is to estimate a long-run frequency distribution rather than to assess a probability distribution directly by thinking in terms of bets or gambles.

After the marketer has thus estimated the long-run frequency distribution of the errors he would make in repeated forecasts, he can go on to assess his probability distribution for the error in his current forecast in the way discussed in Section 8.2.4.

8.3.6
The Meaning of a Forecast

There is just one special point that must be observed by anyone who wishes to evaluate his own accuracy as a forecaster under the circumstances and by the method we have just described, to wit:

■ A decision maker who wishes to assess a probability distribution of the error in his own forecast in a situation where adequate objective data on his forecasting ability are not available must know exactly what he means when he makes his forecast.

If a Mr. Jones forecasts that sales will amount to 300 units, then even if he is not deliberately biassing his forecast to avoid criticism by his superiors after the fact, he may mean that he thinks that sales are more likely to have the value 300 than any other value, or he may mean that he thinks that sales are about as likely to be under 300 as they are to be over, or he may mean that he believes that his company should make decisions as if sales were really going to amount to exactly 300 units, or he may mean still something else. If Jones' forecast can be calibrated before it is used, by looking at a record of the errors he has actually made in past forecasts, it will make no difference what meaning he himself attaches to his forecast, provided that the effect of this meaning on the error in his forecast remains constant from one occasion to the next. (This will not be true if Jones' forecast is actually an indirect recommendation for action that is influenced by factors other than the evidence bearing on sales—e.g., by the state of the company's inventory.) But if Jones is trying to evaluate the accuracy of his own forecast without reference to directly relevant historical data, it is obvious that he cannot logically do so without knowing exactly what he means by his forecast.

8.3.7
Median Forecasts

Although a forecaster can assess a probability distribution of the error in his own point forecast if the forecast has any well defined meaning, he will find it much easier to assess the error distribution if his forecast is a "median" forecast in the sense of the following definition:

- A point forecast or estimate or any uncertain quantity will be called a ≪median forecast≫ or ≪median estimate≫ if in the judgment of the forecaster or estimator the forecast or estimate is exactly as likely to be above as it is to be below the true value of the UQ.

If any particular point forecast is a median forecast in the sense of this definition, then the median of the forecaster's distribution of the A/F ratio is automatically 1.

It might seem at first glance that a forecaster would do better to try his best to hit the exact value "on the nose", i.e., to give as his forecast the sales figure that seems most likely to occur; but even though such a "modal" forecast may in some circumstances be easier to make than the median forecast we recommend, it will usually be very much harder to assess a probability distribution of the A/F ratio that will emerge from a modal forecast than to make the corresponding assessment for a median forecast.

8.4
ASSESSMENT OF EXPECTATIONS

8.4.1
Estimates vs. Expectations

We saw in Section 7.5.5 that under certain very special conditions it is legitimate to replace the complete distribution of an uncertain cost or a UQ such as "demand" by its expectation. The fact that the distribution of a UQ can sometimes be replaced by a particular single number, namely its expectation, does not mean, however, that the distribution can be replaced by an "estimate" of unspecified type; and failure to observe this distinction can lead to serious errors in the analysis of decision problems.

Specifically, a businessman who in a given situation would wish to choose the act with the greatest expected profit if he thought carefully about the matter will in actual practice often base his choice on a point forecast of profit which he calculates from a point forecast of demand in exactly the same way that he would calculate actual profit from actual demand. This procedure would lead to correct action if the forecast profit were equal to the expectation of profit that would be computed from the distribution that the businessman would assess for demand, but this will almost never be true unless it is true *both* that profit is linear over the range of demand *and* that the point forecast of demand can properly be taken as the businessman's expectation of demand. And even if profit is in fact linear over the range of demand, *a person's point forecast of demand will almost never be equal to his expectation of demand unless his distribution of demand is symmetric*. Forecasts that are not intentionally biassed are usually the forecaster's median or mode, and we have seen in Section 7.2.6 that these two quantities almost never agree with the mean when the distribution is asymmetric, the mode usually being even farther than the median from the mean.

8.4.2
Direct Assessment of Expectations

It might seem at first glance that if all that a businessman needs for the purpose at hand is his expectation of demand—i.e., the mean of the distribution that he would assess for demand if he took the trouble—then he would do better to make a point forecast in such a way that it is equal to the mean and not to the median (as we recommended in Section 8.3.7) or to the mode, since in this way he could avoid having to assess his entire distribution and then compute its mean.

This procedure is in general a very poor one, however. By thinking about a few simple uncertain quantities with which he himself has to deal—the temperature at noon tomorrow, for example, or the size of his bank balance just before his next check comes in—the reader can convince himself that while it is usually fairly easy to decide on the median or the mode of a distribution, it is usually very hard to decide directly on the mean. In general, the only reliable method of evaluating one's own expectation of an uncertain quantity is to assess the entire distribution of the UQ and then *compute* the expectation.

It is only when the decision maker's distribution is unimodal and symmetric, so that the median and mode are equal to the mean (Section 7.2.6), that a reliable shortcut can be found. If, after making a median forecast of demand, the decision maker feels that the forecast value is also the most probable value of demand, and if he also feels that his .99 fractile is just about as far above his forecast as his .01 fractile is below it, then he is entitled to conclude that his distribution would be symmetric for all practical purposes and to treat his forecast as being his expectation.

8.4.3
Probability and Expected Long-run Relative Frequency

Exactly this same principle is involved in the problem discussed in Section 8.2.4 of using an "estimate" of the long-run relative frequency of an event as a basis for assessing the probability of that event. We shall show in a later chapter that a decision maker is logically obliged to set his probability for any event equal to his expectation of the long-run frequency with which the event would occur in trials made under conditions indistinguishable from present conditions, and from this it follows that he should set his probability equal to his estimate of the long-run frequency if and in general only if his distribution of the error in this estimate would be unimodal and symmetric.

8.5
SUMMARY

8.5.1
Direct Judgmental Assessment

1 In general, a decision maker should not try to assess directly a distribution of a UQ that takes account of uncertainty about events which can individually have a substantial effect on the value of the UQ. He can apply his judgment and experience to the problem more effectively if he constructs his decision diagram in such a way that it shows all such events explicitly and calls for assessment of a separate distribution of the UQ for every possible combination of the events.

2 If a decision maker's distribution of a UQ does not have to take account of uncertainty about any event which by itself can substantially affect the value of the UQ, the decision maker is likely to feel that his distribution should be unimodal and smooth.

3 If a decision maker feels that his distribution of a UQ should be unimodal and smooth, he can assess the distribution by making separate assessments of only a few points on its cumulative function, plotting these assessments as points, and fairing a smooth curve through the points.

4 If only a very small probability is to be assigned to any one individual value of a UQ $\tilde{x}$, the decision maker can assess points on his cumulative

function by deciding on various fractiles x_k of his distribution and then setting $P(\tilde{x} \leqslant x_k) = k$.

It will often suffice to decide on $x_{.50}, x_{.75}, x_{.25}, x_{.99}$, and $x_{.01}$ before fairing the cumulative function.

8.5.2
Smoothing of Historical Frequencies

In many situations it is useful to think of the value that a UQ will actually have as being generated by a ≪random process≫ that generates (or could generate) values on a very large number of indistinguishable occasions.

> **1** *a* If a decision maker has a record of the values generated by a random process on a number of indistinguishable occasions, he can estimate the cumulative function of the long-run frequency distribution that the process would generate on future indistinguishable occasions by (1) plotting points which show the historical relative frequency of "*x* or less" for every possible *x*, and then (2) drawing a smooth curve whose general shape agrees with his general beliefs about the long-run behavior of the process but which remains as close to the points as possible.

It is absolutely essential to remember that the historical relative frequency of *x* or less must be plotted for *every* possible *x* and not just for the *x*'s that actually occurred.

> **1** *b* The decision maker can then be guided by this estimated long-run frequency distribution in deciding on his probability distribution for the value that the process will generate on the next indistinguishable occasion.

In thinking about the shape of the long-run frequency distribution that would be generated by a random process, the decision maker should remember that:

> **2** If the values generated by a random process consist of some "basic" value plus a "random" element that is the net effect of a large number of *small*, *independent* factors, then the long-run frequency distribution of the values generated by the process will be unimodal and smooth.

8.5.3
Forecasts and Estimates

In many situations where it is difficult to assess the distribution of a UQ directly, it will be more satisfactory to proceed by first getting a point forecast or estimate of the value the UQ will have and then assessing a probability distribution of the

> **1** ≪A /F ratio≫: the ratio of the as yet uncertain actual value of a UQ to an already known point forecast or estimate of its value.

A person who makes point forecasts or estimates repeatedly can be considered a random process generating A/F ratios, and therefore:

> **2** *a* The long-run frequency distribution of the A/F ratios that would be generated by a particular forecaster or estimator can be estimated by smoothing his historical A/F ratios *provided* that the occasions on which the forecasts or estimates are made are all indistinguishable in the sense that there is no known or predictable factor explaining *in advance* why the A/F ratio should be higher or lower on some occasions than on others.

In deciding whether or not occasions are indistinguishable, the decision maker must remember particularly that:

> **2** *b* A known or predictable factor may be related to the A/F ratio either (1) because it affects the forecast or estimate without having a corresponding effect on actual, or (2) because it affects actual without having a corresponding effect on forecast or estimate.

When a decision maker wishes to assess his probability distribution for the A/F ratio that will emerge from his own forecast or estimate, he will usually do well to start by making a

> **3** ≪Median forecast≫ or ≪median estimate≫: a forecast or estimate which the forecaster believes just as likely to be below as it is to be above the true value of the quantity being forecast or estimated.

EXERCISES

A. DIRECT JUDGMENTAL ASSESSMENT

8.1 Suppose that a decision diagram contains an event fork representing the UQ whose distribution is defined by Table 7.15 (page 271), and suppose that the name of this UQ is $\tilde{x}$. If the decision maker's equivalent urn for this fork contains 100 balls, what labels must appear on these balls and how many balls must bear each label?

8.2 Suppose that Mr. J. M. Fraser denotes by $\tilde{c}$ the contribution that will result from his business operations this year and suppose further that he assesses the following probabilities:

$$P(\tilde{c} \leqslant \$6,000) = .01$$
$$P(\tilde{c} \leqslant \$7,500) = .25$$
$$P(\tilde{c} \leqslant \$8,500) = .50$$
$$P(\tilde{c} \leqslant \$9,500) = .75$$
$$P(\tilde{c} \leqslant \$12,000) = .99$$

a In terms of Mr. Fraser's equivalent urn for an event fork representing the UQ $\tilde{c}$, exactly what has Mr. Fraser decided when he makes the "assessment" $P(\tilde{c} \leqslant \$7,500) = .25$?

b Assuming that Mr. Fraser wants the mass function of his distribution of $\tilde{c}$ to have the general shape shown in Figure 8.1 (page 284), construct a graph showing cumulative probabilities $P(\tilde{c} \leqslant c)$ that Mr. Fraser might reasonably assess for every possible value c of $\tilde{c}$.

8.3 Suppose that you are given a choice between lottery tickets A and B. Ticket A will pay $1,000 at a date exactly m months from now if the United States has by then succeeded in putting a man on the moon and bringing him safely back to earth. Ticket B will pay $1,000 at this same date if a red ball emerges in a standard drawing from an urn in which 50% of the balls are red.

a Exactly how large would the number m have to be to make you indifferent between the two tickets?

b Exactly how large would the number m have to be to make you indifferent between the two tickets if the urn contained 75% rather than 50% red balls? If it contained 25%? 99%? 1%?

c Construct a graph from which you can read your "indifference value" of m for every possible percentage of red balls in the urn.

d Read from this graph your probability for the event that the United States succeeds in putting a man on the moon and bringing him safely back within 10 months from now; 20 months; 100 months.

8.4 In order to determine how many men he will need for tomorrow's operations, Frankie Franklin, owner of Frankie's Friendly Car Wash, wants to assess his distribution of the number of car washes he will sell tomorrow. As he thinks carefully about his problem, he realizes that tomorrow's demand will depend very much on whether it rains between now and tomorrow evening, and if so, when it rains. If it rains and then clears before the time at which Frankie would normally open for business tomorrow morning, cars will get dirty and demand for washes will be considerably above the normal level. If, on the other hand, it is raining at the time Frankie would normally open for business, sales will be zero, since in that case Frankie's policy is to remain closed for the entire day.

Taking into consideration his uncertainty about when it will rain and his uncertainty about the demand for washes if it does rain and if it does not, Frankie assesses the following probabilities for tomorrow's sales $\tilde{s}$ of car washes:

$$P(\tilde{s} \leqslant 0) = .25$$
$$P(\tilde{s} \leqslant 135) = .50$$

$$P(\tilde{s} \leqslant 225) = .75$$

$$P(\tilde{s} \leqslant 275) = .99$$

If you were in the position of a consultant to Frankie, how would you advise him to proceed to assess his complete probability distribution for tomorrow's sale of car washes?

B. ASSESSMENT BY SMOOTHING HISTORICAL DATA

8.5 Suppose that as the manufacturer of a certain product you wish to assess your probability distribution of the number of units that will be demanded by customers during the selling season which is about to begin. Table 8.5, which is to be read row by row, shows the number of units demanded during each of the last ten selling seasons. Before any one of these seasons began, you had no reason to think that demand would be higher or lower than during any other of these seasons or during the season that is about to begin; and you believe that over a very great number of selling seasons all of which looked in advance just like these, the frequency distribution of number of units demanded would have the general shape shown in Figure 8.1 (page 284).

TABLE 8.5

Historical Demands

22	57	32
38	29	26
49	42	35
17		

a In what sense is .5 a reasonable estimate of the *long-run* relative frequency of demand for 34 units or less? In what sense is 0 a reasonable estimate of the long-run relative frequency of demand for 16 units or less?

b Make similar estimates of the long-run relative frequency with which demand would be equal to or less than *each one* of the 81 possible values of demand from 0 to 80 units and plot each of these 81 estimates on graph paper.

c Revise the 81 estimates you made in answer to part (b) so that they reflect your beliefs about the general shape of the long-run frequency distribution of demand.

d What was your original estimate and what is your revised estimate of the long-run relative frequency of demand for 30 units or less? 61 or less? 71 or less?

e Assess your *probabilities* for the events "customers demand 30 units or less" (this coming season), "customers demand 61 units or less", and "customers demand 71 units or less".

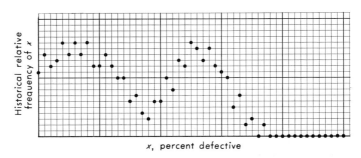

FIGURE 8.9

Historical Record of Fraction Defective

8.6 Inspection of 1,000 successive lots each containing 500 pieces of a certain purchased part has produced the record shown graphically in Figure 8.9. A new lot has just been received and you are faced with a decision problem such that you would like to assess your probability distribution of the number of defectives in the lot. How would you proceed?

C. USE OF FORECASTS AND ESTIMATES

8.7 The actual-to-forecast ratios that have emerged from 15 forecasts made by a certain forecaster are shown in Table 8.6. Suppose that you have convinced yourself (1) that you could not have distinguished any one of these occasions from any other and (2) that if the forecaster were to make a great many forecasts on occasions indistinguishable from the past 15, the mass function of the long-run relative frequency distribution of his A/F ratios would have the general shape shown in Figure 8.1 (page 284). Construct a graph showing the cumulative function that you would assess for the A/F ratio that will emerge from the next forecast that this person makes on an occasion indistinguishable from the 15 past occasions.

TABLE 8.6

Historical A/F Ratios

1.18	.96	.99
.95	1.07	1.31
.78	.98	.92
1.07	.86	1.00
1.00	1.05	.92

8.8 Suppose that you acquire a good deal of experience in marketing after leaving school, suppose that you then forecast that one of your company's new products will sell 27,000 units next year, suppose that one of your superiors subsequently asks you what you can say about the degree of uncertainty in your forecast, and suppose that on the basis of your previous successes and failures in forecasting new product sales you feel that:

1 You have learned to forecast in such a way that in the long run sales would turn out to be greater than your forecast just about as often as they would turn out to be less.

2 You are convinced that on just about half of all occasions sales would be between 20% below and 30% above your forecast, and that when they fell outside this range they would fall above it just about as often as they would fall below.

3 As regards extreme errors, you feel confident that sales would be less than half your forecast on only about 1 occasion in 100, and similarly they would be more than twice your forecast on only about another 1 out of 100 occasions.

4 The general shape of the long-run frequency distribution of the ratio of actual demand to your forecast would resemble Figure 8.1 (page 284).

Construct a graph showing your superior the probability that you would assign to the proposition that actual sales of the new product with which you are currently involved would amount to any given fraction of your forecast or less.

8.9   *a* Without referring to your answers to Exercise 8.3 or looking at the curve you faired in that exercise, make a direct assessment of your expectation of the UQ "number of months until the United States succeeds in putting a man on the moon and returning him safely to earth."

    b Using the distribution you assessed in Exercise 8.3, compute your expectation of this UQ and compare your computed expectation with the expectation you assessed directly in (*a*).

D. REVIEW EXERCISES

8.10   *a* If you have not already done so, plot the five probability assessments made by Mr. Fraser in Exercise 8.2 on the graph paper you used in answering that exercise.

    b If you have not already done so, plot your *original* estimates of the long-run relative frequency with which demand would be equal to or less than each of the ten historical values given in Exercise 8.5 on the graph paper you used in answering that exercise.

    c Do the probability distributions you assessed and plotted in Exercises 8.2 and 8.5 go through the points specified in (*a*) and (*b*) above? If yes, why; if not, why not?

8.11   *American Rubber Products Company (B)*

In the situation described in *American Rubber Products Company (A)* (Exercise 5.20), the sales manager of American Rubber does not believe that sales records more than three years old should be used in forecasting future demand for part XZ714 because the number of machines on which this part is used was steadily increasing until about three years ago. Since then, however, he believes that the number of such machines in service has scarcely changed, and he knows of no other factor that would have caused him to predict higher or lower demand in any one six-months period than any other. The number of parts ordered from American Rubber during the last six semiannual periods has been 2,231, 2,753, 1,970, 2,256, 2,778, and 1,436.

   a Graph the cumulative function of the probability distribution that you would assign to the UQ "demand for part XZ714" if the only information available to you were that given above.

   b Denoting by $\tilde{v}$ the uncertain terminal value that will result from a production order for any given number Q of units of part XZ714, compute your expectation of $\tilde{v}$ given that $Q = 0$; given that $Q = 1,000$.

   c If you were responsible for deciding how many units of part XZ714 to produce and if you were willing to treat your expectations of uncertain monetary values as certainty equivalents in reaching this decision, how could you approximate the number you should produce without actually computing your expectation of $\tilde{v}$ for more than a half dozen different Q's?

8.12 *Morgan Metal Products, Inc.*

On July 1, 1969, Morgan Metal Products, Inc. was invited by the Coventry Aircraft Co. to bid on a subcontract associated with a large Air Force contract that Coventry had recently been awarded. The subcontract required the casting and finishing of 1,000 rotor mounts by the end of the year, according to a design similar to one with which Morgan had had considerable experience. Following general industry practice, two other companies (Farley-Barning and Otis Masterson, both long-standing competitors of Morgan) were also invited to submit bids. The bids were due on August 1. On Monday morning, July 28, a meeting was called by Mr. Earl Grey, Executive Vice-president and Assistant to the President, for the purpose of establishing the bid price. Attending the meeting, besides Grey, were Alton Frye, Vice-president and Controller; Donald Rowe, Production Manager; Werner Bongers, Chief Engineer; and J. D. Philips, Sales Manager.

     Grey opened the meeting by remarking that the subcontract offered an unexpected opportunity to beef up the profit picture for the year, which had been hurt both by start-up costs associated with an expansion of their main manufacturing facilities and by a new labor-wage agreement calling for an average hourly increase of 4.6%. He remarked also that the field had narrowed down to only one competitor, as he had recently been informed that Masterson had notified Coventry that it would be unable to guarantee delivery of the mounts in the time specified because of its current heavy volume of business.

     Rowe spoke up to say that it seemed to be a case of feast or famine, but he wasn't sure how big a feast it was going to be. Only two weeks previously they had discussed the fact that the casting department was operating at only 65% of capacity and had debated, and then rejected, the idea of cutting down the work week in that department to four days. "With this contract we'll be operating at essentially full capacity for the rest of the year—in fact, with maybe a shade of overtime if things go slower than expected." He paused and then added, almost dourly, "The joint will really be jumping, that's for sure."

J. D. Philips remarked that he was delighted that the joint would be jumping, as it was his job to keep it that way. He went on to comment on what he considered to be the crucial nature of the contract. "We've been offered chances at four contracts from Coventry in the past year and a half, and we've overbid on all of them. If we can get this one now, we'll remove some of the tarnish on our image as a company that can come through in the clutch. When the chips are down next time, they'll remember us," he asserted.

Earl Grey broke in to observe dryly that one *sure* way of getting the contract was to bid cost less 25%, but that wouldn't look particularly good on the P and L statement. In fact, he thought it might focus their discussion a bit if they looked at what the current forecasted earnings were. "Show us the figures, Alton," he said.

Frye pulled out a sheet of figures and summarized them as follows. Earnings for the first six months had been about $1.3 million, with the current forecast for second-half earnings slightly below that figure. This forecast could "go $150,000 either way and flip a coin," he admitted, and then explained that what he meant by that was that he felt it was only an even-money bet that the second-half earnings would be between $1.1 million and $1.4 million. One of the factors upon which the forecast was based, he said, was that the casting department would be able to raise its activity from the current level of 65% capacity to its long-run average of 75%. He also added that 3 or 4 hundred thousand dollars of additional profit would certainly look good and go a long way toward washing the bad taste of the new labor settlement from the mouths of the stockholders and the security analysts. Also, he said, it was his understanding that the proposed contract would require a relatively small input of labor for the number of dollars involved, and therefore its profitability would be less affected by the increase in wage rates.

"Well," said Grey, "let's see exactly what the profit potential is. Werner, you've had time to study the specifications pretty thoroughly by now. Do you see any hitches?"

Bongers shook his head slowly and said that he'd convinced himself that the rotor mounts could be produced by a procedure almost identical to that used in two other recent jobs. "The alloy and the molds would be different, and there'd have to be more control over the casting and cooling because of the size of those babies, but basically it's a pretty straightforward operation." He and Rowe had estimated the cost of production to be about $1,500 per unit (see Exhibit 1), of which direct and supervisory labor accounted for only about $450. "There's a lot more uncertainty in this estimate than I'd like," he admitted. "The contract specifies the use of a special copper-magnesium alloy, and we have in stock less than half the tonnage of copper needed to do the job. We'll have to get some more on the market, and the way copper prices are hopping around right now, I can't guarantee what the exact price will be. I've assumed the going price of 50 cents per pound (the average price of the copper we have in stock is 42 cents per pound) in making my estimates. But to get the amount of copper we'll need in the time we need it, we might have to pay a premium of 5 or 6 cents a pound more. Also, I notice that copper futures are up around 58 cents now, which could make things even tighter in a couple of weeks. We can get all we need, no problems there, but it could cost us a good deal more than we'd like, as those mounts require over 700 pounds of copper apiece. On the other cost components I'm pretty satisfied with my estimates—within 5%, say."

"In connection with this, I'd like to bring up another point." Don Rowe was speaking again. "The price we can charge on this contract has to be pegged pretty much around the material costs, as that's by far the biggest item. But materials aren't where we get our best mark-ups. Those come from the labor-intensive jobs. My experience has been that on jobs like this one we end up with only about a 10% margin, whereas on our normal jobs, in which labor represents over 50% of the value added, we get 15% to 20%. We're filling up our shop for sure, but that's both good and bad. We're cutting ourselves off from any other potentially more profitable jobs. If we play the averages we can plan on at least two or three high-margin jobs before the end of the year."

"Another thing that's worth talking about is what Farley-Barning is going to bid," said J. D. Philips. "I've got records of bids they've made against us on nine other occasions in the past three years." (Exhibit 2.) Rowe glanced at the bids and then asked, "What kind of jobs are these? Are they casting jobs, or material-intensive jobs like this one? Are they associated with defense or commercial contracts? How are they comparable?"

"I can give you all that information on each job if you want it," Philips responded rather hotly. "The point is, on each of these jobs we were pretty sure that Farley-Barning's direct production costs would be about the same as ours—either because material costs dominated the other costs, as in this case, or because the contract required the production of pretty standard items. As a result, their bid prices in these cases seem to be affected substantially by how they decided to allocate general overhead costs, and how much they wanted the contract."

"I think J. D.'s got hold of something that may be valuable," said Grey looking at his watch, "but it's time for lunch. Let's give ourselves a chance to digest all this information and meet back here at 3 P.M."

EXHIBIT 1
Estimation of Total Costs

1	Design and construction of molds and special equipment	$ 130,000
2	Cost of copper—150 tons @ $840..........$126,000	
	210 tons @ $1,000........ 210,000	336,000
3	Cost of other metals	380,000
4	Direct and supervisory labor	450,000
5	Miscellaneous	80,000
6	General overhead	180,000
	Total	$1,556,000

EXHIBIT 2
Historical Record of Estimated Costs and Bids
(in thousands)

Job	Morgan Estimated Costs	Morgan Bid	F-B Bid
1	$1,230	$1,390	$1,420
2	850	970	915
3	370	420	450
4	2,120	2,300	2,390
5	790	910	1,000
6	1,510	1,660	1,430
7	200	245	235
8	940	1,050	1,045
9	1,170	1,390	1,360

Describe the procedure that you would use to take account of the various issues raised, and explain how you would go about arriving at a decision on the bid price if you were Mr. Grey. What further information would you desire before making a final decision? How crucial, in terms of its impact on your ultimate decision, do you feel such information would be? What questions would you direct at each of the men present at the meeting in Grey's office? What other people would you want to question?

CHAPTER

9

CONDITIONAL, UNCONDITIONAL, AND JOINT PROBABILITIES; THE USE OF INDIRECTLY RELEVANT INFORMATION

We have emphasized repeatedly that a decision maker must take full account of all relevant information when he assesses his probabilities for the events on any event fork in his decision diagram, but in many situations a decision maker may be unable to see exactly how to use certain relevant information because its relevance seems to him indirect rather than direct. More specifically, a decision maker who wishes to assess his probabilities for the events on a particular event fork will often feel that the available information seems to bear, not directly on the probabilities which should be assigned to the branches of that fork, but on other probabilities that seem to him to be related in some way or another to those probabilities. A typical example of a situation of this kind is described in Section 9.2.1.

Difficult as such assessment problems may seem, they are often quite easy to solve. The probabilities required for analysis of the decision problem are often logically related to the probabilities on which the decision maker's information bears directly in such a way that, if he first directly assesses the latter probabilities, he can then simply compute the former. The logical relations among probabilities which make such computations possible constitute the subject of the present chapter.

Because a decision maker's probabilities for real-world events are by definition equal to standard chances in standard drawings from his equivalent urns, the basic logical relations in which we are interested can be developed by looking at the relations which exist among standard chances in artificial lotteries that are conducted by making one or more standard drawings; and in order to avoid distracting the reader by irrelevant real-world details, this is the way in which we shall actually develop the basic relations in Section 9.1. We can then show in the remainder of the chapter how to apply these relations to the assessment of probabilities for real-world events in real-world decision problems.

Before trying to study this chapter systematically, the reader should orient himself toward the nature of the real-world problems that will be treated by reading the description of an example in Section 9.2.1. He can then study the text and exercises systematically in the following order:

A. INTERRELATED STANDARD CHANCES

1 Sections 9.1.1–9.1.2 and Exercise 9.1*a*.

2 Section 9.1.3 and Exercise 9.1*bc*.

3 Section 9.1.4 and Exercise 9.1*d*.

4 Section 9.1.5 and Exercise 9.1*e*.

5 Section 9.1.6 and Exercise 9.1*fg*.

6 Section 9.1.7 and Exercise 9.1*h*.

7 Exercises 9.2–9.4.

8 Section 9.1.8 and Exercise 9.5.

B. INTERRELATED PROBABILITIES

1 Sections 9.2.1–9.2.8 and Exercises 9.6–9.7.

2 Sections 9.3.1–9.3.4 and Exercises 9.8–9.10.

C. UNCERTAIN QUANTITIES AND EXPECTATIONS

1 Sections 9.3.6–9.3.8 and Exercises 9.11–9.13.

2 Section 9.3.9 and Exercise 9.14.

3 Section 9.3.10 and Exercise 9.15.

D. FUNCTIONS OF SEVERAL UQ's

1 Sections 9.4.1–9.4.3 and Exercises 9.16–9.17.

2 Sections 9.4.4–9.4.5.

3 Section 9.4.6 and Exercises 9.18–9.19.

CONTENTS OF CHAPTER 9

1.
Conditional, Unconditional, and Joint Standard Chances

2.
The Use of Indirectly Relevant Information: An Example

9.1
CONDITIONAL, UNCONDITIONAL,
AND JOINT STANDARD CHANCES

As we said in the introduction to this chapter, we shall start by considering logical relations among chances in completely artificial lotteries that are conducted by making one or more standard drawings. After these basic relations among chances have been made clear in the present section, we shall show in the remainder of the chapter how they can be used in assessing probabilities for real-world events in real-world decision problems.

9.1.1
A Two-stage Standard Gamble

Suppose that John Doe faces a decision problem involving a ticket in a lottery which will be conducted by making two successive standard drawings according to the scheme diagrammed in Figure 9.1. After a ball labelled *A*, *B*, or *C* has been drawn from urn *J*, a ball labelled *X*, *Y*, or *Z* will be drawn from a second-stage urn bearing the same label as the ball drawn from urn *J*; the fraction of balls bearing each label in each of the four urns is shown in parentheses on the branches of the corresponding event fork in the diagram. After both drawings have been made and Doe has arrived at some end position of the diagram, he will receive the prize which the terms of the lottery associate to that end position.

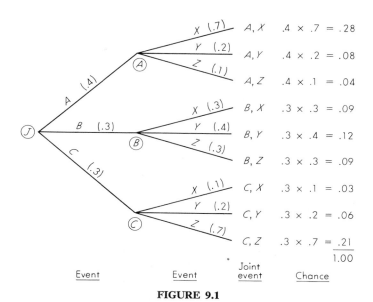

FIGURE 9.1

John Doe's Standard Gamble

The diagram in Figure 9.1 can thus be said to describe a standard gamble that Doe will face if he places himself at the origin of the diagram.

In what follows we shall say that the event *A* occurs if the first drawing yields a ball labelled *A*, that the event *X* occurs if the second drawing yields a ball labelled *X*, that the ≪joint event≫ *A,X* (or "*A* and *X*") occurs if *both* the previously described events occur, and so forth. The joint event *A,X* can also be called the joint event *X,A*: *the order in which the names of two events appear in the name of a joint event indicates neither the order in which the events occur nor the order in which they become known to the decision maker.*

9.1.2
Conditional and Unconditional
Standard Chances

In order to discuss the relations among chances in which we are interested, we must first distinguish between what will be called conditional and unconditional standard chances.

Conditional Standard Chances   If Doe is at the origin of the diagram in Figure 9.1, he will see that *if* the event *A* occurs, *then* the standard chance that the event *X* will occur is .7. This chance as looked at from the origin of Figure 9.1 will be called the "conditional" standard chance of the event *X* "given" the event *A* and will be denoted by the symbol $P(X|A)$, which should be read "*P* of *X* given *A*".[1]

---

[1] We use the symbol *P* to represent a standard chance because the standard chances of interest in the applications are a decision maker's probabilities for real-world events.

In general,

- If F and G are any two events in any standard gamble, the standard chance that F will occur *if* G occurs will be called the ≪conditional≫ standard chance of F ≪given≫ G and will be denoted by $P(F|G)$.

The reader should verify that in the gamble of Figure 9.1

$$P(Y|A) = .2, \qquad P(Y|B) = .4.$$

Unconditional Standard Chances   There is a .4 standard chance that the event A will occur in the gamble of Figure 9.1, nothing being specified about the occurrence of the events X, Y, and Z. This chance will be called the "unconditional" standard chance of the event A and will be denoted by $P(A)$, to be read "P of A". In general,

- If E is any event in any standard gamble, the standard chance that E will occur, nothing being specified about the occurrence or nonoccurence of any other event in the gamble, will be called the ≪unconditional≫ standard chance of E and will be denoted by $P(E)$.

The reader should verify that in the gamble of Figure 9.1

$$P(A) = .4, \qquad P(B) = .3.$$

9.1.3
The Consolidated Equivalent Urn

If the terms of Doe's lottery associate a different prize to each different joint event or end position in Figure 9.1, Doe may want to know the "overall" chance of each of these joint events or end positions.

Although it is intuitively clear enough what Doe means by the "overall" chance of a joint event such as A,X, we have not yet really defined such chances— the only chances that we have as yet defined are "standard" chances, and a standard chance is defined as the fraction of balls in one urn that are labelled with the name of one event. Our next step will therefore be to define chances such as the chance of A,X; and to do so we shall show that by putting an appropriate mix of balls into a single urn, we can make a gamble based on a *single* standard drawing from that urn equivalent to the gamble described by Figure 9.1 in the sense that Doe will be indifferent between the two gambles. Such an urn will be called Doe's ≪consolidated equivalent urn≫ for all the uncertainties involved in the standard gamble described by Figure 9.1.

To construct this consolidated equivalent urn, we shall put a *double* label such as A,X or B,Z on every ball it contains; there will be nine different double labels in all, corresponding to the nine different joint events or end positions in Figure 9.1. If a ball labelled A,X is drawn, we shall say that (1) the event A has occurred, (2) the event X has also occurred, and (3) therefore the joint event A,X has occurred; and we shall assume that Doe will be indifferent between the multistage standard gamble of Figure 9.1 and a standard gamble based on a single drawing from the consolidated urn if (1) the unconditional standard chances of the events *A*, *B*, and *C* are the same in the two gambles, (2) the conditional standard chances of the events *X*, *Y*, and *Z* given the events *A*, *B*, and *C* are the same in the two gambles; and (3) the prizes associated to the nine possible joint events are the same in the two gambles.

In order to make the *unconditional* standard chance of the event *A* of a drawing from the consolidated urn equal to the unconditional standard chance of that event in Figure 9.1 (page 323), we put a first label *A* on .4 *of all the balls in the consolidated urn;* and for similar reasons we put a first label *B* on .3 of the balls and put a first label *C* on .3 of the balls.

In the gamble of Figure 9.1, there is a .7 *conditional* standard chance that the event *X* will occur if, or given that, the event *A* occurs. In order to provide this same conditional standard chance of *X* given *A* in a single drawing from the consolidated urn, we put a second label *X* on .7 *of the balls that bear the first label A.* Similarly we put a second label *Y* on .2 of the balls that bear the first label *A* and put a second label *Z* on .1 of the balls that bear the first label *A*; we then go on to put a second label *X* on .3 of the balls that bear the first label *B*; and we continue in this way until we have put a second label on every ball in the consolidated urn.

9.1.4
Standard Chances of Joint Events

If now Doe wishes to know the "overall" chances of the various possible joint events or end positions in the gamble of Figure 9.1, we are in a position to say what these chances are. They are by definition the unconditional standard chances of these same events in the equivalent gamble based on a single drawing from the consolidated equivalent urn; the unconditional standard chance of any joint event in this single drawing is by definition equal to the fraction of balls in the urn that are labelled with the name of that joint event; and the fraction of balls labelled with the name of any particular joint event is easy to compute.

Taking the joint event *A,X* as an example, we first recall that (1) we first put the label *A* on .4 of all the balls in the consolidated urn, and (2) we then put the label *X* on .7 of the balls that we had previously labelled *A*. It follows that the double label *A,X* appears on $.4 \times .7 = .28$ of all the balls in the consolidated urn, and hence that .28 is the standard chance of the joint event *A,X*.

Now looking back at Figure 9.1 (page 323) we see that the fraction or standard chance .28 that we have just computed is simply the product of the two standard chances that appear on the path from the origin of the diagram to the end position *A,X*; and generalizing we conclude that:

■ The standard chance of the joint event corresponding to any end position of the diagram of a standard gamble can be computed by simply multiplying together the chances on the path from the origin of the diagram to the end position in question.

The standard chances of all possible joint events in the gamble of Figure 9.1 are computed in this way in the right-hand margin of the figure.

Chances like the chance of A,X in our example are sometimes called "joint chances", but it is really only the description of the event which is joint.

■ The so-called "joint" chance of a joint event is in fact an ordinary standard chance—i.e., a fraction of balls in an urn from which a standard drawing is to be made.

9.1.5
Computation of Unconditional
Standard Chances

Suppose now that the terms of Doe's gamble are such that the prize will depend only on the event X, Y, or Z, not on the event A, B, or C. To evaluate such a gamble, Doe will not want to know the individual standard chances of all possible joint events, nor will he want to know the conditional standard chances of the events X, Y, and Z which appear on the branches of the diagram in Figure 9.1. He will want to know the unconditional standard chances of the events X, Y, and Z.

The unconditional standard chances in which Doe is interested can be computed from the unconditional standard chances of joint events which we have already computed and recorded in Figure 9.1 (page 323). Taking the event Z as an example and thinking in terms of the consolidated urn, we argue that Z will occur if the ball which is drawn bears any one of the three double labels A,Z, B,Z, and C,Z; and since the fraction of balls bearing some one or another of these labels is $.04 + .09 + .21 = .34$, the unconditional standard chance of the event Z is .34.

In generalizing from this example, we shall for the sake of brevity say that an event appears at an end position of a diagram when what we really mean is that the event appears on the path from the origin to that end position. Given this convention, the reader should convince himself that:

■ The *unconditional* standard chance of any event in the diagram of a standard gamble is the sum of the standard chances of all the end positions at which that event appears.

The reader can verify the rule by applying it to compute in our example not only

$$P(X) = .28 + .09 + .03 = .40,$$

$$P(Y) = .08 + .12 + .06 = .26,$$

$$P(Z) = .04 + .09 + .21 = .34,$$

but also one of the unconditional chances that were specified by the original terms of the gamble, e.g.,

$$P(B) = .09 + .12 + .09 = .30.$$

This last computation results in the same value that was shown on the branch for *B* in Figure 9.1.

9.1.6

Computation of Conditional Standard Chances

Although the two drawings in Doe's gamble must be made in a predetermined order, the person making the drawings is not obliged to announce their events in that same order. Suppose, then, that the events will be announced to Doe in an order opposite to that in which they actually occur; and suppose that the prizes in the gamble are to be awarded as follows. If the event *X* occurs on the second drawing, Doe will be informed of this fact and will have to pay the house a certain sum of money, after which he will be told the event of the first drawing and will receive a prize which depends on whether that event was *A*, *B*, or *C*. If the event *Y* or *Z* occurs on the second drawing, Doe will make no payment to the house and will receive no prize, whatever the event of the first drawing may have been.

In these circumstances Doe may want to know how the chances of the events *A*, *B*, and *C* will look to him if and when he learns that the event *X* has occurred on the second drawing. In other words, he may want to know, not the unconditional standard chances of *A*, *B*, and *C* which appear on the fork at the origin of Figure 9.1 (page 323), but the conditional standard chances of these events given that the event *X* occurs.

To compute this chance, we again think in terms of the consolidated urn, assume for the moment that it contains 100 balls, and reason as follows. From the results in the right-hand margin of Figure 9.1, the number of balls bearing the label *X* is $100 \times (.28 + .09 + .03) = 40$, while the number of balls bearing not only the label *X* but also the label *A* is $100 \times .28 = 28$. Consequently 28/40 of the balls that bear the label *X* also bear the label *A*; and therefore the conditional standard chance that a ball will bear the label *A* given that it bears the label *X* is 28/40.

This same result could of course have been obtained without making any assumption about the total number of balls in the urn. If we had simply divided the fraction rather than the number of balls bearing both the label *A* and the label *X* by the fraction of balls bearing the label *X*, we would have obtained exactly the same result, $.28/.40 = 28/40$.

Now recalling that (1) the fraction of balls bearing both the label *A* and the label *X* is the unconditional standard chance of the event *A,X*, and (2) the

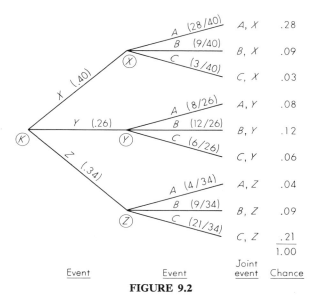

Event	Event	Joint event	Chance

FIGURE 9.2

Reversed Diagram of John Doe's Standard Gamble

fraction of balls bearing the label X is the unconditional standard chance of the event X, we generalize to conclude that:

- If F and G are any two events in a standard gamble, the conditional standard chance of F given G can be found by dividing the unconditional standard chance of F,G by the unconditional standard chance of G. In symbols,

$$P(F \mid G) = \frac{P(F, G)}{P(G)}.$$

It should be remembered that this rule is equivalent to saying that:

- If F and G are any two events in a standard gamble, the conditional chance of F given G can be found by (1) computing the sum of the chances of all end positions at which both F and G appear, (2) computing the sum of the chances of all end positions at which G appears with or without F, and (3) dividing the former sum by the latter.

9.1.7

Reversed Diagram
of the Standard Gamble

Because no forks representing a choice among acts intervene between the forks representing Doe's uncertainties about the two drawings in Figure 9.1, those uncertainties can be diagrammed just as well in the reversed order shown in Figure 9.2 as in the original order.[2]

---

[2] Regarding the names given to the joint events at the end positions of Figure 9.2, recall that A,X means only that both A and X occur; it does not indicate either the order in which A and X occur or the order in which the decision maker learns of their occurrence.

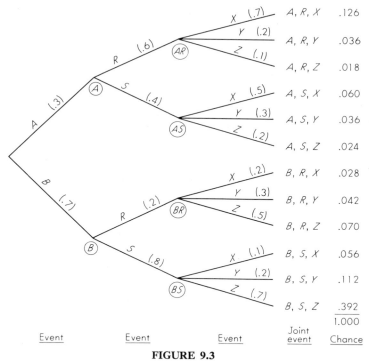

Event	Event	Event	Joint event	Chance
			A, R, X	.126
			A, R, Y	.036
			A, R, Z	.018
			A, S, X	.060
			A, S, Y	.036
			A, S, Z	.024
			B, R, X	.028
			B, R, Y	.042
			B, R, Z	.070
			B, S, X	.056
			B, S, Y	.112
			B, S, Z	.392
				1.000

FIGURE 9.3
A Three-stage Standard Gamble

The unconditional standard chances of the joint events or end positions in Figure 9.2 are simply copied from Figure 9.1 (page 323); and we have already seen in Sections 9.1.5 and 9.1.6 how from these chances we can compute the unconditional standard chance of any branch on the fork at position K in Figure 9.2 or the conditional standard chance of any branch on any one of the forks at positions X, Y, and Z. The results of such computations are shown in parentheses on the branches of Figure 9.2; the reader should verify some of these results before proceeding further.

9.1.8
Standard Gambles with
More than Two Stages

The results which we have now obtained for two-stage standard gambles apply virtually unchanged to standard gambles with any number of stages. The very few additional notions that are required can be brought out by considering the three-stage standard gamble diagrammed in Figure 9.3.

Definition of Joint Events   The terminology of joint events in a multistage standard gamble is illustrated by the following examples. If the three events A, R, and X occur, we say that the joint event A,R,X occurs, and we also say that the joint events A,R, R,X, and A,X occur.

Definition of Conditional and Unconditional Standard Chances of Individual Events
The terminology of conditional and unconditional standard chances for individual events in a multistage standard gamble is illustrated by the following examples.

1. The standard chance of the event A on the fork at the origin of Figure 9.3 is an unconditional standard chance and is denoted by $P(A)$.

2. Viewed from the origin of Figure 9.3, the standard chance of the event R on the fork at position A is conditional on the event A and is denoted by $P(R|A)$.

3. Viewed from the origin of Figure 9.3, the standard chance of the event X on the fork at position AR is conditional on the events A and R (or conditional on the joint event A,R) and is denoted by $P(X|A,R)$.

The Consolidated Equivalent Urn   The balls in a consolidated equivalent urn for the gamble of Figure 9.3 must bear *triple* labels, e.g. A,R,X, A,R,Y, and so forth. The fraction of balls bearing any particular triple label (the standard chance of the corresponding joint event) must be equal to the product of all the standard chances on the path from the origin to the end position at which the label appears.

Computation of Unconditional Standard Chances   Unconditional standard chances that do not appear directly on the branches or at the end positions of Figure 9.3 can be computed by the rule on page 326. The application of the rule is illustrated by the following examples.

1. The unconditional standard chance of the event X is the sum of the unconditional standard chances of all end positions at which X appears:

$$P(X) = .126 + .060 + .028 + .056 = .270.$$

2. The unconditional standard chance of the joint event R,X is the sum of the unconditional standard chances of all end positions at which R,X appears:

$$P(R,X) = .126 + .028 = .154.$$

Computation of Conditional Standard Chances   Conditional standard chances that do not appear directly on the branches of Figure 9.3 can be computed by the rule on page 328. The application of the rule is illustrated by the following examples.

1. The conditional standard chance of the event R given the event X is found by dividing the unconditional standard chance of R *and* X by the unconditional standard chance of X:

$$P(R|X) = P(R,X)/P(X) = .154/.270 = 154/270.$$

2. The conditional standard chance of the event A given the joint event R,X is

$$P(A \mid R,X) = P(A,R,X)/P(R,X) = .126/.154 = 126/154.$$

3. The conditional standard chance of the joint event A,R given the event X is

$$P(A,R \mid X) = P(A,R,X)/P(X) = .126/.270 = 126/270.$$

9.2
THE USE OF INDIRECTLY
RELEVANT INFORMATION: AN EXAMPLE

The essential result of Section 9.1 was this. If we are given the standard chance of every branch in a diagram of a multistage standard gamble, we can compute the unconditional standard chance of every end position of the diagram, and having done this, we can compute any conditional or unconditional standard chance in which we may be interested.

In the present section, we shall show by an example how this result can sometimes be used to compute the probabilities that a decision maker should assign to the branches of the event forks in his decision diagram when the available information bears directly, not on these probabilities, but on other, "related" probabilities.

9.2.1
Mr. Harrison's Decision Problem

Consider a factory manager named Harrison who suspects that a certain newly produced subassembly is defective in the sense that if it is installed in the final assembly for which it is intended, the final assembly will fail to function. By submitting the subassembly to a very thorough process of complete inspection and hand adjustment, Mr. Harrison can make absolutely sure that it will function properly, but this operation will cost about $500. On the other hand, if the subassembly is installed without being put through this operation and the final assembly then fails to function, it will cost about $1,000 just to remove and replace the subassembly, over and above the $500 it will cost to have it put in proper condition. At a cost of only $100, Mr. Harrison can get more information than he now has about the quality of the subassembly by subjecting it to a relatively quick test that his engineers have recently devised, but although this quick test is not very expensive, neither is it completely reliable. The engineers have calibrated the test by applying it to several subassemblies which were known to be good and to others which were known to be defective, and although

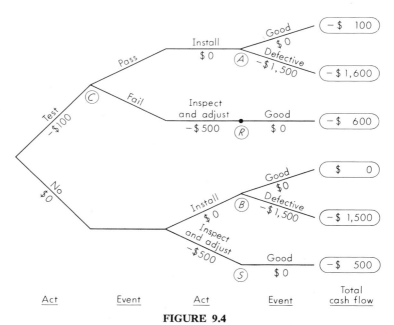

FIGURE 9.4

Mr. Harrison's Decision Problem

most of the good subassemblies passed the test and most of the defectives failed, some good assemblies failed and some defectives passed. No greater reliability can be obtained by repeating the test, since the errors are not associated with the test itself, but rather are due to the fact that the test does not constitute a direct measurement of the characteristics that make the subassembly good or defective.

The decision problem which Mr. Harrison faces is diagrammed in Figure 9.4,[3] and if he wishes to analyze this problem systematically, he must now assess his probabilities for the events on the forks at positions A, B, and C in this diagram. But although the probabilities for the branches of the fork at B will presumably give Mr. Harrison no more than the usual amount of trouble, he may feel quite helpless when he tries to assess his probabilities for the branches of the forks at A and C. His past experience with subassemblies of the same type as the present one gives him a good basis for evaluating the chance at B that an untested subassembly will be good or defective, but he has no basis in experience for evaluating either the chances at A that a subassembly which has passed the quick test will in fact be good or defective or the chances at C that a subassembly of unknown quality will pass or fail the test. The evidence collected by his engineers bears only on the chances that a good assembly will pass or fail the test and the chances that a defective assembly will pass or fail the test.

[3] Certain "obviously inferior" strategies have been omitted from this diagram; for the justification of such omissions, see Section 3.2.2.

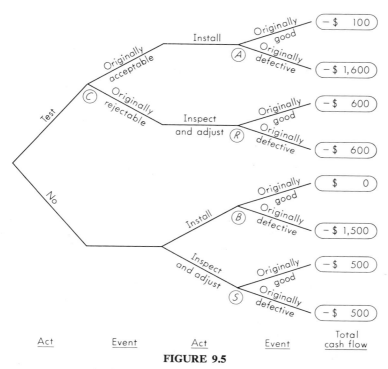

Act Event Act Event Total cash flow

FIGURE 9.5

Mr. Harrison's Decision Problem Described in Terms of Events for Which His Probabilities Are Independent of His Acts

9.2.2
Events Whose Probabilities Are Independent of Acts

This assessment problem is typical of the class of assessment problems that we described in the introduction to this chapter, and ultimately we shall show that if Mr. Harrison will directly assess the probabilities on which the available evidence bears directly, he will be able to compute the probabilities that he should assign to the branches of his decision diagram.

The reasoning underlying these computations would become very complex, however, if we had to take account of the fact that the probability which Mr. Harrison assigns to the branches of an event fork in his decision diagram may depend not only on events but also on acts which precede that fork in the diagram. Our first step toward the solution of Mr. Harrison's assessment problem will therefore be to reexpress his decision problem in terms of events for which his probabilities will be unaffected by his acts, and Figure 9.5 shows how this can be done.

We say that the event "originally acceptable" has occurred if the present state of the subassembly and the test equipment are such that the quick test *would* indicate that the subassembly should be "accepted"—i.e., installed in the final assembly without complete inspection and hand adjustment; and similarly we say that the event "originally rejectable" has occurred if the test *would* indicate that the subassembly should be "rejected"—i.e., inspected and adjusted before it is installed in the final assembly.   Because the events "originally acceptable" and "originally rejectable" as thus defined describe the present state of the subassembly and test equipment rather than the outcome of an actual test, the probabilities Mr. Harrison assigns to them should be the same whether or not he intends actually to subject the subassembly to the quick test and/or alter its present state by having it completely inspected and hand-adjusted before it is installed in the final assembly.

In the same way we say that the event "originally good" has occurred if the present state of the subassembly is such that it *would* function properly if it were installed in the final assembly without complete inspection and hand adjustment, and we say that the event "originally defective" has occurred if the contrary is true.   Again, Mr. Harrison's probabilities for these "present-state" events should be the same whether or not he intends actually to subject the subassembly to the quick test and/or alter its present state by having it completely inspected and hand-adjusted.

The effect (or absence of effect) of the acts "install (without complete inspection and hand adjustment)" and "inspect and adjust" on the *final* state of the subassembly is reflected by the terminal values assigned to the end positions which follow these acts in the decision diagram rather than by branches in the decision diagram itself.   The terminal values at the four end positions following "install" show that if this act is chosen, the final state of the subassembly will be the same as the present state, whatever the present state may be.   The terminal values at the four end positions following "inspect and adjust" show that if this act is chosen, the final state of the subassembly will be good no matter what its present state may be.

There is, of course, no real need to show the event forks at positions R and S in Figure 9.5.   Because both branches of the fork at R lead to exactly the same terminal value, this fork could be replaced by a single, unnamed branch; and similarly for the fork at S.   These two forks are shown in Figure 9.5 only to remind the reader that the events "originally good" and "originally defective" are defined in such a way that they are not only meaningful but also uncertain even after the subassembly has been rendered "finally good" with certainty.

9.2.3
Conditional and Unconditional
Probabilities

Returning now to Mr. Harrison's assessment problem, we shall find it convenient to distinguish between conditional and unconditional probabilities just as we distinguished between conditional and unconditional standard chances in Section 9.1.2. Because all probabilities are by definition standard chances in a standard drawing from an appropriate equivalent urn, we shall use the same symbols to denote conditional and unconditional probabilities that we used in Section 9.1.2 to denote conditional and unconditional standard chances.

Conditional Probabilities   Because probabilities for the branches of any event fork in any decision diagram must be assessed as if the decision maker knew that all events preceding that fork in the diagram had actually occurred or would actually occur, the probability Harrison assigns to the event "originally good" on the fork at position *A* in Figure 9.5 must be the probability which he would assess if he knew that the event "originally acceptable" had occurred. This probability will be called his conditional probability for the event "originally good" given the event "originally acceptable" and will be denoted by the symbol *P*(originally good | originally acceptable).   In general:

- If *E* and *F* are any two real-world events in a decision diagram, the probability that the decision maker would assign to *E* *if* he knew that *F* had occurred or would occur will be called his ≪conditional≫ probability for *E* ≪given≫ *F* and will be denoted by $P(E|F)$.

Unconditional Probabilities   The probability which Harrison assigns to the event "originally good" on the fork at position *B* in Figure 9.5 must be the probability he actually assesses for this event without knowing whether or not any other event in his diagram has occurred or will occur. This probability will be called his unconditional probability for the event "originally good" and will be denoted by the symbol *P*(originally good).   In general:

- If *E* is any real-world event in a decision diagram, the probability that the decision maker assigns to *E* without knowing whether or not any other event in the diagram has occurred or will occur will be called his ≪unconditional≫ probability for *E* and will be denoted by $P(E)$.

Nondependence of Probabilities on Acts   The reader should not fail to observe that conditional and unconditional probabilities are defined with reference to the decision maker's knowledge of events but not with reference to his knowledge of acts.   Complete confusion will therefore arise if the terminology of conditional and unconditional probabilities is used in discussing events for which the decision maker's probabilities can be affected by acts in his decision diagram.

9.2.4
Mr. Harrison's Assessment Gamble

In order to show Mr. Harrison how he can solve his problem of bringing the available information to bear on the probabilities he must assign to the event

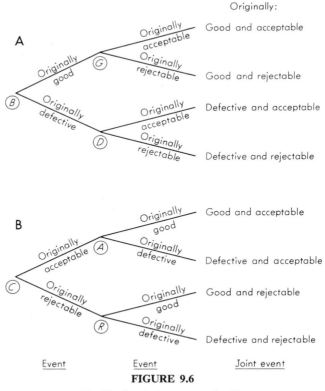

FIGURE 9.6

Mr. Harrison's Assessment Gamble

branches in the diagram of his decision problem, we first ask him to put this real decision problem out of his mind for a moment and imagine that he faces instead a decision problem involving a two-stage ≪assessment gamble≫ in which (1) a prize is associated to every possible combination of the events in which he is interested, and (2) he will make no choice among acts between the earliest and the latest dates at which his uncertainties about these events are resolved.   Because all the uncertainties in this hypothetical assessment gamble will be resolved without any intervening choices among acts, it can be diagrammed equally well in either of the two ways shown in Figure 9.6.

If now the reader will think back to the way in which we calculated the standard chances of the branches in Figure 9.2 (page 328) from the given standard chances of the branches in Figure 9.1 (page 323), the reason for introducing this assessment gamble will be apparent.

1. Harrison can assess his probabilities for all the branches in the *first* diagram of the assessment gamble with no more than the usual difficulty because (1) his previous experience with the actual performance of untested subassemblies bears directly on the unconditional probabilities that he should assign to the branches of the fork at position *B* in Figure 9.6A, and (2) the experience which

his engineers have gained by applying the quick test to subassemblies which were known to be good or known to be defective bears directly on the conditional probabilities that he should assign to the branches of the forks at positions G and D in Figure 9.6A.

2. We shall show in a moment that once Harrison has directly assessed his probabilities for the branches in Figure 9.6A, we can compute the probabilities he should assign to the branches in Figure 9.6B; and among these latter probabilities are the probabilities which Harrison must assess in order to analyze his real decision problem but finds it very hard to assess directly. Specifically, (1) the unconditional probabilities which we shall compute for the branches of the fork at position C in Figure 9.6B are the probabilities that Harrison should assign to the branches of the fork at position C in the diagram of his real decision problem in Figure 9.5 (page 333), and (2) the conditional probabilities given the event "originally acceptable" which we shall compute for the branches of the fork at position A in Figure 9.6B are the probabilities that Harrison should assign to the branches of the fork at position A in Figure 9.5.

9.2.5
Mr. Harrison's Direct Assessments

Suppose therefore that we now ask Mr. Harrison to assess his probabilities for the branches of the first diagram of the assessment gamble—i.e., to decide on his equivalent urn for each of three event forks in Figure 9.6A—and suppose that his assessments are as shown in Table 9.1, where the labels on the balls in his three equivalent urns are shown in the column headed "Label" and the fraction of balls bearing each label in each urn is shown in the column headed "Probability".

TABLE 9.1
Mr. Harrison's Probabilities for the Branches of Figure 9.6A

Position	Preceding Event	Event	Label	Probability
B	none	originally good	G	.7
		originally defective	D	.3
				1.0
G	originally good	originally acceptable	A	.8
		originally rejectable	R	.2
				1.0
D	originally defective	originally acceptable	A	.1
		originally rejectable	R	.9
				1.0

Before proceeding with our argument, we call the reader's attention to the fact that although the same events appear on the forks at positions G and D in

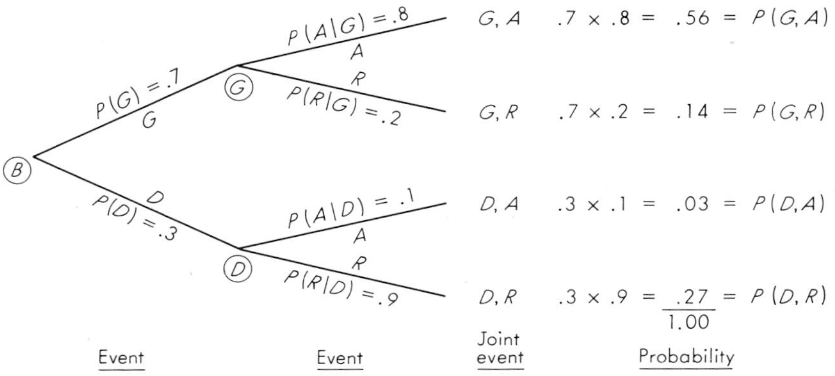

FIGURE 9.7

Probability Diagram for Mr. Harrison's Assessment Gamble

Figure 9.6A, Mr. Harrison's conditional probabilities for these events are not the same on the two forks. His equivalent urn for the fork at position G contains balls with the same labels as his equivalent urn for the event fork at position D, but the proportional mix of balls with these labels is not the same in these two urns. The reason is, of course, that Harrison's assessments at position G are made as if he knew that the subassembly is originally good, whereas his assessments at position D are made as if he knew that the subassembly is originally defective.

9.2.6
Probability Diagram for
the Assessment Gamble

To show how Mr. Harrison can compute the probabilities he should assess for the branches of Figure 9.6B (page 336) from the probabilities he has assessed for the branches of Figure 9.6A, we first use his assessments to reduce the gamble of Figure 9.6A to an equivalent standard gamble in which the only uncertain events are the outcomes of drawings from Harrison's equivalent urns. A diagram of this equivalent standard gamble is shown in Figure 9.7, where each event fork represents a standard drawing from the appropriate one of Harrison's three equivalent urns, the labels on the branches of each fork are the labels on the balls in the corresponding equivalent urn, and the decimal fractions on the branches show the fraction of balls bearing each label in each urn (cf. Table 9.1).

Because the fraction of balls bearing any particular label in any equivalent urn is by definition the decision maker's probability for the corresponding real-world event on the corresponding real-world event fork, we shall hereafter give the name «probability diagram» to any diagram which, like Figure 9.7, shows a decision maker's probabilities for the events in an assessment gamble.

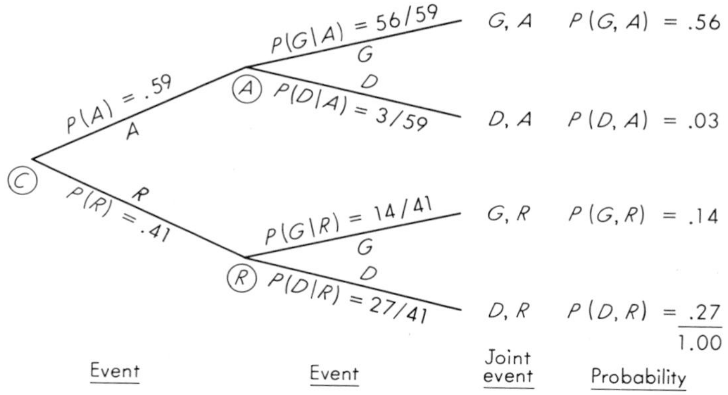

FIGURE 9.8

Reversed Probability Diagram for Mr. Harrison's Assessment Gamble

9.2.7
Mr. Harrison's Consolidated
Equivalent Urn

In order to calculate the probabilities that Mr. Harrison wants to assess from the probabilities that he has already assessed, we next replace the two-stage standard gamble of Figure 9.7 by an equivalent gamble based on a single standard drawing from one urn containing balls with double labels which correspond to the end positions of Figure 9.7.

By the rule in Section 9.1.4, the standard chance or proportion of balls labelled to correspond to any particular end position of the diagram in Figure 9.7 must be equal to the product of the standard chances or probabilities on the path from the origin to that end position. The required calculations and resulting proportions are shown in the right-hand margin of Figure 9.7; an urn containing balls in these proportions can be called Harrison's consolidated equivalent urn for all the uncertainties in his assessment gamble.

9.2.8
Reversed Probability Diagram
for the Assessment Gamble

By simply applying the computational rules that were developed in Sections 9.1.5 and 9.1.6, we can now derive the standard chances of the branches in the reversed probability diagram for Mr. Harrison's assessment gamble that is shown as Figure 9.8; and once this has been done, we shall have solved Mr. Harrison's assessment problem.

Because Mr. Harrison is indifferent between the assessment gamble on real-world events which is diagrammed in Figure 9.6B (page 336) and the equivalent standard gamble which is diagrammed in Figure 9.8, the standard chances on

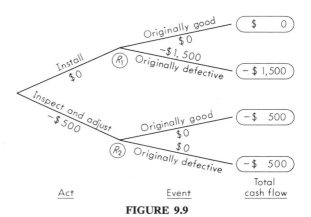

FIGURE 9.9

The Decision Problem Resulting from an Unfavorable Test Indication

the branches in Figure 9.8 are by definition Mr. Harrison's probabilities for the corresponding branches in Figure 9.6B; and as we pointed out when we first introduced the assessment gamble in Section 9.2.4, Mr. Harrison's probabilities for the branches of the event forks at A and C in the diagram of his real decision problem should be equal to his probabilities for the branches of the corresponding forks in Figure 9.6B.

9.2.9
Prior and Posterior Probabilities

Suppose now that instead of carefully analyzing the decision problem described in Section 9.2.1 and finding out whether the expenditure of $100 on a quick test of the subassembly is really justified, Mr. Harrison simply goes ahead and tests the subassembly; and suppose that the test shows that the event "originally rejectable" has in fact occurred—i.e., the test result indicates that the subassembly should be completely inspected and hand-adjusted before being installed in the final assembly. Mr. Harrison now faces the decision problem diagrammed in Figure 9.9; and if he wishes to analyze this problem carefully he must assess his probabilities for the events "originally good" and "originally defective" on the branches of this diagram.[4]

We have already seen, in Section 9.2.1, that the information available to Mr. Harrison does not bear directly on the probabilities that he should assign to the event that an "originally rejectable" assembly is "originally good" or "originally defective"; and this is just as true in the present problem, where "originally rejectable" does not appear as an event on the decision diagram, as it was in the

---

[4] In our original discussion of Mr. Harrison's problem, we assumed that he would not have the quick test performed unless it paid to do so, and this being so we could eliminate from the diagram of his problem any *strategy* which called for testing and then refusing to follow the indication of the test. This does not mean, however, that it is necessarily wrong to choose an *act* which is contrary to the indication of the test if the decision to test was arbitrary. Cf. Section 3.2.2.

problem of Section 9.2.1, where "originally rejectable" did appear as an event in the decision diagram (Figure 9.5 on page 333).

It follows that to exploit the available information effectively in the present situation, Mr. Harrison should follow exactly the same procedure that he should have followed in the earlier situation. Imagining for the moment that he does not in fact know the outcome of the test, Mr. Harrison should directly assess his probabilities for the branches of the first diagram of the assessment gamble in Figure 9.6 (page 336), then compute the probabilities he should assign to the branches of the second diagram of that gamble in Figure 9.6, and finally transfer his probabilities from the fork at position R in Figure 9.6B to the forks at positions R_1 and R_2 in the diagram of his real decision problem in Figure 9.9. As shown by Figure 9.8, the probabilities which Harrison will assess as a result of this procedure will be 14/41 for "originally good" and 27/41 for "originally defective."

We now face a somewhat bothersome problem of terminology. These computed probabilities for the events "originally good" and "originally defective" could properly be called Harrison's *conditional* probabilities for those events given the event "originally rejectable" when he assigned them to the fork at position R in Figure 9.6B (page 336) because the event "originally rejectable" actually appeared in that diagram and the probabilities in question were those that he would assess *if* this event occurred and he arrived as a result at position R. In Figure 9.9, on the contrary, the event "originally rejectable" does not appear in the diagram because Harrison already knows that this event has in fact occurred, and consequently these same computed probabilities for the events "originally good" and "originally defective" cannot be called "conditional" when Harrison assigns them to the forks at positions R_1 and R_2 in Figure 9.9. In this context and on this diagram, they are Harrison's *unconditional* probabilities for the events in question. Their numerical values have of course been affected by Harrison's knowledge that the event "originally rejectable" has occurred, but they are no more "conditional" on this knowledge than they are conditional on any other knowledge that Harrison used in assessing them.

We must, however, be able to distinguish in some way or another between, e.g., (*a*) the .7 unconditional probability which Harrison assigned (or would have assigned) to the event "originally good" in Table 9.1 (page 337) *before* he knew that "originally rejectable" had occurred, and (*b*) the 14/41 unconditional probability that he assigns to "originally good" in Figure 9.9 *after* learning that "originally rejectable" has occurred. To do so, it is customary to say that .7 was his «prior» (unconditional) probability for "originally good" and that 14/41 is his «posterior» (unconditional) probability for this same event. Alternatively, we can say with more precision that .7 was his (unconditional) probability for "originally good" prior to learning that "originally rejectable" had occurred, while 14/41 is his (unconditional) probability for "originally good" posterior to learning that "originally rejectable" has occurred.

9.3
CONDITIONAL, UNCONDITIONAL, AND
JOINT PROBABILITIES AND DISTRIBUTIONS

We can now state the general principles by which indirectly relevant information can be exploited in assessing probabilities. Almost all these principles have already appeared in the two previous sections; in the present section we merely collect them together, restate them more concisely, and point out some simple generalizations.

9.3.1
Events with Probabilities
Independent of Acts

Whenever a decision maker wishes to infer the conditional and unconditional probabilities that he should assess for the event branches of a decision diagram from other conditional and unconditional probabilities that he will assess directly, he must first make sure that all the events involved in his problem have been defined in such a way that his probabilities for these events would be unaffected by any *acts* that appear in his decision diagram. His calculations will not allow for dependence of probabilities on acts, and therefore they will lead to incorrect results if his probabilities ought to depend on his acts.

In order to prevent probabilities from being dependent on acts, it is frequently necessary to think of what first "looks like" one event as actually being two or more different events. In the example of Section 9.2.1, the event "good" on Mr. Harrison's original decision diagram (Figure 9.4 on page 332) looks like one event, but because Mr. Harrison's probability for "good" depended on the acts "install" and "adjust", we had to eliminate "good" from the description of Mr. Harrison's problem and substitute two separate events, "originally good" and "finally good". Although only one of these two events, "originally good", had to appear on the revised diagram (Figure 9.5 on page 333) in that particular example, both of them might have had to appear if the facts of the situation had been slightly different—if, for example, Mr. Harrison had not felt completely sure that complete inspection and hand adjustment would render the subassembly "finally good".

In much the same way, a decision diagram which shows the event "new product succeeds" after the acts "promote heavily" and "do not promote heavily" may have to be revised to show two different events: "product would succeed if heavily promoted" and "product would succeed without heavy promotion". Again, an uncertain quantity such as "unit sales of product X", which might be denoted by $\tilde{s}$ in a decision diagram, may have to be replaced by a whole set of distinct UQ's such as "unit sales of product X if priced at \$4.98", which could be denoted by $\tilde{s}_{498}$.

9.3.2
Joint Events

If two events X and Y both occur, we say that the joint event X,Y (or "X and Y") occurs. If the events X, Y, and Z all occur, we say that the joint events X,Y,Z, X,Y, X,Z, and Y,Z all occur.

9.3.3
Definition of Conditional, Unconditional,
and Joint Probabilities

Conditional and unconditional probabilities were defined in Section 9.2.3 essentially as follows:

1 If E is any event in a decision diagram, the probability that the decision maker assigns to E without knowing whether or not any other event in that diagram has occurred or will occur will be called his unconditional probability for E and will be denoted by $P(E)$.

2 If F and G are any two events in a decision diagram, the probability that the decision maker would assign to F *if* he knew that G had occurred or would occur will be called his conditional probability for F given G and will be denoted by $P(F|G)$.

Because the probabilities assigned to the branches of any event fork in a decision diagram must be assessed as if the decision maker knew that all events preceding that fork in the diagram had actually occurred or would actually occur but did not know whether any events following that fork in the diagram had actually occurred or would actually occur, these definitions imply that:

3 The probabilities assigned to the events on any event fork in a decision diagram must be *conditional* on all events which *precede* that event fork in the diagram but must *not* be conditional on any events which *follow* that fork in the diagram.

The definitions of unconditional and conditional probability that we have just given still hold when some or all of the event names E, F, and G are replaced by names of joint events. For example, the probability that the decision maker would assign to the joint event A,E if he knew that the joint event S,X had occurred will be called his conditional probability for A,E given S,X and will be denoted by $P(A,E|S,X)$.

Probabilities assigned to joint events are sometimes called "joint probabilities", but it must always be remembered that it is really only the descriptions of the events which are joint. The probabilities are just ordinary probabilities, conditional or unconditional as the case may be.

9.3.4
Assessment and Computation
of Probabilities

Suppose that a decision diagram contains event forks representing two or more different sets of mutually exclusive events. The decision maker may feel that he will be better able to exploit the information available to him if, instead of making direct assessments of his probabilities for the event branches in his decision diagram, he makes direct assessments of his probabilities for the event branches in a probability diagram of a hypothetical assessment gamble and then computes the probabilities which logical consistency requires him to assign to the event branches of his decision diagram.

A probability diagram of an assessment gamble involving any number of sets of mutually exclusive events is constructed as follows.

1. One set of mutually exclusive events is selected and is represented by a fork at the origin of the diagram.

2. Another set of mutually exclusive events is represented by a second level of forks, one fork at the end of each branch of the first-level fork.

3. If there are more than two sets of mutually exclusive events, still another set is represented by a third level of forks, one at the end of each branch of each second-level fork; and so forth until all the sets of mutually exclusive events have been duly represented.

In deciding which particular set of mutually exclusive events should appear on the first level of the diagram, which on the second, and so forth, the decision maker will be guided by the fact that after the diagram has been constructed, he will have to assess his probabilities for the branches of each fork in the diagram as if he knew that all events preceding that fork had actually occurred or would actually occur but did not know whether any event following that fork had actually occurred or would actually occur. If the available information bears most directly on the probabilities that he should assign to events $A, B, \ldots$ when he does not know which of the events $X, Y, \ldots$ has occurred, he will put fork(s) on which $A, B, \ldots$ appear *before* the forks on which $X, Y, \ldots$ appear. If on the contrary the available information bears most directly on the probabilities that he should assign to $A, B, \ldots$ if he knew which of the events $X, Y, \ldots$ has occurred, he will put forks on which $A, B, \ldots$ appear *after* the fork(s) on which $X, Y, \ldots$ appear.

In the example of Section 9.2, Mr. Harrison's information bore directly on the probabilities he should assign to the branches of a diagram in which the set of events "originally good" and "originally defective" appeared before the set of events "originally acceptable" and "originally rejectable" (Figure 9.6A on page 336); it did not bear directly on the probabilities he should assign to the branches of a diagram in which these two sets of events appeared in the opposite order (Figure 9.6B); and consequently he chose to make direct assessments of his probabilities for the branches of the first of the two diagrams.

After the decision maker has directly assessed his probabilities for the branches of his probability diagram,

1 The unconditional probability that the decision maker should assign to the joint event represented by any *end position* of the diagram of his assessment gamble can be computed by multiplying together his probabilities for the branches which make up the path from the origin of the diagram to that end position.

As soon as the probability of the joint event corresponding to every end position of the probability diagram has been computed, the probabilities that the decision maker should assign to the branches of the event forks in the diagram of his real decision problem can be computed by use of one or both of the following rules:

2 If E is any event in the diagram of an assessment gamble, the unconditional probability that the decision maker assigns to E should be the sum of the unconditional probabilities that he assigns to all end positions at which E appears.

3 If F and G are any two events in the diagram of an assessment gamble, the conditional probability that the decision maker assigns to F given G should be equal to his unconditional probability for the joint event F,G divided by his unconditional probability for the event G:

$$P(F|G) = \frac{P(F,\ G)}{P(G)}.$$

In other words, the conditional probability that the decision maker should assign to F given G can be computed by (1) computing the sum of his probabilities for all end positions at which both F and G appear, (2) computing the sum of his probabilities for all end positions at which G appears with or without F, and (3) dividing the former sum by the latter.

Rules 2 and 3 still apply when the event names E, F, and/or G are replaced by names of joint events such as A,B or X,Y.

9.3.5
Prior and Posterior Probabilities

Suppose that a decision maker assesses, directly or by computation, both his unconditional probability for an event F and his conditional probability for the event F given an event G; and suppose that he subsequently learns that the event G has in fact occurred. The unconditional probability that he previously assigned to *F* is now invalid because it no longer reflects all the available information about *F*, whereas what was previously his conditional probability for *F* given *G*—i.e., the probability that he decided that he would assign to *F* *if* he knew that *G* had occurred or would occur—now becomes his unconditional probability for *F*—i.e., the probability that he does in fact assign to *F*.

To distinguish between the unconditional probability that the decision maker originally assigned to *F* and the "updated" or "revised" unconditional probability that he assigns to *F* after learning that *G* has in fact occurred, it is customary to call the former his "prior" and the latter his "posterior" unconditional probability for *F*. Because an unconditional probability may be updated or revised more than once as more and more new information is received, it is sometimes necessary to be more precise and distinguish between an unconditional probability assessed prior to learning that some specific event such as *G* has occurred or will occur and the updated or revised unconditional probability assessed posterior to learning that that specific event has occurred or will occur.

Indirect Assessment of Posterior Probabilities   A decision maker who wishes to assign probabilities to events *X*, *Y*, . . . will often feel (like Mr. Harrison in the problem of Section 9.2) that his assessments should be affected by his knowledge that an event *E* has occurred but will find it very difficult to say exactly how they should be affected.

In such a situation, the decision maker can if he chooses make the required assessments indirectly, by the following procedure. Imagining that he is at a point in time just prior to his learning that *E* occurred, he first exploits his prior information by directly assessing (1) his prior unconditional probabilities for *X*, *Y*, . . . , and (2) his conditional probabilities for *E* given *X*, *Y*, ... Next he computes what would have been his conditional probabilities for *X*, *Y*, . . . given *E*; and finally, placing himself once again in the present, he takes these computed conditional probabilities as his posterior unconditional probabilities for *X*, *Y*, ...

If a large part of the information that was available prior to learning that the event *E* has occurred bears directly on the probabilities that the decision maker must assess under this indirect procedure, he should use the procedure. If it does not, he must either make a direct assessment of the probabilities required to analyze his decision problem or find some other way of decomposing his assessment problem.

9.3.6
Conditional and Unconditional
Distributions of a UQ

Just as a decision maker may assess both conditional and unconditional probabilities for the same event, so he may assess both conditional and unconditional probability distributions for an uncertain quantity. For example, consider the subdiagrams or portions of a decision diagram shown in Figure 8.5 (page 289).

1. If the decision maker uses the second subdiagram, Figure 8.5B, then the probability that he assigns to each possible value of the UQ d on the fan at position P must be his conditional probability for that value given the event "competitor markets". The complete set of probabilities that he assigns to all the branches of the fan at position P is called his ≪conditional probability distribution≫ of the UQ d given the event "competitor markets", and similarly the set of probabilities that he assigns to the branches of the fork at position Q in Figure 8.5B is called his conditional probability distribution of d given the event "does not market".

2. If, on the other hand, the decision maker uses the first diagram, Figure 8.5A, then he must assess his unconditional probability for each possible value of d, and his complete set of probabilities for all the branches of the fan is called his ≪unconditional probability distribution≫ of d.

9.3.7
Joint Distributions

The events on which a distribution of a UQ is conditioned may of course be the possible values of another UQ. The probability diagram of an assessment gamble in Figure 9.10 shows (1) a decision maker's unconditional distribution of a UQ $\tilde{x}$, and (2) his conditional distribution of a UQ $\tilde{y}$ given each possible value x of the UQ $\tilde{x}$.

After the decision maker has assessed his probabilities for all the branches of an assessment gamble like the one in Figure 9.10, he can of course compute the unconditional probability that he should assign to any joint event of the form $\tilde{x} = x$, $\tilde{y} = y$ by simply multiplying the probabilities on the path from the origin to the corresponding end position. In Figure 9.10, the decision maker should assign unconditional probability $.3 \times .2 = .06$ to the joint event $\tilde{x} = 0$, $\tilde{y} = 0$, and so forth.

The complete set of unconditional probabilities assigned to all end positions of a diagram like Figure 9.10 is called the decision maker's ≪joint probability distribution≫ of the UQ's in the diagram, and a diagram like Figure 9.10 may be called either a probability diagram of the joint distribution or a ≪joint probability diagram≫. The UQ's themselves are said to be ≪jointly distributed≫ when the decision maker has assessed their joint distribution, either directly, or by assigning probabilities to the branches of a joint probability diagram and thus making it possible to compute the joint distribution.

9.3.8
Conditional and Unconditional Distributions
Implied by a Joint Distribution

Once the joint distribution of any number of UQ's has been assessed, either the unconditional distribution or any desired conditional distribution of any one of

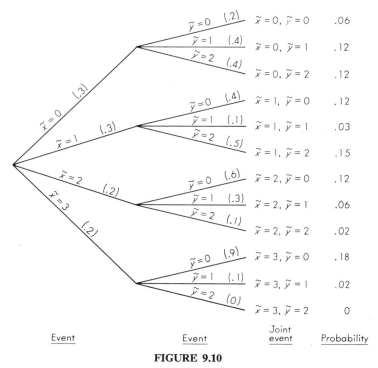

FIGURE 9.10

Probability Diagram of an Assessment Gamble Involving Two Uncertain Quantities

the jointly distributed UQ's can be computed by simply applying the rules given in Section 9.3.4 above for the computation of conditional and unconditional probabilities. By way of review, the reader should verify that the directly assessed unconditional distribution of $\tilde{x}$ and conditional distributions of $\tilde{y}$ that were shown in Figure 9.10 imply the computed unconditional distribution of $\tilde{y}$ and conditional distributions of $\tilde{x}$ that are shown on the branches of the forks in Figure 9.11.

9.3.9

Conditional and Unconditional
Expectations of a UQ

When a UQ is jointly distributed with one or more other UQ's, it has as many different conditional and unconditional expectations as it has conditional and unconditional distributions.

For example, consider the UQ $\tilde{y}$ that is jointly distributed with $\tilde{x}$ via the probability diagrams shown as Figures 9.10 and 9.11. Using the probabilities on the topmost second-level fork in Figure 9.10, which define the conditional distribution of $\tilde{y}$ given $\tilde{x} = 0$, we find that the «conditional expectation» of $\tilde{y}$

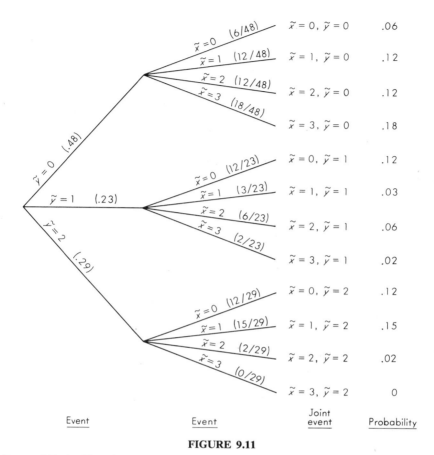

Event	Event	Joint event	Probability

FIGURE 9.11

Reversed Probability Diagram of an Assessment Gamble Involving Two Uncertain Quantities

given $\tilde{x} = 0$ is $0(.2) + 1(.4) + 2(.4) = 1.2$. Using the probabilities on the fork at the origin of Figure 9.11, which constitute the unconditional distribution of $\tilde{y}$, we find that the «unconditional expectation» of $\tilde{y}$ is $0(.48) + 1(.23) + 2(.29) = .81$.

Recall now that it was Figure 9.10 which was directly assessed by the decision maker, and suppose that his only reason for assessing this joint distribution was to find his unconditional expectation of $\tilde{y}$. Instead of going to the trouble of first computing the unconditional distribution of $\tilde{y}$ which appears in Figure 9.11, he could have calculated his unconditional expectation of y directly from Figure 9.10 by use of the following rule:

■ The *unconditional* expectation of any UQ that appears in any probability diagram of a joint distribution can be computed by (1) multiplying the value of the UQ at each end position of the diagram by the probability of that end position, and then (2) adding these products.

The unconditional expectation of y as found by applying this rule to Figure 9.10 is $0(.06) + 1(.12) + 2(.12) + 0(.12) + 1(.03) + 2(.15) + 0(.12) + 1(.06) + 2(.02) + 0(.18) + 1(.02) + 2(0) = .81$, in agreement with the value we found previously by use of the unconditional distribution of $\tilde{y}$. The reader should convince himself that the two methods of computation will necessarily lead to exactly the same result in any problem whatever.

9.3.10
Grouped Approximations

When nonzero probability is assigned to a very large number of possible values of any one of the UQ's appearing in a probability diagram, the exact distributions of that UQ may be replaced by grouped approximations (cf. Section 7.4).

The reader should recall that a grouped approximation is treated exactly as if it were the decision maker's true distribution. In the present context, this implies that after grouped approximations to the decision maker's directly assessed distributions have been used to compute a grouped approximation to some distribution that is required for the analysis of a decision problem, this latter distribution should also be treated as if it were an exact distribution. It should not be "smoothed" in an effort to obtain a better approximation to the distribution that would have resulted from computations based on the decision maker's original, ungrouped distributions.

As we said in Section 7.4.8, grouping and computations based on grouping would in practice be carried out on a digital computer, and the groups would be made small enough to avoid any practical loss of accuracy. Examples and exercises in this book are intended only to bring out the basic logic of the computations that would be performed by the computer, and for this purpose ten equiprobable groups will suffice.

9.4
DISTRIBUTION AND EXPECTATION
OF A FUNCTION OF SEVERAL UQ's

9.4.1
Definition of a Function of Several UQ's

In Section 7.3.2 we said that a UQ such as "sales revenue" is called a function of a UQ such as "demand" if the value of demand determines the value of sales revenue. More generally, $\tilde{z}$ is a function of $\tilde{x}$ if the value of $\tilde{x}$ determines the value of $\tilde{z}$. We shall now say that a UQ $\tilde{z}$ is a function of several UQ's $\tilde{u}$, $\tilde{v}$, $\tilde{w}$, . . . , if the values of these UQ's taken together determine the value of $\tilde{z}$.

For example, if $\tilde{z}$ is related to $\tilde{u}$, $\tilde{v}$, $\tilde{w}$, and $\tilde{x}$ by the formula

$$\tilde{z} = \tilde{u}^2 + 7\tilde{v}\tilde{w} + \frac{1}{\tilde{x}},$$

then $\bar{z}$ is a function of $\bar{u}$, $\bar{v}$, $\bar{w}$, and $\bar{x}$ because we can compute the value of $\bar{z}$ corresponding to any given set of values for $\bar{u}$, $\bar{v}$, $\bar{w}$, and $\bar{x}$. If, say,

$$\bar{u} = 2, \qquad \bar{v} = 3, \qquad \bar{w} = 1, \qquad \bar{x} = 4,$$

then

$$\bar{z} = 2^2 + (7 \times 3 \times 1) + \frac{1}{4} = 25.25.$$

It frequently happens that we wish to compute the distribution of a function of several UQ's whose joint distribution has already been directly assessed, and we shall now explain via an example how this can be done. The method of computation is very similar to the method we described in Section 7.3.3 for computing the distribution of a function of a single UQ, and the reader may do well to review that section before proceeding further.

9.4.2
An Example of a Function of Two UQ's

As an example of a situation in which a decision maker might want to compute the distribution of a function of two UQ's, suppose that the sales manager of a certain company wishes to assess his probability distribution of demand for his company's brand as a function of two other UQ's, namely (1) total demand for all brands of the product in question, and (2) his brand's share of the total. Thinking about the problem in this way, the sales manager might decide that the most effective way to apply his experience and judgment would be to make direct assessments of (1) his unconditional distribution of total demand, and (2) his conditional distribution of his company's share given each possible value of total demand, and then to infer from these distributions his distribution of actual demand for his brand of the product.

If the sales manager feels that information about total demand could affect his judgments about company share, the problem of assessing the conditional distributions of company share may be quite difficult, since the sales manager obviously cannot sit down and assess directly a different conditional distribution of "share" given each of a large number of possible values of the UQ "total demand". Deferring discussion of such difficult assessment problems until Section 9.7, we shall here consider the relatively simple case where the sales manager feels that information about total demand would have absolutely no effect on his judgments about company share. Given this assumption, all of his conditional distributions of "company share" given the various possible values of "total demand" will be *numerically* the same, and he will therefore have only two *numerically* different distributions to assess in all: one of total demand and one of company share.

To bring out as clearly as possible the basic logic by which the sales manager's distribution of company demand can be computed from directly

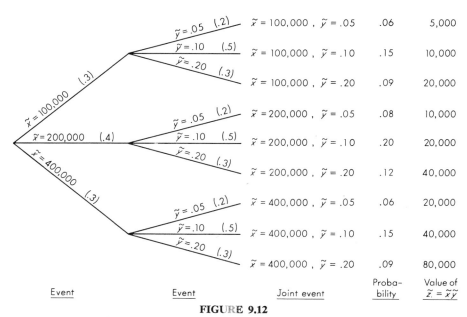

Event	Event	Joint event	Probability	Value of $\tilde{z} = \tilde{x}\tilde{y}$
	$\tilde{y} = .05$ (.2)	$\tilde{x} = 100,000$, $\tilde{y} = .05$	.06	5,000
	$\tilde{y} = .10$ (.5)	$\tilde{x} = 100,000$, $\tilde{y} = .10$	.15	10,000
$\tilde{x} = 100,000$ (.3)	$\tilde{y} = .20$ (.3)	$\tilde{x} = 100,000$, $\tilde{y} = .20$	.09	20,000
	$\tilde{y} = .05$ (.2)	$\tilde{x} = 200,000$, $\tilde{y} = .05$	.08	10,000
$\tilde{x} = 200,000$ (.4)	$\tilde{y} = .10$ (.5)	$\tilde{x} = 200,000$, $\tilde{y} = .10$	.20	20,000
	$\tilde{y} = .20$ (.3)	$\tilde{x} = 200,000$, $\tilde{y} = .20$	.12	40,000
$\tilde{x} = 400,000$ (.3)	$\tilde{y} = .05$ (.2)	$\tilde{x} = 400,000$, $\tilde{y} = .05$	.06	20,000
	$\tilde{y} = .10$ (.5)	$\tilde{x} = 400,000$, $\tilde{y} = .10$	.15	40,000
	$\tilde{y} = .20$ (.3)	$\tilde{x} = 400,000$, $\tilde{y} = .20$	.09	80,000

FIGURE 9.12

Joint Distribution of Total Demand $\tilde{x}$ and Company Share $\tilde{y}$

assessed distributions of total demand and company share, we shall first assume that he assesses the extremely simple distributions that are shown in Table 9.2. Once we have shown how to work with these simple distributions, we shall be ready to show that no complications of any importance arise when the sales manager assesses the realistic distributions of total demand and company share that appear in Figures 9.13 and 9.14.

TABLE 9.2A	
Sales Manager's Unconditional	
Distribution of Total Demand	
Total Demand	*Probability*
x	*P(x)*
100,000	.3
200,000	.4
400,000	.3
	1.0

TABLE 9.2B	
Sales Manager's Conditional	
Distribution of Company Share,	
Given Any Value Whatever of Total Demand	
Company Share	*Probability*
y	$P(y\,\vert\,\tilde{x} = x)$
.05	.2
.10	.5
.20	.3
	1.0

9.4.3
Computation of the Distribution
of the Function

The first step in the computation of the distribution of any function of jointly distributed UQ's is to compute the joint distribution of the UQ's themselves. This computation is carried out for our example in Figure 9.12, where the directly assessed distributions of total demand $\tilde{x}$ and company share $\tilde{y}$ are taken from Table 9.2.

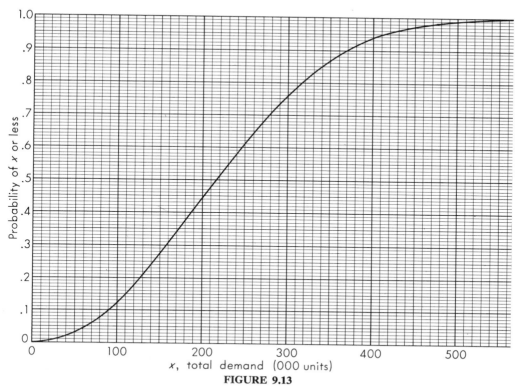

FIGURE 9.13
Sales Manager's Unconditional Distribution of Total Demand

The next step in the computation of the distribution of any function is to calculate the value of the function at each end position of the joint probability diagram. If in our example we denote the function "company demand" by $\bar{z}$, its relation to $\bar{x}$ and $\bar{y}$ is simply $\bar{z} = \bar{x} \times \bar{y}$, and hence the value of $\bar{z}$ corresponding to $\bar{x} = 100,000$ and $\bar{y} = .05$ is $.05 \times 100,000 = 5,000$, and so forth. The value of the function $\bar{z}$ is shown at every end position of Figure 9.12.

We can now find the unconditional probability of any particular value of the function $\bar{z}$ by simply adding the unconditional probabilities of all joint events or end positions in Figure 9.12 that give rise to that value of the function. The complete unconditional distribution of $\bar{z}$ is computed in this way in Table 9.3.

TABLE 9.3
Sales Manager's Unconditional
Distribution of Company Demand

Company Demand z	Probability $P(z)$	
5,000	.06	= .06
10,000	.15 + .08	= .23
20,000	.09 + .20 + .06	= .35
40,000	.12 + .15	= .27
80,000	.09	= .09
		1.00

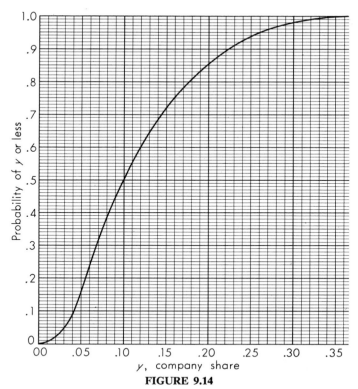

FIGURE 9.14

Sales Manager's Conditional Distribution of Company Share
Given Any Value Whatever of Total Demand

9.4.4
Grouped Approximations

Suppose now that the sales manager assesses, not the three-point distributions of total demand $\tilde{x}$ and company share $\tilde{y}$ that are shown in Table 9.2, but the realistic distributions shown in Figures 9.13 and 9.14. Computation of the exact distribution of company demand $\tilde{z} = \tilde{x}\tilde{y}$ that is implied by these two distributions would be very laborious, but we can easily compute a grouped approximation to the distribution of $\tilde{z}$.

To do so, we first construct grouped approximations to the distributions of $\tilde{x}$ and $\tilde{y}$, representing each distribution by the bracket medians of ten equiprobable brackets; the results are shown in Table 9.4. We next compute the grouped joint distribution shown in Table 9.5 by exactly the same method that we used to compute the joint distribution at the end positions of Figure 9.12; and we also compute the values shown in Table 9.6 of the company share $\tilde{z}$ corresponding to each pair of values of $\tilde{x}$ and $\tilde{y}$. Tables 9.5 and 9.6 completely describe the 100 end positions of the joint probability diagram of $\tilde{x}$ and $\tilde{y}$.

We can now compute the mass function of our approximation to the distribution of the function $\tilde{z}$ by first listing in order of size the values of the function that appear in Table 9.6 and then computing the probability of each value

TABLE 9.4
Grouped Distributions of Total Demand and Company Share

Total Demand x	Probability P(x)	Company Share y	Probability P(y)
65,000	.1	.030	.1
108,000	.1	.048	.1
143,000	.1	.062	.1
173,000	.1	.075	.1
203,000	.1	.092	.1
232,000	.1	.110	.1
261,000	.1	.131	.1
296,000	.1	.158	.1
341,000	.1	.198	.1
415,000	.1	.260	.1
	1.0		1.0

TABLE 9.5
Grouped Joint Distribution of Total Demand and Company Share

Demand x	\ Share y \ .030	.048	.062	.075	.092	.110	.131	.158	.198	.260
65,000	.01	.01	.01	.01	.01	.01	.01	.01	.01	.01
108,000	.01	.01	.01	.01	.01	.01	.01	.01	.01	.01
143,000	.01	.01	.01	.01	.01	.01	.01	.01	.01	.01
173,000	.01	.01	.01	.01	.01	.01	.01	.01	.01	.01
203,000	.01	.01	.01	.01	.01	.01	.01	.01	.01	.01
232,000	.01	.01	.01	.01	.01	.01	.01	.01	.01	.01
261,000	.01	.01	.01	.01	.01	.01	.01	.01	.01	.01
296,000	.01	.01	.01	.01	.01	.01	.01	.01	.01	.01
341,000	.01	.01	.01	.01	.01	.01	.01	.01	.01	.01
415,000	.01	.01	.01	.01	.01	.01	.01	.01	.01	.01

TABLE 9.6
Value of the Function $\bar{z}$ for Given Values of $\bar{x}$ and $\bar{y}$

Demand x	Share y .030	.048	.062	.075	.092	.110	.131	.158	.198	.260
65,000	1,950	3,120	4,030	4,875	5,980	7,150	8,515	10,270	12,870	16,900
108,000	3,240	5,184	6,696	8,100	9,936	11,880	14,148	17,064	21,384	28,080
143,000	4,290	6,864	8,866	10,725	13,156	15,730	18,733	22,594	28,314	37,180
173,000	5,190	8,304	10,726	12,975	15,916	19,030	22,663	27,334	34,254	44,980
203,000	6,090	9,744	12,586	15,225	18,676	22,330	26,593	32,074	40,194	52,780
232,000	6,960	11,136	14,384	17,400	21,344	25,520	30,392	36,656	45,936	60,320
261,000	7,830	12,528	16,182	19,575	24,012	28,710	34,191	41,238	51,678	67,860
296,000	8,880	14,208	18,352	22,200	27,232	32,560	38,776	46,768	58,608	76,960
341,000	10,230	16,368	21,142	25,575	31,372	37,510	44,671	53,878	67,518	88,660
415,000	12,450	19,920	25,730	31,125	38,180	45,650	54,365	65,570	82,170	107,900

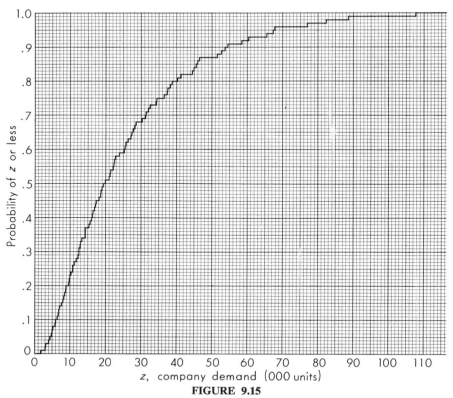

FIGURE 9.15

Sales Manager's Unconditional Distribution of Company Demand

by adding the probabilities, as given by Table 9.5, of all end positions at which that value appears. Instead of showing the results of these computations directly, we go on to compute the cumulative function of $\bar{z}$ from its mass function and graph the cumulative function in Figure 9.15.

Use of a Digital Computer If the distribution of $\bar{z}$ were to be evaluated on a computer, as it would be in practice, then as we explained in Section 7.4.8 the only "hand work" required would be to read the coordinates of about a dozen points and the slopes at three points on each of the graphs in Figures 9.13 and 9.14. The computer would accept these data as inputs, fit mathematical cumulative functions to them, determine from these the bracket medians of $\bar{x}$ and $\bar{y}$ for any specified number of brackets, use these medians to compute tables like Tables 9.5 and 9.6, and finally use these tables to compute the implied mass and cumulative functions of $\bar{z}$.

9.4.5
Distribution of a Function
of Several UQ's

The method of computing the unconditional distribution of a function which was applied in the previous section to a function of two jointly distributed UQ's can be immediately extended to functions of any number of jointly distributed UQ's. The procedure in the general case is as follows.

1 Assess the joint distribution of the underlying UQ's by constructing a joint probability diagram, directly assessing probabilities for all its branches, and then computing the probabilities of all the end positions.

2 Compute the value of the function corresponding to each end position of the diagram.

3 List these function values in order of size and find the unconditional probability of each value by adding the probabilities of all end positions at which the function has that value.

9.4.6

**Expectation of a Function
of Several UQ's**

We saw in Section 7.3.4 that when a UQ $\tilde{z}$ is a function of a single UQ $\tilde{x}$, we can compute the expectation of $\tilde{z}$ in either of two ways. (1) We can *compute the distribution of $\tilde{z}$* from the distribution of $\tilde{x}$ and then compute $E\tilde{z}$ by multiplying each possible value of $\tilde{z}$ by the probability of that value of $\tilde{z}$ and adding the products. (2) We can *work directly from the distribution of $\tilde{x}$*, multiplying the value of $\tilde{z}$ that corresponds to each possible value of $\tilde{x}$ by the probability of that value of $\tilde{x}$ and adding the products.

Essentially the same two methods can be used to compute the unconditional expectation of a UQ $\tilde{z}$ which is a function of several UQ's $\tilde{u}$, $\tilde{v}$, $\tilde{w}$, ...

1 We can *compute the distribution of $\tilde{z}$* from the joint distribution of $\tilde{u}$, $\tilde{v}$, $\tilde{w}$, . . . and then compute $E\tilde{z}$ by multiplying each possible value of $\tilde{z}$ by the probability of that value of $\tilde{z}$ and adding the products.

2 We can *work directly from the joint distribution of $\tilde{u}$, $\tilde{v}$, $\tilde{w}$, . . .* , multiplying the value of $\tilde{z}$ at each end position of the joint probability diagram by the probability of that end position and adding the products.

For example, suppose that a function $\tilde{z}$ of two UQ's $\tilde{x}$ and $\tilde{y}$ is defined by $\tilde{z} = \tilde{x}\tilde{y}$; and suppose that $\tilde{x}$ and $\tilde{y}$ have the joint distribution defined by Figure 9.12 on page 352. To compute $E\tilde{z}$ by the first method, we must first compute the distribution of the function $\tilde{z}$ from the probabilities and values of $\tilde{z}$ shown at the end positions of Figure 9.12, as is done in Table 9.3 on page 335. We can then use the probabilities and values of $\tilde{z}$ in Table 9.3 to compute

$$E\tilde{z} = .06(5{,}000) + .23(10{,}000) + .35(20{,}000) + .27(40{,}000)$$
$$+ .09(80{,}000) = 27{,}600.$$

To compute $E\tilde{z}$ by the second method, we work directly from the probabilities and values of $\tilde{z}$ shown at the end positions in Figure 9.12:

$E\bar{z} = .06(5,000) + .15(10,000) + .09(20,000) + .08(10,000) + .20(20,000)$
$\qquad + .12(40,000) + .06(20,000) + .15(40,000) + .09(80,000) = 27,600.$

The reader should convince himself that the two methods must necessarily lead to exactly the same result, not only in this example, but in any problem whatever.

9.5

INDEPENDENCE

9.5.1

Independence of Two Events

Consider the probability diagram of Figure 9.16A, where X and Y stand for any two events that are not mutually exclusive and $\bar{X}$ (read: not X) and $\bar{Y}$ respectively denote the nonoccurrence of X and Y.

It may be that knowledge of the occurrence or nonoccurrence of the event X would have absolutely no effect on a particular decision maker's judgment about the chance of the event Y. He would be neither more nor less ready to bet on Y if he knew that X had occurred than he would be if he knew that X had not occurred. If this is so, then the probability $P(Y|X)$ that he would assign to Y if he knew that X had occurred will be exactly equal to the probability $P(Y|\bar{X})$ that he would assign to Y if he knew that X had not occurred. In other words, his probability for the event Y on the fork at position A in Figure 9.16A will be exactly equal to his probability for that same event on the fork at position B.

When a decision maker does in fact assess $P(Y|X) = P(Y|\bar{X})$, the event Y may be said to be "independent of the event X" in that decision maker's judgment. It can be proved, however, that if a decision maker assesses $P(Y|X) = P(Y|\bar{X})$, then he is logically obliged to assess $P(X|Y) = P(X|\bar{Y})$. If, in other words, his probability for Y is the same on both second-level forks in Figure 9.16A, then his probability for X should be the same on both second-level forks of the reversed probability diagram in Figure 9.16B.[5] More briefly, if Y is independent of X in his judgment, then X should be independent of Y in his judgment; and therefore we can say simply that "the events X and Y are independent" in his judgment. To sum up:

1 If a decision maker assesses $P(Y|X) = P(Y|\bar{X})$, he is logically obliged to assess $P(X|Y) = P(X|\bar{Y})$, and vice versa.

2 If a decision maker assesses $P(Y|X) = P(Y|\bar{X})$ and $P(X|Y) = P(X|\bar{Y})$, the events X and Y are said to be «independent» in his judgment.

---

[5] The reader will be asked as an exercise to prove this by deriving certain relations between fractions in the decision maker's consolidated equivalent urn.

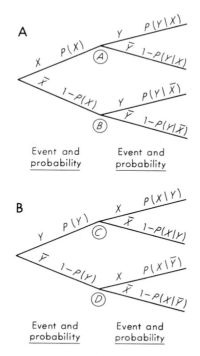

FIGURE 9.16
Probability Diagrams of Two Uncertainties

It frequently happens that a decision maker who assesses $P(Y|X) = P(Y|\bar{X})$ will not at first thought want to assess $P(X|Y) = P(X|\bar{Y})$. It may seem to him that although the occurrence or nonoccurrence of X tells him nothing about Y, the occurrence or nonoccurrence of Y does tell him something about X. This feeling, however, is just another example of the logical inconsistencies that are present in everyone's intuitive opinions, and a decision maker who at first holds such inconsistent opinions should delay analysis of his decision problem until he has convinced himself either that he wants to assess $P(X|Y) = P(X|\bar{Y})$ or that he does not want to assess $P(Y|X) = P(Y|\bar{X})$.

If, knowing that X has occurred, a decision maker would assign the same probability to Y that he would assign if he knew that X had not occurred, then clearly he must assign this same probability to Y when he does not know whether or not X has occurred. In symbols: if he assesses $P(Y|X) = P(Y|\bar{X})$, he must assess $P(Y) = P(Y|X) = P(Y|\bar{X})$.

3 If X and Y are independent in a decision maker's judgment, then not only his two conditional probabilities for X but also his unconditional probability for X must all be *numerically* the same.

9.5.2
Independence of Two UQ's

Consider again the probability diagram in Figure 9.12 (page 352), which represents a joint distribution of total demand $\tilde{x}$ and company share $\tilde{y}$, and observe that the decision maker has assigned the same probability distribution to $\tilde{y}$ on every $\tilde{y}$ fork in the second level of the diagram.

By so doing, the decision maker has said in effect that knowledge of the value of total demand $\tilde{x}$ would have absolutely no effect on his judgments about the share $\tilde{y}$ of that demand that his company would enjoy. Specifically, he has said that if he knew that $\tilde{x} = 200,000$, he would assign the same .2 probability to the event $\tilde{y} = .05$ that he would assign if he knew that $\tilde{x} = 100,000$; and similarly for all other values of $\tilde{x}$ and $\tilde{y}$. His conditional distribution of $\tilde{y}$ *given* a particular value of $\tilde{x}$ does not actually *depend* on the value of $\tilde{x}$.

When a decision maker's conditional distribution of $\tilde{y}$ given any one particular value of $\tilde{x}$ is numerically the same as his conditional distribution of $\tilde{y}$ given any other value of $\tilde{x}$, the UQ $\tilde{y}$ may be said to be independent of the UQ $\tilde{x}$ in his judgment. It can be proved, however, that if a decision maker assigns the same conditional distribution to $\tilde{y}$ given any one particular value of $\tilde{x}$ that he assigns given any other particular value of $\tilde{x}$, then logic obliges him to assign the same conditional distribution to $\tilde{x}$ given any one particular value of $\tilde{y}$ that he assigns given any other particular value of $\tilde{y}$. More briefly, if $\tilde{y}$ is independent of $\tilde{x}$ in the decision maker's judgment, then $\tilde{x}$ should be independent of $\tilde{y}$; and therefore we can say simply that «the UQ's $\tilde{x}$ and $\tilde{y}$ are independent» in his judgment.

If, knowing that $\tilde{x}$ has any one particular value, a decision maker would assign the same distribution to $\tilde{y}$ that he would assign if he knew that $\tilde{x}$ had any other particular value, then clearly he must assign this same distribution to $\tilde{y}$ when the value of $\tilde{x}$ is unknown to him.

■ If two UQ's $\tilde{x}$ and $\tilde{y}$ are independent in a decision maker's judgment, then not only all of his conditional distributions of $\tilde{y}$ given the various possible values of $\tilde{x}$ but also his unconditional distribution of $\tilde{y}$ must be numerically the same.

9.5.3
Independence of Several UQ's

Let $\tilde{x}$, $\tilde{y}$, and $\tilde{z}$ stand for any three UQ's. If a decision maker would assign the same conditional distribution to $\tilde{z}$ given any particular *pair* of values of $\tilde{x}$ and $\tilde{y}$ that he would assign given any other particular pair of values, then the UQ $\tilde{z}$ may be said to be «unconditionally independent» of $\tilde{x}$ and $\tilde{y}$.

More generally, consider a probability diagram which represents the joint distribution of any number of UQ's, recall that all the forks in any one level of the diagram represent the same UQ; suppose that one particular level in the diagram represents a UQ called $\bar{w}$; and recall that the distribution which the decision maker assigns to $\bar{w}$ on any particular fork in this level must be assessed as if he knew all the values of other UQ's which appear on the branches that lead to this fork but did not know the values of any UQ's whose forks follow this fork.

- ■ If a decision maker assigns the same distribution to $\bar{w}$ on every fork in the $\bar{w}$ level of a probability diagram, he is saying in effect that knowledge of the values of all the UQ's which precede $\bar{w}$ in the diagram could not possibly affect his judgments about $\bar{w}$; and therefore $\bar{w}$ may be said to be ≪unconditionally independent≫ of all preceding UQ's.

If a decision maker would assign the same distribution to every $\bar{w}$ fork in a probability diagram in which the $\bar{w}$ level is the *last* level, then $\bar{w}$ may be said to be unconditionally independent of *all* the other UQ's. It can be proved by reference to equivalent urns that:

- ■ If *every* UQ in a probability diagram is unconditionally independent of all preceding UQ's, then every UQ in the diagram is unconditionally independent of *all* other UQ's. In this case: (1) the UQ's in the diagram are said to be ≪mutually independent≫, and (2) any conditional distribution that the decision maker might assign to any one of the UQ's should be numerically the same as his unconditional distribution of that UQ.

9.5.4
Conditional vs. Dependent

The reader must be very careful to distinguish clearly between the words "conditional" and "dependent", and between the words "unconditional" and "independent".

A decision maker's *conditional* distribution of $\bar{z}$ given a particular set of values of $\bar{u}$, $\bar{v}$, $\bar{w}$, . . . is the distribution he would assign to $\bar{z}$ *if he knew* that $\bar{u}$, $\bar{v}$, $\bar{w}$, . . . had the specified values. His *unconditional* distribution of $\bar{z}$ is the distribution he actually assigns to $\bar{z}$ *not knowing* the values of $\bar{u}$, $\bar{v}$, $\bar{w}$, ...

Since knowledge of the values of $\bar{u}$, $\bar{v}$, $\bar{w}$, . . . may or may not actually affect a decision maker's judgments about $\bar{z}$, his conditional distribution of $\bar{z}$ given a particular set of values of $\bar{u}$, $\bar{v}$, $\bar{w}$, . . . may or may not be *numerically* the same as his conditional distribution of $\bar{z}$ given some other set of values of $\bar{u}$, $\bar{v}$, $\bar{w}$, ... If knowledge of the values of $\bar{u}$, $\bar{v}$, $\bar{w}$, . . . would not in fact affect his judgments about $\bar{z}$, with the result that his conditional distribution of $\bar{z}$ given any one set of values of $\bar{u}$, $\bar{v}$, $\bar{w}$, . . . is in fact numerically the same as his conditional distribution of $\bar{z}$ given any other set of values of $\bar{u}$, $\bar{v}$, $\bar{w}$, . . . , then we say that $\bar{z}$ is unconditionally *independent* of $\bar{u}$, $\bar{v}$, $\bar{w}$, ... If on the contrary knowledge of the values of $\bar{u}$, $\bar{v}$, $\bar{w}$, . . . would in fact affect his judgments about $\bar{z}$, with the result that his conditional distributions of $\bar{z}$ are not in fact numerically the same, we say that $\bar{z}$ is unconditionally *dependent* on $\bar{u}$, $\bar{v}$, $\bar{w}$, ...

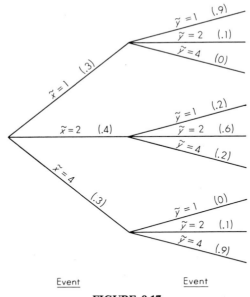

FIGURE 9.17
Joint Distribution of Two Interdependent UQ's

Figure 9.12 on page 352 shows a case where a UQ $\tilde{y}$ is independent of a preceding UQ $\tilde{x}$. Figure 9.17 shows a case where a UQ $\tilde{y}$ is dependent on a preceding UQ $\tilde{x}$.

9.6
SUMMARY MEASURES OF THE DISTRIBUTION
OF A FUNCTION OF SEVERAL UQ's

In many situations where the consequences in a decision problem depend on some UQ $\tilde{z}$, all that really matters about the distribution of $\tilde{z}$ is some summary measure such as its expectation or a certain fractile; if we know the value of this summary measure, we can analyze the problem exactly even though we do not know the complete distribution of $\tilde{z}$. Thus in certain types of inventory problems, all that we need know about the distribution of the UQ "demand" is a certain fractile; in a decision whether or not to market a new product, the expectation of demand is sometimes all that we need when mathematical expectations are treated as certainty equivalents.

When a single summary measure is all that needs to be known about the distribution of some UQ $\tilde{z}$ and when in addition the decision maker finds it convenient to think of $\tilde{z}$ as a function of other UQ's, he may be tempted to try to compute the required summary measure of the distribution of $\tilde{z}$ directly from summary measures of his unconditional distributions of the underlying UQ's, thus avoiding the trouble of first assessing and computing the complete joint distribution of the underlying UQ's, then computing the complete distribution of $\tilde{z}$, and finally computing the required summary measure of this distribution. In the example discussed in Sections 9.4.2 through 9.4.4, it would obviously save a great deal of computation if the decision maker could compute his expectation of demand $\tilde{z}$ for his own company's product by simply multiplying his expectation of total demand $\tilde{x}$ by his expectation of his company's share $\tilde{y}$. But although such shortcut procedures give correct results in certain very special cases, they lead in most cases to errors and in some cases to very serious errors.

The General Case   To see that we cannot in general compute a summary measure of the distribution of a function of several UQ's from summary measures of the unconditional distributions of those UQ's, consider the case where two UQ's $\tilde{x}$ and $\tilde{y}$ have the joint distribution shown in Figure 9.17 and where the function $\tilde{z}$ in which we are interested is the product of $\tilde{x}$ and $\tilde{y}$,

$$\tilde{z} = \tilde{x} \times \tilde{y}.$$

After verifying that the joint distribution of $\tilde{x}$ and $\tilde{y}$ in Figure 9.17 leads to the unconditional distributions in Table 9.7, the reader should verify that:

1. The unconditional expectations of $\tilde{x}$, $\tilde{y}$, and $\tilde{z}$ are respectively 2.00, 2.35, and 6.65, and therefore the unconditional expectation of $\tilde{z}$ is not equal to the product of the unconditional expectations of $\tilde{x}$ and $\tilde{y}$.

2. The .3 fractiles of $\tilde{x}$, $\tilde{y}$, and $\tilde{z}$ are respectively 1, 1, and 2, and therefore the .3 fractile of the unconditional distribution of $\tilde{z}$ is not equal to the product of the .3 fractiles of the unconditional distributions of $\tilde{x}$ and $\tilde{y}$.

TABLE 9.7
Unconditional Distributions of $\tilde{x}$, $\tilde{y}$, and $\tilde{z} = \tilde{x}\tilde{y}$

x	$P(x)$	y	$P(y)$	z	$P(z)$
1	.3	1	.35	1	.27
2	.4	2	.30	2	.11
3	.3	4	.35	4	.24
	———		———	8	.11
	1.0		1.00	16	.27
					———
					1.00

Special Cases   As we have already said, there are a few special cases where we can be sure that shortcut methods will work. The only important ones involve computation of the *mean* of a distribution of a function, i.e., the expectation of the function itself.

1 If a UQ $\tilde{z}$ is a *linear* function of any number of UQ's, i.e., if

$$\tilde{z} = a + b_1\tilde{x}_1 + b_2\tilde{x}_2 + \dots,$$

then

$$E\tilde{z} = a + b_1E\tilde{x}_1 + b_2E\tilde{x}_2 + \dots.$$

In particular,

> The unconditional expectation of a *sum* of UQ's is the sum of the unconditional expectations of the UQ's.

2 If a UQ $\tilde{z}$ is the *product* of *mutually independent* UQ's, possibly multiplied by a constant, i.e., if

$$\tilde{z} = k \times \tilde{x}_1 \times \tilde{x}_2 \times \ldots$$

and the $\tilde{x}$'s are mutually independent, then

$$E(\tilde{z}) = k \times E\tilde{x}_1 \times E\tilde{x}_2 \times \ldots .$$

Do not fail to notice that although the proposition about linear functions (including sums) of UQ's applies to all UQ's without restriction, the proposition about products of UQ's is restricted to mutually independent UQ's.[6]

9.7
ASSESSMENT OF JOINT DISTRIBUTIONS OF INTERDEPENDENT UQ's

We saw in Section 9.3 that when a decision problem involves two uncertain quantities $\tilde{x}$ and $\tilde{y}$, their joint distribution cannot in general be assessed by assessing just one distribution of $\tilde{x}$ and one distribution of $\tilde{y}$. If the decision maker chooses $\tilde{x}$ as the UQ to be represented by the fork at the origin of his probability diagram, he will have only one distribution of $\tilde{x}$ to assess, namely his unconditional distribution of $\tilde{x}$; but when he then goes to the second level of his probability diagram he will have to assess a conditional distribution of $\tilde{y}$ for every $\tilde{x}$ in the range of $\tilde{x}$, and every one of these conditional distributions will in general be different from every other. It is only in the special case where $\tilde{y}$ is independent of $\tilde{x}$ in his judgment—i.e., where knowledge of the value of $\tilde{x}$ would have absolutely no effect on his judgments about $\tilde{y}$—that all his conditional distributions of $\tilde{y}$ will be numerically the same, with the result that he will in effect have only one distribution of $\tilde{y}$ to assess.

If there are only a very few values in the range of $\tilde{x}$—say two or three—the decision maker can assess the required conditional distributions of $\tilde{y}$ by whatever method he would use to assess a single distribution, just as he could assess conditional distributions of demand given the events "competitor markets" and "does not market" by whatever method he would use to assess just one of these distributions. If, however, there are many values in the range of $\tilde{x}$ and correspondingly many conditional distributions of $\tilde{y}$ to assess, the decision maker clearly cannot assess each of these distributions individually, and some other method of assessing the joint distribution of $\tilde{x}$ and $\tilde{y}$ must be found.

---

[6] Technically, the proposition about products can be extended to cases where the UQ's meet a condition somewhat less strict than mutual independence, but the extension is of too little practical use to be worth discussing in an introductory text.

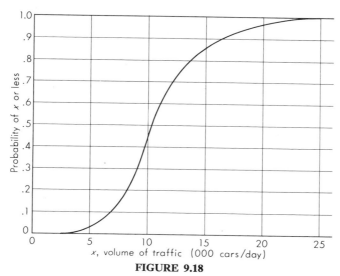

FIGURE 9.18
Unconditional Distribution of Traffic Volume

In the present section we shall first examine a number of typical situations in which there is a difficult problem of assessing the joint distribution of two UQ's and see how the problem can be solved in these particular situations. With these examples in mind, we shall then be able to say something meaningful about general approaches to the problem of assessing joint distributions of interdependent UQ's.

9.7.1
Sales of Gasoline at a Filling Station

Consider the problem faced by an executive of an oil company who is deciding what annual rental he should bid for a filling station on a new turnpike. The decision will clearly turn on a number of factors, one of which is the gallonage that will be sold through the station in each year of the life of the lease for which he is bidding; we consider here only the subproblem of evaluating gallonage for the first year.

The principal factor in determining gallonage will clearly be the volume of traffic on the new turnpike, and it is therefore clear that the executive can usefully decompose the problem of assessing his probability distribution of first-year gallonage by first assessing his unconditional distribution of first-year traffic volume and then assessing conditional distributions of gallonage given each possible value of traffic. An unconditional probability distribution of volume of traffic can be assessed on the basis of the various published forecasts of this volume which were made by experts before it was decided to construct the new turnpike, due allowance being made for errors of the sort that have shown up in expert forecasts of traffic volume on turnpikes already in service. Then given any par-

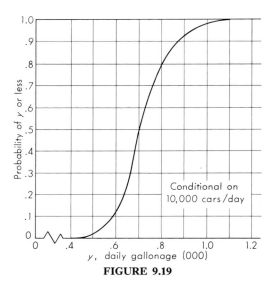

FIGURE 9.19

Conditional Distribution of Gallonage Given 10,000 Cars per Day

ticular traffic volume, a conditional distribution of gallonage can be assessed on the basis of experience with stations on existing turnpikes, duly adjusted for differences in distance between exits, price relative to price off the turnpike, etc.

It would of course be impossible for the executive to make a separate direct assessment of his conditional probability distribution of gallonage for each of several thousand different values of traffic volume, but we shall now suggest a device by which it *may* be very easy to make all the required assessments indirectly.

Assume by way of example that the executive first assesses the unconditional distribution of traffic volume $\tilde{x}$ shown in Figure 9.18 and the conditional distribution of gallonage $\tilde{y}$ given a volume of 10,000 cars a day shown in Figure 9.19. The next question the executive should ask himself is how his conditional distribution of gallonage given traffic volume would change with traffic volume, and depending on his answer to this question his assessment problem may turn out to be very easy to solve. For it is possible that after careful consideration the executive will decide that in his judgment the effect of traffic volume on gallonage is strictly proportional, in the sense that if he assesses at .4 the probability that gallonage will be 680 or less given that there are 10,000 cars per day, then given that there are 9,000 cars per day he would assess at this same .4 the probability that gallonage will be (9/10) 680 = 612 or less, and similarly for any probability and any number of cars per day.

Provided that the executive's judgment is in fact of this nature—and there is absolutely no compelling reason why it must be—his conditional distribution of gallonage given any traffic volume whatever can be calculated from his distribution of the *ratio* of gallonage to traffic volume, which we shall denote

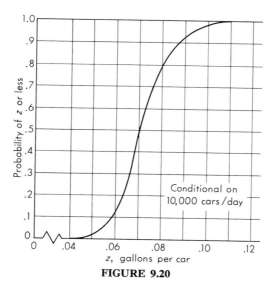

FIGURE 9.20

Conditional Distribution of Gallonage per Car Given 10,000 Cars per Day

by $\tilde{z}$. Figure 9.19 can be converted into such a distribution by simply dividing every gallonage figure on the horizontal axis by the 10,000 cars per day on which that distribution is conditioned; the result of this operation is shown as Figure 9.20. If then we want to know the executive's probability for, say, 1,600 gallons or less given 20,000 cars per day, we have only to calculate that this means $1,600/20,000 = .08$ gallons per car and read the probability as .79 from Figure 9.20.

Formally, what the executive does if he adopts this solution of his problem is to substitute for his original problem of assessing the joint distribution of $\tilde{x}$ (traffic volume) and $\tilde{y}$ (gallonage) a problem of assessing the joint distribution of $\tilde{x}$ and $\tilde{z}$ (gallonage per car). The substitution is *permissible* because the joint distribution of $\tilde{x}$ and $\tilde{z}$ determines the joint distribution of $\tilde{x}$ and $\tilde{y}$—given any pair of values of $\tilde{x}$ and $\tilde{z}$, we can compute the corresponding values of $\tilde{x}$ and $\tilde{y}$, and therefore we can compute the probability that $\tilde{x}$ and $\tilde{y}$ will have any specified pair of values from the distribution of $\tilde{x}$ and $\tilde{z}$. The substitution is *advantageous* if $\tilde{x}$ and $\tilde{z}$ are independent in the executive's judgment, because if they are, then the executive's conditional distributions of $\tilde{z}$ given the various possible values of $\tilde{x}$ are all numerically the same. The joint distribution of the independent UQ's $\tilde{x}$ and $\tilde{z}$ is fully determined by this one distribution of $\tilde{z}$ in conjunction with the unconditional distribution of $\tilde{x}$, whereas it would require a large number of numerically different conditional distributions of $\tilde{y}$ to determine the joint distribution of the interdependent UQ's $\tilde{x}$ and $\tilde{y}$.

It must be emphasized, however, that the executive must ask himself very carefully whether $\tilde{x}$ and $\tilde{z}$ are in fact independent in his judgment before he can conclude that he needs to assess only one distribution for $\tilde{z}$. It is always possible to perform a numerical operation of the type that converted the distribution of $\tilde{y}$ in Figure 9.19 into the distribution of $\tilde{z}$ in Figure 9.20; but if the responsible person does not believe that gallonage per car is independent of the number of cars, then the mere fact that Figure 9.20 is expressed in terms of gallons per car does not make it applicable to any number of cars other than the one for which it was assessed, namely 10,000 cars per day.

9.7.2
Sales in Two Territories

Consider next the problem faced by an executive who wishes to assess his distribution of next year's sales of some product in each of two territories that are supplied from two different factories, so that a single distribution of total sales would not be an adequate basis for production scheduling; and suppose that the fact that certain raw materials with long procurement lead times can be transferred from one territory to the other if need arises means that it will not suffice for the executive to assess merely his unconditional distribution of sales in each of the two territories. To solve his decision problem, he must assess his complete joint distribution of sales in the two territories.

Even so, the executive's assessment problem would be trivial if the executive's judgments about sales in the two territories were independent, i.e., if foreknowledge that sales in territory I would be good or bad would have no effect on the executive's judgments about sales in territory II and vice versa; but for obvious reasons judgments about sales in two territories will ordinarily not be independent, and in this example we shall assume that they are in fact not independent.

If we let $\tilde{x}$ and $\tilde{y}$ denote sales in territories I and II respectively, it may seem that the executive of our present example could solve his assessment problem by essentially the same device that was used by the oil-company executive of our previous example, i.e., by assessing a single distribution of $\tilde{x}$ and a single distribution of the ratio $\tilde{z} = \tilde{y}/\tilde{x}$ of sales in territory II to sales in territory I. Actually, however, it is very unlikely that that device will work in this problem. For any factor such as weather or competitive activity that can affect sales in territory I without affecting sales in territory II proportionally will affect *both* the value of $\tilde{x}$ and the value of $\tilde{z} = \tilde{y}/\tilde{x}$, and therefore the UQ's $\tilde{x}$ and $\tilde{z}$ will not be independent in a reasonable person's judgment. If the executive knew that sales in territory I were going to be half of "normal" because of bad weather that would not affect territory II, he would expect the ratio $\tilde{z} = \tilde{y}/\tilde{x}$ to be about twice "normal", and so forth. This problem is thus quite different from the problem faced by the oil-company executive, where it might very well be reasonable to assume that if some factor caused traffic $\tilde{x}$ to be half of normal, gallonage $\tilde{y}$ would also be half of normal and therefore the ratio $\tilde{z} = \tilde{y}/\tilde{x}$ would be unaffected.

In our present example, the executive may be able to solve his assessment problem by a somewhat different although related device. If we denote total sales in the two territories together by $\tilde{t}$ and denote territory I's share of the total by $\tilde{s}$, it is clear that the joint distribution of the sales $\tilde{x}$ and $\tilde{y}$ in the individual territories is determined by the joint distribution of $\tilde{s}$ and $\tilde{t}$, since given any pair of values of $\tilde{s}$ and $\tilde{t}$ we could compute the values of $\tilde{x}$ and $\tilde{y}$. Now it may be that the executive's judgments about these substitute UQ's $\tilde{s}$ and $\tilde{t}$ *are* independent— it may be, in other words, that learning that territory I would account for less than its usual share of the total (and hence that territory II would account for more than its usual share) would have absolutely no effect on his judgments about total sales because he would have no way of telling whether the change in shares was due to higher than normal sales in territory II or to lower than normal sales in territory I or to both of these factors. If the executive's judgments about $\tilde{s}$ and $\tilde{t}$ are in fact independent, he can solve his assessment problem by assessing just one distribution of $\tilde{s}$ and one distribution of $\tilde{t}$.

9.7.3
Price and Volume of a Crop

As a last example, consider the problem faced by an executive of a canning company who wants to assess his probability distribution for the price of a certain fruit as of the date of the harvest (about two months hence) because he must decide now whether to contract for his company's requirements at a fixed price or to wait until the harvest and then buy on the market; and suppose that this executive believes that the most important factor in determining the price two months hence will be the size of the crop.

Government forecasts of the size of the crop and direct reports on the state of the crop in the fields will provide valuable information bearing on price which would be very hard to use properly if this executive tried to assess his unconditional distribution of price directly, just as it would be hard for a retailer to make proper use of available information about entry of a competitor into the market if he tried to assess his unconditional distribution of demand for his own product directly. We assume therefore that the forecaster would like to handle the crop-size factor by first assessing his unconditional distribution of crop size and then assessing a whole set of conditional distributions of the price of the fruit, one for each possible crop size.

To see how it may be possible for the forecaster to solve his problem, suppose that he first assesses his unconditional distribution of crop size $\tilde{x}$ as shown in Figure 9.21; suppose that he then selects the particular crop size 29 msb (million standard boxes) and assesses his conditional distribution of price $\tilde{y}$ given this crop size as shown in Figure 9.22; and observe that the median of the price distribution in Figure 9.22 can be considered a price "forecast" in the sense of Section 8.3.7, even though this particular forecast is not unconditional but conditional on a crop of 29 msb.

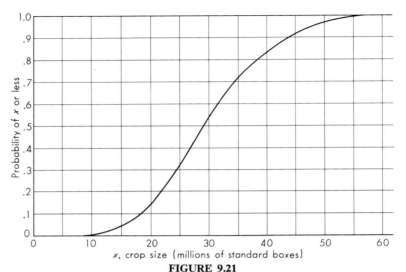

FIGURE 9.21
Unconditional Distribution of Crop Size

The forecaster can now proceed to make a similar conditional forecast of price given every possible crop size, each forecast being a price which is just as likely in the forecaster's judgment to be above as it is to be below the price that will actually prevail if the crop is actually of the given size. The forecaster cannot, of course, think out each of these conditional price forecasts separately, but he does not have to. If he thinks out separately the price forecasts for four additional crop sizes that are plotted as heavy dots in Figure 9.23, and if in addition

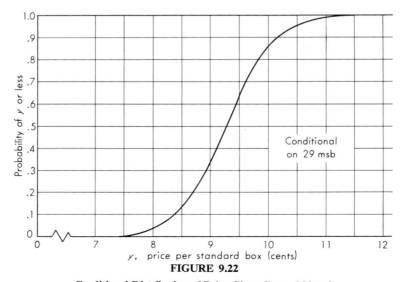

FIGURE 9.22
Conditional Distribution of Price Given Crop of 29 msb

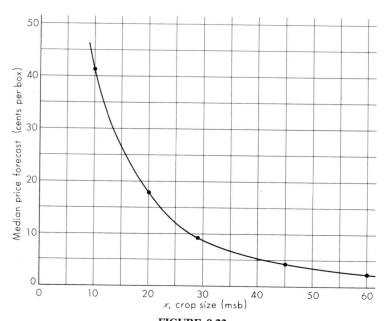

FIGURE 9.23

Median Price Forecast for Each Crop Size

he judges that crop size has a "smooth" effect on price, he can make his price forecast for all other possible crop sizes by simply fairing a smooth curve through the five points in Figure 9.23.

What remains is to evaluate the "reliability" of each of the conditional forecasts specified by Figure 9.23—i.e., to assign a probability distribution rather than a single number to price given every possible crop size. When we dealt with unconditional forecasts in Section 8.3.5, we asked the decision maker to consider whatever evidence was available and then to assign a probability distribution, not to demand (or price) directly, but to the ratio of actual demand (or price) to forecast demand (or price). We shall proceed in that same way in our present problem, although now of course we need a separate conditional distribution of this ratio for every possible crop size.

The forecaster's conditional distribution of the actual-to-forecast ratio $\tilde{z}$ given a crop size of 29 msb can, of course, be obtained directly from the conditional distribution of the actual price in Figure 9.22. Taking the 9.3-cent median of that distribution as his conditional forecast given 29 msb, all that we have to do is divide every number on the horizontal axis of Figure 9.22 by 9.3 cents; the result is shown as Figure 9.24.

Having obtained this result, the forecaster must next ask himself whether or not he thinks that he can forecast prices for crop sizes other than 29 msb as well as he can for a crop size of 29 msb; and it is just conceivable that after due reflection he will decide that he can. It is just conceivable, in other words, that

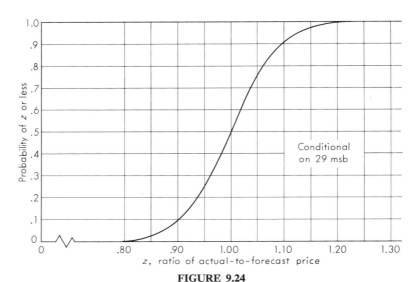

FIGURE 9.24
Conditional Distribution of A/F Ratio Given Crop of 29 msb

he will feel that it is neither more nor less likely that the actual price will amount to, say, 87% or less of forecast when he forecasts a high price for a small crop than when he forecasts a medium price for a medium crop. If he really does feel this way for all crop sizes and for all possible values of the ratio of actual price to forecast price, then his assessment problem is solved. Figure 9.24 applies, not just to the 9.3-cent forecast conditional on 29 msb for which it was originally assessed, but to all the conditional forecasts in Figure 9.23; and the joint distribution of $\bar{x}$ (crop size) and $\bar{y}$ (price) is determined by the independent distributions of $\bar{x}$ and $\bar{z}$ (A/F ratio) together with the conditional forecasts in Figure 9.23.

It is, however, very unlikely that the forecaster will in fact feel that his ability to forecast is as good for very small and very large crops, with which he has probably had very little experience, as it is for medium-sized crops, with which he has probably had much more experience. If so, then he must go on to decide exactly how he thinks his ability varies with crop size.

We shall consider here only the simplest case, where the forecaster decides that the distribution he would assign to the A/F ratio $\bar{z}$ would simply stretch out uniformly to either side of $\bar{z} = 1$ as the crop size departed farther and farther from 29 msb. He might decide, for example, that if he were evaluating his price forecast for an extreme crop size like 10 or 60 msb, his distribution of the A/F ratio would be of the same shape but twice as wide as it was when he evaluated his price forecast for a crop size of 29 msb in Figure 9.24, implying that

$$P(\bar{z} \leqslant 1.6 \,|\, \bar{x} = 10) = P(\bar{z} \leqslant 1.3 \,|\, \bar{x} = 29),$$

$$P(\bar{z} \leqslant .8 \,|\, \bar{x} = 60) = P(\bar{z} \leqslant .9 \,|\, \bar{x} = 29),$$

and so forth.

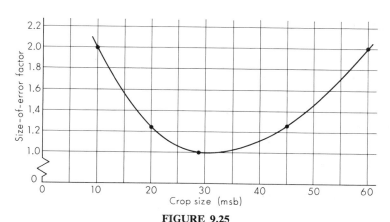

FIGURE 9.25

A/F Spread Factor for Each Crop Size

If this is in fact the forecaster's judgment, we can compute the conditional distribution that he would assign to the A/F ratio $\tilde{z}$ given a crop size $\tilde{x} =$ 10 or 60 msb from his conditional distribution of $\tilde{z}$ given $\tilde{x} = 29$ msb in Figure 9.24; and if he will assess a "spread factor" for every crop size in the same way that he assessed the factor 2 for 10 msb and 60 msb, we can compute all the required conditional distributions of the A/F ratio $\tilde{z}$ from the distribution in Figure 9.24.

Assessment of an A/F spread factor for every possible crop size can be accomplished by a graphic procedure of the same sort that was used to assess a conditional price forecast for every crop size in Figure 9.23. Thus suppose, for example, that the forecaster decides that if he were evaluating his price forecast for a crop size of either 20 or 45 msb, his distribution of the A/F ratio would be 1.25 times as wide as it was when he evaluated his price forecast for a crop size of 29 msb. He can now plot his spread factors for 10, 20, 29, 45, and 60 msb as heavy dots in the way shown in Figure 9.25 and fair through them a curve from which he can read his spread factor for any crop size whatever.

9.7.4

General Approaches to the
Assessment of Joint Distributions

The examples discussed in Sections 9.7.1 through 9.7.3 illustrate several basic approaches to the problem of assessing the joint distribution of two interdependent UQ's $\tilde{x}$ and $\tilde{y}$.

1. The decision maker may be able to express one of the two original UQ's, say $\tilde{y}$, in terms of $\tilde{x}$ and a "substitute" UQ $\tilde{z}$ which is independent of $\tilde{x}$ in his judgment, in which case he can assess a joint distribution of $\tilde{x}$ and $\tilde{y}$ by assessing just one distribution of $\tilde{x}$ and one distribution of $\tilde{z}$. In the example of

Section 9.7.1, where the problem was to assess the joint distribution of traffic $\tilde{x}$ and gallonage $\tilde{y}$, the ratio $\tilde{z} = \tilde{y}/\tilde{x}$ might be independent of $\tilde{x}$ in the decision maker's judgment.

2. The decision maker may be able to express both the original UQ's $\tilde{x}$ and $\tilde{y}$ in terms of *two* substitute UQ's $\tilde{s}$ and $\tilde{t}$ which are independent of each other in his judgment, in which case he can assess the joint distribution of $\tilde{x}$ and $\tilde{y}$ by assessing just one distribution of $\tilde{s}$ and one distribution of $\tilde{t}$. In the example of Section 9.7.2, where the problem was to assess a joint distribution of sales $\tilde{x}$ and $\tilde{y}$ in two territories, total sales $\tilde{t} = \tilde{x} + \tilde{y}$ might be independent of territory I's share of the total $\tilde{s} = \tilde{x}/(\tilde{x} + \tilde{y})$ in the decision maker's judgment.

3. Even if the original UQ's $\tilde{x}$ and $\tilde{y}$ cannot be expressed in terms of independent UQ's $\tilde{x}$ and $\tilde{z}$ or $\tilde{s}$ and $\tilde{t}$, it may be possible to express them in terms of substitute UQ's whose joint distribution is substantially easier to assess than the joint distribution of $\tilde{x}$ and $\tilde{y}$. In the example of Section 9.7.3, where the problem was to assess a joint distribution of crop size $\tilde{x}$ and price $\tilde{y}$, the forecaster might find that it was easier to make a point forecast of price for each value of $\tilde{x}$ and then assess the joint distribution of $\tilde{x}$ and the A/F ratio $\tilde{z}$.

4. The decision maker may feel that even though $\tilde{y}$ is not actually independent of $\tilde{x}$, his conditional distribution of $\tilde{y}$ given a particular value of $\tilde{x}$ should change in some simple way as the conditioning value of $\tilde{x}$ changes, in which case he may be able to assess just one or two conditional distributions of $\tilde{y}$ and then give a rule for computing from this distribution or these distributions the conditional distribution he would assign to $\tilde{y}$ given *any* value of $\tilde{x}$. We saw no example of this procedure applied directly to the original UQ's $\tilde{x}$ and $\tilde{y}$, but after the problem of Section 9.7.3 had been reduced to one of assessing the joint distribution of $\tilde{x}$ and $\tilde{z}$, we saw that a forecaster might feel that his conditional distribution of the A/F ratio $\tilde{z}$ given a particular value of crop size $\tilde{x}$ should spread out uniformly to either side of 1 as the value of $\tilde{x}$ moved away from its median, in which case he could assess his conditional distributions of $\tilde{z}$ for all possible values of $\tilde{x}$ by explicitly assessing his conditional distribution of $\tilde{z}$ for just one value of $\tilde{x}$ and then giving a rule for computing all other conditional distributions from this one.

9.7.5
The Responsibility of the Decision Maker

Our purpose in discussing devices by which the task of assessing a joint distribution of two UQ's can be simplified is very definitely not to prepare the reader to tackle on his own any problem of this sort that he may encounter in business. We have by no means listed all the devices that can be used to simplify the assessment of a joint distribution of two UQ's, and we have not discussed at all the assessment of joint distributions of more than two UQ's. Nor could we give a complete treatment of these assessment problems in an elementary text even if we wanted to, since many of the most useful simplifying devices require description of distributions by mathematical formulas rather than graphs.

The real purposes of this section have been two. First, the businessman should know that what may seem to be an absolutely impossible assessment problem can usually be reduced to a manageable form by some device or another. If he tries to make a systematic analysis of a decision problem but finds that he cannot assess the required distributions, he should not conclude that systematic analysis of the problem is impossible; he should conclude that he needs the aid of a specialist.

Second, and at least equally important, the businessman cannot play his proper role in collaboration with the specialist unless he, the businessman, fully understands the importance of conditionality in assessing joint distributions. A specialist with little knowledge of marketing and less of a particular company's particular problems can easily jump to the conclusion that, for example, the businessman's judgments about the ratio of sales in territory I to sales in territory II can be treated as independent of his judgments about the actual volume of sales in territory I. It is up to the businessman to remember the importance of conditionality and test for himself whether these UQ's are in fact independent in his judgment before letting the specialist proceed as if they were.

The importance of testing assumed independence of UQ's cannot be overemphasized, since treatment of interdependent UQ's as if they were independent is perhaps the most serious error that is commonly made in systematic analyses of decision problems.

9.8
SUMMARY

9.8.1
Events with Probabilities
Independent of Acts

■ When a decision maker wishes to infer the probabilities that he should assign to event branches in his decision diagram from other probabilities that he assesses directly, he must first make sure that all the events involved in his problem have been defined in such a way that none of his probabilities for these events would be affected by any *acts* which appear in his decision diagram.

9.8.2
Conditional, Unconditional, and
Joint Probabilities and Distributions

See Sections 9.3.3 to 9.3.4 and 9.3.6 to 9.3.8.

9.8.3
Conditional and Unconditional
Expectations of a UQ

See Section 9.3.9.

9.8.4
Distribution and Expectation
of a Function of Several UQ's

See Sections 9.4.5 and 9.4.6.

9.8.5
Independence

1 Two events X and Y are ≪independent≫ in the judgment of the decision maker if his conditional probability for X given that Y occurs is *equal* to his conditional probability for X given that Y does not occur.

2 Two UQ's $\bar{x}$ and $\bar{y}$ are independent in the judgment of the decision maker if his conditional distribution of $\bar{y}$ given any possible value of $\bar{x}$ is *numerically* the same as his conditional distribution of $\bar{y}$ given any other possible value of $\bar{x}$.

3 A UQ $\bar{z}$ is ≪unconditionally independent≫ of UQ's $\bar{u}$, $\bar{v}$, $\bar{w}$, . . . if the decision maker's conditional distribution of $\bar{z}$ given any possible set of values of $\bar{u}$, $\bar{v}$, $\bar{w}$, . . . is numerically the same as his conditional distribution of $\bar{z}$ given any other possible set of values.

4 If every UQ in a probability diagram is unconditionally independent of all *preceding* UQ's, then every UQ in the diagram is unconditionally independent of *all* other UQ's and the UQ's are said to be ≪mutually independent≫.

9.8.6
Summary Measures of the Distribution
of a Function

1 In general, a summary measure of the distribution of a function of two or more UQ's can *not* be computed from the corresponding summary measures of the distributions of the individual UQ's. It can only be computed from the complete distribution of the function, and to derive this distribution the decision maker must first assess the complete joint distribution of the underlying UQ's.

The following are the only important exceptions to this rule.

2 The unconditional expectation of the *sum* of several UQ's is the sum of the unconditional expectations of the UQ's.

3 The unconditional expectation of the *product* of several *mutually independent* UQ's is the product of the unconditional expectations of the UQ's.

9.8.7

**Assessment of Joint Distributions
of Interdependent UQ's**

Assessment of the joint distribution of two interdependent UQ's $\bar{x}$ and $\bar{y}$ requires assessment of a numerically different conditional distribution of one of the two UQ's, say $\bar{y}$, for every possible value of the other UQ. For various devices which can sometimes be used to simplify such assessment problems, see Section 9.7.4.

EXERCISES

A. INTERRELATED STANDARD CHANCES

9.1   George Thompson holds a ticket in a two-stage lottery, the terms of which are as follows. After a ball labelled L or M has been selected in a standard drawing from urn T, a ball labelled either U, V, or W will be selected in a standard drawing from an urn bearing the same label as the ball drawn from urn T; the prize will depend on the labels on the two balls drawn. The fraction of balls bearing each label in each urn is shown in parentheses on the branch of the corresponding event fork in the diagram in Figure 9.26.
  a Read from Figure 9.26 each of the following standard chances and explain exactly what it means.

$P(M)$ $P(U|L)$

$P(W|M)$ $P(W|L)$

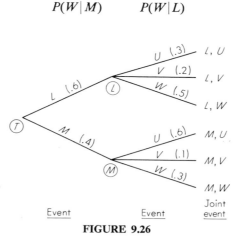

FIGURE 9.26

George Thompson's Standard Gamble

b Suppose that Thompson wants to construct a consolidated urn in such a way that a gamble based on a single standard drawing from that urn will be equivalent to the gamble diagrammed in Figure 9.26. The consolidated urn will contain 100 balls in all. Thompson puts a first label *L* on 60 of the balls and then puts a second label *U* on 18 of these 60 balls. When Thompson is through labelling, exactly how many balls should bear what double labels?

c There should be a .18 standard chance of drawing a ball labelled *L,U* in a single standard drawing from the consolidated urn. What should be the standard chance of drawing a ball labelled *L,W*?

d What should be the standard chance of the joint event *M,U* in a standard drawing from the consolidated urn?

e There should be a .42 unconditional standard chance of drawing a ball bearing the label *U* in a single standard drawing from the consolidated urn. What should be the unconditional standard chance of drawing a ball labelled *V*? *M*?

f If a ball labelled *U* is drawn from the urn, there should be an 18/42 standard chance that it is also labelled *L*. If a ball labelled *V* is drawn, what should be the standard chance that it is also labelled *L*?

g Compute the conditional standard chance of the event *L* given that the event *U* occurs.

h Diagram Thompson's gamble showing the events *U*, *V*, and *W* on the *first*-level fork and the events *L* and *M* on the *second*-level forks; then write on each branch and at each end position of your diagram the appropriate standard chance of the event represented by that branch or end position.

9.2 Suppose that you face the following two-stage standard gamble. After a ball labelled either *D*, *E*, or *F* has been selected in a standard drawing from urn *N*, a ball labelled either *Q*, *R*, or *S* will be selected in a single standard drawing from an urn bearing the same label as the ball drawn from urn *N*; the fraction of balls bearing each label in each urn is shown in parentheses on the branch of the corresponding fork in the diagram in Figure 9.27.

a Read from Figure 9.27 each of the following standard chances and explain exactly what it means.

$$P(S \mid D) \qquad P(S \mid F) \qquad P(F)$$

b Suppose that you want to construct a consolidated urn in such a way that you would be indifferent between the gamble of Figure 9.27 and a gamble based on a single standard drawing from your consolidated urn. What labels should the balls bear and what fraction of balls should bear each label?

c Compute the unconditional standard chance of the joint event represented by each end position of the diagram in Figure 9.27.

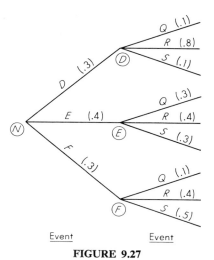

FIGURE 9.27
The Standard Gamble of Exercise 9.2

d Diagram the gamble of Figure 9.27 showing the events Q, R, and S on the
first-level fork and the events D, E, and F on the second-level forks.

e Compute each of the following standard chances and write it on the corresponding branch of the diagram you drew in answer to (*d*).

$$P(D|S) \qquad P(D|R) \qquad P(R)$$

f Compute the appropriate standard chance of the event on each of the remaining branches of the diagram you drew in answer to (*d*) and write it
on that branch.

9.3 Suppose that L. M. Marker holds a ticket in the following two-stage lottery.
After a ball labelled either $\tilde{x} = 1$, $\tilde{x} = 2$, or $\tilde{x} = 3$ has been selected in a
single standard drawing from an urn labelled $\tilde{x}$, a ball labelled W or L will
be selected in a single standard drawing from an urn bearing the same label
as the ball drawn from urn $\tilde{x}$. The unconditional standard chance of each
of the possible joint events of the lottery is shown at the corresponding end
position of the diagram in Figure 9.28; the prize Marker will win depends
on the outcome of both the first and second drawings and is also shown for
every pair of outcomes at the corresponding end position.

a Compute each of the following standard chances and write it on the corresponding branch in Figure 9.28.

$$P(W|\tilde{x} = 2) \qquad P(W|\tilde{x} = 1) \qquad P(\tilde{x} = 1)$$

b Compute each of the following standard chances and write it on the corresponding branch of a reversed diagram.

$$P(\tilde{x} = 1|W) \qquad P(\tilde{x} = 1|L) \qquad P(L)$$

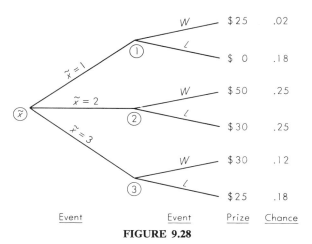

FIGURE 9.28

L. M. Marker's Standard Gamble

9.4   Compute Marker's standard chance of winning $0 in the lottery described by Figure 9.28; his chance of winning $25, $30, $50.

9.5   *a* Rediagram the three-stage standard gamble in Figure 9.3 (page 329) in such a way that you can show on the branches all the standard chances of individual events that were computed in Section 9.1.8.

   b Compute each of the following standard chances and explain exactly what it means.

   $$P(S|Z) \qquad P(R|Y) \qquad P(X,S|B)$$
   $$P(B|S,X) \qquad P(R,Y|Y) \qquad P(A,S|Y)$$

B. INTERRELATED PROBABILITIES

9.6   Assuming that Mr. Harrison is willing to treat mathematical expectations as certainty equivalents, use the probabilities assessed in Sections 9.2.5 to 9.2.8 to determine Harrison's optimal course of action.

9.7   *a* Diagram Harrison's decision problem assuming that he does *not* feel sure that the subassembly will function properly after complete inspection and hand adjustment.

   b Diagram a suitable assessment gamble for this problem.

9.8   Because only 40% of all applicants for jobs as salesmen turn out to be successful under the screening procedure currently used by the Jo-Bo Novelty Company, Jo-Bo's sales manager has just purchased the right to use a newly developed psychological test.   The test will supplement, not replace, the current screening procedure.

   As an inducement to the sales manager to purchase the test, the developers of the test had the sales manager choose a group of 20 salesmen on his staff whom he classified as successful and another group of 10 salesmen whom he classified as unsuccessful. The test was administered to both groups, but although it discriminated between them, it was not infallible; one of Jo-Bo's successful salesmen failed the test while four of the company's unsuccessful salesmen passed it.

    a Jo-Bo's sales manager is about to administer the test to an applicant who has passed the current procedure. Diagram an assessment gamble which shows all possible combinations of the events "would pass test", "would be successful salesman", and their opposites, in an order such that the frequency information available to the sales manager bears directly on the probabilities he should assign to the branches of the diagram.

    b Assuming that the sales manager assesses his probabilities for all events on your diagram by simply equating them to historical relative frequencies, rediagram the assessment gamble showing the events in the reverse order and compute the probability of each branch and end position in this reversed diagram of the assessment gamble.

    c Suppose that an applicant who has passed the initial screening procedure subsequently takes the test and passes it. What probability should the sales manager assign to the event "applicant will make a successful salesman" posterior to observing the test result?

9.9 *a* Returning to the decision problem with which Mr. Smith presented you in Exercise 1.2, consider an assessment gamble which shows all possible combinations of the events "bought", "smoked", and their opposites, and diagram the gamble in both of the two possible orders.

    b Assess your probabilities for all branches on both diagrams directly, as well as you can. (Do *not* compute your probabilities for one diagram from the probabilities you assess for the other.)

    c *After* you have completed both sets of assessments called for in (*b*), take each of your two diagrams and compute the probabilities which your directly assessed probabilities for the branches of that diagram imply that you should assign to the branches of the other diagram.

    d How much solid evidence of what sort underlies each of the *direct* probability assessments you have made?

    e Reconcile your assessments by altering some or all of them in such a way that (1) the probabilities you finally assign to all branches of both diagrams are logically consistent, and (2) you would be willing to base real decisions involving real money on any one of these probabilities.

9.10 Certain serious congenital malformations of a newborn child are often (but not always) associated with the incidence of rubella (German measles) within the first three months of his mother's pregnancy. Before any studies had been made for the purpose of estimating the long-run relative frequency of occurrence of birth defects following a case of rubella in early pregnancy, a number of experienced obstetricians were asked to estimate this relative frequency on the basis of their experience. Subsequent studies revealed that the obstetricians had greatly overestimated the long-run relative frequency in question.

a If you were a medical researcher, how would you go about determining the long-run relative frequency with which birth defects follow a case of rubella?

b Can you think of any reason why the obstetricians so seriously overestimated this long-run relative frequency?

C. UNCERTAIN QUANTITIES AND EXPECTATIONS

9.11 Tables 9.8A and B show a decision maker's directly assessed distributions of total industry sales $\tilde{\imath}$, whose values are measured in thousands of dollars, and of his company's share $\tilde{s}$.

TABLE 9.8A
Unconditional
Distribution of $\tilde{\imath}$

t	$P(\tilde{\imath} = t)$
200	.3
400	.4
800	.3
	1.0

TABLE 9.8B
Conditional Distributions of $\tilde{s}$
Given Each Possible Value of $\tilde{\imath}$

	$P(\tilde{s} = s \mid \tilde{\imath} = t)$		
s	$t = 200$	$t = 400$	$t = 800$
.1	.4	.5	.8
.2	.4	.3	.1
.4	.2	.2	.1
	1.0	1.0	1.0

a Diagram an assessment gamble showing the UQ's $\tilde{\imath}$ and $\tilde{s}$ in an order that allows you to make use of the decision maker's assessments.

b Compute the joint probability distribution of $\tilde{\imath}$ and $\tilde{s}$. Is this a conditional or unconditional distribution?

c Compute (1) the unconditional distribution of $\tilde{s}$, and (2) the conditional distribution of $\tilde{\imath}$ given every possible value s of $\tilde{s}$.

d Do the decision maker's conditional distributions of $\tilde{s}$ *given t* actually *depend* on *t*? Do his conditional distributions of $\tilde{\imath}$ *given s* actually *depend* on *s*?

9.12 Same as Exercise 9.11 except that the distributions in Table 9.8B are replaced by those in Table 9.8C.

TABLE 9.8C
Conditional Distributions of $\tilde{s}$
Given Each Possible Value of $\tilde{\imath}$

	$P(\tilde{s} = s \mid \tilde{\imath} = t)$		
s	$t = 200$	$t = 400$	$t = 800$
.1	.6	.6	.6
.2	.2	.2	.2
.4	.2	.2	.2
	1.0	1.0	1.0

9.13 Let $\tilde{x}$, $\tilde{y}$, and $\tilde{z}$ be uncertain quantities to which a decision maker has assigned the distributions shown in Tables 9.9A, B, and C.

TABLE 9.9A
Unconditional
Distribution of $\tilde{x}$

x	$P(\tilde{x} = x)$
1	.2
2	.4
3	.4
	‾‾‾
	1.0

TABLE 9.9B
Conditional Distributions of $\tilde{y}$
Given Each Possible Value of $\tilde{x}$

$$P(\tilde{y} = y \mid \tilde{x} = x)$$

y	$x = 1$	$x = 2$	$x = 3$
1	.2	.4	.7
2	.8	.6	.3
	‾‾‾	‾‾‾	‾‾‾
	1.0	1.0	1.0

TABLE 9.9C
Conditional Distributions of $\tilde{z}$
Given Each Possible Pair of Values of $\tilde{x}$ and $\tilde{y}$

$$P(\tilde{z} = z \mid \tilde{x} = x, \tilde{y} = y)$$

z	$y = 1$			$y = 2$		
	$x = 1$	$x = 2$	$x = 3$	$x = 1$	$x = 2$	$x = 3$
1	.1	.1	.3	.1	.1	.3
2	.4	.8	.1	.4	.8	.1
3	.5	.1	.6	.5	.1	.6
	‾‾‾	‾‾‾	‾‾‾	‾‾‾	‾‾‾	‾‾‾
	1.0	1.0	1.0	1.0	1.0	1.0

a Diagram an assessment gamble showing the UQ's $\tilde{x}$, $\tilde{y}$, and $\tilde{z}$ in an order that allows you to make use of the decision maker's assessments.

b Compute the joint distribution of $\tilde{x}$, $\tilde{y}$, and $\tilde{z}$.

c Compute the following probabilities:

1. $P(\tilde{z} = 2)$
2. $P(\tilde{y} = 2)$
3. $P(\tilde{y} = 2 \mid \tilde{z} = 2)$
4. $P(\tilde{x} = 2 \mid \tilde{z} = 2)$
5. $P(\tilde{x} = 2 \mid \tilde{y} = 2)$
6. $P(\tilde{x} = 2, \tilde{y} = 2 \mid \tilde{z} = 2)$
7. $P(\tilde{y} = 2, \tilde{z} = 2)$
8. $P(\tilde{x} = 2 \mid \tilde{y} = 2, \tilde{z} = 2)$

d Are the decision maker's judgments about $\tilde{y}$ affected by knowledge of the value x of $\tilde{x}$? Do his conditional distributions of $\tilde{z}$ given x and y actually depend on the values x and y of $\tilde{x}$ and $\tilde{y}$? On the value x of $\tilde{x}$ alone? On the value y of $\tilde{y}$ alone?

9.14 Using the distributions in Tables 9.8A and B and those you computed in answer to Exercise 9.11:

a Compute the unconditional expectation of $\tilde{\imath}$.

b Compute the conditional expectation of $\tilde{s}$ given $\tilde{\imath} = 200$; given $\tilde{\imath} = 400$.

c Compute the unconditional expectation of $\tilde{s}$ using the unconditional distribution of $\tilde{s}$.

d Compute the conditional expectation of $\tilde{\imath}$ given $\tilde{s} = .1$; given $\tilde{s} = .2$.

    e Compute the unconditional expectation of $\tilde{s}$ without using the unconditional distribution of $\tilde{s}$, verify that your answer agrees with your answer to (*c*), and explain why the two methods of computation must necessarily lead to exactly the same result in this or any other problem.

9.15 In Section 8.1.7 it was said that a decision maker should not construct his decision diagram in such a way that it forces him to assess a distribution of a UQ that must allow for uncertainties about events which can individually have a substantial effect on the value of the UQ. Instead, he should decompose his assessment problem by constructing his decision diagram in such a way that all events of the kind just mentioned appear explicitly and forks representing the possible values of the UQ appear *after* the forks representing these events. A very simple example of such decomposition was shown in Figure 8.5 on page 289.

    If, however, a decision problem involves several UQ's and forks representing each of these UQ's must be preceded by several forks representing individually important events, the advice given in Section 8.1.7 will lead to a very complex decision diagram which will be hard to construct and hard to analyze.

    a How could a decision maker describe his decision problem by a diagram containing the single event fork of Figure 8.5A rather than the sequence of forks in Figure 8.5B and yet assess his distribution for the single fork in such a way that he gains all the advantages he would gain by showing the sequence of forks in his decision diagram?

    b In general, how should a decision maker (1) construct his decision diagram, and (2) assess his distributions, when his decision problem involves UQ's whose values may be substantially affected by one or more uncertain events?

D. FUNCTIONS OF SEVERAL UQ's

9.16 Let $\tilde{\imath}$ denote total industry sales of a certain product, measured in thousands of dollars, let $\tilde{s}$ denote a particular company's share of the total, and let $\tilde{c} = \tilde{s}\tilde{\imath}$ denote that company's sales in thousands of dollars.

    a Compute the unconditional distribution of the function $\tilde{c}$ that is implied by the directly assessed distributions of $\tilde{\imath}$ and $\tilde{s}$ in Tables 9.8A and B (page 382).

    b Same as (*a*) except that the decision maker assesses the distributions of $\tilde{s}$ in Table 9.8C rather than those in Table 9.8B.

9.17 Compute the distribution of $\tilde{w} = \tilde{x} + \tilde{y} + \tilde{z}$ that is implied by the directly assessed distributions of $\tilde{x}$, $\tilde{y}$, and $\tilde{z}$ in Tables 9.9A to C (page 383).

9.18 Compute the expectation of $\tilde{c} = \tilde{s}\tilde{\imath}$ that is implied by the distributions of $\tilde{\imath}$ and $\tilde{s}$ in Tables 9.8A and B in each of the two following ways.

a Write down the value of $\tilde{c}$ at every end position of the probability diagram you drew in answer to Exercise 9.11*a* and then multiply the value of $\tilde{c}$ at each end position by the probability of that end position and add the products.

b Using the distribution of $\tilde{c}$ that you derived in answer to Exercise 9.16*a*, multiply each possible value of $\tilde{c}$ by the probability of that value of $\tilde{c}$ and add the products.

9.19 If your answers to Exercise 9.18*a* and *b* do not agree, you have made an error. Why must the two methods of calculation prescribed in Exercise 9.18 always lead to exactly the same result?

E. INDEPENDENCE

9.20 It is asserted in Section 9.5.1 that if a decision maker assesses $P(X|Y) = P(X|\bar{Y})$, then to be consistent he must assess $P(Y|X) = P(Y|\bar{X})$. Prove this by calculation of the relevant fractions in the decision maker's consolidated equivalent urn.

9.21 Are the UQ's $\tilde{s}$ and $\tilde{i}$ independent if they have the distributions defined by Tables 9.8A and B (page 382)? If they have the distributions defined by Tables 9.8A and C?

9.22 Are the UQ's $\tilde{x}$, $\tilde{y}$, and $\tilde{z}$ mutually independent if they have the distributions defined by Tables 9.9A to C (page 383)? Is $\tilde{z}$ independent of the UQ $\tilde{x}$? Is $\tilde{z}$ independent of $\tilde{y}$?

F. SUMMARY MEASURES

9.23 Let total industry sales $\tilde{i}$ have the unconditional distribution defined in Table 9.8A (page 382), let company share $\tilde{s}$ have the conditional distributions shown in Table 9.8C (page 382), consider the function company sales $\tilde{c} = \tilde{i}\tilde{s}$, and recall that you computed the unconditional distributions of $\tilde{s}$ and $\tilde{i}$ in answer to Exercises 9.12 and 9.16*b* respectively.
a What is the unconditionally most probable value of $\tilde{i}$? of $\tilde{s}$? of $\tilde{c}$?
b Is the mode of the product of two independent UQ's necessarily equal to the product of the modes of the UQ's?

9.24 For the UQ's $\tilde{i}$, $\tilde{s}$, and $\tilde{c}$ of Exercise 9.23:
a What is the median of the unconditional distribution of $\tilde{i}$? of $\tilde{s}$? of $\tilde{c}$?
b Is the median of the product of two independent UQ's necessarily equal to the product of the medians of the UQ's?

9.25 For the UQ's $\tilde{i}$, $\tilde{s}$, and $\tilde{c}$ of Exercise 9.23:
a What is the unconditional expectation of $\tilde{i}$? of $\tilde{s}$? of $\tilde{c}$?
b Is the expectation of the product of two UQ's equal to the product of the expectations of the UQ's in this example?

9.26 Let $\tilde{\imath}$ have the unconditional distribution of Table 9.8A as in the last three exercises but now let $\tilde{s}$ have the conditional distributions of Table 9.8B (page 382) rather than Table 9.8C; and recall that you computed the corresponding unconditional expectations of $\tilde{s}$ and of $\tilde{c} = \tilde{\imath}\tilde{s}$ in answer to Exercises 9.14c and 9.18 respectively.

a What is the unconditional expectation of $\tilde{\imath}$? of $\tilde{s}$? of $\tilde{c}$?

b Is the expectation of the product of two UQ's always equal to the product of the expectations of the UQ's? When is it necessarily equal?

9.27 The sales manager of the Ocean Spray Surfboard Company wants to assess his distribution of the company's sales $\tilde{s}$ of surfboards. Ocean Spray markets its surfboards in two different regions and rather than assess his distribution for $\tilde{s}$ directly, the sales manager has assessed the distributions for sales $\tilde{x}$ in Region 1 and sales $\tilde{y}$ in Region 2 shown in Tables 9.10A and B respectively.

TABLE 9.10A Unconditional Distribution of $\tilde{x}$			TABLE 9.10B Conditional Distributions of $\tilde{y}$ Given Each Possible Value of $\tilde{x}$			
				$P(\tilde{y} = y \mid \tilde{x} = x)$		
x	$P(\tilde{x} = x)$		y	$x = 1$	$x = 2$	$x = 3$
$10,000	.80		$10,000	.7	.2	.1
$20,000	.15		$20,000	.2	.6	.2
$30,000	.05		$30,000	.1	.2	.7
	1.00			1.0	1.0	1.0

a Compute the unconditional distributions and expectations of $\tilde{x}$, $\tilde{y}$, and $\tilde{s}$, and the sum of the unconditional expectations of $\tilde{x}$ and $\tilde{y}$.

b Are $\tilde{x}$ and $\tilde{y}$ independent in the sales manager's judgment?

c Under what circumstances does the expectation of the sum of two UQ's equal the sum of their expectations?

PART
3

SAMPLING
AND
SIMULATION

CHAPTER
10

SAMPLES FROM TWO-VALUED POPULATIONS: BASIC PRINCIPLES

In the preceding chapters of this book we set forth the basic principles by means of which any problem of decision under uncertainty can be logically analyzed. In the chapters which follow, we shall discuss in some detail two special applications of these basic principles, namely:

1. The use of information obtained by taking a sample or performing an experiment, together with the problem of deciding how much to spend on sampling or experimentation.

2. The use of what is called "simulation" or the "Monte Carlo method" to analyze decision problems that would be difficult or impossible to analyze by straightforward computation.

Chapters 10 through 12 present an essential core of knowledge about sampling that is essential in both of these seemingly quite different applications. Chapter 13 then takes up the subject of simulation, while Chapters 14 and 15 go more deeply into the subject of sampling and experimentation.

The text and exercises of the present chapter are designed to be studied in the following order:

1 Sections 10.1–10.2.3 and Exercise 10.1*a*.

2 Sections 10.2.4–10.2.5 and Exercise 10.1*b*.

3 Section 10.2.6 and Exercise 10.1*cd*.

4 Section 10.2.7 and Exercise 10.1*e*.

5 Section 10.3.1.

6 Section 10.4.1 and Exercise 10.1*f*.

7 Section 10.4.2 and Exercise 10.1*gh*.

8 Section 10.4.3 and Exercise 10.1*i*.

9 Section 10.4.4 and Exercise 10.2.

10 Section 10.4.5 and Exercises 10.3–10.4.

11 Section 10.5 and Exercises 10.5–10.7.

12 Section 10.3.2 and Exercise 10.8.

13 Section 10.6 and Exercise 10.9.

CONTENTS OF CHAPTER 10

1.
Two-valued Populations

2.
Assessment of Probabilities
Posterior to Sampling

1 An Assessment Problem
2 Indirectly Relevant Information
3 Indirect Assessment: the Assessment Gamble
4 Prior Unconditional Probabilities for the Possible Values of $\tilde{p}$
5 Conditional Probabilities, Given p, for the Possible Sample Observations
6 Conditional Probabilities, Given a Particular Sample Outcome, for the Possible Values of $\tilde{p}$
7 Posterior Unconditional Probabilities for the Possible Values of $\tilde{p}$

3.
The Sampling Process and
the Posterior Distribution

1 Equiprobable Sampling with Replacement
2 Random Digit Generators and "Random Numbers"

4.
Summarization of Sample Information
and Practical Computation
of Posterior Distributions

1 Simplification of the Probability Diagram
2 Worksheet for Computation of a Posterior Distribution
3 Summary Description of a Sample; the Statistics n and r

10.1
TWO-VALUED POPULATIONS

We shall say that a ≪population≫ is ≪two-valued≫ if for the purposes at hand each of its members is to be classified into one or the other of just two categories, e.g., defectives and good pieces, or users and nonusers of a certain product. We shall refer to the members of one of the two categories as ≪successes≫, to the members of the other category as ≪failures≫. Since these terms have no meaning in themselves, we shall in the applications have to state specifically which category will be said to contain the successes.

A two-valued population can be completely described by the two quantities

N: the number of members in the population,

e.g., the number of households in Oshkosh, and

p: the fraction of the members that are successes,

e.g., the fraction of households owning an automatic dishwasher.

The only populations with which we shall be concerned in this chapter are populations that are two-valued in the sense just defined, and our attention will be further restricted to situations in which the only uncertainty that concerns the decision maker is uncertainty about the fraction $\tilde{p}$ of successes in the population. We shall assume, in other words, that the number N of members of the population is known or can be treated for practical purposes as if it were known.

10.2
ASSESSMENT OF PROBABILITIES
POSTERIOR TO SAMPLING

The basic logic by which it is possible to assess a reasonable distribution of $\tilde{p}$ posterior to sampling is the same regardless of the nature of the population or the size of the sample. Accordingly we shall in the present section explain this basic logic by very careful consideration of an extremely simple, artificial example.

10.2.1
An Assessment Problem

Suppose that a bag contains a "population" of poker chips some of which are labelled S(uccess), the others F(ailure), and suppose that a Mr. Warren would like to assess his unconditional probability distribution of the uncertain quantity

$\tilde{p}$: fraction of S's in the population.

Suppose further that the information about $\tilde{p}$ that is available to Mr. Warren is of two sorts.

1. The bag in which Mr. Warren is now interested was chosen by him from a set of four identical-appearing bags, and he knows that in one of these four bags 1/10 of the chips were labelled S, in two of them 2/10 of the chips were labelled S, and in one of them 3/10 of the chips were labelled S.

2. Mr. Warren has made three «sample observations» on the population in his chosen bag by the following method and with the following results. After first stirring the contents of the bag thoroughly, he drew one chip from the bag, observed that it was a S(uccess), and replaced the chip in the bag. He then repeated the entire process, observing a F(ailure) rather than a S(uccess) on this second occasion; and he then repeated the process once more, observing another F(ailure).

10.2.2
Indirectly Relevant Information

The first thing to observe about the information available to Mr. Warren is that none of it bears directly on the probabilities that he should now assign to the possible values of the fraction $\tilde{p}$ of successes in the population in which he is interested.

1. Warren's information about the contents of the four original bags and the way in which "this" bag was chosen among them bears directly, not on the unconditional probabilities he should assign to the various possible values of $\tilde{p}$ *posterior* to observing sample chips labelled S, F, F, but on the unconditional probabilities he should have assigned to the various possible values of $\tilde{p}$ *prior* to these observations.

2. Warren's information about the way in which the sample chips were drawn from the chosen bag bears directly, not on the unconditional probabilities

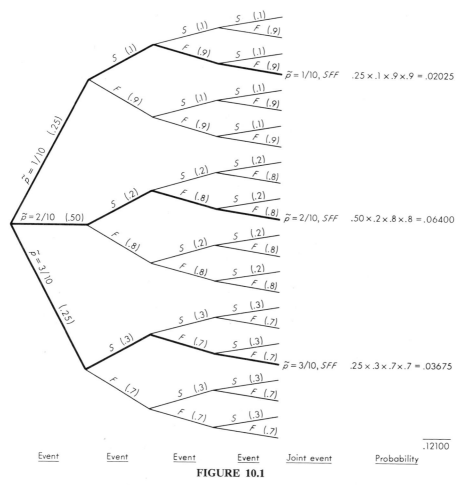

FIGURE 10.1

Probability Diagram of Mr. Warren's Assessment Gamble

he should assign or have assigned *to* the various possible values of $\tilde{p}$, either prior or posterior to sampling, but on the conditional probabilities, *given* the various possible values of $\tilde{p}$, that he should have assigned to the two possible events (S and F) of each sample drawing before he knew which event would actually occur.

10.2.3

Indirect Assessment:

the Assessment Gamble

Mr. Warren thus finds himself facing an assessment problem of exactly the same kind as the one faced by Mr. Harrison in Section 9.2.9, and Mr. Warren should solve his problem in exactly the same way that Mr. Harrison solved his. Mr. Warren should consider the assessment gamble diagrammed in Figure 10.1, which is constructed in such a way that all of Warren's information bears directly on the probabilities he should have assigned to its branches prior to learning what sample outcome actually occurred, and he should assess these probabilities directly. He will then be able to compute the conditional probabilities that he should have assigned to the possible values of $\bar{p}$ given the sample outcome *SFF* before he knew that this outcome would actually occur; and finally he will be entitled to adopt these conditional probabilities as his posterior unconditional probabilities for the possible values of $\bar{p}$ because he knows that the sample outcome *SFF* has in fact occurred.

10.2.4

**Prior Unconditional Probabilities
for the Possible Values of $\bar{p}$**

In assessing his probabilities for the branches of the fork at the origin of Figure 10.1, Mr. Warren will recall that the fraction of chips labelled *S* was 1/10 in exactly one of the four bags from which "his" bag was chosen; and since he had no way of telling which bag was which, he will presumably assign probability .25 to the event that the fraction $\bar{p}$ of chips labelled *S* in his bag has the value 1/10. Similar reasoning will presumably lead him to assign probability .50 to the event $\bar{p} = 2/10$ and probability .25 to the event $\bar{p} = 3/10$, as shown in parentheses on the branches of the fork at the origin of Figure 10.1.

10.2.5

**Conditional Probabilities, Given p,
for the Possible Sample Observations**

In assessing his probabilities for the events *S* and *F* on the uppermost second-level event fork in Figure 10.1, Mr. Warren will presumably argue that because the contents of the bag were thoroughly stirred before the sample was drawn, every chip in the bag had an equal chance of being drawn. If so, he will conclude that because this uppermost second-level fork is preceded by a branch stating that 1/10 of the chips in the bag are labelled *S*, he should *on this fork* assign (conditional) probability .1 to the event *S* and .9 to the event *F*; and similar reasoning will lead to the other assessments shown in parentheses on the branches of the other second-level event forks in Figure 10.1.

When Mr. Warren comes to assess his probabilities for the events *S* and *F* on the third-level event forks in Figure 10.1, representing the possible events of the second sample drawing, he must remember that these probabilities must be conditioned on *all* the information available at the base of each of these forks. In other words, the probabilities must be conditioned, not only on the value of $\bar{p}$, but also on the event *S* or *F* as the case may be of the previous sample observation. Mr. Warren will also remember, however, that his sampling method involved replacing the first sample chip in the bag and restirring the contents before the second chip was drawn; and this fact will presumably lead him to conclude that the event of the first drawing should not actually affect the probabilities he assigns to the possible events of the second drawing. If so, his probability for the event *S* will be .1 on *both* the third-level event forks which follow the event $\bar{p} = 1/10$, it will be .2 on both the third-level forks which follow $\bar{p} = 2/10$, and so forth, as shown in Figure 10.1.

Finally, when he comes to the fourth-level forks in Figure 10.1, representing the possible events of the third sample drawing, Mr. Warren will presumably reason in the same way that he did concerning the third-level forks. His probability for any branch on any fourth-level fork must be *conditional* on all the three events that precede that fork, but because of the replacement and restirring Mr. Warren will presumably conclude that the probabilities he assigns should actually *depend* on only the preceding value of $\bar{p}$. If so, he will presumably assign the probabilities shown on the fourth-level forks in Figure 10.1.

10.2.6
Conditional Probabilities,
Given a Particular Sample Outcome,
for the Possible Values of $\bar{p}$

Now that Mr. Warren has directly assessed probabilities for all the branches of the probability diagram in Figure 10.1, we can use the three rules in Section 9.3.4 to compute the probabilities in which he is really interested, namely the conditional probabilities that he should have assigned to the possible values of $\bar{p}$ given the sample outcome *SFF*. The successive steps in the computations are as follows.

1. The unconditional probability that Mr. Warren should have assigned to each end position of Figure 10.1 is found by multiplying together his probabilities for the branches leading to that end position. These computations are shown in Figure 10.1 itself.

2. The unconditional probability that Mr. Warren should have assigned to the sample outcome *SFF* is found by adding his unconditional probabilities for all the end positions at which this event appears:

$$P(SFF) = .02025 + .06400 + .03675 = .12100.$$

3. The conditional probability that Mr. Warren should have assigned to the event $\bar{p} = 1/10$ given the sample outcome *SFF* is found by dividing his unconditional probability for the occurrence of both $\bar{p} = 1/10$ and *SFF* by his unconditional probability for the occurrence of *SFF*:

$$P(\bar{p} = 1/10 \mid SFF) = \frac{P(\bar{p} = 1/10, \, SFF)}{P(SFF)} = \frac{.02025}{.12100} \doteq .167;$$

and similarly

$$P(\bar{p} = 2/10 \mid SFF) = \frac{P(\bar{p} = 2/10,\ SFF)}{P(SFF)} = \frac{.06400}{.12100} \doteq .529,$$

$$P(\bar{p} = 3/10 \mid SFF) = \frac{P(\bar{p} = 3/10,\ SFF)}{P(SFF)} = \frac{.03675}{.12100} \doteq .304.$$

10.2.7
Posterior Unconditional Probabilities
for the Possible Values of $\bar{p}$

Now for the first time taking account of his knowledge that the sample outcome *SFF* has in fact occurred, Mr. Warren can assess his current *unconditional* probability for any value of $\bar{p}$ by simply equating it to the conditional probability that he would have assigned to that value *given SFF* before he knew that *SFF* would actually occur. In other words, the unconditional distribution that Mr. Warren should now assign to $\bar{p}$ is the one shown in Table 10.1.

TABLE 10.1
Unconditional Probabilities That Mr. Warren Should Assess
Posterior to Learning that *SFF* Has Occurred

Value p	Probability $P(\bar{p} = p)$
1/10	.167
2/10	.529
3/10	.304
	1.000

10.3
THE SAMPLING PROCESS AND
THE POSTERIOR DISTRIBUTION

Now that we have seen one example of the way in which a posterior distribution is derived from a decision maker's prior distribution and a set of sample observations, we are in a position to see how the ≪sampling process≫ by which the sample observations are made plays an essential role in determining the effect of those observations on the posterior distribution.

10.3.1
Equiprobable Sampling with Replacement

Comparing the calculations in Section 10.2.6 with the probability diagram in Figure 10.1 (page 393), the reader will see that the entire effect of the sample observations on Mr. Warren's posterior distribution of $\bar{p}$ was exerted via the conditional probabilities that Mr. Warren assigned to the branches that represented the various possible sample observations. Then examining these probabilities in detail, he will recall that Mr. Warren assessed all of them by simply saying that, given any particular fraction *p* of successes in the population, his conditional probability for an S on any sample drawing was equal to p, regardless of the outcomes of any previous drawings. The facts about Mr. Warren's sampling process that led him to make these assessments were the following.

Because the contents of Mr. Warren's bag were thoroughly stirred before each successive draw was made,

1 The decision maker assigned equal probabilities of selection to all possible candidates for selection on each successive draw.

In what follows, any sampling process which has this property will be said to be ≪equiprobable≫. Observe that the property of equiprobability is an assessment by a decision maker and not an unknowable fact about the "true" chances involved in sampling.

Because each sample chip was replaced in the bag before the next one was drawn,

2 Each member of the entire population was a possible choice on each successive draw, whether or not that member had already been chosen on one or more previous draws.

Because there was no way of distinguishing between one S chip and another, or between one F chip and another,

3 It was not possible to reject any redundant information that may have been obtained by observing the same member of the population more than once.

In what follows, any sampling process that has these last two properties will be said to be ≪with replacement≫, whether or not it involves actual removal and replacement in a physical sense.[1]

Because it obviously does not pay to learn the same facts about a particular household or a particular piece of manufactured product more than once, sampling with replacement is never used in applications such as market surveys or quality control; and even without replacement, equiprobable sampling is used in only a very few applications of this sort. In most applications, more complicated sampling processes such as "stratified" sampling will yield more information per dollar spent. Nevertheless, it is equiprobable sampling with replacement that will concern us exclusively in this chapter and most of the next, primarily because this is the easiest way to gain an understanding of certain basic facts that apply to all sampling processes, but also because equiprobable sampling with

---

[1] A sample of households in Oshkosh can be drawn "with replacement" by listing all households in the population, assigning a serial number to each one, and then drawing serial numbers in such a way that every serial number is a possible choice on each draw whether or not that serial number has been chosen on one or more previous draws. The replacement will not be effective, however, unless the entire sampling and interviewing procedure is conducted in such a way that it is not possible to detect and reject redundant information obtained by interviewing the same household more than once.

replacement is very often actually used in analyzing very complex decision problems by the technique known as "simulation" or the "Monte Carlo method" which we shall study in a later chapter.

10.3.2
Random Digit Generators and
"Random Numbers"

When a statistician wishes to draw a sample in such a way that all reasonable people will agree that every member of the population has an equal chance of being chosen on each successive draw, he frequently does so by assigning a serial number to every member of the population and then using a ≪random digit generator≫ to select as many serial numbers as he wants.

Any physical process which is capable of making a sequence of trials on each of which it generates a digit (i.e., one of the integers 0, 1, . . . , 9) may be called a ≪digit generator≫, and a particular digit generator may be called ≪random≫ for a particular decision maker if, just before any particular trial is made, that decision maker would be just as ready to bet on any one digit as on any other regardless of what digits have appeared on previous trials.

A process which generates digits can, of course, be used to generate numbers containing any desired number of digits—the output of the process can be divided into groups containing three digits each, say, and each such group can be read as a number between 000 and 999. If the process by which the individual digits are generated is random in the sense of the definition above, then just before any sequence of n trials is made the decision maker will be just as ready to bet on any one complete n-digit number as on any other, regardless of what numbers have appeared on previous trials.

As a random digit generator, a decision maker or his statistician might be satisfied with rolling a 10-sided symmetric "cylinder" each of whose faces was labelled with one of the 10 digits, or he could roll a symmetric 20-sided die on which each of the digits appeared on two faces. He might, however, want to use some much more elaborately constructed generator which had been carefully checked out to see that it had no tendency to generate certain digits or patterns of digits more frequently than others.

Instead of actually using a random digit generator to generate a sequence of random numbers for use in drawing a sample, it is often more convenient to take them from a so-called "table of random digits", which is simply a list of digits in the order in which they were generated by someone else's random digit generator.[2] A short table of random digits appears as Table T6 in the collection of tables at the end of this volume.

---

[2] Although it is common usage to refer to the digits in such a list as "random digits", the expression is strictly speaking a misnomer. Randomness is a long-run property of a process which generates digits, not a property of any finite set of digits. The argument for using a table of "random digits" is not that the digits it contains are random; it is that they are as usable a piece of output of a random generator as any new output that might be generated for the purpose at hand.

In using a table of random digits, it is permissible to take the digits either by rows or by columns; it is permissible to take only every second digit or third digit in a row or column, or to take only every second or third column; and so forth. The only schemes for selecting digits from the table that are *not* permissible are schemes which deliberately make the value of the digit selected on one trial depend on the values that were selected on previous trials.

10.4

**SUMMARIZATION OF SAMPLE INFORMATION
AND PRACTICAL COMPUTATION
OF POSTERIOR DISTRIBUTIONS**

In Section 10.2 we showed by an example how a decision maker who is interested in the uncertain fraction $\tilde{p}$ of successes in a population can in principle compute a (posterior) distribution of $\tilde{p}$ which takes due account of both (1) the information about $\tilde{p}$ conveyed by the outcome of a sample drawn from the population by equiprobable sampling with replacement, and (2) the information about $\tilde{p}$ that was available before he knew the sample outcome. In actual practice, however, both the way in which we described the sample outcome and the method by which we computed the posterior distribution become intolerably burdensome as soon as the sample size becomes at all large, and therefore we shall show in the present section how the sample outcome can be more efficiently described and how the computations can be more efficiently organized and can in part be replaced by table lookups.

10.4.1

Simplification of the Probability Diagram

As a first step toward simplification of the procedures described in Section 10.2, we shall show how to simplify the probability diagram which underlies the computation of a posterior distribution, illustrating our discussion by the same example that we used in Section 10.2.

The sample discussed in Section 10.2 consisted of three successive drawings, and the probability diagram in Figure 10.1 (page 393) showed all possible combinations of the two possible events of each of the three drawings. The reader has no doubt already observed, however, that the only probabilities that actually entered into the calculation of the posterior distribution of $\tilde{p}$ were those on the three paths that were heavily inked in Figure 10.1. There was no real need to draw all the lightly inked branches, which represent events that were known not to have occurred; the "abbreviated" probability diagram in Figure 10.2 below would have been just as adequate as Figure 10.1 for the computation of the posterior distribution of $\tilde{p}$ after the sample outcome *SFF* was known.

Even the abbreviated probability diagram in Figure 10.2 is more elaborate than it really needs to be. All the information about structure and probabili-

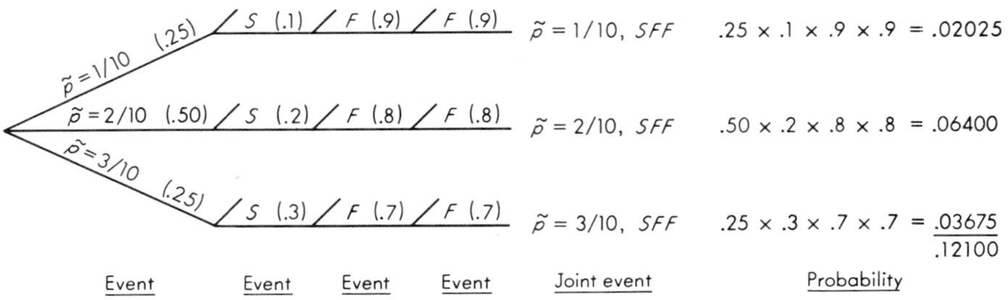

FIGURE 10.2

Abbreviated Probability Diagram of Mr. Warren's Assessment Gamble

ties that is conveyed by this diagram is conveyed by the still simpler diagram in Figure 10.3, where the complete sample outcome *SFF* that actually occurred is represented by a single branch and the suppressed branches represent complete sample outcomes such as *SSS* or *FSF* which did not actually occur.

The decision maker would, of course, find it very difficult to make a direct assessment of his conditional probability for a complete sample outcome such as *SFF* given any particular p, but this creates no real problem. The decision maker can compute his probability for any complete outcome given any p in the way shown on the sample-outcome branches in Figure 10.3, by simply multiplying together his conditional probabilities for the events of the individual sample drawings. The reader should observe that when these computed sample-outcome probabilities are used to compute the probabilities of the various end positions in Figure 10.3, the results are identical to those obtained in the original diagram in Figure 10.1 (page 393).

10.4.2

Worksheet for Computation
of a Posterior Distribution

When the number of possible values of $\tilde{p}$ is very large, as it almost always is in practical applications of sampling, even a condensed probability diagram like Figure 10.3 becomes an inconvenient way of organizing the computations re-

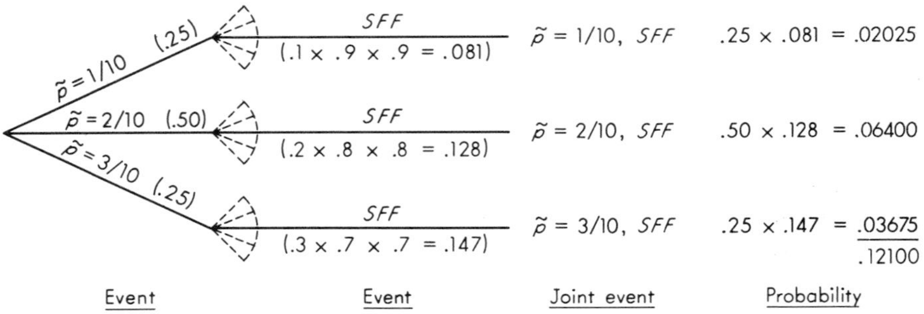

FIGURE 10.3

Further Abbreviated Probability Diagram of Mr. Warren's Assessment Gamble

quired to derive a posterior distribution of $\tilde{p}$. The computations can be more efficiently organized by the use of two worksheets like Tables 10.2 and 10.3. In Table 10.2 the conditional probability of the sample outcome *SFF* given each possible value of $\tilde{p}$ is computed in exactly the same way that it was computed on the corresponding branch of Figure 10.3; computations analogous to those originally described in Section 10.2.6 are then carried out in Table 10.3.

TABLE 10.2
Computation of Mr. Warren's Conditional Probabilities
for the Sample Outcome *SFF* Given *p*

Value *p*	Conditional Probability *P(SFF|p)*
.1	.1 × .9 × .9 = .081
.2	.2 × .8 × .8 = .128
.3	.3 × .7 × .7 = .147

TABLE 10.3
Computation of Mr. Warren's Posterior Distribution of $\tilde{p}$

1 Value *p*	2 Prior *P(p)*	3 Conditional *P(SFF|p)*	4 Joint *P(p, SFF)*	5 Posterior *P(p|SFF)*
.1	.25	.081	.25 × .081 = .02025	.02025/.12100 = .167
.2	.50	.128	.50 × .128 = .06400	.06400/.12100 = .529
.3	.25	.147	.25 × .147 = .03675	.03675/.12100 = .304
	1.00		.12100 = P(SFF)	1.000

Before proceeding further, the reader should make absolutely sure that he understands the logic underlying the computations in Table 10.3, which will serve as a standard model for all of our future work with samples. In particular, the reader should verify and remember that:

1. Column 1 describes each branch of the $\tilde{p}$ fork at the origin of Figure 10.3.

2. Column 2 shows the "prior" unconditional probability that the decision maker (would have) assigned to each branch of the $\tilde{p}$ fork before he knew what sample outcome would actually occur.

3. Column 3 shows the conditional probability that the decision maker (would have) assigned to the sample outcome *SFF* on each second-level branch in Figure 10.3 before he knew what sample outcome would actually occur.

4. Column 4 shows the unconditional probability that the decision maker (should have) assigned to each end position in Figure 10.3, i.e., to each possible joint event of the form *p,SFF*; and therefore its sum is the unconditional probability he (should have) assigned to the sample outcome *SFF* before he knew what sample outcome would actually occur.

5. Column 5 shows the conditional probability that the decision maker (should have) assigned to each possible value of $\tilde{p}$ given the sample outcome *SFF* before he knew what sample outcome would actually occur. The entry for each

value of $\bar{p}$ is obtained by dividing his unconditional probability for the joint occurrence of the sample outcome *SFF and* that value of $\bar{p}$ by his unconditional probability for the sample outcome.

6. The heading of Column 5 reminds us that although what we have actually computed for each value of $\bar{p}$ is the conditional probability given *SFF* that the decision maker (should have) assigned to that value before he knew that *SFF* would actually occur, this probability becomes his "posterior" *unconditional* probability as soon as he knows that *SFF* has in fact occurred.

10.4.3
Summary Description of a Sample;
the Statistics n and r

If a sample consists of only three observations, as it does in the example we have been discussing, it is easy enough to record and work with a complete description of the sample outcome, i.e., a list which shows the successes and failures in the order in which they occurred. If, however, a sample consists of a large number of observations, it is difficult to work with such a record and we would like to find some way of summarizing the information it contains.

Intuition suggests at once that all that we really need to know about a sample is the number of successes and the number of failures it contains, the order of occurrence of these successes and failures being irrelevant, and we leave it to the reader to convince himself that this is true. By reexamining the calculations on the branches representing the sample outcome in Figure 10.3 (page 400), he can convince himself that, given any p, Mr. Warren would have assigned the same conditional probability to the sample outcome *FSF* or *FFS* that he assigned to the actual outcome *SFF*. Next, he can convince himself that the posterior distribution of $\bar{p}$ that would have resulted from *FSF* or *FFS* would have been exactly the same as the one that resulted from *SFF*. Next, he can convince himself that all that really mattered about Mr. Warren's sample outcome was the fact that it consisted of one S and two F's; and finally, he can generalize to the conclusion that:

■ All the information about $\bar{p}$ that is contained in the outcome of any sample drawn by equiprobable sampling with replacement is conveyed by the number of successes and the number of failures in the outcome.

In what follows, it will be more convenient to work with an indirect rather than a direct statement of the number of failures in a sample outcome. We shall say that any sample outcome obtained by equiprobable sampling with replacement is adequately described by the numerical values of the two summary measures or ≪statistics≫

n: total number of observations,

r: number of successes;

the number of failures will be written as $n - r$.

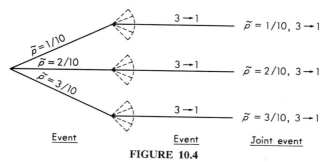

FIGURE 10.4

Mr. Warren's Assessment Gamble Described in Terms of the Statistics n and r

10.4.4
Probability That n Observations
Will Yield r Successes

The fact that a sample outcome is adequately described by the number n of observations and the number r of successes means of course that there is no need to write down the actual sample outcome on the second-level branches of a probability diagram; the values of n and r are all that is required. The diagram in Figure 10.4, where the label $3 \rightarrow 1$ means that 3 observations yielded 1 success, is just as adequate a description of Mr. Warren's assessment gamble as the description in Figure 10.3 (page 400) or the complete description in Figure 10.1 (page 393).

Before he can use a probability diagram like Figure 10.4 to compute his posterior distribution of $\tilde{p}$, the decision maker must of course assign a probability to each second-level branch, and in principle this probability should be his conditional probability given p for the sample outcome that actually occurred—i.e., a sequence of n observations containing r successes and $(n-r)$ failures in a particular order. What we showed in the last section was merely that this probability can be computed even though the probability diagram does not show, and the decision maker does not know, what the order actually was.

It would seem, however, that if the decision maker does not need to know the order in which the successes and failures actually occurred, then he does not need to pay any attention to order at all. It would seem, in other words, that if all that matters is the fact that n observations yielded r successes and $(n-r)$ failures, then the decision maker can assign to each second-level branch of a diagram like Figure 10.4 his conditional probability $P(n \rightarrow r | p)$ for the event that n observations would yield r successes and $(n-r)$ failures, nothing being said about the order in which they occur. In the present section we shall show that this proposition is correct; various reasons why it is important will appear later on.

Applied to the example we have been discussing, the proposition asserts that Mr. Warren can assign to each second-level branch of Figure 10.4 his conditional probability $P(3 \rightarrow 1 | p)$ for the event that 3 observations would yield 1 success and 2 failures in some one or another of the three possible orders

$$SFF, FSF, FFS$$

rather than his conditional probability $P(SFF|p)$ for just one of these three possible outcomes; and we can test the proposition by seeing whether Warren will get the correct posterior distribution of $\tilde{p}$ if he does assign the probability $P(3 \rightarrow 1 | p)$ to each second-level branch of Figure 10.4.

To carry out this test, we must first compute $P(3 \rightarrow 1 | p)$ for each possible value p of $\tilde{p}$, and we can easily do so if we recall that:

1. The event $3 \rightarrow 1$ will occur if and only if some of the three mutually exclusive outcomes or events SFF, FSF, or FFS occurs;

2. Given any particular p, Warren should (as we saw in Section 10.4.3) assign the same conditional probability to any one of these three events that he assigns to any other.

From these two observations it follows that the conditional probability that Warren assigns to the event $3 \rightarrow 1$ given any particular p should be three times the probability that he assigns to the outcome SFF given that same p; and making use of the probabilities for SFF that were computed in Table 10.2 (page 401) we see that Warren should assess

$$P(3 \rightarrow 1 | \tilde{p} = 1/10) = .081 \times 3,$$
$$P(3 \rightarrow 1 | \tilde{p} = 2/10) = .128 \times 3,$$
$$P(3 \rightarrow 1 | \tilde{p} = 3/10) = .147 \times 3.$$

Our next step is to compute the posterior distribution of $\tilde{p}$ that will result if these three probabilities are assigned to the second-level branches of Figure 10.4. Following the model of Table 10.3 (page 401), we lay out our computations on the worksheet shown as Table 10.4, and we obtain the posterior distribution of $\tilde{p}$ that is shown in the last column of the table.

TABLE 10.4
**Computation of Mr. Warren's Posterior Distribution of $\tilde{p}$
by Use of $P(3 \rightarrow 1 | p)$**

1	2	3	4	5
Value p	Prior $P(p)$	Conditional $P(3 \rightarrow 1 | p)$	Joint $P(p, 3 \rightarrow 1)$	Posterior $P(p | 3 \rightarrow 1)$
.1	.25	.081 × 3	.02025 × 3	(.02025 × 3)/(.12100 × 3) = .167
.2	.50	.128 × 3	.06400 × 3	(.06400 × 3)/(.12100 × 3) = .529
.3	.25	.147 × 3	.03675 × 3	(.03675 × 3)/(.12100 × 3) = .304
	1.00		.12100 × 3 = $P(3 \rightarrow 1)$	1.000

Finally, we compare the posterior distribution of $\tilde{p}$ in the last column of Table 10.4 with the distribution we obtained in the last column of Table 10.3, and we see that these two distributions are in fact identical. Nor is the reason hard to see. Every entry in Column 3 of Table 10.4 is exactly 3 times the corresponding entry in Table 10.3; therefore every entry in Column 4 of Table 10.4 is 3 times the corresponding entry in Table 10.3; and the factor 3 simply cancels out when the last column of Table 10.4 is computed.

Now letting $n \to r$ denote the event that any particular number n of observations yields any particular number r of successes (without regard to order), we generalize to conclude that:

> ■ In computing the distribution that he should assign to an uncertain population fraction $\tilde{p}$ after observing the outcome of equiprobable sampling with replacement, the decision maker may assign to each second-level branch of his probability diagram either (1) his conditional probability for the actual sample outcome given the value of $\tilde{p}$ on the preceding branch, or (2) his conditional probability for the event $n \to r$ given the value of $\tilde{p}$ on the preceding branch.

The reader who wishes to prove this generalization can do so by recalling the way the factor 3 cancelled out in Table 10.4 and convincing himself that a similar phenomenon would occur whatever might be the values of n and r that characterized the sample outcome.

10.4.5

Use of Tables of the
Binomial Mass Function

One reason—although by no means the most important reason—for our interest in the result obtained in the last section is the fact that, when sampling is equiprobable with replacement, the conditional probability $P(n \to r | p)$ that the decision maker should assign to the event $n \to r$ given any particular value of the population fraction $\tilde{p}$ can be read from published tables of what is called the «binomial mass function», whereas no tables exist from which one can read the conditional probability that should be assigned to a particular sample outcome given p.

The binomial mass function, which we shall denote by b^*, is a mathematically defined function of three arguments, which we shall denote by n, r, and p; tables of the function show the function value $b^*(n, r, p)$ for various n's, r's, and p's. The formula by which the function is defined is of no real interest to us here; what does interest us is the fact that the following assertion can be shown to be true:

> ■ *If sampling is equiprobable with replacement,* then logical consistency requires that the decision maker's conditional probability $P(n \to r | p)$ for the event $n \to r$ given p should be equal to the function value $b^*(n, r, p)$.

Observe that $P(n \rightarrow r|p)$ and $b^*(n, r, p)$ are most definitely not just two different names for the same thing. $P(n \rightarrow r|p)$ is a probability that is assessed by a decision maker, whereas $b^*(n, r, p)$ is the value of a mathematically defined function. It is only under the very special condition of equiprobable sampling with replacement that logical consistency requires the decision maker's assessed $P(n \rightarrow r|p)$ to be equal to the function value $b^*(n, r, p)$.

A short table of the binomial mass function appears as Table T1 in the collection of tables at the end of this volume, and in Table 10.5 we show how it could have been used to obtain exactly the same results that we obtained in Table 10.4 but with less labor. Each value of $P(3 \rightarrow 1|p)$ in Column 3 of Table 10.5 was obtained by simply reading the corresponding value of $b^*(3, 1, p)$ from Table T1, and comparing Tables 10.4 and 10.5 the reader should observe two things.

1. Every entry in Table 10.5 is numerically equal to the corresponding entry in Table 10.4, even though the factor 3 which appears explicitly in Columns 3, 4, and 5 of Table 10.4 does not appear explicitly in Table 10.5.

2. The reason why the factor 3 does not appear explicitly in Table 10.5 is that the factor 3 is "built in" to the entries in Table T1. The first entry is read directly from Table T1 as

$$b^*(3,1,.1) = .2430,$$

and similarly for the other two entries. The factor cancels out in the end, however, just as well when it is built in to the entries in the table as when it is shown explicitly.

TABLE 10.5
Computation of Mr. Warren's Posterior Distribution of $\tilde{p}$
by Use of Tables of the Binomial Mass Function

1	2	3	4	5
Value p	*Prior* $P(p)$	*Conditional* $P(3 \rightarrow 1|p)$	*Joint* $P(p, 3 \rightarrow 1)$	*Posterior* $P(p|3 \rightarrow 1)$
.1	.25	.2430	.06075	.06075/.363 = .167
.2	.50	.3840	.19200	.19200/.363 = .529
.3	.25	.4410	.11025	.11025/.363 = .304
	1.00		.36300 $= P(3 \rightarrow 1)$	1.000

10.5
GROUPED APPROXIMATIONS

When the fraction $\tilde{p}$ of successes in a population has only a very few possible values, as it did in the example we have been discussing, it is easy for the decision maker to assess his probability for each possible value of $\tilde{p}$ prior to sampling, and after a sample has been observed it is easy to compute his posterior distribution of $\tilde{p}$ by the method illustrated in Table 10.5. In most practical applications of

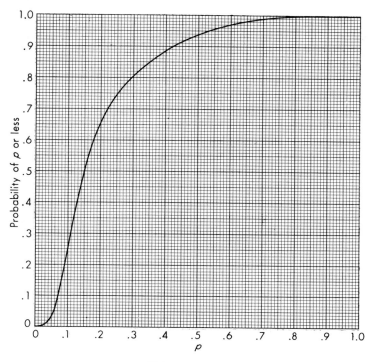

FIGURE 10.5

A Prior Distribution of $\tilde{p}$

sampling, however, the fraction $\tilde{p}$ has thousands or even hundreds of thousands of possible values, and even if the resulting computational difficulties could be overcome by use of a high-speed computer, the decision maker would be completely unable to assess a separate prior probability for each possible value of $\tilde{p}$.

This problem, however, is one that we have studied already, and we already know its solution. The decision maker can assess his prior distribution of $\tilde{p}$ by constructing a graph of its cumulative function, after which the required computations can be carried out by first grouping the distribution assessed by the decision maker and then proceeding exactly as if the grouped distribution were the decision maker's true prior distribution of $\tilde{p}$.

10.5.1

An Example

Suppose, for example, that a decision maker assesses his prior distribution of the fraction $\tilde{p}$ of successes in some population by fairing the cumulative function shown in Figure 10.5, and suppose that he then makes $n = 10$ equiprobable drawings from this population with replacement and observes $r = 3$ successes.

To get a rough idea of the posterior distribution that this decision maker should now assign to $\tilde{p}$, we first group his prior distribution into ten equiprobable brackets, reading the bracket medians to the nearest .01 as shown in the first column of Table 10.6 below. We next use Table T1 to find his conditional probability for the sample event $10 \to 3$ given each bracket median p, and finally we complete the calculations exactly as we did in Table 10.5.

TABLE 10.6
Computation of a Posterior Distribution from a Grouped Prior Distribution

1	2	3	4	5	6	7
					$P(\tilde{p} \leqslant p \mid 10 \to 3)$	
Value	*Prior*	*Conditional*	*Joint*	*Posterior*		
p	*P(p)*	*P(10 → 3│p)*	*P(p, 10 → 3)*	*P(p│10 → 3)*	*Prior*	*Posterior*
.06	.1	.0168	.00168	.013	.1	.013
.08	.1	.0343	.00343	.028	.2	.041
.10	.1	.0574	.00574	.046	.3	.087
.12	.1	.0847	.00847	.068	.4	.155
.14	.1	.1146	.01146	.092	.5	.247
.16	.1	.1450	.01450	.116	.6	.363
.20	.1	.2013	.02013	.161	.7	.524
.25	.1	.2503	.02503	.201	.8	.725
.35	.1	.2522	.02522	.202	.9	.927
.53	.1	.0905	.00905	.073	1.0	1.000
	1.0		.12471	1.000		
			= P(10 → 3)			

10.5.2
Use of Computers

The results obtained in Table 10.6 are admittedly very rough, but they suffice to illustrate the method of computation. In a real problem, the computations would be carried out on a digital computer using a general-purpose program that has been written for this purpose. The user of this program specifies his prior distribution in the way described in Section 7.4.8, by stating the coordinates and slopes of selected points on its cumulative function. Supplied with these inputs, the computer first proceeds, again as described in Section 7.4.8, to group the prior distribution into 100 equiprobable brackets each represented by its bracket median. Then after internally computing the conditional probability of the observed event $10 \to 3$ given each possible p, it goes on to compute a posterior distribution of $\tilde{p}$ by exactly the same arithmetic that was used in Table 10.6.[3]

In Figures 10.6 and 10.7 we show portions of the computer printout for the same example that we analyzed more roughly in Table 10.6. The coordinates and slopes read from the prior cumulative function in Figure 10.5 and supplied to the computer as input appear at the top of Figure 10.6, following by a listing of the bracket medians of the 100 equiprobable brackets into which the computer

---

[3] For a description of this program, see the publication mentioned on page vi of the Preface.

INPUT DATA

VALUE	CUM PROB	SLOPE
0.	0.	0.
0.0320	0.010	
0.0490	0.030	
0.0620	0.070	
0.0800	0.150	
0.0960	0.230	5.747
0.1100	0.310	
0.1390	0.450	
0.1620	0.550	
0.1970	0.650	
0.2520	0.750	
0.3510	0.850	
0.5300	0.950	
0.5960	0.970	
0.7100	0.990	
0.8400	1.000	0.

BRACKET MEDIANS

VALUE	CUM PROB	VALUE	CUM PROB	VALUE	CUM PROB	VALUE	CUM PROB
0.0189	0.005	0.1004	0.255	0.1513	0.505	0.2559	0.755
0.0379	0.015	0.1021	0.265	0.1535	0.515	0.2638	0.765
0.0455	0.025	0.1038	0.275	0.1558	0.525	0.2719	0.775
0.0513	0.035	0.1056	0.285	0.1581	0.535	0.2803	0.785
0.0544	0.045	0.1073	0.295	0.1606	0.545	0.2889	0.795
0.0575	0.055	0.1091	0.305	0.1635	0.555	0.2980	0.805
0.0605	0.065	0.1109	0.315	0.1664	0.565	0.3082	0.815
0.0634	0.075	0.1128	0.325	0.1694	0.575	0.3192	0.825
0.0659	0.085	0.1148	0.335	0.1725	0.585	0.3312	0.835
0.0681	0.095	0.1167	0.345	0.1757	0.595	0.3442	0.845
0.0703	0.105	0.1187	0.355	0.1790	0.605	0.3580	0.855
0.0725	0.115	0.1208	0.365	0.1826	0.615	0.3723	0.865
0.0746	0.125	0.1228	0.375	0.1865	0.625	0.3870	0.875
0.0768	0.135	0.1249	0.385	0.1905	0.635	0.4021	0.885
0.0789	0.145	0.1270	0.395	0.1948	0.645	0.4176	0.895
0.0811	0.155	0.1292	0.405	0.1993	0.655	0.4335	0.905
0.0832	0.165	0.1313	0.415	0.2039	0.665	0.4498	0.915
0.0853	0.175	0.1335	0.425	0.2086	0.675	0.4674	0.925
0.0873	0.185	0.1357	0.435	0.2134	0.685	0.4892	0.935
0.0894	0.195	0.1379	0.445	0.2183	0.695	0.5153	0.945
0.0914	0.205	0.1401	0.455	0.2233	0.705	0.5454	0.955
0.0933	0.215	0.1423	0.465	0.2286	0.715	0.5771	0.965
0.0951	0.225	0.1445	0.475	0.2346	0.725	0.6192	0.975
0.0969	0.235	0.1468	0.485	0.2411	0.735	0.6702	0.985
0.0986	0.245	0.1490	0.495	0.2482	0.745	0.7659	0.995

FIGURE 10.6

Grouped Approximation to the Prior Distribution of $\bar{p}$

grouped the prior distribution. Figure 10.7 then shows how the computer went
on to compute a grouped approximation to the posterior distribution of $\bar{p}$ starting from these 100 bracket medians of the prior distribution. Every column in
Figure 10.7 has exactly the same meaning as the corresponding column in Table
10.6, and except for the conditional probabilities given p, each column is computed in exactly the same way. The conditional probabilities are, as we said before, computed internally instead of being looked up in a table.

10.5.3

"Exactness" of a Grouped Approximation

When we first introduced grouped approximations, in Section 7.4, we said that
after a grouped approximation to any distribution of any UQ has been constructed, it is used exactly as if it were the decision maker's true distribution of
the UQ. In the present context, this implies that as soon as a prior distribution
of $\bar{p}$ has been grouped, we forget that we are working with a grouped approximation and treat any posterior distribution that we compute from it as if it were the
decision maker's true posterior distribution of $\bar{p}$.

```
·AMPLE N    10      SAMPLE R      3
```

VALUE	PRIOR	COND	JOINT	PCST	CUM POST
0.0189	0.0100	0.00071	0.00000712	0.0001	0.C001
0.0379	0.0100	0.00498	0.00004981	0.0004	0.0005
0.0455	0.01C0	0.00817	0.00008167	0.C007	0.0011
0.0513	0.01C0	0.01119	0.00011194	0.C009	0.0020
0.0544	0.0100	0.01309	0.00013089	0.0011	0.0031
0.0575	0.01C0	0.01509	0.00015092	0.0012	0.0043
0.0605	0.01C0	0.01719	0.00017191	0.C014	0.0057
0.0634	0.01C0	0.01933	0.00019334	0.C016	0.0073
0.0659	0.0100	0.02128	0.00021276	0.C017	0.C090
0.0681	0.01C0	0.02311	0.00023111	0.C019	0.0109
0.0703	0.01C0	0.02501	0.00025011	0.0020	0.0129
0.0725	0.01C0	0.02697	0.00026971	0.0022	0.0151
0.1513	0.01C0	0.13177	0.00131773	0.C107	0.2541
0.1535	0.01C0	0.13522	0.00135224	0.0110	0.2651
0.1558	0.0100	0.13868	0.00138681	0.0113	0.2764
0.1581	0.0100	0.14215	0.00142146	0.0115	0.2879
0.1606	0.01C0	0.14595	0.00145946	0.0119	0.2998
0.1635	0.01C0	0.15025	0.00150248	0.0122	0.3120
0.1664	0.0100	0.15467	0.00154674	0.0126	0.3245
0.1694	0.0100	0.15915	0.00159153	0.0129	0.3375
0.1725	0.0100	0.16368	0.00163678	0.0133	0.3508
0.1757	0.0100	0.16827	0.00168272	0.0137	0.3644
0.1790	0.0100	0.17310	0.00173102	0.0141	0.3785
0.1826	0.01C0	0.17818	0.00178178	0.0145	0.3930
0.1865	0.01C0	0.18348	0.00183478	0.0149	0.4079
0.1905	0.01C0	0.18897	0.00188973	0.0154	0.4232
0.1948	0.0100	0.19463	0.00194630	0.0158	0.4390
0.1993	0.01C0	0.20040	0.00200396	0.0163	0.4553
0.2039	0.01C0	0.20612	0.00206115	0.C167	0.4721
0.2086	0.0100	0.21174	0.00211741	0.0172	0.4893
0.2134	0.0100	0.21725	0.00217248	0.0176	0.5069
0.2183	0.0100	0.22261	0.00222610	0.0181	0.5250
0.2233	0.0100	0.22780	0.00227797	0.0185	0.5435
0.2286	0.0100	0.23303	0.00233031	0.0189	0.5624
0.2346	0.0100	0.23842	0.00238421	0.0194	0.5818
0.4021	0.0100	0.21310	0.00213099	0.0173	0.9096
0.4176	0.0100	0.19862	0.00198615	0.0161	0.9258
0.4335	0.01C0	0.18304	0.00183041	0.0149	0.9406
0.4498	0.0100	0.16668	0.00166680	0.0135	0.9542
0.4674	0.0100	0.14894	0.00148943	0.0121	0.9663
0.4892	0.0100	0.12749	0.00127488	0.0104	0.9766
0.5153	0.01C0	0.10320	0.00103196	0.C084	0.9850
0.5454	0.0100	0.07812	0.00078115	0.C063	0.9914
0.5771	0.0100	0.05577	0.00055769	0.0045	0.9959
0.6192	0.0100	0.03306	0.00033056	0.0027	0.9986
0.6702	0.01C0	0.01532	0.00015317	0.C012	0.9998
0.7659	0.0100	0.00208	0.00002079	0.0002	1.0000

```
              UNC PROB OF R      0.12309821

POST MEAN           0.2372
```

Figure 10.7

Computation of the Posterior Distribution of $\bar{p}$

Stated the other way to, we do *not* smooth a grouped approximation to a posterior distribution of $\bar{p}$ in an attempt to obtain more accuracy than we had in our calculations. Instead, we make the original grouping of the prior distribution fine enough to ensure all the accuracy we need for the purpose at hand, and we then treat both the grouped prior and the grouped posterior distributions of $\bar{p}$ as if they were exact.

Grouping that is fine enough to secure all needed accuracy is very easy in real problems, where all the hard work is done by a computer. And since the only purpose of working exercises by hand is to learn the method of computation used by a computer, even the very coarse approximations resulting from the use of only 10 brackets should be treated as if they were exact.

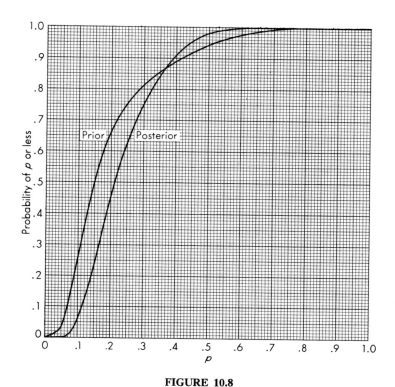

FIGURE 10.8

Prior and Posterior Cumulative Functions Based on Grouping into 100 Equiprobable Brackets

In Figure 10.8 we show smooth graphs of the prior and posterior cumulative functions in our last example as calculated by the computer in Figures 10.6 and 10.7. In Figure 10.9 we show exact graphs of the same functions as calculated by hand in Table 10.6, since use of smooth graphs is not legitimate in a situation where we are proceeding as if there were only 10 possible values of $\tilde{p}$.

In both Figure 10.8 and Figure 10.9, the reader should observe how the information obtained from the sample has led the decision maker to narrow his original distribution of $\tilde{p}$, assigning more probability to values of $\tilde{p}$ that are close to the fraction 3/10 of successes that was actually observed in the sample and less probability to values of $\tilde{p}$ that are substantially different from 3/10.

10.6
SUCCESSIVE SAMPLES

We have already said that although a distribution of $\tilde{p}$ that is revised to take account of sample information is called a "posterior" distribution, it is in fact simply an ordinary probability distribution of $\tilde{p}$ which takes account of all the information available at the time it is assessed, as any distribution of any UQ should do. It follows that if a decision maker who has taken one sample and

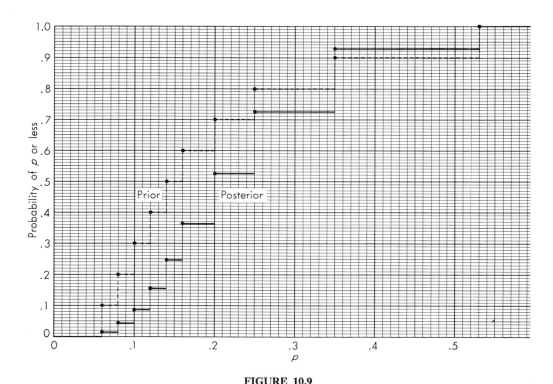

FIGURE 10.9

Prior and Posterior Cumulative Functions Based on Grouping into 10 Equiprobable Brackets

computed his distribution of $\bar{p}$ posterior thereto now takes another sample, the same distribution which was "posterior" as regards the first sample is "prior" as regards the second sample and is used exactly like any prior distribution in computing his distribution posterior to the second sample.

If a decision maker assesses an "original" distribution of $\bar{p}$ and then takes two samples by equiprobable sampling with replacement *without* stopping between them to compute his distribution posterior to the first sample, his distribution posterior to the second sample can be computed by either of two methods, both of which will necessarily give exactly the same result:

1 The decision maker can go back and compute the "posterior" distribution he would have assigned to $\bar{p}$ after observing the first sample alone. This distribution then becomes his "prior" distribution as regards the second sample, and using it he can compute the distribution he should assign to $\bar{p}$ posterior to the second sample.

2 The decision maker can regard all the successes and failures he has observed as constituting a single ≪pooled sample≫, and using his "original" distribution of $\bar{p}$ as his "prior" distribution he can compute the distribution he should assign to $\bar{p}$ posterior to the pooled sample.

If, for example, a first sample of size 25 taken by equiprobable sampling with replacement contained 7 successes and a second sample of size 50 contained 12 successes, the combined effect of the two samples on the decision maker's distribution of $\tilde{p}$ should be exactly the same as if he had taken a single sample of size 75 and found that it contained 19 successes.

10.7
SUMMARY

10.7.1
Description of a Two-valued Population

A two-valued population is one that can be adequately described for the purpose at hand by stating

N: the number of members in the population,

p: the fraction of members who possess some particular attribute.

Members possessing the attribute of interest are called "successes", other members are called "failures".

10.7.2
Equiprobable Sampling with Replacement

1 Sampling is said to be ≪equiprobable≫ if on each successive draw the decision maker assigns equal probabilities of selection to all eligible members of the population.

2 Equiprobable sampling is said to be ≪with replacement≫ if (1) all members of the population are eligible on each successive draw, and (2) it is not possible to identify and reject the redundant information obtained by drawing the same member more than once.

10.7.3
Summarization of Sample Information

The information about $\tilde{p}$ that is contained in a sample drawn by equiprobable sampling with replacement is entirely conveyed by the ≪statistics≫

n: number of sample observations,

r: number of successes among these observations.

10.7.4
Assessment of a Distribution
of $\tilde{p}$ Posterior to Sampling

When a decision maker wishes to assess a distribution of $\tilde{p}$ posterior to equiprobable sampling with replacement, he usually finds that his information bears directly, not on the posterior probabilities he wishes to assess now, but on the

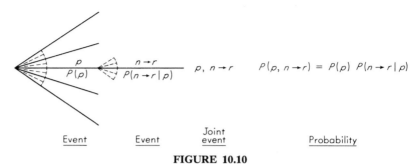

FIGURE 10.10

Probability Diagram for Assessment of a Posterior Distribution of $\tilde{p}$

probabilities he (would have) assigned *prior* to sampling to the branches of the probability diagram in Figure 10.10, where $n \rightarrow r$ stands for the event that n sample observations yield r successes.

When this is true, the decision maker can best bring the available information to bear on his problem by proceeding as follows:

1 The decision maker directly assesses the "prior" unconditional probability $P(p)$ that he (would have) assigned *before* sampling to each possible value of $\tilde{p}$ on the fork at the origin of Figure 10.10.

2 If sampling is equiprobable with replacement, logical consistency requires that the conditional probability $P(n \rightarrow r | p)$ assigned before sampling to each second-level branch be equal to $b^*(n, r, p)$, where b^* is a mathematically defined function known as the ≪binomial mass function≫.

The binomial mass function is tabulated for selected values of n, r, and p in Table T1.

3 The probability that the decision maker (should have) assigned before sampling to each end position of Figure 10.10 can be found by multiplying together the probabilities on the two branches leading to that end position.

4 The conditional probability $P(p | n \rightarrow r)$ that the decision maker should have assigned before sampling to any particular value of $\tilde{p}$ *given* the sample event $n \rightarrow r$ can be computed by dividing the probability of the end position at which that value of $\tilde{p}$ appears together with the event $n \rightarrow r$ by the probability of all end positions at which the event $n \rightarrow r$ appears.

5 Since it is now known that the event $n \rightarrow r$ has actually occurred, the decision maker's "posterior" unconditional probability for any p should be equal to the computed conditional probability $P(p | n \rightarrow r)$.

10.7.5
Grouped Approximations
to Posterior Distributions

1 The distribution that should be assigned to $\tilde{p}$ posterior to sampling can be approximated by grouping the prior distribution of $\tilde{p}$ and then proceeding exactly as if the grouped prior distribution were the true prior distribution of $\tilde{p}$.

2 Accuracy adequate for the purpose at hand should be secured by using an adequately fine grouping of the prior distribution, not by smoothing the computed posterior distribution.

In all exercises, the prior distribution should be grouped into 10 equiprobable brackets and the resulting posterior distribution should be treated as if it were exact. Because this distribution recognizes only 10 possible values of $\tilde{p}$, a smooth graph of the mass or cumulative function of $\tilde{p}$ would be misleading; only exact graphs should be drawn.

10.7.6
Successive Samples

If a decision maker has taken two samples from the same population and wishes to assess a posterior distribution of $\tilde{p}$ that takes account of the information obtained from both the samples, he must start by directly assessing the distribution that he would have assigned to $\tilde{p}$ "originally", before either of the samples were taken. He can then proceed in either of two ways, both of which necessarily lead to exactly the same results.

1 The decision maker can go back and compute the "posterior" distribution he would have assigned to $\tilde{p}$ after observing the first sample alone. This distribution then becomes his "prior" distribution as regards the second sample, and using it he can compute the distribution he should assign to $\tilde{p}$ posterior to the second sample.

2 The decision maker can regard all of the successes and failures he has observed as constituting a single ≪pooled≫ sample, and using his "original" distribution of $\tilde{p}$ as his "prior" distribution he can compute the distribution he should assign to $\tilde{p}$ posterior to the pooled sample.

EXERCISES

10.1 A bag contains an unknown number of poker chips, some of which are red, the remainder white. Mr. Pavlos Stavrou knows that the fraction of red chips in the bag is either .1, .5, or .6, and he feels that there are 3 chances in 5 that the fraction is actually .1, 1 chance in 5 that it is .5, and 1 chance in 5 that it is .6. To get more information about the fraction of red chips in the bag, Stavrou proposes to make two sample observations in the following manner. He will first stir the contents of the bag, draw one chip, observe whether it is red or white, and replace it in the bag. He will then restir the contents of the bag, draw another chip, observe whether it is red or white, and replace it in the bag.

a Diagram an assessment gamble showing all possible combinations of the three possible values of $\tilde{p}$ with the two possible events of each of Stavrou's two proposed sample observations, ordering the forks in whatever way will lead Stavrou to have the greatest possible confidence in the probabilities he assesses for their branches.

b Assuming that before making each observation Stavrou intends to stir the contents of the bag so thoroughly that he believes that every individual chip has an equal chance of being drawn, write on the branches of your diagram the probabilities that Stavrou should assign to them.

c Compute the probabilities that Stavrou should assign to the end positions of his diagram, and then compute the total probability of (1) all end positions at which Stavrou can arrive if the first sample drawing yields a red chip and the second yields a white chip, and (2) all end positions at which he can arrive if $\tilde{p} = .1$ *and* the two sample drawings yield a red and a white chip in that order.

d What should be Stavrou's *conditional* probability for the proposition that .1 of the chips in the bag are red *given* that the first sample drawing yields a red chip and the second yields a white chip? for the proposition that .5 of the chips are red? that .6 are red?

e Mark with an X each end position whose probability you actually used in answering (c) and (d).

f When Mr. Stavrou actually makes his two sample observations, what he actually observes is a white chip on the first drawing and a red chip on the second, rather than the reverse. Construct a diagram like the one in Figure 10.3 (page 400) that Stavrou can use to compute the probabilities he should now assign to the three possible values of the fraction $\tilde{p}$, and compute these probabilities.

g Enter all the data and computational results that you used in answering (f) on two work sheets like Tables 10.2 and 10.3 (page 401).

h If your answers to (f) are not equal to your answers to (d), you have made a mistake. Why must these two sets of answers be equal even though it was assumed in (f) that Stavrou observed first a white and then a red chip whereas it was assumed in (d) that he observed first a red and then a white chip?

i Suppose that in answering (f) you had made a series of mistakes when you calculated the probabilities for the sample-outcome branches and obtained a value that was exactly 10 times the correct value in each and every case. If you had gone ahead and used these erroneous conditional probabilities in computing Stavrou's posterior probabilities for the possible values of $\bar{p}$, what answers would you have obtained? Would they have been the same as the answers you obtained in (*f*) when you used correct conditional probabilities? Why?

10.2 Ten observations are to be made by equiprobable sampling with a replacement on a population containing an unknown fraction of successes; one possible outcome is 3 successes and 7 failures in the order *FSFFFSFSFF*.

a Show that the decision maker's conditional probability for this outcome, given that the fraction of successes in the population is .4, should be $.4^3 \times .6^7$.

b Show that the decision maker should assign this same probability to a sample outcome containing 3 successes and 7 failures in *any* one, particular order.

c The decision maker will receive a prize if he observes 3 successes and 7 failures, *regardless* of the order in which they occur. How could you compute the conditional probability, given $\bar{p} = .4$, that he should assign to winning the prize? How could you compute his conditional probability for this same event given *any* specified value of $\bar{p}$?

d Suppose that the decision maker actually makes 10 observations and observes *FSFFFSFSFF*, and suppose that he then proceeds to compute his posterior distribution of $\bar{p}$ using a worksheet like the one in Table 10.3 (page 401). If in Column 3 he enters, not his conditional probability for *FSFFFSFSFF* given each possible value of $\bar{p}$, but his conditional probability for winning the prize given each possible value of $\bar{p}$, and if he then uses these probabilities to compute his entries in Columns 4 and 5, will the entries in Column 5 be the probabilities that he really should now assign to the possible values of $\bar{p}$? Why?

10.3 a Denoting by $10 \rightarrow 3$ the event that the decision maker of Exercise 10.2 will actually observe 3 successes in 10 observations and thus win the prize, show by use of Table T1 of the binomial mass function that he should assess the following conditional probabilities for winning the prize given various values of $\bar{p}$:

$$P(10 \rightarrow 3 \,|\, \bar{p} = .13) = .0995,$$
$$P(10 \rightarrow 3 \,|\, \bar{p} = .37) = .2394,$$
$$P(10 \rightarrow 3 \,|\, \bar{p} = .63) = .0285,$$
$$P(10 \rightarrow 3 \,|\, \bar{p} = .87) = .0000.$$

b Using a worksheet like the one in Table 10.5 (page 406), compute the posterior distribution that this decision maker should assign to $\bar{p}$ if prior to sampling he would have assigned to $\bar{p}$ the distribution in the table below.

Decision Maker's Prior Distribution of $\bar{p}$

Value p	Probability $P(p)$
.13	.1
.37	.2
.63	.3
.87	.4
	1.0

10.4 (An experiment due to Ward Edwards). You are shown two green baize bags one of which contains 700 red and 300 white poker chips while the other contains 300 red and 700 white, and you choose one of the two bags at random, there being nothing to indicate which is which. You are then allowed to draw a sample of chips from your chosen bag by a process which you assess to be equiprobable with replacement.

a Suppose that 12 drawings yield 8 red and 4 white chips. Without doing any calculations, what probability do you think you should now assign to your having chosen the bag with 70% red chips? (You will find this exercise much more interesting if you answer this question honestly and do not cheat by calculating.)

b Same as (a) except that only 4 drawings are made and all the chips drawn are red.

c Now actually compute the probability that logic obliges you to assign to your having chosen the bag with 70% red chips under the conditions of (a), assuming that prior to sampling you assigned probability 1/2 to this event.

d Same as (c) but under the conditions of (b).

10.5 In order to learn more about the fraction of his 15,000 customers who have ordered less than $50 worth of merchandise during the past six months, Mr. Herbert Zellner has had a clerk make 100 drawings of individual customers by equiprobable sampling with replacement and consult his sales records to find exactly how many dollars worth of merchandise were purchased by the customer selected on each drawing. The clerk has reported that on 23 of his 100 consultations of the sales records, he found that the customer had ordered less than $50 worth of merchandise during the last six months. Compute a grouped approximation to the distribution that Zellner should now assign to the fraction $\bar{p}$ of all 15,000 customers who purchased less than $50 worth of merchandise during the last six months:

a Assuming that prior to sampling Zellner would have assigned to $\bar{p}$ the distribution defined by Figure 10.11, and reading values of $\bar{p}$ from this figure to two decimal places.

b Assuming that prior to sampling Zellner would have assigned exactly the same probability to every possible value of $\bar{p}$.

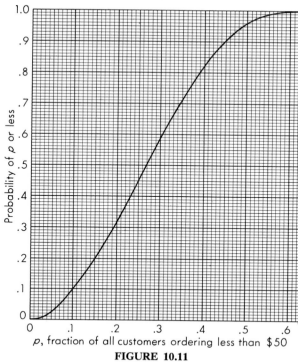

FIGURE 10.11

Mr. Zellner's Prior Distribution of $\bar{p}$

10.6 Prepare the inputs that would be required if you wished to have a more exact answer to Exercise 10.5a computed by the computer program described in Section 10.5.2.

10.7 Rudolph Grauber has constructed a mammoth probability diagram with 1 million end positions and has computed the value of a function $\bar{z}$ at each end position. He would like to know at what fraction of all end positions the function $\bar{z}$ has a value less than 50, but he is so exhausted by the labor of constructing the diagram that he neither has the slightest recollection of the number of times that he labelled an end position with a value of $\bar{z}$ less than 50 nor feels up to counting the end positions where the value of $\bar{z}$ is less than 50. To avoid totally losing the fruit of all his labor, he tries to learn what he can about the fraction in which he is interested by drawing 100 end positions by equiprobable sampling with replacement and observing the value of the function $\bar{z}$ at each end position that he draws. The value of $\bar{z}$ turns out to be less than 50 on 23 of the 100 observations.

a Letting $\bar{p}$ denote the fraction of all 1 million end positions on the probability diagram at which the value of the function $\bar{z}$ is less than 50, what probability distribution should Grauber assign to $\bar{p}$?

b Should Grauber feel that there is any appreciable chance that a complete count of the 1 million end positions would show that $\bar{z}$ has a value below 50 at less than 15% of all end positions?   at more than 35% of all end positions?

10.8 *a* A 10-branched event fork in a probability diagram represents a UQ $\bar{x}$ whose distribution has been grouped into 10 equiprobable brackets, the bracket medians of which are shown in Table 10.7A.   Draw a branch

TABLE 10.7A
Bracket Medians of $\bar{x}$

Serial Number	Bracket Median x	Probability P(x)
0	65,000	.1
1	108,000	.1
2	143,000	.1
3	173,000	.1
4	203,000	.1
5	232,000	.1
6	261,000	.1
7	296,000	.1
8	341,000	.1
9	415,000	.1
		1.0

from this fork by reading the first "random digit" in the first row of Table T6 and selecting the branch whose serial number matches this random digit.

TABLE 10.7B
Bracket Medians of $\bar{y}$

Serial Number	Bracket Median y	Probability P(y|x)
0	.030	.1
1	.048	.1
2	.062	.1
3	.075	.1
4	.092	.1
5	.110	.1
6	.131	.1
7	.158	.1
8	.198	.1
9	.260	.1
		1.0

b The particular *x* branch which you have just drawn is followed in the diagram by a 10-branched fork representing a UQ $\bar{y}$ whose conditional distribution, given the preceding value of $\bar{x}$, has been grouped into 10 equiprobable brackets.   The bracket medians of these 10 brackets are shown in Table 10.7B.   Draw a branch from this fork by reading the second random digit in the first row of Table T6 and selecting the branch whose serial number matches this random digit.

c The decision maker for whom this diagram was constructed is interested in a function of $\tilde{x}$ and $\tilde{y}$, namely $\tilde{z} = \tilde{x} \times \tilde{y}$. What is the value of $\tilde{z}$ at the end position at which you would arrive if you started at the origin and traversed the branches you drew in (a) and (b)?

d Not only the x branch that you drew in (a) but every other branch on the $\tilde{x}$ fork at the origin of the diagram is followed by a $\tilde{y}$ fork with branches representing the bracket medians of 10 equiprobable brackets. Assuming that on every one of these $\tilde{y}$ forks the 10 bracket medians have the values shown in Table 10.7B, use the third random digit in the first row of Table T6 to make another drawing of a branch on the $\tilde{x}$ fork at the origin of the diagram, use the fourth digit in the row to draw a branch on the following $\tilde{y}$ fork, and calculate the value of the function $\tilde{z}$ at the end position to which you are led by the x and y branches you have drawn.

e Since each branch of the 10-branched $\tilde{x}$ fork at the origin of the probability diagram is followed by a 10-branched $\tilde{y}$ fork, the diagram has 100 end positions. Before you actually read the third and fourth digits in the first row of Table T6, what would have been your probability for the event that they would lead you to the particular end position to which they in fact led you? To any other specified end position?

f Suppose that knowledge of the value of $\tilde{x}$ would have a substantial effect on the decision maker's opinions about the value of $\tilde{y}$. Would it be true, as we assumed in (d), that the *same* 10 bracket medians would appear on the branches of all 10 $\tilde{y}$ forks in his probability diagram? If not, would it still be possible to "draw end positions" by reading pairs of random digits from Table T6? What information that you do not now have would you have to have in order to do so?

g The mammoth probability diagram constructed by Mr. Grauber of Exercise 10.7 actually represented the joint distribution of three UQ's, $\tilde{u}$, $\tilde{v}$, and $\tilde{w}$, all of whose distributions had been grouped into 100 equiprobable brackets. Could Grauber have used equiprobable sampling with replacement to draw 100 values of the function $\tilde{z}$ without ever actually constructing his diagram? If he could, what information would he have to have had available in order to do so?

10.9 A decision maker believes that the uncertain fraction $\tilde{p}$ of successes in a certain population must be either .1 or .2, and he assesses

$$P(\tilde{p} = .1) = .3, \qquad P(\tilde{p} = .2) = .7.$$

He then successively draws two members of the population by equiprobable sampling with replacement and observes that the first drawing yields a success, the second a failure.

a Compute the distribution that the decision maker should have assigned to $\bar{p}$ after the first drawing was made but before the second drawing was made.

b Using your answer to (*a*) as a "prior" distribution, compute the distribution that he should assign to $\bar{p}$ posterior to the second drawing.

c Recompute the distribution that he should assign to $\bar{p}$ posterior to both drawings without making use of your answer to (*a*).

d Explain why the assertion in the second paragraph of Section 10.6 is true.

CHAPTER
11

SAMPLES FROM TWO-VALUED POPULATIONS: FURTHER EXAMINATION

In Chapter 10 we discussed the basic logic by which a businessman can assess a "posterior" probability distribution of an uncertain fraction of successes that takes correct account of both the information he has obtained by sampling and the information he had prior to sampling. In the present chapter, we shall try both to deepen and to extend the reader's understanding of this assessment problem in various ways.

    1. First, we try to give the reader a better intuitive understanding of the logic of the combination of sample and prior information by reexamining this logic from a slightly different point of view.

    2. Next, we examine a mathematical shortcut that makes it extremely easy to assess a posterior distribution of an uncertain fraction of successes when the businessman's prior information is negligible relative to the information he has gained by sampling.

    3. Next, we consider situations in which a businessman may legitimately think in terms of an estimate of an uncertain fraction of successes rather than his complete probability distribution of the fraction and show how a reasonable estimate can be computed and its uncertainty can be measured.

    4. Next, we consider problems involving the fraction of successes that would be generated in the long run by a physical process capable in principle of generating an infinite number of successes and failures.

    5. Finally, we very briefly discuss some sampling processes other than equiprobable sampling with replacement.

The text and exercises of this chapter are designed to be studied in the following order:

1 Section 11.1.

2 Sections 11.2.1–11.2.5 and Exercise 11.1.

3 Section 11.2.6 and Exercises 11.2–11.4.

4 Section 11.2.7 and Exercises 11.5–11.6.

5 Section 11.2.8 and Exercise 11.7.

6 Section 11.3.1 and Exercise 11.8*a*.

7 Section 11.3.2 and Exercise 11.8*b*.

8 Section 11.3.3 and Exercise 11.8*c*.

9 Section 11.3.4.

10 Section 11.4 and Exercise 11.9.

11 Section 11.5 and Exercises 11.10–11.12.

12 Section 11.6 and Exercises 11.13–11.16.

3.
Estimates of $\bar{p}$

1 Calculation of an Estimate of $\bar{p}$
2 Measurement of Uncertainty about $\bar{p}$
3 Reduction in Uncertainty to Be Anticipated from Further Sampling
4 Graphs of Uncertainty vs. Cost

4.
Bernoulli Processes

1 Definition of a Bernoulli Process
2 Application to Real Processes
3 Prior Distributions of the Long-run Fraction $\bar{p}$
4 Posterior Distributions of the Long-run Fraction $\bar{p}$
5 Unconditional Probabilities for Events on the Next Trial

5.
Sampling without Replacement

1 Equiprobable Sampling without Replacement
2 Systematic Sampling
3 Stratification and Clustering

6.
Summary

1 Combination of Prior and Sample Information
2 Beta Approximations to Posterior Distributions
3 Estimates of $\bar{p}$
4 Bernoulli Processes
5 Sampling without Replacement

11.1
COMBINATION OF PRIOR
AND SAMPLE INFORMATION

11.1.1
Computation of
Posterior Distributions Reexamined

We have seen repeatedly—e.g., in Table 10.5 on page 406—that two steps are required to compute the probabilities that a decision maker should assign to the possible values of $\bar{p}$ after observing a sample outcome.

   1 We first multiply his prior probability *for* each value of $\bar{p}$ by his condi-

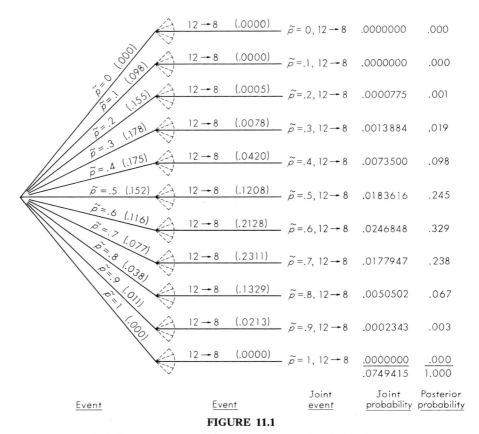

Event	Event	Joint event	Joint probability	Posterior probability
$\tilde{p}=0$ (.000)	$12 \to 8$ (.0000)	$\tilde{p}=0, 12 \to 8$	.0000000	.000
$\tilde{p}=.1$ (.098)	$12 \to 8$ (.0000)	$\tilde{p}=.1, 12 \to 8$	.0000000	.000
$\tilde{p}=.2$ (.155)	$12 \to 8$ (.0005)	$\tilde{p}=.2, 12 \to 8$	.0000775	.001
$\tilde{p}=.3$ (.178)	$12 \to 8$ (.0078)	$\tilde{p}=.3, 12 \to 8$	.0013884	.019
$\tilde{p}=.4$ (.175)	$12 \to 8$ (.0420)	$\tilde{p}=.4, 12 \to 8$	.0073500	.098
$\tilde{p}=.5$ (.152)	$12 \to 8$ (.1208)	$\tilde{p}=.5, 12 \to 8$	.0183616	.245
$\tilde{p}=.6$ (.116)	$12 \to 8$ (.2128)	$\tilde{p}=.6, 12 \to 8$	.0246848	.329
$\tilde{p}=.7$ (.077)	$12 \to 8$ (.2311)	$\tilde{p}=.7, 12 \to 8$	.0177947	.238
$\tilde{p}=.8$ (.038)	$12 \to 8$ (.1329)	$\tilde{p}=.8, 12 \to 8$	.0050502	.067
$\tilde{p}=.9$ (.011)	$12 \to 8$ (.0213)	$\tilde{p}=.9, 12 \to 8$	.0002343	.003
$\tilde{p}=1$ (.000)	$12 \to 8$ (.0000)	$\tilde{p}=1, 12 \to 8$	.0000000	.000
			.0749415	1.000

FIGURE 11.1

Probability Diagram for Computation of a Posterior Distribution of $\tilde{p}$

tional probability for the sample outcome or the event $n \to r$ *given* that value of $\tilde{p}$.

2 We then divide each of these products by their sum, which is his unconditional probability for the sample outcome or the event $n \to r$.

We now observe, however, that since every product obtained in step 1 is divided by the *same* number in step 2, step 2 has no effect on the *relative* magnitudes of the posterior probabilities of the various possible values of $\tilde{p}$. In other words:

3 The posterior probability that a decision maker should assign to each possible value of $\tilde{p}$ is *proportional* (although not in general equal) to the product of just two factors: (1) his prior probability *for* that value of $\tilde{p}$, and (2) his conditional probability for the sample outcome or the event $n \to r$ *given* that value of $\tilde{p}$.

For another illustration of this proposition, consider the computation in Figure 11.1 and Table 11.1 of a decision maker's posterior distribution of $\tilde{p}$ from

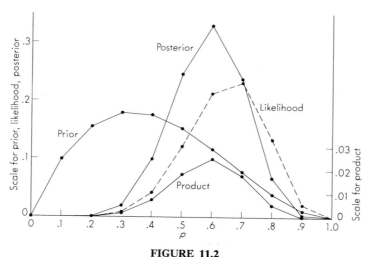

FIGURE 11.2

Mass and Likelihood Functions

his prior distribution of $\bar{p}$ and his conditional probabilities for the sample event $12 \rightarrow 8$ (8 successes in 12 observations). The posterior probabilities in Column 5 are proportional to the joint probabilities in Column 4, from which they differ only by the constant factor $1/.0749415$, and the joint probabilities in Column 4 are the products of the prior probabilities in Column 2 and the conditional probabilities in Column 3.

TABLE 11.1

Computation of a Posterior Distribution of $\bar{p}$

1	2	3	4	5
Value p	*Prior* $P(p)$	*Conditional* $P(12 \rightarrow 8 \mid p)$	*Joint* $P(p, 12 \rightarrow 8)$	*Posterior* $P(p \mid 12 \rightarrow 8)$
.0	.000	.0000	.0000000	.000
.1	.098	.0000	.0000000	.000
.2	.155	.0005	.0000775	.001
.3	.178	.0078	.0013884	.019
.4	.175	.0420	.0073500	.098
.5	.152	.1208	.0183616	.245
.6	.116	.2128	.0246848	.329
.7	.077	.2311	.0177947	.238
.8	.038	.1329	.0050502	.067
.9	.011	.0213	.0002343	.003
1.0	.000	.0000	.0000000	.000
	1.000		.0749415 $= P(12 \rightarrow 8)$	1.000

This same computation is depicted graphically in another way in Figure 11.2 where the various probabilities in Figure 11.1 and Table 11.1 are represented by heavy dots joined together by lines which are merely guides to the eye. Specifically,

1. The dots labelled "prior" show the unconditional probability that the decision maker assigned *to* each possible value of $\bar{p}$ prior to sampling; they depict the decision maker's ≪prior mass function≫ for $\bar{p}$.

2. The dots labelled "likelihood" show the conditional probability that the decision maker assigned to the sample outcome $12 \rightarrow 8$ *given* each possible value of $\bar{p}$; they depict what is called his ≪sample likelihood function≫.

3. The dots labelled "product" show for each possible p the product of the heights of the prior mass function and the sample likelihood function at that value of $\bar{p}$; they correspond to the "joint" probabilities in Figure 11.1 and Table 11.1.

4. Finally, the dots labelled "posterior" show the probability that the decision maker assigned to each possible value of $\bar{p}$ posterior to sampling; they depict his ≪posterior mass function≫ for $\bar{p}$.

The essential thing to observe in Figure 11.2 is this. Because (1) the height of the "product" dot at each possible value of $\bar{p}$ is the product of the heights of the "prior" and "sample likelihood" dots, and (2) the height of the "posterior" dot is simply the height of the "product" dot divided by a constant,

■ The height of the graph of the posterior mass function at any possible value of $\bar{p}$ is proportional to the product of the heights of the graphs of the prior mass function and the sample likelihood function at that value of $\bar{p}$.

To have a clear understanding of the meaning of this observation, the reader must remember that:

■ All four of the graphs in Figure 11.2 represent functions of p, which is the only "variable" present. In particular, the sample likelihood function does *not* represent a probability distribution of the various sample outcomes that might have occurred; it shows the probability of the one sample outcome that actually occurred given the various possible values of $\bar{p}$.

In Figure 11.1, the likelihoods appear on branches representing the same event $12 \rightarrow 8$ on 11 different event forks; they do not appear on branches representing different events on the same event fork, as they would if they constituted a probability distribution of the various sample events that might have occurred.

11.1.2
Effect of Prior and Sample Information

We are now ready to take a systematic look at the way in which the decision maker's prior mass function and sample likelihood function combine to determine his posterior mass function.

In Figure 11.3 we show these three functions for four different cases. In all four of the cases, the possible values of $\bar{p}$ are assumed to be .000, .001, .002, . . . , .999, 1.000, but each case represents a different combination of prior distribution and sample statistics n and r. The values of the sample statistics are indicated at the top of each of the four sets of graphs; the prior distribution is described by the graph of the prior mass function.

Recalling that the height of the posterior mass function at any value of $\bar{p}$ is proportional to the product of the heights of the prior mass function and the sample likelihood function, we now make the following observations.

In part A of Figure 11.3, where neither the prior mass function nor the sample likelihood function is more tightly concentrated than the other, the product curve or posterior mass function is an exact compromise between these two "factor" curves. We can say that the prior information expressed by the prior mass function carries exactly the same weight as three sample observations.

In part B, the prior mass function is more tightly concentrated than the sample likelihood function, and therefore the prior mass function has the greater effect on the product curve or posterior mass function. The information obtained from the sample has an effect on the distribution which the decision maker should assign to $\bar{p}$ after sampling, but its effect is small relative to the effect of the information the decision maker had prior to sampling.

In part C, the situation is the exact opposite of that in part B—the sample likelihood function is more tightly concentrated than the prior mass function and therefore plays the more important role in determining the product curve or posterior mass function. Notice that this is exactly what we would expect in view of the fact that in this case the sample likelihood function expresses the information contained in 12 sample observations whereas the prior information expressed by the prior mass function carries only as much weight as 3 sample observations, as we saw when we examined part A of the figure.

Finally, in part D we have the very common case where a fairly large sample ($n = 99$) produces a sample likelihood function which is very much more tightly concentrated than the prior mass function, with the result that the posterior mass function is almost wholly determined by the sample likelihood function. The information contained in 99 sample observations nearly swamps the 3 observations' worth of information expressed by the prior mass function.

To sum up, these four cases taken together illustrate the two following general principles.

1 The relative importance of prior and sample information in determining a posterior distribution of $\bar{p}$ depends on the relative "tightness" of the prior mass function and the sample likelihood function. If these two functions are about equally tight, the posterior mass function will be a compromise between them; if one of them is much tighter than the other, the posterior mass function will be largely determined by the tighter one.

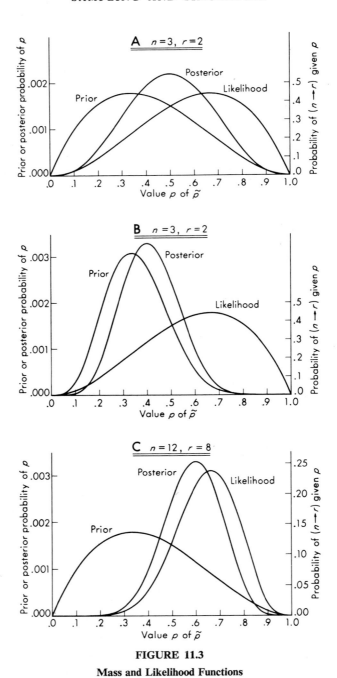

FIGURE 11.3

Mass and Likelihood Functions

2 The tightness of the sample likelihood function increases as the number
of observations n increases while the ratio r/n of successes to observations remains fixed.

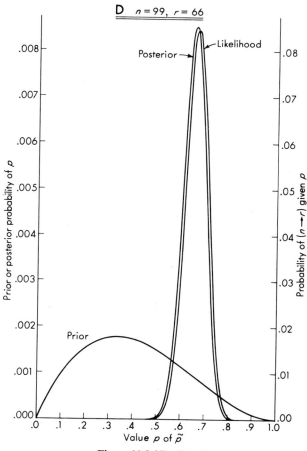

Figure 11.3 (Continued)

Because the tightness of the sample likelihood function can thus be said to express the "amount of information" about $\tilde{p}$ that is contained in the sample, we can think of the tightness of the prior mass function as an expression of the "amount of information" that the decision maker had about $\tilde{p}$ prior to sampling.

11.2

**BETA APPROXIMATIONS
TO POSTERIOR DISTRIBUTIONS OF $\tilde{p}$**

In many practical applications of sampling, the businessman's prior information about $\tilde{p}$ is so slight relative to the information that has been obtained from a sample that the shape of his posterior mass function is for practical purposes wholly determined by the shape of his sample likelihood function. Thus suppose, for example, that a businessman's prior mass function and sample likelihood function are those depicted in Figure 11.3D. When referred to the left rather than the right-hand vertical scale, the likelihood curve defines a possible mass function of $\bar{p}$, and in many situations no harm would be done if the businessman thought and acted as if his posterior mass function were in fact the one defined by the likelihood curve rather than the one defined by the posterior curve in Figure 11.3D.

The fact that a posterior mass function can often be treated for practical purposes as if it were identical in shape to the sample likelihood function is of great importance because the decision maker does not have to make a really careful, quantitative assessment of his prior distribution in order to determine whether this is so. A very rough qualitative assessment of the prior distribution suffices to determine whether an adequately accurate approximation to the posterior mass function can be obtained by merely rescaling the sample likelihood function; and if it can, there are no further demands on the decision maker's time and attention. The rescaling is a completely routine application of arithmetic that can be carried out by either a clerical assistant or a digital computer using a standard, general-purpose program, and in many situations even these calculations are unnecessary. If all that the decision maker really wants to know about his posterior distribution of $\bar{p}$ is its mean, he can compute it by a simple arithmetical operation on the sample statistics n and r, or if all that he wants is certain cumulative probabilities or fractiles, he can read them from published tables.

In this section, we shall ultimately explain and demonstrate all of the assertions we have just made, but in order to do so we shall have to follow a somewhat indirect route. We shall first define what is meant by a ≪uniform≫ prior distribution of $\bar{p}$ and show how the decision maker's posterior distribution of $\bar{p}$ can be very easily derived when his prior distribution is uniform. We shall then be in a position to show that even when the decision maker's prior distribution is not uniform, these same results still apply provided that the prior distribution satisfies certain qualitative conditions.

11.2.1
Uniform Prior Distributions

Suppose that a decision maker is interested in the fraction $\bar{p}$ of successes in a population of size N. Since every member of the population can in principle be either a success or a failure, the possible numbers of successes in the population are $0, 1, 2, \ldots, N - 1, N$, and therefore the possible fractions of successes or values of $\bar{p}$ are $0/N, 1/N, 2/N, \ldots, (N - 1)/N, N/N$.

■ If prior to sampling from a population of size N a decision maker assigns *equal probabilities to all logically possible values of* $\bar{p}$, namely $0/N$, $1/N, \ldots, N/N$, we shall say that his prior distribution of $\bar{p}$ is ≪uniform≫.

11.2.2
The Posterior Mass Function
When the Prior Distribution Is Uniform

Suppose next that a population consists of $N = 1,000$ individuals; suppose that a decision maker assigns a uniform prior distribution to the fraction $\tilde{p}$ of successes in the population; and suppose that he then makes 99 observations on the population by equiprobable sampling with replacement and observes 66 successes. The mass function that this decision maker should now assign to $\tilde{p}$ is computed in the usual manner in the first five columns of Table 11.2, where the reader should observe that because the prior probabilities in Column 2 are all equal, the variation in the posterior probabilities in Column 5 is entirely due to the variation in the sample likelihoods in Column 3. The posterior probability of any particular value of $\tilde{p}$, as shown in Column 5, is equal to the sample likelihood given that value of $\tilde{p}$, as shown in Column 3, divided by a constant which does not depend on p.

TABLE 11.2
Computation of a Posterior Distribution When the Prior Distribution Is Uniform

1	2	3	4	5	6
Value p	Prior P(p)	Likelihood $P(99 \to 66\,\vert\,p)$	Joint $P(p,\ 99 \to 66)$	Posterior $P(p\,\vert\,99 \to 66)$	$P(\tilde{p} \leqslant p\,\vert\,99 \to 66)$
.000	1/1,001	.0000	.0000000	.00000	.00000
.001	1/1,001	.0000	.0000000	.00000	.00000
.....	....	.....	....	....	....
.....	....	.....	....	....	....
.477	1/1,001	.0000	.0000000	.00000	.00000
.478	1/1,001	.0001	.0000001	.00001	.00001
.....	....	.....	....	....	....
.....	....	.....	....	....	....
.597	1/1,001	.0305	.0000305	.00305	.08323
.598	1/1,001	.0314	.0000314	.00314	.08637
.599	1/1,001	.0323	.0000323	.00323	.08960
.600	1/1,001	.0332	.0000332	.00332	.09292
.601	1/1,001	.0341	.0000341	.00341	.09633
.602	1/1,001	.0351	.0000351	.00351	.09984
.603	1/1,001	.0360	.0000360	.00360	.10344
.604	1/1,001	.0370	.0000370	.00370	.10714
.605	1/1,001	.0379	.0000379	.00379	.11093
.606	1/1,001	.0389	.0000389	.00389	.11482
.....	....	.....	....	....	....
.....	....	.....	....	....	....
.825	1/1,001	.0001	.0000001	.00001	1.00000
.826	1/1,001	.0000	.0000000	.00000	1.00000
.....	....	.....	....	....	....
.....	....	.....	....	....	....
.999	1/1,001	.0000	.0000000	.00000	1.00000
1.000	1/1,001	.0000	.0000000	.00000	1.00000
	1		.9990010 = P(99 → 66)	1.00000	

This implies that a graph of the posterior mass function defined by Column 5 of Table 11.2 would be identical in shape to a graph of the sample likelihood function; the only difference between the two graphs would be one of vertical scale. The sample likelihood function for our present example, where $n = 99$ and $r = 66$, has already been graphed in Figure 11.3D on page 431, and the reader can verify that this same curve, when referred to the left- rather than the right-hand vertical scale in the figure, shows the posterior probabilities in Column 5 of Table 11.2.

What we have observed in this example will clearly be true in any case where the decision maker assigns a uniform prior distribution to $\bar{p}$.

1 If the decision maker's prior distribution of $\bar{p}$ is uniform, then his posterior mass function is identical to his sample likelihood function except for a vertical scale factor which does not depend on p.

And because sample likelihoods depend only on n, r, and p when sampling is equiprobable with replacement, we can also say that:

2 If the decision maker's prior distribution of $\bar{p}$ is uniform and sampling is equiprobable with replacement, the *relative* magnitudes of his posterior probabilities for various values of $\bar{p}$ depend only on the sample statistics n and r.

11.2.3
Effect of Population Size on
the Posterior Mass Function

From the conclusion just reached, it is clear that the shape of a graph of the posterior mass function that results from a uniform prior distribution of $\bar{p}$ and equiprobable sampling with replacement depends on the sample statistics n and r. Our next task is to show that it ordinarily does *not* depend to an appreciable extent on the one other fact required to describe the problem completely, namely the size N of the population from which the sample is taken.

To show that the population size ordinarily has a negligible effect on the shape of the posterior mass function, we have only to consider how Table 11.2 would have been altered if the population size had been $N = 500$ rather than 1,000. In this case, every other row of Table 11.2 would have been eliminated and the remaining entries in Column 2 would have been virtually doubled, but because (1) the entries in Column 2 would still all be equal, and (2) the remaining entries in Column 3 would not be changed at all, the *relative* magnitudes of the remaining entries in Columns 4 and 5 would be left completely unchanged.

The effect of population size on the posterior mass function is shown graphically in Figure 11.4, where the reader can see that the *shape* of the posterior mass function is exactly the same when $N = 500$ as when $N = 1,000$, even though its height is twice as great because the total probability is spread out over only half as many possible values of $\bar{p}$.

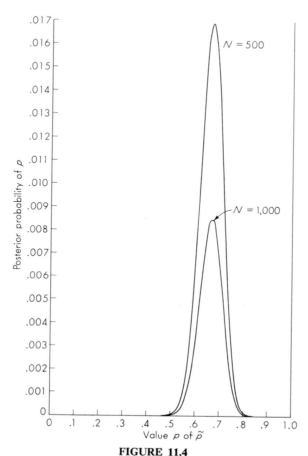

FIGURE 11.4

Effect of Population Size on a Posterior Mass Function

11.2.4
Effect of Population Size
on the Posterior Cumulative Function

Having shown that population size affects the height but not the shape of the posterior mass function of $\tilde{p}$, we next show that population size ordinarily has virtually no effect at all on the posterior cumulative function. To do so, we have only to consider in more detail how Table 11.2 would have been altered if the population size had been $N = 500$ rather than 1,000.

As we have already seen, substitution of $N = 500$ for $N = 1,000$ would have meant that (1) every other individual posterior probability in Column 5 of Table 11.2 would have been eliminated, and (2) every remaining individual posterior probability would have been virtually doubled. It follows at once that while (3) every other cumulative posterior probability in Column 6 of Table 11.2 would have been eliminated, (4) every remaining cumulative posterior probability would have been left virtually unchanged. Each cumulative probability would have been the sum of only half as many individual probabilities as before, but each of the individual probabilities in the sum would have been just about twice as large as before. A smooth graph of the posterior cumulative function for the case where $N = 500$ would be virtually indistinguishable from a smooth graph of that function for the cases where $N = 1,000$.

The same conclusion can be reached by inspection of the graphs of the mass functions for the two cases in Figure 11.4 if we recall that a smooth graph of any mass function simply traces out the tops of the bars that would appear in an exact graph of the function (cf. Figure 7.3A on page 230). The cumulative posterior probability that $\tilde{p}$ is equal, say, to .600 or less is the total height of the bars in an exact graph at all values of $\tilde{p}$ up to and including the bar at $p = .600$. Because reducing the population size from 1,000 to 500 eliminates half the bars in an exact graph of the mass function but virtually doubles the height of each remaining bar, the total height of all bars up to and including the bar at $p = .600$ (or any other specified value of $\tilde{p}$) remains virtually unchanged.

One word of caution is required before we generalize from this example. Our conclusion that a change in the population size would have no appreciable effect on the posterior cumulative function would hold if we changed the population size from 1,000 to, say, 2,000 or 20,000 rather than 500, and it would hold if we changed the population size to, say, 200; but it would *not* hold if we changed the population size to some very low value like 10. In this case, the fact that the likelihood $P(99 \rightarrow 66 | p)$ is virtually zero for any p below .478 or above .825 would lead to concentration of virtually all the posterior probability on just four possible values of $\tilde{p}$, namely, .5, .6, .7, and .8, and most of it would be on the middle two of these values. The corresponding cumulative function would not be at all correctly represented by a smooth graph calculated for the case where $N = 1,000$ and the posterior probability is smoothly spread out over hundreds of possible values of $\tilde{p}$.

With this reservation in mind, we reach the following general conclusion. If (1) prior to sampling the decision maker assigned a uniform prior distribution to $\tilde{p}$—i.e., if he assigned equal prior probabilities to the values $0/N$, $1/N$, $2/N$, ..., N/N, and (2) N is reasonably large relative to n, then the cumulative function that he should assign to $\tilde{p}$ posterior to equiprobable sampling with replacement can be calculated without reference to the exact value of N; it depends essentially on only the uniformity of the prior distribution and the statistics n and r which describe the sample outcome.

11.2.5
Beta Cumulative Functions

The conclusion reached just above shows that in any situation where the decision maker's prior distribution of $\tilde{p}$ is uniform, where sampling is equiprobable with replacement, and where the population size N is large relative to the number of

```
>DO PART 14

            B = 67
            C = 101
   FIRST P: .597    STEP: .001    LAST P: .606

        P       PROB
      .597      .082
      .598      .085
      .599      .088
      .600      .091
      .601      .095
      .602      .098
      .603      .102
      .604      .105
      .605      .109
      .606      .113
   >
```

FIGURE 11.5

Selected Points on the Beta Cumulative Function with Parameters $B = 67$, $C = 101$

sample observations n, there is no need to use the exact value of N in computing the posterior cumulative function of $\bar{p}$. A computer program designed for an arbitrarily chosen N which is large relative to n, or a table computed for such an N, could be used for *any* N that is large relative to n.

What is more important, no material inaccuracy would result from using the calculus to determine the limiting form that the posterior cumulative function approaches as the population size N "approaches infinity" and then designing a computer program that would evaluate this limiting form of the cumulative function. Because the limiting form of the cumulative function is actually much easier to evaluate than the cumulative function for any large finite N, this is what is actually done in practice.

The limiting form of the cumulative function that results from a uniform prior distribution of $\bar{p}$ and any particular pair of sample statistics n and r obtained by equiprobable sampling with replacement is called a ≪beta cumulative function≫ with parameters

$$B = r + 1, \qquad C = n + 2.$$

In the example we have been discussing, where $n = 99$ and $r = 66$, the parameters of the beta cumulative function that approximates the exact posterior cumulative function are $B = 66 + 1 = 67$ and $C = 99 + 2 = 101$.

In Figure 11.5, we show values of this function for selected arguments p as calculated by a time-sharing computer using a general-purpose program called *Betatail*.[1] The time required to calculate these "beta approximations" was only a small fraction of the time it took the same computer to calculate the exact cumulative probabilities in the last column of Table 11.2 on page 433, and the reader can verify that the largest error in the beta approximations is only about .002.

---

[1] Underlined material in Figure 11.5 was typed by the user; everything else was typed by the computer. For a description of this program, see the publication mentioned on page vi of the Preface.

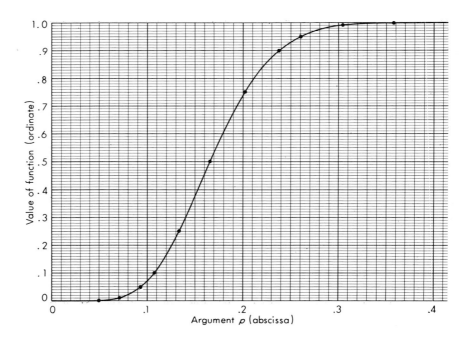

FIGURE 11.6

Beta Cumulative Function with Parameters $B = 9$, $C = 53$

If the population size had been 10,000 or more, rather than 1,000, the beta approximations would be virtually exact.

For use by those who do not have ready access to a time-sharing computer, a table from which it is possible to obtain a number of points on the graph of any beta cumulative function with integral parameters B and C appears as Table T3 in the collection of tables at the end of this volume. This table is an "inverse" table in the sense that, instead of giving the function values (ordinates) which correspond to selected arguments (abscissas), it gives the abscissas which correspond to selected ordinates.

For example, consider the first row and the row for $B = 9$, $C = 53$ on page 681 of the table. The first row shows the selected ordinates, namely .001, .01, .05, .1, . . . , .999. The row for $B = 9$, $C = 53$ describes the beta cumulative function with these parameters by giving the abscissa which corresponds to each of these ordinates. It tells us, for example, that .1072 is the abscissa corresponding to an ordinate of .1—i.e., the curve has height .1 over the point .1072 on the horizontal axis. All the points on the graph of the beta cumulative function with $B = 9$, $C = 53$ which can be read from Table T3 are plotted as heavy dots in Figure 11.6, and a complete graph of the function has been constructed by fairing a smooth curve through the plotted points.

11.2.6
Recapitulation:
the Posterior Distribution of $\tilde{p}$
When the Prior Distribution Is Uniform

What we have said thus far about the posterior distribution of $\tilde{p}$ when the prior distribution is uniform can be summarized as follows:

■ Suppose that a sample of n observations containing r successes has been taken from a population of size N by equiprobable sampling with replacement. If (1) prior to sampling the decision maker assessed a uniform prior distribution of $\tilde{p}$—i.e., if he assigned equal prior probabilities to the values $0/N$, $1/N$, $2/N$, . . . , N/N, and (2) N is reasonably large relative to n, then the cumulative function that the decision maker should assign to $\tilde{p}$ posterior to sampling is almost identical to a beta cumulative function with parameters

$$B = r + 1, \qquad C = n + 2.$$

Any desired cumulative probability or fractile under a distribution with a beta cumulative function can be found directly by use of the computer program *Betatail*. Alternatively, a graph of the complete cumulative function can be constructed by fairing a smooth curve through points read from Table T3, after which any desired cumulative probability or fractile can be read from this graph.

The mean of a distribution with a beta cumulative function can be very easily found by making use of the mathematically demonstrable fact that:

■ If the probability distribution of a discrete UQ has a beta cumulative function with parameters B and C, the mean of the distribution is almost exactly equal to B/C.

11.2.7
Nearly Uniform Prior Distributions

In the previous section we saw that if a decision maker's prior distribution of $\tilde{p}$ is uniform, then the posterior distribution that results from equiprobable sampling with replacement will have a cumulative function that can be closely approximated by a beta cumulative function with parameters $B = r + 1$, $C = n + 2$. We shall now show that this same approximation will be accurate enough for practical purposes whenever the decision maker's prior distribution satisfies certain qualitative conditions which are much less stringent than the condition of strict uniformity.

To start with an example, let us compare the posterior mass function that results from the sample event $99 \rightarrow 66$ and a uniform prior distribution with the posterior mass function that results from that same sample event and the nonuniform prior distribution whose mass function was graphed in Figure 11.3D on page 431. The posterior mass function that results from the nonuniform prior distribution is described by the curve labelled "posterior" in that figure; the posterior mass function that results from a uniform prior distribution is described by the curve labelled "likelihood", as we saw in Section 11.2.2; and the thing to observe is that there is very little difference between them.

The reason why these two posterior mass functions are nearly the same is easy to see if we recall that the height of the graph of any posterior mass function at any value of $\bar{p}$ is proportional to the product of the heights of the prior mass function and the sample likelihood function at that value of $\bar{p}$. With this fact in mind, we observe first of all that because the height of the sample likelihood function in Figure 11.3D is virtually zero outside an interval extending approximately from $p = .50$ to $p = .80$, the height of the posterior mass function must also be virtually zero outside this interval unless the prior mass function has some extremely unusual shape. We then see that inside the interval from $p = .50$ to $p = .80$, the prior mass function actually shown in Figure 11.3D is *nearly* uniform (nearly flat) *relative to the sample likelihood function*, with the result that the posterior mass function has nearly the same shape that it would have if the prior mass function were strictly uniform over the interval from $p = .50$ to $p = .80$.

Now consider any situation in which a decision maker wishes to assess his distribution of an uncertain population fraction $\bar{p}$ after n observations made by equiprobable sampling with replacement have yielded r successes. If in any such situation we were to graph the sample likelihood function, there would be *some* interval on the horizontal axis outside which this function would have virtually zero height. Because the location and width of this interval depend on the sample statistics n and r, we shall call the interval $I_{n,r}$; from Figure 11.3D we already know that when $N = 99$ and $r = 66$, the interval $I_{n,r}$ extends from about .50 to about .80 on the p axis. What we have learned from the example of Figure 11.3D is that:

■ If prior to observing r successes in n observations the decision maker (1) did not assign *extremely* high probabilities to any values of $\bar{p}$ outside $I_{n,r}$, and (2) assigned *roughly* equal probabilities to all values of $\bar{p}$ inside $I_{n,r}$, then the posterior distribution he should assign to $\bar{p}$ will be almost the same as the posterior distribution that would result from a strictly uniform prior distribution, and therefore its cumulative function can be very closely approximated by a beta cumulative function with parameters

$$B = r + 1, \qquad C = n + 2.$$

In order to decide in any particular situation whether he can thus proceed just as if his prior distribution were strictly uniform, the decision maker must first identify the left and right ends of the interval $I_{n,r}$, which depends only on the sample he has taken, not on his prior distribution. This he can do very easily by simply using Table T3 to find the .001 and .999 fractiles of the posterior distribution that he would assess if his prior distribution were in fact strictly uniform, i.e., the distribution defined by a beta cumulative function with parameters $B = r + 1$ and $C = n + 2$. If, for example, $n = 99$ and $r = 66$ as in the example of Figure 11.3D, then he can compute $B = 67$, $C = 101$, and use Table T3 to find that the fractiles in question are respectively .52 and .81, in close agreement with the impression given by the graph of the sample likelihood function in Figure 11.3D.

Having identified the interval $I_{n,r}$ for his particular n and r, the decision maker is in a position to decide whether the prior distribution he would actually assign to $\tilde{p}$ is or is not such that a beta cumulative function with parameters $B = r + 1$ and $C = n + 2$ will be an acceptable approximation to the cumulative function of the posterior distribution that he should now assign to $\tilde{p}$. As we have already said, the approximation will be acceptable provided that the decision maker (1) would not assign extremely high prior probabilities to any values of $\tilde{p}$ outside $I_{n,r}$, and (2) would assign roughly equal prior probabilities to all values of $\tilde{p}$ inside $I_{n,r}$.

As a rule of thumb, prior probabilities can usually be considered as "roughly equal" if the greatest of them is no more than four times the least. The rule itself is a very rough one, but fortunately its roughness rarely matters. In most situations, either it is completely clear that the decision maker's prior information is totally negligible in relation to the information provided by the sample, in which case his prior probabilities should be treated as "roughly equal" even without being formally assessed, or else it is completely clear that his prior information is by no means negligible, in which case he must assess his prior probabilities and actually compute his posterior distribution of $\tilde{p}$.

11.2.8
Successive Samples

We saw in Section 10.6 that when a decision maker has taken more than one sample from the same population by equiprobable sampling with replacement, he can "pool" the observations in all of his samples by computing the total number of observations he has made and the total number of successes he has observed and then calculate his posterior distribution exactly as if the pooled observations had all been taken in a single sample.

We now remark that pooling is not merely a convenient computational device; it is also the only correct way of testing whether a beta approximation to the posterior cumulative function will be acceptably accurate. Such an approximation will be acceptable, as we have already said, if and only if the decision maker's prior distribution is at least nearly uniform relative to the sample likelihood function. Because the tightness of the likelihood function increases with

n, as can be seen by examining the likelihood curves in Figure 11.3 (pages 430 and 431), the decision maker's prior distribution of $\tilde{p}$ may be nearly uniform relative to the likelihood function of the pooled sample even though it cannot be considered nearly uniform relative to the likelihood function of any one of the constituent samples.

11.3

ESTIMATES OF $\tilde{p}$

When the terminal values that will result from acts in a well defined decision problem depend on the uncertain fraction $\tilde{p}$ of successes in some population, and when the degree of uncertainty about $\tilde{p}$ is substantial, the problem cannot in general be carefully analyzed unless the decision maker assesses his complete distribution of $\tilde{p}$ and the analyst uses this complete distribution to compute the decision maker's certainty-equivalent terminal value for every immediate act that is under consideration.[2] In actual business practice, however, most samples are taken, not to provide information that will be used in a well defined decision problem that is immediately at hand, but to provide "background information" that will be useful in the businessman's informal thinking about some general problem area. In such thinking, the businessman cannot practically work with his complete distribution of $\tilde{p}$, or of any other UQ for that matter. What he must do and does do is select some one possible value of $\tilde{p}$ as an "estimate" of $\tilde{p}$ and think mostly in terms of this specific value.

Even while thinking in terms of his estimate, however, the businessman should not forget that it is only an estimate and may be substantially in error. At the same time that he is reaching tentative conclusions based on treating his estimate of $\tilde{p}$ as if it were the true value of $\tilde{p}$, he should keep in the back of his mind some simple quantitative measure of the extent to which he is really uncertain about the true value of $\tilde{p}$. Then if he reaches a stage in his thinking where this measure of his uncertainty suggests that continuing to treat his estimate as a certainty might lead him seriously astray, he can consider the desirability of acquiring more sample information and using it to calculate a new estimate of $\tilde{p}$ that will be subject to less uncertainty.

In the present section we shall first discuss the problem of making a "reasonable" estimate of $\tilde{p}$ when one or more samples have already been taken. We shall then discuss simple quantitative measures of the extent of the uncertainty about the true value of $\tilde{p}$ that accompanies such an estimate; and finally we shall show how to evaluate the reduction in uncertainty that will result from taking another sample of any given size.

---

[2] The only exception is the one we considered in Section 8.4. If preference is linear in terminal value and if the terminal value of every immediate act is linear in $\tilde{p}$, then $\tilde{p}$ can be treated as if it were certain to be equal to the decision maker's expectation of $\tilde{p}$; and if in addition the decision maker can make a good direct assessment of his expectation of $\tilde{p}$ because his distribution of $\tilde{p}$ is unimodal and symmetric, then there is no need for him to assess his complete distribution of $\tilde{p}$.

11.3.1
Calculation of an Estimate of $\tilde{p}$

If a businessman who has obtained sample information bearing on the value of $\tilde{p}$ wants to work with an estimate rather than a complete distribution of $\tilde{p}$, common sense tells us that he should choose as his estimate a value of $\tilde{p}$ that in some sense lies near the "middle" of the posterior distribution of $\tilde{p}$ that he either has assessed or would assess if he took the trouble. Such a value is sometimes called a ≪central≫ value under his posterior distribution of p; the most common examples are the mean and the median, and also the mode if the distribution is unimodal and is not extremely "skewed" to one side or the other.

Common sense does not tell us, however, precisely which one of the many "central" values under a posterior distribution of $\tilde{p}$ should be selected as an estimate of $\tilde{p}$, nor is there any more refined argument that will lead to a definite answer to this question. If the businessman were about to use his estimate in some well defined way to reach a decision in a well defined decision problem, it would be possible to calculate his expectation for the loss that might result from choosing any particular value as an estimate, and the best estimate would then be the one for which the expected loss was least; but when a well defined decision problem is at hand, it is much easier to leave estimates completely out of the picture and carry out a straightforward analysis based on the decision maker's complete distribution of $\tilde{p}$. The only possible conclusion is that in any situation where it makes sense to use an estimate at all, the final choice of the particular central value that is to be used as the estimate is necessarily arbitrary. The natural candidates are the mean, the median, and the mode, and in general any one of them is as likely to be good or bad as any other.

Before any one of these "reasonable" estimates of $\tilde{p}$ can be computed, the businessman's posterior distribution of $\tilde{p}$ must itself be computed, but this computation is trivial in most situations where use of an estimate is legitimate and a sample of any substantial size has been taken. In such situations, the information obtained from the sample usually overwhelms whatever opinions the businessman had about $\tilde{p}$ prior to sampling, in the sense that the distribution he (would have) assigned to $\tilde{p}$ prior to sampling is nearly uniform relative to the likelihood function of the sample; and we already know that when this is so, the businessman's posterior distribution of $\tilde{p}$ can be "computed" by merely asserting that it has a beta cumulative function with parameters $B = r + 1$ and $C = n + 2$.

As regards the computation of an estimate of $\tilde{p}$ under a distribution with a beta cumulative function, we have already seen that the mean of such a distribution is approximately $B/C = (r + 1)/(n + 2)$, and it can be shown that its mode is approximately $(B - 1)/(C - 2) = r/n$. The fraction of successes in the sample is the most probable value for the fraction of successes in the population. The median of the distribution, on the other hand, is not given by any formula, and although it can be easily looked up in Table T3, doing so is not worth the trouble. Since there is no particular reason for preferring any one central value to another, we might as well choose the value that is easiest to calculate from the sample statistics, namely the mode.[3] To sum up:

■ In any situation where (1) it is legitimate to use any estimate of $\tilde{p}$ in place of a complete distribution of $\tilde{p}$, and (2) the distribution which the businessman (would have) assigned to $\tilde{p}$ prior to sampling is nearly uniform relative to the likelihood function of a (possibly pooled) sample that has already been taken, the businessman can usually take the fraction r/n of successes in the (pooled) sample as an estimate of the uncertain fraction $\tilde{p}$ of successes in the population.

Before leaving the subject of choice of an estimate of $\tilde{p}$, we remind the reader that it is *not* true that the sample fraction r/n is *always* a reasonable estimate of the population fraction p. It is reasonable only under very special conditions, and the only conditions under which we have shown it to be reasonable are those in which the decision maker's prior distribution of $\tilde{p}$ is nearly uniform relative to the sample likelihood function.

11.3.2
Measurement of Uncertainty about $\tilde{p}$

We have already said that although a businessman may quite legitimately treat an estimate of $\tilde{p}$ as if it were the true value of $\tilde{p}$ in much of his preliminary thinking about some problem area, he should at the same time keep in the back of his mind some simple quantitative measure of the real extent of his uncertainty about the true value of $\tilde{p}$. A measure that is suitable for this purpose in many situations is the distance between two limits between which the businessman feels "reasonably sure" that the true value of $\tilde{p}$ must lie, and such limits can be found by simply selecting two suitable fractiles of the businessman's posterior distribution of $\tilde{p}$.

For example, suppose that a businessman has observed 4 successes in 25 observations made by equiprobable sampling with replacement, and suppose that his prior distribution was nearly uniform relative to the likelihood function of this sample, so that the cumulative function of his posterior distribution of $\tilde{p}$ is beta with parameters $B = 5$, $C = 27$. By Table T3, the .01 and .99 fractiles of the businessman's posterior distribution of $\tilde{p}$ are .0520 and .3849, implying that he is "98 % sure" that the true value of $\tilde{p}$ lies within the interval of length .3849 —

---

[3] In Section 8.3.7, we recommended use of median estimates rather than modal estimates, but the circumstances were quite different from those we are discussing here. There we were discussing situations in which the businessman wished to work with the complete distribution of some UQ, and we observed that if he started from a median rather than a modal estimate of the UQ, he would find the complete distribution of the UQ easier to assess. Here, the businessman has already assessed his complete distribution of $\tilde{p}$ but wants to work with an estimate instead.

$.0520 \doteq .33$ that has .0520 and .3849 as its end points. If the businessman feels that 98% sure is sure enough, then .33 is a good rough measure of the extent of his uncertainty about $\tilde{p}$.

If the businessman does not think that 98% sure is sure enough, he might measure his uncertainty about $\tilde{p}$ by the distance between two more extreme fractiles of his posterior distribution of $\tilde{p}$. If, for example, he wants an interval within which he can be 99.8% sure that the true value of $\tilde{p}$ actually lies, he can read from Table T3 that the .001 and .999 fractiles of his posterior distribution of $\tilde{p}$ are respectively .0304 and .4621, and he can then take $.4621 - .0304 \doteq .43$ as a measure of his uncertainty about $\tilde{p}$. Exactly which fractiles should be chosen as limits between which the businessman feels "reasonably" sure that the true value of $\tilde{p}$ must lie depends on the seriousness of the loss that may result if he assumes that the true value is between the limits when in fact it is not.

11.3.3
Reduction in Uncertainty to Be
Anticipated from Further Sampling

Suppose now that a businessman has calculated both a point estimate of $\tilde{p}$ based on sample information and the length of an interval within which he feels reasonably sure that the true value of $\tilde{p}$ must lie; and suppose that he feels that his uncertainty about the true value of $\tilde{p}$, as measured by the length of this interval, is uncomfortably great. By acquiring additional sample information he can tighten his distribution of $\tilde{p}$ and thus reduce his uncertainty about $\tilde{p}$, but doing so will cost money and therefore before reaching a final decision about further sampling he would like to know how much of a reduction in uncertainty he can anticipate from a new sample of any given size.

Answering this question is very difficult in the general case, but it is very easy whenever the information obtained from the sample or samples that the businessman has already taken is so great relative to his prior information about $\tilde{p}$ that his current distribution of $\tilde{p}$ has a beta cumulative function. To see how the effect of a new sample on the businessman's uncertainty about $\tilde{p}$ can be calculated when this condition is met, we return to our businessman who has already observed $r = 4$ successes in $n = 25$ observations made by equiprobable sampling with replacement and whose prior distribution of $\tilde{p}$ was such that his current distribution has a beta cumulative function with parameters $B = 5$, $C = 27$; we assume that he has finally decided to take the difference between the .01 and .99 fractiles of his distribution as a measure of his uncertainty about $\tilde{p}$, so that his current uncertainty is

$$p_{.99} - p_{.01} = .3849 - .0520 \doteq .33;$$

and we assume that he is now trying to decide whether he should take a "new" sample of size 50 in order to reduce his uncertainty about $\tilde{p}$.

If this businessman does take the proposed new sample, he will be able to compute his distribution of $\tilde{p}$ posterior to this sample by first pooling it with the sample that has already been taken and then assigning to $\tilde{p}$ a beta cumulative function with parameters determined by the statistics of the pooled sample; and it follows that if the businessman could know in advance how many successes there would be in the new sample, he could easily compute its effect on his uncertainty about $\tilde{p}$. If, for example, the fact that 4/25 of the 25 members of the pilot sample were successes implied that $(4/25) \times 50 = 8$ of the 50 members of the new sample would be successes, then the businessman would know that pooling the new sample with the old would yield statistics

$$n = 25 + 50 = 75, \qquad r = 4 + 8 = 12;$$

therefore he would know that his new distribution of $\tilde{p}$ would be beta with parameters $B = 13$, $C = 77$; and since by Table T3 the .01 and .99 fractiles of this distribution are respectively .0836 and .2791, he would know that his uncertainty about $\tilde{p}$ would be reduced from its current value of .33 to $.2791 - .0836 \doteq .20$.

In actual fact, of course, the fraction of successes in the new sample is not certain to be equal to the fraction of successes in the sample that has already been taken, and therefore the businessman cannot know exactly how much uncertainty about $\tilde{p}$ will remain after the new sample has been taken. If the proposed new sample of size 50 yields 5 rather than 8 successes, the parameters of the resulting distribution of $\tilde{p}$ will be $B = 10$, $C = 77$ instead of $B = 13$, $C = 77$, and by Table T3 the businessman's uncertainty about $\tilde{p}$ will therefore be $.2315 - .0562 \doteq .18$ rather than .20 as it would be if there were 8 successes. If the new sample contains 11 successes, similar calculations show that the businessman's uncertainty will be $.3248 - .1129 \doteq .21$; and so forth.

But although these calculations show that the businessman cannot know exactly how great his uncertainty about $\tilde{p}$ will be after the new sample has been taken, at the same time they show that he can be quite sure approximately how great his uncertainty will be. Intuition suggests, and it can be shown, that the fraction of successes in the proposed new sample of size 50 is not likely to be *very* different from the fraction $4/25 = .16$ in the sample that has already been taken; and we have just seen that if the fraction of successes in the new sample is anywhere in the fairly broad interval from $5/50 = .10$ to $11/50 = .22$, the resulting uncertainty about $\tilde{p}$ will be somewhere within the quite narrow interval from .18 to .21.

Given this information, the businessman will almost certainly feel that the "worth" of the proposed new sample to him is practically the same as it would be if he could be sure that it would reduce his uncertainty about $\tilde{p}$ to exactly .20; and this means that the businessman could have evaluated the proposed new sample by simply (1) computing the uncertainty about $\tilde{p}$ that would result if the fraction of successes in the new sample turned out to be equal to the fraction in the sample already taken, and then (2) treating this estimate of the posterior uncertainty as if it were a known value. Generalizing, we conclude that:

■ In most situations where (1) sample information about a two-valued population is to be used only as "background" information, and (2) a moderately large sample has already been taken, the uncertainty about $\bar{p}$ that will remain after a new sample has been taken can be estimated closely enough for the purpose at hand by calculating it as if the fraction of successes in the new sample would be as nearly equal as possible to the fraction of successes in the original sample.

We say "as nearly equal as possible" because the number of successes in the new sample must be an integer.

11.3.4
Graphs of Uncertainty vs. Cost

So far we have considered only the problem of evaluating the uncertainty about $\bar{p}$ that will remain after a new sample of some specified size has been taken. In order to decide how large an additional sample to take, if any, the businessman will want to compare the cost of additional samples of various sizes with the estimated uncertainty about $\bar{p}$ that will remain after taking such samples.

For example, consider again our businessman who has already observed $r = 4$ successes in $n = 25$ observations and whose prior distribution was nearly uniform relative to the likelihood function of this sample; suppose that he is thinking of making additional sample observations in order to reduce his uncertainty about $\bar{p}$ as measured by the distance between the .01 and .99 fractiles of his distribution of $\bar{p}$; and suppose further that each additional sample observation that he takes will cost \$5.

If this businessman does take a new sample and then pools it with the one he has already taken, his resulting distribution of $\bar{p}$ will have a beta cumulative function with parameters

$$B = r^* + 1, \qquad C = n^* + 2,$$

where r^* and n^* are the statistics of the pooled sample, and therefore we can describe some of the choices open to him by proceeding as follows to construct Table 11.3 below.

1. In Column 1 we show a selection of possible sizes for a new sample.

2. In Column 2, we compute the number of successes that there would be in the new sample if the fraction of successes in that sample were equal to the fraction 4/25 in the sample already taken.

3. In Columns 3 and 4 we show the statistics r^* and n^* of the pooled sample implied by the entries in Columns 1 and 2.

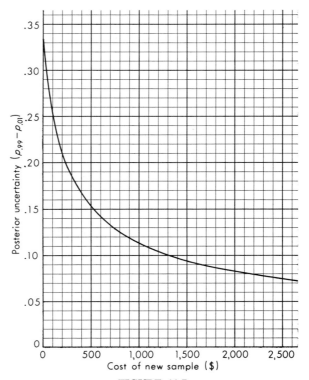

FIGURE 11.7

Cost of Sampling and Posterior Uncertainty about $\bar{p}$

4. In Column 5 we show the uncertainty $(p_{.99} - p_{.01})$ about $\bar{p}$ under a distribution having a beta cumulative function with parameters $B = r^* + 1$, $C = n^* + 2$.

5. Finally, in Column 6 we show the cost of the new sample.

TABLE 11.3

Cost of Sampling and Posterior Uncertainty about $\bar{p}$

1	2	3	4	5	6
New Sample		*Pooled Sample*		*Posterior*	*Cost*
Actual	*Estimated*	*Actual*	*Estimated*	*Uncertainty*	*of New*
n	*r*	*n**	*r**	$p_{.99} - p_{.01}$	*Sample*
0	0	25	4	$.385 - .052 = .333$	\$ 0
25	4	50	8	$.310 - .072 = .238$	125
50	8	75	12	$.279 - .084 = .195$	250
100	16	125	20	$.249 - .097 = .152$	500
150	24	175	28	$.234 - .105 = .129$	750
200	32	225	36	$.220 - .106 = .114$	1,000
300	48	325	52	$.209 - .115 = .094$	1,500
400	64	425	68	$.203 - .120 = .083$	2,000
500	80	525	84	$.199 - .124 = .075$	2,500

Having made these calculations for selected new sample sizes, we construct the graph in Figure 11.7 by first plotting each uncertainty in Table 11.3 against the corresponding cost and then fairing a curve through the plotted points. From this graph the businessman can read an estimate of the uncertainty about $\tilde{p}$ that will remain after spending any amount between \$0 and \$2,500 on additional sampling; it is now up to him to decide how much he wants to spend.

11.4

BERNOULLI PROCESSES

Besides being frequently interested in the fraction of successes in some population of finite size, a businessman is frequently interested in the fraction of successes that would be generated in the long run by some physical process that generates successes and failures. As an example, consider an automatic machine that produces pieces each of which will be classified as either a defective or a good piece. The fraction $\tilde{p}$ of defectives (or "successes") that this machine would produce in the long run is a quantity of considerable interest to a businessman, and he may wish to take a sample of the output of the machine in order to get information about $\tilde{p}$.

When a businessman believes that a particular physical process behaves like what is called a "Bernoulli" process, the sampling theory that we have already studied applies without any modifications whatever to samples from the output of the process. In the present section we shall define a Bernoulli process and show why this is so.

11.4.1

Definition of a Bernoulli Process

Before considering physical processes of the kind that appear in practical business decision problems, let us consider a process that consists of rolling an irregularly shaped die and classifying the outcome of each roll or trial as a success if ace turns up, a failure if it does not; and let us assume that both the die and the surface on which it is rolled are made of material that suffer absolutely no wear as the die is rolled repeatedly. Concerning such a process a decision maker might believe that:

1 If the trials were repeated indefinitely, the fraction of all trials resulting in successes would ultimately become and remain arbitrarily close to some definite number p;

2 The trials would be indistinguishable, so that if the decision maker knew the long-run fraction of successes p, he would assign probability p to success on any trial, regardless of either (1) the number of previous trials or (2) the pattern of successes and failures on previous trials.

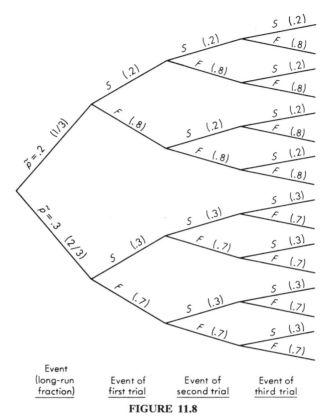

Event
(long-run
fraction)

Event of
first trial

Event of
second trial

Event of
third trial

FIGURE 11.8

Probability Diagram for Three Trials of a Bernoulli Process

If a decision maker does hold these views about a two-valued process, then for him that process is by definition a ≪Bernoulli process≫.

Observe that this definition of a Bernoulli process does not require that the decision maker actually know the numerical value of the long-run fraction of successes p. The definition involves only (1) the decision maker's belief that the fraction of successes would in the long run become and remain equal to *some* definite number p, and (2) the probabilities that he would assign to various events *if* he knew what this number actually was. To say the same thing in different words, the definition involves the conditional probabilities that the decision maker would assign to various events *given* any particular p, not the probabilities he would assign to these events without conditioning on p.

The implications of the definition of a Bernoulli process can be seen by reference to the probability diagram shown as Figure 11.8, where the first fork indicates (unrealistically) that a decision maker believes that the long-run fraction p of successes that would be generated by a certain Bernoulli process must be either .2 or .3, although he does not know which, while the remaining forks describe the possible events, success and failure, of the first three trials of the process. The probability assigned by the decision maker to each branch (event) in the diagram is shown in parentheses.

The probabilities on the branches of the first fork in the diagram show that the decision maker has assigned (1) unconditional probability $1/3$ to the event that *in the long run* .2 of all trials would result in successes, and (2) unconditional probability $2/3$ to the event that in the long run .3 of all trials would result in failures. Observe that these events have nothing to do with the events S and F of any one, particular trial.

The probabilities the decision maker assigns to the events S and F on each of the first three trials of the process appear on the forks which follow the first fork in the diagram, and as usual the probabilities assigned to any one of these later forks are assessed conditionally on all events on the path leading from the origin of the diagram to the base of the fork in question. That the process to which the diagram applies is a Bernoulli process follows from the fact that the probability assigned to S on any fork in the diagram depends only on the value of the long-run fraction $\tilde{p}$ which precedes the fork and is equal to that value of $\tilde{p}$. The probability assigned to S on any fork does *not* depend on either the number of branches preceding that fork or the pattern of S's and F's which appears on those branches.

11.4.2
Application to Real Processes

It is only rarely if ever that a decision maker will feel that a real two-valued process could be operated indefinitely without undergoing a substantial change in its characteristics, but despite this fact a great many of the two-valued processes that appear in business decision problems can legitimately be treated as Bernoulli processes in analyzing those problems.

Suppose, for example, that a decision problem involves a punch press whose output will be classified into defectives (successes) and good pieces (failures), and suppose that the situation is such that at most 10,000 pieces will be turned out by the press. To decide whether the press can legitimately be treated as a Bernoulli process, the decision maker can imagine that after producing 10,000 pieces, the press will be restored to exactly the same condition that it was in at the beginning, after which another 10,000 pieces will be produced, the press will again be restored to its original condition, and so forth ad infinitum. If this imaginary process would be a Bernoulli process in the judgment of the decision maker, then he can treat the real process as being a Bernoulli process as far as the first 10,000 trials are concerned, since the fact that the process will not really be restored to its original condition after 10,000 pieces have been produced should obviously have no effect at all on the probability the decision maker assigns to any event involving only the 10,000 trials that will actually be made.

It is very important, on the other hand, to realize that by no means every two-valued process can legitimately be treated as a Bernoulli process. Use of the Bernoulli model is legitimate only when the decision maker's beliefs about the process (or about a periodically restored version of the process) satisfy the two defining conditions that were stated in Section 11.4.1, or at least come so close to satisfying these conditions that the Bernoulli model can be accepted as an adequately accurate approximation. The first of the two conditions (existence of a long-run process fraction) rarely gives rise to mistakes in practice, but the two parts of the second condition are frequently overlooked, and therefore we shall now examine them more closely.

1 A physical process cannot be treated as a Bernoulli process unless it is ≪stable≫ in the sense that if the decision maker knew the long-run fraction p of successes, he would assign probability p to a success on any trial regardless of the *number* of trials previously made.

If a decision maker knew the long-run fraction defective p of a certain punch press but also knew or believed that the operator tended to become more careless as the day went on, he would assign a probability lower than p to "defective" early in the morning, higher than p to "defective" late in the afternoon. In this case the process is not a Bernoulli process because the process is not stable.

2 A physical process cannot be treated as a Bernoulli process unless the outcomes of successive trials are ≪independent given p≫ in the sense that if the decision maker knew the long-run fraction p of successes, he would assign probability p to success on any trial regardless of the *pattern of successes and failures* that had occurred on previous trials.

If a decision maker knew the long-run fraction defective p of a certain punch press but also knew or believed that after producing a defective the operator tended to be more careful with the next piece, he would assign a probability lower than p to "defective" on a trial following a defective, higher than p to "defective" on a trial following a good piece. If on the contrary he felt that the operator had streaks of carelessness, he would assign a probability higher than p to "defective" on a trial following a defective, lower than p to "defective" on a trial following a good piece. In either of these cases the process is not a Bernoulli process because the outcomes of successive trials are not independent given p.

11.4.3
Prior Distributions of the
Long-run Fraction $\tilde{p}$

Suppose now that a businessman is convinced that a certain physical process behaves like a Bernoulli process but is uncertain about the long-run fraction $\tilde{p}$ that characterizes the process in its present state; suppose that he wishes to assess his probability distribution of this uncertain quantity; and for the moment suppose that he has not as yet observed any successes or failures actually generated by the process in its present state. If the process is a production machine, this could be either because the machine is brand new or because it has just been set up or readjusted. In either case, the businessman would have no observations bearing directly on the long-run fraction $\tilde{p}$ that *currently* characterizes the process.

In such circumstances, the problem of assessing a probability distribution of the long-run fraction $\tilde{p}$ that characterizes a Bernoulli process is very similar to the problem of assessing a distribution of the fraction $\tilde{p}$ of successes in a finite population on which no sample observations have been made. The one difference between the two problems is that whereas the only possible values of the fraction of successes in a finite population of size N are $0/N$, $1/N$, $2/N$, etc., any real number whatever between 0 and 1 is a possible value of the fraction of successes that a process would generate in an infinitely long run. Clearly, however, no seriously wrong conclusions can result if we think about Bernoulli processes *as if* the possible values of $\tilde{p}$ were limited to some finite set of numbers such as .00000, .00001, .00002, etc.; and that is what we shall do in this introductory text.[4]

11.4.4
Posterior Distributions of the
Long-run Fraction $\tilde{p}$

Next consider the case where a businessman who wishes to assess his distribution of the long-run fraction $\tilde{p}$ that characterizes a Bernoulli process has already observed a number of trials of the process in its current state and has noted the successes and failures that were generated, so that his distribution must take account of the information about $\tilde{p}$ that is provided by these observations as well as the information that he had about $\tilde{p}$ prior to making the observations.

In this case too, it should be clear that the general nature of the procedure by which the businessman should assess his probability distribution of the long-run fraction $\tilde{p}$ will be very similar to the procedure by which he would assess his distribution of the fraction $\tilde{p}$ of successes in some finite population after observing the outcomes of a number of sample observations on the population. Because none of the available information bears directly on the probabilities that he should *now* assign to the possible values of $\tilde{p}$, he should construct a diagram of an assessment gamble with a fork at the origin showing the possible values of $\tilde{p}$ and subsequent forks showing the possible trial outcomes that he might have observed; he should assess his "prior" probabilities for the branches of this diagram; he should compute his probabilities for its end positions; and finally he should use these end-position probabilities to compute the "posterior" probabilities that he should now assign to the possible values of $\tilde{p}$ given the trial outcomes he has actually observed.

---

[4] In actual fact, our conclusions will be exact; it is only the logic by which we reach them that will be a little less than rigorous.

Figure 11.8 on page 450 shows what such a probability diagram might look like; and if we compare this diagram with Figure 10.1 on page 393, we can notice a very important similarity. In both cases, the probability assigned to the event S on any fork in the diagram is equal to the preceding value of the UQ $\tilde{p}$.

Because a probability diagram for computing a distribution of the $\tilde{p}$ that characterizes a Bernoulli process posterior to observing a number of trials of the process is thus identical to a probability diagram for computing a distribution of the fraction $\tilde{p}$ of successes in a finite population posterior to equiprobable sampling with replacement, we can conclude at once that:

- Observing r successes in n trials of a Bernoulli process should have exactly the same effect on a businessman's distribution of the long-run fraction $\tilde{p}$ that observing r successes in n observations made by equiprobable sampling with replacement would have on his distribution of the fraction $\tilde{p}$ of successes in a finite population.

As we said in the introduction to this section, all the results that we have derived earlier concerning equiprobable sampling with replacement apply without any modifications whatever to sampling from a Bernoulli process.

11.4.5
Unconditional Probabilities
for Events on the Next Trial

When we first studied the problem of assessing probabilities for events, in Chapter 6, we said that it was often useful to think of a possible event as a possible outcome of the next trial of a physical process that was capable of making an infinite number of trials under conditions indistinguishable from those surrounding the next trial. If a businessman felt that he knew the relative frequency with which the event would occur in an infinite number of such trials, he should set his probability for the event on the next trial equal to that long-run relative frequency, and even if he did not know the long-run relative frequency for certain, he should be guided by whatever he did know about it in assessing his probability for the event on the next trial.

We are now at last in a position to say something definite about just how a businessman should use his information about a process in assessing his probability for some event that may occur on the next trial of the process. If we give the name "success" to the particular event in which we are interested and call the occurrence of any other event a "failure", we see that our problem is simply one of assessing an unconditional probability for success on the next trial of a Bernoulli process; and such problems are usually best solved by proceeding as follows.

1. The businessman starts with certain "prior" judgments about the process derived from knowledge of its mechanism, experience with other processes of the same general sort, etc., and quantifies these judgments by assessing

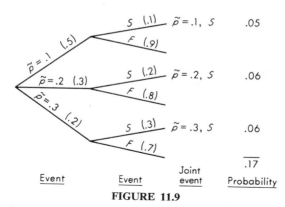

Event   Event   Joint   Probability
                        event

FIGURE 11.9

Computation of the Unconditional Probability of a Success on the Next Trial

his unconditional distribution of the fraction $\tilde{p}$ of successes that the process would generate in the long run.

2. If the businessman has observed any previous trials of the process, he next uses sampling theory to assess a revised or "posterior" unconditional distribution of $\tilde{p}$ that takes account of this sample information.

3. Now considering the "next" trial of the process, he knows that his *conditional* probability for a success, *given* any particular value p of the long-run fraction $\tilde{p}$, should be equal to p; and since he has already assessed his unconditional distribution of $\tilde{p}$, he can compute his unconditional probability for a success by constructing a probability diagram like the one in Figure 11.9 and applying Rule 2 in Section 9.3.4. If his distribution of the long-run fraction $\tilde{p}$ is defined by the probabilities that appear in parentheses on the branches of the fork at the origin of Figure 11.9, his unconditional probability for a success on the next trial is .17, as shown in the right-hand margin of the figure.

It should be observed and remembered that, as shown by this example, the calculations required to find the unconditional probability that the decision maker should assign to the event "success" on the next trial of a Bernoulli process are identical to the calculations that would be required to compute his expectation of the long-run relative frequency $\tilde{p}$ that characterizes the process. We have thus at last proved the assertion made in Section 8.4.3 that

■ A decision maker should set his probability for any event equal to his expectation of the long-run relative frequency with which the event would occur in trials made under conditions indistinguishable from present conditions.

11.5

SAMPLING WITHOUT REPLACEMENT

All the results concerning the use of sample information that we have obtained up to now have been derived on the basis of the assumption that the sample observations were obtained by equiprobable sampling with replacement. As we said earlier, this type of sampling is actually used in what is called the Monte Carlo method, but it is virtually never used in traditional applications of sampling such as acceptance sampling of lots of manufactured product, sample surveys of human populations, and so forth. In the present section we shall briefly discuss some of the sampling processes that are used in such applications.

11.5.1

**Equiprobable Sampling
without Replacement**

In the simplest applications of the general kind now under discussion, it is common practice to draw a sample in such a way that although no member of the population can be drawn more than once, every "eligible" member of the population has an equal chance of being chosen on each successive draw. This kind of sampling is known as

■ ≪Equiprobable Sampling without Replacement≫. A sampling process may be called equiprobable without replacement if, just before each successive draw is made, the decision maker would assign equal probabilities of selection to all members of the population not already selected on previous draws.

To see how the information obtained from a sample drawn by equiprobable sampling without replacement can be used in assessing a posterior distribution of the fraction $\tilde{p}$ of successes in the entire original population, let us return to the example of Section 10.2 and ask what posterior distribution Mr. Warren should have assigned to $\tilde{p}$ if his sample of three chips had been drawn without rather than with replacement.

Looking at the diagram of Mr. Warren's assessment gamble in Figure 10.2 (page 400), we see at once that the only way in which this change in assumption about the sampling process can affect Mr. Warren's posterior distribution of $\tilde{p}$ is by affecting the probabilities he assigns to the sample-outcome branches in this diagram. Once he has assigned appropriate probabilities to these branches, he can compute the probabilities of the end positions and from these compute his posterior distribution of $\tilde{p}$ by exactly the same procedure that he used before.

Whether the probabilities a decision maker should assign to the sample-outcome branches in the case of sampling without replacement should or should not be greatly different from the probabilities he should assign in the case of sampling with replacement depends on the relative sizes of the sample and the population, as we can easily see by considering the probabilities which Mr. Warren should assign to the last sample-outcome branch following the branch for $\tilde{p} = 1/10$ in Figure 10.2.

1. If the population size was $N = 20$—i.e., if there were 20 chips in Mr. Warren's bag—then given $\tilde{p} = 1/10$, there were originally 2 S's and 18 F's in the

population. If then an S and an F had been drawn on the first two draws and had not been replaced, there would have remained 1 S and 17 F's just before the last draw was made; and if Mr. Warren assigned equal probabilities of being drawn to these $1 + 17 = 18$ chips, his probability for the last sample-outcome branch following $\tilde{p} = 1/10$ in Figure 10.2 should have been $17/18 \doteq .944$. Observe that this result differs substantially from the .9 probability that he should have assigned if the chips drawn on the first two draws had been replaced before the third draw was made.

2. If the population size was $N = 100$, then given $\tilde{p} = 1/10$ there were originally 10 S's and 90 F's in the population. Removal of one S and one F without replacement would have left 9 S's and 89 F's; and consequently Mr. Warren's probability for the last sample-outcome branch following $\tilde{p} = 1/10$ in Figure 10.2 should have been $89/98 \doteq .908$, or very nearly equal to the .9 probability that he should have assigned if the chips drawn on the first two draws had been replaced before the third draw was made.

By extending this line of reasoning, the reader should convince himself that in general:

1 If the size of a sample drawn by equiprobable sampling without replacement is small relative to the size of the population from which the sample is drawn, the decision maker's probabilities for the sample-outcome branches in his probability diagram will almost all be virtually the same as if the sample were drawn by equiprobable sampling with replacement.

And since it is only through the probabilities for sample-outcome branches that the sampling process affects the posterior distribution of $\tilde{p}$, we can conclude immediately that:

2 If the size of a sample drawn by equiprobable sampling without replacement is small relative to the size of the population from which the sample is drawn, then the distribution that the decision maker should assign to $\tilde{p}$ posterior to sampling is virtually the same as the distribution he should assign if the sample were drawn by equiprobable sampling with replacement.

In most practical business applications, a sample can be treated as "small relative to the population" if it amounts to no more than 5% of the population.

11.5.2
Systematic Sampling

Another very simple sampling process frequently used in practical applications is one that consists of choosing a number j and then taking every j'th item in a file or list; the first item chosen may be any one of the first j items on the list. This process is known as ≪systematic sampling≫.

In processing the information obtained by systematic sampling, it is *usually* reasonable to proceed as if the information had been obtained by equiprobable sampling without replacement. Such processing is not reasonable, however, if there is reason to suspect that successes and failures tend to be "bunched" in the list or file, since in this case the decision maker (or his statistician delegate—cf. Section 6.5) should clearly assign a higher probability to success on a branch following a success than on a branch following a failure, and so forth.

<h3 style="text-align:center">11.5.3
Stratification and Clustering</h3>

In large surveys of human populations and certain other applications of sampling, it is customary to use sampling processes much more complicated than those we have discussed thus far, primarily because these more complicated processes yield much more information per dollar spent.

≪Stratification≫ is one of the two main devices used to increase the amount of information obtained per dollar spent. The population is first divided into a number of portions or ≪strata≫, and a separate sample is then taken from each stratum. This device is most profitable when the population can be divided into strata in some of which the fraction of successes is quite well known before any sample is taken, since in this case it clearly pays to take relatively large samples from the strata where little is known about the fraction of successes and relatively small samples from the strata where much is known.

The other main device used to increase the amount of information obtained per dollar spent is ≪clustering≫. Instead of drawing members of the population individually, small groups or ≪clusters≫ of nearby individuals are drawn together—e.g., by including several residents of a building in the sample if any resident is included. Clustering obviously reduces the cost of interviewing any given number of individuals, but at the same time it reduces the reliability of the information obtained from a sample of any given size, as can easily be seen by considering an extreme case in which a sample of United States citizens would consist entirely of people living within five miles of some particular point on the map. There is consequently some "best" size of cluster which maximizes reliability per dollar spent.

Even when a sample is drawn by a complex process that involves stratification and/or clustering, the information obtained from it is "processed" by exactly the same basic logic that is used when the sample is drawn by the simplest of all possible processes, namely equiprobable sampling with replacement. The probability diagram consists of a $\tilde{p}$ fork at the origin with one or more sample-outcome branches following each branch of the $\tilde{p}$ fork. After the decision maker has assigned an unconditional probability to each branch of the $\tilde{p}$ fork and his statistician delegate has assigned a conditional probability to each sample-outcome branch, the remaining calculations proceed exactly like those in Section

10.2.6. The probability of each end position of the diagram is found by simply multiplying together the branch probabilities on the path leading to that end position; the posterior probability of each value of $\tilde{p}$ is then found by dividing the probability of the end position at which the actual sample outcome appears together with that value of $\tilde{p}$ by the sum of the probabilities of all end positions at which the actual sample outcome appears.

11.6
SUMMARY

11.6.1
Combination of Prior
and Sample Information

1 Suppose that n sample observations have yielded r successes, and as usual let $P(n \rightarrow r \mid p)$ denote the decision maker's conditional probability for $n \rightarrow r$ given any particular p. Considered as a function of the "variable" p, both n and r being fixed, $P(n \rightarrow r \mid p)$ is called the decision maker's ≪sample likelihood function≫.

2 If the decision maker's prior mass function, sample likelihood function, and posterior mass function are all graphed against p, the height of his posterior mass function at any p is proportional to the product of the heights of his prior mass function and his sample likelihood function at that p.

3 This implies that if the prior mass function and the sample likelihood function are about equally tight, the posterior mass function will be a compromise between them; if one of them is much tighter than the other, the posterior mass function will be largely determined by the tighter one.

4 Since the tightness of the sample likelihood function increases as the number of observations n increases while r/n remains fixed, the tightness of this function can be thought of as an expression of the "amount of information" about $\tilde{p}$ that is contained in the sample; and therefore the tightness of the prior mass function can be said to express the "amount of information" the decision maker had about $\tilde{p}$ prior to sampling.

11.6.2
Beta Approximations
to Posterior Distributions

1 *a* The logically possible values of the fraction $\tilde{p}$ of successes in a population of size N are $0/N, 1/N, 2/N, \ldots, (N-1)/N, N/N$.

  b If a decision maker assigns equal probabilities to all these values, his distribution of $\tilde{p}$ is said to be ≪uniform≫.

2 *a* If (1) prior to sampling a decision maker assigns a uniform distribution to the fraction $\tilde{p}$ of successes in a population of size N, and if (2) equiprobable sampling with replacement then yields r successes in n observations, the decision maker's posterior *mass* function is identical in shape to his sample likelihood function, whose value for any argument p depends only on n, r, and N.

   b If in addition N is large relative to n, his posterior *cumulative* function is very closely approximated by a beta cumulative function with parameters

$$B = r + 1, \qquad C = n + 2.$$

Even if the decision maker's prior distribution of $\tilde{p}$ is not strictly uniform, a beta approximation to his posterior cumulative function will still be accurate enough for most practical purposes if the following conditions are satisfied.

3 Suppose that n observations made by equiprobable sampling with replacement have yielded r successes; consider the beta cumulative function with parameters $B = r + 1$, $C = n + 2$; let $p_{.001}$ and $p_{.999}$ denote the .001 and .999 fractiles of the distribution defined by this cumulative function; and let $I_{n,r}$ denote the interval extending from $p_{.001}$ to $p_{.999}$. If prior to sampling the decision maker (1) did not assign *extremely* high probabilities to any values of $\tilde{p}$ outside $I_{n,r}$, and (2) assigned *roughly* equal probabilities to all values of $\tilde{p}$ inside $I_{n,r}$, then the posterior distribution he should assign to $\tilde{p}$ will be almost the same as the posterior distribution that would result from a strictly uniform prior distribution, and therefore its cumulative function can be very closely approximated by a beta cumulative function with parameters

$$B = r + 1, \qquad C = n + 2.$$

When the conditions of this rule are met, we say that the decision maker's prior distribution of $\tilde{p}$ is "nearly uniform relative to the sample likelihood function".

Whether or not the conditions of Rule 3 above are satisfied is usually obvious in real applications of sampling. In textbook examples and exercises, we shall assume that the probabilities assigned to values of $\tilde{p}$ inside $I_{n,r}$ can be treated as "roughly equal" if the greatest of them is no more than four times the least.

11.6.3
Estimates of $\tilde{p}$

Suppose that a businessman has obtained sample information about the fraction $\tilde{p}$ of successes in some population, not for use in a well defined decision problem, but simply as a guide to his preliminary thinking about some general problem area. In such circumstances the businessman will necessarily think in terms of an estimate of $\bar{p}$ rather than a complete distribution of $\bar{p}$, but at the same time that he does so he should keep in the back of his mind some measure of the extent of his uncertainty about the true value of $\bar{p}$.

1 In any situation where (1) it is legitimate to use any estimate of $\bar{p}$ in place of a complete distribution of $\bar{p}$, and (2) the distribution which the businessman (would have) assigned to $\bar{p}$ prior to sampling is nearly uniform relative to the likelihood function of a (possibly pooled) sample that has already been taken, the businessman can take the fraction r/n of successes in the (pooled) sample as an estimate of the uncertain fraction $\bar{p}$ of successes in the population.

2 In many situations, the extent of the businessman's uncertainty about $\bar{p}$ can be satisfactorily measured by the distance between two limits between which he feels "reasonably" sure that the true value of $\bar{p}$ must lie, and such limits can be found by selecting two suitable fractiles of his posterior distribution of $\bar{p}$.

The .01 and .99 fractiles are possible choices, but which fractiles should be chosen in any particular situation depends on the seriousness of the loss that may result if the businessman assumes that the true value of $\bar{p}$ is between his two limits when in fact it is not.

11.6.4
Bernoulli Processes

1 A physical process which generates either a "success" or a "failure" on each "trial" is said to be a ≪Bernoulli process≫ in the judgment of a particular decision maker if he believes that:

a If trials were repeated indefinitely, the fraction of all trials resulting in successes would become and remain arbitrarily close to some definite number p;

b The trials would be indistinguishable, so that if the decision maker knew the long-run fraction of successes p, he would assign probability p to success on any trial, regardless of either (1) the *number* of previous trials or (2) the *pattern of successes and failures* on previous trials.

2 If a decision maker has assessed a prior distribution of the fraction $\bar{p}$ of successes that a Bernoulli process would generate in the long run, and if he has then observed r successes in n trials of the process, he can compute the posterior distribution that he should now assign to $\bar{p}$ in exactly the same way that he would compute a distribution of the fraction $\bar{p}$ of successes in a finite population posterior to observing r successes in n observations made by equiprobable sampling with replacement.

3 If a decision maker has assessed his current distribution of the fraction $\tilde{p}$ of successes that a Bernoulli process would generate in the long run, the unconditional probability that he assigns to "success" on the next trial of the process should be equal to his expectation of the long-run fraction $\tilde{p}$.

11.6.5
Sampling without Replacement

1 If the size of a sample drawn by equiprobable sampling *without* replacement is small relative to the size of the population from which it is drawn, the posterior distribution that should be assigned to $\tilde{p}$ will be virtually the same as if the sample had been drawn with replacement.

2 A sample drawn by «systematic sampling», i.e., by taking every j'th item on a list, may be treated as if it were taken by equiprobable sampling without replacement provided that there is no reason to suspect that successes and failures tend to be "bunched" in the list.

3 No matter how a sample is drawn, the distribution that should be assigned to $\tilde{p}$ posterior to sampling can be routinely computed once the decision maker has directly assessed his prior distribution of $\tilde{p}$ and his statistician delegate has assessed the conditional probability of the sample outcome given each possible value of $\tilde{p}$.

EXERCISES

A. BETA APPROXIMATIONS

11.1 Consider the beta cumulative function with parameters $B = 24$, $C = 102$, and let p_k denote the argument for which the value of this function is k.
a Verify by use of page 697 of Table T3 that $p_{.001} = .1225$.
b Graph the function.

11.2 A decision maker's posterior distribution of the uncertain fraction $\tilde{p}$ of successes in a certain population has a beta cumulative function with parameters $B = 24$, $C = 102$. Find:
a The three quartiles of his distribution.
b The .05 and .95 fractiles of his distribution.
c The mean of his distribution.

11.3 Recall Mr. Herbert Zellner's desire to learn something about the fraction $\tilde{p}$ of his 15,000 customers who ordered less than \$50 worth of merchandise during the last six months, as described in Exercise 10.5.
a What values of the fraction $\tilde{p}$ are logically possible?
b Approximate as well as you can the median, the mean, and the .05 and

.95 fractiles of the distribution that Mr. Zellner should have assigned to $\bar{p}$ on the assumptions of part (b) of Exercise 10.5.

c On these same assumptions, what probability should Mr. Zellner assign to the proposition that less than 1/4 of all his customers ordered less than $50? to the proposition that at least 9/10 of all his customers ordered at least $50?

11.4 Recall Mr. Rudolph Grauber's mammoth probability diagram with 1 million end positions, as described in Exercise 10.7, and recall that, exhausted as he is, Mr. Grauber very much wants to know at what fraction $\bar{p}$ of these end positions the value of the function z is less than 50.

a What values of the fraction $\bar{p}$ are logically possible on the basis of the information in the exercise?

b Assuming that Grauber would have been just as ready to bet that $\bar{p}$ was equal to any one of these possible values as any other before he took the sample described in Exercise 10.7, approximate as well as you can the median, the mean, and the .05 and .95 fractiles of the distribution that Grauber should assign to $\bar{p}$ posterior to taking the sample.

c What answer would you now give to part (b) of Exercise 10.7?

11.5 Would your answers to Exercise 11.3 above still be approximately correct under the assumptions of part (a) of Exercise 10.5?

11.6 If a decision maker's prior distribution of $\bar{p}$ is grouped into equiprobable brackets, the probabilities assigned to the representative values for the groups are necessarily all equal. Does this mean that (1) such a grouped approximation to a prior distribution is necessarily uniform, and hence (2) a beta approximation to the decision maker's posterior distribution will always be just as accurate as an approximation calculated in the usual manner from the grouped prior?

11.7 A decision maker says that his distribution of $\bar{p}$ has a beta cumulative function with parameters B and C and wants to learn the value of the .25 fractile $p_{.25}$ of his distribution. Show that:

a If $B = 26$, $C = 150$, then $p_{.25} = .1518$.
b If $B = 26$, $C = 210$, then $p_{.25} = .1072$.
c If $B = 26$, $C = 80$, then $p_{.25} = .290$.
d If $B = 26$, $C = 39$, then $p_{.25} = .6172$.
e If $B = 26$, $C = 27$, then $p_{.25} = .9467$.

B. ESTIMATES

11.8 a In the circumstances of Exercise 10.7, what would be Mr. Grauber's median estimate of the fraction $\bar{p}$ of end positions at which $\bar{z} < 50$? His modal estimate? His expectation of $\bar{p}$?

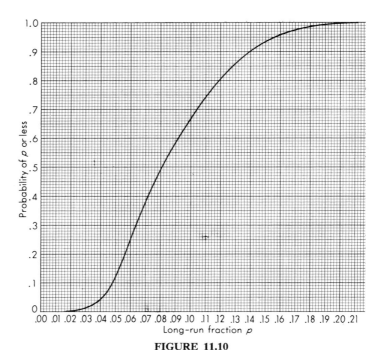

FIGURE 11.10

Manufacturer's Distribution of the Long-run Fraction of Bursts

b If Grauber decides to measure his uncertainty about $\tilde{p}$ by the distance between the .01 and the .99 fractiles of his distribution of $\tilde{p}$, how great was his uncertainty about $\tilde{p}$ before he took his sample? After he took his sample?

c About how great will be his uncertainty about $\tilde{p}$ after making *another* 100 observations on the end positions of his diagram by equiprobable sampling with replacement?

C. BERNOULLI PROCESSES

11.9 In Exercise 6.4, we considered a problem faced by a manufacturer who wished to use a certain pressure vessel for a purpose for which it was not designed. When this abnormal use was first proposed, the manufacturer consulted his chief engineer about the possibility that the vessel would be weakened or damaged thereby. The engineer answered that although the vessel could not be weakened in any way by such use, there was a 1-in-10 chance that it would be burst and completely destroyed by a random pressure surge.

      The manufacturer interpreted this answer as an assertion that if a whose sequence of indistinguishable vessels were put to this use repeatedly, each vessel being replaced by a new one whenever a burst occurred, an

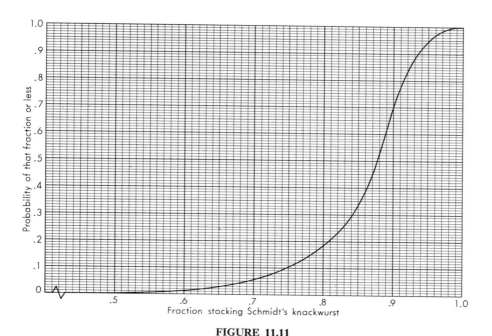

FIGURE 11.11

Schmidt's Distribution of the Fraction of All Delicatessens Stocking His Knackwurst

excessive random surge would occur and the vessel would be burst on 1/10 of all occasions. Knowing, however, that his engineer was a very cautious person inclined toward pessimism in any risky situation, the manufacturer decided that if he had to place bets on the fraction of bursts that would occur in the long run, he would bet 2 to 1 that the fraction would really turn out to be *below* 1/10; and continuing in this vein he ultimately described his probability distribution for the long-run fraction of bursts by constructing the cumulative function shown in Figure 11.10.

After assessing this distribution and thinking about its implications, the manufacturer went ahead and used the vessel for the purpose in question on nine successive occasions. No burst occurred.

In computing your answers to the two following questions, read probabilities from Figure 11.10 to the nearest .01.

a What probability should the manufacturer have assigned to the event "burst" before he first put the vessel to abnormal use?

b What probability should he now assign to the event that the vessel will burst if he puts it to this same use a tenth time?

D. SAMPLING WITHOUT REPLACEMENT

11.10 Herr Hans Schmidt's special knackwurst was distributed through wholesalers to those of the 2,000 delicatessens in the Neustadt metropolitan area who chose to stock it. As shown by his probability distribution in Figure 11.11, Herr Schmidt felt reasonably confident that more than 80% of the 2,000 delicatessens were stocking the knackwurst, but his uncertainty was great enough to lead him to feel that it was worth getting a little more information on the subject, and he therefore drew a sample of 50 delicatessens and sent a man to visit them and see whether they had Schmidt's knackwurst in stock or not. The sample was drawn by assigning a serial number to every delicatessen in the city directory and then using random numbers to select 50 of them. To Schmidt's distress, his agent reported that only 74% of the delicatessens in the sample stocked Schmidt's knackwurst.

What probability should Herr Schmidt now assign to the proposition that more than 80% of the 2,000 delicatessens in the Neustadt metropolitan area stock his special knackwurst? (In computing your answer to this question, read Figure 11.11 to the nearest .01.)

11.11 Besides being interested in the fraction of delicatessens in the Neustadt metropolitan area that stocked his well established brand of knackwurst, Herr Schmidt was anxious to learn what fraction of these same delicatessens would want to stock his newly developed brand of pickled pigs feet, at least on a trial basis. Because there were already several excellent brands of pigs feet for sale in the area in question, Schmidt felt very uncertain about his ability to penetrate the market with a new brand. More specifically, he felt that the fraction of delicatessens that would stock his brand on a trial basis was just about as likely to have any one value between 0/2,000 and 1,000/2,000 as any other value in this range; values above this range were much less probable in his opinion. Since he was already incurring the expense of sending an investigator to look into the knackwurst question, he decided to have this same person solicit orders for the pigs feet, and 13 orders were secured from the 50 delicatessens in the sample.

a What probability should Herr Schmidt now assign to the proposition that if all 2,000 delicatessens in the Neustadt metropolitan area were approached in this same way, at least half of them would stock his pickled pigs feet?

b What should be his expectation of the fraction of all delicatessens that would stock under these conditions? Of the number of delicatessens that would stock?

11.12 An investigator takes a sample of 67 account cards from the file of a downtown department store by taking the 117th card in the file and every 400th card thereafter, and he learns among other things that 12 of these 67 accounts are overdue.

a Approximate as well as you can the mean and the .01, .25, .50, .75, and

.99 fractiles of the distribution *you* should assign, given this information, to the fraction of all accounts in the entire file that are overdue.

b State any reservations you have about your method of computation.

E. SAMPLING AS A BASIS FOR DECISION

11.13 A manufacturer has purchased a certain component in lots of 200 from the same vendor over a considerable period of time. Each lot of parts has been sent directly to the assembly department for use in the final product, and considerable losses have been incurred because some of the components are defective and cause the assembly to fail on final test. Removing such a component from the assembly and replacing it with a good one costs $4 in addition to the cost of reworking the component in the shop. The cost incurred in the assembly department could be avoided by having each incoming lot screened (100% inspected), but this would cost $5 per lot plus $1 per piece in the lot or a total of $205 per lot, and because only 20% of the components in a lot have been defective on the average, the manufacturer has decided that screening every incoming lot would not pay.

The manufacturer is now thinking of taking a sample from each incoming lot and then screening only those lots where the sample results lead him to think that there is a particularly large fraction defective in the lot; a smooth curve fitted to the fractions defective in the last 50 lots was shown as Figure 10.5 on page 407. Sampling inspection would be performed in exactly the same way as screening inspection and would involve the same setup and variable costs, $5 per lot plus $1 per piece inspected; but because the same inspector would go on to screen the remainder of the lot if the occasion arose, screening the remainder would cost only $1 per piece remaining in the lot—there would be no second setup cost.

Assuming that the manufacturer takes a sample of 10 pieces from the next lot to arrive and finds 3 defectives in this sample:

a Write a formula expressing the *number* R_0 of defectives *originally* in the lot in terms of the original lot *fraction* defective p.

b Write a formula expressing the number R of defectives in the part of the lot which has *not yet been inspected* in terms of the *original* lot fraction defective p.

c Assuming that the manufacturer will treat expected monetary values as certainty equivalents in analyzing the decision problem he faces regarding this lot, draw a schematic diagram of the problem and value the typical end positions.

d Analyze the manufacturer's decision problem. [Hint: review Section 7.5.2 and then use Figure 10.7 on page 410.]

e Draw a schematic diagram of the decision problem the manufacturer faced just before he decided to take a sample from this lot and describe exactly how you would analyze this problem, but do not perform any actual computations.

11.14 *Science Books, Inc. (A)*

On February 13, 1969, Mr. L. K. Jensen, the President of Science Books, Inc., was informed by the Wilder Publishing Company that he could have the paperback reprint rights to Q. C. Zbykfy's *Introduction to Game Theory* for a royalty of $.20 per copy sold plus a fixed fee of $2,000 for the use of the original plates. The offer was good for the next 60 days.

Science Books, Inc., was a book club that specialized in the sale of paperback reprints of books on science and mathematics by direct mail only. Members were not required to buy any particular number of books per year, but they were dropped from the mailing list if they failed to buy at least one book during any calendar year. This policy had been adopted after a study had shown that a member who bought no books in any one calendar year almost never bought any books in the next two calendar years.

Each time that the club acquired rights to a new title, the members of the club were sent a circular describing the book and were given 30 days in which to place their order. The press run was made almost immediately after the expiration of this 30-day period, and the books were mailed less than four weeks later to those who had ordered. In order to avoid the expenses that would be entailed by keeping a large variety of books in stock, the club refused to accept orders for any book after the expiration of the 30-day period and limited its press run to the number actually ordered plus a small allowance for spoilage.

The reprints sold by Science Books were uniformly priced at $2.15 plus mailing costs. Mr. Jensen calculated that reprinting of Zbykfy's book would involve fixed costs of about $1,000 for press setup and new plates for the paper cover in addition to the $2,000 payment to Wilder for use of the plates of the text; variable expense for paper, ink, press and binding labor, etc., would amount to about $.45 per copy. Designing the mailing piece that would be sent to the members and preparing the mats would cost only about $50, and the cost of setting up to print the mailing pieces would be negligible; but each copy mailed would give rise to variable costs totalling about $.22 for printing, addressing, stuffing, and postage. At one time Jensen had thought that he should reduce these variable costs by advertising two or three books in a single mailing, but after several experiments in which he had sent combined mailings to some of the members and individual mailings to others, he had concluded that combined mailings reduced sales to such an extent that the resulting loss of contribution was much greater than the saving of cost.

Within the past few years Science Books had reprinted and sold to its members 10 books on subjects which in Jensen's opinion were of roughly the same level of difficulty and roughly the same level of general appeal as Zbykfy's *Introduction*. The number of orders for each of the 10 books is shown in the table below; virtually all orders were for single copies. The membership of the club had remained very close to a constant 45,000 over this entire period, and during this period no book offered to the members had sold less than 1,000 copies.

Book Number	Number of Orders	Book Number	Number of Orders
1	4,017	6	6,912
2	8,493	7	7,356
3	16,238	8	20,571
4	4,551	9	3,944
5	18,014	10	11,173

On the basis of this evidence, Jensen was inclined to believe that he should reprint Zbykfy's *Introduction*, especially since he did not think he had any chance of obtaining rights to any other book on game theory whose sales would be hurt if Zbykfy's book were offered to the members first; but because the club had suffered severe losses on some of the earlier reprints, Jensen felt that it might be worthwhile to get some more information on demand for Zbykfy's book before making a final decision. He could do so by designing the mailing piece that would actually be used if he decided to reprint the book and then sending out a certain number of mailings as if he had actually decided to reprint. Whether or not Jensen ultimately decided to reprint, the orders resulting from the sample mailing would have to be filled with hard-cover copies of the original edition in order to avoid undue delay; these copies would cost the club $8.65 each.

a Putting yourself in Mr. Jensen's position, and assuming that just before each of the 10 books in the record was reprinted its sales prospects looked neither better nor worse to you than the prospects for Zbykfy's *Introduction* look now, assess your probability distribution of the fraction of all club members who will buy the *Introduction* if you reprint it.

b Assuming that you are willing to treat expected monetary values as certainty equivalents, diagram the decision problem you will face if you decide to send a general mailing to all club members *without* first sending a sample mailing, and value the typical end position with a formula expressing the total cash flow in terms of the fraction p of all members who order.

c Analyze this decision problem.

d Suppose now that you do decide to sample, that you send out n sample mailings, that you receive r orders in response, and that you then decide to send a "main" mailing to all members who did not receive a sample mailing. Write a formula expressing the number of orders you receive in response to the *main* mailing in terms of the fraction p of all members who order in response to *both* mailings.

   e Using the symbols n, r, and p as defined in (d) just above, diagram the decision problem you face *before* deciding how large a sample to take if any, and value typical end positions with formulas expressing the total cash flow in terms of n, r, and p.

   f Describe exactly how you could analyze this problem, but do not perform any actual computations.

11.15   *Robinson Abrasives Company* (A)

    The Robinson Abrasives Company manufactures a wide variety of grinding wheels for industrial use. These wheels are subject to extreme stresses, and breakage can result in severe damage to machinery and injury to machine operators. Consequently the company is anxious to maintain high quality output and subjects the wheels to rigorous testing procedures.

    The first step in the manufacture of a grinding wheel is to mix bonding material, abrasive, and water and pour this mixture into molds which are allowed to dry for several days. The dried wheels are then placed on a shaving machine and turned to the desired dimension, after which they are baked in a kiln. Tests for hardness, toughness, and strength are made on the finished product. The strength test consists of placing the wheel in a steel protection shell and rotating it at a speed 50 % greater than the maximum speed that would be used in actual service.

    Failure of finished wheels in the strength test can be due to either or both of two independent causes. (1) If the wheels are improperly loaded in the kiln, warping or cracking or internal stresses can result; on the average, about 5 % of all wheels fail for reasons of this sort. (2) The bonding material itself has been of variable quality, and sometimes a substantial number of wheels in a single batch have failed because the cohesive strength of the material was inadequate.

    The Research Department now announces that it has just developed and has available for immediate use in manufacturing a new vitrified bonding material which is much stronger than the old material. Wheels made of this material are no better or worse than wheels made of the old material which succeed in passing inspection, but the failures due to the raw material are completely eliminated. A batch of the new bonding material costs $1,000.

    The company has on hand one batch of the old bonding material —enough to make 1,000 grinding wheels 36 inches in diameter. The company intends to purchase no more material of the old kind, and the superintendent of manufacturing has raised the question whether the one remaining batch ought to be scrapped in order to avoid the risk of wasting money on wheels which might fail on final test. The variable cost of

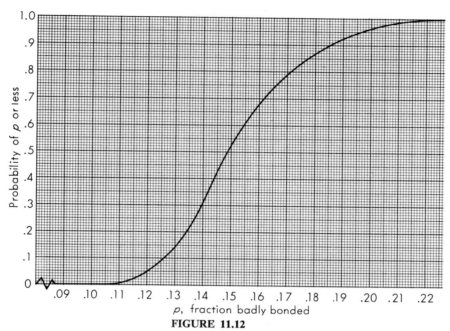

FIGURE 11.12

Badly Bonded Wheels as a Fraction of All Wheels
(Data Apply Only to Batches Containing
at Least One Badly Bonded Wheel)

processing, plus the cost of the materials other than the bonding material, amounts to $15 per wheel.

When the superintendent asks the supervisor of quality control how many rejects they might have if they did not scrap the old bonding material but used it to produce a batch of 1,000 36-inch wheels, the supervisor replies that he is fortunately in a very good position to answer that question because he has been collecting data on the problem for a long time. In about 40% of all batches of 1,000 36-inch wheels, all the wheels appeared to have been well bonded; what failures there were were due exclusively to improper loading in the kiln. In the remaining 60% of all batches, somewhere between 10% and 25% of the wheels appeared to have been badly bonded in the sense that they either were properly loaded and failed solely because of inadequate bonding or else were improperly loaded but would have failed because of inadequate bonding even if they had been properly loaded. The supervisor has just plotted the data on the batches in which badly bonded wheels appeared and faired a curve through the plotted points. His curve is reproduced as Figure 11.12.

a Show that if the remaining batch of old bonding material is used to produce a batch of 36-inch wheels, the replacement cost (cf. Section 2.2.7) of each good wheel produced is $16/.95. Then show that if the superintendent of manufacturing knew that a particular wheel was well bonded but did not know whether or not it had been properly loaded, he should value it at $16.

b Assuming that the superintendent would wish to treat expected monetary values as certainty equivalents in analyzing his decision problem concerning the old bonding material, and letting $\bar{p}$ denote the fraction of wheels made from the old material that will be badly bonded, construct a truncated schematic diagram of his problem in which his uncertainty about the number of wheels that will be improperly loaded does not appear explicitly.

c Taking as your base end position a position at which no wheels have been made from the old bonding material, value the typical end positions of your diagram with either a definite number or a formula which expresses the value as the sum of (1) the total cash flow, and (2) an adjustment for nonmonetary consequences.

d Assuming that the superintendent assesses his distribution of $\bar{p}$ by equating his probabilities to the frequencies or smoothed frequencies supplied by the supervisor of quality control, compute his expectation of $\bar{p}$. [Hint: If you group the distribution of Figure 11.12 into 10 equiprobable brackets, you should assign probability .06 to each bracket median. Why? What should you do with the remaining .4 probability?]

e What decision should the superintendent reach?

11.16 Robinson Abrasives Company (B)

Knowing that the superintendent of manufacturing of the Robinson Abrasives Company is having difficulty in deciding whether or not to scrap the one remaining batch of old bonding material,[5] the supervisor of quality control has suggested to him that it may be desirable to test the remaining batch of old bonding material before deciding whether or not to scrap it. Specifically, he has proposed that several experimental wheels be prepared, processed, and given a strength test; the decision to use or scrap the batch would be based on the number of these experimental wheels that fail the test. The experimental wheels would be loaded into the kiln with enough extra care to make sure that there were no failures due to improper loading.

a Assuming that the superintendent has already produced *n* experimental wheels and that *r* of these wheels have failed the strength test, construct a diagram of the decision problem he now faces and value the typical end positions with either a definite number or a formula in *p*, *n*, and *r*.

b What action should the superintendent take if 10 experimental wheels are produced and none fails the strength test? If one fails?

[5] Cf. *Robinson Abrasives Company* (*A*) Exercise 11.15.

CHAPTER
12

SAMPLES FROM MANY-VALUED POPULATIONS

In the last two chapters we saw how a businessman can make use of the information contained in a sample drawn from a population when the uncertain fact about the population that interests him is the fraction of its members possessing some one, particular attribute. Because each member of the population was to be counted as having one or the other of just two "values", success or failure, we somewhat loosely referred to the population itself as "two-valued". In the present chapter we shall see how a businessman can make use of the information contained in a sample when each member of the population from which the sample is drawn may have any one of several different numerical values and the businessman is interested in the uncertain *average* of the numerical values of all the members of the population.

If, for example, a businessman conducts a sample survey concerning purchases of instant coffee in Oshkosh during the week of July 11, he may think of all Oshkosh housewives as constituting his "population"; he may think of each member of this population as having a "value" equal to the number of ounces of instant coffee she bought during the week in question; and he may be interested in the average of these values, i.e., in the average number of ounces purchased per housewife. Because each member of such a population can have any of a large number of different numerical values, we shall refer to any such population as "many-valued".

Our basic approach to the use of sample information in this chapter will be identical to our basic approach in the last two chapters. We saw there that if the businessman has directly assessed the "prior" probability distribution that he (would have) assigned to the fraction $\tilde{p}$ of successes in a two-valued population before sampling, his statistician can compute the "posterior" distribution that logical consistency requires him to assign to $\tilde{p}$ after observing the successes and failures in a sample drawn from that population. We shall see in the present chapter that if the businessman has directly assessed the prior distribution that he (would have) assigned before sampling to the average $\tilde{A}$ of the values of all the members of a many-valued population, his statistician can compute the posterior distribution that he should assign to $\tilde{A}$ after observing the values of the members drawn in a sample from the population.

The text and exercises of this chapter are designed to be studied in the following order:

CONTENTS OF CHAPTER 12

1.
Many-valued Populations and Samples

2.
Assessment of Probabilities Reflecting All the Information in a Sample

3 Indirect Assessment: the Assessment Gamble
4 Practical Obstacles to the Use of All the Information in a Sample

3.
Assessment of Probabilities Reflecting
Most of the Information in a Sample

1 Summarization of Most of the Information in a Sample; the Statistics n, a, and v
2 Probability That the Values of n Sample Observations Will Have Average a and Variance v
3 Analysis of an Assessment Problem
4 Recapitulation: Large-sample Theory

4.
Grouped Approximations

5.
Successive Samples

6.
Combination of Prior
and Sample Information

7.
Gaussian Approximations
to Posterior Distributions of $\tilde{A}$

1 Uniform Distributions of $\tilde{A}$
2 The Posterior Distribution of $\tilde{A}$ When the Prior Distribution Is Uniform
3 Gaussian Cumulative Functions
4 Recapitulation: the Posterior Distribution of $\tilde{A}$ When the Prior Distribution Is Uniform and Large-sample Theory Applies
5 Nearly Uniform Prior Distributions

8.
Estimates of $\tilde{A}$

9.
Sampling without Replacement

1 Equiprobable Sampling without Replacement
2 Systematic Sampling
3 Stratification and Clustering

10.
Summary

1 Description of a Many-valued Population
2 Summarization of Sample Information; Large-sample Theory
3 Computation of Posterior Distributions
4 Grouped Approximations to Posterior Distributions
5 Successive Samples
6 Gaussian Approximations to Posterior Distributions
7 Estimates of $\tilde{A}$
8 Sampling without Replacement

12.1
MANY-VALUED POPULATIONS AND SAMPLES

12.1.1
Description of Many-valued Populations

As we said in the introduction to this chapter, a population will be called ≪many-valued≫ if for the particular purpose at hand each of its members is to be regarded as having one of a number of possible numerical values. The value of a particular member of a population of housewives may be the number of ounces of instant coffee she purchased last week; the value of a particular member of a population of cans of coffee may be the net weight of the contents; and so forth. It is really the individual members of the population who have many possible values; the expression "many-valued population" is an elliptical way of describing a population whose members are of this sort.

When we studied two-valued populations in the last chapter, we saw that any such population can be completely described by just two numbers, the number of members and the fraction of "successes" among the members. A complete description of a many-valued population would have to be much more complex, since it would have to specify in one way or another the fraction of members having each one of the possible values of the quantity of interest (e.g., amount of instant coffee purchased last week). We shall, however, confine the discussion in this introductory text to the very common case where the only facts about the population as a whole that are of interest to the businessman are the two quantities.

N: the number of members in the population,

e.g., the number of housewives in Oshkosh, and

A: the average of the values of the individual members,

e.g., the average of the amounts of instant coffee purchased by individual housewives last week. We shall further restrict our discussion to the case where the only *uncertain* quantity of interest to the businessman is the population average $\tilde{A}$; we assume, in other words, that the population size N is known or can be treated for practical purposes as if it were known.

12.1.2

Equiprobable Sampling with Replacement

We saw in Chapter 10 that when a sample is taken from a two-valued population in order to learn more about the fraction $\tilde{p}$ of successes in the population, the effect that the information obtained from the sample should have on the business-man's distribution of $\tilde{p}$ depends on the sampling process by which the sample is drawn. Exactly the same thing is true of a sample drawn from a many-valued population in order to learn more about the average $\tilde{A}$ of the values of the in-dividual members. The probability distribution that should be assigned to $\tilde{A}$ posterior to observing some particular sample outcome will in general be one thing if the sample was drawn by equiprobable sampling with replacement, quite another thing if the sample was drawn by stratified sampling without replace-ment, and so forth.

Until we reach Section 12.9 in this chapter, we shall be concerned ex-clusively with samples obtained by equiprobable sampling with replacement.

12.2

ASSESSMENT OF PROBABILITIES REFLECTING
ALL THE INFORMATION IN A SAMPLE

In Section 10.4 we saw that after a businessman has learned the outcome of a sample taken in order to learn more about the uncertain fraction $\tilde{p}$ of successes in some population, he can decide what probability distribution he should now assign to $\tilde{p}$ by considering an assessment gamble of the kind diagrammed in Fig-ure 10.2 (page 400), assigning to its branches the probabilities he (would have) assessed before he knew the sample outcome, and then computing the condi-tional probabilities he should have assigned to the possible values of $\tilde{p}$ given the sample outcome that later actually occurred.

In the present section we shall first show by an example how this same procedure can in principle be used to compute the distribution that a business-man should assign to the uncertain average $\tilde{A}$ of the values of the individual members of a population after observing the values of the members of a sample drawn from the population. We shall then show why this conceptually very simple procedure gives rise in practice to very serious difficulties, after which we shall go on in Section 12.3 to show how these difficulties can usually be avoided by sacrificing a small part of the information in the sample.

12.2.1
An Assessment Problem

Suppose that a bag contains a "population" of poker chips on each of which some number or "value" has been written, and suppose that a Mr. Fraser would like to assess his unconditional distribution of the uncertain quantity

$\tilde{A}$: average of the values of the individual members of the population.

Suppose further that the information which is available to Mr. Fraser is of two sorts.

1. The bag in which Mr. Fraser is now interested was chosen by him from a set of four seemingly identical bags, and he knows that in one of these four bags the average of the values of the individual chips was 10, in two of them the average was 15, and in the last one the average was 20.

2. After choosing one of the four bags, Mr. Fraser successively drew three chips from it by equiprobable sampling with replacement and observed that the values written on these three chips were respectively 13, 17, and 21.

12.2.2
Indirectly Relevant Information

The information on which Mr. Fraser wishes to base his probabilities for the various possible values of the uncertain average $\tilde{A}$ of the values of the individual members of his population of poker chips is exactly like Mr. Warren's information in the example of Sections 10.2 and 10.4 in that it bears only indirectly on the probabilities he wishes to assess.

1. Fraser's information about the contents of the four original bags and the way in which "this" bag was chosen among them bears directly, not on the unconditional probabilities he should assign to the various possible values of $\tilde{A}$ *posterior* to learning the values of the three chips in the sample, but on the unconditional probabilities he should have assigned to the various possible values of $\tilde{A}$ *prior* to learning these values.

2. Fraser's information about the way in which the sample chips were drawn from the chosen bag bears directly, not on the unconditional probabilities he should assign *to* the various possible values of $\tilde{A}$, either prior or posterior to sampling, but on the conditional probabilities, *given* the various possible values of $\tilde{A}$, that he should have assigned to the possible values of each chip drawn in the sample before he knew what the value of each sample chip actually was.

12.2.3
Indirect Assessment:
the Assessment Gamble

Mr. Fraser thus finds himself facing an assessment problem of exactly the same kind as the problem faced by Mr. Warren in Section 10.2, and Mr. Fraser can in

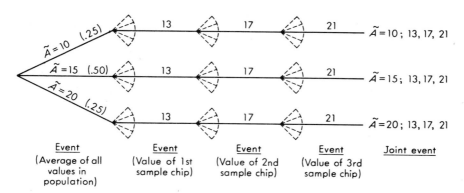

FIGURE 12.1

Mr. Fraser's Assessment Gamble

principle solve his problem in exactly the same way that Mr. Warren solved his. Mr. Fraser can consider the assessment gamble diagrammed in abbreviated form in Figure 12.1, assign to its branches the probabilities he would have assessed for them *before* he knew what value each of the sample chips would actually have, and then compute from these probabilities the conditional probabilities that he should have assigned at that time to the various possible values of $\tilde{A}$ given the sample outcome 13, 17, 21. These computed probabilities for the various possible values of $\tilde{A}$ which would have been conditional on the sample outcome 13, 17, 21 before Mr. Fraser learned that that outcome would actually occur will be the probabilities that he should assign unconditionally now that he knows that the outcome 13, 17, 21 did in fact occur.

12.2.4

Practical Obstacles to the Use
of All the Information in a Sample

It thus appears that if Mr. Fraser can assess his probabilities for the branches of his assessment gamble in Figure 12.1, his problem is solved.

Assessment of unconditional probabilities for the branches of the $\tilde{A}$ fork at the origin of Figure 12.1 presents no new problems. Since the average of the values of the individual chips was 10 in exactly one of the four bags from which Mr. Fraser's bag was chosen, and since Mr. Fraser had no way of telling which bag was which, he will presumably assign probability .25 to the event that the average $\tilde{A}$ of the values on the chips in his chosen bag is 10. Similar reasoning will presumably lead him to assign probability .50 to the event $\tilde{A} = 15$ and probability .25 to the event $\tilde{A} = 20$, as shown on the branches of the $\tilde{A}$ fork in Figure 12.1.

A new and serious problem does arise, however, when Mr. Fraser or his statistician delegate tries to assess probabilities for the sample-outcome branches in Figure 12.1. Any one of these branches presents the same kind of problem; as a typical example, take the first branch following the branch for $\tilde{A} = 10$.

The probability that the assessor must assign to the branch following the branch for $\tilde{A} = 10$ in Figure 12.1 is his conditional probability for the event "value of first sample chip is 13" given that the average A of the values of all the chips in the population is 10. If from the given fact that the average of the values of all the chips in the population is 10 the assessor could deduce what fraction of all chips in the population have the particular value 13, there would be no problem. Because the sampling is equiprobable, the assessor would simply set his probability for the event "value of first sample chip is 13" equal to the fraction of chips having that value in the population. But it is clearly impossible for anyone to deduce what fraction of the chips have the particular value 13 from the given fact that the average of the values is 10, and therefore it is not at all clear what conditional probability anyone should assign to the event "value of sample chip is 13" given $\tilde{A} = 10$.

It is of course true that even though a person does not know what probability he "should" assign to an event, he can always *decide* on his probability for that event. If, for example, Mr. Fraser or his statistician were told that $\tilde{A} = 10$, he could decide before the first chip was actually drawn what standard chance at a prize would be as attractive to him as the right to receive that same prize if the chip turned out to have the value 13. But although such a probability assessment would be a valid expression of the assessor's best judgment concerning the fraction of chips with value 13, this judgment would clearly rest on very little real information; and consequently there is very little to be gained by asking Mr. Fraser or his statistician to make assessments of this kind if there is any way in which a reasonable posterior distribution of $\tilde{A}$ can be derived without them.

In the next section we shall show that although there is no way of avoiding difficult assessment problems when a sample is as small as the one we have been discussing, it is usually very easy to avoid them when the sample is reasonably large and the decision maker is willing to disregard a small part of the information the sample contains.

<h2 style="text-align:center">12.3
ASSESSMENT OF PROBABILITIES REFLECTING
MOST OF THE INFORMATION IN A SAMPLE</h2>

<h3 style="text-align:center">12.3.1
Summarization of Most of the Information
in a Sample; the Statistics n, a, and v</h3>

We saw in Section 10.4.3 that when a sample is taken from a two-valued population by equiprobable sampling with replacement, all the information bearing on the fraction $\bar{p}$ of successes in the population that is contained in the complete sample outcome can be conveyed by merely stating the values of just two summary statistics, the number n of observations in the sample and the number r of successes. We are entitled to say that no information is lost when the outcome is summarized in this way because a person who knows only the statistics n and r will be led to assess the same posterior distribution of $\tilde{p}$ that he would assess if he knew the complete sample outcome.

Summarization of the information in a sample will clearly be more difficult when the information bears on the uncertain average $\tilde{A}$ of the values in a many-valued population than when it bears on the uncertain fraction $\tilde{p}$ of successes in a two-valued population. When an individual member of the population must have one or the other of just two possible values, success or failure, stating the values of the statistics n and r is equivalent to stating exactly how many sample observations had each of these two values. To convey all the information in a sample from a population in which an individual member may have any one of many possible values, it would be necessary to state exactly how many sample observations had each of these many values.

It would not, of course, be particularly difficult simply to *state* the number of sample observations having each possible value, but it would be very difficult indeed to make any use of all the information thus conveyed. In order to compute a posterior distribution of $\tilde{A}$ that took account of all this information, the businessman or his statistician would have to assess his conditional probability for every different value appearing in the sample given every possible value of $\tilde{A}$, exactly as he would if he tried to base a posterior distribution on a detailed list of the sample values in the order in which they were drawn; and we saw in the last section that such conditional probabilities are extremely hard to assess.

It is fortunate, therefore, that when a sample is reasonably large it is usually possible to give a very brief summary description of the sample outcome that preserves *most* of the information in the complete sample outcome and at the same time makes it very easy to derive a posterior distribution of $\tilde{A}$ that is logically consistent with the information that is preserved. When sampling is equiprobable, such a summary description can be given by stating the numerical values of just three summary measures or statistics, namely:

n: total number of observations in the sample,

a: average of the values of the individual observations in the sample,

v: variance of the values of the individual observations in the sample.[1]

Although it is beyond the scope of an elementary text to show that the information about $\tilde{A}$ that is *not* conveyed by these three statistics is usually of

[1] After the average a of the values of the individual observations in the sample has been computed, the variance v can be computed by (1) computing the difference between the average a and the value of each individual observation in the sample, (2) squaring each of these differences, (3) adding the squared differences, and (4) dividing this sum of squares by the number of observations.

relatively little importance, it is easy enough to see that the information that *is* conveyed by each of them usually bears very materially on the probability distribution that should be assigned to $\tilde{A}$ posterior to sampling.

1. The average a of the values of the individual sample observations obviously bears directly on the average A of the values of all the individual members of the population. If a is large, this is evidence that $\tilde{A}$ is probably large, and so forth.

2. The number n of sample observations clearly tells us something about the "weight" that should be attached to the sample average a in assessing a posterior distribution of the population average $\tilde{A}$.

If n is very large, then before taking a sample the assessor will believe that the as yet unknown average of the values in the sample is very likely to be very close to the average A of all the values in the population; and therefore after taking a sample and actually observing the sample average a he will believe that the uncertain population average $\tilde{A}$ is very likely to be very close to the observed sample average a.

If, on the contrary, n is very small, then before taking a sample the assessor will feel that the as yet unknown average of the values in the sample might differ substantially from the average A of all the values in the population; and therefore after taking a sample and actually observing the sample average a he may feel that there is still a substantial chance that the uncertain population average $\tilde{A}$ differs substantially from the observed sample average a.

3. The variance v of the values of the individual sample observations measures the "spread" of these values (in an admittedly rather peculiar way), and we can see how this spread should affect the posterior distribution assigned to $\tilde{A}$ by thinking how knowledge of the spread of the values of all the individual members of the population would affect that distribution.

If the assessor knew that the values of the individual members of the population had very little spread, implying that nearly all of these values were nearly equal to the population average A, then before taking a sample of these values he would believe that the average of the values in the sample was very likely to be very close to the average A of all the values in the population; and therefore after taking a sample and actually observing the sample average a, he would believe that the uncertain population average $\tilde{A}$ was very likely to be very close to the observed sample average a.

If, on the contrary, the assessor knew that the values of the individual members of the population had a great deal of spread, implying that many of these values differed greatly from the population average A, then before taking a sample of these values he would believe that the average of the values in the sample could easily differ very substantially from the average A of all the values in the population; and therefore after taking a sample and actually observing the sample average a, he might feel that there was still a substantial chance that the uncertain population average $\tilde{A}$ might differ substantially from the observed sample average a.

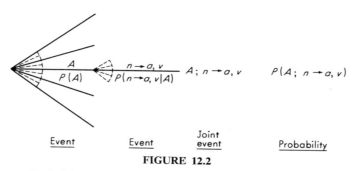

FIGURE 12.2

Typical Assessment Gamble Involving the Statistics *n*, *a*, and *v*

From these observations it is clear that if the assessor knew the spread of the values of all the individual members of the population, he would have to take careful account of this information in assessing his distribution of the population average $\tilde{A}$ posterior to observing the average a of the values in a sample. Usually, however, a person who is uncertain about the average $\tilde{A}$ of the values of the individual members of a population is even more uncertain about their spread, and it is here that the sample statistic v enters the picture. This measure of the spread of the values of the individual observations in the sample constitutes evidence concerning the spread of the values of all the members of the population and therefore must be considered in assessing a posterior distribution of $\tilde{A}$ whenever the population spread is unknown.

12.3.2
Probability That the Values
of *n* Sample Observations
Will Have Average *a* and Variance *v*

If a businessman has taken n sample observations in order to learn more about the uncertain average $\tilde{A}$ of the values of the individual members of some population, and if he has computed the average a and variance v of the values of the sample observations, he can use the assessment gamble diagrammed in Figure 12.2 as a basis for deriving a posterior distribution of $\tilde{A}$ that is consistent with the information conveyed by the values of n, a, and v. The fork at the origin of the diagram is to be understood as having one branch for every possible value of the uncertain population average $\tilde{A}$. The second-level forks, where $n \to a,v$ stands for the event "n observations yield values with average a and variance v", would in a complete diagram have one branch for each possible pair of values for a and v, but after the sample has been taken it is permissible as usual to suppress all branches representing sample events (in this case, values of n, a, and v) which might have occurred but in fact did not occur.

Assessment of "prior" unconditional probabilities for the branches of the $\tilde{A}$ fork at the origin of a diagram like Figure 12.2 presents no new problems, and therefore we turn immediately to the problem of assessing the probabilities for the second-level branches of the diagram. The probability assigned to any second-level branch must of course be conditional on the value of $\tilde{A}$ preceding that branch; it will be denoted by $P(n \rightarrow a,v \mid A)$.

In the general case, it is no easier to assess conditional probabilities of the form $P(n \rightarrow a,v \mid A)$ than it is to assess the conditional probabilities for values of individual sample observations that we discussed in Section 12.2.4 above. Assessment of $P(n \rightarrow a,v \mid A)$ is very easy, however, under certain special conditions that are satisfied in a great many practical applications of sampling, namely, when (1) the sample size or number of observations n is large—at least 25, better 100, and (2) the assessor feels that his prior information about the spread of the values of the individual members of the population is negligible relative to the information on this subject that is supplied by the sample.

Provided that these two basic conditions are met, probabilities of the form $P(n \rightarrow a,v \mid A)$ can be assessed with the aid of tables of a mathematically defined function known as the «Gaussian density function». This function, which we shall denote by g^*, is a function of one argument, which we shall call u; a table showing the function value $g^*(u)$ for various u's appears as Table T2 in the collection of tables at the end of this book. The formula by which the function is defined is of no real interest to us here; what *is* of interest about the function is the following very remarkable proposition, the truth of which rests in part on a mathematical argument and in part on a great deal of accumulated experience.

■ Suppose that n sample observations are to be drawn from some population by equiprobable sampling with replacement. If (1) n is large, and (2) prior information about the spread of the values of the individual members of the population is negligible relative to the information that will be obtained from the sample, then the conditional probability that should be assigned to any event of the form $n \rightarrow a,v$ given any particular value A of the population average $\tilde{A}$ can be very closely approximated by first computing

$$u = (a - A) \sqrt{n/v}$$

and then using the formula

$$P(n \rightarrow a,v \mid A) \doteq k\, g^*(u),$$

where g^* is the Gaussian density function and k is a factor whose value does not depend on A.

If we wanted to know the actual numerical value of $P(n \rightarrow a,v \mid A)$, we would of course have to know not only the value of $g^*(u)$ but also the value of k, which would have to be calculated from a formula. Our real objective, however, is not to evaluate $P(n \rightarrow a,v \mid A)$ for its own sake but to compute the probabilities that should be assigned to the possible values of $\tilde{A}$ after observing the event

$n \rightarrow a, v$; and we can compute these latter probabilities without knowing the value of the factor k because the factor k will cancel out in the course of our computations, as we shall now show by an example.

12.3.3
Analysis of an Assessment Problem

As an example of the use of the method of assessment just described, let us return to the assessment problem faced by Mr. Fraser in Section 12.2.1, but since we are unable to deal with very small samples, let us now assume that Mr. Fraser has taken, not 3, but 25 sample observations. We assume as before that the sampling was equiprobable with replacement; we now assume that the values of the 25 sample observations are those in the second column of Table 12.1. As shown by the self-explanatory calculations in the table, the average of the values of Mr. Fraser's $n = 25$ observations is $a = 18.72$ and their variance is $v = 91.88$.

TABLE 12.1
Mr. Fraser's Sample Information

Observation No.	Value of Observation	Value Minus Average	Square
1	13	− 5.72	32.72
2	17	− 1.72	2.96
3	21	+ 2.28	5.20
4	44	+25.28	639.08
5	20	+ 1.28	1.64
6	23	+ 4.28	18.32
7	17	− 1.72	2.96
8	33	+14.28	203.92
9	22	+ 3.28	10.76
10	10	− 8.72	76.04
11	2	−16.72	279.56
12	17	− 1.72	2.96
13	8	−10.72	114.92
14	23	+ 4.28	18.32
15	35	+16.28	265.04
16	23	+ 4.28	18.32
17	10	− 8.72	76.04
18	19	+ .28	.08
19	24	+ 5.28	27.88
20	9	− 9.72	94.48
21	20	+ 1.28	1.64
22	0	−18.72	350.44
23	15	− 3.72	13.84
24	18	− .72	.52
25	25	+ 6.28	39.44
Sum	468		2297.08
÷ 25	18.72		91.88

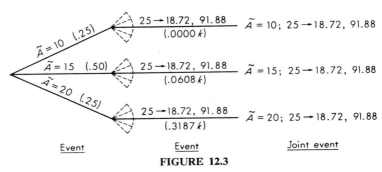

Event   Event   Joint event

FIGURE 12.3

Mr. Fraser's Probability Diagram

If Mr. Fraser is willing to discard a small part of the information in his sample and assign to $\tilde{A}$ a posterior distribution that is logically consistent with the information conveyed by the statistics $n = 25$, $a = 18.72$, and $v = 91.88$, he can base his calculations on the probability diagram in Figure 12.3, where the probabilities shown in parentheses on the branches have been obtained as follows.

1. The (prior) unconditional probabilities $P(A)$ that Mr. Fraser (would have) assigned before sampling to the branches of the $\tilde{A}$ fork at the origin of this diagram are copied from the branches of the $\tilde{A}$ fork in Figure 12.1 (page 479).

2. The conditional probabilities $P(n \rightarrow a,v \mid A)$ that Mr. Fraser (should have) assigned before sampling to the sample-outcome branches in the second level of the diagram are computed by applying the formula for $P(n \rightarrow a,v \mid A)$ that was given in Section 12.3.2; the calculations are shown in Table 12.2, where the value of $\sqrt{.272}$ was read from the table of square roots that appears as Table T5 in the collection of tables at the end of this book.

TABLE 12.2

Computation of $P(n \rightarrow a,v \mid A)$

$n = 25$, $a = 18.72$, $v = 91.88$

$$\sqrt{n/v} = \sqrt{.272} = .522$$

Population Average A	Argument $u = (a - A) \sqrt{n/v}$	Gaussian $g^*(u)$	Conditional $P(n \rightarrow a,v \mid A)$
10	$8.72 \times .522 = +4.55$	.0000	.0000 k
15	$3.72 \times .522 = +1.94$	.0608	.0608 k
20	$-1.28 \times .522 = -.67$	.3187	.3187 k

Having assigned probabilities to the branches of his probability diagram, Mr. Fraser can now go on to compute the distribution that he should assign to the population average $\tilde{A}$ posterior to sampling in exactly the same way that Mr. Warren computed his posterior distribution of $\tilde{p}$ in Table 10.5 (page 406). The calculations are shown in Table 12.3, where the reader should observe that the unknown factor k simply cancels out in the last stage of the computations.

TABLE 12.3
Computation of Mr. Fraser's Posterior Distribution of $\tilde{A}$

1	2	3	4	5
Value *A*	*Prior* *P(A)*	*Conditional* $P(n \to a,v \mid A)$	*Joint* $P(A; n \to a,v)$	*Posterior* $P(A \mid n \to a,v)$
10	.25	.0000 k	.0000 k	.0000 k/.1101 k = .000
15	.50	.0608 k	.0304 k	.0304 k/.1101 k = .276
20	.25	.3187 k	.0797 k	.0797 k/.1101 k = .724
	1.00		.1101 k = $P(n \to a,v)$	1.000

Before leaving this example, we remind the reader of the basic logic underlying the calculations in Table 12.3.

1. The probabilities in Columns 2 and 3 are the probabilities that Mr. Fraser (would have) assigned before sampling to the first- and second-level branches of his probability diagram (Figure 12.3).

2. The probabilities in Column 4 are the probabilities that Mr. Fraser (would have) assigned before sampling to the end positions of his probability diagram.

3. The probabilities in Column 5 are the conditional probabilities that Mr. Fraser should have assigned before sampling to the various possible values of $\tilde{A}$ given that 25 observations yield the statistics $a = 18.72$ and $v = 91.88$.

4. The heading of Column 5 reminds us that these latter probabilities, which were conditional on the event $(25 \to 18.72, 91.88)$ before Mr. Fraser knew that that event would occur, become unconditional probabilities after he knows that that event actually occurred.

In practical work there is, of course, no need to show the constant factor k which appears in Tables 12.2 and 12.3 but has no effect on the final results. Both these tables could be replaced by Table 12.4.

TABLE 12.4
Practical Computation of Mr. Fraser's Posterior Distribution of $\tilde{A}$
$n = 25, a = 18.72, v = 91.88$

$$\sqrt{n/v} = \sqrt{.272} = .522$$

1	2	3a	3b	4	5
Value *A*	*Prior* *P(A)*	*Argument* $u = (a - A)\sqrt{n/v}$	*Gaussian* $g^*(u)$	*Product* $P(A)\,g^*(u)$	*Posterior* $P(A \mid n \to a,v)$
10	.25	8.72 × .522 = +4.55	.0000	.0000	.0000/.1101 = .000
15	.50	3.72 × .525 = +1.94	.0608	.0304	.0304/.1101 = .276
20	.25	−1.28 × .522 = − .67	.3187	.0797	.0797/.1101 = .724
	1.00			.1101	1.000

12.3.4
Recapitulation: Large-sample Theory

Before proceeding to analyze any problem by the method of calculation described above, the reader must be sure to remember that its validity rests on two crucial assumptions:

1 The sample size n is "large"—at least 25, better 100.

2 Prior information concerning the spread of the values of the individual members of the population is negligible relative to the information obtained from the sample.

If these two conditions are not satisfied, it will ordinarily not be true that $P(n \to a, v \mid A)$ is approximately equal to

$$kg^*(u) \qquad \text{where} \qquad u = (a - A)\sqrt{n/v}.$$

The mathematics by which this formula is derived is known as "large-sample theory"; the formula itself will be called the ≪large-sample formula≫ for $P(n \to a, v \mid A)$; and the stated conditions on the sample size n and the prior information about the spread of the values of the individual members of the population will be called the conditions for applicability of large-sample theory.

■ All following discussion of samples from many-valued populations will be restricted to situations where the conditions for the applicability of large-sample theory are satisfied.

12.4
GROUPED APPROXIMATIONS

When the average $\tilde{A}$ of the values of the individual members of a population has a very great number of possible values, as it almost always has in practical applications of sampling, the businessman cannot assess his prior probability for each possible value individually. He can, however, assess his prior distribution of $\tilde{A}$ by constructing a graph of its cumulative function, and after he has done so a grouped approximation to his posterior distribution of $\tilde{A}$ can be computed by first grouping his prior distribution and then proceeding exactly as if this grouped distribution were his true prior distribution of $\tilde{A}$.

Suppose, for example, that a businessman is interested in a population of file cards on each of which is written the value of his company's inventory of a certain item; suppose that before sampling he assigns the prior distribution shown in Figure 12.4 to the uncertain average $\tilde{A}$ of the dollar amounts on the individual cards; suppose that $n = 100$ cards are then drawn from the population by equiprobable sampling with replacement; suppose that the average and variance of the 100 dollar amounts on these cards are respectively $a = 173.2$ and

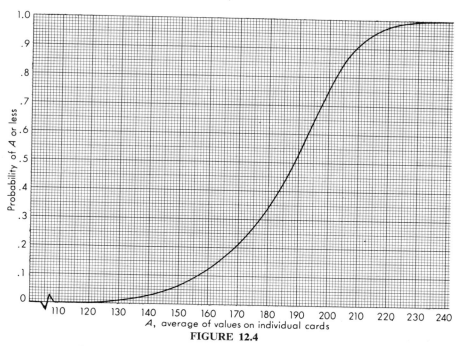

FIGURE 12.4

A Businessman's Prior Distribution of a Population Average $\tilde{A}$

$v = 8897$; and suppose that the businessman feels that his prior information about the spread of the dollar amounts on all the cards in the file was negligible relative to the information obtained from the sample, so that large-sample theory applies.

To get a rough idea of the revised or posterior distribution that the businessman should assign to $\tilde{A}$ after observing the sample, we first group the prior distribution of $\tilde{A}$ by reading from Figure 12.4 the bracket medians of 10 equiprobable brackets of values of A. These bracket medians and the probabilities assigned to them are shown in the first two columns of Table 12.5. Then treating the distribution defined by the first two columns of Table 12.5 exactly as if it were the businessman's true prior distribution of $\tilde{A}$, we proceed in the remainder of the table to compute the distribution that he should assign to $\tilde{A}$ posterior to observing $a = 173.2$, $v = 8897$ in a sample of $n = 100$ observations. These calculations follow the model of Table 12.4 exactly.

In a real business application of sampling, a statistician would of course use a computer to carry out all calculations of the sort we have just carried out by hand, and he would have the computer base all of its calculations on a much finer grouping of the businessman's prior distribution of $\tilde{A}$ than the one we used in the last section. In Figure 12.5 we show portions of the computer output obtained by first using the program described in Section 7.4.8 to group the prior distribution of Figure 12.4 into 100 equiprobable brackets and then using a pro-

TABLE 12.5

Computation of a Posterior Distribution of $\tilde{A}$ from a Grouped Prior Distribution

$n = 100, a = 173.2, v = 8897$

$\sqrt{n/v} = .106$

1	2	3a	3b	4	5
Value A	Prior P(A)	Argument $u = (a - A)\sqrt{n/v}$	Gaussian $g^*(u)$	Product $P(A)\,g^*(u)$	Posterior $P(A\|n \to a,v)$
146.6	.1	$26.6 \times .106 = +2.82$	.0075	.00075	.006
163.3	.1	$9.9 \times .106 = +1.05$	.2299	.02299	.194
173.3	.1	$-\ .1 \times .106 = -\ .01$	.3989	.03989	.336
180.6	.1	$-\ 7.4 \times .106 = -\ .78$	.2943	.02943	.248
186.2	.1	$-13.0 \times .106 = -1.38$	.1539	.01539	.130
190.9	.1	$-17.7 \times .106 = -1.88$	.0681	.00681	.057
195.2	.1	$-22.0 \times .106 = -2.33$	.0264	.00264	.022
199.8	.1	$-26.6 \times .106 = -2.82$	.0075	.00075	.006
205.1	.1	$-31.9 \times .106 = -3.38$	.0013	.00013	.001
214.8	.1	$-41.6 \times .106 = -4.41$	.0000	.00000	.000
	1.0			.11878	1.000

gram which causes the computer to carry out exactly the same arithmetic that was carried out by hand in Table 12.5. At the top of the printout is a proof list of the coordinates and slopes of various points that were read from Figure 12.4 and supplied to the computer as input. After fitting a smooth mathematical curve to these points and slopes, the computer proceeded automatically to produce the main body of the printout, every column of which has exactly the same meaning and was derived in essentially the same way as the corresponding column in Table 12.5. The one difference is that instead of looking up the values $g^*(u)$ in a table, the computer calculated them internally from the formula for $g^*(u)$.

In Figure 12.6 we show smooth graphs of the prior and posterior cumulative functions corresponding to the computer printout in Figure 12.5. The reader should observe how the sample evidence has both tightened the businessman's distribution of $\tilde{A}$ and moved its "center" in the direction of the observed sample average $a = 173.2$.

Exact graphs of the coarser approximations to these same functions that were calculated by hand in Table 12.5 are shown in Figure 12.7; use of smooth graphs is not legitimate when we are proceeding as if there were only 10 possible values of $\tilde{A}$. We remind the reader that a grouped approximation to a posterior distribution is always to be treated as if it were exact. When a computer is used, all necessary accuracy should be secured by making a fine enough original grouping of the prior distribution, not by trying to improve on the computed results. And since the only purpose of working examples by hand is to learn the method of computation used by a computer, even the very coarse approximations resulting from the use of only 10 brackets should be treated as if they were exact.

INPUT DATA

VALUE	CUM PROB	SLOPE
120.0	0.	0.
130.0	0.010	
140.0	0.030	
160.0	0.124	
170.0	0.213	
180.0	0.341	
193.0	0.598	0.02330
200.0	0.753	
205.0	0.848	
210.0	0.911	
215.0	0.951	
225.0	0.990	
240.0	1.000	0.

SAMPLE N 100.   SAMPLE A   173.2   SAMPLE V   8897.

VALUE	PRIOR	G(U)	PRODUCT	POST	CUM POST
125.5	0.0100	0.00000	0.00000001	0.0000	0.0000
133.0	0.0100	0.00004	0.00000045	0.0000	0.0000
137.7	0.0100	0.00034	0.00000338	0.0000	0.0000
142.1	0.0100	0.00174	0.00001737	0.0001	0.0002
145.4	0.0100	0.00515	0.00005152	0.0004	0.0006
147.6	0.0100	0.00995	0.00009950	0.0008	0.0015
149.5	0.0100	0.01714	0.00017140	0.0014	0.0029
151.4	0.0100	0.02790	0.00027897	0.0024	0.0053
153.3	0.0100	0.04305	0.00043054	0.0036	0.0089
155.1	0.0100	0.06322	0.00063220	0.0053	0.0142
156.8	0.0100	0.08862	0.00088619	0.0075	0.0217
158.5	0.0100	0.11897	0.00118972	0.0101	0.0318
180.3	0.0100	0.30114	0.00301138	0.0255	0.6728
180.9	0.0100	0.28476	0.00284757	0.0241	0.6969
181.6	0.0100	0.26842	0.00268416	0.0227	0.7196
182.2	0.0100	0.25233	0.00252325	0.0213	0.7409
182.8	0.0100	0.23665	0.00236654	0.0200	0.7609
183.4	0.0100	0.22154	0.00221541	0.0187	0.7796
184.0	0.0100	0.20709	0.00207085	0.0175	0.7971
184.6	0.0100	0.19336	0.00193363	0.0163	0.8135
185.1	0.0100	0.18042	0.00180420	0.0153	0.8287
185.6	0.0100	0.16828	0.00168283	0.0142	0.8430
186.1	0.0100	0.15696	0.00156961	0.0133	0.8562
186.6	0.0100	0.14636	0.00146360	0.0124	0.8686
187.0	0.0100	0.13621	0.00136212	0.0115	0.8801
187.5	0.0100	0.12651	0.00126513	0.0107	0.8908
188.0	0.0100	0.11727	0.00117274	0.0099	0.9007
188.4	0.0100	0.10850	0.00108503	0.0092	0.9099
188.9	0.0100	0.10020	0.00100200	0.0085	0.9184
189.3	0.0100	0.09236	0.00092364	0.0078	0.9262
189.8	0.0100	0.08499	0.00084990	0.0072	0.9333
190.2	0.0100	0.07807	0.00078070	0.0066	0.9399
190.7	0.0100	0.07159	0.00071592	0.0061	0.9460
191.1	0.0100	0.06554	0.00065544	0.0055	0.9515
191.6	0.0100	0.05991	0.00059912	0.0051	0.9566
207.7	0.0100	0.00050	0.00000504	0.0000	0.9999
208.5	0.0100	0.00037	0.00000369	0.0000	0.9999
209.4	0.0100	0.00025	0.00000254	0.0000	1.0000
210.4	0.0100	0.00016	0.00000165	0.0000	1.0000
211.5	0.0100	0.00010	0.00000103	0.0000	1.0000
212.7	0.0100	0.00006	0.00000062	0.0000	1.0000
214.0	0.0100	0.00003	0.00000034	0.0000	1.0000
215.8	0.0100	0.00001	0.00000015	0.0000	1.0000
217.8	0.0100	0.00001	0.00000005	0.0000	1.0000
220.1	0.0100	0.00000	0.00000001	0.0000	1.0000
222.5	0.0100	0.00000	0.00000000	0.0000	1.0000
231.5	0.0100	0.00000	0.00000000	0.0000	1.0000

TOTAL   0.11829904

POST MEAN   176.4

FIGURE 12.5

The Posterior Distribution of $\bar{A}$ as Evaluated by a Digital Computer

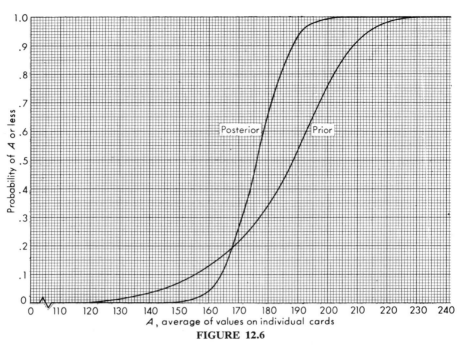

FIGURE 12.6

Prior and Posterior Cumulative Functions Based on Grouping into 100 Equiprobable Brackets

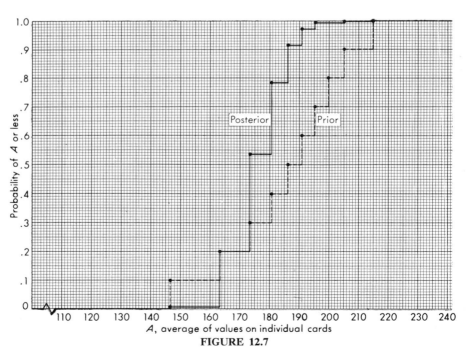

FIGURE 12.7

Prior and Posterior Cumulative Functions Based on Grouping into 10 Equiprobable Brackets

12.5
SUCCESSIVE SAMPLES

We have already said that although a distribution that is revised to take account of sample information is called a "posterior" distribution, it is in fact simply an ordinary probability distribution which takes account of all the information available at the time it is assessed, as any distribution of any UQ should do. Exactly as in the case of a population fraction $\tilde{p}$, it follows that if a decision maker who has taken one sample and computed his distribution of $\tilde{A}$ posterior thereto now takes another sample, the same distribution that was "posterior" as regards the first sample is "prior" as regards the second sample and can be used exactly like any prior distribution in computing his distribution posterior to the second sample.

In problems of the kind with which we are now dealing, however, computation of a distribution posterior to a second sample from a distribution posterior to a first sample gives rise to a difficulty that did not appear in problems of the kind with which we dealt in Chapters 10 and 11. The difficulty does not concern the basic logic, which is exactly the same as before. It concerns the assessment of the businessman's conditional probabilities for the event $n \rightarrow a, v$ of the second sample given the possible values of the population average $\tilde{A}$. Because the first sample has supplied a substantial amount of information about the spread of the values of the individual members of the population, these probabilities cannot be calculated by use of large-sample theory (cf. Section 12.3.4), and the way in which they actually can be calculated is not a subject for an introductory text.

Elementary methods can, however, be used to compute the distribution that should be assigned to $\tilde{A}$ posterior to two or more samples if the samples are pooled. Provided that the size of the pooled sample is "large", and provided that the information about the spread of the values of the individual members of the population that was available prior to taking *any* sample is negligible relative to the information supplied by the pooled sample, the posterior distribution of $\tilde{A}$ can be computed by use of large-sample theory exactly as if all the observations in the pooled sample had been taken as a single sample. Observe that the pooled sample may be large enough to justify the use of large-sample theory even though none of the individual samples is large enough by itself.

If we let n^*, a^*, and v^* denote the statistics that summarize the pooled sample, their values can be calculated from the pooled observations in the ordinary way. If the pooled sample consists of two samples which have been summarized separately by statistics n_1, a_1, v_1, and n_2, a_2, v_2, the statistics of the pooled sample can be computed by use of the formulas

$$n^* = n_1 + n_2, \qquad a^* = \frac{n_1 \, a_1 + n_2 \, a_2}{n_1 + n_2}, \qquad v^* \doteq \frac{n_1 \, v_1 + n_2 \, v_2}{n_1 + n_2}.$$

The last of these three formulas is an approximation, but unless one of the two samples is very small, the approximation is nearly exact.

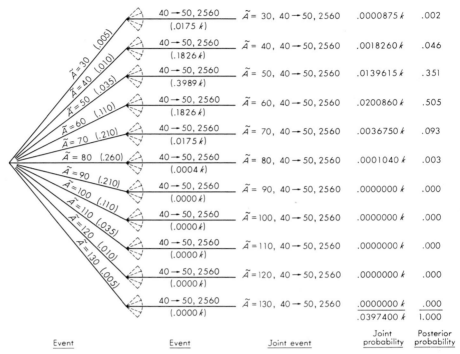

Event	Event	Joint event	Joint probability	Posterior probability

FIGURE 12.8

Computation of a Posterior Distribution of $\tilde{A}$

12.6
COMBINATION OF PRIOR
AND SAMPLE INFORMATION

In order to gain more insight into the way in which prior and sample information combine to determine a businessman's posterior distribution of a population average $\tilde{A}$, let us examine the computation of a posterior distribution that is shown in Figure 12.8 and Table 12.6. After the businessman and his statistician have assessed the probabilities shown in Columns 2 and 3 of the table for the first- and second-level branches in the figure, the businessman's posterior probability for each possible value of $\tilde{A}$ is computed in two steps:

1 We first multiply his prior probability *for* each value of $\tilde{A}$ by his conditional probability for the sample event $n \rightarrow a,v$ *given* that value of $\tilde{A}$ to obtain the product shown in Column 4 of the table.

2 We then divide each of these products by their sum, which is the businessman's unconditional probability for the event $n \rightarrow a,v$.

Since every product computed in step 1 is divided by the *same* number in step 2, this second step has no effect on the *relative* magnitudes of the posterior

TABLE 12.6
Computation of a Posterior Distribution of $\tilde{A}$

$$n = 40, a = 50, v = 2560$$

$$\sqrt{n/v} = \sqrt{1/64} = 1/8$$

1	2	3	4	5
Value A	Prior $P(A)$	Conditional* $P(n \rightarrow a,v \mid A)$	Joint $P(A;\, n \rightarrow a,v)$	Posterior $P(A \mid n \rightarrow a,v)$
30	.005	.0175 k	.0000875 k	.002
40	.010	.1826 k	.0018260 k	.046
50	.035	.3989 k	.0139615 k	.351
60	.110	.1826 k	.0200860 k	.505
70	.210	.0175 k	.0036750 k	.093
80	.260	.0004 k	.0001040 k	.003
90	.210	.0000 k	.0000000 k	.000
100	.110	.0000 k	.0000000 k	.000
110	.035	.0000 k	.0000000 k	.000
120	.010	.0000 k	.0000000 k	.000
130	.005	.0000 k	.0000000 k	.000
	1.000		.0397400 k $= P(n \rightarrow a,v)$	1.000

* $P(n \rightarrow a,v \mid A) = kg^*(u)$ where $u = (a - A)\sqrt{n/v} = (a - A)/8$

probabilities of the various possible values of $\tilde{A}$. It can be thought of as merely a rescaling operation which causes the posterior probabilities to add to 1, as they should. In other words:

■ The posterior probability that should be assigned to each possible value of $\tilde{A}$ is *proportional* (although not in general equal) to the product of just two factors: (1) the businessman's prior probability *for* that value of $\tilde{A}$, and (2) his conditional probability for the sample event $n \rightarrow a,v$ *given* that value of $\tilde{A}$.

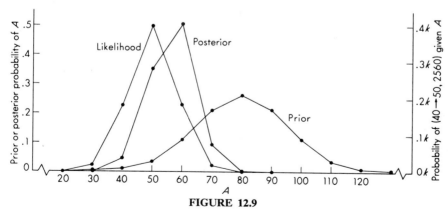

FIGURE 12.9
Mass and Likelihood Functions

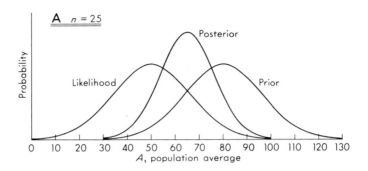

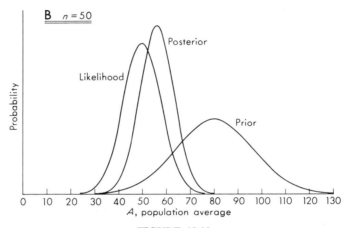

FIGURE 12.10

Mass and Likelihood Functions

The relation just described is shown graphically in Figure 12.9, where the heavy dots labelled "prior" represent the probabilities that appear on the first-level branches of Figure 12.8 and in Column 2 of Table 12.6, the dots labelled "likelihood" represent the probabilities that appear on the second-level branches and in Column 3, and the dots labelled "posterior" represent the probabilities that appear in Column 5. If we use the terms "prior mass function", "sample likelihood function", and "posterior mass function" to denote these three sets of probabilities, we can say that:

■ The height of a graph of the posterior mass function at any possible value of $\tilde{A}$ is proportional to the product of the heights of the graphs of the prior mass function and the sample likelihood function at that value of $\tilde{A}$.

With this fact in mind, we can now see how various amounts of sample information combine with a fixed amount of prior information by examining

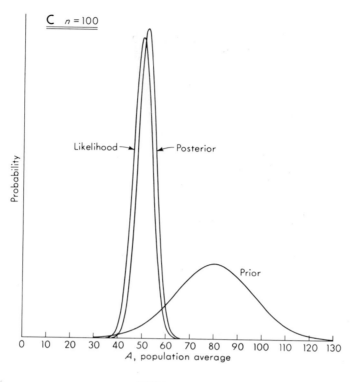

FIGURE 12.10
(Continued)

Figure 12.10.   The figure depicts three cases in all of which it is assumed that the population average $\tilde{A}$ has an extremely large number of possible values evenly spaced out along the horizontal axis; the reader can think of 100,000 or 1 million possible values on the part of the A axis that is actually shown in the figure.   The three cases are also exactly alike as regards the prior mass function and the average and variance of the sample observations, which are assumed to be $a = 50$, $v = 1,600$.   The cases differ only in respect to the number of sample observations, which is indicated at the top of each part of the figure.   Comparing the three parts of Figure 12.10, the reader should observe that:

1 As the number of sample observations increases, the tightness of the sample likelihood function increases.

2 As the tightness of the sample likelihood function increases while the tightness of the prior mass function remains fixed, the posterior mass function (1) becomes tighter, and (2) moves closer to the sample likelihood function.

GAUSSIAN APPROXIMATIONS
TO POSTERIOR DISTRIBUTIONS OF $\tilde{A}$

Suppose now that a businessman's prior mass function, sample likelihood function, and posterior mass function are those depicted in Figure 12.10C. When referred to a suitable vertical scale, the likelihood curve defines a possible mass function; and this mass function is so close to the businessman's posterior mass function that in many situations no harm would be done if the businessman thought and acted as if his posterior mass function were in fact the one defined by the likelihood curve rather than the one defined by the posterior curve.

We saw in Section 11.2 that the fact that a posterior mass function of a population fraction $\tilde{p}$ can often be treated as if it were identical in shape to the sample likelihood function is of great practical importance. When a posterior mass function can be treated in this way, the businessman has to make only a qualitative assessment of his prior distribution of $\tilde{p}$, and computations are greatly simplified or can even be replaced by table lookups. In the present section, we shall show that these same statements are true and that very similar computational methods can be used when the businessman wishes to assess a posterior distribution of a population average $\tilde{A}$ rather than a population fraction $\tilde{p}$. The line of argument that we shall follow will also be very similar to the line of argument that we followed in Section 11.2, but we shall rely on the reader to remember here what he learned there and shall not spell out all the details.

12.7.1
Uniform Distributions of $\tilde{A}$

If each individual member of a population of size N can have any one of the values $0, 1, 2, \ldots, 7$, then the total of the individual values of all members of the population can be any one of the numbers $0, 1, 2, \ldots, 7N$, and consequently the logically possible values of the average $\tilde{A}$ of the values of the individual members of the population are $0/N, 1/N, 2/N, \ldots, 7N/N$. This means that the logically possible values of $\tilde{A}$ are evenly spaced; and we leave it to the reader to convince himself that even if the individual members of a population can have negative and/or fractional values, the possible values of the population average $\tilde{A}$ will be evenly spaced in any circumstances likely to be encountered in practical business applications of sampling.

With this fact in mind, we now generalize the definition of a uniform distribution that we gave in Section 11.2.1.

> ■ If a decision maker (1) believes that the possible values of any UQ are *equally spaced*, and (2) assigns *equal probabilities* to all the possible values, we shall say that his distribution of the UQ is ≪uniform≫.

12.7.2
The Posterior Distribution of $\tilde{A}$
When the Prior Distribution Is Uniform

We have already seen in Section 12.6 that the height of a posterior mass function is proportional to the product of the heights of the prior mass function and the sample likelihood function. This implies that:

- When the prior probabilities of all possible values of $\tilde{p}$ are equal, the posterior mass function is identical in shape to the sample likelihood function. The only difference between the two functions is one of vertical scale.

If the decision maker of Figure 12.10C had assigned equal prior probabilities to all possible values of $\tilde{A}$, rather than the unequal prior probabilities depicted in the figure, the likelihood curve in the figure would define his exact posterior mass function when referred to a suitable vertical scale.

Now think of the likelihood curve in Figure 12.10C as tracing the tops of the vertical bars, one for each possible value of $\tilde{A}$, that would be present in an exact graph of either a likelihood or a posterior mass function (cf. Figure 7.3A on page 230). If the heights of these bars are measured on a scale suitable for a posterior mass function, then (1) the "cumulative" probability of an event such as $\tilde{A} \leqslant 43$ is the sum of the heights of the bars up to and including the bar for $\tilde{A} = 43$, and (2) the total height of *all* the bars in the graph must be 1. It follows that if the heights of the bars are measured on a scale suitable for a likelihood function, the probability of $\tilde{A} \leqslant 43$ is given by the ratio

$$\frac{\text{total height of bars up to and including the bar for } \tilde{A} = 43}{\text{total height of all bars}}.$$

This means that if all possible values of $\tilde{A}$ have equal prior probabilities, all that we need to compute the cumulative posterior probability of any event such as $\tilde{A} \leqslant 43$ is (1) a list of the possible values of $\tilde{A}$, and (2) the mathematically determined likelihood of the sample event $n \to a,v$ given each of these possible values of $\tilde{A}$.

Finally, assume that the possible values of $\tilde{A}$ not only have equal prior probabilities but also are (1) equally spaced, so that the prior distribution of $\tilde{A}$ can be called uniform, and (2) very close together. In this case, the ratio

$$\frac{\text{total height of bars up to and including the bar for } \tilde{A} = 43}{\text{total height of all bars}}$$

in an exact graph of the sample likelihood function will scarcely depend on *exactly* how close the possible values are together, and similarly for any other value of $\tilde{A}$. It follows that if (1) prior to sampling the businessman assigns a uniform prior distribution to $\tilde{A}$, and (2) the possible values of $\tilde{A}$ are very close together, then the cumulative function that he should assign to $\tilde{A}$ posterior to sampling can be calculated without reference to the exact spacing between the possible values of $\tilde{A}$. It depends essentially on only the uniformity of the prior distribution and the sample outcome.

12.7.3
Gaussian Cumulative Functions

The conclusion just reached implies that if the possible values of $\tilde{A}$ are very close together, the posterior cumulative function resulting from a uniform prior distribution can be very closely approximated by first using the calculus to find the limiting form that the function approaches as the spacing approaches 0 and then designing a computer program to evaluate this limiting form of the cumulative function. Because the limiting cumulative function is much easier to evaluate than the exact cumulative function for any finite spacing between possible values of $\tilde{A}$, this is what is actually done in practice.

When the likelihood function is computed by use of large-sample theory, so that its values are determined by the Gaussian density function, the limiting form of the cumulative function that results from a uniform prior distribution and the sample event $n \rightarrow a,v$ is what is called a «Gaussian cumulative function» with parameters.

$$M = a, \qquad S = \sqrt{v/n}.$$

All Gaussian cumulative functions have the following properties, which are illustrated by the graphs in Figure 12.11 of Gaussian cumulative functions with three specific pairs of values for the parameters M and S.

1 The value (ordinate) of the function is $1/2$ when the argument (abscissa) is equal to the parameter M.

2 The lateral "spread" of the function is proportional to the parameter S.

3 The function is symmetric in the sense that its graph has exactly the same shape when viewed from above that it has when viewed from below.

4 No matter how large the argument A becomes, the value of the function never quite reaches 1, but it is nearly 1 for any A greater than $M + 3S$. Similarly, no matter how (algebraically) small the argument A becomes, the value of the function never quite reaches 0, but it is nearly 0 for any A less than $M - 3S$.

There exist many general-purpose computer programs that can be used to calculate the value of a Gaussian cumulative function with any parameters M and S for any argument A. For use by those without ready access to a computer,

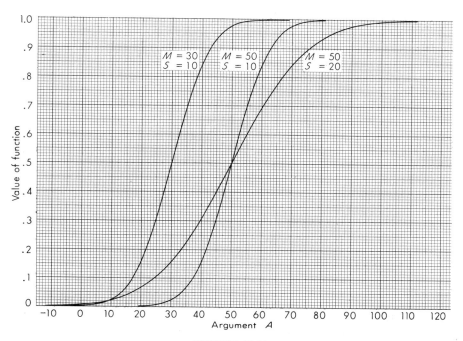

FIGURE 12.11

Gaussian Cumulative Functions

a table from which it is easy to obtain a number of points on the graph of any Gaussian cumulative function appears as Table T4 in the collection of tables at the end of this book.

Table T4 is a table of what is called the «unit» Gaussian cumulative function, i.e., the Gaussian cumulative function with parameters $M = 0$, $S = 1$. The table is an inverse table, showing abscissas u_k for selected ordinates k rather than the reverse. The table can be used to evaluate other Gaussian cumulative functions by making use of the fact that, for any pair of values of the parameters M and S, the argument A_k for which the value of the function is k is given by the formula

$$A_k = M + u_k S.$$

For example, suppose that we are interested in the Gaussian cumulative function with parameters $M = 30$, $S = 10$, and suppose that we wish to find the argument (abscissa) $A_{.1}$ corresponding to the function value (ordinate) .1. We simply read $u_{.1} = -1.282$ from Table T4 and then compute

$$A_{.1} = M + u_{.1} S = 30 - 1.282 \times 10 = 17.18,$$

in agreement with the graph in Figure 12.11.

12.7.4

**Recapitulation: the Posterior Distribution
of $\tilde{A}$ When the Prior Distribution Is Uniform
and Large-sample Theory Applies**

What we have said thus far about Gaussian approximations to posterior distributions of $\tilde{A}$ can be summarized as follows:

■ Suppose that a sample yielding statistics n, a, and v has been taken from a population by equiprobable sampling with replacement. If (1) prior to sampling the decision maker assigned a uniform distribution to $\tilde{A}$, (2) the possible values of $\tilde{A}$ are very close together, and (3) the sample likelihood function would be calculated by use of large-sample theory, then the cumulative function that the decision maker should assign to $\tilde{A}$ posterior to sampling is almost identical to a Gaussian cumulative function with parameters

$$M = a, \qquad S = \sqrt{v/n}.$$

Any desired cumulative probability or fractile under a distribution with a Gaussian cumulative function can be found directly by use of any one of a number of generally available computer programs or published tables of the unit Gaussian function. Alternatively, a graph of the complete cumulative function can be constructed by fairing a smooth curve through points calculated by use of Table T4 and the relation

$$A_k = M + u_k S,$$

after which any desired cumulative probability or fractile can be read from this graph.

We have already seen that the value of a Gaussian cumulative function is .5 when the argument of the function is equal to the parameter M. This implies that the median of a distribution having a Gaussian cumulative function with parameters M and S is equal to M, and the symmetry of the function then implies that the mean and the mode of the distribution are also equal to M (cf. Section 7.2.6).

12.7.5

Nearly Uniform Prior Distributions

The results just stated for the case where the decision maker's prior distribution of $\tilde{A}$ is strictly uniform can be used as good working approximations in many situations where his prior distribution is not strictly uniform. Thus in Figure 12.10C on page 497, the likelihood curve when referred to a suitable vertical scale describes the posterior mass function that would have resulted from a strictly uniform prior distribution, and there is not a great deal of difference between this mass function and the one that actually resulted from the nonuniform prior distribution depicted in the figure.

The reason why the nonuniformity of the prior mass function in Figure 12.10C has so little effect on the posterior mass function is easy to see if we recall that the height of the posterior mass function is proportional to the product of the heights of the prior mass function and the sample likelihood function. Since the height of the likelihood function is virtually 0 outside an interval extending from about $A = 35$ to $A = 65$ on the horizontal axis, the height of the posterior mass function has to be virtually 0 outside this interval unless the prior mass function has some extremely unusual shape. And since the variation in the height of the prior mass function inside this interval is small compared with the variation in the height of the sample likelihood function, the shape of the posterior mass function inside the interval is primarily determined by the shape of the sample likelihood function.

In order to generalize from this example, we first observe that in any situation where the sample likelihood function would be evaluated by use of large-sample theory, the value of the likelihood function will be virtually 0 outside an interval extending from $A = a - 3\sqrt{v/n}$ to $A = a + 3\sqrt{v/n}$, as the reader should verify. Consequently:

> ■ Suppose that equiprobable sampling with replacement has yielded statistics n, a, and v, and suppose that large-sample theory would be used to evaluate the likelihood function of this sample. If prior to sampling the decision maker (1) did not assign *extremely* high probabilities to any values of $\tilde{A}$ outside an interval extending from $A = a - 3\sqrt{v/n}$ to $A = a + 3\sqrt{v/n}$, and (2) assigned *roughly* equal probabilities to all values of $\tilde{A}$ inside this interval, then the posterior distribution he should assign to $\tilde{A}$ will be almost the same as the posterior distribution that would result from a strictly uniform prior distribution, and therefore its cumulative function can be very closely approximated by a Gaussian cumulative function with parameters
>
> $$M = a, \qquad S = \sqrt{v/n}.$$

12.8
ESTIMATES OF $\tilde{A}$

We saw in Section 11.3 that when a businessman wishes to use sample information about a fraction $\tilde{p}$, not in analyzing a well defined decision problem, but in preliminary thinking about some general problem area, he will necessarily make use, not of his complete posterior distribution of $\tilde{p}$, but of a point estimate of $\tilde{p}$ accompanied by a simple measure of the extent of his uncertainty about the true value of $\tilde{p}$. Exactly the same thing will be true when the businessman is interested in the average $\tilde{A}$ of the values of the individual members of a population rather than the fraction $\tilde{p}$ of successes in the population.

   Furthermore, most of what we said in Section 11.3 about choice of an estimate and measurement of uncertainty applies with only minor modifications when the businessman is interested in a population average $\tilde{A}$ rather than a population fraction $\tilde{p}$. He should choose as his estimate some value which is "central" under his posterior distribution of $\tilde{A}$, and he can usually find a satisfactory measure of his uncertainty by computing the distance between two fractiles of his posterior distribution, e.g., the .01 and .99 fractiles.

   When the businessman's posterior distribution of $\tilde{A}$ has a Gaussian cumulative function with parameters $M = a$ and $S = \sqrt{v/n}$, selection of an estimate and computation of the distance between two chosen fractiles are very easy. Since the mean, median, and mode of his distribution are all equal to M, as we saw in Section 12.7.4, $M = a$ is the only estimate that needs to be considered when the estimate is to be used as a guide to purely informal thinking. As regards the measure of his uncertainty about $\tilde{A}$, we have shown by Table T4 that the distance between $A_{.01}$ and $A_{.99}$ is

$$(M + 2.326\ S) - (M - 2.326\ S) = 4.652\ S = 4.652\sqrt{v/n}.$$

If the businessman chooses some pair of fractiles other than $A_{.01}$ and $A_{.99}$, the corresponding measure will be equally easy to compute.

   Finally, what we said in Section 11.3 about the reduction in uncertainty that the businessman can anticipate if he takes additional sample observations also applies with minor changes when the businessman is interested in an average $\tilde{A}$ rather than a fraction $\tilde{p}$. If his distribution of $\tilde{A}$ posterior to the sample that has already been taken could be calculated by treating his "original" distribution of $\tilde{A}$ as if it were uniform, then certainly he will be able to use this same method of calculation to find the distribution he should assign to $\tilde{A}$ posterior to taking additional sample observations and pooling them with the observations already taken. This means that if he takes $A_{.99} - A_{.01}$ as the measure of his uncertainty about $\tilde{A}$, his uncertainty posterior to any new sample will be $4.652\sqrt{v^*/n^*}$, where v^* and n^* are statistics calculated from the pooled sample, and similarly if he chooses fractiles other than $A_{.01}$ and $A_{.99}$. The value of n^* is known in advance; and although v^* is not known in advance, it is not likely to be *very* different from the statistic v calculated from the observations already taken. The businessman can get a good enough estimate of the uncertainty that will remain after a new sample has been taken by calculating it as if the v^* of the pooled sample were certain to be equal to the v of the sample already taken.

   For example, suppose that a businessman has already made $n = 100$ observations by equiprobable sampling with replacement; suppose that the variance of these sample observations is $v = 14.9$; suppose that his prior information about the average and spread of the individual values in the population

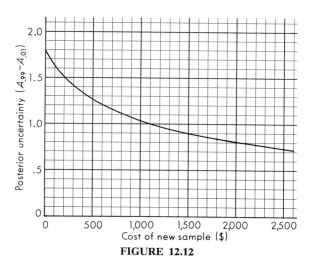

FIGURE 12.12

Cost of Sampling and Posterior Uncertainty about $\tilde{A}$

was negligible relative to the information obtained from this sample, so that his current distribution of $\tilde{A}$ has a Gaussian cumulative function; suppose that he measures his uncertainty about $\tilde{A}$ by $A_{.99} - A_{.01}$, so that his current uncertainty is $4.652 \times \sqrt{14.9/100} = 4.652 \times .386 = 1.80$; suppose that he is thinking of taking an additional sample of some as yet undetermined size in order to reduce this uncertainty; and suppose that taking any additional sample will cost $5 per observation.

In order to describe to this businessman the choices that are open to him, we first construct Table 12.7 by proceeding as follows.

1. In Column 1 we show a selection of possible sizes for a new sample.

2. In Column 2 we show the total size n^* of the sample that will result from pooling the new sample with the 100 observations already taken.

3. In Column 3 we show the parameter $S = \sqrt{v^*/n^*}$ of the posterior distribution of $\tilde{A}$ as calculated on the assumption that $v^* = 14.9$.

4. In Column 4 we show the corresponding uncertainty

$$A_{.99} - A_{.01} = 4.652\ S.$$

5. Finally, in Column 5 we show the cost of the new sample.

Having made these calculations for selected new sample sizes, we construct the graph in Figure 12.12 by first plotting each uncertainty in Column 4 of Table 12.7 against the corresponding cost in Column 5 and then fairing a curve through the plotted points. From this graph the businessman can read an estimate of the uncertainty about $\tilde{A}$ that will remain after spending any amount between $0 and $2,600 on additional sampling; it is now up to him to decide how much he wants to spend.

TABLE 12.7
Cost of Sampling and Posterior Uncertainty about $\tilde{A}$

1	2	3	4	5
Size of New Sample n	*Size of Pooled Sample* n^*	*Posterior Parameter* S	*Posterior Uncertainty* $A_{.99} - A_{.01}$	*Cost of New Sample*
0	100	.386	1.80	$ 0
50	150	.315	1.47	250
100	200	.273	1.27	500
200	300	.223	1.04	1,000
300	400	.193	.90	1,500
500	600	.158	.74	2,500

12.9
SAMPLING WITHOUT REPLACEMENT

All the results concerning the use of sample information from many-valued populations that we have obtained up to now have been derived on the basis of the assumption that the sample observations were obtained by equiprobable sampling with replacement. As we said earlier, this type of sampling is actually used in Monte Carlo calculations, but it is virtually never used in traditional applications of sampling such as market tests, sample surveys, and so forth. Some of the sampling processes that are used in such applications were discussed in Section 11.5 in connection with sampling from two-valued populations; in the present section we shall briefly review what was said there, making such modifications as are necessary to adapt our remarks to sampling from many-valued populations.

12.9.1
Equiprobable Sampling
without Replacement

As we said in Section 11.5, it is common practice in the simplest applications of the general kind now under discussion to use equiprobable sampling without replacement, i.e., to draw a sample in such a way that although no member of the population can be drawn more than once, every "eligible" member of the population has an equal chance of being chosen on each successive draw.

The way in which the information in a sample outcome is processed in order to assign a reasonable posterior distribution to $\tilde{A}$ is virtually the same when the sample is drawn by equiprobable sampling without replacement as when it is drawn by equiprobable sampling with replacement. In both cases it is very difficult to make use of all the information in the sample outcome, for the reasons set forth in Section 12.2.4; in both cases it is usually true that most of the information about $\tilde{A}$ that is contained in the sample is conveyed by the values of the three summary statistics n, a, and v that were defined in Section 12.3.1; and in both cases it is usually very easy to compute the posterior distribution of $\tilde{A}$ that is consistent with the information conveyed by these three statistics provided that (1) n is "large", and (2) the assessor's prior information about the spread of the values of the individual members of the population is negligible relative to the information obtained from the sample.

When these two conditions are satisfied, the distribution that should be assigned to $\tilde{A}$ posterior to equiprobable sampling without replacement can be computed by a procedure which is identical to the one described in Section 12.3.2 and 12.3.3 except for a change in the input u to the large-sample formula

$$P(n \rightarrow a, v \,|\, A) \doteq k \, g^*(u).$$

Instead of setting

$$u = (a - A)\sqrt{n/v},$$

as we do when the sample is taken with replacement, we must in principle set

$$u = (a - A)\sqrt{n/v} \, \sqrt{(N - 1)/(N - n)},$$

where N is the size of the population from which the sample is taken. In most applications, however, the sample size n is so small relative to the population size N that the factor $\sqrt{(N - 1)/(N - n)}$ is virtually equal to 1 and therefore has virtually no effect on the posterior distribution of $\tilde{A}$. The reader should neither try to remember the formula for the factor nor use it in working any of the exercises in this book.

The fact that the procedure for actually computing a distribution of $\tilde{A}$ posterior to equiprobable sampling is essentially the same when the sample is taken without replacement as it is when the sample is taken with replacement implies that virtually everything that was said in Section 12.7 about Gaussian approximations to posterior cumulative functions still applies when the sample is taken without replacement. The only difference when the sample is taken without replacement is in the formula for the parameter S of the Gaussian cumulative function, which becomes

$$S = \sqrt{v/n} \, \sqrt{(N - n)/(N - 1)}$$

instead of simply $\sqrt{v/n}$. In most applications, however, the additional factor $\sqrt{(N - n)/(N - 1)}$ is so close to 1 that its effect is negligible, and the reader should not use it in working any of the exercises in this book.

12.9.2
Systematic Sampling

Systematic sampling is another very simple process frequently used in practical applications. As we said in Section 11.5.2, it consists in choosing a number j and then taking every j'th item in a file or list; the first item chosen may be any one of the first j items in the list.

In processing the information obtained by systematic sampling, it is usually reasonable to proceed as if the information had been obtained by equiprobable sampling without replacement. Such processing is not reasonable, however, if there is reason to suspect that high or low values may appear in some definite pattern in the list or file, since this would invalidate the large-sample formula for $P(n \rightarrow a, v \mid A)$.

12.9.3
Stratification and Clustering

In large surveys of human populations and certain other applications of sampling, it is customary to use sampling processes which involve stratification and/or clustering, for reasons which were explained in Section 11.5.3.

Although the computational procedures for processing information obtained by stratified and/or clustered sampling differ in many details from the procedures used in the case of equiprobable sampling, the basic logic of the procedures is exactly the same in all cases. The probability diagram consists of an $\tilde{A}$ fork at the origin with a sample-outcome branch following each branch of the $\tilde{A}$ fork. After the decision maker has assigned an unconditional probability to each branch of the $\tilde{A}$ fork and his statistician delegate has assigned a conditional probability to each sample-outcome branch, the remaining calculations proceed exactly as in the case of equiprobable sampling. The probability of each end position of the diagram is found by multiplying together the branch probabilities on the path leading to that end position, and the posterior probability of each value of $\tilde{A}$ is then found by dividing the probability of the end position at which the actual sample outcome appears together with that value of $\tilde{A}$ by the sum of the probabilities of all end positions at which the actual sample outcome appears.

12.10
SUMMARY

12.10.1
Description of a Many-valued Population

1 A population will be called many-valued if for the purpose at hand each of its members is regarded as having one of many possible numerical values.

2 The discussion in this chapter is restricted to situations where (1) the only facts about the population as a whole that interest the decision maker are

  N: the number of members in the population,

  A: the average of the values of the individual members,

  and (2) the quantity N can be treated as known.

12.10.2
Summarization of Sample Information;
Large-sample Theory

In order to assess a posterior distribution of $\tilde{A}$ that reflects all the information in a sample, it is necessary to use a probability diagram like Figure 12.1 (page 479) and assess the conditional probability, given each possible A, that each individual sample observation will have a particular value. These assessments are very difficult to make, however, and are usually avoided by exploiting the fact that:

1 In most situations encountered in practice, most of the information about $\tilde{A}$ obtained by equiprobable sampling with replacement is conveyed by the statistics

  n: number of sample observations,

  a: average of the values of the individual observations,

  v: variance of the values of the individual observations.[2]

This fact permits use of a probability diagram like Figure 12.2 (page 483), and probabilities for the second-level branches in such a diagram are usually easy to assess because:

2 Suppose that n sample observations are to be made by equiprobable sampling with replacement. If (1) n is "large"—at least 25, better 100— and (2) prior information about the spread of the individual values in the population is negligible relative to the information that will be obtained from the sample, then probabilities for sample-outcome branches may be assessed by use of the ≪large-sample formula≫

  $$P(n \rightarrow a,v \,|\, A) \doteq k\,g^*(u) \qquad \text{where} \qquad u = (a - A)\sqrt{n/v},$$

g^* is the Gaussian density function, and k is a factor whose value does not depend on A and which will therefore cancel out in computing the posterior distribution of $\tilde{A}$.

12.10.3
Computation of Posterior Distributions

1 After the probabilities that would have been assessed prior to sampling have been assigned to the branches of a diagram like Figure 12.2 (page 483), the probability of each end position can be computed by multiplying together the probabilities on the two branches leading to that end position.

---

[2] The variance v is the average of the squares of the differences between the values of the individual observations and their average a.

2 The probability that should be assigned to each value of $\tilde{A}$ posterior to sampling can then be computed by dividing the probability of the end position at which that value of $\tilde{A}$ appears together with the event $n \rightarrow a,v$ by the probability of all end positions at which the event $n \rightarrow a,v$ appears.

12.10.4
Grouped Approximations
to Posterior Distributions

1 The distribution that should be assigned to $\tilde{A}$ posterior to sampling can be approximated by grouping the prior distribution of $\tilde{A}$ and then proceeding exactly as if the grouped prior distribution were the true prior distribution of $\tilde{A}$.

2 Accuracy adequate for the purpose at hand should be secured by using an adequately fine grouping of the prior distribution, not by smoothing the computed posterior distribution.

In all exercises, the prior distribution should be grouped into 10 equiprobable brackets and the resulting posterior distribution should be treated as if it were exact. Because this distribution recognizes only 10 possible values of $\tilde{A}$, a smooth graph of the mass or cumulative function of $\tilde{A}$ would be misleading; only exact graphs should be drawn.

12.10.5
Successive Samples

1 If a decision maker has taken two or more samples from the same population by equiprobable sampling with replacement, he can calculate his distribution posterior to all the samples by proceeding exactly as if all the observations constituted a single sample.

2 If two samples have already been summarized by statistics n_1, a_1, v_1, and n_2, a_2, v_2, the sample obtained by pooling the two samples has statistics

$$n^* = n_1 + n_2, \qquad a^* = \frac{n_1\,a_1 + n_2\,a_2}{n_1 + n_2}, \qquad v^* \doteq \frac{n_1\,v_1 + n_2\,v_2}{n_1 + n_2}.$$

12.10.6
Gaussian Approximations
to Posterior Distributions

1 If (1) the logically possible values of any UQ are *equally spaced*, and (2) a decision maker assigns *equal* probabilities to all the logically possible values, his distribution of the UQ may be said to be ≪uniform≫.

2 Suppose that a sample yielding statistics n, a, and v has been taken from a population by equiprobable sampling with replacement. If (1) prior to sampling the decision maker assigned a uniform prior distribution to $\tilde{A}$, (2) the possible values of $\tilde{A}$ are very close together, and (3) the sample likelihood function would be calculated by use of large-sample theory, then the cumulative function that the decision maker should assign to $\tilde{A}$ posterior to sampling is almost identical to a Gaussian cumulative function with parameters

$$M = a, \qquad S = \sqrt{v/n}.$$

3 Suppose that equiprobable sampling with replacement has yielded statistics n, a, and v, and suppose that large-sample theory would be used to evaluate the likelihood function of this sample. If prior to sampling the decision maker (1) did not assign extremely high probabilities to any values of $\tilde{A}$ outside an interval extending from $A = a - 3\sqrt{v/n}$ to $A = a + 3\sqrt{v/n}$, and (2) assigned roughly equal probabilities to all values of $\tilde{A}$ inside this interval, then the posterior distribution he should assign to $\tilde{A}$ will be almost the same as the posterior distribution that would result from a strictly uniform prior distribution, and therefore its cumulative function can be very closely approximated by a Gaussian cumulative function with parameters

$$M = a, \qquad S = \sqrt{v/n}.$$

When the conditions of this last rule are satisfied, we may say that the decision maker's prior distribution of $\tilde{A}$ is "nearly uniform relative to the sample likelihood function".

4 If $\tilde{A}$ has a Gaussian cumulative function with parameters M and S:

  a The mean, median, and mode of the distribution are all equal to M.

  b The k fractile of the distribution can be found by use of the formula

$$A_k = M + u_k S,$$

where u_k is a factor whose value for various k's can be found in Table T4.

12.10.7

Estimates of $\tilde{A}$

When a businessman uses sample information about $\tilde{A}$ as a guide to his preliminary thinking about some problem area, he necessarily thinks in terms of a "point estimate" of $\tilde{A}$ rather than a complete probability distribution of $\tilde{A}$, but at the same time he should keep in mind some measure of his uncertainty about the true value of $\tilde{A}$.

1 In any situation where (1) a businessman may legitimately use a point estimate of $\tilde{A}$ rather than a complete distribution of $\tilde{A}$, and (2) the distribution he (would have) assigned to $\tilde{A}$ prior to sampling is nearly uniform relative to the likelihood function of a (possibly pooled) sample which has already been taken, he can take the average a of the values in the (pooled) sample as an estimate of the uncertain average $\tilde{A}$ of the values of all the individual members of the population.

2 In many situations, the businessman's uncertainty about the true value of $\tilde{A}$ can be satisfactorily measured by the distance between two limits between which he feels "reasonably" sure that the true value must lie, and such limits can be found by computing two suitable fractiles of his posterior distribution of $\tilde{A}$.

The .01 and .99 fractiles are possible choices, but which fractiles should be chosen in any particular situation depends on the seriousness of the loss that may result if the businessman assumes that the true value of $\tilde{A}$ is between his two limits when in fact it is not.

12.10.8
Sampling without Replacement

1 Let N denote the size of the population and let n denote the size of a sample drawn from this population by equiprobable sampling ≪without replacement≫. If $\sqrt{(N - n)/(N - 1)}$ is close to 1, the posterior distribution that should be assigned to the population average $\tilde{A}$ is practically the same as if the sample had been taken with replacement.

2 Sample information obtained by ≪systematic sampling≫ may be processed as if it had been obtained by equiprobable sampling without replacement unless the decision maker suspects that high and low values may be arranged in some definite pattern in the file or list from which the sample is drawn.

EXERCISES

A. LARGE-SAMPLE THEORY AND POSTERIOR DISTRIBUTIONS

12.1   The values of successive observations made by equiprobable sampling with replacement are 13, 17, 21, and 9. Verify that for this sample the summary statistics defined in Section 12.3.1 have the values

$$n = 4, \qquad a = 15, \qquad v = 20.$$

12.2   A population consists of 10,000 inventory cards on each of which is written the dollar value of Mr. Herbert Zellner's inventory of a particular item. Mr. Zellner is uncertain about the average $\tilde{A}$ of these 10,000 dollar values, and in order to learn more about $\tilde{A}$ he proposes to make 100 drawings from his population of cards by equiprobable sampling with replacement and observe the value on each card that is drawn. As regards the spread of the values on the 10,000 cards, Mr. Zellner feels that his present information is negligible relative to the information that he will obtain from 100 sample observations.

When the 100 observations are actually taken and their values observed, it may happen that the average and variance of the 100 values turn out to be 72 and 3,600 respectively.

a Show that Zellner should regard this event as being about 3,521/2,420 times as likely to occur if $\tilde{A} = 69$ as it is if $\tilde{A} = 78$.

b Should another person necessarily hold this same opinion? Why?

12.3   Suppose that the values of the 100 observations of Exercise 12.2 do in fact turn out to have average 72 and variance 3,600; and for the moment suppose unrealistically that before learning this fact Zellner felt that 69 and 78 were the only possible values of the population average $\tilde{A}$ and assessed

$$P(\tilde{A} = 69) = .5, \qquad P(\tilde{A} = 78) = .5.$$

Construct the probability diagram that Zellner should use in order to compute the probabilities that he should now assign to the two possible values of $\tilde{A}$, and show that these probabilities are

$$P(\tilde{A} = 69) = (.5 \times .3521)/.2970 \doteq .59,$$

$$P(\tilde{A} = 78) = (.5 \times .2420)/.2970 \doteq .41.$$

12.4   After taking the sample and assessing the posterior probabilities described in Exercise 12.3, Mr. Zellner draws another 100 cards by equiprobable sampling with replacement in order to learn still more about $\tilde{A}$, and the values on these 100 cards turn out to have average 76 and variance 4,000. In deciding what probabilities he should now assign to the two possible values of $\tilde{A}$:

a Can Mr. Zellner assign probabilities .59 and .41 respectively to the branches for $\tilde{A} = 69$ and $\tilde{A} = 78$ in a new probability diagram?

b Can he use the large-sample formula for $P(n \to a,v \,|\, A)$ to compute the probabilities he assigns to the event $(100 \to 76, 4{,}000)$ on the second-level branches of this new probability diagram?

B. GROUPED APPROXIMATIONS

12.5   Compute a grouped approximation to the distribution that Mr. Zellner should assign to $\tilde{A}$ after taking the sample described in Exercise 12.3:

a Assuming that prior to sampling Zellner would have assigned to $\tilde{A}$ the distribution defined by Figure 12.13;

b Assuming that prior to sampling Zellner would have assigned exactly the same probability to every possible value of $\tilde{A}$ between 21 and 120 and zero probability to every other possible value of $\tilde{A}$.

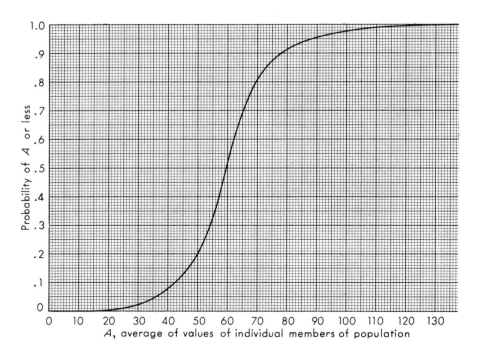

FIGURE 12.13

Mr. Zellner's Prior Distribution of Average Investment in Inventory per Item Stocked

12.6 Prepare the inputs that would be required if you wished to have a more exact answer to Exercise 12.5*a* calculated by the computer program described in Section 12.4.

12.7 We saw in Exercise 10.7 that after constructing a mammoth probability diagram and writing down the value of a function $\bar{z}$ at each of its 1 million end positions, Mr. Rudolph Grauber was too exhausted to count the number of end positions at which $\bar{z}$ had each of its possible values. In order to learn what he could about the frequency with which $\bar{z}$ had a value less than 50, he used equiprobable sampling with replacement to draw 100 end positions and observed the value of $\bar{z}$ on each of these draws.

Besides being interested in the fraction of all 1 million end positions at which $\bar{z}$ has a value less than 50, Grauber is interested in the average of the 1 million values of $\bar{z}$ that he has written down, and he thinks that he can learn something about this average from the 100 values of $\bar{z}$ that he drew in his sample. The average of these 100 sample values of $\bar{z}$ was 72; their variance was 3,600.

a Should Grauber feel that there is a substantial chance that the average of all 1 million values of $\bar{z}$ is less than 54? Greater than 90? [Hint: compute $P(n \rightarrow a,v \,|\, A)$ for $A = 54$, 72, and 90, and then take the argument from there.]

b Suppose that Grauber constructed the diagram for a decision maker who wished to know what expectation he should assign to $\bar{z}$ in analyzing a decision problem. Show that if Grauber had been physically able to complete his assigned task, he could have answered his employer's question by simply averaging the values of $\tilde{z}$ at the 1 million equally probable end positions of his diagram. [Hint: review Section 9.4.6.]

c Things being as they are, what kind of answer can Grauber give his employer?

C. SUCCESSIVE SAMPLES

12.8 In the situation of Exercise 12.4, what distribution should Mr. Herbert Zellner assign to $\tilde{A}$ if prior to taking any sample he assessed $P(\tilde{A} = 69) = .5$ and $P(\tilde{A} = 78) = .5$?

D. GAUSSIAN APPROXIMATIONS TO POSTERIOR DISTRIBUTIONS

12.9 Consider the Gaussian cumulative function with parameters $M = 72$ and $S = 6$, and let A_k denote the argument for which the value of this function is k.

a Compute A_k for $k = .001, .01, .05, .1, .2, \ldots , .8, .9, .95, .99, .999$.

b Graph the function.

12.10 Suppose that a statistician tells a businessman that his distribution of the average of the values of the individual members of a certain population should have the cumulative function described in Exercise 12.9. Find the three quartiles and the mean of the distribution thus defined.

12.11 Suppose that prior to sampling in the situation of Exercise 12.2, Mr. Zellner had felt that any one possible value of $\tilde{A}$ was just about as likely as another.

a If the values on the cards in Zellner's file are recorded to the nearest cent, what are the first three logically possible values of their average $\tilde{A}$ expressed in dollars?

b Describe the distribution Zellner should assign to $\tilde{A}$ after learning that the values of 100 sample observations have average 72 and variance 3,600.

c What should be his expectation of $\tilde{A}$ posterior to learning this sample outcome?

d Describe the distribution Zellner should assign to $\tilde{A}$ after taking a second sample of 100 observations and finding that these observations have average 76 and variance 4,000.

e What should be his expectation of $\tilde{A}$ posterior to this second sample?

12.12 Would your answers to Exercise 12.11*bc* be valid if prior to sampling Zellner had felt that:

a Although $\tilde{A}$ was rather unlikely to be less than 50 or greater than 95, he would be just about as ready to bet on any one possible value of $\tilde{A}$ between 50 and 95 as on any other?

   b Although $\tilde{A}$ was very unlikely to be less than 70 or greater than 75, he would be just about as ready to bet on any one possible value of $\tilde{A}$ between 70 and 75 as on any other?

E. ESTIMATES

12.13 a In the situation of Exercise 12.7, what would be Mr. Grauber's modal estimate of the average of the values of the function $\tilde{z}$ at the 1 million end positions of his probability diagram? His median estimate? His expectation of the average?

   b Find an interval of possible values of the average within which Grauber can be 98% sure that the true average actually lies.

   c Suppose that before receiving Grauber's report Grauber's employer was very uncertain about the expectation that he should assign to $\tilde{z}$ in analyzing his decision problem. Would he now be justified in assessing $E\tilde{z} = 72$ and proceeding to analyze his decision problem on this basis?

   d What can Grauber's employer hope to gain by ordering Grauber to draw 300 more end positions and average the values of $\tilde{z}$ at these end positions together with the values at his original 100 end positions?

F. SAMPLING WITHOUT REPLACEMENT

12.14 Mar-Pruf Finishes, Inc. (A)

   Mar-Pruf Finishes, Inc., was a relatively small firm operating in a segment of the industrial-finishes market which was dominated by the American Paint and Lacquer Company. Mar-Pruf's research chemists had recently developed a product to compete with American's type A–1 lacquer and the company was trying to decide whether or not to put this product on the market. Some preliminary market research had shown that while some firms considered the new Mar-Pruf product to be superior to American's A–1, the difference was not great enough to permit Mar-Pruf to charge a price appreciably higher than American's price of $8.75 per gallon. On the other hand, any attempt to seize American's market by charging a lower price was almost certain to produce a price war which American was sure to win because of its superior financial resources. It was clear that if the product was to be marketed at all it would have to be marketed at a price of $8.75 per gallon.

   Mar-Pruf's management figured that if it installed the necessary equipment for economical manufacture of the new product it could realize a net contribution (selling price less variable cost of production, selling, and delivery) amounting to about $.40 per gallon; and after considering

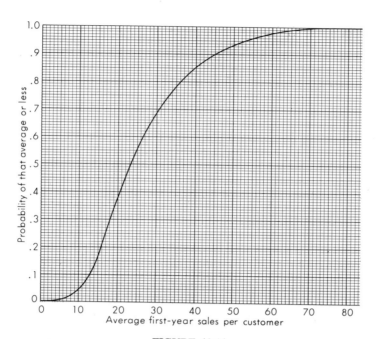

FIGURE 12.14
Mar-Pruf's Prior Distribution of Average First-year Sales per Customer

the amount of time during which a customer could be expected to continue buying the product, management had decided that the "present value" of the whole stream of contributions to be expected from a customer who was initially sold on the new product would be about $2 for each gallon-per-year of initial sales. In other words: management would have been just willing to accept $2x$ spot cash in lieu of the uncertain total contribution to be derived from a customer who bought x gallons in the first year after the product was marketed.

Mar-Pruf's hesitation about entering the market with this new product arose from the fact that the total cost of installing and debugging the necessary equipment for volume manufacture plus the cost of the required introductory sales effort would amount to about $600,000, so that unless a sales volume of $600,000/$2 = 300,000 gallons per year could be attained in the first year, the introduction of the product could be expected to result in a net loss. Mar-Pruf's market research had shown that there were about 10,000 firms who could be considered potential customers for the product, so that the breakeven point could also be considered as achieving first-year sales averaging 30 gallons per firm.

a Assuming that Mar-Pruf wishes to choose the course of action that maximizes expected monetary value, diagram the decision problem faced by Mar-Pruf's management.

b Give a formula or formulas for valuing the end positions of your diagram.

c If various members of Mar-Pruf's management have different views about the UQ "average first-year sales per customer", can it possibly be meaningful to talk about *management's* distribution of this UQ? If the expression *is* meaningful, what does it mean?

d If on the basis of present information Mar-Pruf's management assigns the probability distribution shown in Figure 12.14 to average first-year sales per potential customer, and if no further information is obtained, should Mar-Pruf market the product?

e Instead of basing a final decision on the distribution of Figure 12.14, management decides to obtain additional information by sampling. The marketing-research department draws 100 of the 10,000 potential customers for the new product in such a way that each of them has an equal chance of being drawn, and the sales manager then dispatches salesmen to give free samples of the product to these customers and to ask whether the customer would buy the product if it were actually placed on the market, and if so, how many gallons in the first year. The results of this survey are shown in simplified form in Table 12.8.

TABLE 12.8

First-year Purchase	Number of Firms
0	60
60	10
90	20
120	10
	100

Show that the average of the 100 responses was $a = 36$ and that their variance was $v = 2124$.

f If management believes that any customer who is interviewed would actually buy exactly the amount he says he would buy, what distribution should management now assign to the average first year's purchase?

(It is of course much more likely that management will *not* believe that every customer who is interviewed will in fact buy exactly the amount he says he will buy. The problem of assessing a distribution of the average first year's actual purchase under such circumstances will be examined in Chapter 15.)

12.15 *Grand Western Railroad (A)*

In January, 1957, a number of American railroads were offering a special passenger tariff known as the "Family-Fare Plan". There were some variations in the details from road to road, but basically the tariff provided that if a husband bought a round trip at the regular rate, his wife could buy a round trip at half price and his children could buy their round trips at still lower prices. A single ticket was issued to cover the transportation of the entire family, and to prevent misuse of the ticket, certain lines recorded the names and addresses of the persons entitled to use it on the stub which was surrendered to the conductor on the last leg of the trip.

There was great disagreement among passenger officers of the various roads concerning the effect of the Family-Fare Plan on revenue and profit, and the Grand Western Railroad was seriously considering its abandonment. A good deal of revenue was at stake: sales of Family-Fare tickets amounted to about $4 million per year on the Grand Western, and if the same passengers had been carried at full fare this figure would have been substantially greater. While the general passenger agent of the Grand Western believed that 90% of the passenger-miles sold under the special tariff would not have been sold at all under the normal tariff, the senior executives of the Grand Western knew that the general passenger agent of another railroad serving exactly the same major cities believed that all but 10% of the passenger-miles sold under the special tariff *could* have been sold at regular fares.

The President of the Grand Western, Mr. H. B. Jones, was particularly puzzled by the fact that both his own GPA and the GPA of the other road based their contradictory statements on the results of surveys carried out by having ticket agents ask purchasers of Family-Fare tickets whether or not they would have made the same trip if the special rates had not been in effect. Jones was inclined to believe that the samples taken by the two men were too small to be reliable, and since there was no one among the road's personnel who was an expert in such matters he called in a representative of a marketing-research agency specializing in consumer surveys and laid the problem before him. The agency representative answered that both the samples were so large that sampling error as such could not possibly account for more than 1 or 2 of the 80 percentage points of difference and went on to assert that the real difficulty was that reliable answers to a question like the one asked of the ticket buyers could not possibly be obtained through hurried interviews conducted by ticket clerks under unfavorable conditions. Even if the Grand Western sample were extended to a 100% count, there would in his opinion be no more real knowledge than there was before any data were collected. He recommended that the railroad employ his agency to draw a small equal-probability sample of purchasers of Family-Fare tickets and have the persons in the sample interviewed in their homes by really skilled interviewers.

When asked about the cost of such a survey, the agency representative quoted a price of $1,000 for general expenses plus $100 per family in the sample, explaining the high cost per head as due in part to the fees of the skilled interviewers and in part to the time and expense required to secure interviews with people selected with equal probabilities among all persons who had surrendered Family-Fare ticket stubs during the preceding year. It seemed to Jones that this obviously implied that a sample large enough to give reliable results would be prohibitive in cost, but the agency representative argued that this was not necessarily true and that in any case a good deal of very useful information could be obtained by taking a very small pilot sample and analyzing its results. Since the total amount of Grand Western revenue at stake was really substantial, Jones finally decided to contract with the marketing-research agency to interview a sample of 50 families at a cost of $6,000.

Before taking the sample the agency examined the available data on the values of the individual Family-Fare tickets sold during the previous year and found that the large majority of the tickets were for short trips and actually accounted for only a small part of the total dollar sales; 80% of the dollars came from individual sales of $150 and over. The railroad and the agency quickly agreed that the sample should be drawn exclusively from families who had paid over $150 for their tickets, since it seemed very likely that the behavior of these families alone would determine whether the plan was or was not profitable overall.

The pilot sample was promptly drawn and interviewed with the results shown in simplified form in Table 12.9 below. The figure shown in the column headed "effect of cancellation" was calculated by subtracting the amount the family actually spent on its Family-Fare ticket from the amount it would have spent travelling on the Grand Western if Family-Fares had not been available.

TABLE 12.9

Effect of Cancellation	Number of Families
− $200	10
− 100	12
0	7
+ 100	16
+ 200	5
	50

After these results were in, Jones was still very unsure about what to do next. It was easy to calculate that the effect of cancellation of the plan on families in the sample would have been a reduction in revenue amounting to $600 in total or $12 per family on the average. Jones also knew that Grand Western had sold about 20,000 Family-Fare tickets for amounts of $150 and over in the past year, so that if the $12 sample figure held for the entire population, about $240,000 would have been lost in one year by abandoning the plan. Because the road's passenger-train schedules and consists were such that the reduction in passenger-miles travelled would have had no appreciable effect on train costs, this loss of revenue would have been an out-and-out loss of that much net contribution to overhead and profit.

Jones believed that conditions were changing so rapidly that the entire question would have to be reexamined next year, so that there was no sense in projecting profit or loss further than a year in advance, but he was nevertheless seriously disturbed about basing his decision on a sample of only 50 families.

Suppose that before learning the results of the pilot sample Jones had decided that the available evidence on the effect of cancelling the Family-Fare Plan was worthless and that so far as he could see cancellation would have been just as likely to increase average per-family expenditure by any one amount between +$150 and −$150 as by any other. If he believes that the answers given by the 50 families in the sample accord strictly with the facts, what distribution should he now assign to the effect that cancellation would have had on last year's average per-family expenditure?

(It is of course much more likely that Jones would *not* believe that the answers accord strictly with the facts. We shall see in Chapter 15 how he can assess his distribution of the true effect of cancellation if this is so.)

CHAPTER
13

THE MONTE CARLO
METHOD; SIMULATION

In order to analyze a business decision problem, it is often necessary to compute the distribution or expectation of a function of jointly distributed UQ's. When only two or three UQ's are involved, this is not particularly hard to do. With the aid of a digital computer, we can group each of the distributions involved into 100 equiprobable brackets, compute the probability of every end position of the joint probability diagram, and compute the value of the function at every end position. We can then compute the implied probability of each possible value of the function by adding the probabilities of all end positions at which the UQ has that value, or we can compute the implied expectation of the function by multiplying the value of the function at each end position by the probability of that end position and adding these products.

This method of computation becomes excessively costly, however, when the number of jointly distributed UQ's is at all large; and as we shall see in this chapter, practical business decision problems often involve hundreds or even thousands of jointly distributed UQ's. Even if a problem involves only 30 UQ's, and even if the distribution of each UQ is grouped into only 2 equiprobable brackets, the joint probability diagram will have $2^{30} \doteq 1$ billion end positions, and evaluation of a billion end positions is a very large task for even a very fast computer. Clearly, some method of evaluation other than straightforward grouping and computation must be used in problems involving a large number of jointly distributed UQ's, and in this chapter we shall examine one of the methods most commonly used in practice, namely, the one known as the "Monte Carlo" method or "simulation".

The logical essence of the Monte Carlo method is very simple indeed: it consists in taking a sample of the end positions that would be present in a probability diagram based on very fine grouping of the distributions of the jointly distributed UQ's and using the information supplied by this sample to estimate the results that would be obtained by straightforward computations based on such a diagram. In Section 13.1 we shall show that once such a sample has been drawn by an appropriate sampling process, the required estimates can be made and their reliability can be evaluated by procedures we have already studied in Chapters 11 and 12. We shall then show in Sections 13.2 and 13.3 how a sample of end positions can be drawn in a way that makes these procedures legitimate even though the probability diagram is far too large to be actually written down. Finally, we shall show why this sampling procedure is sometimes equivalent to "simulation" of the way in which events might occur or a particular business strategy might operate in the real world.

The text and exercises of this chapter are designed to be studied in the following order:

1 Sections 13.1.1–13.1.3 and Exercise 13.1*a*.

2 Section 13.1.4 and Exercise 13.1*b*.

3 Section 13.1.5 and Exercise 13.1*c*.

4 Section 13.1.6 and Exercise 13.2.

5 Sections 13.1.7–13.1.8 and Exercises 13.3–13.4.

6 Sections 13.2.1–13.2.2 and Exercise 13.5.

7 Section 13.2.3 and Exercise 13.6.

8 Section 13.2.4 and Exercises 13.7–13.8.

9 Sections 13.3.1–13.3.3 and Exercise 13.9.

10 Section 13.3.4 and Exercises 13.10–13.11.

11 Section 13.3.5 and Exercise 13.12.

12 Section 13.4.

CONTENTS OF CHAPTER 13

1.
Estimates Based on
Samples of End Positions

1 A Probability Diagram with Equally Probable End Positions
2 Equiprobable Sampling with Replacement

2.
Sampling of End Positions
with Matched Probabilities

3.
Practical Execution of
Monte Carlo Trials

4.
Simulation of Real-world Events

5.
Summary

13.1
ESTIMATES BASED ON
SAMPLES OF END POSITIONS

In Sections 11.3 and 12.8 we showed how to estimate the fraction of successes or the average of the values in a population on the basis of information obtained by equiprobable sampling with replacement, and we also showed how the reliability of such estimates could be evaluated and how a businessman could decide whether or not it would be worthwhile to do additional sampling in the hope of

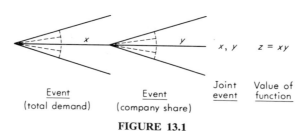

FIGURE 13.1

Probability Diagram of the Joint Distribution of $\tilde{x}$ and $\tilde{y}$

improving the reliability of his estimates. In the present section we shall first show that exactly these same procedures can be applied to a problem of estimating the distribution or expectation of a function of jointly distributed UQ's when all the end positions of the probability diagram have equal probabilities and a sample of these end positions has been drawn by equiprobable sampling with replacement. We shall then go on to show that these same procedures can still be used even though the end positions have unequal probabilities provided that the sample is drawn by what we shall call sampling with matched probabilities.

To simplify our explanation of the basic logic underlying the use of these procedures for this purpose, we shall in the present section use examples that are simple enough to allow us actually to list all the end positions of the probability diagram. Once this basic logic has been made clear, we shall go on in Sections 13.2 and 13.3 to show how a sample of end positions can be drawn with matched probabilities in situations of the sort where the Monte Carlo method is really useful, i.e., situations where the end positions of the probability diagram are so numerous that they cannot be explicitly listed.

13.1.1

A Probability Diagram
with Equally Probable End Positions

As a first example to illustrate the Monte Carlo method of estimation, we shall reconsider the example discussed in Section 9.4.4, where a sales manager used the probability diagram shown in Figure 13.1 to decompose a problem of assessing an unconditional distribution of demand $\tilde{z}$ for his company's product into separable problems of assessing an unconditional distribution of total demand $\tilde{x}$ and a set of conditional distributions of company share $\tilde{y}$, one for each possible value x of $\tilde{x}$.

In this particular example, the sales manager's conditional distribution of $\tilde{y}$ given x was the same for every x—he assigned the same distribution to every second-level $\tilde{y}$ fork in Figure 13.1—and therefore he had only two different distributions to assess. After he had assessed these two distributions by constructing the graphs of their cumulative functions that appear in Figure 9.13 (page 353) and Figure 9.14 (page 354), we grouped each of them into 10 equiprobable brackets represented by their bracket medians, as shown in Table 9.4 (page 355). Then thinking of the probability diagram in Figure 13.1 as having $10 \times 10 = 100$ end positions, we found by straightforward computations that the sales manager's grouped distributions of $\tilde{x}$ and $\tilde{y}$ implied the equal end-position probabilities that appear in Table 9.5 (page 355); we also found by straightforward computation that the value of the function $\tilde{z} = \tilde{x}\tilde{y}$ at each end position was as shown in Table 9.6 (page 355); and from these two tables we derived the distribution of $\tilde{z}$ that is graphed in Figure 9.15 (page 356).

In order to distinguish between these results of straightforward computation and the Monte Carlo estimates that we are about to discuss, we shall in what follows refer to the joint distribution of $\tilde{x}$ and $\tilde{y}$ that is described by Table 9.5 as the sales manager's "exact" joint distribution, even though it is in fact only a grouped approximation to the joint distribution that is really implied by his basic assessments in Figures 9.13 and 9.14. Similarly we shall refer to the distribution of $\tilde{z}$ that is graphed in Figure 9.15 as his "exact" distribution of $\tilde{z}$; and we shall talk as if the probability diagram in Figure 13.1 really had only 100 end positions even though it is only a particular grouped approximation to that diagram that in fact has 100 end positions.

13.1.2
Equiprobable Sampling with Replacement

We shall now show that if the sales manager did not already know the exact distribution of the function $\tilde{z}$ that appears in Figure 9.15, he could arrive at a reasonable estimate of this distribution *without* calculating the value of $\tilde{z}$ at every one of the 100 end positions in Figure 13.1. Specifically, we shall show how he can arrive at such an estimate after calculating the values of $\tilde{z}$ at a number of end positions drawn by equiprobable sampling with replacement from the "population" of 100 equally probable end positions defined by Figure 13.1.

TABLE 13.1

Description of a Sample Consisting of 10 End Positions Drawn from the Population Consisting of All End Positions in Figure 13.1

1	2		3
Draw Number	Description of End Position		Value of $\tilde{z} = \tilde{x}\tilde{y}$
	Value of $\tilde{x}$	Value of $\tilde{y}$	at That End Position
1	261,000	.092	24,012
2	143,000	.131	18,733
3	65,000	.110	7,150
4	296,000	.092	27,232
5	143,000	.030	4,290
6	173,000	.048	8,304
7	261,000	.131	34,191
8	203,000	.198	40,194
9	108,000	.048	5,184
10	232,000	.092	21,344

Since for the moment we are interested only in the basic logic of the estimation procedure, we shall simplify our calculations and tables by assuming that the sales manager is willing to base his estimate of the distribution of $\tilde{z}$ on the outcome of only 10 sample observations; and by way of example we shall assume that 10 successive sample draws yield the 10 end positions shown in Column 2 of Table 13.1. Observe that each of these end positions is identified by a specific pair of values for $\tilde{x}$ and $\tilde{y}$, exactly as end positions are identified on the probability diagram in Figure 13.1.

The value of the function $\tilde{z}$ at each of the 10 sample end positions is shown in the last column of Table 13.1, and the reader should observe that although in this example we could read these function values from the list of function values at all end positions that appears as Table 9.6, we did not really need to have any such complete list. We could have computed the values of $\tilde{z} = \tilde{x}\tilde{y}$ at the sample end positions directly from the descriptions of those end positions in Table 13.1; and if we had been dealing with a realistic sample of, say, 1,000 end positions from a population of 10 billion end positions, the saving that would have resulted from having to compute only 1,000 rather than 10 billion function values would have been very substantial.

13.1.3
Estimation of a Cumulative Probability

In order to show how we could use the sample of Table 13.1 to estimate the complete distribution of $\tilde{z}$ that appears in Figure 9.15, we start by showing how the sample could be used to estimate the exact probability of any particular event of the form $\tilde{z} \leqslant z$.

Taking the event $\tilde{z} \leqslant 10,000$ as an example, we first recall that the exact probability of this event is equal to the sum of the probabilities of all end positions at which $\tilde{z}$ has a value no greater than 10,000 (cf. Rule 2 in Section 9.3.4). Next, we observe that because all the end positions in Figure 13.1 have equal probabilities, as shown by Table 9.5, the total probability of all end positions at which $\tilde{z}$ has a value no greater than 10,000 is equal to the *fraction* of all end positions at which $\tilde{z}$ has a value no greater than 10,000. Next, thinking of an end position at which $\tilde{z} \leqslant 10,000$ as a "success", we recall from Section 11.3.1 that under appropriate conditions the fraction of successes in a sample is a reasonable estimate of the fraction of successes in the population from which the sample is drawn; and we conclude that:

■ We can estimate the exact probability of the event $\tilde{z} \leqslant 10,000$ by computing the fraction of end positions in the sample at which $\tilde{z}$ has a value no greater than 10,000.

By use of Table 9.6, we find that the value of $\tilde{z}$ is no greater than 10,000 at 22 of the 100 end positions in the complete population, so that the exact prob-

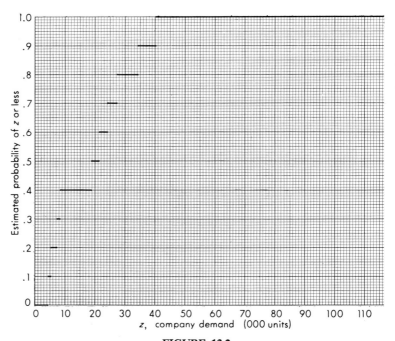

FIGURE 13.2

Estimated Distribution of $\tilde{z}$

ability of the event $\tilde{z} \leqslant 10,000$ is $22/100 = .22$. Table 13.1 shows that the value of $\tilde{z}$ is no greater than 10,000 at 4 of the 10 end positions in the sample, so that our estimate of the probability of the event $\tilde{z} \leqslant 10,000$ would be $4/10 = .40$. The agreement with the exact value is no worse than we would expect in view of the fact that the estimate is based on so small a sample.

13.1.4
Estimation of a Complete Distribution

To estimate the complete distribution of $\tilde{z}$ that is implied by the sales manager's basic assessments, we simply estimate its cumulative function by estimating $P(\tilde{z} \leqslant z)$ for every possible value z of $\tilde{z}$ in exactly the same way that we estimated $P(z \leqslant 10,000)$ in Section 13.1.3 just above.

Our estimates are shown in Table 13.2 and graphed in Figure 13.2, where each heavy horizontal line really represents a whole collection of distinct points, one for each possible value of $\tilde{z}$ in the interval covered by the line. The graph in Figure 13.2 can be thought of as an estimate of the graph in Figure 9.15 of the exact distribution of $\tilde{z}$.

Before proceeding further, the reader should verify some of the estimates in Table 13.2 and Figure 13.2. He should observe, for example, that because there is no sample end position in Table 13.1 at which $\tilde{z} \leqslant 2,000$, we estimate

TABLE 13.2
Estimated Distribution of $\bar{z}$

Value z	Estimated $P(\bar{z} \leqslant z)$
0– 4,289	.0
4,290– 5,183	.1
5,184– 7,149	.2
7,150– 8,303	.3
8,304–18,732	.4
18,733–21,343	.5
21,344–24,011	.6
24,012–27,231	.7
27,232–34,190	.8
34,191–40,193	.9
40,194+	1.0

$P(\bar{z} \leqslant 2,000) = 0$; because $\bar{z} \leqslant 5,000$ at 1 of the 10 sample end positions in Table 13.2, we estimate $P(\bar{z} \leqslant 5,000) = 1/10$; and so forth.

Smoothing the Estimated Distribution of $\bar{z}$ Even if we had not already computed the exact distribution of $\bar{z}$ in Figure 9.15, we would know that the only reason why the estimates in Figure 13.2 increase from 0 to 1 in 10 big jumps was that we had only 10 end positions in our sample. In principle, we should treat the estimates in Figure 13.2 as "preliminary" rather than "final" estimates of $P(\bar{z} \leqslant z)$, exactly as we treated the heavy dots in Figure 8.8 (page 297) as preliminary rather than final estimates; and in principle we should go on to derive an improved estimate of the distribution of $\bar{z}$ by smoothing the preliminary estimates in Figure 13.2 in exactly the same way that we smoothed the preliminary estimates in Figure 8.8.

In actual practice, however, smoothing is rarely required in problems where an estimate of a probability distribution is based on a sample of the end positions of a probability diagram. Although we are illustrating the principles of such estimation by an example in which the sample size is very small, the samples used in practice are ordinarily very large and consequently the preliminary estimates are usually smooth enough to be treated as final. In this respect the problems discussed in the present chapter are quite different from those discussed in Section 8.2.5, where the preliminary estimates were derived from very sparse historical data and it was important to make the very best use possible of those data.

13.1.5

Estimation of an Expectation

If the sales manager wishes to estimate the mean of the distribution of $\bar{z}$ that is implied by his basic assessments—if, in other words, he wishes to estimate the exact expectation of $\bar{z}$—he can do so by computing the mean of the estimated distribution of $\bar{z}$ that appears in Table 13.2 and Figure 13.2. If, however, the mean is the *only* aspect of the distribution of $\bar{z}$ that interests the sales manager, he can arrive at exactly the same final result without going to the trouble of first estimating the complete distribution of $\bar{z}$.

To show how this can be done, we first recall that we could compute the exact expectation of $\bar{z}$ without first computing the exact distribution of $\bar{z}$. As shown in Section 9.4.6, we could simply multiply the value of $\bar{z}$ at each end position of Figure 13.1 by the probability of that end position and add the products. Next, we observe that because all the end positions in Figure 13.1 have equal probabilities, this probability-weighted average of the values of $\bar{z}$ is equal to the ordinary or unweighted average of those values. Finally, thinking of the end positions in Figure 13.1 as constituting a "population" of end positions and recalling what we learned about estimation of population averages in Section 12.8, we conclude that

■ We can estimate the exact expectation of $\bar{z}$ by computing the average of the values of $\bar{z}$ at the end positions in the sample.

By averaging the 100 values of $\bar{z}$ in the complete population as given by Table 9.6, we find that the exact expectation of $\bar{z}$ is 26,039. By averaging the 10 values of $\bar{z}$ in the sample as given by Table 13.1, we arrive at 19,063 as our estimate of the expectation. The agreement with the exact value is no worse than we would expect in view of the fact that the estimate is based on so small a sample.

13.1.6
Evaluation of the Reliability
of Estimates Derived from Samples

It is now time to ask how we could evaluate the reliability of estimates of the kind we have just discussed in a situation where we did not know the exact value of the probability or expectation being estimated. This is, of course, the only kind of situation that is of any practical interest, since the whole point of Monte Carlo estimation is to avoid the need for computing exact values.

The reliability of a Monte Carlo estimate can be evaluated by use of the sampling theory that was set forth in Chapters 10–12. We shall illustrate the method by applying it to two of the estimates we have already made.

Reliability of an Estimate of a Cumulative Probability   To evaluate the reliability of our estimate of the probability of the event $\bar{z} \leqslant 10,000$, we first translate the problem into the language of Chapters 10 and 11. We say that a member of the population of 100 end positions in Figure 13.1 is a "success" if and only if the value of $\bar{z}$ is no greater than 10,000 at that end position, and we define

p: fraction of successes among the 100 end positions in the population;

n: number of end positions in the sample;

r: number of successes in the sample.

In this language, what we said in Section 13.1.3 was that (1) if the sales manager knew the population fraction p, he should assess $P(\tilde{z} \leqslant 10{,}000) = p$, but (2) if he did not know p, he could take the sample fraction r/n as an estimate of $p = P(\tilde{z} \leqslant 10{,}000)$.

Suppose now that the sales manager does not know the population fraction p and could therefore treat it as an uncertain quantity $\tilde{p}$; all that he knows is that there were $r = 4$ successes in the sample of size $n = 10$ that is described by Table 13.1. If prior to observing this sample the sales manager had only very vague ideas about the value of $\tilde{p}$, then we have shown by Section 11.2.7 that posterior to observing the sample he should assign to $\tilde{p}$ a distribution having a beta cumulative function with parameters

$$B = r + 1 = 5, \qquad C = n + 2 = 12.$$

By Table T3 the .01 and .99 fractiles of this distribution are .1344 and .7378, so that all that the sales manager can feel 98 % sure of is that the population fraction $\tilde{p}$ is somewhere between .1344 and .7378.

Recalling now that the sales manager's basic assessments imply that he should assess $P(\tilde{z} \leqslant 10{,}000)$ as equal to p, we see that his estimate $r/n = 4/10$ of this implied probability is not at all reliable. If he wants a more reliable estimate, he must acquire more information about the population of end positions by taking another sample; to decide how large this sample should be, he can use the methodology described in Sections 11.3.3–11.3.4.

Reliability of an Approximation to an Expectation   To evaluate the reliability of our estimate of the expectation of the function $\tilde{z}$, we first translate the problem into the language of Chapter 12. We say that the "value" of any member of the population of 100 end positions in Figure 13.1 is the value of the function $\tilde{z}$ at that end position, and we define

A: average of the values of the 100 end positions in the population;

n: number of end positions in the sample;

a: average $\Big\}$
v: variance$\Big\}$ of the values of the end positions in the sample.

In this language, what we said in Section 13.1.5 was that (1) if the sales manager knew the population average A, he should assess $E\tilde{z} = A$, but (2) if he did not know A, then he could take the sample average a as an estimate of $A = E\tilde{z}$.

Suppose now that the sales manager does not know the population average A and could therefore treat it as an uncertain quantity $\tilde{A}$; all that he knows is that the sample described in Table 13.1 can be summarized by the statistics

$$n = 10, \qquad a = 19{,}063, \qquad v = 144{,}046{,}000.$$

If prior to observing this sample the sales manager would have assigned equal probabilities to all possible values of $\tilde{A}$, then we have shown by Section 12.7 that posterior to observing the sample he should assign to $\tilde{A}$ a distribution having a Gaussian cumulative function[1] with parameters

$$M = a = 19{,}063, \qquad S = \sqrt{v/n} = 3{,}795.$$

By Table T4 the .01 and .99 fractiles of this distribution of $\tilde{A}$ are

$$A_{.01} = 19{,}063 - 2.326 \times 3{,}795 = +10{,}236,$$

$$A_{.99} = 19{,}063 + 2.326 \times 3{,}795 = +27{,}890,$$

and we see that the sample of Table 13.1 is so small that it tells the sales manager very little about the population average $\tilde{A}$.

Recalling now that the sales manager's basic assessments imply that he should assess $E\tilde{z}$ as equal to A, we see that his estimate $a = 19{,}063$ of this implied expectation is very unreliable. If he wants a more reliable estimate, he must acquire more information about the population of end positions by taking another sample; to decide how large this sample should be, he can use the methodology described in Section 12.8.

13.1.7
Recapitulation: Estimation When All
End Positions Have Equal Probabilities

Everything that we have said thus far applies only in the case where the decision maker's basic assessments imply equal probabilities for all the end positions of the probability diagram. Before we go on to the general case, where the decision maker's basic assessments may imply different probabilities for different end positions, it will be well to review the logic underlying the results we have obtained for the case of equal probabilities.

1. *Estimation of Cumulative Probabilities.* As in the previous section, let us take the event $\tilde{z} \leqslant 10{,}000$ as an example and call any end position at which $\tilde{z} \leqslant 10{,}000$ a "success". If we draw a sample by equiprobable sampling from the population consisting of all end positions on any probability diagram, the fraction of successes in the sample is a reasonable estimate of the fraction of successes in the population. It is only, however, when the decision maker has assigned equal probabilities to all the end positions in the population that his *probability* for the event $\tilde{z} \leqslant 10{,}000$ should be equal to the fraction of successes

---

[1] A sample size of 10 is not large enough to make the Gaussian approximation very good, but a *very* rough approximation is all that we need here.

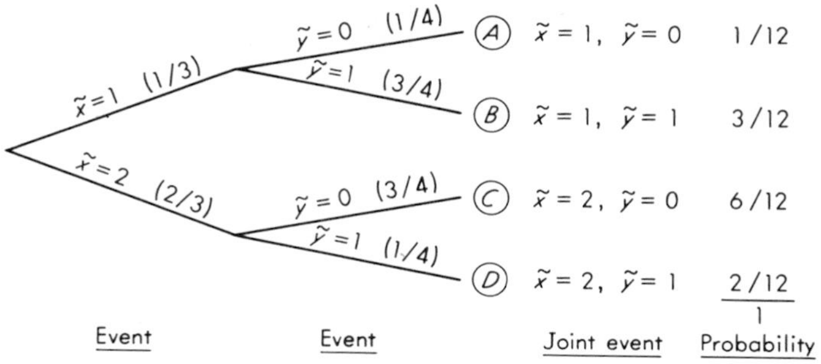

FIGURE 13.3

Probability Diagram in Which the End Positions Have Unequal Probabilities

in the population; and therefore it is only in this case that this probability can be estimated by the fraction of successes in a sample drawn by equiprobable sampling.

2. *Estimation of Expectations.* As in the previous section, let us think of each end position in the population as itself having a "value" equal to the value of some function $\tilde{z}$ at that end position. If we draw a sample from any population of end positions by equiprobable sampling, the unweighted average of the values of the end positions in the sample is a reasonable estimate of the unweighted average of the values of all the end positions in the population. It is only, however, when the decision maker has assigned equal probabilities to all the end positions in the population that his *expectation* of $\tilde{z}$ should be equal to the unweighted average of the values of the end positions in the population; and therefore it is only in this case that his expectation can be estimated by the unweighted average of the values of the end positions in a sample drawn by equiprobable sampling.

13.1.8

Estimation in the General Case:
Sampling with Matched Probabilities

We now turn to the problem of estimating the distribution or expectation of a function of jointly distributed UQ's in situations where the probabilities of the end positions of the probability diagram are not all equal. We have just seen that if we were to draw a sample of the end positions of such a diagram by equiprobable sampling, we would not be able to apply any of the methodology developed in Sections 13.1.3 to 13.1.6 to the solution of our problem. We shall now show that this methodology *can* be applied, without any changes whatever, if we draw the sample, not by equiprobable sampling, but by what we shall call sampling with matched probabilities.

To see what is meant by sampling with matched probabilities, consider the probability diagram shown in Figure 13.3, where the decision maker's basic assessments of probabilities for the branches imply that his probabilities for end positions *A, B, C,* and *D* should be 1/12, 3/12, 6/12, and 2/12. To draw a sample of the end positions of this diagram by sampling with matched probabilities, the drawing must be done in such a way that, in the decision maker's judgment, the probability that end position *A* will be selected on any draw is 1/12, the probability that end position *B* will be selected is 3/12, and so forth. In general,

> ■ A sample of the end positions of a probability diagram will be said to be drawn ≪with matched probabilities≫ if, on each successive draw, the decision maker's probability for the *selection of any particular end position* is equal to his probability for the *occurrence of the joint event* represented by that end position.

Observe that when all the end positions of a probability diagram have equal probabilities, sampling with matched probabilities is the same thing as equiprobable sampling with replacement.

Having defined sampling with matched probabilities, we now must show that all the methodology for estimation of distributions and expectations that we have developed for the case of equiprobable sampling from a population of equally probable end positions can be applied unchanged in the case of sampling with matched probabilities from a population of unequally probable end positions. We can show this by a simple example.

Consider two different probability diagrams which might have been constructed to evaluate the distribution of a function $\tilde{w}$. Diagram I has 100 equally probable end positions; at 15 of these end positions $\tilde{w} = 1$ while at the other 85 end positions $\tilde{w} = 2$. Diagram II has only two end positions, one with probability .15 and another with probability .85; at the first of these end positions $\tilde{w} = 1$ while at the other $\tilde{w} = 2$. Both diagrams thus imply exactly the same distribution of the function $\tilde{w}$.

Now suppose that we draw a sample of the end positions of the first diagram by equiprobable sampling with replacement; suppose that we draw a sample from the end positions of the second diagram by sampling with matched probabilities; and suppose that in order to draw these samples we proceed as follows. In the case of Diagram I, we first take the 100 possible 2-digit random numbers from 00 to 99 and assign a different one of them to each branch of the diagram. We then draw each successive sample end position by generating a two-digit random number and taking the end position to which that number was assigned. In the case of Diagram II, we first assign 15 of the 100 possible 2-digit random numbers to the end position with probability .15, the remaining 85 numbers to the end position with probability .85. We then draw each successive sample end position by generating a 2-digit random number and taking the end position to which that number was assigned.

Clearly we can assign the possible random numbers to the end positions of the two diagrams in such a way that each possible random number is associated to the same value of the function $\tilde{w}$ in both diagrams; and if we do, then no matter what sequence of random numbers we subsequently generate, it is clear that (1) we will get exactly the same sequence of $\tilde{w}$ values if we use these numbers to draw from Diagram I that we will get if we use them to draw from Diagram II, and (2) this sample of $\tilde{w}$ values will tell us neither more nor less about the exact distribution of $\tilde{w}$ if it is drawn from Diagram II than if it is drawn from Diagram I. It follows at once that if we have already drawn a sample from Diagram II in the way just described, we can use exactly the same methodology to estimate the distribution or expectation of $\tilde{w}$ and to evaluate the reliability of our estimates that we could use if we had drawn the sample from Diagram I by equiprobable sampling with replacement.

Finally, we observe that the implications of a sample drawn from the end positions of a probability diagram by the use of random numbers obviously cannot depend on which particular random numbers were assigned to which particular end position; the implications depend only on *how many* numbers were assigned to each end position. Accordingly the real reason why any given sample would have exactly the same implications if drawn from Diagram II in our example that it would have if drawn from Diagram I is simply that in both cases we assigned the random numbers to the end positions in such a way that the probability of drawing any particular end position was equal to the probability assigned to that end position in the probability diagram. In other words, the implications of the sample were the same in both cases because in both cases the end positions were drawn with matched probabilities; and generalizing from this example we conclude that:

■ If a sample is drawn with matched probabilities from the end positions of any probability diagram, its implications are exactly the same as if it had been drawn by equiprobable sampling with replacement from a population of equally probable end positions. In particular, the same methodology that can be used to estimate the distribution or expectation of a function and to evaluate the reliability of an estimate when a sample has been taken by equiprobable sampling with replacement from a population of equally probable end positions can be used when a sample has been taken by sampling with matched probabilities from any population of end positions.

13.2
SAMPLING OF END POSITIONS
WITH MATCHED PROBABILITIES

In the last section we showed how to estimate the distribution or expectation of a function of jointly distributed UQ's on the basis of the information in a sample drawn with matched probabilities from the end positions of the joint probability diagram, but we said nothing about the problem of actually drawing such a sam-

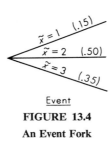

Event

FIGURE 13.4
An Event Fork

ple from a diagram whose end positions are too numerous to list. In this and the following sections we shall show how this sampling problem can be practically solved.

    1. First, we shall show how to draw a branch from a single event fork with matched probabilities—i.e., in such a way that the decision maker's probability for the selection of any particular branch is equal to his conditional probability for the occurrence of the event represented by that branch given the information available at the base of that fork.

    2. Next, we shall show that if we start at the origin of a probability diagram and select a path to an end position by drawing individual branches on successive forks with matched probabilities, the decision maker's probability for the selection of any particular path or end position will be equal to the probability he should assign to the joint event represented by that end position.

    3. Finally, after this much has been accomplished in Section 13.2, we shall go on in Section 13.3 to show how this sampling procedure can be applied even in situations where the probability diagram is far too large to be written down.

13.2.1
Drawing with Matched Probabilities
from the Branches of an Event Fork

As we have already said, the basis of the sampling method we are about to describe is the drawing of branches from event forks with probabilities which are "matched" in the sense of the following definition.

    ■ If a branch is drawn from an event fork in such a way that the decision maker's probability for the *selection* of any particular branch on the fork is equal to his conditional probability for the *occurrence of the event* represented by that branch given the information available at the base of that fork, the drawing may be said to be made ≪with matched probabilities≫.

For example, consider the event fork in Figure 13.4, where the decision maker's assessed probabilities for the events represented by the branches are shown in parentheses. To draw a branch from this fork with matched probabilities, the drawing must be made in such a way that in the decision maker's judgment there is probability .15 that the topmost branch will be chosen, probability .50 that the middle branch will be chosen, and probability .35 that the bottom branch will be chosen.

The easiest practical way of drawing branches from event forks with matched probabilities is by use of random numbers. To make such a drawing from the event fork of Figure 13.4, we first list the branches and the probabilities of the corresponding events in the first two columns of Table 13.3. Next, we assign every possible 2-digit random number to some one branch in such a way that the *number of random numbers* assigned to each branch is proportional to the decision maker's assessed probability for the event represented by that branch; our assignments are shown in the third column of the table. Finally, we use a random digit generator to generate one 2-digit random number, and we select the branch to which that random number was assigned. If, for example, the number which is generated is 48, we say that we have drawn the branch for $\tilde{x} = 2$.

TABLE 13.3
Assignment of Random Numbers to the Branches of an Event Fork

Branch	Probability	Random Numbers
$\tilde{x} = 1$	.15	00–14
$\tilde{x} = 2$	.50	15–64
$\tilde{x} = 3$	.35	65–99
	1.00	

That a drawing made in the way we have just described does in fact make the probability of drawing any branch equal to the decision maker's probability for the corresponding event is easy to see. If the digit generator which is used is random for the decision maker in the sense of Section 10.3.2, he must assign probability .01 to every possible 2-digit random number, and therefore his probability for drawing any particular branch is .01 times the number of random numbers assigned to that branch. Since we have assigned 15 random numbers to the branch for $\tilde{x} = 1$, it follows that his probability for drawing this branch must be .15, the same as the probability he assessed for the event represented by that branch; and similarly for the other two branches.

Generalizing from this example, we see that if we wish to draw a branch from an event fork with matched probabilities by generating an *n*-digit random number, we must first assign all possible *n*-digit random numbers to the various branches of the fork in proportion to the probabilities assigned to the corresponding events on that fork. Assignment of all possible *n*-digit random numbers in accordance with this rule will always be possible if *n* is at least equal to the number of decimal places in the probabilities assigned to the events represented by the branches of the fork. If the probabilities are specified to 3 decimal places rather than 2 as in our example, it will be possible to assign the 1,000

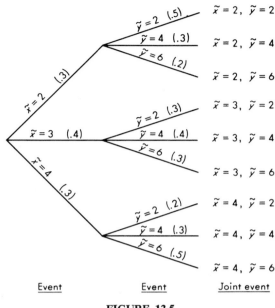

FIGURE 13.5

A Probability Diagram

possible 3-digit random numbers to the branches in proportion to their probabilities, and so forth.

Which particular random numbers are assigned to which particular branches makes absolutely no difference at all, since the probability of drawing any particular branch depends only on the *number* of random numbers assigned to that branch.

13.2.2

Drawing with Matched Probabilities
from the End Positions
of a Probability Diagram

We are now ready to show how we can select a path to an end position of a probability diagram with matched probabilities by drawing successive branches with matched probabilities. We shall first merely exhibit the nature of the drawing process by using it to draw several end positions from the probability diagram in Figure 13.5. We shall then be able to show that the nature of the process obliges the decision maker to assign the same probability to the selection of any particular end position that he should assign to the occurrence of the joint event represented by that end position.

Since the probabilities on the branches of Figure 13.5 are all specified to just one decimal place, we can draw a branch with matched probabilities from any event fork in the diagram by use of a 1-digit random number. We therefore set up our sampling process by proceeding as shown in Table 13.4 to consider each of the event forks in Figure 13.5 in turn and assign all possible 1-digit random numbers to its branches in proportion to the decision maker's probabilities for the corresponding events on that fork.

TABLE 13.4
Assignment of Random Numbers to the Branches of Figure 13.5

Fork at Origin		*Second-level Fork Following:*					
		$\bar{x} = 2$		$\bar{x} = 3$		$\bar{x} = 4$	
Branch	*Numbers*	*Branch*	*Numbers*	*Branch*	*Numbers*	*Branch*	*Numbers*
$\bar{x} = 2$	0–2	$\bar{y} = 2$	0–4	$\bar{y} = 2$	0–2	$\bar{y} = 2$	0–1
$\bar{x} = 3$	3–6	$\bar{y} = 4$	5–7	$\bar{y} = 4$	3–6	$\bar{y} = 4$	2–4
$\bar{x} = 4$	7–9	$\bar{y} = 6$	8–9	$\bar{y} = 6$	7–9	$\bar{y} = 6$	5–9

To draw *one* end position from Figure 13.5, we can now (1) generate one 1-digit random number and use it to select a branch on the $\bar{x}$ fork at the origin, and then (2) generate another 1-digit random number and use it to select a branch on the particular $\bar{y}$ fork which follows the x branch drawn in step 1. If our first random number is 7, the first pair of columns in Table 13.4 tells us that we have drawn the branch for $\bar{x} = 4$ on the fork at the origin and that we must next draw a branch from the $\bar{y}$ fork which follows this particular x branch. If our second random number is 5, the pair of columns headed $\bar{x} = 4$ in Table 13.4 tells us that we have drawn the branch for $\bar{y} = 6$ on the fork following $\bar{x} = 4$ and have thus arrived at the end position ($\bar{x} = 4$, $\bar{y} = 6$) in Figure 13.5.

To draw additional end positions from Figure 13.5, we simply repeat this procedure, each time using *two* random numbers to draw *one* path or end position. In Table 13.5, we show the five sample end positions that we would draw if 10 successive trials of our random digit generator yielded the 1-digit random numbers 7, 5, 0, 5, 4, 4, 1, 4, 9, 7 in that order. Before proceeding further, the reader should verify every step in the process by which these 10 random numbers led to the entries in Table 13.5.

TABLE 13.5
Sample of End Positions of Figure 13.5

First Random Number	*Branch on Fork at Origin*	*Second Random Number*	*Branch on Second-level Fork*	*Resulting End Position*
7	$\bar{x} = 4$	5	$\bar{y} = 6$	$\bar{x} = 4, \bar{y} = 6$
0	$\bar{x} = 2$	5	$\bar{y} = 4$	$\bar{x} = 2, \bar{y} = 4$
4	$\bar{x} = 3$	4	$\bar{y} = 4$	$\bar{x} = 3, \bar{y} = 4$
1	$\bar{x} = 2$	4	$\bar{y} = 2$	$\bar{x} = 2, \bar{y} = 2$
9	$\bar{x} = 4$	7	$\bar{y} = 6$	$\bar{x} = 4, \bar{y} = 6$

That the drawing process which we have just described does in fact make the probability of drawing any end position equal to the decision maker's implied probability for the corresponding joint event can now be demonstrated by a very simple argument.

Consider the selection of any one end position in our example. Because the first branch on the path to this end position is drawn with matched probabilities, the probability that the branch for $\bar{x} = 2$ (say) will be selected is equal to the decision maker's .3 unconditional probability for the event $\bar{x} = 2$. If the branch for $\bar{x} = 2$ is in fact selected on the fork at the origin, the second branch on the path will be drawn with matched probabilities from the $\bar{y}$ fork which follows this branch and therefore the probability that the branch for $\bar{y} = 2$ (say) will be selected is equal to the decision maker's .5 conditional probability for the event $\bar{y} = 2$ given the event $\bar{x} = 2$. It follows that the probability that the end position $(\bar{x} = 2, \bar{y} = 2)$ will be selected is $.3 \times .5 = .15$ and equal to the probability that the decision maker should assign to the joint event $(\bar{x} = 2, \bar{y} = 2)$.

We leave it to the reader to convince himself that a similar conclusion can be reached concerning any other end position in our example, and more generally, concerning any end position in any probability diagram to which the method of sampling which we have just illustrated is applied.

13.2.3
Drawing a Value from
a Probability Distribution

In order to draw a sample of end positions by the procedure just described, it is necessary to assign random numbers to the branches of each fork in the probability diagram in proportion to their probabilities, but it is not necessary actually to write down all these assignments. All that is really needed is a description of the cumulative function of the distribution that has been assigned to each fork in the diagram. Given this information, we can draw a branch from any fork with matched probabilities by a method which can best be explained by two examples, one in which every possible value of a UQ is represented by a separate branch on the event fork, and one in which the branches represent the bracket medians of equiprobable groups of possible values of the UQ.

Ungrouped Distributions Suppose that the cumulative probabilities in Column 2 of Table 13.6 define the distribution that has been assigned to a UQ $\bar{v}$ on a particular event fork in a probability diagram. We could set up for drawing from this fork by first computing the individual probabilities in Column 3 from the cumulative probabilities in Column 2 and then making the random number assignments shown in Column 4, but we can achieve exactly the same result by simply generating a 2-digit random number and then applying the following rules:

    1 Put a decimal point in front of the random number, thus converting it into a decimal fraction which we shall call k;

2 Select the branch representing the smallest value of the UQ whose cumulative probability is greater than k.

In Table 13.7 we show the branches or values of the UQ that various random numbers would select under this procedure.

TABLE 13.6
Probability Distribution Assigned to an Event Fork

1	2	3	4
Branch (Value of the UQ)	Probability of that Value or Less	Probability of that Value	Random Numbers
$\tilde{v} = 1$	.53	.53	00–52
$\tilde{v} = 2$	.82	.29	53–81
$\tilde{v} = 3$	1.00	.18	82–99
		1.00	

TABLE 13.7
Branches Selected by Various Random Numbers

Random Number	Fraction k	Branch Selected
00	.00	$\tilde{v} = 1$
52	.52	$\tilde{v} = 1$
53	.53	$\tilde{v} = 2$
81	.81	$\tilde{v} = 2$
82	.82	$\tilde{v} = 3$
99	.99	$\tilde{v} = 3$

To convince himself that the procedure we have just described does in fact select branches with matched probabilities, the reader should first verify that the branch selections in Table 13.7 agree with the two rules stated just above, and he should then verify that exactly the same branches would have been selected if the selection had been made by use of Column 4 of Table 13.6. He will then be able to see why in our example any possible random number will select the same branch or value of the UQ under either procedure; and having done so he will be able to see that:

- To draw a branch with matched probabilities from any event fork representing a UQ whose cumulative function is given, all that is needed is to generate a random number containing at least as many digits as there are decimal places in the cumulative probabilities and then apply the two rules stated just above.

For obvious reasons, the drawing procedure that we have just illustrated is often called «drawing a value from the distribution of a UQ», and henceforth we shall frequently use this expression in place of the expression "drawing a branch from an event fork with matched probabilities".

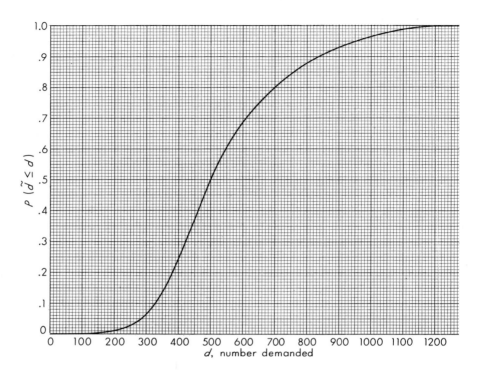

FIGURE 13.6

Probability Distribution Assigned to an Event Fan

Grouped Distributions   Suppose next that the distribution assigned to a UQ $\tilde{d}$ on a particular event fan in a probability diagram has been defined by the graphic cumulative function in Figure 13.6. To draw a value from this distribution we could first group the distribution and then proceed exactly as if the grouped distribution were the exact distribution of the UQ. If, for example, we would be satisfied with the use of only 10 equiprobable groups, we could enter Figure 13.6 at each of the points on the vertical axis that appear in Column 1 of Table 13.8, read over to the curve and down to find the corresponding bracket median that appears in Column 2, assign to each bracket median the probability in Column 3, use these probabilities to compute the grouped cumulative probabilities in Column 4, and then use a 1-digit random number to draw a value from the distribution defined by Columns 2 and 4 in exactly the same way that we drew values in the previous example. If we generated the random number 6, we would write $k = .6$ and then take the value $\tilde{d} = 576$ because this is the smallest value of $\tilde{d}$ whose grouped cumulative probability as given in Column 4 is greater than .6.

We can, however, achieve exactly this same result without first grouping the distribution defined by Figure 13.6. To do so we simply generate a 1-digit random number and then apply the following rules:

TABLE 13.8
Grouped Distribution Derived from Figure 13.6

1	2	3	4
Exact Probability of d or Less	*Bracket Median* *d*	*Grouped* *of d*	*Probability* *of d or less*
.05	285	.1	.1
.15	358	.1	.2
.25	402	.1	.3
.35	441	.1	.4
.45	480	.1	.5
.55	522	.1	.6
.65	576	.1	.7
.75	650	.1	.8
.85	757	.1	.9
.95	952	.1	1.0
		1.0	

1 Put the digit 5 at the end of the random number, put a decimal point in front of the number, and call the result k;

2 Select the value of the UQ whose ungrouped cumulative probability is equal to k.

If we generate the random number 6, we compute $k = .65$ by putting a 5 after the 6 and a decimal point in front; we then enter Figure 13.6 at .65 on the vertical axis, read over to the curve and down to find 576 on the horizontal axis; and we say that we have drawn the value 576 from the distribution of the UQ.

Recalling that $d = 576$ is the same value that we obtained when we used the random number 6 to select a value from the grouped distribution defined by Columns 2 and 4 of Table 13.8, the reader should convince himself that any 1-digit random number would select the same value of the UQ under either procedure. He will then be able to convince himself that as regards any distribution of any UQ:

- If we draw from a distribution by generating an n-digit random number and then applying the two rules stated just above, we will select the same value of the UQ that we would have selected if we had first grouped the values of the UQ into 10^n equiprobable brackets each represented by its bracket median and then drawn from the resulting grouped distribution of the UQ.

If we use 3-digit random numbers, we will achieve the effect of grouping into $10^3 = 1,000$ equiprobable brackets, and so forth.

13.2.4
Monte Carlo Trials and Trial Values

Because the method of sampling end positions that we have described in this section involves making two or more drawings of branches in order to draw one end position, expressions such as "the second drawing" become ambiguous. To avoid confusion, we shall henceforth restrict the use of the word "drawing" to the drawing of a branch from a single event fork; the selection of a complete path or end position will be called a ≪Monte Carlo trial≫. Thus we may say that Table 13.5 on page 539 describes the results of five Monte Carlo trials each of which required two drawings of branches from event forks.

Although the immediate result of a Monte Carlo trial is the selection of an end position, the end position as such is of no real interest. What is of interest is the value of some function at the selected end position, and henceforth we shall refer to the function value that results from any Monte Carlo trial as the ≪trial value≫ of the function. If, for example, we had drawn the sample described in Table 13.5 in order to approximate the distribution of the function $\tilde{w} = \tilde{x} + \tilde{y}$, we could say that the first trial value of $\tilde{w}$ was $4 + 6 = 10$, that the second trial value was $2 + 4 = 6$, and so forth.

13.3
PRACTICAL EXECUTION
OF MONTE CARLO TRIALS

In real problems involving a large number of jointly distributed UQ's each of which has a large number of possible values, a schematic probability diagram is valuable as a conceptual framework for visualizing both the basic unconditional and conditional assessments that are required of the decision maker and the general nature of the Monte Carlo process by which a sample of end positions will be drawn, but such a diagram is not a very practical guide to the actual execution of Monte Carlo trials. What is needed for this purpose is a set of computing instructions which specify (1) exactly what conditional distribution of what UQ is to be drawn from as each successive branch is selected in the course of any one Monte Carlo trial, and (2) exactly how the trial value of the function is to be computed after an end position has been selected by the trial. In the present section we shall illustrate the nature of such instructions by a series of examples.

13.3.1
Symmetric Probability Diagrams

Instructions for the conduct of Monte Carlo trials are simplest when the underlying probability diagram is symmetric in the sense that the path from the origin to any end position contains the same number of branches representing actual events as the path to any other end position. This was true of the diagram in Figure 13.5 (page 538), where every path consisted of two branches, one representing a value of $\tilde{x}$, the other a value of $\tilde{y}$.

Suppose then that instead of actually constructing the probability diagram of Figure 13.5 and writing his assessed probabilities on its branches, the decision maker had merely said that his unconditional distribution of $\tilde{x}$ and his conditional distributions of $\tilde{y}$ given x had the cumulative functions in Table 13.9; and suppose that the decision maker wishes to approximate the distribution

TABLE 13.9A
Unconditional Distribution of $\tilde{x}$

x	$P(\tilde{x} \leqslant x)$
2	.3
3	.7
4	1.0

TABLE 13.9B
Conditional Distributions of $\tilde{y}$ Given x

y	$P(\tilde{y} \leqslant y \mid \tilde{x} = 2)$	$P(\tilde{y} \leqslant y \mid \tilde{x} = 3)$	$P(\tilde{y} \leqslant y \mid \tilde{x} = 4)$
2	.5	.3	.2
4	.8	.7	.5
6	1.0	1.0	1.0

of the function $\tilde{z} = \tilde{x} + \tilde{y}$ by the Monte Carlo method. In this case, instructions for the conduct of one Monte Carlo trial could be written as follows:

1 Draw a value x from the unconditional distribution of $\tilde{x}$ in Table 13.9A.

2 Draw a value y from the particular conditional distribution of $\tilde{y}$ in Table 13.9B that applies given the x drawn in step 1.

3 Compute the sum z of the values x and y drawn in steps 1 and 2.

One execution of this whole set of instructions yields *one* trial value of the function $\tilde{z} = \tilde{x} + \tilde{y}$. By repeatedly executing the whole set of instructions, the decision maker's statistician could obtain a sample of values of the function on the basis of which he could estimate the distribution or expectation of $\tilde{z}$ in the way described in Sections 13.1.3 to 13.1.5 and evaluate the reliability of his estimates in the way described in Section 13.1.6.

13.3.2
Asymmetric Probability Diagrams

In many practical problems the probability diagram is asymmetric in the sense that the paths from the origin to some end positions contain more branches representing actual events than the paths to other end positions, and when this is true the computing instructions for Monte Carlo trials become somewhat more complicated.

As the simplest possible example of such a problem, suppose that a manufacturer wishes to derive his distribution of next week's demand for a certain product from directly assessed distributions of (1) the number of orders received during the week, and (2) the number of units demanded in each order. If the manufacturer believes that neither the number of orders nor the number of units

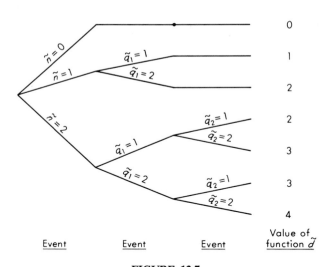

FIGURE 13.7
An Asymmetric Probability Diagram

demanded in any one order can exceed 2, his probability diagram will have the form shown in Figure 13.7, where the following names have been given to the various UQ's:

$\tilde{n}$:   number of orders received,

$\tilde{q}_1$:   number of units demanded in the first order if a first order is received,

$\tilde{q}_2$:   number of units demanded in the second order if a second order is received,

$\tilde{d}$:   total number of units demanded.

When a probability diagram is asymmetric as in this example, the computing instructions for a Monte Carlo trial must take account of the fact that not only the distribution but the very identity of the UQ that will be involved in the "next" drawing in a Monte Carlo trial depends on the values of UQ's that were selected in earlier drawings in that trial. In our example, suppose that the manufacturer feels that $\tilde{n}$, $\tilde{q}_1$, and $\tilde{q}_2$ are mutually independent (cf. Section 9.5.3), so that he has only one distribution of each UQ to assess; suppose that he assigns to $\tilde{n}$ the distribution shown in Table 13.10A; and suppose that he assigns to both $\tilde{q}_1$ and $\tilde{q}_2$ the distribution shown in Table 13.10B. Instructions for the conduct of one Monte Carlo trial leading to one trial value of the function $\tilde{d}$ might then be written as follows:

1 Draw a value n from the distribution of $\tilde{n}$ in Table 13.10A.

2 Draw n values of $\tilde{q}$ from the distribution in Table 13.10B.

3 Compute the sum d of the n values of $\tilde{q}$ that were drawn in step 2.

If $\tilde{n} = 2$ was drawn in step 1, there will be 2 values of $\tilde{q}$ to add in step 3, but if $\tilde{n} = 1$ was drawn in step 1, there will be just 1 value of $\tilde{q}$ to "add", and if $\tilde{n} = 0$ was drawn in step 1, there will be no values of $\tilde{q}$ to add.

TABLE 13.10A Distribution of Number of Orders				TABLE 13.10B Distribution of Number of Units Demanded in One Order	
n	$P(\tilde{n} \leqslant n)$			q	$P(\tilde{q} \leqslant q)$
0	.2			1	.8
1	.7			2	1.0
2	1.0				

13.3.3
Worksheets

In even moderately complex applications of the Monte Carlo method, confusion will almost certainly result unless the results of the successive steps in each Monte Carlo trial are recorded on a carefully designed worksheet.

As an example of an only moderately complex application, consider a plant in which there are various tool cribs to which mechanics come to obtain special tools needed in their work. Currently each tool crib is manned by a single attendant, and because finding a required tool sometimes takes a very long time, there may be many mechanics waiting in line at the crib which carries the tools they want while other cribs have no customers at all. For this reason the production manager is thinking of consolidating two or more cribs into one, even though this will somewhat increase the average distance mechanics will have to travel from their work places to the cribs; but before doing so he would like to know what saving in waiting time he can expect to result.

As regards the consolidation of cribs E and F in particular, the production manager has collected data on the basis of which he has assessed the distributions in Table 13.11 of (1) the "interarrival time" $\tilde{x}$ that will elapse between the arrival of one mechanic at the consolidated crib and the arrival of the next mechanic, and (2) the "service time" $\tilde{y}$ that will be required for an attendant to find a tool after a mechanic has asked for it; and he has said that he would assign these distributions to any interarrival time or any service time regardless of the values of previous interarrival and service times. More accurately expressed, he has considered successive interarrival times $\tilde{x}_1, \tilde{x}_2, \ldots$ and successive service times $\tilde{y}_1, \tilde{y}_2, \ldots$ and said that (1) he assesses the $\tilde{x}$'s and $\tilde{y}$'s as mutually independent, and (2) he assigns the distribution in Table 13.11A to every $\tilde{x}$ and the distribution in Table 13.11B to every $\tilde{y}$.

If the distribution that these basic assessments imply for the UQ "total time lost during one day by mechanics waiting in line" is to be estimated by the Monte Carlo method, the following computing instructions for a single Monte Carlo trial could be used together with a worksheet like the one shown in Table

<table>
<tr><td colspan="2" align="center">**TABLE 13.11A**
Distribution of Interarrival Time
(In Minutes)</td><td colspan="2" align="center">**TABLE 13.11B**
Distribution of Service Time
(In Minutes)</td></tr>
</table>

x	$P(\tilde{x} \leqslant x)$	$\tilde{y}$	$P(\tilde{y} \leqslant y)$
0	.20	0	0
1	.35	1	.80
2	.47	2	.85
3	.56	3	.88
4	.64	4	.90
5	.70	5	.91
6	.75	6	.92
7	.79	7	.93
8	.83	8	.94
9	.86	9	.95
10	.89	10	.96
11	.92	11	.97
12	.94	12	.98
13	.96	13	.99
14	.98	14	1.00
15	1.00		

13.12. All times are measured in minutes; we assume that there are 480 minutes in a working day; and we assume that a mechanic who arrives at the crib before the end of the day will wait until he has been served even if overtime results.

TABLE 13.12
Worksheet for Simulating a Day's Waiting Time

First Random Number	Inter- arrival Time	Second Random Number	Serv- ice Time	Time of Arrival	Server 1		Server 2		Wait- ing Time
					Service Begins	Service Ends	Service Begins	Service Ends	
				0		0		0	
42	2	15	1	2	2	3			0
67	5	96	11	7	7	18			0
15	0	89	4	7			7	11	0
23	1	27	1	8			11	12	3
35	2	39	1	10			12	13	2
61	4	62	1	14			14	15	0
72	6	83	2	20	20	22			0

1 ≪Initialize≫ the computations by entering 0's as indicated in the first line of the worksheet.

2 *a* Draw an interarrival time from the distribution of Table 13.11A and a service time from the distribution of Table 13.11B.

    b Add the interarrival time to the most recent entry under "Time of Arrival" and enter the sum under "Time of Arrival". Then if the entry just made is greater than 480, skip to step 3 below; otherwise continue with step 2*c*.

c Select the server for whom the most recent entry under "Service Ends" is smallest; if there is a tie, select Server 1.

d Under "Service Begins" for the selected server, enter the greater of the following times: (1) the last entry under "Time of Arrival", (2) the last entry under "Service Ends" for the selected server.

e If the time entered under "Service Begins" in step (*d*) was greater than the last entry under "Time of Arrival", enter the difference between them under "Waiting Time"; otherwise enter 0.

f Add the service time drawn in step (*a*) to the time entered under "Service Begins" in step (*d*); enter the sum under "Service Ends" for the selected server; and return to step 2*a*.

3 Add the recorded waiting times to obtain the trial value of the UQ "total time lost during one day by mechanics waiting in line" for this one Monte Carlo trial.

Assuming that the random numbers shown in the first and third columns of Table 13.12 were obtained by use of a random digit generator, the reader should make sure before proceeding further that he understands exactly how every other entry in the table was calculated.

13.3.4
Evaluation of Strategies

Since the only forks in the diagram of a strategy are event forks, all acts being prescribed by the strategy, any strategy diagram can be thought of as being simply the probability diagram of a number of jointly distributed UQ's, and the uncertain terminal value that will result from the strategy can be thought of as a function of these UQ's. Accordingly the distribution or expectation of the uncertain terminal value that is implied by the decision maker's basic assessments can be estimated by the Monte Carlo method; we illustrate by an example.

Suppose that a wholesaler proposes to control his inventory of a certain product by a strategy of the following kind. At the end of each day's business a clerk will compute the total number of units of this product that are on hand and on order from the factory, and whenever he finds that this quantity has fallen to or below some predetermined reorder point *R*, he will place an order with the factory for just enough units to raise the total quantity on hand and on order to some predetermined maximum *S*.

If a customer's order for this product cannot be completely filled on the day it is placed, the customer cancels the order and places it with a competing wholesaler; and although the wholesaler believes that no appreciable loss of goodwill results, he is worried about the resulting direct loss of cash contribution. Accordingly, one of the things he wants to know for any given *R* and *S* is the sales volume he can expect to lose during the next year as a result of stockouts, and this loss will of course depend, not only on R and S, but also on the day-to-day regularity or irregularity of customer demand and the regularity or irregularity of the lead time on factory orders, i.e., the time elapsing between the placing of a factory order and the arrival of the goods at the wholesaler's warehouse.

As regards customer demand, we shall assume that the wholesaler assesses distributions of (1) the number of customer orders received on each of the 260 working days in the coming year, and (2) the quantity (number of units of the product) demanded in each successive customer order. Denoting by $\tilde{n}_1$, $\tilde{n}_2$, $\tilde{n}_3$, . . . the number of orders received on the 1st, 2nd, 3rd, . . . working days of the year, and denoting by $\tilde{q}_1$, $\tilde{q}_2$, $\tilde{q}_3$, . . . the quantity demanded in the 1st, 2nd, 3rd, . . . customer orders received, the wholesaler assesses the probability distributions shown in Table 13.13A and B and says that they respectively apply to any one of the $\tilde{n}$'s and any one of the $\tilde{q}$'s regardless of the values of all previous $\tilde{n}$'s and $\tilde{q}$'s.

As regards factory lead time, we assume that he assesses the distribution shown in Table 13.13C and says that he would assign it to the lead time on any order placed during the next year regardless of lead times actually experienced on previous orders or previous values of number of customer orders or number of units demanded.[2]

<table>
<tr><td colspan="2">TABLE 13.13A
Distribution of
Number of Customer Orders
Received in One Day</td><td colspan="2">TABLE 13.13B
Distribution of
Number of Units Demanded
in One Customer Order</td></tr>
<tr><td>Number
of
Orders</td><td>Probability of
That Number
or Less</td><td>Number
of
Units</td><td>Probability of
That Number
or Less</td></tr>
<tr><td>0</td><td>.15</td><td>1</td><td>.06</td></tr>
<tr><td>1</td><td>.50</td><td>2</td><td>.17</td></tr>
<tr><td>2</td><td>.75</td><td>3</td><td>.32</td></tr>
<tr><td>3</td><td>.90</td><td>4</td><td>.50</td></tr>
<tr><td>4</td><td>1.00</td><td>5</td><td>.65</td></tr>
<tr><td></td><td></td><td>6</td><td>.77</td></tr>
<tr><td></td><td></td><td>7</td><td>.87</td></tr>
<tr><td></td><td></td><td>8</td><td>.94</td></tr>
<tr><td></td><td></td><td>9</td><td>.98</td></tr>
<tr><td></td><td></td><td>10</td><td>1.00</td></tr>
</table>

If the distribution of the UQ "sales lost next year" that is implied by these basic assessments is to be approximated by the Monte Carlo method, each

----

[2] The assessment of the lead times as independent of each other implies that two factory orders may "cross" in the sense that the one which was placed earlier may be the later to arrive. The wholesaler may believe that this can really happen, or he may believe that even though it cannot really happen, the results of his analysis will not be seriously in error if he simplifies his assessment problem by making assessments that imply that it can happen.

single Monte Carlo trial could be made according to the following instructions, using a worksheet like the one shown as Table 13.14; as we have already said, we assume that there are 260 working days in one year.

TABLE 13.13C
Distribution of
Factory Lead Time
in Working Days

Number of Days	Probability of That Number or Less
4	.00
5	.05
6	.15
7	.35
8	.65
9	.85
10	.95
11	1.00

TABLE 13.14
Worksheet for Monte Carloing Lost Sales
$R = 10, S = 30$

1	2	3	4	5	6	7	8	9	10	11
		Customer Orders		Factory Orders						
Day	Random Number	Number of Orders	Quantity Ordered	Quantity Ordered	Lead Time	Arrival Date	Quantity Received	Quantity on Hand	On Hand and on Order	Lost Sales
				—		—		11	11	
1	63	2								
	82		7					4	4	
	55		5							5
	14			26	6	7			30	
2	12	0								
3	48	1								
	38		4					0	26	
4	05	0								
5	37	1								
	18		3							3
6	14	0								
7							26	26		
	20	1								
	74		6					20	20	
8	07	0								

1 Initialize the computations by (1) entering in Column 9 the number of units currently on hand, (2) entering in Column 10 the number of units currently on hand and on order from the factory, (3) entering in Columns 5 and 7 the quantity ordered in each outstanding factory order and the estimated date of arrival of the order.

2 Iterate the following routine 260 times.

a Enter a serial number under "Day".

b If there is an entry under "Arrival Date" equal to this serial number, enter the corresponding "Quantity Ordered" (Column 5) under "Quantity Received"; then add the quantity received to the last entry under "Quantity on Hand" and enter the sum in that column.

c Draw the number of customer orders received today from the distribution in Table 13.13A.

d For each customer order, draw the quantity ordered from the distribution in Table 13.13B, compare it with the most recent entry under "On Hand", and then:

If quantity ordered is no greater than quantity on hand, subtract quantity ordered from the most recent entries under both "Quantity on Hand" and "On Hand and on Order" and enter the results in those columns, but

If quantity ordered is greater than quantity on hand, enter quantity ordered under "Lost Sales".

e After the last customer order received today has been processed, check whether "On Hand and on Order" is greater than R. If it is not, increase "On Hand and on Order" to S and enter the amount by which "On Hand and on Order" was increased under "Factory Orders: Quantity Ordered" (Column 5); then draw a lead time from the distribution of Table 13.13C, enter it in Column 6, add it to the serial number of the current "Day", and enter the sum under "Arrival Date" (Column 7).

3 After steps *2a* to *e* have been iterated 260 times, add the entries under "Lost Sales" to obtain the trial value of the UQ "sales lost next year" for this one Monte Carlo trial.

The numerical entries in Table 13.14 represent merely the *beginning* of *one* Monte Carlo trial made to evaluate a strategy under which $R = 10$, $S = 30$. Assuming that the random numbers in Column 2 were obtained by use of a random digit generator, the reader should make sure before proceeding further that he understands exactly how every other entry in the table was calculated.

13.3.5
Use of Digital Computers

Monte Carlo trials can be made on a high-speed computer in almost exactly the same way that they can be made by hand. The required probability distributions are supplied as data; random numbers can either be supplied from tape or generated internally. The computer then carries out the same drawings and computations that would be carried out by hand, being directed by a program which gives computing instructions of exactly the same sort that would be used to direct hand computations.

The computer can be programmed so that at the end of a run it not only computes all required estimates but also evaluates the reliability of these estimates in the way described in Section 13.1.6. Alternatively, the computer can be instructed to pause at the end of every so many trials, compute tentative estimates on the basis of the trial values obtained up to that point, evaluate the reliability of those estimates, compare these evaluations with predetermined standards set by the user, and then either stop and print out the results if the standards have been met or make additional trials if they have not.

For example, a user who wants a Monte Carlo estimate of the expectation of the function "profit from strategy X" might specify in advance that the Monte Carlo run should continue until a person who was originally very vague about profit from strategy X could feel 98 % sure that the exact value of expected profit did not differ by more than $1,000 from the Monte Carlo estimate of that expectation.

13.4
SIMULATION OF REAL-WORLD EVENTS

In the examples discussed in Sections 13.3.2 to 13.3.4, the sequence of events (values of UQ's) which made up any one Monte Carlo trial were drawn in the order in which they might have actually occurred in the real world. In such cases, the selection of a number of end positions by a sequence of Monte Carlo trials is often called «simulation» of the corresponding real-world events; and when the probability diagram is actually the diagram of a possible strategy, as it is in the example of Section 13.3.4, the Monte Carlo process is often called simulation of what might happen if that strategy were actually adopted in the real world.

We remind the reader, however, that events do not have to appear on a probability diagram in either the order in which they actually occur or the order in which they will become known to the decision maker. They should appear in the order that makes it easiest for the decision maker to assess the unconditional and conditional probabilities required by the probability diagram; and the basic logic by which the results of Monte Carlo trials can be used to estimate the distribution or expectation of a function is exactly the same whether the events that make up each trial are drawn in the order in which they might really occur or in some quite different order which makes their probabilities easier to assess.

We also call the reader's particular attention to a very common kind of misunderstanding of the nature and uses of simulation. Much that has been published would lead one to think that simulation constitutes a really different approach to the formulation and analysis of problems of decision under uncertainty and that this approach is one which is somehow exceptionally easy to apply. Thus a recent advertisement by a major computer manufacturer describes a general-purpose simulation program as an "easy-to-use tool for . . . analysis of environments that are difficult to describe mathematically", and a recent article aimed at informing businessmen about the uses of simulation says that "simulation is recommended when the problem cannot be solved by . . . mathematical approaches".

From the discussion in this chapter, it should be clear that simulation is in fact of absolutely no help whatever in either formulating a decision problem or making the basic assessments that determine the probability distributions required for its analysis. Before the operation of a strategy can be simulated, the strategy must be diagrammed, either literally or by giving rules which state exactly what event fork would follow any given sequence of branches if the diagram were in fact to be drawn on paper; rules must be given for finding the value that the decision maker would assign to any end position of the diagram; and rules must be given for finding the probability that he would assign to any event branch in the diagram. It is only *after* a complete and exact mathematical statement of the problem has been given by stating these rules that simulation can enter the picture; and if it does enter, it enters purely and simply as a *computational* shortcut which may or may not be economically more efficient in a given problem than some other computational shortcut.

A great many different computational shortcuts exist, some of which involve purely numerical operations while others involve substitution of the calculus for numerical operations, and many of the "basic" shortcuts have many variations. The Monte Carlo method itself, for example, can be based on sampling processes other than sampling with matched probabilities, and the efficiency of the method can often be very greatly increased by so doing. The subject of efficient computation is thus far too complex to be discussed in an introductory or even an intermediate text, but fortunately all that the businessman needs to know about this subject is that many different computational techniques do exist and that their relative merits depend on the technical details of the problem that is to be analyzed. Selection of the most efficient technique for the problem at hand should be left to a mathematician who specializes in such matters; the businessman should devote his attention to seeing to it that his problem has been correctly formulated and that his values, preferences, and probabilities have been correctly assessed.

13.5
SUMMARY

Suppose that a decision maker has already assessed his joint distribution of a set of UQ's by directly assessing his distribution for every event fork in their joint probability diagram; and suppose that he would now like to assign a distribution to some function of the jointly distributed UQ's. The distribution he "should" assign to the function is logically implied by the assessments he has already made, as we saw in Section 9.4, but the probability diagram may have so many end positions that it is not feasible actually to compute this ≪implied distribution≫ of the function. In such circumstances, the decision maker may be satisfied with an estimate of the implied distribution of the function derived from a sample of the end positions of the probability diagram.

The way in which estimates can be made and evaluated depends on the way in which the sample of end positions is drawn; we consider only the simplest case, where the sample is drawn "with matched probabilities" in the sense of the following definition:

1 If an end position is drawn from a probability diagram in such a way that the decision maker's probability for the selection of any end position is equal to the unconditional probability that he should assign to the occurrence of the corresponding joint event, the drawing may be said to be made ≪with matched probabilities≫.

An end position can be drawn without actually constructing the probability diagram if there is available a set of computing instructions which specify (1) what event fork comes next after any possible sequence of branches in the diagram, and (2) what probabilities have been assigned to its branches. Following these instructions, an end position can be selected with matched probabilities by starting at the origin of the diagram and drawing branches on successive forks until an end position is reached, each branch being drawn with matched probabilities in the sense of the following definition:

2 If a branch is drawn from an event fork in such a way that the decision maker's probability for the selection of any branch is equal to the probability that he would assign to the occurrence of the event represented by that branch if he were in the position at the base of that fork, the drawing may be said to be made ≪with matched probabilities≫.

The most convenient way of drawing a branch from an event fork with matched probabilities is by use of random numbers.

3 A branch can be drawn from any event fork with matched probabilities by first assigning all possible *n*-digit random numbers to the branches in proportion to their probabilities and then generating an *n*-digit random number and taking the branch to which it was assigned.

The required proportional assignments will always be possible if the number of digits n is at least equal to the number of decimal places in the probabilities assigned to the branches.

When an event fork represents an uncertain quantity, drawing a branch from the fork with matched probabilities is also called ≪drawing a value from the distribution≫ of the UQ.

4 If the distribution of a UQ has been defined by a smooth graph of its cumulative function, the effect of first grouping the distribution into 10^n equiprobable brackets each represented by its bracket median and then drawing from the grouped distribution with matched probabilities can be achieved with less effort as follows:

a Generate an n-digit random number, put a 5 at its end and a decimal point in front, and call the result k;

b Take the value of the UQ whose ungrouped cumulative probability is equal to k.

The selection of an end position by drawing a sequence of branches or values of a UQ is called a ≪Monte Carlo trial≫; the value of the function of interest at the end position selected on any one trial is called the ≪trial value≫ of the function. After a number of trial values have been obtained, they can be used to estimate the distribution or expectation of the function that is implied by the probabilities assigned by the decision maker to the branches of the probability diagram.

5 If a number of trial values of a function have been drawn with matched probabilities:

a The fraction of all trial values that are no greater than any specified value can be taken as an estimate of the implied probability that the function is no greater than that value.

b The unweighted average of the trial values can be taken as an estimate of the implied expectation of the function.

Provided that all other evidence about an implied probability or expectation is negligible compared with the evidence obtained from a number of Monte Carlo trials, the reliability of estimates based on these trials can be evaluated by the following rules, where $\tilde{z}$ stands for any function and z for any specified value of the function.

6 *a* Let p denote the implied probability that $\tilde{z} \leqslant z$. If r out of n Monte Carlo trial values of $\tilde{z}$ are less than or equal to z, the decision maker would be justified in assigning to $\tilde{p}$ a distribution having a beta cumulative function with parameters $B = r + 1$ and $C = n + 2$.

b Let A denote the implied expectation of $\tilde{z}$. If a is the average and v the variance of n Monte Carlo trial values of $\tilde{z}$, the decision maker would be justified in assigning to $\tilde{A}$ a distribution having a Gaussian cumulative function with parameters $M = a$ and $S = \sqrt{v/n}$.

EXERCISES

13.1 Suppose that after the sample of 10 end positions described in Table 13.1 (page 526) was drawn, 10 more end positions were drawn with the results shown in Table 13.15 below. On the basis of the total sample of 20 end positions now available:

a Show that $6/20 = .3$ is a reasonable estimate of the probability that the sales manager's directly assessed distributions of $\tilde{x}$ and $\tilde{y}$ imply that he should assign to the event $\tilde{z} \leqslant 10,000$.

b Estimate the complete cumulative function that the sales manager should assign to $\tilde{z}$ and graph your estimate.

c Estimate the mean of the distribution that he should assign to $\tilde{z}$.

TABLE 13.15
Description of a Second Sample of the End Positions in Figure 13.1

Draw Number	Description of End Position Value of $\tilde{x}$	Value of $\tilde{y}$	Value of $\tilde{z} = \tilde{x}\tilde{y}$ at That End Position
11	261,000	.092	24,012
12	108,000	.131	14,148
13	203,000	.062	12,586
14	203,000	.030	6,090
15	341,000	.062	21,142
16	296,000	.260	76,960
17	203,000	.030	6,090
18	261,000	.092	24,012
19	203,000	.260	52,780
20	296,000	.131	38,776

13.2 The average and variance of the 20 values of $\tilde{z}$ in Tables 13.1 (page 526) and 13.15 (just above) are respectively 23,361 and 320,220,000. Evaluate the reliability of the two estimates you verified or made in answer to Exercise 13.1*a* and *c*.

13.3 A decision maker has assessed the joint distribution of UQ's $\tilde{x}$, $\tilde{y}$, and $\tilde{z}$ by constructing a three-level probability diagram and assessing appropriate unconditional or conditional probabilities for all of its branches. The diagram has 1 million end positions with various probabilities.

The decision maker must assign a distribution to a function $\tilde{w}$ of $\tilde{x}$, $\tilde{y}$, and $\tilde{z}$, and in order to estimate the distribution of $\tilde{w}$ that is implied by his directly assessed distributions of $\tilde{x}$, $\tilde{y}$, and $\tilde{z}$, he draws 25 end positions with matched probabilities and computes the value of $\tilde{w}$ at each of them. The computed values of $\tilde{w}$ and the number of drawings on which each one occurred are shown in Table 13.16.

a Show that the decision maker can take .76 as an estimate of the probability which his directly assessed distributions of $\tilde{x}$, $\tilde{y}$, and $\tilde{z}$ imply that he should assign to the event $\tilde{w} \leqslant 300$.

b Estimate the probability that he should assign to the event $\tilde{w} \leqslant 500$.

c Show that he can take 189.92 as an estimate of the mean of the distribution that he should assign to $\tilde{w}$.

13.4 The variance of the 25 (not all different) values of $\tilde{w}$ described by Table 13.16 is 110,400. Evaluate the reliability of the two estimates you verified or made in answer to Exercise 13.3*a* and *c*.

13.5 In the example of Section 13.1.1, the 100 end positions described by Tables 9.5 and 9.6 (page 355) are those which correspond to the grouped unconditional distribution of total demand $\tilde{x}$ and the grouped conditional distribution of company share $\tilde{y}$ given any possible value of $\tilde{x}$ that appear in Table 9.4.

TABLE 13.16
Values of the Function $\tilde{w}$ at the End Positions
Obtained by 25 Draws with Matched Probabilities

Value w	Number of Occurrences
0	16
137	1
213	1
264	1
317	1
335	1
492	1
784	1
991	1
1,215	1
	25

a Verify that the sample of end positions in Table 13.1 (page 526) and 13.15 (page 557) could have been obtained by reading pairs of 1-digit random numbers from Columns 1 and 2 of Table T6, starting from the top, and using the first random number in each pair to select a value of $\tilde{x}$ from the distribution of $\tilde{x}$ in Table 9.4, the second to select a value of $\tilde{y}$ from the distribution of $\tilde{y}$ in Table 9.4. (The first two pairs of random numbers obtained in the way described would be 6, 4; 2, 6.)

b Continuing to obtain random numbers in this same way, add 3 more sample end positions to the 20 already obtained and calculate the value of the function $\tilde{z} = \tilde{x}\tilde{y}$ at each of them.

13.6 The distributions of total demand $\tilde{x}$ and company share $\tilde{y}$ that were actually assessed by the sales manager in the example of Section 13.1.1 are shown in Figures 9.13 (page 353) and 9.14 (page 354). Using 2-digit random numbers taken from Columns 6 and 7 of Table T6, starting at the top, draw 3 sample end positions from the population of end positions that would result from grouping each of these distributions into 100 equiprobable brackets represented by their bracket medians. (Your first two random numbers should be 63, 44.)

13.7 An executive, Mr. Merton Benz, has assessed his unconditional distribution of domestic sales and his unconditional distribution of foreign sales and now wishes to use the Monte Carlo method to estimate the distribution that he should assign to total sales. He proposes to make each Monte Carlo by generating two random numbers and using the first one to draw a value from his unconditional distribution of domestic sales, the second to draw a value from his unconditional distribution of foreign sales. Although domestic and foreign sales are not independent in his judgment, he believes that he is justified in using the two unconditional distributions in the way described because the fact that his random numbers are independently distributed means that the values drawn from his two distributions will be independently distributed.

Is Benz's argument correct?

13.8 Mr. Benz's assistant is not convinced that Benz's proposed method of assessing a distribution of total sales (cf. Exercise 13.7) is valid; in his opinion, Benz cannot legitimately avoid assessing a separate conditional distribution of sales in one of the two markets for each possible value of sales in the other market. Benz's assistant does believe, however, that some economy of effort can be achieved in the actual conduct of the Monte Carlo trials that will be used to estimate Benz's implied distribution of total sales after the required assessments have been made. Specifically, he believes that after a random number has been generated and used to draw a value from the unconditional distribution of sales in one of the two markets, this same number can be used to draw a value from the appropriate conditional distribution of sales in the other market.

Comment on the proposal made by Benz's assistant.

13.9 The worksheet in Table 13.12 (page 548) shows the results of simulating the first 7 arrivals in a day's operation of the mechanics' tool crib described in Section 13.3.3. Extend the worksheet to simulate the next 5 arrivals, obtaining the required random numbers by reading Columns 51 and 52 of Table T6 from the top. (Your first two random numbers should be 59, 99.)

13.10 The worksheet in Table 13.14 (page 551) shows the results of simulating the first 8 days' operations of the inventory-control system described in Section 13.3.4. Extend the worksheet to simulate the next 9 days' operations, obtaining the required random numbers by reading Columns 50 and 51 of Table T6 from the bottom up. (Your first two random numbers should be 91, 32.)

13.11 Regarding the inventory problem described in Section 13.3.4, suppose that

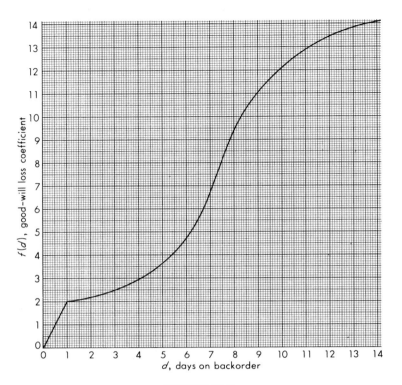

FIGURE 13.8
The Wholesaler's Goodwill-Loss Function

instead of cancelling orders that are not filled immediately, the customers allow the wholesaler to place unfilled orders on backorder and then fill them when stock arrives from the manufacturer. To reduce expense and confusion in the shipping and billing departments, no partial shipments are made.

Even though customer orders that cannot be filled immediately are not cancelled this time, the wholesaler believes that failure to fill an order immediately increases the chance that a customer will later transfer his entire business to another wholesaler. This risk seems so serious to him that he has decided that if, instead of holding a customer order for n units on backorder for d days, he could fill it immediately by paying a premium to the manufacturer for instantaneous delivery of the required stock, he would be willing to pay any premium up to $\$2n\,f(d)$, where $f(d)$ can be read from a curve he has assessed, shown here as Figure 13.8. In other words, the wholesaler has decided that the loss of goodwill that he suffers by holding an order for n units on backorder for d days is equivalent in his judgment to a loss of $\$2n\,f(d)$ cash from the till; and accordingly one of the things he would like to know about any particular inventory-control strategy is the total goodwill loss that it can be expected to cause during the next year.

Because of the possibility of customer backorders, the wholesaler feels that he cannot maintain proper control of his stock by having his clerk look only at the total quantity on hand and on order from the factory at the end of each day's business; he will have to look at this quantity less the quantity on customer backorder. This net amount, quantity on hand plus quantity due in minus quantity due out, is sometimes called the "status" of an item carried in inventory. The wholesaler will control his inventory by a strategy which calls for the clerk to compute status at the end of each business day, check whether it has fallen to or below a predetermined reorder point R, and if it has, order enough units from the factory to raise it to a predetermined maximum S.

The wholesaler intends to put his new inventory-control strategy into effect tomorrow morning. As of the close of business today, he has 11 units on hand and no customer orders on backorder. There is one factory order for 21 units outstanding, and the factory has assured him that it will arrive on the 4th working day after today. His probability distributions are those shown in Tables 13.13A–C on pages 550–551.

Devise computing instructions and a worksheet for making a Monte Carlo estimate of the expectation in which the wholesaler is interested, and simulate the first 5 days of the first trial under the strategy $R = 10$, $S = 30$. In carrying out your simulation, use 2-digit random numbers read from the first two rows of Table T6, starting from the left; your first three random numbers should be 62, 46, 25.

13.12 A manufacturer of grinding wheels controls his inventory of each type and size of wheel by a policy which calls for daily calculation of "status" (quantity on hand and on order from the factory less quantity due out on customer backorders). Whenever status is found to have fallen to or below some predetermined reorder point R, a factory order is issued for a quantity sufficient to raise the status to a predetermined maximum S. The manufacturer would now like to decide what R and S to use in controlling his stock of item no. 53026.

Stock of item no. 53026 is affected by fluctuations in the number of customer orders received in one day, in the number of units ordered in one customer order, and in the lead time between placing a factory order and delivery of finished goods by the factory. On the basis of his past experience, the manufacturer has assigned to these three uncertain quantities the distributions shown in Exhibit 1 below. More specifically, he has said that he would assign the first of these three distributions to the number of customer orders in any one day regardless of anything that may happen before that day arrives, and similarly for the other two distributions.

Control of stock of item no. 53026 (or any other item) is complicated by the fact that the number of wheels delivered by the factory usually differs from the number ordered by the inventory-control department because of rejections during the manufacturing process. The factory adds a rejection allowance based on the average rejection rate to the number ordered by inventory control, and on the average this allowance is correct, but the number of rejections in individual batches varies from batch to batch. The manufacturer believes that it is impossible to find any predictable cause for this variation. Historically, the average rejection rate on item no. 53026 has been 5%, and the manufacturer feels that there is a 5% chance that any particular new wheel of this type will be rejected, regardless of the size of the production batch or the number of other wheels in the batch that are rejected.

Control of stock of item no. 53026 is further complicated by the fact that in order to avoid cancellation of customer orders or loss of customer goodwill, the manufacturer has adopted a policy of expediting factory orders whenever there is any chance that a customer order would otherwise remain on backorder for more than one week. Expedited orders invariably arrive within a week of the time at which they are expedited, and customers never cancel orders that are backordered for only a week or less.

To implement this policy, the manufacturer has instructed the inventory-control department that whenever a customer order is backordered, outstanding factory orders should be checked to see whether or not it will be possible to fill the order within a week even if the lead times on all nonexpedited orders turn out to have the largest value to which he has assigned nonzero probability, namely 49 days. If it will not be possible to fill the order within one week under this pessimistic assumption, the inventory-control department is to expedite the oldest outstanding nonexpedited factory order.

Because no customer orders will be cancelled under this policy, the manufacturer's choice of an R and an S for control of item no. 53026 will have no effect on sales revenue, and therefore his objective in choosing R and S is simply to minimize his costs of production (including expediting) and of carrying inventory. In order to evaluate these costs with any particular pair of values for R and S, the manufacturer wants to know the probability that any particular factory order will have to be expedited under that policy and he also wants to know the expectations of two uncertain quantities, namely, the number of pieces that will be ordered in one factory order, and the number of direct labor hours that may have to be performed on overtime because the order is expedited.

To aid in the computation of these two expectations, the manufacturer's chief cost accountant has developed formulas which relate the number of hours of direct labor hours that will actually be performed on overtime if any particular batch is expedited to the size of the batch and a quantity he calls the "fraction expedited", viz.,

$$f = \frac{\text{(date of completion if not expedited)} - \text{(date expedited)}}{\text{(date of completion if not expedited)} - \text{(date ordered)}}.$$

In terms of this quantity, the number of hours of setup labor that will be done on overtime is

$$f \times H_s,$$

where H_s is the total number of hours of setup labor required to produce the batch. The number of hours of piece labor that will be done on overtime is

$$f \times (N_g + \tfrac{1}{2}fN_r) \times H_g,$$

where N_g is the number of good pieces in the batch, N_r is the number of rejections, and H_g is the number of hours of piece labor required to produce one good piece. The somewhat peculiar nature of this last formula derives from the cost accountant's assumptions concerning the average timing and amount of work that will be done on a rejected wheel up to the point at which it is rejected.

An analyst on the manufacturer's staff has written a computer program in Fortran for Monte Carlo estimation of the expectations in which the manufacturer is interested. Because the analyst wishes to use this same program to evaluate control policies for a number of different items, he has not written into the program any specifications that are peculiar to any one item. These specifications (the relevant probability distributions and the numerical values of the average reject rate, the number of setup hours required to produce a batch, and the number of piece-labor hours required to produce a good piece) will be supplied to the program as data each time it is run. A list of the variable names used in the program appears in Exhibit 2 below; a somewhat simplified description of the program itself appears in Exhibit 3.

a Be prepared to explain exactly what real-world event, operation, or calculation is being simulated by each instruction in Exhibit 3.

b Before having the program punched and compiled, the analyst has started to check it out by following its instructions by hand, using data pertaining to item no. 53026. His probability distributions are those in Exhibit 1 below; his "parameter values" are:

Average reject rate: 5%.

Setup hours to produce one batch: 12.

Piece hours to produce one good piece: 4.

Reorder point: 60.

Maximum status: 117.

The balances and running totals he has obtained after simulating 181 days of operation appear at the head of the worksheet that appears as Exhibit 4.

Simulate the next 15 days of operation, assuming that the next random numbers produced by your random-digit generator are as follows:

> 432, 115, 969, 443, 702, 637, 865, 973, 392, 925, 783,
> 221, 193, 841, 207, 355, 339, 602, 823, 758, 007.

If in the course of your simulation you have occasion to execute instruction D2, do *not* proceed from there to instruction D3; instead, execute the following instruction:

D3*. Set STARTD $\doteq$ FCORQ$/(1 -$ AVRJRT) and round to nearest integer.
Set REJECS = STARTD $-$ FCORQ $- 1$.
Go to D7.

EXHIBIT 1
Probability Distributions for Item 53026

Number of Customer Orders in One Day		*Leadtime on Factory Orders*	
Number of Orders	*Probability of That Number or Less*	*Number of Days*	*Probability of That Number or Less*
0	0.850	27	0.009
1	0.963	28	0.020
2	0.997	29	0.033
3	1.000	30	0.052
		31	0.079
		32	0.110
		33	0.146
		34	0.188
Number of Units Demanded in One Customer Order		35	0.237
		36	0.296
Number of Units	*Probability of That Number or Less*	37	0.359
		38	0.435
1	0.194	39	0.526
2	0.333	40	0.610
4	0.625	41	0.703
5	0.708	42	0.782
6	0.722	43	0.846
8	0.833	44	0.897
10	0.930	45	0.935
12	0.944	46	0.964
15	0.958	47	0.983
20	0.986	48	0.996
24	1.000	49	1.000

EXHIBIT 2
Variable Names Used in the Computing Instructions

I. Inputs

Parameters

R	Reorder point.
S	Maximum status.
HSET	Hours of setup labor to produce one batch.
HPC	Hours of piece labor to produce one good piece.
AVRJRT	Average reject rate.
NDAYS	Number of days' operations to be simulated.

Uncertain Quantities and Their Probability Distributions

NCSOR	Number of customer orders in one day.
PNCSOR	Probability of NCSOR or less.
CSORQ	Quantity ordered by customer.
PCSORQ	Probability of CSORQ or less.
LEADTM	Lead time.
PLDTM	Probability of LEADTM or less.

II. Internally Computed

Dating

M	Date (day number).

Balances (initial values supplied as inputs)

ONHAND	Quantity on hand.
DUEOUT	Quantity due out.
STATUS	Status.
DUINEX	Quantity due in on expedited orders.

Customer Orders

NTCSOR	Total number of orders to date.
TCSORQ	Total quantity ordered to date.

Backorder List

Each order on the list of orders due out to customers has values of the following quantities associated to it:

MBACK	Date received.
QBACK	Quantity ordered.

Factory Orders

FCORQ	Quantity ordered from factory.
STARTD	Quantity put into production (including rejection allowance).
REJECS	Rejects in this order.
TFCORQ	Total quantity ordered to date.
NTFCOR	Total number of orders to date.

Factory List

Each order on the list of orders due in from the factory has values of the following quantities associated to it:

QORD	Quantity ordered from factory.
QREJ	Quantity of rejections.
QDEL	Quantity actually delivered.
QEXP	= QORD if order is expedited, 0 if not.

NLDTM	Lead time if not expedited.
MDELAC	Actual delivery date.
MDELMX	Latest possible delivery date.

Expediting

FRCEXP	Fraction expedited.
HSETX	Setup hours expedited.
HPCX	Piece hours expedited.
THSETX	Total setup hours expedited to date.
THPCX	Total piece hours expedited to date.
NFCORX	Number of orders expedited to date.

Defined by Context

KOUNT
SHORT
Q

EXHIBIT 3
Computing Instructions for Monte Carlo Evaluation of Alternative Strategies

I. Initialization

A. Read in all parameters, probability distributions, and initial balances.

B. Set all running totals equal to 0.

C. Set $M = 1$.

II. Daily Operations

A. Receipt of Goods from Factory

A1. Is the factory list empty? If yes, go to B1; if no, go to A2.

A2. Is the MDELAC of the earliest factory order in the factory list equal to M? If yes, go to A3; if no, go to B1.

A3. Add QDEL for that order to ONHAND.
Add (QDEL–QORD) for that order to STATUS.
Subtract QEXP for that order from DUINEX.
Eliminate that order from the factory list and return to A1.

B. Filling of Backorders (Unfilled Customer Orders)

B1. Is the backorder list empty? If yes, go to C1; if no, go to B2.

B2. Find the oldest backorder on the list for which QBACK $\leqslant$ ONHAND. If none can be found, go to C1; otherwise, go to B3.

B3. Subtract QBACK of that backorder from ONHAND and DUEOUT. Eliminate that backorder from the backorder list and return to B1.

C. Receipt of Customer Orders

C1. Generate a random number, find the smallest value of PNCSOR which is larger than this random number, find the corresponding value of NCSOR, and set KOUNT = NCSOR.

C2. Is KOUNT equal to 0? If yes, go to D1; if no, go to C3.

C3. Generate a random number, find the smallest value of PCSORQ which is larger than this random number, find the corresponding value of CSORQ, and set Q = CSORQ.
Subtract Q from STATUS, add Q to TCSORQ, and add 1 to NTCSOR.

C4. Is ONHAND $\geqslant$ Q? If yes, go to C5; if no, go to C6.

C5. Subtract Q from ONHAND and go to C7.

C6. Add Q to DUEOUT.
Enter the order in the backorder list accompanied by the quantities
MBACK = M and QBACK = Q.

C7. Subtract 1 from KOUNT and return to C2.

D. *Placement of Factory Orders*

D1. Is STATUS $\leqslant$ R? If yes, go to D2; if no, go to E1.

D2. Set FCORQ = S − STATUS.
Add FCORQ to STATUS and TFCORQ and add 1 to NTFCOR.

D3. Set STARTD = FCORQ/(1 − AVRJRT) and round to nearest integer.
Set REJECS = 0 and set KOUNT = STARTD.

D4. Generate a random number. Is it < AVRJRT? If yes, go to D5; if no, go to D6.

D5. Add 1 to REJECS.

D6. Subtract 1 from KOUNT. Is KOUNT > 0? If yes, return to D4; if no, go to D7.

D7. Generate a random number, find the smallest value of PLDTM which is larger than this random number, and find the corresponding value of LEADTM. Enter the order in the factory list accompanied by the quantities

QORD	= FCORQ	QREJ	= REJECS
QDEL	= STARTD − REJECS	QEXP	= 0
NLDTM	= LEADTM	MDELAC	= M + LEADTM
MDELMX	= M + greatest possible value of LEADTM		

E. *Expediting of Factory Orders*

E1. Is DUEOUT > 0? If yes, go to E2; if no, go to E9.

E2. Set SHORT = DUEOUT.

E3. Is SHORT > DUINEX? If yes, go to E4; if no, go to E9.

E4. Find oldest non-expedited factory order on factory list. Is its MDELMX $\leqslant$ M + 7? If yes, go to E5; if no, go to E6.

E5. Subtract its QORD from SHORT, remove the order from further current expediting consideration, and return to E3.

E6. Set FRCEXP = (MDELAC − M)/NLDTM.
Set HSETX = FRCEXP × HSET.
Set HPCX   = FRCEXP × (QDEL + ½ × FRCEXP × QREJ) × HPC.
Add HSETX to THSETX, add HPCX to THPCX, and add 1 to NFCORX.

E7. Set the order's QEXP = QORD and add QEXP to DUINEX. Is the order's MDELAC > M + 7? If yes, go to E8; if no, return to E3.

E8. Set MDELAC = M + 7 and return to E3.

E9. Add 1 to M. Is M > NDAYS? If yes, go to IIIA; if no, return to A1.

III. Summary Results

A. Compute and Print:

Number of Factory Orders Placed = NTFCOR
Average Factory Order Quantity = TFCORQ/NTFCOR
Fraction of Factory Orders Expedited = NFCORX/NTFCOR
Setup hours expedited per factory order placed = THSETX/NTFCOR
Piece hours expedited per piece ordered = THPCX/TFCORQ

B. Stop.

EXHIBIT 4

Worksheet for Simulation of Inventory Behavior

Date	Random	Transactions		Balances				Running Totals						
M	Number	NCSOR	CSORQ	ONHAND	DUEOUT	STATUS	DUINEX	TCSORQ	NTCSOR	TFCORQ	NTFCOR	NFCORX	THSETX	THPCX
181	- - -	- - -	- - -	31	0	98	0	151	47	182	3	0	0	0
182	432													

Backorder List

MBACK	QBACK

Factory List

QORD	QREJ	QDEL	QEXP	NLDTM	MDELAC	MDELMX
67	5	66	0	46	204	207

568

CHAPTER
14

DETERMINATION OF
OPTIMAL SAMPLE SIZE

In Chapters 10, 11, and 12 we saw how a businessman can take systematic account of the information provided by a sample of any given size, and we also saw how he can informally weigh benefits against costs when he must decide whether or not to spend money on additional sample information that is to be used as a guide to informal thinking about some general problem area. In the present chapter we shall consider situations where sample information is to be used as part of the basis for decision in a well defined decision problem, and we shall show how the businessman can determine the optimal amount to spend on sampling in the simplest situations of this kind.

Even when sample information is ultimately to be used as a basis for some definite decision, there is in general no reason why only one sample can be taken before reaching a decision, and consequently problems of determining the proper size for any one sample are in general quite complex. The analysis must take account of the fact that although a large sample will give a better basis for decision than a small sample, it may nevertheless be better to take a fairly small sample now, and then take another sample if the information obtained from this small sample seems an insufficient basis for a final decision. In some situations, however, the problem is much simpler because whether or not one or more samples have already been taken, it is now either impossible or clearly uneconomical to take more than one (more) sample before the date at which the information obtained by sampling is to be used. In this introductory text we shall consider only problems of this simpler type.

In the first section of the present chapter, we shall show that when sample information is wanted for use in a well defined decision problem, the sample-size problem becomes an integral part of the decision problem, which is then solved by standard methods. We shall then go on to show that although it may sometimes be very difficult to carry out an exact analysis of a sample-size problem of this general type, it is sometimes very easy to obtain an approximation to the optimal sample size, and it is always very easy to get a rough indication of the desirability of purchasing (more) sample information by computing how much the businessman could just afford to pay for complete or perfect information about the uncertain quantity of interest to him.

The text and exercises of the present chapter are designed to be studied in the following order:

1 Sections 14.1.1–14.1.10 and Exercise 14.1*a*.

2 Section 14.1.11.

3 Section 14.2.1.

4 Appendix to Chapter 14 and Exercises 14.1*b* and 14.2.

5 Section 14.2.2 and Exercise 14.1*c*.

6 Exercises 14.3–14.4.

CONTENTS OF CHAPTER 14

1.
Computation of Optimal Sample Size

1 A Decision Problem
2 The Decision Diagram
3 Valuation of End Positions
4 The Assessment Problem and the Probability Diagram
5 The Decision Maker's Direct Assessments
6 Computation of the Distributions Required for Analysis
7 First Reduction of the Decision Diagram
8 Second Reduction of the Decision Diagram
9 Third Reduction of the Decision Diagram
10 Expected Net Gain of Sampling and Optimal Sample Size
11 Sampling in Terminal-action Problems: the General Case

2.
Approximations to Optimal Sample Size
and Upper Bounds on the Net Gain of Sampling

1 Approximations to Optimal Sample Size
2 Upper Bounds on the Net Gain of Sampling: the Expected Value of Perfect Information

3.
Summary

1 Computation of Optimal Sample Size
2 Expected Net Gain of Sampling and Expected Value of Perfect Information

Appendix
Description of Computer Program CP-2

14.1
COMPUTATION OF OPTIMAL SAMPLE SIZE

14.1.1
A Decision Problem

To show how it is possible to determine the optimal amount to spend on sampling in situations of the kind described in the introduction to this chapter, we shall analyze a very simple example from the field of quality control.

A manufacturer has purchased a certain component in lots of 200 from the same vendor over a considerable period of time. Each lot of parts has been sent directly to the assembly department for use in the final product, and considerable losses have been incurred because some of the components are defective and cause the complete assembly to fail on final test. Removing such a component from the assembly and replacing it with a good one costs $4 in addition to the cost of reworking the component in the shop. The cost incurred in the assembly department could be avoided by having each incoming lot screened (100% inspected), but this would cost $5 per lot plus $1 per piece in the lot, making a total of $205 per lot, and because only 20% of the components in a lot have been defective on the average, the manufacturer has decided that screening every incoming lot would not pay.

The manufacturer is now thinking of taking a sample from each incoming lot and then screening the lot if the number of defectives in the sample exceeds some predetermined limit. Such sampling inspection would be performed in exactly the same way as screening inspection and would involve the same kinds of costs, a setup cost of $5 per lot plus a variable cost of $1 per piece inspected; but because the same inspector would go on to screen the remainder of the lot if the sample findings led to a decision to do so, screening the remainder would entail only the variable cost of $1 per piece remaining in the lot—there would be no second setup cost.

The manufacturer's immediate problem is to decide how large a sample, if any, he should take from one lot of components which has just been received. Because the stakes in this decision problem are very small compared with the overall scale of his operations, the manufacturer wishes to act in whatever way maximizes his expected monetary value.

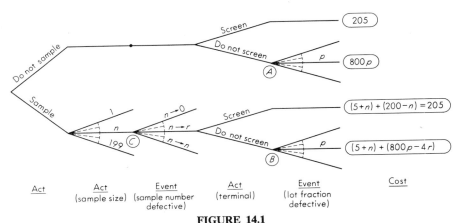

FIGURE 14.1

The Manufacturer's Decision Problem

14.1.2

The Decision Diagram

The manufacturer's decision problem concerning the lot just received can be diagrammed as shown in Figure 14.1, where the following points should be particularly noticed.

1. Following the branch for the act "sample" on the fork at the origin there is an act fork representing the choice of a sample size n. The largest sample size is $n = 199$ because the act $n = 200$ means inspecting every piece in the lot and is therefore identical to the sequence "do not sample, screen" that is already shown on the diagram.

2. Following the branch for each sample size n, there is an event fork showing every possible number of defectives r in a sample of that size.

3. The next level of the diagram shows the choice between the ≪terminal acts≫ "screen" and "do not screen" that the manufacturer will have to make after the sample has been taken and the number r of successes is known.

4. The last level of the diagram contains event forks showing the fraction p of defectives that were *originally* in the lot, before the sample was taken from it. The reader must keep this definition of p in mind as he reads what follows.

14.1.3

Valuation of End Positions

The terminal values at the end positions of the diagram in Figure 14.1 are expressed in terms of cash outflow or "cost" rather than cash inflow. In computing these values, both the purchase cost of the components and the cost of reworking defectives in the shop can be disregarded because neither of these costs will be affected by any act in the decision problem. Omitting such costs reduces the expected cost of every act by the same amount and therefore has no effect on the rankings of the acts. The costs that do have to be considered are:

1. The ≪sample-stage cost≫ that results directly from taking a sample size n; the facts in Section 14.1.1 imply that this cost will amount to $0 if $n = 0$, to $(5 + n)$ if n is greater than 0.

2. The ≪terminal-stage cost≫, which will consist of either (a) the cost of screening the $(200 - n)$ pieces that have not already been inspected in the sample, or (b) the cost of accepting defective product which will be incurred in the assembly department if these $(200 - n)$ pieces, among which there are $(200p - r)$ defectives, are sent there without being screened. The facts in Section 14.1.1 imply that the cost of screening will be $205 if no sample has previously been taken, $(200 - n)$ if one has; they imply that the cost of accepting defective product is given by the formula $4(200p - r) = \$(800p - 4r)$ for any sample size n.

14.1.4
The Assessment Problem
and the Probability Diagram

Before we can analyze the decision problem diagrammed in Figure 14.1, we must have or be able to compute for each possible sample size n:

1. The *unconditional* probability distribution that the manufacturer would assign to the $\tilde{r}$ fork which follows the branch for that n, i.e., his unconditional distribution of the number $\tilde{r}$ of defectives in a sample of size n;

2. The *conditional* distribution that the manufacturer would assign to the $\tilde{p}$ fork following each possible value of $\tilde{r}$, i.e., the conditional distribution that he would assign to the lot (or "population") fraction defective $\tilde{p}$ given any particular number r of defectives in a sample of the given size n.

The manufacturer will not, however, want to assess these required distributions directly, because he could not in this way make effective use of the information available to him. One part of the available information is the history of fractions defective in lots previously received from this vendor, and this information bears on the "prior" unconditional distribution that should be assigned to the fraction defective $\tilde{p}$ in the present lot *before* sampling rather than on the conditional distribution that should be assigned to $\tilde{p}$ given any particular number r of defectives in a sample of any particular size n. The other part of the available information concerns the procedure that will be used in drawing a sample, and this information bears on the *conditional* distribution that should be assigned to the number $\tilde{r}$ of defectives in a sample of size n given any particular value of the lot fraction defective $\tilde{p}$ rather than on the unconditional distribution of $\tilde{r}$.

We therefore assume that for each possible sample size n the manufacturer structures his assessment problem by use of a probability diagram like the one in Figure 14.2, where the probabilities that should be assigned to the

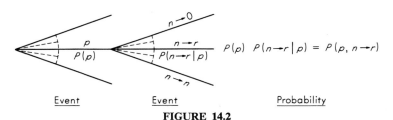

FIGURE 14.2

Probability Diagram for Computation of the Distributions Required for Any One Sample Size *n*

branches of the forks are those on which the available information bears directly. After these branch probabilities for the probability diagram for any particular *n* have been directly assessed, we will be able to compute the probabilities that should be assigned to the branches which follow that *n* in the decision diagram of Figure 14.1.

14.1.5
The Decision Maker's Direct Assessments

As regards the probabilities assigned to the branches of the probability diagram for any particular sample size *n*, we make the following assumptions.

1. By smoothing his data on fractions defective in previous lots in the way described in Section 8.2.5, the manufacturer—or his quality-control engineer acting on his behalf—directly assesses the unconditional distribution of the lot fraction defective $\tilde{p}$ that is defined by the cumulative function in Figure 10.5 on page 407.

2. The manufacturer directly assesses the sampling process as equi-probable, implying as we saw in Section 11.5.1 that if the sample size *n* is not too large relative to the population or lot size of 200, his conditional distribution of the number $\tilde{r}$ of defectives in the sample given any particular lot fraction defective *p* is approximately binomial. (We say that the *distribution* of $\tilde{r}$ given *p* is binomial if $P(n \rightarrow r|p)$ is equal to the value $b^*(n, r, p)$ of the binomial mass function and *n* is fixed before the sample is taken.)

14.1.6
Computation of the Distributions
Required for Analysis

Grouping of the Unconditional Distribution of $\tilde{p}$ Our computation of the probability distributions required for the analysis of the manufacturer's decision problem will be based on a grouped approximation to the unconditional distribution of $\tilde{p}$ that the manufacturer assessed in Figure 10.5. Specifically, we shall use the 100-bracket grouping that was shown in Figure 10.6 on page 409.

Computation of the Conditional Distributions of $\tilde{p}$ Given $n \to r$ All the conditional distributions of $\tilde{p}$ given $n \to r$ that are required for analysis of the problem were evaluated by a digital computer. As an example of these calculations, we have already shown in Figure 10.7 (page 410) the calculation of the conditional distribution of $\tilde{p}$ given the sample event $10 \to 3$, i.e., 3 successes in a sample of size 10.

Unconditional Distribution of $\tilde{r}$ The unconditional probability of the event $n \to r$ is the sum of the probabilities of all end positions at which that event appears in a probability diagram like Figure 14.2; and for any fixed n, the unconditional distribution of the UQ $\tilde{r}$ is found by simply evaluating $P(n \to r)$ for every possible r from 0 to n inclusive. The unconditional probability $P(10 \to 3)$ was computed as .12309821 in Figure 10.7; Table 14.1 shows the complete unconditional distribution of $\tilde{r}$ for $n = 10$ as evaluated by the computer.

TABLE 14.1
Unconditional Distribution of $\tilde{r}$ in Sample of Size $n = 10$

Number of Defectives *r*	Unconditional Probability *P(r)*
0	.2241
1	.2686
2	.1986
3	.1231
4	.0746
5	.0468
6	.0300
7	.0185
8	.0103
9	.0044
10	.0010
	1.0000

14.1.7
First Reduction of the Decision Diagram

Having valued all the end positions of the decision diagram in Figure 14.1 (page 572) and having computed all the probability distributions that are required for its analysis, we are ready to begin the actual analysis by evaluation of individual acts.

To show how the analysis goes, we shall work in terms of the decision diagram in Figure 14.3, which shows typical numerical values for n and r, rather than the original diagram in Figure 14.1, where everything was expressed in terms of literal symbols. The reader should verify that the values for particular end positions in Figure 14.3 agree with the general formulas for end-position values in Figure 14.1.

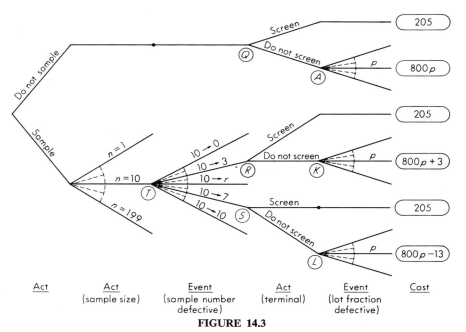

| Act | Act (sample size) | Event (sample number defective) | Act (terminal) | Event (lot fraction defective) | Cost |

FIGURE 14.3

Decision Diagram Showing Typical Numerical Values

In carrying out the analysis, we shall avoid use of any shortcuts that are available in this particular problem but might not be available in other sample-size problems that are generally similar to this one. Specifically, we shall not exploit the fact that the terminal values in Figures 14.1 and 14.3 are linear in $\tilde{p}$.

Evaluation of Position A   Because the $\tilde{p}$ fork at position A in Figure 14.3 is not preceded by any sample event, the distribution assigned to it must be the manufacturer's unconditional distribution of $\tilde{p}$ that was shown in Figure 10.6 (page 409). In Table 14.2 we show how this distribution was used by the computer to evaluate the manufacturer's mathematical expectation (and certainty equivalent) for the uncertain terminal value $\$800\ \tilde{p}$ that he will face at position A.

Evaluation of Position K   On the $\tilde{p}$ fork at position K in Figure 14.3, the distribution of $\tilde{p}$ must be the manufacturer's conditional distribution of $\tilde{p}$ given the sample event $10 \rightarrow 3$ which precedes the fork in the diagram. In Table 14.3 we show how this distribution, which was computed in Figure 10.7 (page 410), was used to evaluate the manufacturer's mathematical expectation (and certainty equivalent) for the uncertain terminal value $\$(800\tilde{p} + 3)$ that he will face at position K.

Evaluation of Position L   Position L in Figure 14.3 is exactly like position K except that the uncertain terminal value is $\$(800\tilde{p} - 13)$ rather than $\$(800\tilde{p} + 3)$ and the required distribution of $\tilde{p}$ is the manufacturer's conditional distribution

TABLE 14.2
Computation of Expected Cost at Position *A*

1	2	3	4
Value *p*	*Probability* *P(p)*	*Cost* *$800 p*	*Product* **2 × 3**
.0189	.01	$ 15.1	$ .151
.0379	.01	30.3	.303
.0455	.01	36.4	.364
.....	....	......	....
.....	....	......	....
.6192	.01	495.4	4.954
.6702	.01	536.2	5.362
.7659	.01	612.7	6.127
	1.00		$160.78

TABLE 14.3
Computation of Expected Cost at Position *K*

1	2	3	4
Value *p*	*Probability* $P(p\,|\,10 \rightarrow 3)$	*Cost* $\$(800p + 3)$	*Product* **2 × 3**
.0189	.0001	$ 18.1	$ .002
.0379	.0004	33.3	.013
.0455	.0007	39.4	.028
.....	......	......	....
.....	......	......	....
.6192	.0027	498.4	1.347
.6702	.0012	539.2	.647
.7659	.0002	615.7	.123
	1.0000		$192.74

given the sample event $10 \rightarrow 7$ rather than $10 \rightarrow 3$. Calculations of exactly the same sort as those used to evaluate position *K* lead to a value of $431.90 for position *L*.

After all the $\bar{p}$ forks in Figure 14.3 have been evaluated in the same way as the forks at positions *A*, *K*, and *L*, that diagram can be reduced to the one in Figure 14.4.

14.1.8
Second Reduction of the Decision Diagram

At positions *Q*, *R*, and *S* in Figure 14.4, the manufacturer is free to choose between the two available acts, and he will of course choose the act with the lower cost or expected cost. At position *Q*, he will choose not to screen at an expected cost of $160.78 in preference to screening at a known cost of $205.00. At position *R* he will likewise choose not to screen at an expected cost of $192.74 in preference to screening at a known cost of $205.00; but at position *S* he will

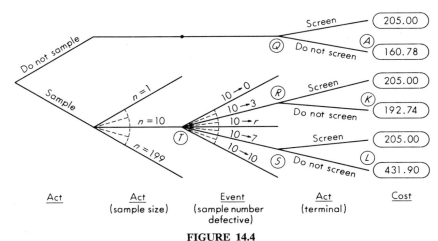

Act   Act   Event   Act   Cost
       (sample size)   (sample number   (terminal)
                         defective)

FIGURE 14.4

First Reduction of the Decision Diagram

choose to screen at a known cost of $205.00 in preference to not screening at an expected cost of $431.90.

The diagram in Figure 14.4 can now be reduced to the one in Figure 14.5.

14.1.9

Third Reduction of the Decision Diagram

To evaluate the fork at position *T* in Figure 14.5, we first compute the value of the position at the end of each of its branches in exactly the same way that we computed the values of positions *R* and *S*, namely, by first computing the expected cost of not screening at each position, comparing this with the known $205 cost of screening, and selecting the lower of the two costs. The results of this analysis are shown in the first three columns of Table 14.4.

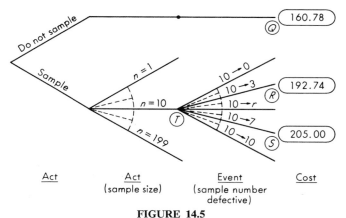

Act   Act   Event   Cost
       (sample size)   (sample number
                         defective)

FIGURE 14.5

Second Reduction of the Decision Diagram

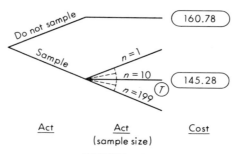

FIGURE 14.6

Third Reduction of the Decision Diagram

TABLE 14.4

Computation of Expected Cost at Position *T*

1	2	3	4	5
Value	\multicolumn{2}{c}{*(Expected) Cost of:*}	*Probability*	*Product*
r	*Not Screening*	*Optimal Act*	$P(n \rightarrow r)$	*3 × 4*
0	$ 97.94	$ 97.94	.2241	$ 21.95
1	119.14	119.14	.2686	32.00
2	148.85	148.85	.1986	29.56
3	192.74	192.74	.1231	23.73
4	250.75	205.00	.0746	15.29
5	314.17	205.00	.0468	9.59
6	375.09	205.00	.0300	6.15
7	431.90	205.00	.0185	3.79
8	482.65	205.00	.0103	2.11
9	522.12	205.00	.0044	.90
10	547.53	205.00	.0010	.21
			1.0000	$145.28

Next, we write down in Column 4 of Table 14.4 the manufacturer's probabilities for the branches of the fork at position *T* in Figure 14.5. These probabilities are the manufacturer's unconditional probabilities for the possible numbers of defectives *r* in a sample of size 10; they were derived by the computer from the manufacturer's direct assessments and have already been shown in Table 14.1 on page 575.

After these probabilities have been used to compute the manufacturer's mathematical expectation (and certainty equivalent) for the fork at position *T* in the last column of Table 14.4, the diagram in Figure 14.5 can be reduced to the one in Figure 14.6, where we see that it would be better to take a sample of size *n* = 10 and then decide whether or not to screen than it is to make the best possible choice without sampling, which is to send the lot to the assembly department without screening.

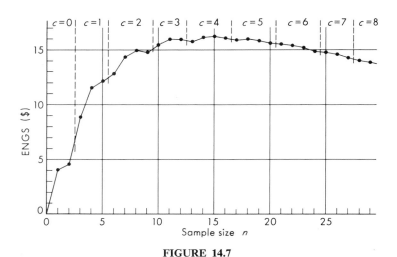

FIGURE 14.7

Expected Net Gain of Sampling as a Function of Sample Size

14.1.10
Expected Net Gain of Sampling
and Optimal Sample Size

We can find the manufacturer's optimal first-stage act, i.e., the optimal sample size, by first computing his expected cost at the end of every n branch in Figure 14.6 in exactly the same way that we have just computed this expectation for $n = 10$ and then selecting the branch for which this expectation is smallest. It will be more instructive, however, to look at the problem, not in terms of expected cost, but in terms of what we shall call the ≪expected net gain of sampling≫.

In our example, we have already seen that (*a*) if the manufacturer does not sample, he should choose the act "do not screen", which has an expected cost of \$160.78, whereas (*b*) if he decides to take a sample of size 10 and then decide whether or not to screen, his expected cost is \$145.28. We may therefore say that the expected *net gain* of taking a sample of size 10 is \$160.78 − \$145.28 = \$15.50; and in general we define:

■ For any given sample size in any decision problem, the ≪expected net gain of sampling≫ (ENGS) is the *difference* between the decision maker's current expectations of (*a*) the terminal value that will result if he chooses his terminal act as well as he can without obtaining any information that he does not already have, and (*b*) the terminal value that will result if he first takes a sample of the size in question and then chooses his terminal act as well as he can.

In Figure 14.7 we show ENGS for our example for sample sizes from $n = 0$ to 29, a range which includes the sample size $n = 15$ that gives rise to the greatest ENGS achievable with a sample of any size and is therefore the optimal sample size.[1]

14.1.11

Sampling in Terminal-action Problems:
the General Case

The general principle that is illustrated by the example that we have just analyzed is this:

> **1** Whenever information to be obtained by (further) sampling will be used in connection with a well defined problem of choice among terminal acts and only in that connection, the sample-size problem becomes an integral part of the decision problem and is solved by straightforward application of the usual procedures for analyzing a problem of decision under uncertainty.

In the applications there will often be many possible terminal acts, rather than just two as in our example, and the value of the chosen act may depend on some ≪characteristic≫ of the population other than the fraction of successes it contains—it may depend on the average of the values of the members of the population or on some still other characteristic. But no matter what the terminal acts may be and no matter what the relevant population characteristic may be, the basic nature of the decision problem will be the same:

> **2** After a sample size has been chosen and the sample has been taken, the information the sample provides about the relevant population characteristic will be summarized by one or more statistics, of which the statistics r, a, and v that we have studied are only a few examples. In the light of the information provided by these statistics, the decision maker will choose a terminal act, and his terminal value will then be determined by the relevant population characteristic.

The structure of any such decision problem is shown in the decision diagram in Figure 14.8, where C represents the characteristic of the population that will determine the terminal value resulting from the chosen terminal act and s stands for the statistic or statistics that will convey the information about C that has been obtained from the sample.

---

[1] The irregularities in the general shape of the ENGS curve are related to the fact that corresponding to each possible sample size n, there is an ≪acceptance number≫ c such that if the number of defectives in the sample is c or less, the manufacturer should accept the remainder of the lot without screening, whereas if the number of defectives is greater than c, he should screen the remainder of the lot. Table 14.4 showed that $c = 3$ when $n = 10$.

As n increases, the resulting increases in ENGS become smaller and smaller except that when an increase in n is accompanied by an increase in c, either that increase in n or the next one may produce an increase in ENGS which is larger than the preceding one.

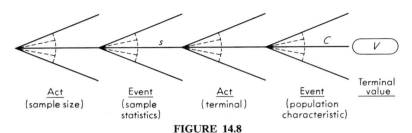

FIGURE 14.8

General Decision Diagram for Optimal Sample Size in Terminal-action Problems

To analyze such a decision problem by evaluation of individual acts, it will be necessary to assign an unconditional distribution to the statistic (or statistics) $\tilde{s}$ and a conditional distribution to the relevant population characteristic $\tilde{C}$ given each possible value of $\tilde{s}$. Usually the available information will bear on these distributions only indirectly, and it will be best to structure the assessment problem by a probability diagram like the one in Figure 14.9. After the decision maker has assessed his unconditional distribution of $\tilde{C}$ and his statistician has assessed the required conditional distributions of $\tilde{s}$ given C, it will be a routine matter to compute the distributions called for by the decision diagram in Figure 14.8 and then to find the optimal sample size by analysis of that diagram.

14.2
APPROXIMATIONS TO OPTIMAL SAMPLE SIZE
AND UPPER BOUNDS ON THE NET GAIN OF SAMPLING

14.2.1
Approximations to Optimal Sample Size

In the acceptance-sampling problem that was analyzed in Section 14.1, the exact ENGS of a sample of any given size could be evaluated in less than a second on a large digital computer, and because the optimal sample size was only 15, it could be found at reasonable cost by straightforwardly evaluating the exact ENGS of successive sample sizes $n = 1, 2, \ldots$, until the maximum was located. In other problems, however, it might take much longer to evaluate the exact ENGS of any one sample size, and it might be necessary to evaluate hundreds or thousands

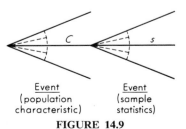

FIGURE 14.9

Probability Diagram for Assessment of the Distributions Required by Figure 14.8

of sample sizes before the maximum of the ENGS was found. In such situations, a determination of the exact optimal sample size might be prohibitively expensive, and therefore it naturally occurs to us to ask whether a good approximation to optimal sample size might be calculated at substantially less cost.

An approximation to optimal sample size can often be found at very small cost by exploiting the fact that in many classes of decision problems it is very easy to find the exact optimal sample size when the decision maker's prior distribution of the population characteristic in which he is interested is defined, not by a graph, but by a formula which is "mathematically tractable" in the sense that it allows a large part of the required analysis to be carried out by algebra or calculus rather than numerical computation. When the economic structure of a real decision problem is such that it could be very easily solved exactly if the prior distribution were of a certain type, an approximation to the optimal sample size for the real problem can easily be found by computing the exact optimal sample size for a substitute problem in which the prior distribution has the same mean and standard deviation[2] as the decision maker's real prior distribution but is defined by a formula of the required type.

Among the types of decision problems for which such methods of analysis have already been worked out are "two-action" problems with "linear economics" of the sort typified by the acceptance-sampling problem that we analyzed in Section 14.1. An approximate analysis of this latter problem will serve to give the reader some idea of both the results obtainable by this general method of approximation and the cost of obtaining them.

To obtain an approximation to optimal sample size in the problem of Section 14.1, the mean and standard deviation of the grouped approximation to the manufacturer's unconditional distribution of $\tilde{p}$ that was shown in Figure 10.6 (page 409) were computed and found to be

$$E\tilde{p} = .2010, \qquad S\tilde{p} = .1491.$$

A ready-to-use computer program which is described in the appendix to this chapter was then supplied with these values and with the essential data on costs:

Sampling cost

Fixed:	$5
Variable:	$1 per piece

Cost of screening after sampling

Fixed:	$0
Variable:	$1 per piece

Cost of not screening after sampling

Fixed:	$0
Variable:	$4 per defective

---

[2] For the definition of the standard deviation of a probability distribution, see Section 7.2.7.

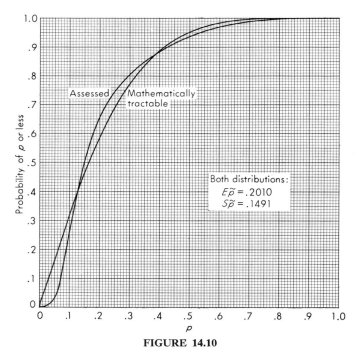

FIGURE 14.10

Mathematically Tractable Approximation to a Directly Assessed Prior Distribution

The computer then automatically selected the prior distribution with mean .2010 and standard deviation .1491 whose cumulative function is depicted by the curve labelled "mathematically tractable" in Figure 14.10; using this prior distribution it calculated the ENGS of every possible sample size from 1 to 199; and finally it printed out a statement that the sample size yielding the greatest ENGS was 13. The complete computer printout is shown in Figure 14.11.

As regards the cost of such an analysis, the total computation time was less than a second in our example, and it would be very small in almost any problem of this type because the net gains of successive sample sizes are evaluated at a rate of several hundred per second.

As regards the accuracy of the approximation, we have already seen that the sample size that is optimal for the prior distribution actually assessed by the manufacturer is 15 rather than 13, but a comparison of the two sample sizes as such is irrelevant, and it would be equally irrelevant to ask whether the prior distribution on which the computer's results are based is "close" to the prior distribution that the manufacturer actually assessed. The proof of the pudding is in the eating, and referring back to the data underlying the ENGS curve in Figure 14.7 (page 580) we find that the $15.76 ENGS achieved with $n = 13$ is 97% of the $16.22 ENGS achieved with the truly optimal $n = 15$. The 46-cent difference is far from sufficient to repay the extra cost of computing the exact optimum.

It is important to observe that the approximation to optimal sample size in our example could have been even further from the truly optimal $n = 15$ than

```
                           INPUT SPECIFICATIONS
TOTAL NUMBER OF UNITS =        200.
SAMPLE UNITS NOT SUBJECTED TO TERMINAL ACT

REVENUE COEFFICIENTS        FIXED         PER UNIT         PER SUCCESS
         SAMPLE             -5.00         -1.000              0.
         ACT 1              0.            -1.000              0.
         ACT 2              0.             0.                -4.000

PROBLEM INVOLVES UNKNOWN FRACTION OF SUCCESSES IN A FINITE POPULATION.
PRIOR DISTRIBUTION OF THIS FRACTION IS HYPERBINOMIAL WITH
     MEAN     = .20100
     S.D.     = .14910
     VARIANCE = .02223080

IMPLIED BETA MIXING DISTRIBUTION HAS
     MEAN   = .20100      RHO =   1.298
     S.D.   = .14675      NU  =   6.457

GREATEST SAMPLE SIZE TO BE EVALUATED =     199.

              ALL SAMPLE SIZES WERE EVALUATED AS INSTRUCTED


                    SUMMARY STATEMENT OF RESULTS

OF ALL SAMPLE SIZES EVALUATED, THE BEST IS      13
FOR WHICH THE CRITICAL NUMBER IS      3
WITH A SAMPLE OF THIS SIZE
SELECT ACT 1 IF SAMPLE SUCCESSES EXCEED CRITICAL NUMBER, OTHERWISE ACT 2
     SAMPLING REVENUE      =      -18.00
     TERMINAL REVENUE      =     -127.08
     TOTAL REVENUE         =     -145.08
     NET GAIN              =       15.72
WITHOUT SAMPLING
     REVENUE               =     -160.80
```

FIGURE 14.11

Optimal Sample Size for a Mathematically Tractable Prior Distribution

it actually was without resulting in any serious loss of net gain. Referring once more to the data underlying Figure 14.7, we find that any sample size from $n = 11$ to $n = 19$ would yield an ENGS equal to at least 97% of the ENGS of the optimal $n = 15$; and this example is typical. In almost all decision problems encountered in business, a curve showing ENGS as a function of sample size is very flat in the neighborhood of its maximum, and therefore reasonably small departures from the optimal sample size cause only extremely small losses of net gain. What is important in practice is not to choose the exactly optimal sample size but to choose a sample size that is within 10 or 20% of the optimal; and an approximation to optimal sample size that meets *this* requirement is often very easy to compute.

14.2.2

Upper Bounds on the Net Gain
of Sampling: the Expected Value
of Perfect Information

Although a very good approximation to optimal sample size can be calculated quite easily in many situations, there are many other situations in which it is not easy to obtain even an approximate evaluation of the net gain of sampling with a

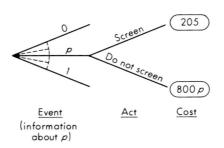

Event   Act   Cost
(information
about p)

FIGURE 14.12

Diagram for Computation of Expected Cost of Action Subsequent to Receipt of

Perfect Information

sample of one given size, let alone find the optimal sample size. It is almost always very easy, however, to compute an upper bound on the expected net gain of sampling, and if this upper bound turns out to be very small, the decision maker can conclude without further ado that he should stop thinking about sampling and proceed to choose whatever terminal act is optimal in the light of the information already available.

To find an upper bound on the ENGS of a real sample taken to provide information about some population characteristic, the decision maker simply computes the expected net gain of a mythical sample of size 0 that costs nothing to take but nevertheless yields exact or "perfect" information concerning the characteristic in question. The expected net gain of such a mythical sample will be called the ≪expected value of (free) perfect information≫ (EVPI) concerning that particular characteristic.

The computation of EVPI is carried out in two steps. First, imagining that he will in fact be given perfect information about the relevant population characteristic before he has to choose his terminal act, the decision maker computes his current expectation of the revenue or cost that will result from his choice. He then finds the expected value of the perfect information by computing the *difference* between this expectation and his expectation of the revenue or cost that will result if he chooses his terminal act as well as he can without first obtaining any additional information about the characteristic.

The two steps in the computation of EVPI in any terminal-action problem can be illustrated by applying them to the acceptance-sampling problem that we analyzed in Section 14.1, where the relevant population characteristic was the fraction $\tilde{p}$ of defectives in the lot that had just been received.

1. The diagram in Figure 14.12 shows how to carry out the first step, namely to find what expectation the manufacturer should assign now to the cost that he would ultimately incur if he were in fact to be told the exact value of the lot fraction defective $\tilde{p}$ before he had to decide whether or not to screen the lot. The first fork in the diagram represents the possible values of the lot fraction $\tilde{p}$;

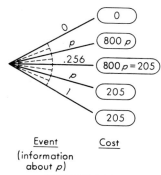

Event   Cost
(information
about p)

FIGURE 14.13

Reduced Diagram for Computation of Expected Cost of Action Subsequent to Receipt of Perfect Information

the second-level forks represent the choice between terminal acts that hypothetically will be made after learning the true value of $\bar{p}$.

Since screening costs \$205 (\$5 fixed cost plus \$1 per piece in the lot) while not screening costs \$800p (\$4 for each of the 200p defectives in the lot), the manufacturer will screen if and only if p exceeds $205/800 = .256$. From this it follows that we can reduce the diagram in Figure 14.12 to the single fork in Figure 14.13, and all that remains is to compute the manufacturer's mathematical expectation for the uncertain cost represented by this fork.

Using the grouped distribution of $\bar{p}$ that was originally shown in Figure 10.6 (page 409), the computer carried out this computation in the way indicated in Table 14.5, where it appears that \$128.57 should be the manufacturer's current expectation of the cost that he would ultimately incur if he were in fact to be told the true value of the lot fraction defective $\bar{p}$ before deciding whether or not to screen.

2. We have already seen in Figure 14.4 (page 578) that if the manufac-

TABLE 14.5
Computation of Expected Cost of Action
Subsequent to Receipt of Perfect Information

1	2	3	4
Value p	*Probability* $P(p)$	*Cost of Optimal Act*	*Product* 2×3
.0189	.01	\$ 15.1	\$ .151
.0379	.01	30.3	.303
.0455	.01	36.4	.364
. . . . .	. . . .	. . . . . .	. . . .
. . . . .	. . . .	. . . . . .	. . . .
.6192	.01	205.0	2.050
.6702	.01	205.0	2.050
.7659	.01	205.0	2.050
	1.00		\$128.57

turer decides whether or not to screen without obtaining any information he does not already have, his better choice is not to screen and his expectation of the cost that will result is $160.78. Since this is $160.78 − $128.57 = $32.21 more than his expectation of the cost he would incur if he could learn the true value of $\tilde{p}$ before deciding whether or not to screen, we can say that in this situation the expected value of perfect information about $\tilde{p}$ is $32.21.

We remind the reader that the EVPI is interesting because no real sample, which costs money to take and then provides only "imperfect" information about $\tilde{p}$, can possibly have an ENGS as high as the EVPI. In our example, we have already seen (Figure 14.7 on page 580) that the greatest ENGS achievable with a real sample is only $16.22.

14.3
SUMMARY

14.3.1
Computation of Optimal Sample Size

1 In many decision problems, the terminal values that will result from the ≪terminal acts≫ that are under consideration depend on some ≪characteristic≫ of a population, such as p or A, and the information about this characteristic that is provided by a sample can be summarized by computing the values of an appropriate ≪statistic≫ or statistics, such as n, r, a, or v.

2 If sample information is to be used as a basis for decision in a terminal-action problem, and if at most one (more) sample can be taken, the possible sample sizes are shown on the first fork in the decision diagram, the possible values of the sample statistic(s) on the second-level forks, the possible terminal acts on the third-level forks, and the possible values of the relevant population characteristic on the fourth-level forks.

3 The probability distributions required for analysis by evaluation of individual acts are an unconditional distribution of the sample statistic(s) and a conditional distribution of the relevant population characteristic given every possible value (or set of values) of the sample statistic(s).

4 The decision maker will usually do well to assess the required distributions indirectly, by directly assessing his unconditional distribution of the population characteristic and making an assessment of the sampling process that implies conditional distributions of the sample statistic(s) given the population characteristic. The distributions required for analysis can then be computed from these directly assessed distributions.

14.3.2
Expected Net Gain of Sampling
and Expected Value of Perfect Information

1 In any terminal-action problem, the ≪expected net gain of sampling≫ (ENGS) with a sample of any given size is the *difference* between the decision maker's current expectations of (*a*) the terminal value that will result if he chooses his terminal act as well as he can without obtaining any information that he does not already have, and (*b*) the terminal value that will result if he first takes a sample of the size in question and then chooses his terminal act.

2 In any terminal-action problem, the ≪expected value of (free) perfect information≫ (EVPI) concerning a given population characteristic is the *difference* between the decision maker's current expectations of (*a*) the terminal value that will result if he chooses his terminal act as well as he can without obtaining any information that he does not already have, and (*b*) the terminal value that would result if he were to be told the true value of the characteristic before choosing his terminal act.

3 The expected net gain of sampling is necessarily smaller for all sample sizes than the expected value of (free) perfect information.

Harvard Business School
Computer Programs for Managerial Economics
MEPD–1
Robert Schlaifer, 4/9/66

OPTIMAL SAMPLE SIZE FOR BINOMIAL OR HYPERGEOMETRIC SAMPLING IN TWO-ACTION PROBLEMS WITH LINEAR ECONOMICS

PREFACE

The computer program discussed in the present memorandum, Program CP–2, can be used to find either the optimal or a near-optimal sample size in decision problems where:

1 The decision maker must ultimately choose one or the other of just two possible terminal acts in circumstances where the profit or cost of at least one of these acts will depend on the unknown number of "successes" that are contained in some "population" or that have been or will be generated by some "process".

2 Whether or not any sample units from this population or process have already been drawn and observed, at most one (additional) sample can now be drawn before choosing a terminal act.

3 The profits or costs of sampling and of both terminal acts are linear in all relevant variables.

4 The sampling distribution of the number of successes in a sample of any size is either binomial or hypergeometric.

Problems having these characteristics typically arise when a decision must be made whether or not to:

a Produce a certain number of pieces on a certain machine or by a certain process when there is uncertainty about the process fraction defective. The problem

---

[3] For a complete description of this program, see the publication mentioned on page vi of the Preface.

may specify either the total number of pieces to be produced or the number of pieces to be produced in addition to the sample pieces, if any.

b Reject (screen) a lot of manufactured pieces when there is uncertainty about either the fraction of all pieces in the lot that are defective or the process fraction defective of the process that produced the lot.

c Administer a certain treatment (offer a certain product) to all members of a certain population when there is uncertainty about either the fraction of all members who will respond favorably or the "true probability" that any particular member will respond favorably.

Program CP–2 can find the strictly optimal sample size only if the decision maker's uncertainties about the fraction of successes or the true probability of a success can be expressed by a prior distribution of an appropriate mathematical type, to be discussed in Section 1.5 below. As will be explained in that section, however, the user's prior distribution will often be necessarily of virtually the required type if any substantial number of sample units have already been drawn and observed; and even when the user's prior distribution is not of the required type, a close approximation to the optimal sample size can usually be obtained by substituting for the decision maker's true prior distribution a distribution of the required type that has the correct mean and variance. If the user's prior distribution is essentially determined by sample observations that have already been made, he can specify his prior distribution by merely stating the number of these observations and the number of successes among them. If this is not the case but the user is willing to accept an analysis based on a prior distribution of the required type that has the same mean and variance as his true prior distribution, all that he has to specify is the mean and variance in question.

*   *   *

Program CP–2 was written by Ronald Rubel and edited by Robert Glauber. According to the particular problem being analyzed, it makes use of one or the other of two basic recursive computational schemes, one of which was developed by Howard Raiffa and Robert Schlaifer, the other by José Faus. The programming of the Raiffa-Schlaifer scheme was done by Ronald Rubel, that of the Faus scheme by Faus.

1

THE PROBLEMS THAT CAN BE ANALYZED

1.1

Subjection of Sample Units
to the Terminal Act

In most situations sample "units" drawn from a population or process are not later subjected to the chosen terminal act. This is the case, for example, when sample units drawn from a population are "treated" in the course of sampling inspection, will not be treated again if the chosen terminal act is to treat the remainder of the population, and cannot be "detreated" if the chosen terminal act is not to treat the remainder of the population. This is also the case when sample units drawn from a process are destructively inspected, so that they cannot be used to fill requirements whether the chosen terminal act is to use this process to fill requirements or to reject this process and use another.

In some situations, however, sample units *are* later subjected to the chosen terminal act, exactly like units not included in the sample. This is the case, for example, when sampling inspection consists in determining as regards each member of the sample whether he would buy a product if it were offered for sale, and the terminal act will consist in either offering or not offering the product to all members of population, those who were included as well as those who were not included in the sample.

Program CP–2 can be used to analyze decision problems when sample units that will be drawn as the result of the decision either will or will not be later subjected to the chosen terminal act. If any sample units have already been drawn and observed at the time the decision problem is analyzed, the program can be used whether or not these units will be handled in the same way as the units that will be drawn as a result of the decision.

1.2
Total Number of Units and Number
Subjected to the Terminal Act

In some situations, the number of units that will be subjected to the terminal act depends on the sample size because the total number of units that exist in a "population" or that have been and are to be produced by a "process" is fixed and all units except the sample units (if any) will be subjected to the chosen terminal act.

In other situations, the number of units that will be subjected to the terminal act is fixed or predetermined, either (*a*) because the sample is taken from a process capable of generating an unlimited number of units and the units to be subjected to the terminal act will be produced in predetermined number after the sample has been produced and inspected, or (*b*) because even though the total number of units existing or to be produced is fixed, all units including the sample units (if any) will be subjected to the terminal act.

To state these possible cases more concisely, we first define the following notation for use in referring to *units that have NOT been already drawn and observed:*

n_s: number of units that *will* be included in the (new) *sample*, excluding any units already drawn and observed;

n_t: number of units not already drawn and observed that will be subjected to the chosen *terminal act;*

N: *total* number of units not already observed that exist in a "population" or have been and are to be produced by a "process".

In this notation, the categories of problems that can be analyzed by Program CP–2 are:

1 N is fixed while n_t depends on n_s via $n_t = N - n_s$.

2 n_t is fixed while N depends on n_s via $N = n_s + n_t$.

3 N is fixed and $n_t = N$ regardless of n_s.

The user must specify to which category his problem belongs, and he must specify the numerical value of N if N is fixed, of n_t if N depends on n_s. In either case, he must *exclude units already drawn and observed* in determining the numerical value in question.

1.3

Economics of Sampling
and Terminal Action

Two conditions concerning the economics of sampling and terminal action must be met if a problem is to be analyzed by Program CP–2. In stating these conditions we shall use the word "now" to denote the time at which the analysis is made; "past" and "future" are defined relative to "now".

1 *Terminal Economics.* The *revenue* (positive or negative) that will result from choice of terminal act a_i ($i = 1, 2$) either "now" or in the "future" must be expressible in the form

$$V_t(a_i, n_t, r_t) = F_i + A_i n_t + B_i r_t, \qquad i = 1, 2, \tag{1}$$

where the F_i, A_i, and B_i are constants each of which may be positive, zero, or negative, n_t is the number of units *not* already inspected in the "past" that will be subjected to the chosen terminal act, and r_t is the as yet unknown number of successes among these n_t units. Observe that:

a If sample units already inspected in the "past" are to be subjected ("now" or in the "future") to the chosen terminal act, the revenue that will result from subjecting them to terminal act a_i must be included in the "fixed" revenue F_i, since these units and the successes among them are not counted in n_t and r_t.

b If sample units drawn and inspected in either the "past" or the "future" are to be later subjected to the chosen terminal act, the revenue that has resulted or will result purely from inclusion of these units in a sample, regardless of the choice of terminal act, is to be excluded from the terminal revenue expressed by formula (1) above.

2 *Sampling Economics.* The *revenue* (positive or negative) that will result from "future" sampling prior to choice of a terminal act must be expressible in the form

$$V_s(n_s, r_s) = \begin{cases} 0 & \text{if} & n_s = 0, \\ F_s + A_s n_s + B_s r_s & \text{if} & n_s > 0, \end{cases} \tag{2}$$

where F_s, A_s, and B_s are constants, n_s is the number of sample units inspected in the "future", and r_s is the number of successes among these n_s units. The coefficients F_s and A_s will usually be negative, representing respectively the fixed cost associated with taking a sample of any size and the incremental cost per unit in the sample; the coefficient B_s may be either negative (e.g., if the defectives in a sample are reworked at a cost regardless of the choice of terminal act), zero, or positive (e.g., if a sample mailing of a catalog results in orders from customers that give rise to a profit regardless of the choice of terminal act). Observe that:

a If sample units inspected in the "future" are later to be subjected to the chosen terminal act, the sampling revenue expressed by formula (2) must include only revenue that is independent of the choice of terminal act.

b Revenue that has resulted or will result from drawing and inspecting units already inspected in the "past" is irrelevant to the decision problem and must be excluded from the revenue due to "future" sampling as expressed by formula (2) as well as from the terminal revenue expressed by formula (1).

1.4
Sampling Distributions

Program CP–2 can be used when either:

1 The problem is expressed in terms of a finite population which contains a *fixed but unknown fraction $\tilde{f}$ of successes*, so that the sampling distribution of $\tilde{r}_s$ given f is hypergeometric, or

2 The problem is expressed in terms of either a finite population containing, or a process generating, units all of which have the same *fixed but unknown probability $\tilde{p}$* of being a success, so that the sampling distribution of $\tilde{r}_s$ given p is binomial.

The user must specify in which of these two ways he is expressing his problem; if his problem involves a "finite population", he should observe that he can express it either in terms of the fraction $\tilde{f}$ of successes actually contained in the population or in terms of the probability $\tilde{p}$ that any member of the population would or will be a success.

1.5
Prior Distributions

1.5.1
Assumptions and Specifications
Required of the User

The computational methods used in Program CP–2 are based on the assumption that:

1 If the problem is expressed in terms of an unknown probability $\tilde{p}$, so that sampling is binomial, the prior distribution assigned to $\tilde{p}$ will be of the beta type defined and parametrized in Section 1.5.4 below.

2 If the problem is expressed in terms of an unknown fraction $\tilde{f}$, so that sampling is hypergeometric, the prior distribution assigned to $\tilde{f}$ will be of the hyper-binomial type defined and parametrized in Section 1.5.5 below.

The user must specify either:

    a The mean and variance of his prior distribution of $\tilde{p}$ or $\tilde{f}$; or

    b The parameters ρ and ν of the distribution as defined below.

1.5.2
Specification When Sample Units
Have Already Been Drawn and Observed

If a number of sample units have already been drawn and observed at the time the decision concerning a new sample is being analyzed, and if the user feels that any other information he may have about the value of $\tilde{p}$ or $\tilde{f}$ is negligible in comparison with the information contained in these sample observations, then it can usually be shown that (1) the user's prior distribution of $\tilde{p}$ or $\tilde{f}$ should logically be of the corresponding type named in Section 1.5.1 just above, and (2) that the parameters of this distribution should logically have nearly if not exactly the values

        ν = number of units already observed,

        ρ = number of successes among these units.

The user who finds himself in this situation has no need to read the remainder of Section 1.5.

1.5.3
Specification Required to Obtain
a Near-optimal Plan for Practical Use

When the conditions of the previous section do not obtain, the user's "true" prior distribution of $\tilde{p}$ or $\tilde{f}$ may or may not be of the form required for exact analysis by Program CP–2, but if the user's objective is simply to obtain a near-optimal plan for practical use, he will run little risk of going far astray if he pays no attention to the exact form of prior distribution that will be automatically assumed by the program and specifies merely that this distribution shall have a mean and variance equal to the mean and variance of his "true" prior distribution of $\tilde{p}$ or $\tilde{f}$, whatever the form of that distribution may be, continuous or discrete. Many numerical examples indicate that a sampling plan which is optimal under one prior distribution will be nearly optimal— i.e., will have nearly the greatest achievable net gain—under another prior distribution having the same mean and variance even though the "shapes" of the two distributions are substantially different. The only important exception discovered to date is the case where the true prior distribution assigns a very substantial probability mass to $\tilde{p}$ or $\tilde{f}$ = 0 or 1, but the result of an analysis based on a substitute prior distribution should be questioned whenever the analysis shows that although the optimal sample size is presumably zero, there is some nonzero sample size that it would be nearly profitable to take. For the information on this point that can be provided by Program CP–2, see Sections 2.1 and 2.2 below.

1.5.4
Beta Distributions

The beta distribution assumed in Program CP–2 when a problem is stated in terms of an unknown probability $\bar{p}$ is defined with parameters ρ and ν by writing its density in the form

$$f(p) \propto p^{\rho-1} (1 - p)^{\nu-\rho-1}.$$

As stated in Section 1.5.1 just above, the user must specify the parameters ρ and ν, either directly or by specifying the mean and variance of the distribution. The program will automatically compute and print out that one of the two alternative forms of specification which is not supplied by the user.

1.5.5
Hyperbinomial Distributions

A hyperbinomial distribution with parameters N, ρ, and ν is ordinarily defined as a beta mixture of binomial distributions of a *number* $\tilde{R}$ of successes by writing its mass function in the form

$$f(R|N, \rho, \nu) \propto \int_0^1 p^R (1 - p)^{N-R} p^{\rho-1} (1 - p)^{\nu-\rho-1} \, dp.$$

We shall, however, refer to the corresponding distribution of the *fraction* $\tilde{f} = \tilde{R}/N$ of successes among N units as hyperbinomial with parameters N, ρ, and ν.

It is assumed in Program CP–2 that the parameter N is fixed by the size of the finite population from which a sample is to be taken. As stated in Section 1.5.1 above, the parameters ρ and ν must be specified by the user, either directly or by specifying the mean and variance of $\tilde{f}$; the program will automatically compute and print out that one of the two alternative specifications which is not supplied by the user, and will also compute and print out the mean and variance of the implied beta mixing distribution.

2
THE RESULTS THAT CAN BE OBTAINED

2.1
Available Output

Given the input data required to define a problem meeting the conditions discussed in Section 1 above, Program CP–2 will if so instructed recursively compute and print out all of the following quantities for sample sizes 1, 2, . . . up to a maximum which must be specified by the user and which must not exceed 99,999.

> **1** Critical number to use in a decision rule for choice of a terminal act after the sample has been taken.
>
> **2** Expectation of the revenue that will result directly from taking the sample. If n_t is fixed, this can be interpreted as the negative of the expected cost of

sampling; if N is fixed and $n_t = N - n_s$, it can only be interpreted as expected sample-stage revenue.

3 Expectation of the revenue that will result directly from choosing the terminal act which appears better after the sample has been taken.

4 Expectation of the total revenue that will result from taking the sample and then choosing the terminal act, the sum of (2) and (3).

5 Expectation of the net gain of sampling (ENGS), i.e., the difference between (4) and the expectation of the revenue that will result from choosing the terminal act which appears better before sampling.

6 If n_t is fixed, the difference between (5) and (2), which can be interpreted as the expected gross value of the information to be obtained from the sample (EVSI), before deduction of the expected cost of obtaining this information.

2.2

Output Needed to Determine
Optimal Sample Size

If the user is interested only in determining the optimal sample size, he can increase running speed and decrease output volume by instructing the program to compute recursively only the ENGS (net gain) of sample sizes 1, 2, . . . up to a maximum which he must specify (but which must not exceed 99,999) and then to compute and print the quantities listed in Section 2.1 above for that sample size whose computed ENGS is greatest.

2.3

Running Time

Running time on an IBM 7094 amounts to approximately 4,000 successive sample sizes per minute when results for all sample sizes are listed, 20,000 per minute when only the results pertaining to optimal sample size are printed.

3

SUMMARY OF REQUIRED INPUTS

A. Concerning the entire run:

    1 Number of separate problems to be analyzed in the run.

    2 Maximum running time.

B. For each separate problem:

    1 Classification of the relations among n_s, n_t, and N:
      a N is fixed while n_t depends on n_s via $n_t = N - n_s$.
      b n_t is fixed while N depends on n_s via $N = n_t + n_s$.
      c N is fixed and $n_t = N$ regardless of n_s.

    2 Numerical value of N if fixed, of n_t if N depends on n_s.

3 Revenue coefficients defined by formulas (1) and (2) above. Each coefficient must be prefixed by an algebraic sign, $-$ if it represents a *cost* or cash outflow, $+$ if it represents a *profit* or cash inflow; no coefficient may contain more than eight significant digits or more than eight digits on either side of the decimal point. There are nine coefficients to be specified altogether, as follows.

Terminal Revenue:

F_1: fixed revenue resulting from
A_1: revenue per unit subjected to $\}$ act 1,
B_1: revenue per success resulting from

F_2: fixed revenue resulting from
A_2: revenue per unit subjected to $\}$ act 2.
B_2: revenue per success resulting from

Sampling Revenue:

F_s: fixed revenue resulting from taking a sample of any nonzero size,
A_s: revenue per unit in the sample,
B_s: revenue per success in the sample.

4 Statement of greatest sample size to be evaluated.

5 Output desired: statement whether the user wants:
  a Only the results relating to optimal sample size, or
  b Complete listing of results for every sample size evaluated.

6 Prior distribution: statement whether the unknown quantity to which a prior distribution is assigned is
  a the fixed but unknown *fraction $\tilde{f}$* of successes among a known, fixed number N of units, or
  b the fixed but unknown *probability $\tilde{p}$* that any unit is or will be a success.

7 Specification of the prior distribution via *either:*
  a Statement of its *mean* and *variance*, or
  b Statement of its *parameters ρ and ν.*

EXERCISES

14.1 Science Books, Inc. (B)

  a Diagram the decision problem that was faced by Mr. Jensen of *Science Books, Inc. (A)* (Exercise 11.14) before he decided to send out a sample mailing concerning Zbykfy's *Introduction to Game Theory*, and be prepared to describe every step in the process by which you could analyze this decision problem.
  b Prepare all the inputs that are needed for an approximate analysis of Mr. Jensen's problem by the computer program described in Section 14.2.1 and the Appendix to Chapter 14.
  c If Mr. Jensen had not been able to send out a sample mailing, how much should he have been just willing to pay to a clairvoyant for revealing the exact number of club members who would order Zbykfy's *Introduction?*

14.2 *Robinson Abrasives Company (C)*

The superintendent of manufacturing of the Robinson Abrasives Company must decide whether or not to scrap a batch of possibly defective bonding material that the company has on hand, and the supervisor of quality control has suggested that before making his decision the superintendent should conduct an experiment by producing a small number of wheels with bonding material from this batch and then observing how many of these wheels fail on final test.[4] The superintendent is hesitant about conducting such an experiment, however, because the results will be uninformative unless the experimental wheels are loaded in the kiln with enough extra care to make sure that none of them fail due to improper loading, and this special care will cost $10 per wheel over and above the normal costs of manufacturing.

a Could the superintendent of manufacturing use the computer program described in Section 14.2.1 and the Appendix to Chapter 14 to decide whether or not to conduct the proposed experiment, and if so, how many experimental wheels to produce?

b If he could, prepare all the inputs that he would have to supply to the program.

14.3 *Mar-Pruf Finishes, Inc. (B)*

In the context of the decision problem described in *Mar-Pruf Finishes, Inc. (A)* (Exercise 12.14), Mar-Pruf's management might have wished to know the expected value of perfect information (EVPI) concerning the average first-year sales per customer that would be realized if the new product were actually put on the market.

a Compute the EVPI in the situation of part (*d*) of Exercise 12.14, *before* the sample described in part (*e*) was taken.

b Compute the EVPI in the situation of part (*f*) of Exercise 12.14, *after* the sample described in part (*e*) was taken, assuming that management believes that every sample customer would actually buy exactly as much as he said he would buy.

14.4 *Grand Western Railroad (B)*

In the context of the decision problem described in *Grand Western Railroad (A)* (Exercise 12.15), Mr. H. B. Jones might have wished to know the expected value of perfect information (EVPI) concerning the average amount by which cancellation of the Family-Fare tariff would increase an individual family's expenditure on travel on the Grand Western Railroad during the coming year.

a Compute the EVPI as of the time of Jones' original interest in the problem, *before* the pilot sample described in the case was taken.

b Compute the EVPI *after* the pilot sample was taken, assuming that Jones believes (*a*) that every person in the sample stated correctly the amount by which cancellation would have reduced his last year's expenditure, and (*b*) that the average effect that cancellation will have on next year's expenditures is exactly equal to the average effect that cancellation would have had on last year's expenditures.

---

[4] Cf. *Robinson Abrasives Company (A)* and (*B*) (Exercises 11.15 and 11.16).

CHAPTER
15

TOPICS IN SAMPLING

In the present chapter we take up three special topics that are of very considerable importance in practical applications of sampling.

1. In Section 15.1, we show how a businessman can assess a probability distribution of the difference between the fraction of successes or the average of the values in one population and the corresponding fraction or average in another population. Such distributions are very frequently useful in deciding, for example, to which of two groups of people a product should be promoted, or in deciding which of two methods of promotion is more effective.

2. In Section 15.2, we show how a businessman can take reasoned account of the fact that sample observations are often subject to various forms of "bias". This may happen, for example, because the values of the members of the sample are incorrectly reported by interviewers, or because some members of the population refuse to be interviewed, or for many other reasons.

3. Finally, in Section 15.3 we leave the problems faced by a decision maker who wishes to take account of sample information in assessing his own distribution of some UQ and briefly discuss the problems faced by a researcher who has obtained sample information that may be of interest to many different decision makers and wishes to state the implications of this information as clearly as possible.

The text and exercises of the present chapter are designed to be studied in the following order:

1 Section 15.1.1 and Exercise 15.1.

2 Section 15.1.2 and Exercise 15.2.

3 Section 15.1.3 and Exercise 15.3.

4 Section 15.1.4 and Exercises 15.4–15.6.

5 Sections 15.2.1–15.2.4 and Exercise 15.7.

6 Section 15.2.5 and Exercise 15.8.

7 Section 15.2.7 and Exercises 15.9–15.10.

8 Section 15.2.8 and Exercises 15.11–15.13.

9 Section 15.3 and Exercises 15.14–15.16.

10 Exercises 15.17–15.19.

CONTENTS OF CHAPTER 15

1.
Differences between Populations

1 Prior Distributions of Differences between Fractions
2 Posterior Distributions of Differences between Fractions
3 Negligible Prior Information
4 Distributions of Differences between Averages

2.
Biassed Samples

1 Errors of Measurement
2 An Assessment Problem
3 Restructuring of the Problem
4 Analysis of the Problem; the Effect of Uncertainty about Errors of Measurement
5 Practical Assessment of the Required Distributions
6 Alternative Structures and Effective Use of the Available Information
7 Samples from Many-valued Populations
8 Sampling Bias in General

3.
General-purpose Reporting of the
Implications of Sample Information

1 The Nature of the Problem
2 Reports Based on Uniform Priors
3 Confidence Intervals
4 Reporting in the Face of Uncertainty about Bias

4.
Summary

1 Differences between Fractions
2 Differences between Averages
3 Biassed Sampling
4 General-purpose Reporting

15.1
DIFFERENCES BETWEEN POPULATIONS

In many situations where a businessman has imperfect information concerning the fractions of successes or the averages of the values in each of two different populations, he will want to know what this information implies concerning the difference between the two fractions or the two averages.

For example, a businessman may want to know what the available information allows him to believe about the difference between the fraction of housewives aged 40 or less who use Product X and the corresponding fraction of housewives over 40. If we think of all housewives aged 40 or less as constituting a first population and think of all housewives over 40 as constituting a second population, and if we define

$$\tilde{p}_1 = \text{fraction of users in the first population,}$$

$$\tilde{p}_2 = \text{fraction of users in the second population,}$$

we can express the businessman's problem as one of assessing a probability distribution of the *uncertain difference*

$$\tilde{x} = \tilde{p}_1 - \tilde{p}_2$$

prior or posterior to sampling from the two populations.

As a second example, suppose that this same businessman is also interested in the difference between the *amount* of Product X purchased last week by the "average housewife" aged 40 or less and the corresponding amount for the "average housewife" over 40. If we define the same two populations that we defined in our first example, think of each housewife in either population as having a "value" equal to the amount of Product X she purchased last week, and define

$$\tilde{A}_1 = \text{average of the values of the individual members of the first population,}$$

$$\tilde{A}_2 = \text{average of the values of the individual members of the second population,}$$

then we can express the businessman's present problem as one of assessing a probability distribution of the uncertain difference

$$\tilde{y} = \tilde{A}_1 - \tilde{A}_2$$

prior or posterior to sampling from the two populations.

In the present section we shall discuss ways of assessing prior and posterior distributions of UQ's like $\tilde{x}$ and $\tilde{y}$ as defined above.

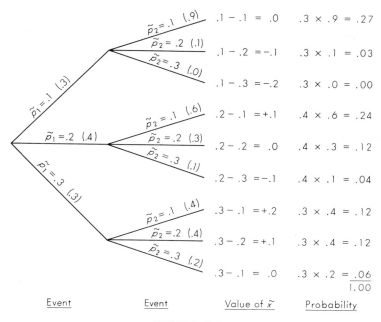

FIGURE 15.1

Probability Diagram for Assessment of a Prior Distribution of $\tilde{x} = \tilde{p}_1 - \tilde{p}_2$

15.1.1
Prior Distributions of
Differences between Fractions

When a businessman thinks about two related fractions or averages like those in the examples just given, he will usually feel that learning the true value of one of the two quantities could have a material effect on his opinions about the other or about the difference between them.

For example, suppose that a businessman feels that (1) the fraction $\tilde{p}_1$ of users of Product X in the 40-or-under population is probably near .8, and (2) the corresponding fraction $\tilde{p}_2$ in the over-40 population is probably near .6, implying that (3) the difference $\tilde{x} = \tilde{p}_1 - \tilde{p}_2$ is probably near .2. If this businessman should learn that in fact $\tilde{p}_1$ is only .4, he might quite conceivably conclude that $\tilde{p}_2$ is probable near .3 rather than .6, implying that the difference $\tilde{x} = \tilde{p}_1 - \tilde{p}_2$ is probably near .1 rather than .2. If so, information about $\tilde{p}_1$ has affected his judgments about both $\tilde{p}_2$ and $\tilde{x}$.

If in such a situation the businessman wishes to assess his probability distribution of the difference $\tilde{x} = \tilde{p}_1 - \tilde{p}_2$, he must be sure to take full account, not only of experience and information that bear directly on $\tilde{x}$, but also of experience and information that bear directly on $\tilde{p}_1$ or $\tilde{p}_2$ and hence bear indirectly on the difference $\tilde{x}$ between $\tilde{p}_1$ and $\tilde{p}_2$. There are various ways in which he can organize his thinking in order to accomplish this objective; one way is illustrated by the artificially simple example that is diagrammed in Figure 15.1.

In the example of Figure 15.1, the businessman has expressed his basic judgments by proceeding as follows. First, thinking only about the first of the two populations in which he is interested, he assessed his unconditional distribution of the fraction $\tilde{p}_1$ of successes in that population, making use as he did so of all experience and information that bore directly on $\tilde{p}_1$. Then, considering every possible value of $\tilde{p}_1$ in turn, he assessed his conditional distribution of $\tilde{p}_2$ given that particular value of $\tilde{p}_1$, making use as he did so of all experience and information that bore directly on either $\tilde{p}_2$ or the relation between $\tilde{p}_2$ and $\tilde{p}_1$.

After the businessman has made these direct assessments, his statistician can compute the unconditional distribution that the businessman should assign to $\tilde{x} = \tilde{p}_1 - \tilde{p}_2$. To do so, he first computes the value of the function $\tilde{x}$ at each end position of Figure 15.1 and the unconditional probability of each end position; the results of these computations are shown in Figure 15.1 itself. He then computes the required distribution of $\tilde{x}$ by making use of the fact that the unconditional probability of any value of $\tilde{x}$ is the sum of the unconditional probabilities of all end positions at which that value appears; his results are shown in Table 15.1.

TABLE 15.1
Prior Distribution of $\tilde{x} = \tilde{p}_1 - \tilde{p}_2$
Implied by the Assessments in Figure 15.1

Value x	Prior Probability $P(\tilde{x} = x)$		
$-.2$	.00	$=$	.00
$-.1$	.03 + .04	$=$	.07
.0	.27 + .12 + .06	$=$	.45
$+.1$	.24 + .12	$=$	.36
$+.2$	.12	$=$	.12
			1.00

15.1.2

Posterior Distributions of Differences between Fractions

Suppose now that after assessing the prior distributions shown in Figure 15.1, the businessman proceeds to take a sample from each of the two populations in order to learn more about $\tilde{x} = \tilde{p}_1 - \tilde{p}_2$; suppose that both samples are taken by equiprobable sampling without replacement; and suppose that the sample outcomes are described by the following statistics:

$$\left. \begin{array}{l} n_1 = 10 \\ r_1 = 4 \end{array} \right\} \text{ sample from first population}$$

$$\left. \begin{array}{l} n_2 = 15 \\ r_2 = 3 \end{array} \right\} \text{ sample from second population.}$$

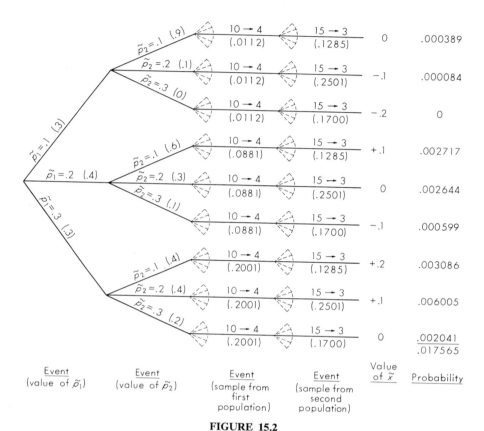

FIGURE 15.2

Probability Diagram for Assessment of a Posterior Distribution of $\tilde{x} = \tilde{p}_1 - \tilde{p}_2$

If the businessman wishes to assign to $\tilde{x}$ a posterior distribution which reflects the sample information just described as well as the prior information that led him to assess the prior probabilities on the branches of Figure 15.1, his statistician can compute the required distribution by use of the abbreviated probability diagram shown as Figure 15.2.

Like any other probability diagram, Figure 15.2 is constructed in such a way that the available information bears directly and cleanly on the probabilities that the businessman or his statistician delegate must assign to its branches.

1. Because the $\tilde{p}_1$ and $\tilde{p}_2$ forks precede the sample-event branches in the diagram, the businessman assigns to them probabilities which reflect only his prior information about $\tilde{p}_1$ and $\tilde{p}_2$. We have already discussed the assessment of such probabilities in Section 15.1.1, and the probabilities in parentheses on the branches of the $\tilde{p}_1$ and $\tilde{p}_2$ forks in Figure 15.2 are simply copied from Figure 15.1.

2. The probabilities assigned to each sample-event branch in the third and fourth levels of Figure 15.2 must be conditioned on the events represented by all preceding branches. Clearly, however, the only preceding event that should

actually affect the probability assigned to getting 3 successes in 15 draws from population 2 is the fraction p_2 of successes in population 2, and similarly for population 1. It follows that if the size of the sample from the first population is small relative to the size of that population, the businessman can assess his probability for the event $10 \rightarrow 4$ on any third-level branch by simply setting it equal to $b^*(10, 4, p_1)$, where p_1 is the value of $\tilde{p}_1$ that precedes the third-level branch in question; and similarly he can equate his probability for any fourth-level branch to $b^*(15, 3, p_2)$. It is these values of b^*, as read from Table T1, which appear in parentheses on the third- and fourth-level branches in Figure 15.2.

Once probabilities have been assigned to the branches of Figure 15.2, the probability of each end position in the figure can be found in the usual way, by multiplying together the probabilities that appear on the path from the origin to the end position in question. And once these end-position probabilities have been computed, we can compute the posterior distribution of $\tilde{x} = \tilde{p}_1 - \tilde{p}_2$ by applying the usual rule for computing conditional probabilities. The probability of any particular value of $\tilde{x}$ given the (joint) sample event $(10 \rightarrow 4, 15 \rightarrow 3)$ is found by dividing the total probability of all end positions at which the sample event appears together with that value of $\tilde{x}$ by the total probability of all end positions at which the sample event appears. The required computations and the resulting posterior distribution of $\tilde{x}$ are shown in Table 15.2.

TABLE 15.2
Computation of the Posterior Distribution of $x = \tilde{p}_1 - \tilde{p}_2$

Value x	*Joint Probability* $P(x, n_1 \rightarrow r_1, n_2 \rightarrow r_2)$		*Posterior Probability* $P(x \mid n_1 \rightarrow r_1, n_2 \rightarrow r_2)$
$-.2$	$.000000$	$= .000000$	$.000$
$-.1$	$.000084 + .000599$	$= .000683$	$.039$
0	$.000389 + .002644 + .002041$	$= .005074$	$.289$
$+.1$	$.002717 + .006005$	$= .008722$	$.496$
$+.2$	$.003086$	$= .003086$	$.176$
		$.017565$	1.000

15.1.3

Negligible Prior Information

The example we have just analyzed is completely representative of real problems concerning the difference between two $\tilde{p}$'s except for the assumption that the businessman believed that $\tilde{p}_1$ and $\tilde{p}_2$ must each have one of just three possible values, .1, .2, or .3. In a real problem, a businessman would ordinarily assign nonzero prior probabilities to a very large number of possible values of $\tilde{p}_1$ and $\tilde{p}_2$.

As far as computations are concerned, realistic prior distributions would not give rise to any substantial difficulties. Using a computer, the statistician could replace the businessman's true unconditional prior distribution of $\tilde{p}_1$ by a grouped distribution; he could replace the businessman's conditional prior distribution[1] of $\tilde{p}_2$ given each of these values of $\tilde{p}_1$ by a grouped distribution; and he could then derive all the required posterior distributions by exactly the same logic that we used in the simple example we have just discussed.

As regards assessments, on the other hand, the procedure we have described could easily impose a very burdensome task on the businessman himself. Assessment of an unconditional prior distribution of $\tilde{p}_1$ presents no unusual difficulties, nor does assessment of a conditional prior distribution of $\tilde{p}_2$ given any one value of $\tilde{p}_1$; but direct assessment of a conditional prior distribution of $\tilde{p}_2$ given each of a large number of values of $\tilde{p}_1$ is clearly an impossible task. Some suggestions for reducing such a task to a manageable size have been given in Section 9.7, but when large samples have been taken from both populations it is sometimes possible to do even better and show that the businessman does not have to make any quantitative prior assessments at all.

We saw in Section 11.2 that if the prior distribution that a businessman would assign to the fraction $\tilde{p}$ of successes in a single population is nearly uniform relative to the likelihood function of a sample drawn from that population by equiprobable sampling with replacement, then his posterior distribution of $\tilde{p}$ will have a beta cumulative function with parameters $B = r + 1$ and $C = n+2$; and in Section 11.5.1 we saw that this same result holds even when the sample is drawn without replacement if the sample is small relative to the population from which it is drawn. When two populations are involved, a similar proposition can be proved.

■ Suppose that samples yielding statistics n_1, r_1, and n_2, r_2 have been taken from two populations by equiprobable sampling; and if the samples were drawn without replacement, suppose further that each sample is small relative to the population from which it was drawn. If (1) the decision maker's unconditional prior distribution of $\tilde{p}_1$ is nearly uniform relative to the likelihood function of the sample from population 1, and (2) his conditional prior distribution of $\tilde{p}_2$ given every value in the range of $\tilde{p}_1$ is nearly uniform relative to the likelihood function of the sample from population 2, then:

1 The UQ's $\tilde{p}_1$ and $\tilde{p}_2$ should be independent in the "posterior judgment" of the decision maker, and

2 His posterior distributions of $\tilde{p}_1$ and $\tilde{p}_2$ should have beta cumulative functions with parameters determined in the usual way by the statistics of the samples from populations 1 and 2 respectively.

When the businessman's prior distributions of $\tilde{p}_1$ and $\tilde{p}_2$ satisfy the qualitative conditions of near uniformity that we have just stated, the distribu-

---

[1] Although a prior distribution is always unconditional as regards the sample outcome, it may be conditional on some other event or events. In Figure 15.2, each of the businessman's three prior distributions of $\tilde{p}_2$ is conditional on the preceding value of $\tilde{p}_1$.

```
>DO PART 1

SPECIFY PARAMETERS OF THE DISTRIBUTIONS OF P1 AND P2
        B(1)  =  5
        C(1)  =  12
        B(2)  =  4
        C(2)  =  17

                 FRACTILES OF THE DISTRIBUTION OF X = P1 - P2
    •001      •01       •1       •25       •5       •75       •9       •99       •999
  -0•335   -0•211   -0•037    0•066    0•181    0•298    0•401    0•566    0•671


>DO PART 2 FOR X = -•4 BY •1 TO •7

   VALUE    PROBABILITY
  -0•400       0•000
  -0•300        •002
  -0•200        •012
  -0•100        •049
   0•000        •144
   0•100        •318
   0•200        •543
   0•300        •754
   0•400        •899
   0•500        •971
   0•600        •995
   0•700       1•000
>


>DO PART 3 FOR K = •025, •975

  PROBABILITY      VALUE
     •025        -0•150
     •975         0•511
```

FIGURE 15.3

Distribution of $\tilde{x} = \tilde{p}_1 - \tilde{p}_2$

tion of $\tilde{x} = \tilde{p}_1 - \tilde{p}_2$ is determined by the fact that $\tilde{p}_1$ and $\tilde{p}_2$ are independent and have distributions with well defined beta cumulative functions; and the distribution thus determined can be easily evaluated by use of a computer program called *Betadif.* For example, suppose as we did in Section 15.1.2 that samples drawn by equiprobable sampling from two large populations have yielded the statistics

$$n_1 = 10, \qquad r_1 = 4, \qquad\qquad n_2 = 15, \qquad r_2 = 3;$$

but now suppose that the businessman who took these samples feels that the information he had about $\tilde{p}_1$ and $\tilde{p}_2$ prior to sampling is totally negligible relative to the information provided by the samples, so that any conditional or unconditional prior distribution he would have assigned to either $\tilde{p}_1$ or $\tilde{p}_2$ would have been nearly uniform relative to the likelihood function of the corresponding sample. To find the distribution that he should now assign to the difference $\tilde{x} = \tilde{p}_1 - \tilde{p}_2$, the businessman must first compute the parameters of the beta cumulative functions of the distributions that he should now assign to the independent UQ's $\tilde{p}_1$ and $\tilde{p}_2$:

$$B_1 = r_1 + 1 = 5, \qquad\qquad B_2 = r_2 + 1 = 4,$$
$$C_1 = n_1 + 2 = 12, \qquad\qquad C_2 = n_2 + 2 = 17.$$

He can then call the program *Betadif* on a time-sharing computer and obtain the output shown in Figure 15.3, where the underlined material was typed by the

608

user and everything else was typed by the computer. In response to the command "Do Part 1", the computer calculated a grouped approximation to the distribution of $\tilde{x} = \tilde{p}_1 - \tilde{p}_2$ and automatically gave the user a very rough description of this distribution by printing out a few fractiles. The user then obtained the cumulative probability of x or less for selected values of x by giving the command "Do Part 2 for $x = \ldots$", after which he obtained selected fractiles x_k of $\tilde{x}$ by giving the command "Do Part 3 for $k = \ldots$".

15.1.4

Distributions of Differences

between Averages

Except for purely technical details (the use of binomial mass functions and beta cumulative functions), everything that we have said about distributions of differences between two population fractions $\tilde{p}_1$ and $\tilde{p}_2$ applies to distributions of differences between two population averages $\tilde{A}_1$ and $\tilde{A}_2$.

When the businessman's prior information about $\tilde{A}_1$ and $\tilde{A}_2$ is negligible relative to the information obtained by sampling and the conditions for applicability of large-sample theory (Section 12.3.4) are satisfied, the businessman's posterior distribution of $\tilde{y} = \tilde{A}_1 - \tilde{A}_2$ can be found almost as easily as his posterior distribution of the average $\tilde{A}$ of the individual values in a single population. For:

■ Suppose that samples yielding statistics n_1, a_1, v_1 and n_2, a_2, v_2 have been taken from two populations by equiprobable sampling; if the samples were drawn without replacement, suppose that each sample is small relative to the population from which it was drawn; and suppose that the conditions for applicability of large-sample theory are satisfied as regards each sample considered by itself. If (1) the decision maker's unconditional prior distribution of $\tilde{A}_1$ is nearly uniform relative to the likelihood function of the sample from population 1, and (2) his conditional prior distribution of $\tilde{A}_2$ given every value in the range of $\tilde{A}_1$ is nearly uniform relative to the likelihood function of the sample from population 2, then:

1 The UQ's $\tilde{A}_1$ and $\tilde{A}_2$ should be independent in the "posterior judgment" of the decision maker;

2 His posterior distributions of $\tilde{A}_1$ and $\tilde{A}_2$ should have Gaussian cumulative functions with parameters M_1, S_1 and M_2, S_2 determined in the usual way by the statistics of the samples from populations 1 and 2 respectively;

3 His posterior distribution of the difference

$$\tilde{y} = \tilde{A}_1 - \tilde{A}_2$$

should have a Gaussian cumulative function with parameters

$$M_y = M_1 - M_2, \qquad S_y = \sqrt{S_1^2 + S_2^2}.$$

15.2
BIASSED SAMPLES

15.2.1
Errors of Measurement

Up to now we have assumed that when a sample is taken from a two-valued population, it is possible to tell for sure which of the sample members are successes and which are failures; and similarly we have assumed that it is possible to determine with complete accuracy the "value" of each member of a sample from a many-valued population. Very frequently, however, these assumptions are invalid in practical business applications of sampling.

For example, consider a businessman who must decide whether or not to put a newly developed product on the market, and suppose that before making his decision he draws a sample from the population of potential customers and asks each member of the sample whether he will buy the product. Almost certainly some persons who will not in fact buy the product will nevertheless say that they will buy, and some who will in fact buy will say that will not buy. Only by luck will the total number of sample members who will in fact buy be equal to the number who say they will buy.

If each member of the sample is asked, not simply whether he will buy the new product, but how much of it he will buy, a similar phenomenon will occur. Some members of the sample will overstate the amount they will buy, others will understate, and only by luck will the average of the stated amounts equal the average of the amounts that will actually be bought.

In this second example, the amount that an individual member of the sample says he will buy can be called the ≪measured value≫ of that member; the amount he will in fact buy can be called his ≪true value≫; and the difference can be called the ≪error of measurement≫. The same language is often used in discussing the two-valued case. An error of measurement is made if a true success (a person who will in fact buy) is reported as a failure because he says he will not buy, and similarly when a true failure is reported as a success.

15.2.2
An Assessment Problem

To show how sample information can be used when the sample observations are subject to errors of measurement, we shall start by considering a simplified version of the first of the two examples suggested above. A businessman who has certain prior judgments concerning the fraction of all members of a certain population who will in fact buy a certain new product wishes to revise these judgments in order to take account of the information provided by a sample some of whose members said they would buy while others said they would not. The sample was taken by equiprobable sampling without replacement from a population large

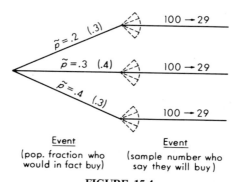

FIGURE 15.4

Usual Probability Diagram for Computation of a Posterior Distribution

enough to allow the data to be processed as if the sample had been taken with replacement; the sample statistics are:

$n = 100$: number of individuals in the sample,

$r = 29$: number of these individuals who *said* they would buy.

We shall assume that before sampling the businessman (would have) assigned the distribution in Table 15.3 to the UQ

$\tilde{p}$: fraction of all members of the population who would *in fact* buy.

TABLE 15.3
Prior Distribution of the Fraction Who Will Actually Buy

Value p	Probability $P(\tilde{p} = p)$
.2	.3
.3	.4
.4	.3
	1.0

In Figure 15.4 we show a probability diagram of the kind we have used hitherto for computation of a distribution of $\tilde{p}$ posterior to sampling. The businessman's prior distribution of $\tilde{p}$ is shown on the fork at the origin, and it would be a routine matter to compute his posterior distribution of $\tilde{p}$ if he or someone acting on his behalf could assess a reasonable conditional probability for the event $100 \rightarrow 29$ on each second-level branch in the diagram given the preceding value of $\tilde{p}$.

It is not a routine matter, however, to assess these second-level branch probabilities when the sample observations are subject to errors of measurement. The fact that the sampling was equiprobable implies, for example, that the conditional probability of the event "29 *true* successes in a sample of 100" given that $\tilde{p} = .2$ of the members of the population are true successes should be assessed as

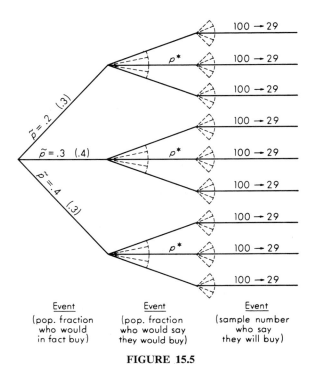

Event	Event	Event
(pop. fraction who would in fact buy)	(pop. fraction who would say they would buy)	(sample number who say they will buy)

FIGURE 15.5

Probability Diagram for Computation of a Posterior Distribution When There Is Uncertainty about Errors of Measurement

equal to $b^*(100, 29, .2)$, but "29 true successes in a sample of 100" is not the event with which we are concerned.   The event that appears on each second-level branch in Figure 15.4 is "29 *reported* successes in a sample of 100", and direct assessment of a conditional probability for *this* event given that .2 of the members of the population are true successes would be extremely difficult because it is impossible to obtain any information that bears directly on such a probability.

15.2.3
Restructuring of the Problem

To avoid the need for the very difficult direct assessments required by Figure 15.4, we introduce an additional UQ

$\tilde{p}^*$:   fraction of all members of the population who would *say* they would buy if they were drawn in a sample and asked;

and we then restructure the assessment problem by replacing the probability diagram in Figure 15.4 by the one in Figure 15.5, where every second-level fork is to be understood as having a branch for every possible value of the UQ $\tilde{p}^*$ which we have just defined.

When the assessment problem is structured in the way shown in Figure 15.5, probabilities for the first- and third-level branches can be assessed by exactly the same kind of reasoning that would be used if there were no uncertainty about errors of measurement. Because the fork at the origin represents the fraction $\tilde{p}$ of all customers who will in fact buy, the businessman can assess his probabilities for its branches without worrying about what customers would say they would do. And because each third-level branch is preceded by some definite value of the fraction $\tilde{p}^*$ of all customers who would say they would buy, the conditional probabilities that should be assigned to these branches are completely determined by the fact that the sampling process was equiprobable. Given that some definite fraction p^* of the whole population would say they would buy, the probability that 29 customers in a sample of 100 would say they would buy should be assessed as equal to $b^*(100, 29, p^*)$, regardless of how many customers in either the population or the sample would in fact buy.

Uncertainty about errors of measurement enters the assessment problem only when the businessman comes to assigning probabilities to the branches of the second-level forks in Figure 15.5, each of which calls for a conditional distribution of the fraction $\tilde{p}^*$ of all customers who would say they would buy given the value on the preceding branch of the fraction $\tilde{p}$ of all customers who would in fact buy. These probability distributions should reflect all available experience and information bearing on the difference between what people actually do and what they say they will do in sample surveys of this general sort, and the task of assessing the distributions is therefore one that the businessman should very probably delegate to someone with broad experience in the use of sample surveys to predict actual buying behavior.

15.2.4
Analysis of the Problem; the Effect
of Uncertainty about Errors of Measurement

Once probabilities have been assigned to all the branches of the probability diagram in Figure 15.5, it is a routine matter to compute the distribution that the businessman should assign to the fraction $\tilde{p}$ of all customers who would in fact buy.

For example, suppose that the basic assessments are those shown on the branches of Figure 15.6, where for the sake of simplicity we have unrealistically assumed, not only that the businessman believes that $\tilde{p}$ must have one of just three possible values, but also that his market researcher believes that, given any particular value of $\tilde{p}$, $\tilde{p}^*$ must have one of just three possible values. The probabilities on the fork at the origin are those assessed by the businessman in Table 15.3; the probabilities on the second-level forks are those assessed by the market researcher; the probabilities on the third-level branches are function values $b^*(100, 29, p^*)$ read from Table T1 of the binomial mass function.

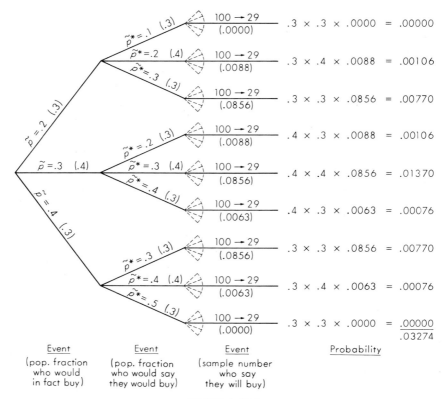

FIGURE 15.6

Special Case of Figure 15.5

The posterior distribution of $\tilde{p}$ can now be computed in the usual way. The probability that is assigned to any particular value p of $\tilde{p}$ posterior to observing the event $100 \rightarrow 29$ should be equal to the conditional probability, given the event $100 \rightarrow 29$, that would have been assigned to p before sampling; and this conditional probability should have been equal to the total probability of all end positions at which the event $100 \rightarrow 29$ appears together with p divided by the total probability of all end positions at which the event $100 \rightarrow 29$ appears. This rule results in the posterior distribution of $\tilde{p}$ that is shown in Table 15.4.

TABLE 15.4

Posterior Distribution of $\tilde{p}$ Implied by Figure 15.6

Value p	Posterior Probability $P(p \mid 100 \rightarrow 29)$
.2	(.00000 + .00106 + .00770)/.03274 = .268
.3	(.00106 + .01370 + .00076)/.03274 = .474
.4	(.00770 + .00076 + .00000)/.03274 = .258
	1.000

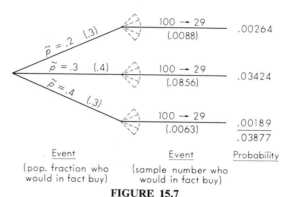

	Event	Event	Probability

(pop. fraction who would in fact buy)   (sample number who would in fact buy)

FIGURE 15.7

Probability Diagram Assuming No Errors of Measurement

It is instructive to contrast the posterior distribution of $\tilde{p}$ in Table 15.4 with the distribution the businessman would have assessed if he had neglected his uncertainty about errors of measurement and simply assumed that the number of sample customers who would in fact buy was 29. This assumption would have led to the probability diagram shown in Figure 15.7 and the posterior distribution in Table 15.5, and the difference between this distribution and the one in Table 15.4 is striking.

TABLE 15.5

Posterior Distribution of $\tilde{p}$ Assuming No Errors of Measurement

Value p	Posterior Probability $P(p \mid 100 \to 29)$	
.2	.00264/.03877 =	.068
.3	.03424/.03877 =	.883
.4	.00189/.03877 =	.049
		1.000

The reason for the difference between the two posterior distributions is easy to see if we observe that the *fraction* of sample customers who said they would buy was $29/100 = .29$. If it were really known that .29 of the sample customers would in fact buy, this would be very strong evidence for the proposition that the fraction $\tilde{p}$ of all customers in the population who would in fact buy is actually .3 rather than .2 or .4, and accordingly the businessman would assign a very high probability to $\tilde{p} = .3$ and very low probabilities to $\tilde{p} = .2$ and $\tilde{p} = .4$, as shown in Table 15.5. If, on the contrary, there is substantial uncertainty about the relation between saying and doing, then the evidence provided by the sample is much weaker, and accordingly the businessman assigns a much lower probability to $\tilde{p} = .3$ and much higher probabilities to $\tilde{p} = .2$ and $\tilde{p} = .4$ in Table 15.4 than he does in Table 15.5. The posterior probabilities in Table 15.4 are in fact only a little different from the businessman's prior probabilities in Table 15.3.

15.2.5
Practical Assessment
of the Required Distributions

The example just analyzed is completely representative of real problems involving uncertainty about errors of measurement except for the fact that (1) the businessman assigned nonzero probabilities to only three values of $\tilde{p}$, and (2) given each possible value of $\tilde{p}$, the market researcher assigned nonzero probabilities to only three values of $\tilde{p}^*$. In a real problem, both the businessman and the market researcher would ordinarily assign nonzero probabilities to very many values of $\tilde{p}$ and $\tilde{p}^*$ respectively.

As far as computations are concerned, realistic prior distributions do not give rise to any substantial difficulties. Using a computer, a statistician could replace the businessman's true unconditional distribution of $\tilde{p}$ by a grouped distribution; he could replace the market researcher's conditional distribution of $\tilde{p}^*$ given each of these values of $\tilde{p}$ by a grouped distribution; and he could then derive the required posterior distribution of $\tilde{p}$ by exactly the same logic that we used in the simple example we analyzed in Section 15.2.4.

Nor does direct assessment of a realistic unconditional distribution of $\tilde{p}$ present the businessman with a particularly difficult problem. He has only one such distribution to assess, and the task is no more difficult than it would be in the absence of uncertainty about errors of measurement.

Serious difficulties can arise, however, when the market researcher tries to assess his conditional distribution of $\tilde{p}^*$ given each of a large number of values of $\tilde{p}$. Direct assessment of any one of these distributions presents no unusual problems, but direct assessment of all of them is impossible.

Often, however, it is surprisingly easy to reduce a task of this sort to manageable size. For example, suppose that the businessman feels fairly sure that $\tilde{p}$ has a value p somewhere between .1 and .3, so that it is only for p's within this interval that the market researcher has to assess conditional distributions of $\tilde{p}^*$ given p. If instead of thinking directly about the UQ $\tilde{p}^*$, the market researcher thinks about the *ratio* of $\tilde{p}^*$ to $\tilde{p}$, he may decide that his opinions about this ratio would for all practical purposes be the same if he were told that $\tilde{p}$ had any one particular value between .1 and .3 as they would be if he were told that $\tilde{p}$ had any other value in that interval. It may be, for example, that (1) if he knew that $\tilde{p} = .1$, he would feel that there was 1 chance in 4 that $\tilde{p}^*$ was at least twice as great as $\tilde{p}$, and (2) if he knew that $\tilde{p} = .3$ rather than .1, he would still feel that there was 1 chance in 4 that $\tilde{p}^*$ was at least twice as great as $\tilde{p}$; and so forth.

If the market researcher does feel this way about the ratio of $\tilde{p}^*$ to $\tilde{p}$, then a single distribution of the UQ

$$\tilde{z} = \tilde{p}^*/p$$

will express his conditional judgments about $\tilde{p}^*$ given *any* value p of $\tilde{p}$. Once he has assessed this one distribution, his implied conditional distribution of $\tilde{p}^*$ given any p can be found by use of the relation

$$P(\tilde{p}^* = p^* | \tilde{p} = p) = P(\tilde{z} = p^*/p).$$

Observe, however, that we have not asserted that the market researcher's opinions about the ratio $\tilde{p}^*/p$ either will or should necessarily be the same regardless of $\tilde{p}$. All that we have said is that this may be true in a particular case.

If in a particular case the market researcher's opinions about the UQ $\tilde{z} = \tilde{p}^*/p$ are not the same given all p's that he has to consider—i.e., given all p's to which the businessman attaches a substantial probability—then he can look for some other substitute UQ (cf. Section 9.7.4) concerning which his opinions do have this property. It may be, for example, that he will decide that his opinions about the *difference* between $\tilde{p}^*$ and p would be the same given any p he has to consider, in which case he can solve his assessment problem by assessing one distribution of the UQ

$$\tilde{w} = \tilde{p}^* - p$$

and then using the relation

$$P(\tilde{p}^* = p^* | \tilde{p} = p) = P(\tilde{w} = p^* - p).$$

If neither the ratio $\tilde{p}^*/p$ nor the difference $\tilde{p}^* - p$ has the required property, he can consider, e.g., the ratio $(1 - \tilde{p}^*)/(1 - p)$, and ultimately, if he is ingenious, he may succeed in finding *some* substitute UQ by use of which he can solve his assessment problem. If he does not, he will have to proceed along the lines suggested in Section 9.7.3 and paragraph 4 of Section 9.7.4.

15.2.6
Alternative Structures
and Effective Use
of the Available Information[2]

The probability diagram in Figure 15.5 (page 612) is only one of many possible ways of structuring an assessment problem when there is uncertainty about errors of measurement.

One possible alternative structure is shown in Figure 15.8, where the order of the $\tilde{p}$ and $\tilde{p}^*$ forks is the reverse of that in Figure 15.5. Whereas the structure of Figure 15.5 calls for direct assessment of an unconditional distribution of $\tilde{p}$ and a set of conditional distributions of $\tilde{p}^*$ given p, this new structure calls for direct assessment of an unconditional distribution of $\tilde{p}^*$ and a set of conditional distributions of $\tilde{p}$ given p^*.

Another, quite different possible structure is shown in Figure 15.9, where each branch of the first fork represents a possible value of the uncertain

---

[2] This section should be omitted on a first reading.

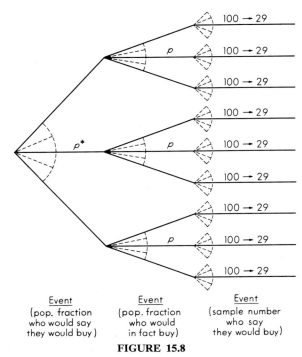

Event	Event	Event
(pop. fraction who would say they would buy)	(pop. fraction who would in fact buy)	(sample number who say they would buy)

FIGURE 15.8

First Alternative to Figure 15.5

number of *sample* customers who will in fact buy the product. The idea is that, instead of allowing for measurement errors by assessing distributions of the fractions $\tilde{p}$ and $\tilde{p}^*$ of true and reported successes in the entire population, the businessman or his delegate can allow for these errors by assessing a distribution of the uncertain number of *true* successes in the sample that has actually been taken and then assess a conditional distribution of the fraction of true successes in the population given each possible number of true successes in the sample. The observed event "29 reported successes in a sample of 100" does not appear explicitly in this assessment scheme but it will affect the final result by affecting the judgmentally assessed probabilities that are assigned to the branches of the fork at the origin.

The fact that the problem of deriving a posterior distribution of $\tilde{p}$ can be structured in more than one way means that the first step in the process must be the choice of some one, particular structure, and there are two important facts to keep in mind when this choice is made.

1. As regards the computations that will be made after a structure has been chosen and the required direct assessments of branch probabilities have been made, any one structure is as good as any other. No matter what structure is chosen, the required arithmetic can be carried out on a computer at very small cost.

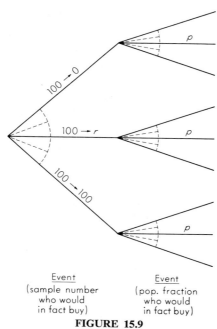

Event
(sample number
who would
in fact buy)

Event
(pop. fraction
who would
in fact buy)

FIGURE 15.9

Second Alternative to Figure 15.5

2. As regards the required direct assessments of branch probabilities, on the other hand, it is by no means true that any one structure is as good as any other. The reason why a posterior distribution of $\tilde{p}$ is computed from other assessments instead of being assessed directly is that this indirect procedure allows more effective use of the available experience and information; and the structure that allows the most effective use of the available experience and information is the one that should be chosen. If we examine the structures of Figures 15.5, 15.8, and 15.9 from this point of view, we can quickly see that the structure of Figure 15.5 is much superior to the other two.

In Figure 15.5 (page 612), each different kind of relevant experience and information bears cleanly and directly on one and only one set of probability assessments. (1) The businessman's knowledge of the proposed new product and his experience with similar products bears on the unconditional distribution he should assign before sampling to the fraction $\tilde{p}$ of potential customers who will in fact buy. (2) The market researcher's experience with differences between stated intentions and actual behavior in other situations bears on the conditional distribution he should assign to $\tilde{p}^*$ given any particular value of $\tilde{p}$. (3) The nature of the sampling process completely determines the conditional probabilities that should be assigned to the event "29 reported successes in a sample of 100" given each possible value of $\tilde{p}^*$.

In Figure 15.8 (page 618), the third-level probabilities are as easy to assess as in Figure 15.5, but the first- and second-level probabilities are much harder. (1) Whoever assesses the unconditional distribution of $\bar{p}*$ for the fork at the origin must take *simultaneous* account of experience bearing on actual demand for the new product and experience bearing on the difference between actual demand and stated intentions. (2) Whoever assesses the second-level conditional distributions of $\bar{p}$ given $p*$ must then again take simultaneous account of both these kinds of experience. When, for example, he assesses his conditional distribution of $\bar{p}$ given a very low value of $\bar{p}*$, he must remember that the fact that very few customers would say they would buy can indicate either that very few customers would actually buy, in which case $\bar{p}$ must be quite small, or that many actual buyers misstate their intentions, in which case $\bar{p}$ may be fairly large; and he cannot strike a balance between these possible interpretations without making use of both the available experience bearing on actual demand and the available experience bearing on differences between stated intentions and actual demand.

In Figure 15.9 (page 619), the required direct assessments involve a still more complex use of the available experience and information. Whoever assesses the first-level distribution of the number of *sample* customers who will in fact buy must take simultaneous account of (1) the fact that 29 of these customers said they would buy, together with all experience bearing on the difference between stated intentions and actual behavior, and (2) all experience bearing on the fraction of all customers who will in fact buy, together with the fact that he is dealing with only a small sample of all customers. Whoever then assesses the second-level conditional distributions of $\bar{p}$ given the various possible numbers of buyers in the sample will have to take simultaneous account of much of the information that already had to be used in assessing the first-level distribution. It would, in fact, be far easier to make a direct assessment of the desired posterior distribution of $\bar{p}$ itself than to make the direct assessments required by Figure 15.9.

To sum up, we merely repeat what we said at the outset. The assessment structure of Figure 15.5 is superior to the structures of Figures 15.8 and 15.9 because the available experience and information bear cleanly and directly on the direct assessments called for by the structure of Figure 15.5 and do not bear cleanly and directly on the direct assessments called for by the other two structures.

15.2.7

Samples from Many-valued Populations

Virtually everything that has been said about errors of measurement in samples from two-valued populations applies essentially unchanged to samples from many-valued populations. All that is needed is to define the two UQ's

$\tilde{A}$: average of the *true* values of all individual members of the population,

$\tilde{A}^*$: average of the values that would be *reported* if all the members of the population were drawn in the sample,

and then substitute $\tilde{A}$ for $\bar{p}$ and $\tilde{A}^*$ for $\bar{p}^*$ in the text above.

15.2.8
Sampling Bias in General

Errors of measurement are only one of a great many possible causes of what is called ≪bias≫ in a sample, or better, in the process by which the sample was drawn and measured. A sample or sampling process may be biassed because, for example, people who are unwilling to answer the interviewer's questions are less likely to be successes than those who are willing, or because the sample is drawn in such a way that high-valued members of the population are less likely to be drawn than low-valued members, or for many other reasons.

Whatever may be the cause or causes of possible bias in a sampling and measuring process, the problem of using the information obtained from such a sample can always be solved by essentially the same approach that we used to deal with errors of measurement, although the quantities $\bar{p}^*$ and $\tilde{A}^*$ must be defined in a somewhat different way if all cases are to be covered. If we are interested in a sample of size n from a two-valued population in which the fraction of true successes is $\bar{p}$, we define

$\bar{p}^*$: fraction of all observations that would be reported as successes if an infinite number of samples of size n were to be drawn and measured in exactly the same way that "this" sample was or will be drawn and measured.

If we are interested in a sample of size n from a many-valued population in which the average of the true values of the individual members is $\tilde{A}$, we define

$\tilde{A}^*$: average of all values that would be reported if an infinite number of samples of size n were to be drawn and measured in exactly the same way that "this" sample was or will be drawn and measured.

In both cases, we assume that even if each individual sample is drawn without replacement, the sample as a whole is replaced before the next sample is drawn.

Using these definitions of $\bar{p}^*$ and $\tilde{A}^*$ we can define exactly what we mean by a biassed sampling and measuring process.

■ A sampling and measuring process is ≪biassed≫ unless $\bar{p}^* = \bar{p}$ or $\tilde{A}^* = \tilde{A}$; there exists uncertainty about bias unless the decision maker feels completely sure that $\bar{p}^* = \bar{p}$ or $\tilde{A}^* = \tilde{A}$.

When the decision maker feels sure that the process is not biassed, he simply treats reported successes as true successes or reported values as true values and processes the sample information in the way described in Chapters 10 through 12; the quantities $\bar{p}^*$ and $\tilde{A}^*$ never enter his analysis explicitly. When on the contrary the decision maker suspects that $\bar{p}^*$ may be different from $\bar{p}$ or $\tilde{A}^*$ from $\tilde{A}$, for whatever reason or reasons, he must allow for his uncertainty about bias by proceeding in the way described in Sections 15.2.3 and 15.2.4 and symbolized by Figure 15.5 on page 612.

15.3
GENERAL-PURPOSE REPORTING
OF THE IMPLICATIONS OF SAMPLE INFORMATION

15.3.1
The Nature of the Problem

Hitherto we have discussed samples from the point of view of a particular *user* of sample information, i.e., from the point of view of a person who wants to know what he himself is logically entitled to believe about some UQ on the basis of all the relevant information available to him. We shall now briefly consider the problem that faces a *producer* of sample information which is to be used by others, i.e., a person who has made a number of sample observations and now wishes to tell people in general about the implications of these observations.

One fact about the problem that faces this producer of sample information should be completely clear in the light of our earlier discussion of sample information from the user's point of view.

■ It is flatly impossible for a producer of sample information to tell a user what probability distribution the user should assign to a UQ posterior to receiving the sample information unless the producer knows what distribution the user would have assigned to the UQ prior to receiving the sample information.

This means, for example, that a person who has taken a sample from a two-valued population cannot under any conditions write in a general-purpose report that, for example, "the sample evidence shows that there are 99 chances in 100" that the fraction of successes in the population is between some pair of specified values.

15.3.2
Reports Based on Uniform Priors

It is tempting to conclude that a producer of sample information should report nothing but a description of the sampling process and the sample outcome, leaving it up to each user to decide for himself on the implications. The producer will often be reluctant to accept this conclusion, however, because he will feel sure that many of the users of the information will be unable to evaluate its implications on their own; and often he can in fact be of considerable help to many users by briefly and informally describing the posterior distribution that a user should assess *if* his prior distribution was nearly uniform relative to the likelihood function of the sample.

For example, suppose that a researcher takes a sample of size 100 from a two-valued population and finds 20 successes. Given a uniform prior distribution of the fraction $\bar{p}$ of successes in the population, this sample outcome would lead to a beta posterior cumulative function with parameters $B = 21$ and $C = 102$, and by Table T3 this would imply that the posterior distribution has fractiles as follows:

$$p_{.001} = .1006, \qquad p_{.75} = .2318,$$
$$p_{.01} = .1222, \qquad p_{.99} = .3064,$$
$$p_{.25} = .1779, \qquad p_{.999} = .3433.$$

The researcher could therefore state in his report that: "Unless the reader has really strong outside evidence to the contrary, he can infer that $\bar{p}$ is almost certainly between .10 and .34; and if the outside evidence is more or less neutral as regards values of $\bar{p}$ between .10 and .34, he can further infer that (1) there are about 98 chances in 100 that $\bar{p}$ is between .12 and .31, and (2) about an even chance that $\bar{p}$ is between .18 and .23."

A report of essentially the same kind as the one just described can be made when the producer of sample information has sampled from two populations and wishes to say something about the difference between the $\bar{p}$'s or $\tilde{A}$'s of the populations.

For example, suppose that samples from two many-valued populations have yielded statistics

$$n_1 = 100, \qquad a_1 = 26, \qquad v_1 = 878,$$
$$n_2 = 100, \qquad a_2 = 22, \qquad v_2 = 1147.$$

We saw in Section 15.1.4 that under certain conditions concerning prior information, these samples should lead to a posterior distribution of $\tilde{y} = \tilde{A}_1 - \tilde{A}_2$ that has a Gaussian cumulative function with parameters

$$M_y = a_1 - a_2 = 4, \qquad S_y = \sqrt{v_1/n_1 + v_2/n_2} = 4.50;$$

and it follows that after using Table T4 to compute

$$y_{.001} = 4 - 3.090 \times 4.50 = -9.9, \qquad y_{.75} = 4 + .674 \times 4.50 = +7.0,$$
$$y_{.01} = 4 - 2.326 \times 4.50 = -6.5, \qquad y_{.99} = 4 + 2.326 \times 4.50 = +14.5,$$
$$y_{.25} = 4 - .674 \times 4.50 = +1.0, \qquad y_{.999} = 4 + 3.090 \times 4.50 = +17.9,$$

the researcher could make a statement of the following sort in a general-purpose report. "If the reader feels that all other evidence concerning $\tilde{A}_1$, $\tilde{A}_2$, and the difference $\tilde{y} = \tilde{A}_1 - \tilde{A}_2$ is very weak in comparison with the evidence provided by these two samples, he can infer that (1) $\tilde{y}$ is almost certainly between -9.9

and $+17.9$, (2) there are about 98 chances in 100 that $\bar{y}$ is between -6.5 and $+14.5$, and (3) there is about an even chance that $\bar{y}$ is between $+1.0$ and $+7.0$."

15.3.3
Confidence Intervals

Instead of making statements like those suggested in the preceding section, many researchers resort to what are called ≪confidence-interval≫ statements. For example, a researcher who had obtained the data about a population fraction $\tilde{p}$ that was described on page 623 might report that: "With confidence .98, the value of $\tilde{p}$ is between .12 and .31."

Confidence-interval statements are derived by a logic that is entirely different from the logic that underlies posterior probabilities, and they are not supposed to be assertions concerning posterior probabilities. What the word "confidence" *is* supposed to suggest is not at all clear, but it does not mean probability in the sense in which that word is used in this book. It happens to be true, however, that *in certain very special cases* confidence-interval statements agree fairly well with statements about posterior probabilities that are based on uniform prior distributions. Specifically:

1. If on the basis of a *large* sample it is stated that "with confidence .98" some population average $\tilde{A}$ lies between two specified values, the reader may infer that a uniform prior distribution of $\tilde{A}$ would lead to a posterior probability of .98 for the proposition that A lies between the two stated values; and similarly for any ≪level of confidence≫ other than .98.

2. If on the basis of a sample of any size it is stated that "with confidence .98" some population fraction $\tilde{p}$ lies between two specified values, the reader may infer that a uniform prior distribution of $\tilde{p}$ would lead to a posterior probability of approximately .98 for the proposition that $\tilde{p}$ lies between the two stated values; and similarly for any level of confidence other than .98. The approximation is very close if the sample is large, less close if the sample is small.

3. Confidence-interval statements about the difference between two $\tilde{A}$'s or two $\tilde{p}$'s agree approximately with posterior probabilities based on uniform priors when *both* samples are large.

In all other cases, a businessman should consult a statistician if he wishes to know what useful meaning, if any, he can attach to a confidence-interval statement.

15.3.4
Reporting in the Face
of Uncertainty about Bias

When a researcher who has taken a sample suspects that the sampling and/or measuring process which he has used may be biassed, he will usually be unable to make any statement of the kind discussed in Section 15.3.2 about the fraction $\tilde{p}$ of true successes or the average $\tilde{A}$ of the true values in the population from which he sampled.

As we saw in Section 15.2, the posterior distribution of $\tilde{p}$ or $\tilde{A}$ cannot be computed until the user has directly assessed distributions of $\tilde{p}^*$ or $\tilde{A}^*$ which in effect express his prior judgments about the possible amount of bias in the sampling process, and *the posterior distribution of $\tilde{p}$ or $\tilde{A}$ will be strongly affected by these judgments about bias even if the user's prior distribution of $\tilde{p}$ or $\tilde{A}$ itself is uniform and has little effect on the posterior distribution of $\tilde{p}$ or $\tilde{A}$.* The researcher will of course have his own opinions about the amount of bias that may be present, but if he quantifies these judgments in the form of distributions of $\tilde{p}^*$ or $\tilde{A}^*$ and then computes a posterior distribution of $\tilde{p}$ or $\tilde{A}$, he cannot present this distribution as being in any sense an expression of the implications of the sample evidence alone. It represents the implications of the sample evidence in combination with his personal judgments, and these judgments may differ greatly from any particular user's judgments.

If in such a situation the researcher wishes to do more than merely report the sample data, about all that he can do is to describe the posterior distribution that the user should assign to the *biassed* quantity $\tilde{p}^*$ or $\tilde{A}^*$ if his prior distribution of *that* quantity is uniform or nearly uniform, leaving it to the user to decide for himself what he can infer from this description about the UQ $\tilde{p}$ or $\tilde{A}$ in which he is really interested.

For example, suppose that a researcher takes a sample of size 100 from a certain population and asks each member of the sample whether he will buy a new automobile during the next six months; suppose that 20 of the 100 sample members say that they will buy; and define

$\tilde{p}$: fraction of all members of the population who will in fact buy,

$\tilde{p}^*$: fraction of all members of the population who would say they would buy if asked.

Using the computations and results in Section 15.3.2, the researcher is entitled to report, for example, that unless the user has very strong evidence to the contrary, he can infer that the fraction $\tilde{p}^*$ of all members of the population who would *say* they would buy is almost certainly between .10 and .34. He must, however, leave it to each individual user to decide for himself what he can conclude about the fraction $\tilde{p}$ of all members of the population who will in fact buy.

15.4
SUMMARY

15.4.1
Differences between Fractions

1 Let $\tilde{p}_1$ and $\tilde{p}_2$ denote the fractions of successes in two populations. The problem of assessing a distribution of the difference $\tilde{x} = \tilde{p}_1 - \tilde{p}_2$ which takes account of all relevant information about $\tilde{p}_1$, $\tilde{p}_2$, and $\tilde{x}$ can be structured by a probability diagram of the kind shown in Figure 15.10.

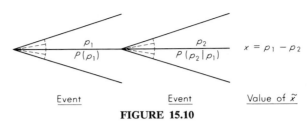

FIGURE 15.10

Probability Diagram for Assessment of a Prior Distribution of $\tilde{x} = \tilde{p}_1 - \tilde{p}_2$

The diagram calls for assessment of one unconditional distribution of $\tilde{p}_1$ and one conditional distribution of $\tilde{p}_2$ given each possible value p_1 in the range of $\tilde{p}_1$.

    2 After samples have been taken from the two populations, the posterior distribution that should be assigned to $\tilde{x}$ can be computed by use of a probability diagram of the kind shown in Figure 15.11.

The distributions assigned to the forks in the first and second levels of Figure 15.11 are those that were or would have been assessed before the samples were taken. The probabilities assigned to the third-level branches are those that would be assessed if the first population were the only population involved in the problem; and similarly for the fourth level and the second population.

    3 If (1) a businessman's unconditional prior distribution of $\tilde{p}_1$ is nearly uniform relative to the likelihood function of the sample from population 1, and (2) his conditional prior distribution of $\tilde{p}_2$ given every value p_1 in the range of $\tilde{p}_1$ is nearly uniform relative to the likelihood function of the sample from population 2, then

        a The UQ's $\tilde{p}_1$ and $\tilde{p}_2$ should be independent in his posterior judgment, and

        b His posterior distribution of the $\tilde{p}$ of either population can be computed without reference to the sample from the other population.

    4 If $\tilde{p}_1$ and $\tilde{p}_2$ are independent in the businessman's judgment and his distributions of $\tilde{p}_1$ and $\tilde{p}_2$ have beta cumulative functions with parameters B_1, C_1 and B_2, C_2, he can use the computer program *Betadif* to find his posterior distribution of $\tilde{x} = \tilde{p}_1 - \tilde{p}_2$.

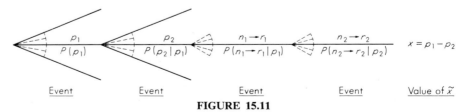

FIGURE 15.11

Probability Diagram for Assessment of a Posterior Distribution of $\tilde{x} = \tilde{p}_1 - \tilde{p}_2$

15.4.2
Differences between Averages

1 Let $\tilde{A}_1$ and $\tilde{A}_2$ denote the averages of the values of the individual members of two populations. The problem of assessing a distribution of the difference $\tilde{y} = \tilde{A}_1 - \tilde{A}_2$ can be structured by a diagram exactly like Figure 15.10 except that A_1, A_2, and y are substituted for p_1, p_2, and x.

2 After samples have been taken from the two populations, the posterior distribution that should be assigned to $\tilde{y}$ can be computed by use of a diagram like Figure 15.11 except for the obviously necessary changes in the names of the UQ's and the statistics.

3 Rule 3 in Section 15.4.1 just above holds when A_1 and A_2 are substituted for p_1 and p_2.

4 If $\tilde{A}_1$ and $\tilde{A}_2$ are independent in the businessman's judgment and his distributions of $\tilde{A}_1$ and $\tilde{A}_2$ have Gaussian cumulative functions with parameters M_1, S_1 and M_2, S_2, his distribution of $\tilde{y} = \tilde{A}_1 - \tilde{A}_2$ should have a Gaussian cumulative function with parameters

$$M_y = M_1 - M_2, \qquad S_y = \sqrt{S_1^2 + S_2^2}.$$

15.4.3
Biassed Sampling

If a sample of size n has been or is to be taken from a two-valued population by a particular sampling and measuring process, this process can be characterized by the uncertain quantity

$\tilde{p}^*$: fraction of all observations that would be *reported* as successes if an infinite number of samples of size n were to be drawn and measured in exactly the same way that "this" sample was or is to be drawn and measured.

If the population is many-valued, the process can be characterized by

$\tilde{A}^*$: average of all values that would be *reported* if an infinite number of samples of size n were to be drawn and measured in exactly the same way that "this" sample was or is to be drawn and measured.

In terms of these definitions:

1 A sampling and measuring process is ≪biassed≫ unless $\tilde{p}^* = \tilde{p}$ or $\tilde{A}^* = \tilde{A}$; there exists uncertainty about bias unless the decision maker feels *sure* that $\tilde{p}^* = \tilde{p}$ or $\tilde{A}^* = \tilde{A}$.

If a businessman does feel sure that the process by which a particular sample was drawn and measured is not biassed, he can process the sample information without further reference to $\tilde{p}^*$ or $\tilde{A}^*$, but:

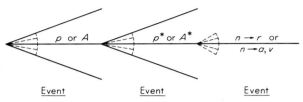

FIGURE 15.12

Probability Diagram for Assessment of a Posterior Distribution in the Presence of Uncertainty about Bias

2 If a businessman suspects that $\tilde{p}^*$ may differ from $\tilde{p}$ (or $\tilde{A}^*$ from $\tilde{A}$), he should usually structure the problem of assessing his posterior distribution of $\tilde{p}$ (or $\tilde{A}$) by use of a probability diagram like Figure 15.12, where the conditional probability that should be assigned to any third-level branch depends only on the preceding value of $\tilde{p}^*$ (or $\tilde{A}^*$), not on the preceding value of $\tilde{p}$ (or $\tilde{A}$).

Figure 15.12 calls for direct assessment of a different conditional distribution of $\tilde{p}^*$ or $\tilde{A}^*$ given each possible value of $\tilde{p}$ or $\tilde{A}$, but:

3 The task of assessing a different conditional distribution of $\tilde{p}^*$ or $\tilde{A}^*$ given each possible value of $\tilde{p}$ or $\tilde{A}$ can sometimes be avoided by finding a substitute UQ such as

$$\tilde{z} = \tilde{p}^*/p \qquad \text{or} \qquad \tilde{w} = \tilde{A}^* - A$$

to which the assessor would assign the same conditional distribution given any value in the range of $\tilde{p}$ or $\tilde{A}$.

15.4.4
General-purpose Reporting

1 The distribution that any individual should assign to any characteristic (such as $\tilde{p}$ or $\tilde{A}$) of a population after observing a sample from the population necessarily depends on his prior judgments as well as the sample data. It is logically impossible to say what distribution should be assessed on the basis of the sample data alone.

2 A producer of sample information can, however, sometimes be of help to many users by briefly describing the distribution that they should assign to a population characteristic *if* they feel that their other information is negligible relative to the information conveyed by the sample.

    a If the researcher feels sure that his sampling process is unbiased, he can make such a statement about the quantity actually of interest to the users, e.g., $\tilde{A}$ or $\tilde{p}$ or $\tilde{x} = \tilde{p}_1 - \tilde{p}_2$.

    b If, however, the researcher suspects that his sampling process may be biased, his statement must concern the corresponding biased quantity, e.g., $\tilde{A}^*$ or $\tilde{p}^*$ or $\tilde{x}^* = \tilde{p}_1^* - \tilde{p}_2^*$, since any user's distribution of the unbiassed quantity will necessarily depend substantially on his personal judgments about the amount of bias that may be present.

EXERCISES

A. DIFFERENCES BETWEEN POPULATIONS

15.1 The manager of a large machine shop is interested in the difference between the fractions defective $\tilde{p}_1$ and $\tilde{p}_2$ in two lots of components that he has just purchased from the same vendor. If he assesses the probability distributions of $\tilde{p}_1$ and $\tilde{p}_2$ that are shown in Table 15.6, what distribution should he assign to $\tilde{x} = \tilde{p}_1 - \tilde{p}_2$?

TABLE 15.6A
Unconditional Distribution of $\tilde{p}_1$

Value p_1	*Probability* $P(p_1)$
.01	.8
.02	.2
	1.0

TABLE 15.6B
Conditional Distributions of $\tilde{p}_2$ Given p_1

Value p_2	*Conditional Probabilities*	
	$P(p_2\|\tilde{p}_1 = .01)$	$P(p_2\|\tilde{p}_1 = .02)$
.01	.9	.4
.02	.1	.6
	1.0	1.0

15.2 If the manager of Exercise 15.1 uses equiprobable sampling without replacement to draw a sample of 100 units from each of the two lots, each of which contains 5,000 units, and if he finds two defectives in the sample from lot 1 but none in the sample from lot 2, what distribution should he now assign to $\tilde{x} = \tilde{p}_1 - \tilde{p}_2$?

15.3 Suppose that, instead of assessing the distributions in Table 15.6, the manager of Exercise 15.1 had said before sampling that (1) he considered all values of $\tilde{p}_1$ between 0 and .1 to be equally likely, and (2) he considered all values of $\tilde{p}_2$ between 0 and .1 to be equally likely and would continue to hold this opinion even if he learned the value of $\tilde{p}_1$, no matter what that value might be. How could you compute the distribution that he should assign to $\tilde{x} = \tilde{p}_1 - \tilde{p}_2$ after sampling?

15.4 The manager of a large specialty store is interested in the difference between the average Tuesday sales check $\tilde{A}_1$ and the average Wednesday sales check $\tilde{A}_2$. If he assesses the probability distributions of $\tilde{A}_1$ and $\tilde{A}_2$ that are shown in Table 15.7 below, what distribution should he assign to $\tilde{y} = \tilde{A}_1 - \tilde{A}_2$?

TABLE 15.7A
Unconditional Distribution of $\tilde{A}_1$

Value A_1	Probability $P(A_1)$
$3	.8
$5	.2
	1.0

TABLE 15.7B
Conditional Distributions of $\tilde{A}_2$ Given A_1

Value A_2	Conditional Probability	
	$P(A_2 \mid \tilde{A}_1 = 3)$	$P(A_2 \mid \tilde{A}_1 = 5)$
$3	.9	.4
$5	.1	.6
	1.0	1.0

15.5 The manager of Exercise 15.4 has an assistant use systematic sampling to draw 100 of the 5,286 sales checks written on Tuesday and 100 of the 7,334 sales checks written on Wednesday, and a clerk computes the summary statistics

$$n_1 = 100, \qquad a_1 = 3.90, \qquad v_1 = 16,$$
$$n_2 = 100, \qquad a_2 = 4.20, \qquad v_2 = 25.$$

What distribution should the manager now assign to $\tilde{y} = \tilde{A}_1 - \tilde{A}_2$?

15.6 Suppose that instead of assessing the distributions in Table 15.7, the manager of Exercise 15.4 had said before sampling that (1) he considered all values of $\tilde{A}_1$ between $2.00 and $6.00 to be about equally likely, and (2) he considered all values of $\tilde{A}_2$ between $2.00 and $6.00 to be about equally likely and would continue to hold this view even if he learned the value of $\tilde{A}_1$, no matter what that value might be. After taking the samples described in Exercise 15.5, what distribution should he assign to $\tilde{y} = \tilde{A}_1 - \tilde{A}_2$?

B. UNCERTAINTY ABOUT BIAS

15.7 A production manager has just received a lot of 5,000 units of a certain part and is interested in the fraction of these parts that will not function properly. To learn more about this fraction, he uses equiprobable sampling without replacement to draw 100 parts from the lot, submits these 100 parts to a test devised by his quality-control engineers, and finds that 18 of the parts fail the test.

a If the production manager believes that the test shows infallibly whether or not a part will function properly, and if prior to sampling he assigned the distribution shown in Table 15.8 to the fraction of parts that would not function properly, what distribution should he now assign to this fraction?

TABLE 15.8
Production Manager's Distribution of
Fraction That Would Not Function Properly

Fraction	Probability
.1	.6
.2	.4
	1.0

b Suppose now that the production manager does *not* believe that the test is infallible, and suppose that at his request one of the quality-control engineers assigns the distributions shown in Table 15.9 to the fraction that would fail the test given various values of the fraction that would not function properly. What distribution should the production manager now assign to the fraction that would not function properly?

TABLE 15.9
Quality-control Engineer's Distribution of
Fraction That Would Fail the Test

Fraction Failing Test	Probability, Given That Fraction Not Functioning Is:	
	.1	.2
.0	.3	.0
.1	.4	.3
.2	.3	.4
.3	.0	.3
	1.0	1.0

15.8 Same as Exercise 15.7*b* except that instead of assessing the distributions in Table 15.9 the quality-control engineer says that, given *any* value of the fraction not functioning, he would assign the distribution shown in Table 15.10 to the *difference*

(fraction failing test) − (fraction not functioning).

Is it true that uncertainty about errors of measurement can be disregarded if the expected error is zero?

TABLE 15.10
Quality-control Engineer's Distribution of the Difference
between Fraction Failing Test and Fraction Not Functioning

Difference	Probability
−.1	.3
.0	.4
+.1	.3
	1.0

15.9 Suppose that the businessman of Section 15.2.2 asks each respondent in a
      sample of 100, not simply whether he will buy the new product, but how
      many gallons he will buy during the first year after it is put on the market;
      suppose that the sample statistics are

$$n = 100, \qquad a = 36, \qquad v = 2124;$$

and suppose that before sampling the businessman assigned the distribution shown in Table 15.11 to the amount that would actually be bought
during the first year by the "average customer".

TABLE 15.11
Businessman's Distribution of
Average Amount Actually Bought

Number of Gallons	Probability
35	.6
45	.4
	1.0

a If the businessman believes that any respondent will in fact buy exactly
   as much as he says he will buy, what distribution should the businessman now assign to the amount that would be bought by the "average
   customer" during the first year?
b Suppose now that the businessman does *not* believe that a respondent
   will necessarily buy exactly as much as he says he will buy, and suppose
   that at the businessman's request an experienced market researcher
   assigns the distributions shown in Table 15.12 to the average of the
   amounts that the potential customers would say they would buy if they
   were all drawn in a 100% sample. What distribution should the businessman now assign to the amount that would actually be bought during the first year by the "average customer"?

15.10 Same as Exercise 15.9b except that instead of assessing the distributions in
      Table 15.12 the market researcher says that, given *any* value of the average
      amount actually bought, he would assess the distribution shown in Table
      15.13 of the *difference*

(average response in 100% sample) − (average amount actually bought).

Can the fact that respondents may over- or understate the amounts they
will actually buy be disregarded if respondents are just as likely to understate as to overstate?

TABLE 15.12
Market Researcher's Distribution of
Average Response in a 100% Sample

Average Response (Gallons)	Probability, Given That Average Amount Actually Bought Is:	
	35 Gallons	45 Gallons
30	.3	0
35	.4	0
40	.3	.3
45	0	.4
50	0	.3
	1.0	1.0

TABLE 15.13
Market Researcher's Distribution of the Difference
between Average Response in a 100% Sample and
Average Amount Actually Bought

Difference	Probability
−5	.3
0	.4
+5	.3
	1.0

15.11 *Mar-Pruf Finishes, Inc.* (C)

To help management decide whether or not to market a new product that would compete with the American Paint and Lacquer Company's A-1 lacquer, the marketing-research department of Mar-Pruf Finishes, Inc., drew 100 of the 10,000 potential customers for the product and then had salesmen give free samples to the selected customers and ask them how much, if any, of the product they would buy during the next year if the product were actually placed on the market. The sample responses and management's prior judgments about first-year sales are described in *Mar-Pruf Finishes, Inc. (A)* (Exercise 12.14).

Mar-Pruf's management now wish to decide how their prior judgments about first-year sales should be modified to take account of the information obtained from the sample. They are inclined to give very little weight to this information because they believe that responses obtained in the way these responses were obtained tend to be highly unreliable. More specifically, they feel that if every one of the 10,000 customers were to be interviewed, there would be 2 chances in 3 that the average response would be higher than the true average sales and 1 chance in 3 that the average response would be high by 10 gallons or more. All that they feel fairly sure of is that the average response would not be more than 20 gallons above actual sales or more than 10 gallons below.

Placing yourself in the position of the director of marketing research, and assuming that you can command the services of a computer programmer who knows almost everything there is to know about computers and almost nothing about anything else, prepare precise instructions for computing an answer to management's question and prepare all the data that will enter into these computations.

15.12 *Grand Western Railroad (B)*

In order to get information to use in deciding whether or not to cancel the Family-Fare tariff currently offered by the Grand Western Railroad, the president of Grand Western, Mr. H. B. Jones, employed a marketing research agency to draw a sample of the 20,000 families who had used the tariff during the past year and ask them how their expenditures would have been affected if the tariff had not been available. The method of drawing the sample and the responses obtained are described in *Grand Western Railroad (A)* (Exercise 12.15).

Before he learned the sample responses, Mr. Jones felt that if the Family-Fare tariff had not been available last year, the average per-family revenue obtained from the 20,000 families who used the tariff might have been anywhere between $150 less and $150 greater than it actually was with the tariff available, and he felt that any effect between these two extremes was about as likely as any other. The information obtained from the sample responses seemed to him much more solid than any other information available to him, but he was inclined to place rather little reliance in even the sample information. The marketing research agency who had conducted the sample survey for Jones assured him that thoroughly trained interviewers had been used, but Jones felt nevertheless that even if all 20,000 users of the tariff were to be interviewed, the average amount by which these users would say that their expenditures would have been altered might be anywhere between $50 below and $50 above the truth, any one value between these limits being about as likely in his opinion as any other.

a If you had the use of a computer and the services of a programmer available to you, how could you figure out what opinions Jones should now hold concerning the amount by which last year's average per-family expenditure would have been altered if the Family-Fare tariff had not been available? Exactly what computing instructions would you ask the programmer to program and exactly what data would you give him?

b What really interests Jones is of course not the effect that cancellation would have had on last year's revenues but the effect that cancellations may have on next year's revenues. If you were in Jones' position and had available the services of a competent probabilist, what information would you give him and what would you ask him to calculate for you?

15.13 In Section 14.2.2 we saw that if the expected value of free perfect information about a given population characteristic is very small, a decision maker can conclude without further calculations that it is almost certainly not worthwhile spending money to obtain imperfect sample information about that characteristic. In Section 15.2 we saw that when sample observations are subject to errors of measurement, we must distinguish carefully between two different population characteristics, namely (1) the average $\tilde{A}$ of the true values of all the members of the population (or fraction $\tilde{p}$ of true successes), and (2) the average $\tilde{A}^*$ of the values that would be measured (or fraction $\tilde{p}^*$ of successes that would be reported) if a certain sampling and measuring process were to be applied to the entire population.

    a In answer to Exercise 14.3*a* you have already computed the expected value of perfect information concerning the average amount of lacquer that would be actually purchased by individual customers in the first year if Mar-Pruf Finishes, Inc., puts its new lacquer on the market. Now describe exactly how you could compute the expected value of free perfect information concerning the average amount of lacquer that individual customers would say they would purchase if all 10,000 potential customers were interviewed. Exactly what probability assessments are required as inputs to this computation?

    b Will the expected value of perfect information about the average amount that customers would say they would buy be greater or less than the expected value of perfect information about what they would actually buy?

    c If management wants an upper bound on the net gain that can be expected from a real sample of the best possible size, which of these two EVPI's should be computed?

C. GENERAL-PURPOSE REPORTING

15.14 The top executives of a drug-manufacturing firm are thinking of developing and marketing a new cold remedy and wish to learn, among other things, what fraction of all choices of such a remedy are due to a doctor's advice. The director of marketing research decides to conduct an inexpensive sample survey in order to get more information on this point. To keep the costs low, he employs an agency specializing in telephone surveys and has this agency call telephone numbers chosen by equiprobable sampling from all telephone numbers in just one large city and ask each person who answers the telephone (1) whether when he last bought a cold remedy his choice of product was due to any individual's advice and (2) if so, whose advice; the calls are to be continued until 1,000 answers have been obtained.

    The agency reports that of the 1,000 persons answering the questions, 148 had not bought any cold remedy that they could remember, 221 had been buying the same product for so long that they had forgotten what led them to start, 476 had made their choice because of advertising in mass media, 56 because of advice from friends, 67 because of advice from doctors, and 32 because of advice from druggists.

The director of the marketing-research department now wishes to describe the results of the survey and their implications in a written report that will be circulated to all top executives of the company and to various other persons in the marketing department.

If the director of marketing research were to ask you to prepare this report, what would you write?

15.15 In the fall of 1965, students in a class in marketing were asked to study the level of awareness for Gillette razors in different segments of the Boston market. One group of students interviewed 200 men in barber shops in, to quote them, "a cross section of locations". High, medium, and low awareness was defined in terms of specific patterns of response to a structured questionnaire. The students considered both the question of overall awareness in the area and the relation between awareness and population characteristics like age, social class, etc.

One of their tabulations which seemed of particular interest is reproduced in Table 15.14. Without introducing any judgments of your own, what can you report on the basis of this tabulation about:

TABLE 15.14
Numbers of Respondents in Selected Categories

Awareness	White Collar	Blue Collar	Service	Total
High	34	10	10	54
Medium	27	13	14	54
Low	14	9	8	31
Total	75	32	32	139

a The percentage of the adult male population of Boston who have high awareness (as measured by the questionnaire)?

b The proportion of white collar workers who have high awareness?

c The difference in awareness between white and blue collar workers?

15.16 The following story appeared under the title "Trying too Hard for the Fast Knockout" in *Time* for January 6, 1967.

> Many cases of meningitis are caused by viruses, but by far the most deadly is the bacterial form. The disease, which causes inflammation of the membranes covering the brain and spinal cord, often strikes without warning and can kill a husky young man within hours. Fatal in at least 10% of cases, it understandably causes public panic when it breaks out. Yet, little is known about it or about the best way to treat it. In fact, careful

studies have only served to deepen some of its mysteries. But, as the University of Southern California's Dr. Paul F. Wehrle told the New York Academy of Sciences, there is at least one new lesson in treating meningitis that doctors could well learn.

Several antibiotics are effective against the infection, and because the disease is so severe, doctors have been inclined to combine them, hoping for a fast knockout. As Dr. Wehrle puts it, "There is a fixed and mystical belief that if one antibiotic is good, two must be better, and three even more efficacious." Not so, the Wehrle team found. In a twelve-month study at Los Angeles County General Hospital, every meningitis patient got intravenous ampicillin, a fast-acting form of penicillin, while alternate patients received, in addition, chloramphenicol and streptomycin. There were five deaths among 129 patients on ampicillin alone, but 13 among the 111 who got all three drugs. Using an antibiotic combination is evidently detrimental, perhaps because it interferes with the action of ampicillin.

a Although the experimental results strongly suggest that ampicillin alone is more effective than a combination of drugs, the numbers of deaths are not very large in either case and the apparent superiority of ampicillin alone could be due purely to chance. What could Dr. Wehrle have said about this possibility?

b If you were a doctor and now had to decide how to treat a patient for meningitis, how would you assess your probability for the correctness of Dr. Wehrle's conclusion?

D. REVIEW PROBLEMS

15.17 A student at the Beaumanvia Institute of Business Technology undertakes as a marketing-research project to investigate the fraction of women in Beaconia, the Beaumanvian city in which the Institute is located, who prefer to shop at Fellini's rather than at Gordon Bogg's, the only other major department store in the city. In an initial inquiry, he telephones and interviews 25 women selected at random from the Beaconia telephone directory and discovers that 68% of these women say that they prefer Fellini's.

With the outcome of this small sample in hand, the student is still uncertain whether he should poll any additional women. He would like to turn in a sharp and definitive report concerning the preferences of all women in Beaconia, but on the other hand he hesitates to divert any more time from his other studies, in some of which his marks are far from distinguished. He estimates that it will take him about 2½ minutes to select a number from the telephone directory, dial the number, and interview the housewife, and after the interviews are completed it will take him 30 minutes to analyze the results.

   a What does the information this student has already collected entitle him to say in his report about the subject he has set out to investigate?

   b How would you advise this student to go about deciding whether to enlarge his sample and if so by how much?

15.18 Tables 15.15 to 15.18 below show sample data obtained respectively by a manufacturer of small electrical appliances, a candy manufacturer, a manufacturer of phonograph records, and the manager of a regional dairy.[3] Putting yourself in the position of the marketing researcher who obtained each of these sets of data for the interested businessman:

   a Decide exactly what statements of significant findings you would make to the businessman if (1) the sample included the entire population in which the businessman was interested, and (2) you felt sure that every response was "true", and write out these statements to be read in class. (Remember that your objective is to call the businessman's attention to what is important, not to tell him everything you know.)

   b Still assuming that you feel sure that all responses are "true", decide how you should modify each of your statements to allow for the "sampling error" that might be present if the data represented the results of interviews with only 100 persons chosen by equiprobable sampling from the population of interest, and write out your modified statements to be read in class. (If you feel that any of these statements should quote probabilities that would be slow to compute by hand, leave a blank for the numerical value in your statement and be prepared to describe in class how the numerical value could be evaluated by someone able to use a computer.)

   c Decide what further modifications you would make in your statements if you were not sure that all responses were "true", and write out your modified statements to be read in class.

TABLE 15.15
Out-of-store Source of Information Felt to Be Most
Useful by Buyers of Small Electrical Appliances

Source	Percent Finding Most Useful
Newspaper advertising	10%
Magazine advertising	3%
Television advertising	4%
Other	83%
	100%

[3] Fictitious data adapted from real data given by H. Zeisel, *Say It With Figures* (New York: Harper & Row, Publishers, 1968).

TABLE 15.16
Candy-eating Habits of Women

	Eat Regularly		Do Not Eat Regularly		Total	
Single						
Aged 18–30	21%		5%		26%	
Aged over 30	4%		3%		7%	
Subtotal		25%		8%		33%
Married						
Aged 18–30	14%		3%		17%	
Aged over 30	29%		21%		50%	
Subtotal		43%		24%		67%
Total		68%		32%		100%

TABLE 15.17
Liking of Adults for Classical Music

	Like		Do Not Like		Total	
Aged under 40						
High education	11%		19%		30%	
Low education	1%		9%		10%	
Subtotal		12%		28%		40%
Aged 40 or over						
High education	6%		19%		25%	
Low education	12%		23%		35%	
Subtotal		18%		42%		60%
Total		30%		70%		100%

TABLE 15.18
Weekly Family Milk Consumption

	Consumption (Quarts)		Percent of All Families	
Upper economic status				
Family size 3 or less	8.0		34%	
Family size over 3	17.1		16%	
All upper e.s.		10.9		50%
Lower economic status				
Family size 3 or less	6.2		22%	
Family size over 3	14.4		28%	
All lower e.s.		10.8		50%
All respondents:		10.85		100%

15.19 Loeb Drama Center

During the fall of 1965, Mr. Schwalbe, the business manager of the Loeb Drama Center, a nonprofit theater affiliated with Harvard University, became concerned by the number of empty seats at Loeb performances and contacted the staff of the first-year course in Marketing at the Harvard Business School. The problem was assigned to a seven-man group as a part of the requirements of the course.

In an interview with the group, Mr. Schwalbe indicated that he felt strongly that the Loeb should cater to an audience which was larger than the Harvard community and that he desired substantiated recommendations concerning the marketing strategy (especially as regards advertising and promotion) that the Loeb should follow to attract a broader audience and fill the theater for every performance.

Before making recommendations to Mr. Schwalbe, the group decided to conduct a survey to determine the characteristics of the people who currently attended the Loeb and the extent to which people who did not attend the Loeb were aware of its existence. A sample was drawn from the residents of three suburban communities within six miles of the Loeb and a questionnaire was administered to those adults who answered the phone and were willing to cooperate; the questionnaire contained 47 questions and took about 15 minutes to answer. The number of persons answering was 190, of whom 79 had attended some theater during the last year and 29 had attended the Loeb; the number of nonrespondents was not recorded. The total population of the three communities which were sampled was about 200,000.

To determine respondents' awareness of the Loeb, an aided-recall technique was used. Of the 50 people who had attended a theater but had not attended the Loeb, 58% reported that they had heard of the Loeb, and the researchers concluded that awareness was not a serious problem for the Loeb.

The interpretation of some of the other information obtained did not seem so simple, however. Education was thought to be a critical factor in determining attendance at the Loeb because of the nature of the plays produced, which included works by Genet, Shaw, Shakespeare, and Pirandello, and therefore each respondent who had attended a theater during the last year was asked whether he had graduated from college; the answers obtained are shown in Table 15.19 below. Census data showed that the median education of the population sampled was about 13 years of schooling, so that it seemed clear that theatergoers as a whole were more highly educated than nontheatergoers, but the researchers were not sure what conclusions could be drawn from their sample about differences in education between theatergoers who attended the Loeb and theatergoers who did not.

TABLE 15.19
Education of Persons Who Attended a Theater

College Education	Attended Loeb (n = 29)	Did Not Attend Loeb (n = 50)	Total (n = 79)
Graduated	90%	69%	77%
Did not graduate	10%	31%	23%
Total	100%	100%	100%

Another demographic classification was made by family income. According to *Sales Management*, the median annual income in the communities sampled was $10,000; sample respondents reported family incomes as shown in Table 15.20.

TABLE 15.20
Family Income of Respondents

Family Income	Attended a Theater — Attended Loeb (n = 29)	Attended a Theater — Did not Attend Loeb (n = 50)	Did not Attend a Theater (n = 111)	Total (n = 190)
Under $7,000	24%	4%	11%	11%
$7,000–$10,999	10%	20%	15%	16%
$11,000 & over	35%	60%	50%	50%
No answer	31%	16%	24%	23%
	100%	100%	100%	100%

Another interesting finding of the survey was the fact that the people who had attended the Loeb attended some theater or another more often than people who had not attended the Loeb. Table 15.21 shows the sample results.

TABLE 15.21
Frequency of Theater Attendance

Persons Who:	Average Number of Times Attended a Theater
Attended Loeb (n = 29)	6.3
Did Not Attend Loeb (n = 50)	3.9
Total sample (n = 190)	2.0

a If the percentages or averages in the tables above represented the results of a complete count of the population of interest to Mr. Schwalbe, and if you felt sure that all answers obtained were "true", exactly what statements of significant findings would you have made to Mr. Schwalbe?

b How would you have modified these statements to allow for the "sampling error" that might be present in the sample data actually obtained if the 190 responses had been obtained by making exactly 190 phone calls (no nonrespondents) and you felt sure that all answers were "true"?

c How would you report your findings on the basis of the data actually obtained?

APPENDIX

SETS, FUNCTIONS, AND WEIGHTED AVERAGES

A.1
SETS

A.1.1
Meaning of the Word "Set"

The word ≪set≫ is used in mathematics with essentially the same meaning that it is used in ordinary English. Thus we can talk about the set of all first-year students currently registered in a certain school, the set of all books currently on the shelves of the library, the set of all books purchased by the library during the past 12 months, and so forth.

A set is well defined if for any given ≪element≫ it is possible to say definitely whether that element belongs to the set or not. "All residents of Massachusetts" would not define a set unless the expression were accompanied by a precise rule for determining who is and who is not to be classified as a resident of Massachusetts.

A.1.2
Sets of Numbers

In this Appendix we shall be primarily interested in sets of numbers, e.g., the set of all integers from 1 through 10 inclusive, the (infinite) set of all positive integers, the set of all positive numbers, the set of all nonnegative numbers expressed to two decimal places (.00, .01, .02, . . .), and so forth.

We shall have occasion to refer frequently to the set of ≪real numbers≫. All positive and negative integers and common and decimal fractions are members of this set, as is the number zero.   The set also includes the so-called transcendental numbers, like $\sqrt{2}$ or the π of geometry, but these numbers will be of no interest in the problems discussed in this book.

A.1.3
Intervals

The set of all real numbers between a specified lower limit and a specified upper limit is called an ≪interval≫; the definition of any particular interval must state concerning each of the two limits whether that limit is or is not included in the interval.   All the real numbers from 3 to 7 inclusive constitute an interval; all the real numbers from 3 to 7 including 3 but excluding 7 constitute another interval; and so forth.

A.2
FUNCTIONS OF ONE ARGUMENT

A.2.1
Definition of a Function

A ≪function≫ associates one and only one member of some ≪output set≫ to each member of some ≪input set≫; it may or may not associate the same member of the output set to more than one member of the input set.   The elements of the two sets may be entities of any sort whatever.

      For example, a list which assigns one and only one account number to each customer of a certain firm defines a function.   The customers are the elements of the input set; the account numbers are the elements of the output set; the function is well defined because given any input it is possible to find a unique corresponding output.   If no two customers have the same account number, this same list also defines *another* function, called the ≪inverse≫ of the first function, which associates one and only one customer (output) to each account number (input).   If, however, two or more customers—e.g., a man and his wife—may have the same account number, then no such second function exists.   We repeat: a function may associate more than one element of its input set to the same element of its output set, but it must associate one and only one member of its output set to each member of its input set.

A.2.2
Real-valued Functions
of One Real Argument

A function which associates one and only one member of an output set consisting of single real numbers to each member of an input set consisting of single real numbers is called a ≪real-valued≫ function ≪of one real argument≫.   Any member of the input set is a permissible ≪argument≫ of the function; the corresponding member of the output set is the ≪value≫ of the function for that argument.

      A particular real-valued function of one real argument—or function of one argument for short—may be defined in various ways, of which the following are the most important for our purposes.

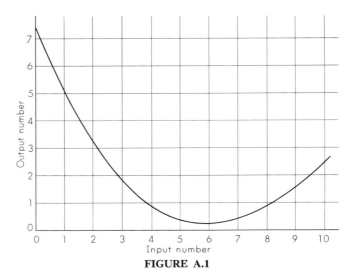

FIGURE A.1

Graph Defining a Function

1. A particular function may be defined by a *list* which shows the output number that corresponds to every member of a set of permissible input numbers. Thus Table A.1 defines a function because it specifies an output number corresponding to every member of the set of

TABLE A.1
Definition of a Function

Input Number	Output Number
1	6 2/3
2	−23
3	7 1/4
4	$\sqrt{2}$
5	−23

permissible input numbers listed in the table. We remind the reader once more that, as illustrated in this table, a function may associate the same output to more than one input; it cannot, however, associate more than one output to the same input.

2. A particular function may be defined by a *graph* which shows the output number that corresponds to every member of a set of permissible input numbers. Thus Figure A.1 defines a function because it specifies the output number that corresponds to every input number on the horizontal axis, i.e., to every real number from 0 to 10 inclusive. The output number corresponding to the input number 2.0 is 3.2, and so forth.

3. Finally, a particular function may be defined by a *formula* from which the output number that corresponds to any permissible input number can be computed. Thus each of the following two formulas defines a particular function to which any real number is a permissible input.

1 Output number = input number + 3,

2 Output number = input number squared.

If the input number to the function defined by the second of these formulas is 7, we can immediately calculate that the corresponding output number is 49, and so forth.

A.2.3
Functional Notation

In talking about functions, it is often convenient to let some letter stand for *any* one, particular argument or member of the set of permissible input numbers and to let some other letter stand for the corresponding value or output number. If, for example, we denote the argument by x and the value by y, the function defined by Table A.1 could equally well be defined by Table A.2,

TABLE A.2

Argument x	Value y
1	6 2/3
2	-23
3	7 1/4
4	$\sqrt{2}$
5	-23

and the two functions defined above by formulas could be equally well defined by writing

1 $y = x + 3$,

2 $y = x^2$.

It is also often convenient to let some letter denote a particular function itself. We might, for example, give the name f to the function defined by Table A.2, the name g to the function defined by formula 1, and so forth.

Finally, it is often convenient to let $f(x)$ denote the value associated to an argument x by a function f, even when we are also using a letter y to denote the value associated by f to x. For example, it is often convenient to write

$$y = f(x),$$

thus reminding ourselves in very compact form that we are dealing with a function which we have agreed to call f and that we have also agreed to let the symbol x stand for any one, particular input number or argument of this function and to let y stand for the corresponding output number or value of the function.

Instead of saying that we shall give the name g, say, to the function defined by the formula

$$y = x + 3$$

we can say that we define the function g by the formula

$$g(x) = x + 3.$$

A.2.4
The Expression "y is a function of x"

When there is an output number y corresponding to every input number x that belongs to some specified set, it is often said that "y is a function of x." This expression is really shorthand for the statement "y is the *value* of a function whose *argument* is x."

Similarly, if there is a definite output number called "production cost" for any permissible input number called "number of units produced", we can say that production cost "is a function of" number of units produced, meaning that production cost is the value of a function whose argument is the number of units produced.

A.2.5
Permissible Input Numbers

Let Q denote the quantity (number of units) of Product X that a businessman will produce next year, suppose that to produce this quantity he must incur a cost of $5,000 for setup plus $5 per unit produced, and denote his production cost by p.   Then the relation

$$p = 5,000 + 5Q$$

defines what we may call his "cost function"; or if we give the name f to this function, we can say that f is defined by

$$f(Q) = 5,000 + 5Q.$$

The input number or argument of the cost function f is the number Q of units produced; the output number or value of the cost function f is the production cost p.

If a businessman untrained in mathematics were to graph his production cost p against the number Q of units produced, he would draw a continuous line even if it were impossible to produce a fractional number of units, implying that his continuous graph would show a meaningless cost above each fractional number of units on the horizontal axis.   In thinking about the set of permissible input numbers to the cost function f which we defined above, we shall find it convenient to imitate the businessman.   Formally, we shall say that any real number Q is a permissible input to f and simply keep in the back of our minds the fact that the value of the function f corresponds to a real production cost only if Q is some nonnegative, integral number of units that the businessman can actually produce.

A.3
FUNCTIONS OF MORE THAN ONE ARGUMENT

A.3.1
Real-valued Functions
of Several Real Arguments

Besides dealing with functions which associate single output numbers to single input numbers, we shall have to deal with functions which associate single output numbers to groups of input numbers.   One particular function of this sort is defined by Table A.3, where we see, for example, that if the first input number is -2 and the second input number is $+3$, then the output number is -17.   In general, a ≪real-valued function of two real arguments≫, or function of two arguments for short, associates *one and only one* output number or *value* to each permissible *pair* of *arguments;* and similarly for functions of more than two arguments.

Like functions of one argument, functions of two or more arguments can be defined by formulas as well as by tables.   The function defined by Table A.3 could alternatively have

TABLE A.3
Definition of a Function of Two Arguments

First Input Number	Second Input Number	Output Number
−2	+1	− 1
−2	+2	− 7
−2	+3	−17
0	+1	+ 1
0	+2	+ 1
0	+3	+ 1
+2	+1	+ 3
+2	+2	+ 9
+2	+3	+19

been defined by calling the function f, letting u and v stand for any permissible pair of arguments, and writing

$$f(u, v) = uv^2 + 1.$$

In a strict sense, the function defined by this formula is not the same function that was defined by Table A.3 unless we specify that the formula is to be applied to only those pairs of arguments that were listed in Table A.3, but in the applications we have in mind such niceties are unnecessary.

A.3.2

Example of Application

Suppose in the example introduced in Section A.2.5 that the businessman collects $7 net for each unit that he sells, and define or redefine the following notation:

Q: number of units produced,
d: number of units demanded by customers,
s: number of units sold,
p: production cost,
r: sales revenue,
$c = r − p$: contribution to overhead and profit.

Since

$$r = 7s \quad \text{and} \quad p = 5,000 + 5Q,$$

we have

$$c = 7s − (5,000 + 5Q).$$

Then since sales will equal demand unless demand is greater than the quantity produced, in which case sales will equal the quantity produced,

$$s = \begin{cases} d & \text{if} & d \leqslant Q, \\ Q & \text{if} & d > Q; \end{cases}$$

and therefore

$$c = \begin{cases} 7d − (5,000 + 5Q) & \text{if} & d \leqslant Q, \\ 7Q − (5,000 + 5Q) & \text{if} & d > Q. \end{cases}$$

Contribution thus "is a function of" quantity produced and customer demand. If we denote the contribution *function* by g, we can say that g is defined by

$$g(d, Q) = \begin{cases} 7d - (5,000 + 5Q) & \text{if} & d \leqslant Q, \\ 7Q - (5,000 + 5Q) & \text{if} & d > Q. \end{cases}$$

The input numbers or arguments of the function g are d and Q; the output number or value of the function g is the contribution $g(d, Q) = c$.

A.3.3
Parameters of a Function

Suppose now that the businessman of the example we have been discussing is thinking of producing some particular quantity, say $Q = 8,000$ units; and suppose that he wants to examine how the contribution he earns as a result will depend on the number of units d demanded by his customers. By substituting 8,000 for Q in the last formula above he can derive the formula

$$g(d, 8,000) = \begin{cases} 7d - 45,000 & \text{if} & d \leqslant Q, \\ 11,000 & \text{if} & d > Q; \end{cases}$$

after which he can investigate the relation between demand and contribution by substituting various values of d in this new formula. If he then wishes to carry out a similar investigation for some other production decision, say $Q = 9,000$, he can substitute 9,000 for Q in the original formula for $g(d, Q)$, thus obtaining

$$g(d, 9,000) = \begin{cases} 7d - 50,000 & \text{if} & d \leqslant Q, \\ 13,000 & \text{if} & d > Q, \end{cases}$$

after which he can again investigate the relation between demand and contribution by substituting various values of d in the formula he had derived.

Observe now that although the original formula for $g(d, Q)$ defines a function of two arguments, the formula we derived from it by substituting 8,000 for Q defines a function of just one argument, d, while the formula we derived by substituting 9,000 for Q defines *another* function of the one argument d. Accordingly we can if we like think of the original formula for $g(d, Q)$ as defining, not a single function of two arguments d and Q, but a whole family of functions of a single argument d, within which we select one particular function by giving one particular numerical value to the symbol Q. If we do think of the formula for $g(d, Q)$ in this way, we say that Q is a «parameter» rather than an argument of the function defined by the formula.

To indicate that we are thinking of Q as a parameter of a function of one argument rather than as an argument of a function of two arguments, we can write $g_Q(d)$ instead of $g(d, Q)$. If the context is such that no confusion can result, we can simply eliminate the parameter from the name of the function and write $g(d)$.

A.4
LINEAR FUNCTIONS

A.4.1
Linear Functions of One Argument

A function f of one argument x is said to be a «linear» function if the value it associates to *any* permissible input x is or could be given by a *single* formula of the type

$$f(x) = a + bx,$$

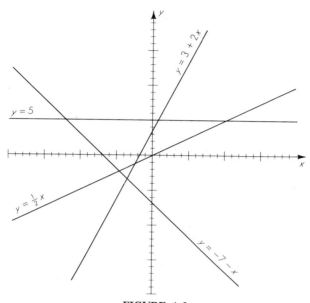

FIGURE A.2

Graphs of Linear Functions

where a and b stand for fixed numbers or constants in contradistinction to x, which stands for any member of the set of permissible input numbers.[1] For example, a function f would be linear if the value $f(x)$ which it associates to any argument x were given by any *one* of the following formulas:

$$f(x) = 3 + 2x \qquad (a = 3, b = 2),$$
$$f(x) = -7 - x \qquad (a = -7, b = -1),$$
$$f(x) = x/2 \qquad (a = 0, b = 1/2),$$
$$f(x) = 5 \qquad (a = 5, b = 0).$$

Such functions are called linear because their graphs are straight lines. The graphs of the four examples just given are shown in Figure A.2.

A.4.2

Piecewise Linear Functions

It is very important to understand that the function h defined by

$$h(x) = \begin{cases} 3 + 2x & \text{if} & x \leqslant 6, \\ 15 - x & \text{if} & x > 6, \end{cases}$$

is not a linear function, nor is it two linear functions; it is one, nonlinear function. Such functions are sometimes called "piecewise linear", but they do not have the very important property of truly linear functions that we shall study in Section A.5.4 below.

---

[1] We could if we liked say that a and b are "parameters" of the function of one argument defined by the formula $a + bx$.

A.4.3
Linear Functions of
More than One Argument

A function f of several arguments x, y, z, . . . is said to be a linear function if its value for any group of permissible input numbers x, y, z, . . . is or could be given by a single formula of the type

$$f(x, y, z, \ldots) = a + b_1x + b_2y + b_3z + \ldots$$

where a, b_1, b_2, . . . are fixed numbers or constants.

A.5
WEIGHTED AVERAGES

A.5.1
Definition of a Weighted Average

Table A.4 illustrates the application of the following definition of a weighted average of a set of numbers.

Given (1) a set of (positive, zero, or negative) numbers, and (2) a nonnegative ≪weight≫ associated to each number, the ≪weighted average≫ of the numbers is computed by (1) multiplying each number by its weight to form a product, and (2) dividing the sum of the products by the sum of the weights.

TABLE A.4
Computation of a Weighted Average

Number	Weight	Product
−1	4	−4
0	2	0
+1	3	+3
2	4	8
3	0	0
4	7	28
Total	20	35

Weighted average: 35/20 = 1.75

A.5.2
Weighting Functions

It will be convenient in what follows to think of weights like those in Table A.4 as being values of a ≪weighting function≫ which associates a weight to every member of some specified set of real numbers. Thus in the example of Table A.4, we can regard the weights in the second column as values of a weighting function whose permissible arguments are the numbers in the first column.

If we give the name w to the weighting function which associates weights to the numbers in the first column of Table A.4, and if we let x stand for any member of this set of numbers, the weight associated to x can be denoted by $w(x)$. The second column of the table shows that $w(-1) = 4$, $w(0) = 2$, and so forth.

A.5.3
Weighted Average of the Values
of a Function of One Argument

Now consider the set of numbers x defined by Column 1 of Table A.5; suppose that a weighting function associates to each x the weight $w(x)$ shown in Column 2; and suppose that another function f (*not* a weighting function) associates to each x the value

$$f(x) = x^2$$

shown in Column 3. The weighted average of *the values of the function f* is computed in Column 4 of Table A.5 according to the following definition:

> Given (1) a set of real numbers x, (2) a function f which associates a value to each x, and (3) a weighting function w which associates a weight to each x, the «weighted average of the values $f(x)$ of the function f» is the number obtained by (1) multiplying the value $f(x)$ associated to each x in the set by the corresponding weight $w(x)$, and (2) dividing the sum of these products by the sum of the weights.

In the example of Table A.5, the weighted average of the function values $f(x)$ is 6.6.

TABLE A.5
Weighted Average of the Values of a Function

1	2	3	4
Argument	*Weight*	*Value*	*Product*
x	$w(x)$	$f(x)$	2×3
1	4	1	4
2	3	4	12
3	1	9	9
4	1	16	16
5	1	25	25
Total	10		66
Weighted Average:			$66/10 = 6.6$

Example of Application   If x in Table A.5 is the length in feet of one side of the top of a square table, then $f(x) = x^2$ is the area in square feet of the top; and if $w(x)$ is the number of tables on hand whose side-length is x, then 6.6 square feet is the average area of a table top.

A.5.4
Weighted Average of the Values
of a Linear Function of One Argument

In Table A.6 we show the computation of the weighted averages of both (1) the arguments x originally shown in Column 1 of Table A.5 and shown again in Column 1 of Table A.6, and (2) the values of a linear function g defined by

$$g(x) = 2 + 3x.$$

The weighted average of the arguments x is 2.2; the weighted average of the function values $g(x)$ is 8.6.

TABLE A.6
Weighted Average of the Values of a Linear Function

1 *Argument* *x*	**2** *Weight* *w(x)*	**3** *Product* **1 × 2**	**4** *Value* *g(x)*	**5** *Product* **4 × 2**
1	4	4	5	20
2	3	6	8	24
3	1	3	11	11
4	1	4	14	14
5	1	5	17	17
Total	10	22		86
Weighted Average:		22/10 = 2.2		86/10 = 8.6

We can now observe two very important facts about weighted averages of values of functions.

1. The weighted average of the values $g(x)$ of the *linear* function g which we considered in Table A.6 could have been computed by simply substituting the weighted average of its arguments in the formula defining g. The weighted average of the arguments was shown to be 2.2 in Table A.6; substituting this number in the formula for g we get

$$g(2.2) = 2 + (3 \times 2.2) = 8.6;$$

and 8.6 was shown in Table A.6 to be the weighted average of the values $g(x)$ of the function g.

2. The weighted average of the values $f(x)$ of the *nonlinear* function f which we considered in Table A.5 could *not* have been computed by simply substituting the weighted average of its arguments in the formula defining f. If we substitute the argument average 2.2 in the formula defining f we get

$$f(2.2) = 2.2^2 = 4.84,$$

whereas we showed in Table A.5 that the weighted average of the values of f is actually 6.6.

These two examples are typical of what happens with any set of numbers x and any weighting function w. To state the general principles which the examples illustrate, let h denote any function, let x denote any argument of the function h, let $y = h(x)$ denote any value of the function h, let $\bar{x}$ (read: x bar) denote the weighted average of the arguments x, and let $\bar{y}$ denote the weighted average of the values y.

1 If h is a *linear* function, then it can be proved that

$$\bar{y} \text{ is } \textit{necessarily} \text{ equal to } h(\bar{x}).$$

2 If h is a *nonlinear* function, then as shown by our example

$$\bar{y} \text{ is } \textit{not} \text{ in general equal to } h(\bar{x}).$$

TABLES

CONTENTS

A.
Mass and Density Functions

B.
Cumulative Functions

C.
Miscellaneous

TABLE T1
BINOMIAL MASS FUNCTION[1]

The following table gives values of the binomial mass function defined by

$$b^*(N, R, P) = \binom{N}{R} P^R (1 - P)^{N-R}$$

for

$$N = 1(1)15, \ 100,$$

$$R = 0(1)N,$$

$$P = .01(.01).99.$$

The values of R at the left of any section of the table are to be used in conjunction with the values of P at the top of that section; the values of R at the right of any section are to be used in conjunction with the values of P at the bottom of that section. A decimal point is to be inserted immediately before each value of P and each entry in the body of the table.

Example. To evaluate $b^*(N, R, P)$ for $N = 6$, $R = 2$, $P = .17$, locate the section for $N = 6$, the column for $P = .17$, and the row for $R = 2$, and read

$$b^*(6, 2, .17) = .2057 = b^*(6, 4, .83).$$

---

[1] Table computed and edited by Stanley I. Buchin.

N = 1

R	P	01	02	03	04	05	06	07	08	09	10	
0		9900	9800	9700	9600	9500	9400	9300	9200	9100	9000	1
1		0100	0200	0300	0400	0500	0600	0700	0800	0900	1000	0
		99	98	97	96	95	94	93	92	91	90	P R

R	P	11	12	13	14	15	16	17	18	19	20	
0		8900	8800	8700	8600	8500	8400	8300	8200	8100	8000	1
1		1100	1200	1300	1400	1500	1600	1700	1800	1900	2000	0
		89	88	87	86	85	84	83	82	81	80	P R

R	P	21	22	23	24	25	26	27	28	29	30	
0		7900	7800	7700	7600	7500	7400	7300	7200	7100	7000	1
1		2100	2200	2300	2400	2500	2600	2700	2800	2900	3000	0
		79	78	77	76	75	74	73	72	71	70	P R

R	P	31	32	33	34	35	36	37	38	39	40	
0		6900	6800	6700	6600	6500	6400	6300	6200	6100	6000	1
1		3100	3200	3300	3400	3500	3600	3700	3800	3900	4000	0
		69	68	67	66	65	64	63	62	61	60	P R

R	P	41	42	43	44	45	46	47	48	49	50	
0		5900	5800	5700	5600	5500	5400	5300	5200	5100	5000	1
1		4100	4200	4300	4400	4500	4600	4700	4800	4900	5000	0
		59	58	57	56	55	54	53	52	51	50	P R

N = 2

R	P	01	02	03	04	05	06	07	08	09	10	
0		9801	9604	9409	9216	9025	8836	8649	8464	8281	8100	2
1		0198	0392	0582	0768	0950	1128	1302	1472	1638	1800	1
2		0001	0004	0009	0016	0025	0036	0049	0064	0081	0100	0
		99	98	97	96	95	94	93	92	91	90	P R

R	P	11	12	13	14	15	16	17	18	19	20	
0		7921	7744	7569	7396	7225	7056	6889	6724	6561	6400	2
1		1958	2112	2262	2408	2550	2688	2822	2952	3078	3200	1
2		0121	0144	0169	0196	0225	0256	0289	0324	0361	0400	0
		89	88	87	86	85	84	83	82	81	80	P R

R	P	21	22	23	24	25	26	27	28	29	30	
0		6241	6084	5929	5776	5625	5476	5329	5184	5041	4900	2
1		3318	3432	3542	3648	3750	3848	3942	4032	4118	4200	1
2		0441	0484	0529	0576	0625	0676	0729	0784	0841	0900	0
		79	78	77	76	75	74	73	72	71	70	P R

R	P	31	32	33	34	35	36	37	38	39	40	
0		4761	4624	4489	4356	4225	4096	3969	3844	3721	3600	2
1		4278	4352	4422	4488	4550	4608	4662	4712	4758	4800	1
2		0961	1024	1089	1156	1225	1296	1369	1444	1521	1600	0
		69	68	67	66	65	64	63	62	61	60	P R

R	P	41	42	43	44	45	46	47	48	49	50	
0		3481	3364	3249	3136	3025	2916	2809	2704	2601	2500	2
1		4838	4872	4902	4928	4950	4968	4982	4992	4998	5000	1
2		1681	1764	1849	1936	2025	2116	2209	2304	2401	2500	0
		59	58	57	56	55	54	53	52	51	50	P R

N = 3

R	P	01	02	03	04	05	06	07	08	09	10	
0		9703	9412	9127	8847	8574	8306	8044	7787	7536	7290	3
1		0294	0576	0847	1106	1354	1590	1816	2031	2236	2430	2
2		0003	0012	0026	0046	0071	0102	0137	0177	0221	0270	1
3		0000	0000	0000	0001	0001	0002	0003	0005	0007	0010	0
		99	98	97	96	95	94	93	92	91	90	P R

R	P	11	12	13	14	15	16	17	18	19	20	
0		7050	6815	6585	6361	6141	5927	5718	5514	5314	5120	3
1		2614	2788	2952	3106	3251	3387	3513	3631	3740	3840	2
2		0323	0380	0441	0506	0574	0645	0720	0797	0877	0960	1
3		0013	0017	0022	0027	0034	0041	0049	0058	0069	0080	0
		89	88	87	86	85	84	83	82	81	80	P R

R	P	21	22	23	24	25	26	27	28	29	30	
0		4930	4746	4565	4390	4219	4052	3890	3732	3579	3430	3
1		3932	4015	4091	4159	4219	4271	4316	4355	4386	4410	2
2		1045	1133	1222	1313	1406	1501	1597	1693	1791	1890	1
3		0093	0106	0122	0138	0156	0176	0197	0220	0244	0270	0
		79	78	77	76	75	74	73	72	71	70	P R

R	P	31	32	33	34	35	36	37	38	39	40	
0		3285	3144	3008	2875	2746	2621	2500	2383	2270	2160	3
1		4428	4439	4444	4443	4436	4424	4406	4382	4354	4320	2
2		1989	2089	2189	2289	2389	2488	2587	2686	2783	2880	1
3		0298	0328	0359	0393	0429	0467	0507	0549	0593	0640	0
		69	68	67	66	65	64	63	62	61	60	P R

R	P	41	42	43	44	45	46	47	48	49	50	
0		2054	1951	1852	1756	1664	1575	1489	1406	1327	1250	3
1		4282	4239	4191	4140	4084	4024	3961	3894	3823	3750	2
2		2975	3069	3162	3252	3341	3428	3512	3594	3674	3750	1
3		0689	0741	0795	0852	0911	0973	1038	1106	1176	1250	0
		59	58	57	56	55	54	53	52	51	50	P R

N = 4

R	P	01	02	03	04	05	06	07	08	09	10	
0		9606	9224	8853	8493	8145	7807	7481	7164	6857	6561	4
1		0388	0753	1095	1416	1715	1993	2252	2492	2713	2916	3
2		0006	0023	0051	0088	0135	0191	0254	0325	0402	0486	2
3		0000	0000	0001	0002	0005	0008	0013	0019	0027	0036	1
4		0000	0000	0000	0000	0000	0000	0000	0000	0001	0001	0
		99	98	97	96	95	94	93	92	91	90	P R

R	P	11	12	13	14	15	16	17	18	19	20	
0		6274	5997	5729	5470	5220	4979	4746	4521	4305	4096	4
1		3102	3271	3424	3562	3685	3793	3888	3970	4039	4096	3
2		0575	0669	0767	0870	0975	1084	1195	1307	1421	1536	2
3		0047	0061	0076	0094	0115	0138	0163	0191	0222	0256	1
4		0001	0002	0003	0004	0005	0007	0008	0010	0013	0016	0
		89	88	87	86	85	84	83	82	81	80	P R

R	P	21	22	23	24	25	26	27	28	29	30	
0		3895	3702	3515	3336	3164	2999	2840	2687	2541	2401	4
1		4142	4176	4200	4214	4219	4214	4201	4180	4152	4116	3
2		1651	1767	1882	1996	2109	2221	2331	2439	2544	2646	2
3		0293	0332	0375	0420	0469	0520	0575	0632	0693	0756	1
4		0019	0023	0028	0033	0039	0046	0053	0061	0071	0081	0
		79	78	77	76	75	74	73	72	71	70	P R

R	P	31	32	33	34	35	36	37	38	39	40	
0		2267	2138	2015	1897	1785	1678	1575	1478	1385	1296	4
1		4074	4025	3970	3910	3845	3775	3701	3623	3541	3456	3
2		2745	2841	2933	3021	3105	3185	3260	3330	3396	3456	2
3		0822	0891	0963	1038	1115	1194	1276	1361	1447	1536	1
4		0092	0105	0119	0134	0150	0168	0187	0209	0231	0256	0
		69	68	67	66	65	64	63	62	61	60	P R

R	P	41	42	43	44	45	46	47	48	49	50	
0		1212	1132	1056	0983	0915	0850	0789	0731	0677	0625	4
1		3368	3278	3185	3091	2995	2897	2799	2700	2600	2500	3
2		3511	3560	3604	3643	3675	3702	3723	3738	3747	3750	2
3		1627	1719	1813	1908	2005	2102	2201	2300	2400	2500	1
4		0283	0311	0342	0375	0410	0448	0488	0531	0576	0625	0
		59	58	57	56	55	54	53	52	51	50	P R

N = 5

R	P	01	02	03	04	05	06	07	08	09	10	
0		9510	9039	8587	8154	7738	7339	6957	6591	6240	5905	5
1		0480	0922	1328	1699	2036	2342	2618	2866	3086	3280	4
2		0010	0038	0082	0142	0214	0299	0394	0498	0610	0729	3
3		0000	0001	0003	0006	0011	0019	0030	0043	0060	0081	2
4		0000	0000	0000	0000	0000	0001	0001	0002	0003	0004	1
		99	98	97	96	95	94	93	92	91	90 P	R

R	P	11	12	13	14	15	16	17	18	19	20	
0		5584	5277	4984	4704	4437	4182	3939	3707	3487	3277	5
1		3451	3598	3724	3829	3915	3983	4034	4069	4089	4096	4
2		0853	0981	1113	1247	1382	1517	1652	1786	1919	2048	3
3		0105	0134	0166	0203	0244	0289	0338	0392	0450	0512	2
4		0007	0009	0012	0017	0022	0028	0035	0043	0053	0064	1
5		0000	0000	0000	0001	0001	0001	0001	0002	0002	0003	0
		89	88	87	86	85	84	83	82	81	80 P	R

R	P	21	22	23	24	25	26	27	28	29	30	
0		3077	2887	2707	2536	2373	2219	2073	1935	1804	1681	5
1		4090	4072	4043	4003	3955	3898	3834	3762	3685	3601	4
2		2174	2297	2415	2529	2637	2739	2836	2926	3010	3087	3
3		0578	0648	0721	0798	0879	0962	1049	1138	1229	1323	2
4		0077	0091	0108	0126	0146	0169	0194	0221	0251	0283	1
5		0004	0005	0006	0008	0010	0012	0014	0017	0021	0024	0
		79	78	77	76	75	74	73	72	71	70 P	R

R	P	31	32	33	34	35	36	37	38	39	40	
0		1564	1454	1350	1252	1160	1074	0992	0916	0845	0778	5
1		3513	3421	3325	3226	3124	3020	2914	2808	2700	2592	4
2		3157	3220	3275	3323	3364	3397	3423	3441	3452	3456	3
3		1418	1515	1613	1712	1811	1911	2010	2109	2207	2304	2
4		0319	0357	0397	0441	0488	0537	0590	0646	0706	0768	1
5		0029	0034	0039	0045	0053	0060	0069	0079	0090	0102	0
		69	68	67	66	65	64	63	62	61	60 P	R

R	P	41	42	43	44	45	46	47	48	49	50	
0		0715	0656	0602	0551	0503	0459	0418	0380	0345	0313	5
1		2484	2376	2270	2164	2059	1956	1854	1755	1657	1562	4
2		3452	3442	3424	3400	3369	3332	3289	3240	3185	3125	3
3		2399	2492	2583	2671	2757	2838	2916	2990	3060	3125	2
4		0834	0902	0974	1049	1128	1209	1293	1380	1470	1562	1
5		0116	0131	0147	0165	0185	0206	0229	0255	0282	0312	0
		59	58	57	56	55	54	53	52	51	50 P	R

N = 6

R	P	01	02	03	04	05	06	07	08	09	10	
0		9415	8858	8330	7828	7351	6899	6470	6064	5679	5314	6
1		0571	1085	1546	1957	2321	2642	2922	3164	3370	3543	5
2		0014	0055	0120	0204	0305	0422	0550	0688	0833	0984	4
3		0000	0002	0005	0011	0021	0036	0055	0080	0110	0146	3
4		0000	0000	0000	0000	0001	0002	0003	0005	0008	0012	2
5		0000	0000	0000	0000	0000	0000	0000	0000	0000	0001	1
		99	98	97	96	95	94	93	92	91	90 P	R

R	P	11	12	13	14	15	16	17	18	19	20	
0		4970	4644	4336	4046	3771	3513	3269	3040	2824	2621	6
1		3685	3800	3888	3952	3993	4015	4018	4004	3975	3932	5
2		1139	1295	1452	1608	1762	1912	2057	2197	2331	2458	4
3		0188	0236	0289	0349	0415	0486	0562	0643	0729	0819	3
4		0017	0024	0032	0043	0055	0069	0086	0106	0128	0154	2
5		0001	0001	0002	0003	0004	0005	0007	0009	0012	0015	1
6		0000	0000	0000	0000	0000	0000	0000	0000	0000	0001	0
		89	88	87	86	85	84	83	82	81	80 P	R

R	P	21	22	23	24	25	26	27	28	29	30	
0		2431	2252	2084	1927	1780	1642	1513	1393	1281	1176	6
1		3877	3811	3735	3651	3560	3462	3358	3251	3139	3025	5
2		2577	2687	2789	2882	2966	3041	3105	3160	3206	3241	4
3		0913	1011	1111	1214	1318	1424	1531	1639	1746	1852	3
4		0182	0214	0249	0287	0330	0375	0425	0478	0535	0595	2
5		0019	0024	0030	0036	0044	0053	0063	0074	0087	0102	1
6		0001	0001	0001	0002	0002	0003	0004	0005	0006	0007	0
		79	78	77	76	75	74	73	72	71	70 P	R

R	P	31	32	33	34	35	36	37	38	39	40	
0		1079	0989	0905	0827	0754	0687	0625	0568	0515	0467	6
1		2909	2792	2673	2555	2437	2319	2203	2089	1976	1866	5
2		3267	3284	3292	3290	3280	3261	3235	3201	3159	3110	4
3		1957	2061	2162	2260	2355	2446	2533	2616	2693	2765	3
4		0660	0727	0799	0873	0951	1032	1116	1202	1291	1382	2
5		0119	0137	0157	0180	0205	0232	0262	0295	0330	0369	1
6		0009	0011	0013	0015	0018	0022	0026	0030	0035	0041	0
		69	68	67	66	65	64	63	62	61	60	P R

R	P	41	42	43	44	45	46	47	48	49	50	
0		0422	0381	0343	0308	0277	0248	0222	0198	0176	0156	6
1		1759	1654	1552	1454	1359	1267	1179	1095	1014	0937	5
2		3055	2994	2928	2856	2780	2699	2615	2527	2436	2344	4
3		2831	2891	2945	2992	3032	3065	3091	3110	3121	3125	3
4		1475	1570	1666	1763	1861	1958	2056	2153	2249	2344	2
5		0410	0455	0503	0554	0609	0667	0729	0795	0864	0937	1
6		0048	0055	0063	0073	0083	0095	0108	0122	0138	0156	0
		59	58	57	56	55	54	53	52	51	50	P R

$$N = 7$$

R	P	01	02	03	04	05	06	07	08	09	10	
0		9321	8681	8080	7514	6983	6485	6017	5578	5168	4783	7
1		0659	1240	1749	2192	2573	2897	3170	3396	3578	3720	6
2		0020	0076	0162	0274	0406	0555	0716	0886	1061	1240	5
3		0000	0003	0008	0019	0036	0059	0090	0128	0175	0230	4
4		0000	0000	0000	0001	0002	0004	0007	0011	0017	0026	3
5		0000	0000	0000	0000	0000	0000	0000	0001	0001	0002	2
		99	98	97	96	95	94	93	92	91	90	P R

R	P	11	12	13	14	15	16	17	18	19	20	
0		4423	4087	3773	3479	3206	2951	2714	2493	2288	2097	7
1		3827	3901	3946	3965	3960	3935	3891	3830	3756	3670	6
2		1419	1596	1769	1936	2097	2248	2391	2523	2643	2753	5
3		0292	0363	0441	0525	0617	0714	0816	0923	1033	1147	4
4		0036	0049	0066	0086	0109	0136	0167	0203	0242	0287	3
5		0003	0004	0006	0008	0012	0016	0021	0027	0034	0043	2
6		0000	0000	0000	0000	0001	0001	0001	0002	0003	0004	1
		89	88	87	86	85	84	83	82	81	80	P R

R	P	21	22	23	24	25	26	27	28	29	30	
0		1920	1757	1605	1465	1335	1215	1105	1003	0910	0824	7
1		3573	3468	3356	3237	3115	2989	2860	2731	2600	2471	6
2		2850	2935	3007	3067	3115	3150	3174	3186	3186	3177	5
3		1263	1379	1497	1614	1730	1845	1956	2065	2169	2269	4
4		0336	0389	0447	0510	0577	0648	0724	0803	0886	0972	3
5		0054	0066	0080	0097	0115	0137	0161	0187	0217	0250	2
6		0005	0006	0008	0010	0013	0016	0020	0024	0030	0036	1
7		0000	0000	0000	0000	0001	0001	0001	0001	0002	0002	0
		79	78	77	76	75	74	73	72	71	70	P R

R	P	31	32	33	34	35	36	37	38	39	40	
0		0745	0672	0606	0546	0490	0440	0394	0352	0314	0280	7
1		2342	2215	2090	1967	1848	1732	1619	1511	1407	1306	6
2		3156	3127	3088	3040	2985	2922	2853	2778	2698	2613	5
3		2363	2452	2535	2610	2679	2740	2793	2838	2875	2903	4
4		1062	1154	1248	1345	1442	1541	1640	1739	1838	1935	3
5		0286	0326	0369	0416	0466	0520	0578	0640	0705	0774	2
6		0043	0051	0061	0071	0084	0098	0113	0131	0150	0172	1
7		0003	0003	0004	0005	0006	0008	0009	0011	0014	0016	0
		69	68	67	66	65	64	63	62	61	60	P R

R	P	41	42	43	44	45	46	47	48	49	50	
0		0249	0221	0195	0173	0152	0134	0117	0103	0090	0078	7
1		1211	1119	1032	0950	0872	0798	0729	0664	0604	0547	6
2		2524	2431	2336	2239	2140	2040	1940	1840	1740	1641	5
3		2923	2934	2937	2932	2918	2897	2867	2830	2786	2734	4
4		2031	2125	2216	2304	2388	2468	2543	2612	2676	2734	3
5		0847	0923	1003	1086	1172	1261	1353	1447	1543	1641	2
6		0196	0223	0252	0284	0320	0358	0400	0445	0494	0547	1
7		0019	0023	0027	0032	0037	0044	0051	0059	0068	0078	0
		59	58	57	56	55	54	53	52	51	50	P R

N = 8

R	P	01	02	03	04	05	06	07	08	09	10	
0		9227	8508	7837	7214	6634	6096	5596	5132	4703	4305	8
1		0746	1389	1939	2405	2793	3113	3370	3570	3721	3826	7
2		0026	0099	0210	0351	0515	0695	0888	1087	1288	1488	6
3		0001	0004	0013	0029	0054	0089	0134	0189	0255	0331	5
4		0000	0000	0001	0002	0004	0007	0013	0021	0031	0046	4
5		0000	0000	0000	0000	0000	0000	0001	0001	0002	0004	3
		99	98	97	96	95	94	93	92	91	90	P R

R	P	11	12	13	14	15	16	17	18	19	20	
0		3937	3596	3282	2992	2725	2479	2252	2044	1853	1678	8
1		3892	3923	3923	3897	3847	3777	3691	3590	3477	3355	7
2		1684	1872	2052	2220	2376	2518	2646	2758	2855	2936	6
3		0416	0511	0613	0723	0839	0959	1084	1211	1339	1468	5
4		0064	0087	0115	0147	0185	0228	0277	0332	0393	0459	4
5		0006	0009	0014	0019	0026	0035	0045	0058	0074	0092	3
6		0000	0001	0001	0002	0002	0003	0005	0006	0009	0011	2
7		0000	0000	0000	0000	0000	0000	0000	0000	0001	0001	1
		89	88	87	86	85	84	83	82	81	80	P R

R	P	21	22	23	24	25	26	27	28	29	30	
0		1517	1370	1236	1113	1001	0899	0806	0722	0646	0576	8
1		3226	3092	2953	2812	2670	2527	2386	2247	2110	1977	7
2		3002	3052	3087	3108	3115	3108	3089	3058	3017	2965	6
3		1596	1722	1844	1963	2076	2184	2285	2379	2464	2541	5
4		0530	0607	0689	0775	0865	0959	1056	1156	1258	1361	4
5		0113	0137	0165	0196	0231	0270	0313	0360	0411	0467	3
6		0015	0019	0025	0031	0038	0047	0058	0070	0084	0100	2
7		0001	0002	0002	0003	0004	0005	0006	0008	0010	0012	1
8		0000	0000	0000	0000	0000	0000	0000	0000	0001	0001	0
		79	78	77	76	75	74	73	72	71	70	P R

R	P	31	32	33	34	35	36	37	38	39	40	
0		0514	0457	0406	0360	0319	0281	0248	0218	0192	0168	8
1		1847	1721	1600	1484	1373	1267	1166	1071	0981	0896	7
2		2904	2835	2758	2675	2587	2494	2397	2297	2194	2090	6
3		2609	2668	2717	2756	2786	2805	2815	2815	2806	2787	5
4		1465	1569	1673	1775	1875	1973	2067	2157	2242	2322	4
5		0527	0591	0659	0732	0808	0888	0971	1058	1147	1239	3
6		0118	0139	0162	0188	0217	0250	0285	0324	0367	0413	2
7		0015	0019	0023	0028	0033	0040	0048	0057	0067	0079	1
8		0001	0001	0001	0002	0002	0003	0004	0004	0005	0007	0
		69	68	67	66	65	64	63	62	61	60	P R

R	P	41	42	43	44	45	46	47	48	49	50	
0		0147	0128	0111	0097	0084	0072	0062	0053	0046	0039	8
1		0816	0742	0672	0608	0548	0493	0442	0395	0352	0312	7
2		1985	1880	1776	1672	1569	1469	1371	1275	1183	1094	6
3		2759	2723	2679	2627	2568	2503	2431	2355	2273	2187	5
4		2397	2465	2526	2580	2627	2665	2695	2717	2730	2734	4
5		1332	1428	1525	1622	1719	1816	1912	2006	2098	2187	3
6		0463	0517	0575	0637	0703	0774	0848	0926	1008	1094	2
7		0092	0107	0124	0143	0164	0188	0215	0244	0277	0312	1
8		0008	0010	0012	0014	0017	0020	0024	0028	0033	0039	0
		59	58	57	56	55	54	53	52	51	50	P R

N = 9

R P	01	02	03	04	05	06	07	08	09	10	
0	9135	8337	7602	6925	6302	5730	5204	4722	4279	3874	9
1	0830	1531	2116	2597	2985	3292	3525	3695	3809	3874	8
2	0034	0125	0262	0433	0629	0840	1061	1285	1507	1722	7
3	0001	0006	0019	0042	0077	0125	0186	0261	0348	0446	6
4	0000	0000	0001	0003	0006	0012	0021	0034	0052	0074	5
5	0000	0000	0000	0000	0000	0001	0002	0003	0005	0008	4
6	0000	0000	0000	0000	0000	0000	0000	0000	0000	0001	3
	99	98	97	96	95	94	93	92	91	90	P R

R P	11	12	13	14	15	16	17	18	19	20	
0	3504	3165	2855	2573	2316	2082	1869	1676	1501	1342	9
1	3897	3884	3840	3770	3679	3569	3446	3312	3169	3020	8
2	1927	2119	2295	2455	2597	2720	2823	2908	2973	3020	7
3	0556	0674	0800	0933	1069	1209	1349	1489	1627	1762	6
4	0103	0138	0179	0228	0283	0345	0415	0490	0573	0661	5
5	0013	0019	0027	0037	0050	0066	0085	0108	0134	0165	4
6	0001	0002	0003	0004	0006	0008	0012	0016	0021	0028	3
7	0000	0000	0000	0000	0000	0001	0001	0001	0002	0003	2
	89	88	87	86	85	84	83	82	81	80	P R

R P	21	22	23	24	25	26	27	28	29	30	
0	1199	1069	0952	0846	0751	0665	0589	0520	0458	0404	9
1	2867	2713	2558	2404	2253	2104	1960	1820	1685	1556	8
2	3049	3061	3056	3037	3003	2957	2899	2831	2754	2668	7
3	1891	2014	2130	2238	2336	2424	2502	2569	2624	2668	6
4	0754	0852	0954	1060	1168	1278	1388	1499	1608	1715	5
5	0200	0240	0285	0335	0389	0449	0513	0583	0657	0735	4
6	0036	0045	0057	0070	0087	0105	0127	0151	0179	0210	3
7	0004	0005	0007	0010	0012	0016	0020	0025	0031	0039	2
8	0000	0000	0001	0001	0001	0001	0002	0002	0003	0004	1
	79	78	77	76	75	74	73	72	71	70	P R

R P	31	32	33	34	35	36	37	38	39	40	
0	0355	0311	0272	0238	0207	0180	0156	0135	0117	0101	9
1	1433	1317	1206	1102	1004	0912	0826	0747	0673	0605	8
2	2576	2478	2376	2270	2162	2052	1941	1831	1721	1612	7
3	2701	2721	2731	2729	2716	2693	2660	2618	2567	2508	6
4	1820	1921	2017	2109	2194	2272	2344	2407	2462	2508	5
5	0818	0904	0994	1086	1181	1278	1376	1475	1574	1672	4
6	0245	0284	0326	0373	0424	0479	0539	0603	0671	0743	3
7	0047	0057	0069	0082	0098	0116	0136	0158	0184	0212	2
8	0005	0007	0008	0011	0013	0016	0020	0024	0029	0035	1
9	0000	0000	0000	0001	0001	0001	0001	0002	0002	0003	0
	69	68	67	66	65	64	63	62	61	60	P R

R P	41	42	43	44	45	46	47	48	49	50	
0	0087	0074	0064	0054	0046	0039	0033	0028	0023	0020	9
1	0542	0484	0431	0383	0339	0299	0263	0231	0202	0176	8
2	1506	1402	1301	1204	1110	1020	0934	0853	0776	0703	7
3	2442	2369	2291	2207	2119	2027	1933	1837	1739	1641	6
4	2545	2573	2592	2601	2600	2590	2571	2543	2506	2461	5
5	1769	1863	1955	2044	2128	2207	2280	2347	2408	2461	4
6	0819	0900	0983	1070	1160	1253	1348	1445	1542	1641	3
7	0244	0279	0318	0360	0407	0458	0512	0571	0635	0703	2
8	0042	0051	0060	0071	0083	0097	0114	0132	0153	0176	1
9	0003	0004	0005	0006	0008	0009	0011	0014	0016	0020	0
	59	58	57	56	55	54	53	52	51	50	P R

N = 10

R	P	01	02	03	04	05	06	07	08	09	10	
0		9044	8171	7374	6648	5987	5386	4840	4344	3894	3487	10
1		0914	1667	2281	2770	3151	3438	3643	3777	3851	3874	9
2		0042	0153	0317	0519	0746	0988	1234	1478	1714	1937	8
3		0001	0008	0026	0058	0105	0168	0248	0343	0452	0574	7
4		0000	0000	0001	0004	0010	0019	0033	0052	0078	0112	6
5		0000	0000	0000	0000	0001	0001	0003	0005	0009	0015	5
6		0000	0000	0000	0000	0000	0000	0000	0000	0001	0001	4
		99	98	97	96	95	94	93	92	91	90	P R

R	P	11	12	13	14	15	16	17	18	19	20	
0		3118	2785	2484	2213	1969	1749	1552	1374	1216	1074	10
1		3854	3798	3712	3603	3474	3331	3178	3017	2852	2684	9
2		2143	2330	2496	2639	2759	2856	2929	2980	3010	3020	8
3		0706	0847	0995	1146	1298	1450	1600	1745	1883	2013	7
4		0153	0202	0260	0326	0401	0483	0573	0670	0773	0881	6
5		0023	0033	0047	0064	0085	0111	0141	0177	0218	0264	5
6		0002	0004	0006	0009	0012	0018	0024	0032	0043	0055	4
7		0000	0000	0000	0001	0001	0002	0003	0004	0006	0008	3
8		0000	0000	0000	0000	0000	0000	0000	0000	0001	0001	2
		89	88	87	86	85	84	83	82	81	80	P R

R	P	21	22	23	24	25	26	27	28	29	30	
0		0947	0834	0733	0643	0563	0492	0430	0374	0326	0282	10
1		2517	2351	2188	2030	1877	1730	1590	1456	1330	1211	9
2		3011	2984	2942	2885	2816	2735	2646	2548	2444	2335	8
3		2134	2244	2343	2429	2503	2563	2609	2642	2662	2668	7
4		0993	1108	1225	1343	1460	1576	1689	1798	1903	2001	6
5		0317	0375	0439	0509	0584	0664	0750	0839	0933	1029	5
6		0070	0088	0109	0134	0162	0195	0231	0272	0317	0368	4
7		0011	0014	0019	0024	0031	0039	0049	0060	0074	0090	3
8		0001	0002	0002	0003	0004	0005	0007	0009	0011	0014	2
9		0000	0000	0000	0000	0000	0000	0001	0001	0001	0001	1
		79	78	77	76	75	74	73	72	71	70	P R

R	P	31	32	33	34	35	36	37	38	39	40	
0		0245	0211	0182	0157	0135	0115	0098	0084	0071	0060	10
1		1099	0995	0898	0808	0725	0649	0578	0514	0456	0403	9
2		2222	2107	1990	1873	1757	1642	1529	1419	1312	1209	8
3		2662	2644	2614	2573	2522	2462	2394	2319	2237	2150	7
4		2093	2177	2253	2320	2377	2424	2461	2487	2503	2508	6
5		1128	1229	1332	1434	1536	1636	1734	1829	1920	2007	5
6		0422	0482	0547	0616	0689	0767	0849	0934	1023	1115	4
7		0108	0130	0154	0181	0212	0247	0285	0327	0374	0425	3
8		0018	0023	0028	0035	0043	0052	0063	0075	0090	0106	2
9		0002	0002	0003	0004	0005	0006	0008	0010	0013	0016	1
10		0000	0000	0000	0000	0000	0000	0000	0001	0001	0001	0
		69	68	67	66	65	64	63	62	61	60	P R

R	P	41	42	43	44	45	46	47	48	49	50	
0		0051	0043	0036	0030	0025	0021	0017	0014	0012	0010	10
1		0355	0312	0273	0238	0207	0180	0155	0133	0114	0098	9
2		1111	1017	0927	0843	0763	0688	0619	0554	0494	0439	8
3		2058	1963	1865	1765	1665	1564	1464	1364	1267	1172	7
4		2503	2488	2462	2427	2384	2331	2271	2204	2130	2051	6
5		2087	2162	2229	2289	2340	2383	2417	2441	2456	2461	5
6		1209	1304	1401	1499	1596	1692	1786	1878	1966	2051	4
7		0480	0540	0604	0673	0746	0824	0905	0991	1080	1172	3
8		0125	0147	0171	0198	0229	0263	0301	0343	0389	0439	2
9		0019	0024	0029	0035	0042	0050	0059	0070	0083	0098	1
10		0001	0002	0002	0003	0003	0004	0005	0006	0008	0010	0
		59	58	57	56	55	54	53	52	51	50	P R

N = 11

R	P	01	02	03	04	05	06	07	08	09	10	
0		8953	8007	7153	6382	5688	5063	4501	3996	3544	3138	11
1		0995	1798	2433	2925	3293	3555	3727	3823	3855	3835	10
2		0050	0183	0376	0609	0867	1135	1403	1662	1906	2131	9
3		0002	0011	0035	0076	0137	0217	0317	0434	0566	0710	8
4		0000	0000	0002	0006	0014	0028	0048	0075	0112	0158	7
5		0000	0000	0000	0000	0001	0002	0005	0009	0015	0025	6
6		0000	0000	0000	0000	0000	0000	0000	0001	0002	0003	5
		99	98	97	96	95	94	93	92	91	90	P R

R	P	11	12	13	14	15	16	17	18	19	20	
0		2775	2451	2161	1903	1673	1469	1288	1127	0985	0859	11
1		3773	3676	3552	3408	3248	3078	2901	2721	2541	2362	10
2		2332	2507	2654	2774	2866	2932	2971	2987	2980	2953	9
3		0865	1025	1190	1355	1517	1675	1826	1967	2097	2215	8
4		0214	0280	0356	0441	0536	0638	0748	0864	0984	1107	7
5		0037	0053	0074	0101	0132	0170	0214	0265	0323	0388	6
6		0005	0007	0011	0016	0023	0032	0044	0058	0076	0097	5
7		0000	0001	0001	0002	0003	0004	0006	0009	0013	0017	4
8		0000	0000	0000	0000	0000	0000	0001	0001	0001	0002	3
		89	88	87	86	85	84	83	82	81	80	P R

R	P	21	22	23	24	25	26	27	28	29	30	
0		0748	0650	0564	0489	0422	0364	0314	0270	0231	0198	11
1		2187	2017	1854	1697	1549	1408	1276	1153	1038	0932	10
2		2907	2845	2768	2680	2581	2474	2360	2242	2121	1998	9
3		2318	2407	2481	2539	2581	2608	2619	2616	2599	2568	8
4		1232	1358	1482	1603	1721	1832	1937	2035	2123	2201	7
5		0459	0536	0620	0709	0803	0901	1003	1108	1214	1321	6
6		0122	0151	0185	0224	0268	0317	0371	0431	0496	0566	5
7		0023	0030	0039	0050	0064	0079	0098	0120	0145	0173	4
8		0003	0004	0006	0008	0011	0014	0018	0023	0030	0037	3
9		0000	0000	0001	0001	0001	0002	0002	0003	0004	0005	2
		79	78	77	76	75	74	73	72	71	70	P R

R	P	31	32	33	34	35	36	37	38	39	40	
0		0169	0144	0122	0104	0088	0074	0062	0052	0044	0036	11
1		0834	0744	0662	0587	0518	0457	0401	0351	0306	0266	10
2		1874	1751	1630	1511	1395	1284	1177	1075	0978	0887	9
3		2526	2472	2408	2335	2254	2167	2074	1977	1876	1774	8
4		2269	2326	2372	2406	2428	2438	2436	2423	2399	2365	7
5		1427	1533	1636	1735	1830	1920	2003	2079	2148	2207	6
6		0641	0721	0806	0894	0985	1080	1176	1274	1373	1471	5
7		0206	0242	0283	0329	0379	0434	0494	0558	0627	0701	4
8		0046	0057	0070	0085	0102	0122	0145	0171	0200	0234	3
9		0007	0009	0011	0015	0018	0023	0028	0035	0043	0052	2
10		0001	0001	0001	0001	0002	0003	0003	0004	0005	0007	1
		69	68	67	66	65	64	63	62	61	60	P R

R	P	41	42	43	44	45	46	47	48	49	50	
0		0030	0025	0021	0017	0014	0011	0009	0008	0006	0005	11
1		0231	0199	0171	0147	0125	0107	0090	0076	0064	0054	10
2		0801	0721	0646	0577	0513	0454	0401	0352	0308	0269	9
3		1670	1566	1462	1359	1259	1161	1067	0976	0888	0806	8
4		2321	2267	2206	2136	2060	1978	1892	1801	1707	1611	7
5		2258	2299	2329	2350	2360	2359	2348	2327	2296	2256	6
6		1569	1664	1757	1846	1931	2010	2083	2148	2206	2256	5
7		0779	0861	0947	1036	1128	1223	1319	1416	1514	1611	4
8		0271	0312	0357	0407	0462	0521	0585	0654	0727	0806	3
9		0063	0075	0090	0107	0126	0148	0173	0201	0233	0269	2
10		0009	0011	0014	0017	0021	0025	0031	0037	0045	0054	1
11		0001	0001	0001	0001	0002	0002	0002	0003	0004	0005	0
		59	58	57	56	55	54	53	52	51	50	P R

N = 12

R	P	01	02	03	04	05	06	07	08	09	10	
0		8864	7847	6938	6127	5404	4759	4186	3677	3225	2824	12
1		1074	1922	2575	3064	3413	3645	3781	3837	3827	3766	11
2		0060	0216	0438	0702	0988	1280	1565	1835	2082	2301	10
3		0002	0015	0045	0098	0173	0272	0393	0532	0686	0852	9
4		0000	0001	0003	0009	0021	0039	0067	0104	0153	0213	8
5		0000	0000	0000	0001	0002	0004	0008	0014	0024	0038	7
6		0000	0000	0000	0000	0000	0000	0001	0001	0003	0005	6
		99	98	97	96	95	94	93	92	91	90	P R

R	P	11	12	13	14	15	16	17	18	19	20	
0		2470	2157	1880	1637	1422	1234	1069	0924	0798	0687	12
1		3663	3529	3372	3197	3012	2821	2627	2434	2245	2062	11
2		2490	2647	2771	2863	2924	2955	2960	2939	2897	2835	10
3		1026	1203	1380	1553	1720	1876	2021	2151	2265	2362	9
4		0285	0369	0464	0569	0683	0804	0931	1062	1195	1329	8
5		0056	0081	0111	0148	0193	0245	0305	0373	0449	0532	7
6		0008	0013	0019	0028	0040	0054	0073	0096	0123	0155	6
7		0001	0001	0002	0004	0006	0009	0013	0018	0025	0033	5
8		0000	0000	0000	0000	0001	0001	0002	0002	0004	0005	4
9		0000	0000	0000	0000	0000	0000	0000	0000	0000	0001	3
		89	88	87	86	85	84	83	82	81	80	P R

R	P	21	22	23	24	25	26	27	28	29	30	
0		0591	0507	0434	0371	0317	0270	0229	0194	0164	0138	12
1		1885	1717	1557	1407	1267	1137	1016	0906	0804	0712	11
2		2756	2663	2558	2444	2323	2197	2068	1937	1807	1678	10
3		2442	2503	2547	2573	2581	2573	2549	2511	2460	2397	9
4		1460	1589	1712	1828	1936	2034	2122	2197	2261	2311	8
5		0621	0717	0818	0924	1032	1143	1255	1367	1477	1585	7
6		0193	0236	0285	0340	0401	0469	0542	0620	0704	0792	6
7		0044	0057	0073	0092	0115	0141	0172	0207	0246	0291	5
8		0007	0010	0014	0018	0024	0031	0040	0050	0063	0078	4
9		0001	0001	0002	0003	0004	0005	0007	0009	0011	0015	3
10		0000	0000	0000	0000	0000	0001	0001	0001	0001	0002	2
		79	78	77	76	75	74	73	72	71	70	P R

R	P	31	32	33	34	35	36	37	38	39	40	
0		0116	0098	0082	0068	0057	0047	0039	0032	0027	0022	12
1		0628	0552	0484	0422	0368	0319	0276	0237	0204	0174	11
2		1552	1429	1310	1197	1088	0986	0890	0800	0716	0639	10
3		2324	2241	2151	2055	1954	1849	1742	1634	1526	1419	9
4		2349	2373	2384	2382	2367	2340	2302	2254	2195	2128	8
5		1688	1787	1879	1963	2039	2106	2163	2210	2246	2270	7
6		0885	0981	1079	1180	1281	1382	1482	1580	1675	1766	6
7		0341	0396	0456	0521	0591	0666	0746	0830	0918	1009	5
8		0096	0116	0140	0168	0199	0234	0274	0318	0367	0420	4
9		0019	0024	0031	0038	0048	0059	0071	0087	0104	0125	3
10		0003	0003	0005	0006	0008	0010	0013	0016	0020	0025	2
11		0000	0000	0000	0001	0001	0001	0001	0002	0002	0003	1
		69	68	67	66	65	64	63	62	61	60	P R

R	P	41	42	43	44	45	46	47	48	49	50	
0		0018	0014	0012	0010	0008	0006	0005	0004	0003	0002	12
1		0148	0126	0106	0090	0075	0063	0052	0043	0036	0029	11
2		0567	0502	0442	0388	0339	0294	0255	0220	0189	0161	10
3		1314	1211	1111	1015	0923	0836	0754	0676	0604	0537	9
4		2054	1973	1886	1794	1700	1602	1504	1405	1306	1208	8
5		2284	2285	2276	2256	2225	2184	2134	2075	2008	1934	7
6		1851	1931	2003	2068	2124	2171	2208	2234	2250	2256	6
7		1103	1198	1295	1393	1489	1585	1678	1768	1853	1934	5
8		0479	0542	0611	0684	0762	0844	0930	1020	1113	1208	4
9		0148	0175	0205	0239	0277	0319	0367	0418	0475	0537	3
10		0031	0038	0046	0056	0068	0082	0098	0116	0137	0161	2
11		0004	0005	0006	0008	0010	0013	0016	0019	0024	0029	1
12		0000	0000	0000	0001	0001	0001	0001	0001	0002	0002	0
		59	58	57	56	55	54	53	52	51	50	P R

N = 13

R	P	01	02	03	04	05	06	07	08	09	10	
0		8775	7690	6730	5882	5133	4474	3893	3383	2935	2542	13
1		1152	2040	2706	3186	3512	3712	3809	3824	3773	3672	12
2		0070	0250	0502	0797	1109	1422	1720	1995	2239	2448	11
3		0003	0019	0057	0122	0214	0333	0475	0636	0812	0997	10
4		0000	0001	0004	0013	0028	0053	0089	0138	0201	0277	9
5		0000	0000	0000	0001	0003	0006	0012	0022	0036	0055	8
6		0000	0000	0000	0000	0000	0001	0001	0003	0005	0008	7
7		0000	0000	0000	0000	0000	0000	0000	0000	0000	0001	6
		99	98	97	96	95	94	93	92	91	90	P R

R	P	11	12	13	14	15	16	17	18	19	20	
0		2198	1898	1636	1408	1209	1037	0887	0758	0646	0550	13
1		3532	3364	3178	2979	2774	2567	2362	2163	1970	1787	12
2		2619	2753	2849	2910	2937	2934	2903	2848	2773	2680	11
3		1187	1376	1561	1737	1900	2049	2180	2293	2385	2457	10
4		0367	0469	0583	0707	0838	0976	1116	1258	1399	1535	9
5		0082	0115	0157	0207	0266	0335	0412	0497	0591	0691	8
6		0013	0021	0031	0045	0063	0085	0112	0145	0185	0230	7
7		0002	0003	0005	0007	0011	0016	0023	0032	0043	0058	6
8		0000	0000	0001	0001	0001	0002	0004	0005	0008	0011	5
9		0000	0000	0000	0000	0000	0000	0000	0001	0001	0001	4
		89	88	87	86	85	84	83	82	81	80	P R

R	P	21	22	23	24	25	26	27	28	29	30	
0		0467	0396	0334	0282	0238	0200	0167	0140	0117	0097	13
1		1613	1450	1299	1159	1029	0911	0804	0706	0619	0540	12
2		2573	2455	2328	2195	2059	1921	1784	1648	1516	1388	11
3		2508	2539	2550	2542	2517	2475	2419	2351	2271	2181	10
4		1667	1790	1904	2007	2097	2174	2237	2285	2319	2337	9
5		0797	0909	1024	1141	1258	1375	1489	1600	1705	1803	8
6		0283	0342	0408	0480	0559	0644	0734	0829	0928	1030	7
7		0075	0096	0122	0152	0186	0226	0272	0323	0379	0442	6
8		0015	0020	0027	0036	0047	0060	0075	0094	0116	0142	5
9		0002	0003	0005	0006	0009	0012	0015	0020	0026	0034	4
10		0000	0000	0001	0001	0001	0002	0002	0003	0004	0006	3
11		0000	0000	0000	0000	0000	0000	0000	0000	0000	0001	2
		79	78	77	76	75	74	73	72	71	70	P R

R	P	31	32	33	34	35	36	37	38	39	40	
0		0080	0066	0055	0045	0037	0030	0025	0020	0016	0013	13
1		0469	0407	0351	0302	0259	0221	0188	0159	0135	0113	12
2		1265	1148	1037	0933	0836	0746	0663	0586	0516	0453	11
3		2084	1981	1874	1763	1651	1538	1427	1317	1210	1107	10
4		2341	2331	2307	2270	2222	2163	2095	2018	1934	1845	9
5		1893	1974	2045	2105	2154	2190	2215	2227	2226	2214	8
6		1134	1239	1343	1446	1546	1643	1734	1820	1898	1968	7
7		0509	0583	0662	0745	0833	0924	1019	1115	1213	1312	6
8		0172	0206	0244	0288	0336	0390	0449	0513	0582	0656	5
9		0043	0054	0067	0082	0101	0122	0146	0175	0207	0243	4
10		0008	0010	0013	0017	0022	0027	0034	0043	0053	0065	3
11		0001	0001	0002	0002	0003	0004	0006	0007	0009	0012	2
12		0000	0000	0000	0000	0000	0000	0001	0001	0001	0001	1
		69	68	67	66	65	64	63	62	61	60	P R

R	P	41	42	43	44	45	46	47	48	49	50	
0		0010	0008	0007	0005	0004	0003	0003	0002	0002	0001	13
1		0095	0079	0066	0054	0045	0037	0030	0024	0020	0016	12
2		0395	0344	0298	0256	0220	0188	0160	0135	0114	0095	11
3		1007	0913	0823	0739	0660	0587	0519	0457	0401	0349	10
4		1750	1653	1553	1451	1350	1250	1151	1055	0962	0873	9
5		2189	2154	2108	2053	1989	1917	1838	1753	1664	1571	8
6		2029	2080	2121	2151	2169	2177	2173	2158	2131	2095	7
7		1410	1506	1600	1690	1775	1854	1927	1992	2048	2095	6
8		0735	0818	0905	0996	1089	1185	1282	1379	1476	1571	5
9		0284	0329	0379	0435	0495	0561	0631	0707	0788	0873	4
10		0079	0095	0114	0137	0162	0191	0224	0261	0303	0349	3
11		0015	0019	0024	0029	0036	0044	0054	0066	0079	0095	2
12		0002	0002	0003	0004	0005	0006	0008	0010	0013	0016	1
13		0000	0000	0000	0000	0000	0000	0001	0001	0001	0001	0
		59	58	57	56	55	54	53	52	51	50	P R

N = 14

R	P	01	02	03	04	05	06	07	08	09	10	
0		8687	7536	6528	5647	4877	4205	3620	3112	2670	2288	14
1		1229	2153	2827	3294	3593	3758	3815	3788	3698	3559	13
2		0081	0286	0568	0892	1229	1559	1867	2141	2377	2570	12
3		0003	0023	0070	0149	0259	0398	0562	0745	0940	1142	11
4		0000	0001	0006	0017	0037	0070	0116	0178	0256	0349	10
5		0000	0000	0000	0001	0004	0009	0018	0031	0051	0078	9
6		0000	0000	0000	0000	0000	0001	0002	0004	0008	0013	8
7		0000	0000	0000	0000	0000	0000	0000	0000	0001	0002	7
		99	98	97	96	95	94	93	92	91	90	P R

R	P	11	12	13	14	15	16	17	18	19	20	
0		1956	1670	1423	1211	1028	0871	0736	0621	0523	0440	14
1		3385	3188	2977	2759	2539	2322	2112	1910	1719	1539	13
2		2720	2826	2892	2919	2912	2875	2811	2725	2620	2501	12
3		1345	1542	1728	1901	2056	2190	2303	2393	2459	2501	11
4		0457	0578	0710	0851	0998	1147	1297	1444	1586	1720	10
5		0113	0158	0212	0277	0352	0437	0531	0634	0744	0860	9
6		0021	0032	0048	0068	0093	0125	0163	0209	0262	0322	8
7		0003	0005	0008	0013	0019	0027	0038	0052	0070	0092	7
8		0000	0001	0001	0002	0003	0005	0007	0010	0014	0020	6
9		0000	0000	0000	0000	0000	0001	0001	0001	0002	0003	5
		89	88	87	86	85	84	83	82	81	80	P R

R	P	21	22	23	24	25	26	27	28	29	30	
0		0369	0309	0258	0214	0178	0148	0122	0101	0083	0068	14
1		1372	1218	1077	0948	0832	0726	0632	0548	0473	0407	13
2		2371	2234	2091	1946	1802	1659	1519	1385	1256	1134	12
3		2521	2520	2499	2459	2402	2331	2248	2154	2052	1943	11
4		1843	1955	2052	2135	2202	2252	2286	2304	2305	2290	10
5		0980	1103	1226	1348	1468	1583	1691	1792	1883	1963	9
6		0391	0466	0549	0639	0734	0834	0938	1045	1153	1262	8
7		0119	0150	0188	0231	0280	0335	0397	0464	0538	0618	7
8		0028	0037	0049	0064	0082	0103	0128	0158	0192	0232	6
9		0005	0007	0010	0013	0018	0024	0032	0041	0052	0066	5
10		0001	0001	0001	0002	0003	0004	0006	0008	0011	0014	4
11		0000	0000	0000	0000	0000	0001	0001	0001	0002	0002	3
		79	78	77	76	75	74	73	72	71	70	P R

R	P	31	32	33	34	35	36	37	38	39	40	
0		0055	0045	0037	0030	0024	0019	0016	0012	0010	0008	14
1		0349	0298	0253	0215	0181	0152	0128	0106	0088	0073	13
2		1018	0911	0811	0719	0634	0557	0487	0424	0367	0317	12
3		1830	1715	1598	1481	1366	1253	1144	1039	0940	0845	11
4		2261	2219	2164	2098	2022	1938	1848	1752	1652	1549	10
5		2032	2088	2132	2161	2178	2181	2170	2147	2112	2066	9
6		1369	1474	1575	1670	1759	1840	1912	1974	2026	2066	8
7		0703	0793	0886	0983	1082	1183	1283	1383	1480	1574	7
8		0276	0326	0382	0443	0510	0582	0659	0742	0828	0918	6
9		0083	0102	0125	0152	0183	0218	0258	0303	0353	0408	5
10		0019	0024	0031	0039	0049	0061	0076	0093	0113	0136	4
11		0003	0004	0006	0007	0010	0013	0016	0021	0026	0033	3
12		0000	0000	0001	0001	0001	0002	0002	0003	0004	0005	2
13		0000	0000	0000	0000	0000	0000	0000	0000	0000	0001	1
		69	68	67	66	65	64	63	62	61	60	P R

R	P	41	42	43	44	45	46	47	48	49	50	
0		0006	0005	0004	0003	0002	0002	0001	0001	0001	0001	14
1		0060	0049	0040	0033	0027	0021	0017	0014	0011	0009	13
2		0272	0233	0198	0168	0141	0118	0099	0082	0068	0056	12
3		0757	0674	0597	0527	0462	0403	0350	0303	0260	0222	11
4		1446	1342	1239	1138	1040	0945	0854	0768	0687	0611	10
5		2009	1943	1869	1788	1701	1610	1515	1418	1320	1222	9
6		2094	2111	2115	2108	2088	2057	2015	1963	1902	1833	8
7		1663	1747	1824	1892	1952	2003	2043	2071	2089	2095	7
8		1011	1107	1204	1301	1398	1493	1585	1673	1756	1833	6
9		0469	0534	0605	0682	0762	0848	0937	1030	1125	1222	5
10		0163	0193	0228	0268	0312	0361	0415	0475	0540	0611	4
11		0041	0051	0063	0076	0093	0112	0134	0160	0189	0222	3
12		0007	0009	0012	0015	0019	0024	0030	0037	0045	0056	2
13		0001	0001	0001	0002	0002	0003	0004	0005	0007	0009	1
14		0000	0000	0000	0000	0000	0000	0000	0000	0000	0001	0
		59	58	57	56	55	54	53	52	51	50	P R

N = 15

R	P	01	02	03	04	05	06	07	08	09	10	
0		8601	7386	6333	5421	4633	3953	3367	2863	2430	2059	15
1		1303	2261	2938	3388	3658	3785	3801	3734	3605	3432	14
2		0092	0323	0636	0988	1348	1691	2003	2273	2496	2669	13
3		0004	0029	0085	0178	0307	0468	0653	0857	1070	1285	12
4		0000	0002	0008	0022	0049	0090	0148	0223	0317	0428	11
5		0000	0000	0001	0002	0006	0013	0024	0043	0069	0105	10
6		0000	0000	0000	0000	0000	0001	0003	0006	0011	0019	9
7		0000	0000	0000	0000	0000	0000	0000	0001	0001	0003	8
		99	98	97	96	95	94	93	92	91	90	P R

R	P	11	12	13	14	15	16	17	18	19	20	
0		1741	1470	1238	1041	0874	0731	0611	0510	0424	0352	15
1		3228	3006	2775	2542	2312	2090	1878	1678	1492	1319	14
2		2793	2870	2903	2897	2856	2787	2692	2578	2449	2309	13
3		1496	1696	1880	2044	2184	2300	2389	2452	2489	2501	12
4		0555	0694	0843	0998	1156	1314	1468	1615	1752	1876	11
5		0151	0208	0277	0357	0449	0551	0662	0780	0904	1032	10
6		0031	0047	0069	0097	0132	0175	0226	0285	0353	0430	9
7		0005	0008	0013	0020	0030	0043	0059	0081	0107	0138	8
8		0001	0001	0002	0003	0005	0008	0012	0018	0025	0035	7
9		0000	0000	0000	0000	0001	0001	0002	0003	0005	0007	6
10		0000	0000	0000	0000	0000	0000	0000	0000	0001	0001	5
		89	88	87	86	85	84	83	82	81	80	P R

R	P	21	22	23	24	25	26	27	28	29	30	
0		0291	0241	0198	0163	0134	0109	0089	0072	0059	0047	15
1		1162	1018	0889	0772	0668	0576	0494	0423	0360	0305	14
2		2162	2010	1858	1707	1559	1416	1280	1150	1029	0916	13
3		2490	2457	2405	2336	2252	2156	2051	1939	1821	1700	12
4		1986	2079	2155	2213	2252	2273	2276	2262	2231	2186	11
5		1161	1290	1416	1537	1651	1757	1852	1935	2005	2061	10
6		0514	0606	0705	0809	0917	1029	1142	1254	1365	1472	9
7		0176	0220	0271	0329	0393	0465	0543	0627	0717	0811	8
8		0047	0062	0081	0104	0131	0163	0201	0244	0293	0348	7
9		0010	0014	0019	0025	0034	0045	0058	0074	0093	0116	6
10		0002	0002	0003	0005	0007	0009	0013	0017	0023	0030	5
11		0000	0000	0000	0001	0001	0002	0002	0003	0004	0006	4
12		0000	0000	0000	0000	0000	0000	0000	0000	0001	0001	3
		79	78	77	76	75	74	73	72	71	70	P R

R	P	31	32	33	34	35	36	37	38	39	40	
0		0038	0031	0025	0020	0016	0012	0010	0008	0006	0005	15
1		0258	0217	0182	0152	0126	0104	0086	0071	0058	0047	14
2		0811	0715	0627	0547	0476	0411	0354	0303	0259	0219	13
3		1579	1457	1338	1222	1110	1002	0901	0805	0716	0634	12
4		2128	2057	1977	1888	1792	1692	1587	1481	1374	1268	11
5		2103	2130	2142	2140	2123	2093	2051	1997	1933	1859	10
6		1575	1671	1759	1837	1906	1963	2008	2040	2059	2066	9
7		0910	1011	1114	1217	1319	1419	1516	1608	1693	1771	8
8		0409	0476	0549	0627	0710	0798	0890	0985	1082	1181	7
9		0143	0174	0210	0251	0298	0349	0407	0470	0538	0612	6
10		0038	0049	0062	0078	0096	0118	0143	0173	0206	0245	5
11		0008	0011	0014	0018	0024	0030	0038	0048	0060	0074	4
12		0001	0002	0002	0003	0004	0006	0007	0010	0013	0016	3
13		0000	0000	0000	0000	0001	0001	0001	0001	0002	0003	2
		69	68	67	66	65	64	63	62	61	60	P R

R	P	41	42	43	44	45	46	47	48	49	50	
0		0004	0003	0002	0002	0001	0001	0001	0001	0000	0000	15
1		0038	0031	0025	0020	0016	0012	0010	0008	0006	0005	14
2		0185	0156	0130	0108	0090	0074	0060	0049	0040	0032	13
3		0558	0489	0426	0369	0318	0272	0232	0197	0166	0139	12
4		1163	1061	0963	0869	0780	0696	0617	0545	0478	0417	11
5		1778	1691	1598	1502	1404	1304	1204	1106	1010	0916	10
6		2060	2041	2010	1967	1914	1851	1780	1702	1617	1527	9
7		1840	1900	1949	1987	2013	2028	2030	2020	1997	1964	8
8		1279	1376	1470	1561	1647	1727	1800	1864	1919	1964	7
9		0691	0775	0863	0954	1048	1144	1241	1338	1434	1527	6
10		0288	0337	0390	0450	0515	0585	0661	0741	0827	0916	5
11		0091	0111	0134	0161	0191	0226	0266	0311	0361	0417	4
12		0021	0027	0034	0042	0052	0064	0079	0096	0116	0139	3
13		0003	0004	0006	0008	0010	0013	0016	0020	0026	0032	2
14		0000	0000	0001	0001	0001	0002	0002	0003	0004	0005	1
		59	58	57	56	55	54	53	52	51	50	P R

N = 100

R	P	01	02	03	04	05	06	07	08	09	10	
0		3660	1326	0476	0169	0059	0021	0007	0002	0001	0000	00
1		3697	2707	1471	0703	0312	0131	0053	0021	0008	0003	99
2		1849	2734	2252	1450	0812	0414	0198	0090	0039	0016	98
3		0610	1823	2275	1973	1396	0864	0486	0254	0125	0059	97
4		0149	0902	1706	1994	1781	1338	0888	0536	0301	0159	96
5		0029	0353	1013	1595	1800	1639	1283	0895	0571	0339	95
6		0005	0114	0496	1052	1500	1657	1529	1233	0895	0596	94
7		0001	0031	0206	0589	1060	1420	1545	1440	1188	0889	93
8		0000	0007	0074	0285	0649	1054	1352	1455	1366	1148	92
9		0000	0002	0023	0121	0349	0687	1040	1293	1381	1304	91
10		0000	0000	0007	0046	0167	0399	0712	1024	1243	1319	90
11		0000	0000	0002	0016	0072	0209	0439	0728	1006	1199	89
12		0000	0000	0000	0005	0028	0099	0245	0470	0738	0988	88
13		0000	0000	0000	0001	0010	0043	0125	0276	0494	0743	87
14		0000	0000	0000	0000	0003	0017	0058	0149	0304	0513	86
15		0000	0000	0000	0000	0001	0006	0025	0074	0172	0327	85
16		0000	0000	0000	0000	0000	0002	0010	0034	0090	0193	84
17		0000	0000	0000	0000	0000	0001	0004	0015	0044	0106	83
18		0000	0000	0000	0000	0000	0000	0001	0006	0020	0054	82
19		0000	0000	0000	0000	0000	0000	0000	0002	0009	0026	81
20		0000	0000	0000	0000	0000	0000	0000	0001	0003	0012	80
21		0000	0000	0000	0000	0000	0000	0000	0000	0001	0005	79
22		0000	0000	0000	0000	0000	0000	0000	0000	0000	0002	78
23		0000	0000	0000	0000	0000	0000	0000	0000	0000	0001	77
		99	98	97	96	95	94	93	92	91	90	P R

R	P	11	12	13	14	15	16	17	18	19	20	
1		0001	0000	0000	0000	0000	0000	0000	0000	0000	0000	99
2		0007	0003	0001	0000	0000	0000	0000	0000	0000	0000	98
3		0027	0012	0005	0002	0001	0000	0000	0000	0000	0000	97
4		0080	0038	0018	0008	0003	0001	0001	0000	0000	0000	96
5		0189	0100	0050	0024	0011	0005	0002	0001	0000	0000	95
6		0369	0215	0119	0063	0031	0015	0007	0003	0001	0001	94
7		0613	0394	0238	0137	0075	0039	0020	0009	0004	0002	93
8		0881	0625	0414	0259	0153	0086	0047	0024	0012	0006	92
9		1112	0871	0632	0430	0276	0168	0098	0054	0029	0015	91
10		1251	1080	0860	0637	0444	0292	0182	0108	0062	0034	90
11		1265	1205	1051	0849	0640	0454	0305	0194	0118	0069	89
12		1160	1219	1165	1025	0838	0642	0463	0316	0206	0128	88
13		0970	1125	1179	1130	1001	0827	0642	0470	0327	0216	87
14		0745	0954	1094	1143	1098	0979	0817	0641	0476	0335	86
15		0528	0745	0938	1067	1111	1070	0960	0807	0640	0481	85
16		0347	0540	0744	0922	1041	1082	1044	0941	0798	0638	84
17		0212	0364	0549	0742	0908	1019	1057	1021	0924	0789	83
18		0121	0229	0379	0557	0739	0895	0998	1033	1000	0909	82
19		0064	0135	0244	0391	0563	0736	0882	0979	1012	0981	81
20		0032	0074	0148	0258	0402	0567	0732	0870	0962	0993	80
21		0015	0039	0084	0160	0270	0412	0571	0728	0859	0946	79
22		0007	0019	0045	0094	0171	0282	0420	0574	0724	0849	78
23		0003	0009	0023	0052	0103	0182	0292	0427	0576	0720	77
24		0001	0004	0011	0027	0058	0111	0192	0301	0433	0577	76
25		0000	0002	0005	0013	0031	0064	0119	0201	0309	0439	75
26		0000	0001	0002	0006	0016	0035	0071	0127	0209	0316	74
27		0000	0000	0001	0003	0008	0018	0040	0076	0134	0217	73
28		0000	0000	0000	0001	0004	0009	0021	0044	0082	0141	72
29		0000	0000	0000	0000	0002	0004	0011	0024	0048	0088	71
30		0000	0000	0000	0000	0001	0002	0005	0012	0027	0052	70
31		0000	0000	0000	0000	0000	0001	0002	0006	0014	0029	69
32		0000	0000	0000	0000	0000	0000	0001	0003	0007	0016	68
33		0000	0000	0000	0000	0000	0000	0000	0001	0003	0008	67
34		0000	0000	0000	0000	0000	0000	0000	0001	0002	0004	66
35		0000	0000	0000	0000	0000	0000	0000	0000	0001	0002	65
36		0000	0000	0000	0000	0000	0000	0000	0000	0000	0001	64
		89	88	87	86	85	84	83	82	81	80	P R

R	21	22	23	24	25	26	27	28	29	30	
7	0001	0000	0000	0000	0000	0000	0000	0000	0000	0000	93
8	0003	0001	0001	0000	0000	0000	0000	0000	0000	0000	92
9	0007	0003	0002	0001	0000	0000	0000	0000	0000	0000	91
10	0018	0009	0004	0002	0001	0000	0000	0000	0000	0000	90
11	0038	0021	0011	0005	0003	0001	0001	0000	0000	0000	89
12	0076	0043	0024	0012	0006	0003	0001	0001	0000	0000	88
13	0136	0082	0048	0027	0014	0007	0004	0002	0001	0000	87
14	0225	0144	0089	0052	0030	0016	0009	0004	0002	0001	86
15	0343	0233	0152	0095	0057	0033	0018	0010	0005	0002	85
16	0484	0350	0241	0159	0100	0061	0035	0020	0011	0006	84
17	0636	0487	0356	0248	0165	0106	0065	0038	0022	0012	83
18	0780	0634	0490	0361	0254	0171	0111	0069	0041	0024	82
19	0895	0772	0631	0492	0365	0259	0177	0115	0072	0044	81
20	0963	0881	0764	0629	0493	0369	0264	0182	0120	0076	80
21	0975	0947	0869	0756	0626	0494	0373	0269	0186	0124	79
22	0931	0959	0932	0858	0749	0623	0495	0376	0273	0190	78
23	0839	0917	0944	0919	0847	0743	0621	0495	0378	0277	77
24	0716	0830	0905	0931	0906	0837	0736	0618	0496	0380	76
25	0578	0712	0822	0893	0918	0894	0828	0731	0615	0496	75
26	0444	0579	0708	0814	0883	0906	0883	0819	0725	0613	74
27	0323	0448	0580	0704	0806	0873	0896	0873	0812	0720	73
28	0224	0329	0451	0580	0701	0799	0864	0886	0864	0804	72
29	0148	0231	0335	0455	0580	0697	0793	0855	0876	0856	71
30	0093	0154	0237	0340	0458	0580	0694	0787	0847	0868	70
31	0056	0098	0160	0242	0344	0460	0580	0691	0781	0840	69
32	0032	0060	0103	0165	0248	0349	0462	0579	0688	0776	68
33	0018	0035	0063	0107	0170	0252	0352	0464	0579	0685	67
34	0009	0019	0037	0067	0112	0175	0257	0356	0466	0579	66
35	0005	0010	0021	0040	0070	0116	0179	0261	0359	0468	65
36	0002	0005	0011	0023	0042	0073	0120	0183	0265	0362	64
37	0001	0003	0006	0012	0024	0045	0077	0123	0187	0268	63
38	0000	0001	0003	0006	0013	0026	0047	0079	0127	0191	62
39	0000	0001	0001	0003	0007	0015	0028	0049	0082	0130	61
40	0000	0000	0001	0002	0004	0008	0016	0029	0051	0085	60
41	0000	0000	0000	0001	0002	0004	0008	0017	0031	0053	59
42	0000	0000	0000	0000	0001	0002	0004	0009	0018	0032	58
43	0000	0000	0000	0000	0000	0001	0002	0005	0010	0019	57
44	0000	0000	0000	0000	0000	0000	0001	0002	0005	0010	56
45	0000	0000	0000	0000	0000	0000	0000	0001	0003	0005	55
46	0000	0000	0000	0000	0000	0000	0000	0001	0001	0003	54
47	0000	0000	0000	0000	0000	0000	0000	0000	0001	0001	53
48	0000	0000	0000	0000	0000	0000	0000	0000	0000	0001	52
	79	78	77	76	75	74	73	72	71	70	P R

R	P	31	32	33	34	35	36	37	38	39	40	
15		0001	0001	0000	0000	0000	0000	0000	0000	0000	0000	85
16		0003	0001	0001	0000	0000	0000	0000	0000	0000	0000	84
17		0006	0003	0002	0001	0000	0000	0000	0000	0000	0000	83
18		0013	0007	0004	0002	0001	0000	0000	0000	0000	0000	82
19		0025	0014	0008	0004	0002	0001	0000	0000	0000	0000	81
20		0046	0027	0015	0008	0004	0002	0001	0001	0000	0000	80
21		0079	0049	0029	0016	0009	0005	0002	0001	0001	0000	79
22		0127	0082	0051	0030	0017	0010	0005	0003	0001	0001	78
23		0194	0131	0085	0053	0032	0018	0010	0006	0003	0001	77
24		0280	0198	0134	0088	0055	0033	0019	0011	0006	0003	76
25		0382	0283	0201	0137	0090	0057	0035	0020	0012	0006	75
26		0496	0384	0286	0204	0140	0092	0059	0036	0021	0012	74
27		0610	0495	0386	0288	0207	0143	0095	0060	0037	0022	73
28		0715	0608	0495	0387	0290	0209	0145	0097	0062	0038	72
29		0797	0710	0605	0495	0388	0292	0211	0147	0098	0063	71
30		0848	0791	0706	0603	0494	0389	0294	0213	0149	0100	70
31		0860	0840	0785	0702	0601	0494	0389	0295	0215	0151	69
32		0833	0853	0833	0779	0698	0599	0493	0390	0296	0217	68
33		0771	0827	0846	0827	0774	0694	0597	0493	0390	0297	67
34		0683	0767	0821	0840	0821	0769	0691	0595	0492	0391	66
35		0578	0680	0763	0816	0834	0816	0765	0688	0593	0491	65
36		0469	0578	0678	0759	0811	0829	0811	0761	0685	0591	64
37		0365	0471	0578	0676	0755	0806	0824	0807	0757	0682	63
38		0272	0367	0472	0577	0674	0752	0802	0820	0803	0754	62
39		0194	0275	0369	0473	0577	0672	0749	0799	0816	0799	61
40		0133	0197	0277	0372	0474	0577	0671	0746	0795	0812	60
41		0087	0136	0200	0280	0373	0475	0577	0670	0744	0792	59
42		0055	0090	0138	0203	0282	0375	0476	0576	0668	0742	58
43		0033	0057	0092	0141	0205	0285	0377	0477	0576	0667	57
44		0019	0035	0059	0094	0143	0207	0287	0378	0477	0576	56
45		0011	0020	0036	0060	0096	0145	0210	0289	0380	0478	55
46		0006	0011	0021	0037	0062	0098	0147	0211	0290	0381	54
47		0003	0006	0012	0022	0038	0063	0099	0149	0213	0292	53
48		0001	0003	0007	0012	0023	0039	0064	0101	0151	0215	52
49		0001	0002	0003	0007	0013	0023	0040	0066	0102	0152	51
50		0000	0001	0002	0004	0007	0013	0024	0041	0067	0103	50
51		0000	0000	0001	0002	0004	0007	0014	0025	0042	0068	49
52		0000	0000	0000	0001	0002	0004	0008	0014	0025	0042	48
53		0000	0000	0000	0000	0001	0002	0004	0008	0015	0026	47
54		0000	0000	0000	0000	0000	0001	0002	0004	0008	0015	46
55		0000	0000	0000	0000	0000	0000	0001	0002	0004	0008	45
56		0000	0000	0000	0000	0000	0000	0000	0001	0002	0004	44
57		0000	0000	0000	0000	0000	0000	0000	0001	0001	0002	43
58		0000	0000	0000	0000	0000	0000	0000	0000	0001	0001	42
59		0000	0000	0000	0000	0000	0000	0000	0000	0000	0001	41
		69	68	67	66	65	64	63	62	61	60	P R

R	P = 41	42	43	44	45	46	47	48	49	50	
23	0001	0000	0000	0000	0000	0000	0000	0000	0000	0000	77
24	0002	0001	0000	0000	0000	0000	0000	0000	0000	0000	76
25	0003	0002	0001	0000	0000	0000	0000	0000	0000	0000	75
26	0007	0003	0002	0001	0000	0000	0000	0000	0000	0000	74
27	0013	0007	0004	0002	0001	0000	0000	0000	0000	0000	73
28	0023	0013	0007	0004	0002	0001	0000	0000	0000	0000	72
29	0039	0024	0014	0008	0004	0002	0001	0000	0000	0000	71
30	0065	0040	0024	0014	0008	0004	0002	0001	0001	0000	70
31	0102	0066	0041	0025	0014	0008	0004	0002	0001	0001	69
32	0152	0103	0067	0042	0025	0015	0008	0004	0002	0001	68
33	0218	0154	0104	0068	0043	0026	0015	0008	0004	0002	67
34	0298	0219	0155	0105	0069	0043	0026	0015	0009	0005	66
35	0391	0299	0220	0156	0106	0069	0044	0026	0015	0009	65
36	0491	0391	0300	0221	0157	0107	0070	0044	0027	0016	64
37	0590	0490	0391	0300	0222	0157	0107	0070	0044	0027	63
38	0680	0588	0489	0391	0301	0222	0158	0108	0071	0045	62
39	0751	0677	0587	0489	0391	0301	0223	0158	0108	0071	61
40	0796	0748	0675	0586	0488	0391	0301	0223	0159	0108	60
41	0809	0793	0745	0673	0584	0487	0391	0301	0223	0159	59
42	0790	0806	0790	0743	0672	0583	0487	0390	0301	0223	58
43	0740	0787	0804	0788	0741	0670	0582	0486	0390	0301	57
44	0666	0739	0785	0802	0786	0739	0669	0581	0485	0390	56
45	0576	0666	0737	0784	0800	0784	0738	0668	0580	0485	55
46	0479	0576	0665	0736	0782	0798	0783	0737	0667	0580	54
47	0382	0480	0576	0665	0736	0781	0797	0781	0736	0666	53
48	0293	0383	0480	0577	0665	0735	0781	0797	0781	0735	52
49	0216	0295	0384	0481	0577	0664	0735	0780	0796	0780	51
50	0153	0218	0296	0385	0482	0577	0665	0735	0780	0796	50
51	0104	0155	0219	0297	0386	0482	0578	0665	0735	0780	49
52	0068	0105	0156	0220	0298	0387	0483	0578	0665	0735	48
53	0043	0069	0106	0156	0221	0299	0388	0483	0579	0666	47
54	0026	0044	0070	0107	0157	0221	0299	0388	0484	0580	46
55	0015	0026	0044	0070	0108	0158	0222	0300	0389	0485	45
56	0008	0015	0027	0044	0071	0108	0158	0222	0300	0390	44
57	0005	0009	0016	0027	0045	0071	0108	0158	0223	0301	43
58	0002	0005	0009	0016	0027	0045	0071	0108	0159	0223	42
59	0001	0002	0005	0009	0016	0027	0045	0071	0109	0159	41
60	0001	0001	0002	0005	0009	0016	0027	0045	0071	0108	40
61	0000	0001	0001	0002	0005	0009	0016	0027	0045	0071	39
62	0000	0000	0001	0001	0002	0005	0009	0016	0027	0045	38
63	0000	0000	0000	0001	0001	0002	0005	0009	0016	0027	37
64	0000	0000	0000	0000	0001	0001	0002	0005	0009	0016	36
65	0000	0000	0000	0000	0000	0001	0001	0002	0005	0009	35
66	0000	0000	0000	0000	0000	0001	0001	0002	0005	0009	34
67	0000	0000	0000	0000	0000	0000	0000	0001	0001	0002	33
68	0000	0000	0000	0000	0000	0000	0000	0000	0001	0001	32
69	0000	0000	0000	0000	0000	0000	0000	0000	0000	0001	31
	59	58	57	56	55	54	53	52	51	50 P	R

TABLE T2
GAUSSIAN DENSITY FUNCTION[2]

The following table gives values of the Gaussian density function defined by

$$g^*(u) = (2\pi)^{-1/2} e^{-u^2/2}$$

for all arguments u from -4.3 to $+4.3$ inclusive. Because $g^*(-u) = g^*(u)$, the table should be entered with the absolute value of u—i.e., a negative value of u should be treated as if it were positive. A decimal point is to be inserted immediately before each value in the table.

Example 1. To find either $g^*(2.16)$ or $g^*(-2.16)$, enter the table in the row headed 2.1, read 0387 in the column headed 6, and prefix a decimal point to obtain .0387.

The five columns at the extreme right of the table show "tenths of the tabular difference", which are used as shown by the following two examples.

Example 2. To find either $g^*(2.164)$ or $g^*(-2.164)$, enter the table in the row headed 2.1, read 0387 in the column headed 6, read 3 in the 4th difference column, compute $0387 - 3 = 0384$, and prefix a decimal point to obtain .0384. Notice that the difference is *subtracted* from 0387 because the entries in the table *decrease* from left to right.

Example 3. To find either $g^*(2.166)$ or $g^*(-2.166)$, enter the table in the row headed 2.1, read 0379 in the column headed 7, read 3 in the 4th difference column, compute $0379 + 3 = 0382$, and prefix a decimal point to obtain .0382. Notice that the difference is *added* to 0379.

[2] Table computed and edited by Arthur Schleifer, Jr.

U	0	1	2	3	4	5	6	7	8	9	10					
0.0	3989	3989	3989	3988	3986	3984						0	0	0	0	0
						3984	3982	3980	3977	3973	3970	0	1	1	1	1
0.1	3970	3965	3961	3956	3951	3945						0	1	1	2	2
						3945	3939	3932	3925	3918	3910	1	1	2	3	3
0.2	3910	3902	3894	3885	3876	3867						1	2	3	3	4
						3867	3857	3847	3836	3825	3814	1	2	3	4	5
0.3	3814	3802	3790	3778	3765	3752						1	2	4	5	6
						3752	3739	3725	3712	3697	3683	1	3	4	6	7
0.4	3683	3668	3653	3637	3621	3605						2	3	5	6	8
						3605	3589	3572	3555	3538	3521	2	3	5	7	8
0.5	3521	3503	3485	3467	3448	3429						2	4	5	7	9
						3429	3410	3391	3372	3352	3332	2	4	6	8	10
0.6	3332	3312	3292	3271	3251	3230						2	4	6	8	10
						3230	3209	3187	3166	3144	3123	2	4	6	9	11
0.7	3123	3101	3079	3056	3034	3011						2	4	7	9	11
						3011	2989	2966	2943	2920	2897	2	5	7	9	11
0.8	2897	2874	2850	2827	2803	2780						2	5	7	9	12
						2780	2756	2732	2709	2685	2661	2	5	7	10	12
0.9	2661	2637	2613	2589	2565	2541						2	5	7	10	12
						2541	2516	2492	2468	2444	2420	2	5	7	10	12
1.0	2420	2396	2371	2347	2323	2299						2	5	7	10	12
						2299	2275	2251	2227	2203	2179	2	5	7	10	12
1.1	2179	2155	2131	2107	2083	2059						2	5	7	10	12
						2059	2036	2012	1989	1965	1942	2	5	7	9	12
1.2	1942	1919	1895	1872	1849	1826						2	5	7	9	12
						1826	1804	1781	1758	1736	1714	2	5	7	9	11
1.3	1714	1691	1669	1647	1626	1604						2	4	7	9	11
						1604	1582	1561	1539	1518	1497	2	4	6	9	11
1.4	1497	1476	1456	1435	1415	1394						2	4	6	8	10
						1394	1374	1354	1334	1315	1295	2	4	6	8	10
1.5	1295	1276	1257	1238	1219	1200						2	4	6	8	10
						1200	1182	1163	1145	1127	1109	2	4	5	7	9
1.6	1109	1092	1074	1057	1040	1023						2	3	5	7	9
						1023	1006	0989	0973	0957	0940	2	3	5	7	8
1.7	0940	0925	0909	0893	0878	0863						2	3	5	6	8
						0863	0848	0833	0818	0804	0790	1	3	4	6	7
1.8	0790	0775	0761	0748	0734	0721						1	3	4	6	7
						0721	0707	0694	0681	0669	0656	1	3	4	5	6
1.9	0656	0644	0632	0620	0608	0596						1	2	4	5	6
						0596	0584	0573	0562	0551	0540	1	2	3	4	6
2.0	0540	0529	0519	0508	0498	0488	0478	0468	0459	0449	0440	1	2	3	4	5
2.1	0440	0431	0422	0413	0404	0396	0387	0379	0371	0363	0355	1	2	3	3	4
2.2	0355	0347	0339	0332	0325	0317	0310	0303	0297	0290	0283	1	1	2	3	4
2.3	0283	0277	0270	0264	0258	0252	0246	0241	0235	0229	0224	1	1	2	2	3
2.4	0224	0219	0213	0208	0203	0198	0194	0189	0184	0180	0175	0	1	1	2	2
2.5	0175	0171	0167	0163	0158	0154	0151	0147	0143	0139	0136	0	1	1	2	2
2.6	0136	0132	0129	0126	0122	0119	0116	0113	0110	0107	0104	0	1	1	1	2
2.7	0104	0101	0099	0096	0093	0091	0088	0086	0084	0081	0079	0	1	1	1	1
2.8	0079	0077	0075	0073	0071	0069	0067	0065	0063	0061	0060	0	0	1	1	1
2.9	0060	0058	0056	0055	0053	0051	0050	0048	0047	0046	0044	0	0	0	1	1
3.0	0044	0043	0042	0040	0039	0038	0037	0036	0035	0034	0033	0	0	0	0	1
3.1	0033	0032	0031	0030	0029	0028	0027	0026	0025	0025	0024	0	0	0	0	0
3.2	0024	0023	0022	0022	0021	0020	0020	0019	0018	0018	0017	0	0	0	0	0
3.3	0017	0017	0016	0016	0015	0015	0014	0014	0013	0013	0012	0	0	0	0	0
3.4	0012	0012	0012	0011	0011	0010	0010	0010	0009	0009	0009	0	0	0	0	0
3.5	0009	0008	0008	0008	0008	0007	0007	0007	0007	0006	0006	0	0	0	0	0
3.6	0006	0006	0006	0005	0005	0005	0005	0005	0005	0004	0004	0	0	0	0	0
3.7	0004	0004	0004	0004	0004	0004	0003	0003	0003	0003	0003	0	0	0	0	0
3.8	0003	0003	0003	0003	0003	0002	0002	0002	0002	0002	0002	0	0	0	0	0
3.9	0002	0002	0002	0002	0002	0002	0002	0002	0001	0001	0001	0	0	0	0	0
4.0	0001	0001	0001	0001	0001	0001	0001	0001	0001	0001	0001	0	0	0	0	0
4.1	0001	0001	0001	0001	0001	0001	0001	0001	0001	0001	0001	0	0	0	0	0
4.2	0001	0001	0001	0001	0000	0000	0000	0000	0000	0000	0000	0	0	0	0	0

TABLE T3
BETA CUMULATIVE FUNCTIONS[3]

A beta cumulative function with argument p and parameters B and C is defined by

$$k(p;\, B,\, C) = \int_0^p \frac{\Gamma(C)}{\Gamma(B)\,\Gamma(C-B)}\, t^{B-1}\,(1-t)^{C-B-1}\, dt.$$

For all integral values of the parameters, the following tables either give directly or tell how to approximate the argument p_k corresponding to each of the function values

$$k = .001,\ .01,\ .05,\ .1,\ .25,\ .50,\ .75,\ .9,\ .95,\ .99,\ .999.$$

There is one table for each value of B from 1 to 100, followed by a table for all B over 100. In each such table, there will be for any given C a row in which either (1) the value of p_k can be read under the column heading k, or else (2) reference is made to a footnote telling how to find p_k or compute an approximation to p_k.

Examples. To find the argument $p_{.01}$ corresponding to the function value .01 for beta cumulative functions with parameter $B = 27$ and various parameters C, we proceed as follows:

$B = 27$, $C = 150$: In the table for $B = 27$ and the row for $C = 150$, read

$$p_{.01} = .1139$$

under the column heading .01.

$B = 27$, $C = 220$: In the table for $B = 27$ and the row for $C = 203+$, read 16.40 * under the column heading .01; then follow the instruction in the footnote referenced by * and compute

$$p_{.01} = 16.40\,/(C-1) = 16.40\,/219 = .0749.$$

$B = 27$, $C = 80$: Read "See note ***" in the table for $B = 27$ and the row for $C = 42$–124, and following the instructions in the note compute

$m = B/C = 27\,/80 = .3375,$

$s = \sqrt{m(1-m)\,/(C+1)} = \sqrt{.3375 \times .6625\,/81} = \sqrt{.002760} = .0525,$

$u_{.01} = -2.326 \qquad$ (from Table T4),

$p_{.01} = m + u_{.01}\, s = .3375 - 2.326 \times .0525 = .2154.$

$B = 27$, $C = 40$: Read "See note**" in the table for $B = 27$ and the row for $C = 28$–41; then following the instructions in the note compute $B^* = 40 - 27 =$

---

[3] Table computed and edited by Arthur Schleifer, Jr. with the assistance of Joseph Dolben.

13; in the table for $B = 13$ and the row for $C = 40$, read $p_{.99}^* = .5052$ under the column heading .99 ($= 1 - .01$); then compute

$$p_{.01} = 1 - .5052 = .4948.$$

$B = 27, C = 28$: Read "See note**" in the table for $B = 27$ and the row for $C = 28\text{–}41$; then following the instructions in the note compute $B^* = 28 - 27 = 1$; in the table for $B = 1$ and the row for $C = 20+$, read 4.605* under the column heading .99; following the instruction in the footnote, compute $p_{.99}^* = 4.605/(C-1) = 4.605/27 = .1706$; and compute

$$p_{.01} = 1 - .1706 = .8294.$$

Accuracy of the Approximations   Let $\hat{p}_k$ denote an approximation to p_k. The tables give instructions for computing approximations to all p_k for those and only those values of the parameters B and C for which

$$.005 < k(\hat{p}_{.01}; B, C) < .015 \qquad and \qquad .985 < k(\hat{p}_{.99}; B, C) < .995.$$

The accuracy of the approximations for k other than .01 and .99 has not been investigated but is presumably quite good for k between .01 and .99, quite poor for $k = .001$ or .999.

B	C	.001	.01	.05	.1	.25	.5	.75	.9	.95	.99	.999
1	2	.0010	.0100	.0500	.1000	.2500	.5000	.7500	.9000	.9500	.9900	.9990
	3	.0005	.0050	.0253	.0513	.1340	.2929	.5000	.6838	.7764	.9000	.9684
	4	.0003	.0033	.0170	.0345	.0914	.2063	.3700	.5358	.6316	.7846	.9000
	5	.0003	.0025	.0127	.0260	.0694	.1591	.2929	.4377	.5271	.6838	.8222
	6	.0002	.0020	.0102	.0209	.0559	.1294	.2421	.3690	.4507	.6019	.7488
	7	.0002	.0017	.0085	.0174	.0468	.1091	.2063	.3187	.3930	.5358	.6838
	8	.0001	.0014	.0073	.0149	.0403	.0943	.1797	.2803	.3482	.4821	.6272
	9	.0001	.0013	.0064	.0131	.0353	.0830	.1591	.2501	.3123	.4377	.5783
	10	.0001	.0011	.0057	.0116	.0315	.0741	.1428	.2257	.2831	.4005	.5358
	11	.0001	.0010	.0051	.0105	.0284	.0670	.1294	.2057	.2589	.3690	.4988
	12	.0001	.0009	.0047	.0095	.0258	.0611	.1184	.1889	.2384	.3421	.4663
	13	.0001	.0008	.0043	.0087	.0237	.0561	.1091	.1746	.2209	.3187	.4377
	14	.0001	.0008	.0039	.0081	.0219	.0519	.1011	.1623	.2058	.2983	.4122
	15	.0001	.0007	.0037	.0075	.0203	.0483	.0943	.1517	.1926	.2803	.3895
	16	.0001	.0007	.0034	.0070	.0190	.0452	.0883	.1423	.1810	.2644	.3690
	17	.0001	.0006	.0032	.0066	.0178	.0424	.0830	.1340	.1707	.2501	.3506
	18	.0001	.0006	.0030	.0062	.0168	.0400	.0783	.1267	.1616	.2373	.3339
	19	.0001	.0006	.0028	.0058	.0159	.0378	.0741	.1201	.1533	.2257	.3187
	20+	.0010*	.0101*	.0513*	.1054*	.2877*	.6931*	1.386*	2.303*	2.996*	4.605*	6.908*
2	3	SEE NOTE**										
	4	.0184	.0589	.1354	.1958	.3264	.5000	.6736	.8042	.8646	.9411	.9816
	5	.0130	.0420	.0976	.1426	.2430	.3857	.5437	.6795	.7514	.8591	.9360
	6	.0101	.0327	.0764	.1122	.1938	.3138	.4542	.5839	.6574	.7779	.8780
	7	.0083	.0268	.0628	.0926	.1612	.2644	.3895	.5103	.5818	.7057	.8186
	8	.0070	.0227	.0534	.0788	.1380	.2285	.3407	.4526	.5207	.6434	.7625
	9	.0060	.0197	.0464	.0686	.1206	.2011	.3027	.4062	.4707	.5899	.7113
	10	.0053	.0174	.0410	.0608	.1072	.1796	.2723	.3684	.4291	.5440	.6651
	11	.0048	.0155	.0368	.0545	.0964	.1623	.2474	.3368	.3942	.5044	.6237
	12	.0043	.0141	.0333	.0495	.0876	.1480	.2266	.3102	.3644	.4698	.5866
	13	.0039	.0128	.0305	.0452	.0803	.1360	.2091	.2875	.3387	.4395	.5534
	14	.0036	.0118	.0281	.0417	.0741	.1258	.1941	.2678	.3163	.4128	.5234
	15	.0034	.0110	.0260	.0387	.0688	.1170	.1810	.2507	.2967	.3891	.4963
	16	.0031	.0102	.0242	.0360	.0642	.1094	.1697	.2356	.2794	.3679	.4718
	17	.0029	.0095	.0227	.0337	.0602	.1027	.1596	.2222	.2640	.3483	.4495
	18	.0027	.0090	.0213	.0317	.0566	.0968	.1507	.2102	.2501	.3316	.4292
	19	.0026	.0085	.0201	.0299	.0535	.0915	.1427	.1995	.2377	.3160	.4105
	20	.0025	.0080	.0190	.0283	.0507	.0868	.1355	.1898	.2264	.3018	.3934
	21	.0023	.0076	.0181	.0269	.0481	.0825	.1290	.1810	.2161	.2888	.3776
	22	.0022	.0072	.0172	.0256	.0458	.0786	.1232	.1729	.2067	.2768	.3630
	23	.0021	.0069	.0164	.0244	.0437	.0751	.1178	.1656	.1981	.2658	.3494
	24	.0020	.0066	.0157	.0234	.0418	.0719	.1128	.1588	.1902	.2557	.3369
	25	.0019	.0063	.0150	.0224	.0401	.0690	.1083	.1526	.1829	.2462	.3252
	26	.0019	.0060	.0144	.0215	.0385	.0662	.1041	.1469	.1761	.2375	.3142
	27	.0018	.0058	.0138	.0206	.0370	.0637	.1002	.1415	.1698	.2293	.3040
	28	.0017	.0056	.0133	.0199	.0356	.0614	.0966	.1366	.1640	.2217	.2944
	29	.0016	.0054	.0128	.0192	.0344	.0592	.0933	.1319	.1585	.2146	.2854
	30+	.0454*	.1486*	.3554*	.5318*	.9613*	1.678*	2.693*	3.890*	4.744*	6.638*	9.233*
3	4-5	SEE NOTE**										
	6	.0476	.1056	.1893	.2466	.3594	.5000	.6406	.7534	.8107	.8944	.9524
	7	.0379	.0847	.1532	.2009	.2969	.4214	.5532	.6668	.7287	.8269	.9060
	8	.0316	.0708	.1288	.1696	.2531	.3641	.4861	.5962	.6587	.7637	.8562
	9	.0270	.0608	.1111	.1469	.2206	.3205	.4332	.5382	.5997	.7068	.8073
	10	.0237	.0533	.0977	.1295	.1955	.2862	.3905	.4901	.5496	.6563	.7612
	11	.0210	.0475	.0873	.1158	.1756	.2586	.3554	.4496	.5069	.6117	.7185
	12	.0189	.0428	.0788	.1048	.1593	.2358	.3261	.4152	.4701	.5723	.6793
	13	.0172	.0390	.0719	.0957	.1459	.2167	.3012	.3855	.4381	.5373	.6436
	14	.0158	.0358	.0660	.0880	.1345	.2004	.2798	.3598	.4101	.5062	.6110
	15	.0146	.0331	.0611	.0815	.1248	.1865	.2612	.3372	.3854	.4783	.5812
	16	.0135	.0307	.0568	.0759	.1163	.1743	.2450	.3173	.3634	.4532	.5539
	17	.0126	.0287	.0531	.0710	.1090	.1637	.2306	.2996	.3438	.4305	.5290
	18	.0119	.0269	.0499	.0667	.1025	.1542	.2178	.2837	.3262	.4099	.5060
	19	.0112	.0254	.0470	.0629	.0968	.1458	.2064	.2694	.3103	.3912	.4849
	20	.0105	.0240	.0445	.0595	.0916	.1383	.1961	.2565	.2958	.3741	.4654
	21	.0100	.0227	.0422	.0564	.0870	.1315	.1867	.2448	.2826	.3583	.4474
	22	.0095	.0216	.0401	.0537	.0828	.1253	.1783	.2340	.2706	.3439	.4306
	23	.0090	.0206	.0382	.0512	.0790	.1197	.1705	.2242	.2595	.3305	.4151
	24	.0086	.0196	.0365	.0489	.0756	.1146	.1634	.2152	.2492	.3181	.4006
	25	.0083	.0188	.0350	.0468	.0724	.1099	.1569	.2069	.2398	.3066	.3870
	26	.0079	.0180	.0335	.0449	.0695	.1055	.1509	.1991	.2310	.2959	.3743
	27	.0076	.0173	.0322	.0432	.0668	.1015	.1453	.1920	.2229	.2859	.3624

* To approximate p_k, divide the starred entry under k by $(C - 1)$.

** Compute $B^* = C - B$, find p^*_{1-k} for B^* and C, and compute $p_k = 1 - p^*_{1-k}$.

B	C	.001	.01	.05	.1	.25	.5	.75	.9	.95	.99	.999
3	28	.0073	.0166	.0310	.0415	.0643	.0978	.1401	.1853	.2153	.2766	.3512
	29	.0070	.0160	.0298	.0400	.0620	.0944	.1353	.1791	.2082	.2679	.3407
	30	.0068	.0155	.0288	.0386	.0599	.0911	.1308	.1733	.2016	.2596	.3308
	31	.0066	.0149	.0278	.0373	.0579	.0881	.1265	.1678	.1953	.2519	.3214
	32	.0063	.0144	.0269	.0361	.0560	.0853	.1226	.1627	.1895	.2446	.3126
	33	.0061	.0140	.0260	.0349	.0542	.0827	.1189	.1579	.1839	.2377	.3042
	34	.0059	.0135	.0252	.0339	.0526	.0802	.1154	.1533	.1787	.2312	.2963
	35	.0058	.0131	.0245	.0329	.0510	.0779	.1121	.1490	.1738	.2251	.2887
	36	.0056	.0127	.0238	.0319	.0496	.0757	.1090	.1450	.1692	.2192	.2815
	37	.0054	.0124	.0231	.0310	.0482	.0736	.1060	.1412	.1647	.2137	.2747
	38+	.1905*	.4360*	.8177*	1.102*	1.727*	2.674*	3.920*	5.322*	6.296*	8.406*	11.23*
4	5-7	SEE NOTE**										
	8	.0767	.1423	.2253	.2786	.3788	.5000	.6212	.7214	.7747	.8577	.9233
	9	.0648	.1210	.1929	.2397	.3291	.4402	.5555	.6554	.7108	.8018	.8804
	10	.0562	.1053	.1688	.2104	.2910	.3931	.5020	.5994	.6551	.7500	.8371
	11	.0496	.0932	.1500	.1876	.2609	.3551	.4577	.5517	.6066	.7029	.7954
	12	.0444	.0837	.1351	.1692	.2364	.3238	.4205	.5108	.5644	.6604	.7559
	13	.0402	.0759	.1229	.1542	.2162	.2976	.3888	.4753	.5273	.6222	.7192
	14	.0368	.0695	.1127	.1416	.1991	.2753	.3615	.4443	.4946	.5878	.6851
	15	.0338	.0640	.1040	.1309	.1846	.2561	.3377	.4170	.4657	.5567	.6537
	16	.0314	.0594	.0967	.1218	.1720	.2394	.3169	.3928	.4398	.5285	.6246
	17	.0292	.0554	.0903	.1138	.1611	.2247	.2985	.3712	.4166	.5029	.5977
	18	.0273	.0519	.0846	.1068	.1514	.2118	.2821	.3519	.3956	.4796	.5729
	19	.0257	.0488	.0797	.1006	.1429	.2002	.2674	.3344	.3767	.4583	.5499
	20	.0242	.0461	.0753	.0951	.1353	.1899	.2541	.3186	.3594	.4387	.5286
	21	.0229	.0436	.0714	.0902	.1284	.1805	.2421	.3042	.3437	.4207	.5087
	22	.0218	.0414	.0678	.0858	.1222	.1721	.2312	.2910	.3292	.4041	.4903
	23	.0207	.0394	.0646	.0817	.1166	.1644	.2212	.2789	.3159	.3887	.4730
	24	.0198	.0376	.0617	.0781	.1114	.1573	.2120	.2678	.3036	.3745	.4569
	25	.0189	.0360	.0590	.0747	.1068	.1509	.2036	.2575	.2923	.3612	.4419
	26	.0181	.0345	.0566	.0717	.1024	.1449	.1958	.2480	.2817	.3488	.4277
	27	.0174	.0331	.0543	.0688	.0985	.1394	.1886	.2392	.2719	.3372	.4144
	28	.0167	.0318	.0522	.0662	.0948	.1343	.1819	.2309	.2627	.3264	.4019
	29	.0161	.0306	.0503	.0638	.0914	.1296	.1756	.2232	.2542	.3162	.3901
	30	.0155	.0295	.0485	.0615	.0882	.1252	.1698	.2160	.2461	.3066	.3790
	31	.0149	.0285	.0469	.0594	.0852	.1210	.1644	.2093	.2386	.2976	.3685
	32	.0144	.0275	.0453	.0575	.0824	.1172	.1592	.2030	.2315	.2891	.3585
	33	.0140	.0267	.0438	.0556	.0798	.1136	.1544	.1970	.2248	.2811	.3490
	34	.0135	.0258	.0425	.0539	.0774	.1101	.1499	.1914	.2185	.2735	.3401
	35	.0131	.0250	.0412	.0523	.0751	.1069	.1456	.1860	.2125	.2663	.3315
	36	.0127	.0243	.0400	.0508	.0729	.1039	.1416	.1810	.2069	.2594	.3234
	37	.0124	.0236	.0389	.0493	.0709	.1011	.1378	.1762	.2015	.2530	.3157
	38	.0120	.0229	.0378	.0480	.0690	.0983	.1342	.1717	.1964	.2468	.3083
	39	.0117	.0223	.0368	.0467	.0671	.0958	.1307	.1674	.1916	.2409	.3013
	40	.0114	.0217	.0358	.0455	.0654	.0933	.1275	.1633	.1870	.2353	.2945
	41	.0111	.0212	.0349	.0443	.0638	.0910	.1244	.1594	.1826	.2299	.2881
	42	.0108	.0206	.0340	.0432	.0622	.0888	.1214	.1557	.1784	.2248	.2819
	43	.0105	.0201	.0332	.0422	.0607	.0867	.1186	.1522	.1744	.2199	.2760
	44	.0103	.0196	.0324	.0412	.0593	.0847	.1159	.1488	.1706	.2152	.2703
	45	.0100	.0192	.0317	.0402	.0579	.0828	.1134	.1456	.1669	.2107	.2649
	46+	.4286*	.8232*	1.366*	1.745*	2.535*	3.672*	5.109*	6.681*	7.754*	10.05*	13.06*
5	6-9	SEE NOTE**										
	10	.1025	.1710	.2514	.3010	.3920	.5000	.6080	.6990	.7486	.8290	.8975
	11	.0898	.1504	.2224	.2673	.3507	.4517	.5555	.6458	.6965	.7817	.8587
	12	.0799	.1344	.1996	.2405	.3173	.4119	.5111	.5995	.6502	.7378	.8206
	13	.0721	.1215	.1810	.2187	.2898	.3785	.4731	.5590	.6091	.6976	.7841
	14	.0656	.1108	.1657	.2005	.2668	.3502	.4403	.5234	.5726	.6609	.7497
	15	.0602	.1019	.1527	.1851	.2471	.3258	.4117	.4920	.5400	.6274	.7173
	16	.0556	.0944	.1417	.1720	.2301	.3045	.3865	.4640	.5108	.5969	.6871
	17	.0517	.0878	.1321	.1606	.2154	.2859	.3642	.4389	.4844	.5690	.6590
	18	.0483	.0822	.1238	.1506	.2024	.2694	.3444	.4164	.4605	.5434	.6328
	19	.0454	.0772	.1164	.1418	.1909	.2547	.3265	.3960	.4389	.5199	.6083
	20	.0427	.0728	.1099	.1339	.1806	.2415	.3105	.3775	.4191	.4983	.5856
	21	.0404	.0688	.1041	.1269	.1714	.2297	.2959	.3607	.4010	.4783	.5643
	22	.0383	.0653	.0988	.1206	.1631	.2189	.2826	.3452	.3844	.4600	.5444
	23	.0364	.0621	.0941	.1149	.1556	.2091	.2705	.3310	.3691	.4426	.5258
	24	.0347	.0593	.0898	.1097	.1487	.2001	.2593	.3180	.3549	.4267	.5084
	25	.0331	.0566	.0859	.1050	.1424	.1919	.2490	.3059	.3418	.4118	.4920

*** To approximate p_k, compute $m = B/C$ and $s = \sqrt{m(1-m)/(C+1)}$, find u_k in Table T4 on page 715 below, and compute $p_k \doteq m + u_k s$.

B	C	.001	.01	.05	.1	.25	.5	.75	.9	.95	.99	.999
5	26	.0317	.0542	.0823	.1006	.1366	.1843	.2396	.2947	.3296	.3979	.4766
	27	.0304	.0520	.0790	.0966	.1313	.1774	.2308	.2842	.3182	.3849	.4621
	28	.0292	.0500	.0759	.0929	.1264	.1709	.2226	.2745	.3076	.3727	.4485
	29	.0281	.0481	.0731	.0895	.1218	.1648	.2150	.2655	.2977	.3613	.4356
	30	.0271	.0463	.0705	.0863	.1175	.1592	.2079	.2570	.2884	.3505	.4234
	31	.0261	.0447	.0681	.0834	.1136	.1540	.2012	.2490	.2796	.3403	.4118
	32	.0252	.0432	.0658	.0806	.1099	.1491	.1950	.2415	.2714	.3307	.4009
	33	.0244	.0418	.0637	.0780	.1064	.1444	.1891	.2344	.2636	.3216	.3905
	34	.0236	.0405	.0617	.0756	.1031	.1401	.1836	.2278	.2563	.3130	.3806
	35	.0229	.0392	.0598	.0733	.1001	.1360	.1784	.2215	.2493	.3049	.3712
	36	.0222	.0381	.0580	.0712	.0972	.1322	.1734	.2155	.2427	.2971	.3622
	37	.0215	.0370	.0564	.0691	.0944	.1285	.1688	.2099	.2365	.2898	.3537
	38	.0209	.0359	.0548	.0672	.0919	.1251	.1644	.2045	.2305	.2828	.3456
	39	.0203	.0349	.0533	.0654	.0894	.1218	.1602	.1994	.2249	.2761	.3377
	40	.0198	.0340	.0519	.0637	.0871	.1187	.1562	.1946	.2195	.2697	.3303
	41	.0193	.0331	.0506	.0621	.0849	.1158	.1524	.1900	.2144	.2636	.3231
	42	.0188	.0323	.0493	.0605	.0828	.1130	.1488	.1856	.2095	.2578	.3163
	43	.0183	.0315	.0481	.0591	.0808	.1103	.1453	.1814	.2048	.2522	.3097
	44	.0179	.0307	.0470	.0577	.0789	.1078	.1421	.1774	.2004	.2469	.3034
	45	.0175	.0300	.0459	.0563	.0771	.1054	.1389	.1735	.1961	.2418	.2974
	46	.0171	.0293	.0448	.0550	.0754	.1030	.1359	.1698	.1920	.2369	.2916
	47	.0167	.0287	.0438	.0538	.0738	.1008	.1330	.1663	.1880	.2321	.2860
	48	.0163	.0280	.0429	.0527	.0722	.0987	.1303	.1629	.1843	.2276	.2806
	49	.0160	.0274	.0420	.0515	.0707	.0966	.1276	.1597	.1806	.2232	.2754
	50	.0156	.0269	.0411	.0505	.0692	.0947	.1251	.1566	.1771	.2190	.2704
	51	.0153	.0263	.0402	.0494	.0678	.0928	.1226	.1535	.1738	.2150	.2656
	52	.0150	.0258	.0394	.0485	.0665	.0910	.1203	.1507	.1706	.2111	.2609
	53	.0147	.0253	.0387	.0475	.0652	.0892	.1180	.1479	.1674	.2073	.2564
	54+	.7394*	1.279*	1.970*	2.433*	3.369*	4.671*	6.274*	7.994*	9.154*	11.60*	14.79*
6	7-11	SEE NOTE**										
	12	.1249	.1940	.2712	.3177	.4016	.5000	.5984	.6823	.7288	.8060	.8751
	13	.1120	.1746	.2453	.2882	.3663	.4595	.5547	.6377	.6848	.7651	.8401
	14	.1016	.1588	.2240	.2637	.3368	.4251	.5167	.5982	.6452	.7271	.8062
	15	.0929	.1457	.2061	.2432	.3117	.3954	.4835	.5631	.6096	.6920	.7738
	16	.0857	.1346	.1909	.2256	.2902	.3697	.4543	.5317	.5774	.6597	.7432
	17	.0794	.1251	.1778	.2104	.2714	.3471	.4283	.5035	.5483	.6299	.7143
	18	.0741	.1168	.1664	.1972	.2549	.3270	.4051	.4781	.5219	.6025	.6872
	19	.0694	.1096	.1563	.1855	.2404	.3092	.3843	.4550	.4978	.5772	.6617
	20	.0653	.1032	.1475	.1751	.2274	.2932	.3655	.4340	.4758	.5538	.6378
	21	.0616	.0975	.1396	.1659	.2157	.2788	.3484	.4149	.4556	.5321	.6154
	22	.0584	.0925	.1324	.1575	.2052	.2657	.3329	.3973	.4370	.5120	.5944
	23	.0554	.0879	.1260	.1500	.1956	.2538	.3187	.3812	.4198	.4933	.5747
	24	.0528	.0838	.1202	.1432	.1870	.2430	.3056	.3663	.4039	.4758	.5561
	25	.0504	.0800	.1149	.1369	.1790	.2330	.2936	.3525	.3891	.4595	.5386
	26	.0482	.0765	.1101	.1312	.1717	.2238	.2824	.3397	.3754	.4443	.5222
	27	.0462	.0734	.1056	.1260	.1650	.2153	.2721	.3277	.3626	.4300	.5066
	28	.0443	.0705	.1015	.1211	.1588	.2074	.2625	.3166	.3506	.4166	.4919
	29	.0426	.0678	.0977	.1166	.1530	.2001	.2536	.3062	.3394	.4039	.4780
	30	.0410	.0653	.0942	.1125	.1476	.1933	.2452	.2965	.3289	.3920	.4649
	31	.0395	.0630	.0909	.1086	.1426	.1869	.2374	.2874	.3190	.3808	.4524
	32	.0382	.0609	.0878	.1050	.1380	.1809	.2300	.2788	.3096	.3702	.4406
	33	.0369	.0588	.0850	.1016	.1336	.1753	.2231	.2707	.3008	.3601	.4293
	34	.0357	.0570	.0823	.0984	.1295	.1701	.2166	.2630	.2925	.3506	.4186
	35	.0346	.0552	.0798	.0954	.1256	.1651	.2105	.2558	.2846	.3416	.4084
	36	.0335	.0535	.0774	.0926	.1220	.1605	.2047	.2490	.2772	.3330	.3987
	37	.0326	.0520	.0752	.0900	.1186	.1560	.1992	.2425	.2701	.3248	.3894
	38	.0316	.0505	.0731	.0875	.1153	.1519	.1940	.2363	.2634	.3170	.3805
	39	.0307	.0491	.0711	.0851	.1123	.1479	.1891	.2305	.2570	.3096	.3721
	40	.0299	.0478	.0692	.0829	.1093	.1441	.1844	.2249	.2509	.3025	.3639
	41	.0291	.0466	.0674	.0807	.1066	.1406	.1799	.2196	.2450	.2957	.3562
	42	.0284	.0454	.0657	.0787	.1040	.1372	.1757	.2145	.2395	.2893	.3487
	43	.0277	.0442	.0641	.0768	.1015	.1339	.1716	.2097	.2342	.2831	.3416
	44	.0270	.0432	.0626	.0750	.0991	.1308	.1677	.2051	.2291	.2771	.3347
	45	.0263	.0422	.0611	.0732	.0968	.1279	.1640	.2006	.2242	.2714	.3281
	46	.0257	.0412	.0597	.0716	.0946	.1251	.1605	.1964	.2195	.2659	.3217
	47	.0252	.0402	.0584	.0700	.0925	.1224	.1571	.1923	.2151	.2607	.3156
	48	.0246	.0394	.0571	.0684	.0906	.1198	.1538	.1884	.2108	.2556	.3097
	49	.0241	.0385	.0559	.0670	.0887	.1173	.1507	.1847	.2066	.2508	.3041
	50	.0235	.0377	.0547	.0656	.0868	.1149	.1477	.1811	.2027	.2461	.2986
	51	.0231	.0369	.0536	.0643	.0851	.1126	.1448	.1776	.1988	.2416	.2933
	52	.0226	.0362	.0525	.0630	.0834	.1105	.1421	.1743	.1952	.2372	.2882

* To approximate p_k, divide the starred entry under k by $(C - 1)$.
** Compute $B^* = C - B$, find p_{1-k}^* for B^* and C, and compute $p_k = 1 - p_{1-k}^*$.

B	C	.001	.01	.05	.1	.25	.5	.75	.9	.95	.99	.999
6	53	.0221	.0354	.0515	.0617	.0818	.1083	.1394	.1711	.1916	.2330	.2833
	54	.0217	.0348	.0505	.0606	.0802	.1063	.1368	.1680	.1882	.2289	.2785
	55	.0213	.0341	.0495	.0594	.0787	.1044	.1344	.1650	.1849	.2250	.2739
	56	.0209	.0335	.0486	.0583	.0773	.1025	.1320	.1621	.1817	.2213	.2695
	57	.0205	.0328	.0477	.0573	.0759	.1006	.1297	.1593	.1786	.2176	.2652
	58	.0201	.0322	.0468	.0562	.0746	.0989	.1274	.1566	.1756	.2141	.2610
	59	.0198	.0317	.0460	.0552	.0733	.0972	.1253	.1541	.1728	.2106	.2569
	60	.0194	.0311	.0452	.0543	.0720	.0956	.1232	.1515	.1700	.2073	.2530
	61	.0191	.0306	.0445	.0534	.0708	.0940	.1212	.1491	.1673	.2041	.2492
	62+	1.107*	1.785*	2.613*	3.152*	4.219*	5.670*	7.423*	9.275*	10.51*	13.11*	16.45*
7	8-13	SEE NOTE**										
	14-15	SEE NOTE***										
	16	.1209	.1795	.2437	.2822	.3518	.4348	.5204	.5965	.6404	.7177	.7936
	17	.1119	.1665	.2267	.2629	.3289	.4082	.4909	.5654	.6090	.6866	.7645
	18	.1041	.1552	.2119	.2461	.3088	.3847	.4646	.5374	.5803	.6577	.7369
	19	.0974	.1454	.1990	.2314	.2910	.3637	.4409	.5118	.5540	.6309	.7108
	20	.0915	.1368	.1875	.2183	.2752	.3449	.4195	.4886	.5300	.6060	.6861
	21	.0862	.1292	.1773	.2067	.2610	.3280	.4000	.4673	.5078	.5829	.6628
	22	.0816	.1223	.1682	.1962	.2482	.3126	.3823	.4477	.4874	.5613	.6409
	23	.0774	.1162	.1599	.1867	.2366	.2986	.3660	.4297	.4685	.5412	.6202
	24	.0736	.1107	.1525	.1782	.2260	.2858	.3511	.4131	.4510	.5224	.6007
	25	.0702	.1056	.1457	.1703	.2164	.2741	.3373	.3976	.4347	.5048	.5823
	26	.0671	.1010	.1395	.1632	.2075	.2632	.3246	.3833	.4195	.4884	.5649
	27	.0642	.0968	.1338	.1566	.1994	.2532	.3128	.3700	.4054	.4729	.5485
	28	.0616	.0929	.1285	.1505	.1918	.2440	.3018	.3575	.3921	.4584	.5329
	29	.0592	.0894	.1237	.1449	.1848	.2354	.2915	.3459	.3797	.4447	.5181
	30	.0570	.0860	.1192	.1397	.1784	.2274	.2819	.3349	.3680	.4317	.5041
	31	.0549	.0830	.1150	.1348	.1723	.2199	.2730	.3247	.3570	.4195	.4908
	32	.0530	.0801	.1111	.1303	.1666	.2128	.2646	.3150	.3467	.4080	.4782
	33	.0512	.0774	.1074	.1261	.1613	.2063	.2566	.3059	.3369	.3970	.4662
	34	.0495	.0749	.1040	.1221	.1564	.2001	.2492	.2973	.3276	.3866	.4547
	35	.0480	.0726	.1008	.1184	.1517	.1942	.2422	.2892	.3189	.3767	.4438
	36	.0465	.0704	.0978	.1149	.1473	.1887	.2355	.2815	.3106	.3674	.4334
	37	.0451	.0683	.0950	.1116	.1431	.1836	.2292	.2742	.3027	.3584	.4234
	38	.0438	.0664	.0923	.1085	.1392	.1786	.2232	.2673	.2952	.3499	.4139
	39	.0426	.0645	.0898	.1056	.1355	.1740	.2176	.2607	.2880	.3418	.4048
	40	.0414	.0628	.0874	.1028	.1320	.1696	.2122	.2544	.2812	.3340	.3960
	41	.0403	.0611	.0851	.1001	.1286	.1654	.2071	.2485	.2747	.3266	.3877
	42	.0393	.0596	.0830	.0976	.1255	.1614	.2022	.2427	.2685	.3195	.3796
	43	.0383	.0581	.0809	.0952	.1224	.1575	.1975	.2373	.2626	.3127	.3719
	44	.0373	.0567	.0790	.0929	.1196	.1539	.1931	.2321	.2569	.3062	.3645
	45	.0365	.0553	.0771	.0908	.1168	.1504	.1888	.2271	.2515	.2999	.3574
	46	.0356	.0540	.0754	.0887	.1142	.1471	.1847	.2223	.2463	.2939	.3506
	47	.0348	.0528	.0737	.0867	.1117	.1439	.1808	.2177	.2413	.2882	.3440
	48	.0340	.0516	.0720	.0848	.1093	.1409	.1771	.2133	.2365	.2826	.3376
	49	.0333	.0505	.0705	.0830	.1070	.1380	.1735	.2091	.2319	.2773	.3315
	50	.0325	.0495	.0690	.0813	.1048	.1352	.1701	.2050	.2274	.2721	.3256
	51	.0319	.0484	.0676	.0796	.1026	.1325	.1668	.2011	.2232	.2671	.3198
	52	.0312	.0474	.0662	.0780	.1006	.1299	.1636	.1974	.2191	.2624	.3143
	53	.0306	.0465	.0649	.0765	.0987	.1274	.1605	.1937	.2151	.2577	.3090
	54	.0300	.0456	.0637	.0750	.0968	.1251	.1576	.1903	.2113	.2533	.3038
	55	.0294	.0447	.0625	.0736	.0950	.1227	.1547	.1869	.2076	.2490	.2989
	56	.0288	.0439	.0613	.0722	.0932	.1205	.1520	.1836	.2040	.2448	.2940
	57	.0283	.0431	.0602	.0709	.0915	.1184	.1493	.1805	.2006	.2408	.2894
	58	.0278	.0423	.0591	.0697	.0899	.1163	.1468	.1775	.1972	.2369	.2848
	59	.0273	.0415	.0580	.0684	.0884	.1143	.1443	.1745	.1940	.2331	.2804
	60	.0268	.0408	.0570	.0672	.0869	.1124	.1419	.1717	.1909	.2295	.2762
	61	.0263	.0401	.0561	.0661	.0854	.1105	.1396	.1689	.1879	.2259	.2720
	62	.0259	.0394	.0551	.0650	.0840	.1087	.1373	.1663	.1849	.2225	.2680
	63	.0255	.0388	.0542	.0639	.0826	.1070	.1352	.1637	.1821	.2191	.2641
	64	.0250	.0381	.0533	.0629	.0813	.1053	.1331	.1612	.1793	.2159	.2603
	65	.0246	.0375	.0525	.0619	.0800	.1037	.1310	.1588	.1767	.2128	.2567
	66	.0242	.0369	.0516	.0609	.0788	.1021	.1291	.1564	.1741	.2097	.2531
	67	.0239	.0363	.0508	.0600	.0776	.1005	.1271	.1541	.1716	.2067	.2496
	68	.0235	.0358	.0501	.0591	.0764	.0991	.1253	.1519	.1691	.2039	.2462
	69+	1.520*	2.330*	3.285*	3.895*	5.083*	6.670*	8.558*	10.53*	11.84*	14.57*	18.06*
8	9-14	SEE NOTE**										
	15-18	SEE NOTE***										
	19	.1289	.1844	.2440	.2792	.3427	.4182	.4964	.5667	.6078	.6814	.7560
	20	.1209	.1733	.2297	.2633	.3239	.3966	.4725	.5413	.5819	.6553	.7309

*** To approximate p_k, compute $m = B/C$ and $s = \sqrt{m(1 - m)/(C + 1)}$, find u_k in Table T4 on page 715 below, and compute $p_k \doteq m + u_k s$.

B	C	.001	.01	.05	.1	.25	.5	.75	.9	.95	.99	.999
8	21	.1139	.1634	.2171	.2491	.3071	.3771	.4507	.5180	.5580	.6309	.7070
	22	.1076	.1546	.2057	.2363	.2920	.3594	.4308	.4966	.5359	.6082	.6844
	23	.1020	.1468	.1956	.2248	.2783	.3433	.4126	.4768	.5155	.5868	.6630
	24	.0969	.1397	.1863	.2144	.2658	.3286	.3959	.4586	.4964	.5669	.6427
	25	.0923	.1332	.1780	.2049	.2544	.3151	.3804	.4416	.4787	.5481	.6235
	26	.0882	.1273	.1703	.1962	.2440	.3027	.3661	.4258	.4622	.5306	.6054
	27	.0844	.1220	.1633	.1883	.2344	.2912	.3528	.4111	.4468	.5140	.5881
	28	.0809	.1170	.1568	.1809	.2255	.2806	.3405	.3974	.4323	.4984	.5718
	29	.0777	.1125	.1509	.1741	.2172	.2707	.3290	.3845	.4187	.4837	.5562
	30	.0747	.1083	.1453	.1678	.2096	.2614	.3182	.3725	.4060	.4699	.5415
	31	.0720	.1044	.1402	.1620	.2024	.2528	.3081	.3611	.3939	.4567	.5274
	32	.0694	.1007	.1354	.1565	.1958	.2447	.2986	.3505	.3826	.4443	.5141
	33	.0671	.0973	.1309	.1514	.1895	.2372	.2897	.3404	.3719	.4325	.5013
	34	.0649	.0942	.1268	.1466	.1837	.2301	.2813	.3309	.3618	.4213	.4892
	35	.0628	.0912	.1228	.1421	.1782	.2234	.2734	.3219	.3522	.4107	.4776
	36	.0608	.0884	.1191	.1379	.1730	.2170	.2659	.3134	.3430	.4005	.4665
	37	.0590	.0858	.1157	.1339	.1681	.2111	.2588	.3053	.3344	.3909	.4559
	38	.0573	.0833	.1124	.1302	.1635	.2054	.2521	.2976	.3262	.3817	.4458
	39	.0557	.0810	.1093	.1266	.1591	.2001	.2457	.2903	.3183	.3729	.4361
	40	.0541	.0788	.1064	.1233	.1550	.1950	.2397	.2834	.3108	.3645	.4268
	41	.0527	.0767	.1036	.1201	.1510	.1901	.2339	.2767	.3037	.3565	.4179
	42	.0513	.0747	.1010	.1171	.1473	.1855	.2284	.2704	.2969	.3488	.4093
	43	.0500	.0729	.0985	.1142	.1437	.1812	.2231	.2643	.2904	.3414	.4011
	44	.0488	.0711	.0961	.1115	.1403	.1770	.2181	.2586	.2841	.3343	.3932
	45	.0476	.0694	.0938	.1089	.1371	.1730	.2133	.2530	.2781	.3276	.3856
	46	.0465	.0678	.0917	.1064	.1340	.1692	.2087	.2477	.2724	.3210	.3783
	47	.0454	.0662	.0896	.1040	.1311	.1655	.2043	.2426	.2669	.3148	.3712
	48	.0444	.0647	.0876	.1017	.1282	.1620	.2001	.2377	.2616	.3087	.3644
	49	.0434	.0633	.0857	.0995	.1255	.1587	.1961	.2330	.2565	.3029	.3578
	50	.0425	.0620	.0839	.0974	.1229	.1555	.1922	.2285	.2516	.2973	.3515
	51	.0416	.0607	.0822	.0954	.1205	.1524	.1884	.2242	.2469	.2920	.3454
	52	.0407	.0594	.0805	.0935	.1181	.1494	.1848	.2200	.2424	.2868	.3395
	53	.0399	.0582	.0789	.0917	.1158	.1465	.1814	.2160	.2380	.2817	.3338
	54	.0391	.0571	.0774	.0899	.1136	.1438	.1781	.2121	.2338	.2769	.3282
	55	.0383	.0560	.0759	.0882	.1114	.1411	.1748	.2084	.2297	.2722	.3229
	56	.0376	.0549	.0745	.0866	.1094	.1386	.1717	.2047	.2258	.2677	.3177
	57	.0369	.0539	.0731	.0850	.1074	.1361	.1688	.2012	.2220	.2633	.3127
	58	.0362	.0529	.0718	.0835	.1055	.1338	.1659	.1979	.2183	.2591	.3078
	59	.0356	.0520	.0705	.0820	.1037	.1315	.1631	.1946	.2148	.2549	.3031
	60	.0349	.0511	.0693	.0806	.1019	.1293	.1604	.1914	.2113	.2510	.2985
	61	.0343	.0502	.0681	.0792	.1002	.1271	.1578	.1884	.2080	.2471	.2941
	62	.0337	.0493	.0670	.0779	.0985	.1250	.1552	.1854	.2048	.2434	.2898
	63	.0332	.0485	.0659	.0766	.0969	.1230	.1528	.1826	.2016	.2397	.2856
	64	.0326	.0477	.0648	.0754	.0954	.1211	.1504	.1798	.1986	.2362	.2815
	65	.0321	.0469	.0637	.0742	.0939	.1192	.1481	.1771	.1956	.2328	.2776
	66	.0316	.0462	.0627	.0730	.0924	.1174	.1459	.1744	.1928	.2295	.2737
	67	.0311	.0455	.0618	.0719	.0910	.1156	.1437	.1719	.1900	.2262	.2700
	68	.0306	.0448	.0608	.0708	.0896	.1139	.1416	.1694	.1873	.2231	.2663
	69	.0301	.0441	.0599	.0697	.0883	.1122	.1396	.1670	.1847	.2200	.2628
	70	.0297	.0434	.0590	.0687	.0870	.1106	.1376	.1647	.1821	.2171	.2593
	71	.0292	.0428	.0582	.0677	.0858	.1090	.1357	.1624	.1796	.2142	.2560
	72	.0288	.0422	.0573	.0667	.0845	.1075	.1338	.1602	.1772	.2113	.2527
	73	.0284	.0416	.0565	.0658	.0834	.1060	.1320	.1581	.1749	.2086	.2495
	74	.0280	.0410	.0557	.0649	.0822	.1046	.1302	.1560	.1726	.2059	.2464
	75	.0276	.0404	.0549	.0640	.0811	.1032	.1285	.1539	.1703	.2033	.2433
	76+	1.971*	2.906*	3.981*	4.656*	5.956*	7.669*	9.684*	11.77*	13.15*	16.00*	19.63*
9	10-16	SEE NOTE**										
	17-21	SEE NOTE***										
	22	.1362	.1891	.2450	.2778	.3366	.4063	.4787	.5442	.5828	.6528	.7252
	23	.1289	.1793	.2327	.2642	.3207	.3881	.4585	.5227	.5609	.6304	.7033
	24	.1224	.1705	.2216	.2518	.3062	.3715	.4400	.5029	.5405	.6094	.6824
	25	.1166	.1625	.2116	.2406	.2931	.3562	.4229	.4845	.5214	.5896	.6626
	26	.1112	.1553	.2024	.2303	.2810	.3422	.4071	.4673	.5036	.5711	.6437
	27	.1064	.1467	.1940	.2209	.2698	.3292	.3924	.4513	.4870	.5535	.6258
	28	.1019	.1426	.1862	.2122	.2596	.3171	.3787	.4364	.4714	.5370	.6088
	29	.0978	.1370	.1791	.2042	.2500	.3059	.3660	.4224	.4567	.5214	.5926
	30	.0940	.1318	.1725	.1968	.2412	.2955	.3540	.4092	.4429	.5066	.5771
	31	.0905	.1270	.1663	.1899	.2330	.2858	.3428	.3968	.4299	.4927	.5624
	32	.0873	.1225	.1606	.1834	.2253	.2766	.3323	.3852	.4177	.4794	.5484
	33	.0843	.1184	.1553	.1774	.2181	.2681	.3224	.3742	.4061	.4668	.5350
	34	.0815	.1145	.1503	.1718	.2113	.2600	.3131	.3638	.3951	.4549	.5223

* To approximate p_k, divide the starred entry under k by $(C - 1)$.

** Compute $B^* = C - B$, find p^*_{1-k} for B^* and C, and compute $p_k = 1 - p^*_{1-k}$.

B	C	.001	.01	.05	.1	.25	.5	.75	.9	.95	.99	.999
9	35	.0788	.1109	.1456	.1665	.2050	.2525	.3043	.3540	.3847	.4435	.5101
	36	.0764	.1075	.1412	.1615	.1990	.2453	.2960	.3446	.3748	.4327	.4984
	37	.0741	.1043	.1371	.1569	.1933	.2386	.2882	.3358	.3654	.4223	.4872
	38	.0719	.1012	.1332	.1524	.1880	.2322	.2807	.3274	.3564	.4125	.4765
	39	.0698	.0984	.1295	.1483	.1830	.2261	.2736	.3194	.3479	.4031	.4663
	40	.0679	.0957	.1260	.1443	.1782	.2204	.2669	.3118	.3398	.3941	.4565
	41	.0661	.0931	.1227	.1406	.1737	.2149	.2604	.3045	.3320	.3854	.4470
	42	.0643	.0907	.1196	.1370	.1694	.2097	.2543	.2976	.3246	.3772	.4380
	43	.0627	.0884	.1166	.1337	.1653	.2048	.2485	.2909	.3175	.3693	.4292
	44	.0611	.0863	.1138	.1304	.1614	.2000	.2429	.2846	.3107	.3617	.4209
	45	.0596	.0842	.1111	.1274	.1576	.1955	.2376	.2785	.3042	.3544	.4128
	46	.0582	.0822	.1085	.1245	.1541	.1912	.2325	.2727	.2980	.3474	.4050
	47	.0568	.0803	.1060	.1217	.1507	.1871	.2276	.2671	.2920	.3407	.3975
	48	.0556	.0785	.1037	.1190	.1474	.1831	.2229	.2617	.2862	.3342	.3903
	49	.0543	.0768	.1015	.1164	.1443	.1794	.2184	.2566	.2807	.3279	.3833
	50	.0531	.0751	.0993	.1140	.1413	.1757	.2141	.2516	.2754	.3219	.3766
	51	.0520	.0736	.0972	.1116	.1385	.1722	.2099	.2469	.2702	.3161	.3701
	52	.0509	.0721	.0953	.1094	.1357	.1689	.2059	.2423	.2653	.3105	.3638
	53	.0499	.0706	.0934	.1072	.1331	.1656	.2021	.2379	.2605	.3051	.3577
	54	.0489	.0692	.0916	.1052	.1305	.1625	.1984	.2336	.2559	.2999	.3519
	55	.0479	.0679	.0898	.1032	.1281	.1595	.1948	.2295	.2515	.2948	.3462
	56	.0470	.0666	.0881	.1012	.1257	.1567	.1913	.2255	.2472	.2900	.3406
	57	.0461	.0653	.0865	.0994	.1235	.1539	.1880	.2217	.2430	.2852	.3353
	58	.0453	.0641	.0849	.0976	.1213	.1512	.1848	.2180	.2390	.2807	.3301
	59	.0445	.0630	.0834	.0959	.1191	.1486	.1817	.2144	.2351	.2762	.3251
	60	.0437	.0619	.0820	.0942	.1171	.1461	.1787	.2109	.2314	.2719	.3202
	61	.0429	.0608	.0805	.0926	.1151	.1437	.1758	.2075	.2277	.2678	.3155
	62	.0422	.0598	.0792	.0910	.1132	.1413	.1730	.2043	.2242	.2637	.3109
	63	.0415	.0588	.0779	.0895	.1114	.1391	.1703	.2011	.2208	.2598	.3064
	64	.0408	.0578	.0766	.0881	.1096	.1369	.1676	.1981	.2175	.2560	.3021
	65	.0401	.0569	.0754	.0867	.1079	.1347	.1651	.1951	.2143	.2523	.2979
	66	.0394	.0559	.0742	.0853	.1062	.1327	.1626	.1922	.2111	.2487	.2938
	67	.0388	.0551	.0730	.0840	.1046	.1307	.1602	.1894	.2081	.2452	.2898
	68	.0382	.0542	.0719	.0827	.1030	.1287	.1578	.1867	.2051	.2418	.2859
	69	.0376	.0534	.0708	.0815	.1015	.1269	.1556	.1841	.2023	.2385	.2821
	70	.0371	.0526	.0698	.0803	.1000	.1250	.1533	.1815	.1995	.2353	.2784
	71	.0365	.0518	.0687	.0791	.0985	.1233	.1512	.1790	.1968	.2322	.2748
	72	.0360	.0511	.0678	.0780	.0971	.1215	.1491	.1766	.1941	.2292	.2713
	73	.0355	.0503	.0668	.0769	.0958	.1198	.1471	.1742	.1916	.2262	.2679
	74	.0349	.0496	.0658	.0758	.0945	.1182	.1451	.1719	.1891	.2233	.2646
	75	.0345	.0489	.0649	.0747	.0932	.1166	.1432	.1697	.1866	.2205	.2613
	76	.0340	.0482	.0641	.0737	.0919	.1151	.1413	.1675	.1842	.2177	.2581
	77	.0335	.0476	.0632	.0727	.0907	.1136	.1395	.1654	.1819	.2150	.2550
	78	.0331	.0469	.0623	.0718	.0895	.1121	.1377	.1633	.1797	.2124	.2520
	79	.0326	.0463	.0615	.0708	.0883	.1107	.1360	.1613	.1775	.2099	.2491
	80	.0322	.0457	.0607	.0699	.0872	.1093	.1343	.1593	.1753	.2074	.2462
	81	.0318	.0451	.0600	.0690	.0861	.1079	.1326	.1574	.1732	.2049	.2434
	82	.0314	.0446	.0592	.0682	.0850	.1066	.1310	.1555	.1712	.2026	.2406
	83+	2.452*	3.507*	4.695*	5.432*	6.838*	8.669*	10.80*	12.99*	14.43*	17.40*	21.16*
10	11-17	SEE NOTE**										
	18-25	SEE NOTE***										
	26	.1361	.1848	.2356	.2653	.3184	.3816	.4476	.5080	.5439	.6100	.6802
	27	.1300	.1768	.2257	.2544	.3058	.3671	.4315	.4907	.5262	.5916	.6617
	28	.1245	.1695	.2166	.2443	.2941	.3537	.4165	.4746	.5095	.5742	.6441
	29	.1194	.1627	.2082	.2350	.2833	.3412	.4025	.4594	.4938	.5578	.6273
	30	.1148	.1565	.2005	.2264	.2732	.3296	.3895	.4452	.4790	.5422	.6113
	31	.1105	.1508	.1933	.2184	.2638	.3187	.3772	.4319	.4651	.5274	.5960
	32	.1065	.1454	.1866	.2110	.2551	.3086	.3657	.4193	.4519	.5134	.5814
	33	.1027	.1404	.1804	.2040	.2469	.2990	.3548	.4074	.4394	.5001	.5674
	34	.0993	.1358	.1746	.1975	.2393	.2900	.3446	.3961	.4276	.4874	.5541
	35	.0960	.1315	.1691	.1914	.2321	.2816	.3350	.3855	.4165	.4754	.5413
	36	.0930	.1274	.1640	.1857	.2253	.2736	.3258	.3754	.4058	.4639	.5291
	37	.0902	.1236	.1591	.1803	.2189	.2661	.3172	.3658	.3957	.4529	.5174
	38	.0875	.1199	.1546	.1752	.2128	.2590	.3090	.3567	.3861	.4424	.5062
	39	.0850	.1165	.1503	.1704	.2071	.2522	.3012	.3480	.3769	.4324	.4954
	40	.0826	.1133	.1462	.1658	.2017	.2458	.2938	.3397	.3682	.4228	.4851
	41	.0803	.1103	.1424	.1615	.1966	.2397	.2867	.3318	.3598	.4137	.4752
	42	.0782	.1074	.1387	.1574	.1917	.2339	.2800	.3243	.3518	.4049	.4657
	43	.0762	.1047	.1353	.1535	.1870	.2284	.2736	.3171	.3442	.3964	.4565
	44	.0743	.1021	.1320	.1498	.1826	.2231	.2675	.3102	.3368	.3883	.4477
	45	.0724	.0996	.1288	.1463	.1784	.2181	.2616	.3036	.3298	.3806	.4392

*** To approximate p_k, compute $m = B/C$ and $s = \sqrt{m(1-m)/(C+1)}$, find u_k in Table T4 on page 715 below, and compute $p_k \doteq m + u_k s$.

B	C	.001	.01	.05	.1	.25	.5	.75	.9	.95	.99	.999
10	46	.0707	.0973	.1258	.1429	.1744	.2133	.2560	.2973	.3231	.3731	.4310
	47	.0691	.0950	.1230	.1397	.1705	.2087	.2506	.2912	.3166	.3659	.4231
	48	.0675	.0929	.1202	.1366	.1668	.2043	.2455	.2854	.3104	.3590	.4154
	49	.0660	.0908	.1176	.1337	.1633	.2000	.2405	.2798	.3044	.3523	.4081
	50	.0645	.0889	.1151	.1309	.1599	.1960	.2358	.2744	.2986	.3459	.4010
	51	.0631	.0870	.1127	.1282	.1567	.1921	.2312	.2692	.2931	.3397	.3941
	52	.0618	.0852	.1104	.1256	.1535	.1883	.2268	.2642	.2877	.3337	.3875
	53	.0606	.0835	.1082	.1231	.1505	.1847	.2226	.2594	.2826	.3279	.3810
	54	.0593	.0818	.1061	.1207	.1477	.1813	.2185	.2548	.2776	.3224	.3748
	55	.0582	.0802	.1041	.1184	.1449	.1779	.2146	.2503	.2728	.3170	.3688
	56	.0571	.0787	.1021	.1162	.1422	.1747	.2108	.2460	.2682	.3117	.3629
	57	.0560	.0772	.1002	.1141	.1397	.1716	.2071	.2418	.2637	.3067	.3573
	58	.0549	.0758	.0984	.1120	.1372	.1686	.2036	.2378	.2594	.3018	.3518
	59	.0539	.0744	.0966	.1100	.1348	.1657	.2002	.2339	.2552	.2970	.3465
	60	.0530	.0731	.0949	.1081	.1325	.1630	.1969	.2301	.2511	.2925	.3413
	61	.0520	.0718	.0933	.1063	.1302	.1603	.1937	.2264	.2472	.2880	.3363
	62	.0511	.0706	.0917	.1045	.1281	.1576	.1906	.2229	.2433	.2837	.3314
	63	.0503	.0694	.0902	.1027	.1260	.1551	.1876	.2195	.2396	.2795	.3267
	64	.0494	.0683	.0887	.1011	.1240	.1527	.1847	.2161	.2361	.2754	.3221
	65	.0486	.0672	.0873	.0995	.1220	.1503	.1819	.2129	.2326	.2714	.3176
	66	.0478	.0661	.0859	.0979	.1201	.1480	.1791	.2098	.2292	.2676	.3133
	67	.0471	.0650	.0846	.0964	.1183	.1458	.1765	.2067	.2259	.2639	.3090
	68	.0463	.0640	.0833	.0949	.1165	.1436	.1739	.2038	.2227	.2602	.3049
	69	.0456	.0631	.0820	.0935	.1147	.1415	.1714	.2009	.2196	.2567	.3009
	70	.0449	.0621	.0808	.0921	.1131	.1394	.1690	.1981	.2166	.2532	.2970
	71	.0442	.0612	.0796	.0907	.1114	.1375	.1666	.1954	.2136	.2499	.2931
	72	.0436	.0603	.0785	.0894	.1098	.1355	.1643	.1927	.2108	.2466	.2894
	73	.0430	.0594	.0773	.0882	.1083	.1337	.1621	.1901	.2080	.2434	.2858
	74	.0423	.0586	.0762	.0869	.1068	.1318	.1599	.1876	.2053	.2403	.2823
	75	.0417	.0578	.0752	.0857	.1054	.1301	.1578	.1852	.2026	.2373	.2788
	76	.0412	.0570	.0742	.0846	.1039	.1283	.1557	.1828	.2001	.2343	.2754
	77	.0406	.0562	.0732	.0834	.1026	.1267	.1537	.1805	.1975	.2315	.2722
	78	.0401	.0554	.0722	.0823	.1012	.1250	.1518	.1782	.1951	.2287	.2689
	79	.0395	.0547	.0712	.0813	.0999	.1234	.1499	.1760	.1927	.2259	.2658
	80	.0390	.0540	.0703	.0802	.0986	.1219	.1480	.1739	.1904	.2232	.2627
	81	.0385	.0533	.0694	.0792	.0974	.1204	.1462	.1718	.1881	.2206	.2597
	82	.0380	.0526	.0685	.0782	.0962	.1189	.1444	.1697	.1859	.2181	.2568
	83	.0375	.0519	.0677	.0772	.0950	.1174	.1427	.1677	.1837	.2156	.2540
	84	.0370	.0513	.0668	.0763	.0938	.1160	.1410	.1658	.1816	.2131	.2512
	85	.0366	.0507	.0660	.0753	.0927	.1146	.1393	.1639	.1795	.2108	.2484
	86	.0361	.0501	.0652	.0744	.0916	.1133	.1377	.1620	.1775	.2084	.2457
	87	.0357	.0495	.0645	.0736	.0905	.1120	.1362	.1602	.1755	.2061	.2431
	88	.0353	.0489	.0637	.0727	.0895	.1107	.1346	.1584	.1736	.2039	.2405
	89	.0349	.0483	.0630	.0719	.0885	.1095	.1331	.1566	.1717	.2017	.2380
	90+	2.961*	4.130*	5.425*	6.221*	7.726*	9.669*	11.91*	14.21*	15.71*	18.78*	22.66*
11	12-19	SEE NOTE**										
	20-28	SEE NOTE***										
	29	.1425	.1896	.2383	.2665	.3169	.3765	.4388	.4958	.5300	.5930	.6606
	30	.1368	.1823	.2293	.2567	.3056	.3637	.4246	.4806	.5143	.5767	.6441
	31	.1316	.1755	.2211	.2476	.2951	.3517	.4112	.4663	.4994	.5612	.6282
	32	.1268	.1693	.2134	.2391	.2853	.3405	.3987	.4528	.4854	.5465	.6131
	33	.1223	.1634	.2062	.2312	.2761	.3299	.3869	.4400	.4721	.5324	.5986
	34	.1182	.1580	.1995	.2238	.2675	.3200	.3758	.4279	.4596	.5191	.5848
	35	.1143	.1529	.1932	.2168	.2594	.3107	.3653	.4165	.4476	.5064	.5715
	36	.1106	.1481	.1873	.2103	.2518	.3019	.3554	.4056	.4363	.4943	.5588
	37	.1072	.1436	.1818	.2042	.2447	.2936	.3460	.3953	.4255	.4827	.5466
	38	.1040	.1394	.1765	.1984	.2379	.2857	.3371	.3855	.4152	.4716	.5349
	39	.1010	.1354	.1716	.1929	.2315	.2783	.3286	.3762	.4054	.4610	.5237
	40	.0981	.1317	.1669	.1877	.2254	.2712	.3205	.3673	.3960	.4509	.5129
	41	.0954	.1281	.1625	.1828	.2197	.2645	.3129	.3588	.3871	.4412	.5025
	42	.0929	.1248	.1583	.1782	.2142	.2581	.3055	.3507	.3785	.4319	.4925
	43	.0905	.1216	.1544	.1738	.2090	.2520	.2985	.3429	.3703	.4230	.4829
	44	.0882	.1185	.1506	.1695	.2040	.2462	.2919	.3355	.3625	.4144	.4737
	45	.0860	.1157	.1470	.1655	.1993	.2406	.2855	.3284	.3549	.4062	.4648
	46	.0839	.1129	.1436	.1617	.1948	.2353	.2794	.3216	.3477	.3982	.4562
	47	.0819	.1103	.1403	.1581	.1905	.2302	.2735	.3150	.3408	.3906	.4479
	48	.0801	.1078	.1372	.1546	.1864	.2254	.2679	.3087	.3341	.3833	.4399
	49	.0783	.1054	.1342	.1512	.1824	.2207	.2625	.3027	.3277	.3762	.4321
	50	.0765	.1031	.1313	.1480	.1786	.2162	.2573	.2969	.3215	.3694	.4247
	51	.0749	.1009	.1286	.1450	.1750	.2119	.2524	.2913	.3156	.3628	.4175
	52	.0733	.0988	.1259	.1420	.1715	.2078	.2476	.2859	.3099	.3564	.4105

* To approximate p_k, divide the starred entry under k by $(C-1)$.

** Compute $B^* = C - B$, find p_{1-k}^* for B^* and C, and compute $p_k = 1 - p_{1-k}^*$.

B	C	.001	.01	.05	.1	.25	.5	.75	.9	.95	.99	.999
11	53	.0718	.0968	.1234	.1392	.1682	.2039	.2430	.2807	.3043	.3503	.4037
	54	.0703	.0949	.1210	.1365	.1649	.2000	.2385	.2757	.2990	.3444	.3972
	55	.0690	.0930	.1186	.1339	.1618	.1963	.2342	.2709	.2938	.3386	.3908
	56	.0676	.0913	.1164	.1314	.1589	.1928	.2301	.2662	.2889	.3331	.3847
	57	.0663	.0895	.1142	.1290	.1560	.1894	.2261	.2617	.2841	.3277	.3787
	58	.0651	.0879	.1122	.1266	.1532	.1861	.2222	.2574	.2794	.3225	.3729
	59	.0639	.0863	.1102	.1244	.1505	.1829	.2185	.2531	.2749	.3174	.3673
	60	.0627	.0848	.1082	.1222	.1479	.1798	.2149	.2491	.2705	.3126	.3619
	61	.0616	.0833	.1064	.1201	.1454	.1768	.2114	.2451	.2663	.3078	.3566
	62	.0606	.0818	.1045	.1181	.1430	.1739	.2081	.2413	.2622	.3032	.3515
	63	.0595	.0805	.1028	.1162	.1407	.1711	.2048	.2376	.2582	.2987	.3465
	64	.0585	.0791	.1011	.1143	.1384	.1684	.2016	.2340	.2544	.2944	.3416
	65	.0576	.0778	.0995	.1124	.1362	.1658	.1986	.2305	.2506	.2902	.3369
	66	.0566	.0766	.0979	.1107	.1341	.1633	.1956	.2271	.2470	.2861	.3323
	67	.0557	.0754	.0964	.1089	.1321	.1608	.1927	.2238	.2434	.2821	.3278
	68	.0548	.0742	.0949	.1073	.1301	.1584	.1899	.2206	.2400	.2782	.3235
	69	.0540	.0731	.0934	.1057	.1281	.1561	.1871	.2175	.2367	.2745	.3192
	70	.0532	.0720	.0921	.1041	.1263	.1539	.1845	.2145	.2334	.2708	.3151
	71	.0524	.0709	.0907	.1026	.1244	.1517	.1819	.2115	.2303	.2672	.3111
	72	.0516	.0698	.0894	.1011	.1227	.1496	.1794	.2087	.2272	.2637	.3071
	73	.0508	.0688	.0881	.0997	.1209	.1475	.1770	.2059	.2242	.2603	.3033
	74	.0501	.0679	.0869	.0983	.1193	.1455	.1746	.2032	.2213	.2570	.2996
	75	.0494	.0669	.0857	.0969	.1176	.1435	.1723	.2005	.2184	.2538	.2959
	76	.0487	.0660	.0845	.0956	.1161	.1416	.1701	.1980	.2157	.2507	.2924
	77	.0480	.0651	.0833	.0943	.1145	.1398	.1679	.1955	.2130	.2476	.2889
	78	.0474	.0642	.0822	.0930	.1130	.1380	.1657	.1930	.2103	.2446	.2855
	79	.0468	.0633	.0811	.0918	.1115	.1362	.1636	.1906	.2078	.2417	.2822
	80	.0461	.0625	.0801	.0906	.1101	.1345	.1616	.1883	.2052	.2388	.2789
	81	.0455	.0617	.0791	.0895	.1087	.1328	.1596	.1860	.2028	.2360	.2758
	82	.0450	.0609	.0781	.0884	.1074	.1312	.1577	.1838	.2004	.2333	.2727
	83	.0444	.0602	.0771	.0873	.1061	.1296	.1558	.1817	.1981	.2307	.2696
	84	.0438	.0594	.0761	.0862	.1048	.1280	.1540	.1795	.1958	.2281	.2667
	85	.0433	.0587	.0752	.0851	.1035	.1265	.1522	.1775	.1936	.2255	.2638
	86	.0427	.0580	.0743	.0841	.1023	.1250	.1504	.1755	.1914	.2230	.2609
	87	.0422	.0573	.0734	.0831	.1011	.1236	.1487	.1735	.1893	.2206	.2582
	88	.0417	.0566	.0726	.0821	.0999	.1222	.1470	.1716	.1872	.2182	.2555
	89	.0412	.0559	.0717	.0812	.0988	.1208	.1454	.1697	.1851	.2159	.2528
	90	.0407	.0553	.0709	.0803	.0976	.1194	.1438	.1678	.1831	.2136	.2502
	91	.0403	.0546	.0701	.0794	.0965	.1181	.1422	.1660	.1812	.2114	.2476
	92	.0398	.0540	.0693	.0785	.0955	.1168	.1407	.1642	.1793	.2092	.2451
	93	.0394	.0534	.0685	.0776	.0944	.1155	.1392	.1625	.1774	.2070	.2427
	94	.0389	.0528	.0678	.0768	.0934	.1143	.1377	.1608	.1756	.2049	.2403
	95	.0385	.0522	.0670	.0759	.0924	.1131	.1363	.1592	.1738	.2029	.2379
	96	.0381	.0517	.0663	.0751	.0914	.1119	.1348	.1575	.1720	.2008	.2356
	97+	3.491*	4.771*	6.169*	7.021*	8.620*	10.67*	13.02*	15.41*	16.96*	20.14*	24.13*
12	13-20	SEE NOTE**										
	21-32	SEE NOTE***										
	33	.1430	.1873	.2326	.2589	.3055	.3609	.4188	.4721	.5042	.5639	.6288
	34	.1380	.1810	.2250	.2505	.2960	.3500	.4068	.4592	.4909	.5499	.6145
	35	.1334	.1751	.2179	.2427	.2870	.3398	.3954	.4470	.4782	.5366	.6007
	36	.1291	.1696	.2112	.2354	.2786	.3302	.3847	.4354	.4661	.5239	.5875
	37	.1251	.1644	.2049	.2285	.2707	.3211	.3746	.4244	.4547	.5117	.5749
	38	.1213	.1595	.1990	.2220	.2632	.3125	.3649	.4139	.4438	.5001	.5628
	39	.1178	.1550	.1934	.2158	.2561	.3044	.3558	.4039	.4333	.4890	.5511
	40	.1144	.1506	.1881	.2100	.2493	.2966	.3471	.3944	.4234	.4783	.5398
	41	.1113	.1466	.1831	.2045	.2430	.2893	.3388	.3853	.4139	.4681	.5290
	42	.1083	.1427	.1784	.1993	.2369	.2823	.3309	.3767	.4048	.4583	.5187
	43	.1054	.1390	.1739	.1943	.2311	.2756	.3233	.3684	.3961	.4489	.5086
	44	.1027	.1355	.1696	.1896	.2256	.2693	.3161	.3604	.3877	.4399	.4990
	45	.1002	.1322	.1655	.1851	.2204	.2632	.3092	.3528	.3797	.4312	.4897
	46	.0977	.1291	.1617	.1808	.2154	.2574	.3026	.3455	.3720	.4228	.4807
	47	.0954	.1260	.1580	.1767	.2106	.2518	.2963	.3385	.3646	.4148	.4721
	48	.0932	.1232	.1544	.1728	.2061	.2465	.2902	.3318	.3575	.4071	.4637
	49	.0911	.1204	.1510	.1691	.2017	.2414	.2843	.3253	.3507	.3996	.4556
	50	.0891	.1178	.1478	.1655	.1975	.2365	.2787	.3191	.3441	.3924	.4478
	51	.0872	.1153	.1447	.1620	.1935	.2318	.2734	.3131	.3378	.3854	.4402
	52	.0853	.1129	.1417	.1588	.1896	.2273	.2682	.3073	.3317	.3786	.4329
	53	.0836	.1106	.1389	.1556	.1859	.2230	.2632	.3018	.3258	.3722	.4259
	54	.0819	.1084	.1362	.1526	.1823	.2188	.2584	.2964	.3201	.3659	.4190
	55	.0802	.1062	.1335	.1496	.1789	.2147	.2538	.2912	.3146	.3599	.4124

*** To approximate p_k, compute $m = B/C$ and $s = \sqrt{m(1-m)/(C+1)}$, find u_k in Table T4 on page 715 below, and compute $p_k \doteq m + u_k s$.

B	C	.001	.01	.05	.1	.25	.5	.75	.9	.95	.99	.999
12	56	.0787	.1042	.1310	.1468	.1756	.2109	.2493	.2862	.3093	.3540	.4059
	57	.0772	.1022	.1286	.1441	.1724	.2071	.2450	.2814	.3041	.3483	.3997
	58	.0757	.1003	.1262	.1415	.1694	.2035	.2408	.2767	.2992	.3428	.3936
	59	.0743	.0985	.1239	.1390	.1664	.2000	.2368	.2722	.2943	.3375	.3877
	60	.0730	.0968	.1218	.1366	.1635	.1967	.2329	.2678	.2897	.3323	.3820
	61	.0717	.0951	.1197	.1342	.1608	.1934	.2291	.2636	.2852	.3273	.3765
	62	.0704	.0934	.1176	.1320	.1581	.1902	.2254	.2595	.2808	.3224	.3711
	63	.0692	.0918	.1157	.1298	.1555	.1872	.2219	.2555	.2765	.3177	.3658
	64	.0680	.0903	.1137	.1276	.1530	.1842	.2185	.2516	.2724	.3131	.3607
	65	.0669	.0888	.1119	.1256	.1506	.1814	.2151	.2479	.2684	.3086	.3558
	66	.0658	.0874	.1101	.1236	.1482	.1786	.2119	.2442	.2645	.3043	.3509
	67	.0648	.0860	.1084	.1217	.1460	.1759	.2088	.2407	.2608	.3001	.3462
	68	.0637	.0847	.1067	.1198	.1438	.1733	.2058	.2373	.2571	.2959	.3417
	69	.0628	.0834	.1051	.1180	.1416	.1708	.2028	.2339	.2535	.2919	.3372
	70	.0618	.0821	.1035	.1163	.1395	.1683	.1999	.2307	.2501	.2881	.3329
	71	.0609	.0809	.1020	.1146	.1375	.1659	.1971	.2275	.2467	.2843	.3286
	72	.0600	.0797	.1005	.1129	.1356	.1636	.1944	.2245	.2434	.2806	.3245
	73	.0591	.0785	.0991	.1113	.1337	.1613	.1918	.2215	.2402	.2770	.3205
	74	.0582	.0774	.0977	.1097	.1318	.1591	.1892	.2186	.2371	.2735	.3165
	75	.0574	.0763	.0963	.1082	.1300	.1570	.1867	.2157	.2340	.2701	.3127
	76	.0566	.0753	.0950	.1067	.1282	.1549	.1843	.2130	.2311	.2667	.3090
	77	.0558	.0742	.0937	.1053	.1265	.1529	.1819	.2103	.2282	.2635	.3053
	78	.0551	.0732	.0925	.1039	.1249	.1509	.1796	.2077	.2254	.2603	.3017
	79	.0543	.0722	.0912	.1025	.1233	.1490	.1774	.2051	.2226	.2572	.2982
	80	.0536	.0713	.0901	.1012	.1217	.1471	.1752	.2026	.2199	.2542	.2948
	81	.0529	.0704	.0889	.0999	.1202	.1452	.1730	.2002	.2173	.2512	.2915
	82	.0522	.0695	.0878	.0987	.1187	.1435	.1709	.1978	.2148	.2483	.2882
	83	.0515	.0686	.0867	.0974	.1172	.1417	.1689	.1955	.2123	.2455	.2850
	84	.0509	.0677	.0856	.0962	.1158	.1400	.1669	.1932	.2098	.2427	.2819
	85	.0503	.0669	.0845	.0951	.1144	.1384	.1649	.1910	.2074	.2400	.2789
	86	.0496	.0661	.0835	.0939	.1130	.1367	.1630	.1888	.2051	.2374	.2759
	87	.0490	.0653	.0825	.0928	.1117	.1352	.1612	.1867	.2028	.2348	.2729
	88	.0484	.0645	.0816	.0917	.1104	.1336	.1594	.1846	.2006	.2323	.2701
	89	.0479	.0638	.0806	.0907	.1091	.1321	.1576	.1826	.1984	.2298	.2673
	90	.0473	.0630	.0797	.0896	.1079	.1306	.1558	.1806	.1963	.2274	.2645
	91	.0468	.0623	.0788	.0886	.1067	.1292	.1541	.1786	.1942	.2250	.2618
	92	.0462	.0616	.0779	.0876	.1055	.1278	.1525	.1767	.1921	.2227	.2592
	93	.0457	.0609	.0770	.0866	.1043	.1264	.1508	.1749	.1901	.2204	.2566
	94	.0452	.0602	.0762	.0857	.1032	.1250	.1493	.1731	.1882	.2182	.2541
	95	.0447	.0596	.0753	.0848	.1021	.1237	.1477	.1713	.1863	.2160	.2516
	96	.0442	.0589	.0745	.0839	.1010	.1224	.1462	.1695	.1844	.2138	.2491
	97	.0437	.0583	.0737	.0830	.1000	.1211	.1447	.1678	.1825	.2117	.2468
	98	.0433	.0577	.0730	.0821	.0989	.1199	.1432	.1661	.1807	.2097	.2444
	99	.0428	.0570	.0722	.0812	.0979	.1187	.1418	.1645	.1789	.2077	.2421
	100	.0424	.0565	.0715	.0804	.0969	.1175	.1404	.1629	.1772	.2057	.2398
	101	.0419	.0559	.0707	.0796	.0959	.1163	.1390	.1613	.1755	.2037	.2376
	102	.0415	.0553	.0700	.0788	.0950	.1151	.1376	.1598	.1738	.2018	.2355
	103	.0411	.0547	.0693	.0780	.0940	.1140	.1363	.1582	.1722	.1999	.2333
	104+	4.042*	5.428*	6.924*	7.829*	9.519*	11.67*	14.12*	16.60*	18.21*	21.49*	25.59*
13	14-22	SEE NOTE**										
	23-36	SEE NOTE***										
	37	.1439	.1859	.2285	.2532	.2969	.3486	.4029	.4531	.4834	.5401	.6023
	38	.1395	.1803	.2219	.2459	.2886	.3393	.3926	.4420	.4719	.5280	.5898
	39	.1353	.1751	.2156	.2391	.2808	.3305	.3828	.4314	.4609	.5163	.5777
	40	.1315	.1702	.2097	.2326	.2734	.3221	.3734	.4213	.4503	.5052	.5661
	41	.1278	.1655	.2041	.2265	.2664	.3141	.3645	.4116	.4403	.4945	.5549
	42	.1243	.1611	.1988	.2207	.2598	.3065	.3560	.4024	.4307	.4842	.5441
	43	.1210	.1570	.1938	.2152	.2534	.2992	.3479	.3935	.4214	.4744	.5337
	44	.1179	.1530	.1890	.2099	.2474	.2923	.3402	.3851	.4126	.4649	.5237
	45	.1150	.1492	.1845	.2049	.2417	.2857	.3327	.3770	.4041	.4558	.5140
	46	.1122	.1457	.1801	.2002	.2362	.2794	.3256	.3692	.3960	.4470	.5047
	47	.1095	.1423	.1760	.1956	.2309	.2734	.3188	.3618	.3881	.4385	.4957
	48	.1069	.1390	.1720	.1913	.2259	.2676	.3123	.3546	.3806	.4304	.4869
	49	.1045	.1359	.1683	.1871	.2211	.2621	.3061	.3477	.3734	.4225	.4785
	50	.1022	.1329	.1646	.1832	.2165	.2568	.3000	.3411	.3664	.4150	.4704
	51	.1000	.1301	.1612	.1794	.2121	.2517	.2942	.3347	.3597	.4077	.4625
	52	.0978	.1273	.1579	.1757	.2079	.2468	.2887	.3285	.3532	.4006	.4549
	53	.0958	.1247	.1547	.1722	.2038	.2421	.2833	.3226	.3469	.3938	.4475
	54	.0938	.1222	.1516	.1688	.1999	.2375	.2782	.3169	.3409	.3872	.4403
	55	.0919	.1198	.1487	.1656	.1961	.2332	.2732	.3114	.3350	.3808	.4334
	56	.0901	.1175	.1458	.1625	.1925	.2289	.2684	.3060	.3294	.3746	.4267

* To approximate p_k, divide the starred entry under k by $(C - 1)$.

** Compute $B^* = C - B$, find p_{1-k}^* for B^* and C, and compute $p_k = 1 - p_{1-k}^*$.

B	C	.001	.01	.05	.1	.25	.5	.75	.9	.95	.99	.999
13	57	.0884	.1153	.1431	.1595	.1890	.2249	.2637	.3009	.3239	.3686	.4202
	58	.0867	.1131	.1405	.1566	.1856	.2210	.2592	.2959	.3187	.3628	.4138
	59	.0851	.1111	.1380	.1538	.1824	.2172	.2549	.2911	.3136	.3572	.4077
	60	.0836	.1091	.1355	.1511	.1792	.2135	.2507	.2864	.3086	.3517	.4017
	61	.0821	.1072	.1332	.1485	.1762	.2100	.2467	.2819	.3038	.3464	.3959
	62	.0807	.1053	.1309	.1460	.1733	.2065	.2427	.2775	.2992	.3413	.3903
	63	.0793	.1035	.1287	.1435	.1704	.2032	.2389	.2732	.2946	.3363	.3848
	64	.0779	.1018	.1266	.1412	.1677	.2000	.2352	.2691	.2903	.3315	.3795
	65	.0766	.1001	.1245	.1389	.1650	.1969	.2317	.2651	.2860	.3267	.3743
	66	.0754	.0985	.1226	.1367	.1624	.1939	.2282	.2612	.2819	.3222	.3692
	67	.0742	.0969	.1206	.1346	.1599	.1910	.2248	.2575	.2779	.3177	.3643
	68	.0730	.0954	.1188	.1325	.1575	.1881	.2215	.2538	.2740	.3134	.3595
	69	.0718	.0939	.1170	.1305	.1552	.1854	.2184	.2502	.2702	.3092	.3548
	70	.0707	.0925	.1152	.1286	.1529	.1827	.2153	.2468	.2665	.3051	.3503
	71	.0697	.0911	.1135	.1267	.1507	.1801	.2123	.2434	.2629	.3011	.3458
	72	.0686	.0898	.1118	.1249	.1485	.1776	.2094	.2401	.2594	.2972	.3415
	73	.0676	.0885	.1102	.1231	.1464	.1751	.2065	.2369	.2560	.2934	.3373
	74	.0666	.0872	.1087	.1214	.1444	.1727	.2038	.2338	.2527	.2897	.3332
	75	.0657	.0860	.1072	.1197	.1424	.1704	.2011	.2308	.2495	.2861	.3292
	76	.0648	.0848	.1057	.1180	.1405	.1682	.1985	.2278	.2463	.2825	.3252
	77	.0639	.0836	.1043	.1164	.1387	.1660	.1959	.2250	.2432	.2791	.3214
	78	.0630	.0825	.1029	.1149	.1368	.1638	.1934	.2222	.2402	.2757	.3176
	79	.0621	.0814	.1015	.1134	.1351	.1617	.1910	.2194	.2373	.2725	.3140
	80	.0613	.0803	.1002	.1119	.1333	.1597	.1886	.2168	.2345	.2693	.3104
	81	.0605	.0793	.0989	.1105	.1316	.1577	.1863	.2142	.2317	.2661	.3069
	82	.0597	.0782	.0976	.1091	.1300	.1558	.1841	.2116	.2290	.2631	.3035
	83	.0590	.0772	.0964	.1077	.1284	.1539	.1819	.2091	.2263	.2601	.3001
	84	.0582	.0763	.0952	.1064	.1268	.1520	.1797	.2067	.2237	.2572	.2969
	85	.0575	.0753	.0940	.1051	.1253	.1502	.1776	.2043	.2212	.2543	.2937
	86	.0568	.0744	.0929	.1038	.1238	.1485	.1756	.2020	.2187	.2515	.2905
	87	.0561	.0735	.0918	.1026	.1224	.1467	.1736	.1997	.2163	.2488	.2875
	88	.0554	.0726	.0907	.1014	.1209	.1451	.1716	.1975	.2139	.2461	.2844
	89	.0548	.0718	.0897	.1002	.1196	.1434	.1697	.1954	.2116	.2435	.2815
	90	.0541	.0709	.0886	.0991	.1182	.1418	.1678	.1932	.2093	.2410	.2786
	91	.0535	.0701	.0876	.0980	.1169	.1402	.1660	.1912	.2071	.2384	.2758
	92	.0529	.0693	.0866	.0969	.1156	.1387	.1642	.1891	.2049	.2360	.2730
	93	.0523	.0686	.0857	.0958	.1143	.1372	.1625	.1871	.2028	.2336	.2703
	94	.0517	.0678	.0847	.0947	.1131	.1357	.1608	.1852	.2007	.2312	.2676
	95	.0511	.0670	.0838	.0937	.1119	.1343	.1591	.1833	.1986	.2289	.2650
	96	.0505	.0663	.0829	.0927	.1107	.1329	.1574	.1814	.1966	.2266	.2625
	97	.0500	.0656	.0820	.0917	.1095	.1315	.1558	.1796	.1946	.2244	.2600
	98	.0495	.0649	.0811	.0908	.1084	.1302	.1542	.1778	.1927	.2222	.2575
	99	.0489	.0642	.0803	.0898	.1072	.1288	.1527	.1760	.1908	.2201	.2551
	100	.0484	.0635	.0795	.0889	.1062	.1275	.1512	.1743	.1890	.2180	.2527
	101	.0479	.0629	.0786	.0880	.1051	.1263	.1497	.1726	.1872	.2160	.2504
	102	.0474	.0623	.0778	.0871	.1040	.1250	.1482	.1710	.1854	.2139	.2481
	103	.0469	.0616	.0771	.0862	.1030	.1238	.1468	.1693	.1836	.2119	.2458
	104	.0465	.0610	.0763	.0854	.1020	.1226	.1454	.1678	.1819	.2100	.2436
	105	.0460	.0604	.0755	.0845	.1010	.1214	.1440	.1662	.1802	.2081	.2415
	106	.0456	.0598	.0748	.0837	.1000	.1203	.1427	.1646	.1786	.2062	.2393
	107	.0451	.0592	.0741	.0829	.0991	.1191	.1414	.1631	.1770	.2044	.2372
	108	.0447	.0587	.0734	.0821	.0982	.1180	.1401	.1617	.1754	.2026	.2352
	109	.0442	.0581	.0727	.0814	.0972	.1169	.1388	.1602	.1738	.2008	.2332
	110	.0438	.0575	.0720	.0806	.0963	.1159	.1375	.1588	.1723	.1990	.2312
	111+	4.611*	6.099*	7.690*	8.646*	10.42*	12.67*	15.22*	17.78*	19.44*	22.82*	27.03*
14	15-23	SEE NOTE**										
	24-40	SEE NOTE***										
	41	.1450	.1851	.2255	.2488	.2901	.3389	.3901	.4376	.4663	.5203	.5800
	42	.1410	.1801	.2196	.2424	.2828	.3307	.3810	.4278	.4562	.5096	.5689
	43	.1373	.1754	.2141	.2363	.2759	.3229	.3724	.4184	.4464	.4993	.5581
	44	.1337	.1710	.2088	.2305	.2693	.3154	.3641	.4095	.4371	.4894	.5477
	45	.1303	.1667	.2037	.2250	.2630	.3083	.3562	.4009	.4282	.4799	.5377
	46	.1271	.1627	.1989	.2198	.2571	.3015	.3486	.3927	.4196	.4707	.5281
	47	.1241	.1589	.1943	.2148	.2513	.2950	.3413	.3847	.4113	.4618	.5187
	48	.1212	.1552	.1899	.2100	.2459	.2888	.3343	.3772	.4034	.4533	.5097
	49	.1184	.1517	.1857	.2054	.2406	.2828	.3276	.3698	.3957	.4451	.5009
	50	.1157	.1484	.1817	.2011	.2356	.2770	.3212	.3628	.3884	.4372	.4925
	51	.1132	.1452	.1779	.1969	.2308	.2715	.3150	.3560	.3813	.4295	.4843
	52	.1108	.1422	.1742	.1928	.2262	.2663	.3091	.3495	.3744	.4221	.4764
	53	.1085	.1392	.1707	.1890	.2218	.2612	.3033	.3432	.3678	.4149	.4687
	54	.1062	.1364	.1673	.1853	.2175	.2563	.2978	.3372	.3614	.4080	.4613

*** To approximate p_k, compute $m = B/C$ and $s = \sqrt{m(1-m)/(C+1)}$, find u_k in Table T4 on page 715 below, and compute $p_k \doteq m + u_k s$.

B	C	.001	.01	.05	.1	.25	.5	.75	.9	.95	.99	.999
14	55	.1041	.1337	.1641	.1817	.2134	.2516	.2925	.3313	.3553	.4013	.4540
	56	.1020	.1311	.1609	.1783	.2094	.2470	.2873	.3256	.3493	.3948	.4470
	57	.1001	.1286	.1579	.1750	.2056	.2426	.2824	.3202	.3435	.3886	.4403
	58	.0982	.1262	.1550	.1718	.2020	.2384	.2776	.3149	.3380	.3825	.4337
	59	.0963	.1239	.1522	.1687	.1984	.2343	.2729	.3097	.3326	.3766	.4273
	60	.0946	.1217	.1495	.1658	.1950	.2304	.2685	.3048	.3273	.3708	.4210
	61	.0929	.1195	.1469	.1629	.1917	.2265	.2641	.3000	.3222	.3653	.4150
	62	.0912	.1175	.1444	.1602	.1885	.2228	.2599	.2953	.3173	.3599	.4091
	63	.0897	.1154	.1420	.1575	.1854	.2193	.2558	.2908	.3126	.3547	.4034
	64	.0881	.1135	.1396	.1549	.1824	.2158	.2519	.2864	.3079	.3496	.3978
	65	.0867	.1116	.1374	.1524	.1795	.2125	.2481	.2822	.3034	.3446	.3924
	66	.0852	.1098	.1352	.1500	.1767	.2092	.2444	.2781	.2991	.3398	.3872
	67	.0839	.1081	.1330	.1476	.1740	.2060	.2408	.2741	.2948	.3351	.3820
	68	.0825	.1064	.1310	.1454	.1714	.2030	.2373	.2702	.2907	.3306	.3770
	69	.0812	.1047	.1290	.1432	.1688	.2000	.2339	.2664	.2867	.3261	.3721
	70	.0800	.1031	.1270	.1410	.1663	.1971	.2306	.2627	.2828	.3218	.3674
	71	.0788	.1016	.1252	.1390	.1639	.1943	.2274	.2591	.2790	.3176	.3628
	72	.0776	.1001	.1233	.1370	.1616	.1916	.2242	.2556	.2753	.3135	.3582
	73	.0764	.0986	.1216	.1350	.1593	.1890	.2212	.2522	.2717	.3095	.3538
	74	.0753	.0972	.1198	.1331	.1571	.1864	.2182	.2489	.2681	.3056	.3495
	75	.0743	.0958	.1182	.1313	.1549	.1839	.2154	.2457	.2647	.3018	.3453
	76	.0732	.0945	.1165	.1295	.1529	.1814	.2126	.2426	.2614	.2981	.3412
	77	.0722	.0932	.1149	.1277	.1508	.1791	.2098	.2395	.2581	.2945	.3372
	78	.0712	.0919	.1134	.1260	.1488	.1767	.2072	.2366	.2550	.2910	.3333
	79	.0702	.0907	.1119	.1243	.1469	.1745	.2046	.2336	.2519	.2875	.3295
	80	.0693	.0895	.1104	.1227	.1450	.1723	.2020	.2308	.2488	.2842	.3257
	81	.0684	.0883	.1090	.1212	.1432	.1701	.1996	.2280	.2459	.2809	.3221
	82	.0675	.0872	.1076	.1196	.1414	.1680	.1972	.2253	.2430	.2777	.3185
	83	.0666	.0861	.1063	.1181	.1397	.1660	.1948	.2227	.2402	.2745	.3150
	84	.0658	.0850	.1050	.1167	.1380	.1640	.1925	.2201	.2374	.2714	.3116
	85	.0650	.0840	.1037	.1153	.1363	.1621	.1903	.2176	.2348	.2684	.3082
	86	.0642	.0829	.1024	.1139	.1347	.1602	.1881	.2151	.2321	.2655	.3049
	87	.0634	.0819	.1012	.1125	.1331	.1583	.1859	.2127	.2296	.2626	.3017
	88	.0626	.0809	.1000	.1112	.1315	.1565	.1838	.2104	.2270	.2598	.2986
	89	.0619	.0800	.0988	.1099	.1300	.1547	.1818	.2081	.2246	.2571	.2955
	90	.0611	.0791	.0977	.1086	.1286	.1530	.1798	.2058	.2222	.2544	.2925
	91	.0604	.0781	.0966	.1074	.1271	.1513	.1778	.2036	.2198	.2517	.2895
	92	.0597	.0773	.0955	.1062	.1257	.1496	.1759	.2014	.2175	.2491	.2866
	93	.0590	.0764	.0944	.1050	.1243	.1480	.1740	.1993	.2152	.2466	.2838
	94	.0584	.0755	.0934	.1039	.1230	.1464	.1722	.1972	.2130	.2441	.2810
	95	.0577	.0747	.0923	.1027	.1217	.1449	.1704	.1952	.2109	.2417	.2783
	96	.0571	.0739	.0913	.1016	.1204	.1434	.1686	.1932	.2087	.2393	.2756
	97	.0565	.0731	.0904	.1006	.1191	.1419	.1669	.1913	.2067	.2369	.2730
	98	.0559	.0723	.0894	.0995	.1179	.1404	.1652	.1894	.2046	.2347	.2704
	99	.0553	.0715	.0885	.0985	.1166	.1390	.1636	.1875	.2026	.2324	.2678
	100	.0547	.0708	.0876	.0975	.1154	.1376	.1620	.1857	.2006	.2302	.2654
	101	.0541	.0701	.0867	.0965	.1143	.1362	.1604	.1839	.1987	.2280	.2629
	102	.0536	.0693	.0858	.0955	.1131	.1349	.1588	.1821	.1968	.2259	.2605
	103	.0530	.0686	.0849	.0945	.1120	.1336	.1573	.1804	.1950	.2238	.2582
	104	.0525	.0680	.0841	.0936	.1109	.1323	.1558	.1787	.1932	.2218	.2559
	105	.0519	.0673	.0833	.0927	.1099	.1310	.1543	.1770	.1914	.2197	.2536
	106	.0514	.0666	.0824	.0918	.1088	.1298	.1528	.1754	.1896	.2178	.2514
	107	.0509	.0660	.0816	.0909	.1078	.1285	.1514	.1738	.1879	.2158	.2492
	108	.0504	.0653	.0809	.0900	.1067	.1273	.1500	.1722	.1862	.2139	.2470
	109	.0500	.0647	.0801	.0892	.1057	.1262	.1487	.1706	.1845	.2120	.2449
	110	.0495	.0641	.0793	.0884	.1048	.1250	.1473	.1691	.1829	.2102	.2428
	111	.0490	.0635	.0786	.0875	.1038	.1239	.1460	.1676	.1813	.2084	.2408
	112	.0485	.0629	.0779	.0867	.1029	.1228	.1447	.1662	.1797	.2066	.2388
	113	.0481	.0623	.0772	.0859	.1019	.1217	.1434	.1647	.1782	.2049	.2368
	114	.0477	.0618	.0765	.0852	.1010	.1206	.1422	.1633	.1767	.2031	.2348
	115	.0472	.0612	.0758	.0844	.1001	.1195	.1410	.1619	.1752	.2015	.2329
	116	.0468	.0607	.0751	.0837	.0993	.1185	.1398	.1605	.1737	.1998	.2310
	117	.0464	.0601	.0745	.0829	.0984	.1175	.1386	.1592	.1723	.1982	.2292
	118+	5.195*	6.782*	8.464*	9.470*	11.33*	13.67*	16.31*	18.96*	20.67*	24.14*	28.45*
15	16-24	SEE NOTE**										
	25-45	SEE NOTE***										
	46	.1426	.1802	.2180	.2397	.2781	.3235	.3714	.4159	.4429	.4940	.5509
	47	.1391	.1759	.2129	.2342	.2719	.3166	.3636	.4075	.4342	.4848	.5413
	48	.1359	.1718	.2081	.2290	.2660	.3099	.3562	.3995	.4259	.4759	.5319
	49	.1327	.1680	.2035	.2240	.2603	.3035	.3491	.3918	.4178	.4673	.5229
	50	.1297	.1642	.1991	.2192	.2548	.2973	.3423	.3844	.4101	.4590	.5141

* To approximate p_k, divide the starred entry under k by $(C - 1)$.

** Compute $B^* = C - B$, find p^*_{1-k} for B^* and C, and compute $p_k = 1 - p^*_{1-k}$.

B	C	.001	.01	.05	.1	.25	.5	.75	.9	.95	.99	.999
15	51	.1269	.1607	.1949	.2146	.2496	.2914	.3357	.3772	.4026	.4510	.5056
	52	.1241	.1573	.1908	.2102	.2446	.2857	.3293	.3703	.3954	.4433	.4974
	53	.1215	.1540	.1870	.2060	.2398	.2803	.3232	.3637	.3885	.4358	.4895
	54	.1190	.1509	.1833	.2019	.2352	.2750	.3174	.3572	.3817	.4286	.4818
	55	.1166	.1479	.1797	.1980	.2308	.2700	.3117	.3511	.3753	.4216	.4743
	56	.1143	.1450	.1762	.1943	.2265	.2651	.3062	.3451	.3690	.4148	.4670
	57	.1121	.1423	.1729	.1907	.2224	.2604	.3009	.3393	.3629	.4082	.4600
	58	.1099	.1396	.1697	.1872	.2184	.2558	.2958	.3337	.3570	.4019	.4531
	59	.1079	.1370	.1667	.1839	.2146	.2514	.2909	.3283	.3513	.3957	.4465
	60	.1059	.1346	.1637	.1806	.2109	.2472	.2861	.3230	.3458	.3897	.4400
	61	.1040	.1322	.1609	.1775	.2073	.2431	.2815	.3180	.3405	.3839	.4337
	62	.1022	.1299	.1581	.1745	.2038	.2391	.2770	.3130	.3353	.3782	.4276
	63	.1004	.1276	.1554	.1716	.2005	.2353	.2727	.3083	.3303	.3727	.4217
	64	.0987	.1255	.1529	.1688	.1972	.2316	.2685	.3036	.3254	.3674	.4159
	65	.0970	.1234	.1504	.1660	.1941	.2280	.2644	.2991	.3206	.3622	.4103
	66	.0954	.1214	.1480	.1634	.1911	.2245	.2605	.2948	.3160	.3572	.4048
	67	.0939	.1195	.1456	.1608	.1881	.2211	.2566	.2905	.3116	.3523	.3994
	68	.0924	.1176	.1434	.1584	.1853	.2178	.2529	.2864	.3072	.3475	.3942
	69	.0909	.1158	.1412	.1560	.1825	.2146	.2493	.2824	.3030	.3429	.3892
	70	.0895	.1140	.1390	.1536	.1798	.2116	.2458	.2785	.2989	.3384	.3842
	71	.0881	.1123	.1370	.1514	.1772	.2085	.2424	.2747	.2949	.3340	.3794
	72	.0868	.1106	.1350	.1492	.1747	.2056	.2390	.2710	.2910	.3297	.3747
	73	.0855	.1090	.1330	.1470	.1722	.2028	.2358	.2674	.2872	.3255	.3701
	74	.0843	.1074	.1311	.1450	.1698	.2000	.2327	.2640	.2835	.3214	.3656
	75	.0831	.1059	.1293	.1429	.1675	.1973	.2296	.2605	.2798	.3174	.3612
	76	.0819	.1044	.1275	.1410	.1653	.1947	.2266	.2572	.2763	.3135	.3570
	77	.0807	.1030	.1258	.1391	.1631	.1922	.2237	.2540	.2729	.3097	.3528
	78	.0796	.1016	.1241	.1372	.1609	.1897	.2209	.2508	.2695	.3060	.3487
	79	.0786	.1002	.1224	.1354	.1588	.1872	.2181	.2478	.2663	.3024	.3447
	80	.0775	.0989	.1208	.1337	.1568	.1849	.2154	.2447	.2631	.2989	.3408
	81	.0765	.0976	.1193	.1319	.1548	.1826	.2128	.2418	.2600	.2954	.3370
	82	.0755	.0963	.1178	.1303	.1529	.1803	.2102	.2389	.2569	.2921	.3333
	83	.0745	.0951	.1163	.1286	.1510	.1782	.2077	.2362	.2540	.2888	.3296
	84	.0736	.0939	.1148	.1271	.1491	.1760	.2052	.2334	.2511	.2855	.3261
	85	.0726	.0927	.1134	.1255	.1473	.1739	.2029	.2307	.2482	.2824	.3226
	86	.0717	.0916	.1120	.1240	.1456	.1719	.2005	.2281	.2454	.2793	.3191
	87	.0709	.0905	.1107	.1225	.1439	.1699	.1982	.2256	.2427	.2763	.3158
	88	.0700	.0894	.1094	.1211	.1422	.1680	.1960	.2231	.2401	.2733	.3125
	89	.0692	.0883	.1081	.1197	.1406	.1661	.1938	.2207	.2375	.2704	.3093
	90	.0683	.0873	.1069	.1183	.1390	.1642	.1917	.2183	.2349	.2676	.3062
	91	.0675	.0863	.1056	.1169	.1374	.1624	.1896	.2159	.2324	.2648	.3031
	92	.0668	.0853	.1044	.1156	.1359	.1606	.1876	.2136	.2300	.2621	.3000
	93	.0660	.0844	.1033	.1143	.1344	.1589	.1856	.2114	.2276	.2595	.2971
	94	.0653	.0834	.1021	.1131	.1329	.1572	.1836	.2092	.2253	.2568	.2942
	95	.0645	.0825	.1010	.1119	.1315	.1555	.1817	.2071	.2230	.2543	.2913
	96	.0638	.0816	.0999	.1107	.1301	.1539	.1798	.2050	.2208	.2518	.2885
	97	.0631	.0807	.0989	.1095	.1287	.1523	.1780	.2029	.2186	.2493	.2858
	98	.0624	.0798	.0978	.1083	.1274	.1507	.1762	.2009	.2164	.2469	.2831
	99	.0618	.0790	.0968	.1072	.1261	.1492	.1744	.1989	.2143	.2446	.2804
	100	.0611	.0782	.0958	.1061	.1248	.1477	.1727	.1969	.2122	.2422	.2778
	101	.0605	.0774	.0948	.1050	.1235	.1462	.1710	.1950	.2102	.2400	.2753
	102	.0599	.0766	.0938	.1040	.1223	.1447	.1693	.1932	.2082	.2377	.2728
	103	.0592	.0758	.0929	.1029	.1211	.1433	.1677	.1913	.2062	.2355	.2703
	104	.0586	.0750	.0920	.1019	.1199	.1419	.1661	.1895	.2043	.2334	.2679
	105	.0581	.0743	.0911	.1009	.1187	.1406	.1645	.1878	.2024	.2313	.2655
	106	.0575	.0736	.0902	.0999	.1176	.1393	.1630	.1860	.2006	.2292	.2632
	107	.0569	.0728	.0893	.0990	.1165	.1379	.1615	.1843	.1987	.2271	.2609
	108	.0564	.0721	.0884	.0980	.1154	.1367	.1600	.1827	.1970	.2251	.2587
	109	.0558	.0714	.0876	.0971	.1143	.1354	.1585	.1810	.1952	.2232	.2565
	110	.0553	.0708	.0868	.0962	.1132	.1342	.1571	.1794	.1935	.2212	.2543
	111	.0548	.0701	.0860	.0953	.1122	.1329	.1557	.1778	.1918	.2193	.2522
	112	.0542	.0695	.0852	.0944	.1112	.1317	.1543	.1763	.1901	.2175	.2500
	113	.0537	.0688	.0844	.0936	.1102	.1306	.1530	.1747	.1885	.2156	.2480
	114	.0533	.0682	.0836	.0927	.1092	.1294	.1516	.1732	.1869	.2138	.2459
	115	.0528	.0676	.0829	.0919	.1082	.1283	.1503	.1718	.1853	.2120	.2439
	116	.0523	.0670	.0822	.0911	.1073	.1272	.1490	.1703	.1838	.2103	.2420
	117	.0518	.0664	.0814	.0903	.1063	.1261	.1478	.1689	.1822	.2086	.2400
	118	.0514	.0658	.0807	.0895	.1054	.1250	.1465	.1675	.1807	.2069	.2381
	119	.0509	.0652	.0800	.0887	.1045	.1240	.1453	.1661	.1792	.2052	.2363
	120	.0505	.0646	.0793	.0880	.1036	.1229	.1441	.1647	.1778	.2036	.2344
	121	.0500	.0641	.0787	.0872	.1028	.1219	.1429	.1634	.1764	.2020	.2326
	122	.0496	.0635	.0780	.0865	.1019	.1209	.1418	.1621	.1750	.2004	.2308

*** To approximate p_k, compute $m = B/C$ and $s = \sqrt{m(1 - m)/(C + 1)}$, find u_k in Table T4 on page 715 below, and compute $p_k \doteq m + u_k s$.

B	C	.001	.01	.05	.1	.25	.5	.75	.9	.95	.99	.999
15	123	.0492	.0630	.0773	.0858	.1011	.1199	.1406	.1608	.1736	.1988	.2290
	124	.0488	.0625	.0767	.0851	.1002	.1189	.1395	.1595	.1722	.1973	.2273
	125+	5.794*	7.477*	9.246*	10.30*	12.24*	14.67*	17.40*	20.13*	21.89*	25.45*	29.85*
16	17–26	SEE NOTE**										
	27–49	SEE NOTE***										
	50	.1442	.1804	.2167	.2375	.2742	.3176	.3632	.4057	.4316	.4805	.5353
	51	.1410	.1765	.2121	.2325	.2686	.3113	.3562	.3982	.4237	.4722	.5266
	52	.1379	.1728	.2077	.2277	.2632	.3052	.3495	.3909	.4162	.4641	.5181
	53	.1350	.1692	.2035	.2231	.2580	.2994	.3431	.3839	.4089	.4564	.5099
	54	.1322	.1657	.1994	.2187	.2530	.2938	.3368	.3772	.4018	.4488	.5019
	55	.1295	.1624	.1955	.2145	.2482	.2884	.3308	.3706	.3950	.4415	.4941
	56	.1269	.1592	.1918	.2104	.2436	.2831	.3250	.3643	.3885	.4345	.4866
	57	.1244	.1562	.1881	.2065	.2392	.2781	.3194	.3583	.3821	.4276	.4793
	58	.1221	.1533	.1847	.2028	.2349	.2733	.3140	.3524	.3759	.4210	.4722
	59	.1198	.1504	.1813	.1991	.2308	.2686	.3088	.3467	.3699	.4145	.4653
	60	.1176	.1477	.1781	.1956	.2268	.2641	.3037	.3411	.3642	.4083	.4587
	61	.1154	.1451	.1750	.1922	.2229	.2597	.2988	.3358	.3585	.4022	.4521
	62	.1134	.1425	.1720	.1890	.2192	.2554	.2941	.3306	.3531	.3963	.4458
	63	.1114	.1401	.1691	.1858	.2156	.2514	.2895	.3256	.3478	.3906	.4396
	64	.1095	.1377	.1663	.1827	.2121	.2474	.2850	.3207	.3427	.3850	.4337
	65	.1076	.1354	.1635	.1798	.2088	.2435	.2807	.3159	.3377	.3796	.4278
	66	.1059	.1332	.1609	.1769	.2055	.2398	.2765	.3113	.3329	.3744	.4221
	67	.1041	.1311	.1584	.1741	.2023	.2362	.2725	.3069	.3282	.3692	.4166
	68	.1025	.1290	.1559	.1715	.1993	.2327	.2685	.3025	.3236	.3643	.4112
	69	.1008	.1270	.1535	.1689	.1963	.2293	.2647	.2983	.3192	.3594	.4059
	70	.0993	.1250	.1512	.1663	.1934	.2260	.2609	.2942	.3148	.3547	.4008
	71	.0978	.1232	.1489	.1639	.1906	.2228	.2573	.2902	.3106	.3501	.3958
	72	.0963	.1213	.1468	.1615	.1879	.2196	.2538	.2863	.3065	.3456	.3909
	73	.0949	.1196	.1446	.1592	.1852	.2166	.2504	.2825	.3025	.3412	.3861
	74	.0935	.1178	.1426	.1569	.1826	.2136	.2470	.2788	.2986	.3370	.3815
	75	.0921	.1161	.1406	.1547	.1801	.2108	.2438	.2753	.2948	.3328	.3769
	76	.0908	.1145	.1386	.1526	.1777	.2080	.2406	.2718	.2911	.3287	.3725
	77	.0895	.1129	.1367	.1506	.1753	.2053	.2375	.2683	.2875	.3248	.3681
	78	.0883	.1114	.1349	.1485	.1730	.2026	.2345	.2650	.2840	.3209	.3639
	79	.0871	.1099	.1331	.1466	.1708	.2000	.2316	.2618	.2806	.3171	.3597
	80	.0859	.1084	.1314	.1447	.1686	.1975	.2287	.2586	.2772	.3134	.3557
	81	.0848	.1070	.1297	.1428	.1665	.1950	.2259	.2555	.2739	.3098	.3517
	82	.0837	.1056	.1280	.1410	.1644	.1926	.2232	.2525	.2707	.3063	.3478
	83	.0826	.1043	.1264	.1392	.1623	.1903	.2205	.2495	.2676	.3028	.3441
	84	.0815	.1030	.1248	.1375	.1604	.1880	.2179	.2466	.2646	.2995	.3403
	85	.0805	.1017	.1233	.1358	.1584	.1858	.2154	.2438	.2616	.2962	.3367
	86	.0795	.1004	.1218	.1342	.1565	.1836	.2129	.2411	.2586	.2929	.3331
	87	.0785	.0992	.1203	.1326	.1547	.1815	.2105	.2384	.2558	.2898	.3297
	88	.0776	.0980	.1189	.1310	.1529	.1794	.2081	.2357	.2530	.2867	.3262
	89	.0767	.0969	.1175	.1295	.1511	.1774	.2058	.2332	.2503	.2837	.3229
	90	.0757	.0957	.1161	.1280	.1494	.1754	.2035	.2306	.2476	.2807	.3196
	91	.0749	.0946	.1148	.1266	.1477	.1734	.2013	.2282	.2450	.2778	.3164
	92	.0740	.0935	.1135	.1251	.1461	.1715	.1992	.2258	.2424	.2750	.3133
	93	.0731	.0925	.1122	.1238	.1445	.1697	.1970	.2234	.2399	.2722	.3102
	94	.0723	.0914	.1110	.1224	.1429	.1679	.1950	.2211	.2374	.2695	.3071
	95	.0715	.0904	.1098	.1211	.1414	.1661	.1929	.2188	.2350	.2668	.3042
	96	.0707	.0894	.1086	.1198	.1399	.1643	.1909	.2166	.2327	.2642	.3013
	97	.0699	.0885	.1074	.1185	.1384	.1626	.1890	.2144	.2616	.2616	.2984
	98	.0692	.0875	.1063	.1172	.1370	.1610	.1871	.2123	.2281	.2591	.2956
	99	.0684	.0866	.1052	.1160	.1356	.1593	.1852	.2102	.2259	.2566	.2928
	100	.0677	.0857	.1041	.1148	.1342	.1577	.1834	.2081	.2237	.2542	.2901
	101	.0670	.0848	.1030	.1136	.1328	.1562	.1816	.2061	.2215	.2518	.2875
	102	.0663	.0839	.1020	.1125	.1315	.1546	.1798	.2042	.2194	.2494	.2849
	103	.0656	.0831	.1009	.1114	.1302	.1531	.1781	.2022	.2174	.2471	.2823
	104	.0650	.0822	.0999	.1103	.1289	.1516	.1764	.2003	.2154	.2449	.2798
	105	.0643	.0814	.0989	.1092	.1277	.1502	.1747	.1985	.2134	.2427	.2773
	106	.0637	.0806	.0980	.1081	.1264	.1487	.1731	.1966	.2114	.2405	.2749
	107	.0631	.0798	.0970	.1071	.1252	.1473	.1715	.1948	.2095	.2384	.2725
	108	.0624	.0791	.0961	.1061	.1240	.1460	.1699	.1931	.2076	.2363	.2702
	109	.0618	.0783	.0952	.1051	.1229	.1446	.1684	.1913	.2058	.2342	.2679
	110	.0612	.0776	.0943	.1041	.1217	.1433	.1668	.1896	.2040	.2322	.2656
	111	.0607	.0768	.0934	.1031	.1206	.1420	.1653	.1880	.2022	.2302	.2634
	112	.0601	.0761	.0926	.1022	.1195	.1407	.1639	.1863	.2004	.2282	.2612
	113	.0595	.0754	.0917	.1012	.1185	.1395	.1624	.1847	.1987	.2263	.2590
	114	.0590	.0747	.0909	.1003	.1174	.1382	.1610	.1831	.1970	.2244	.2569
	115	.0584	.0740	.0901	.0994	.1164	.1370	.1596	.1816	.1954	.2225	.2548

* To approximate p_k, divide the starred entry under k by $(C - 1)$.

** Compute $B^* = C - B$, find p_{1-k}^* for B^* and C, and compute $p_k = 1 - p_{1-k}^*$.

B	C	.001	.01	.05	.1	.25	.5	.75	.9	.95	.99	.999
16	116	.0579	.0734	.0893	.0985	.1153	.1358	.1583	.1800	.1937	.2207	.2528
	117	.0574	.0727	.0885	.0977	.1143	.1347	.1569	.1785	.1921	.2189	.2508
	118	.0569	.0721	.0877	.0968	.1133	.1335	.1556	.1770	.1905	.2171	.2488
	119	.0564	.0715	.0869	.0960	.1124	.1324	.1543	.1756	.1890	.2154	.2468
	120	.0559	.0708	.0862	.0952	.1114	.1313	.1530	.1741	.1874	.2137	.2449
	121	.0554	.0702	.0855	.0944	.1105	.1302	.1518	.1727	.1859	.2120	.2430
	122	.0549	.0696	.0847	.0936	.1096	.1291	.1505	.1713	.1845	.2103	.2411
	123	.0545	.0690	.0840	.0928	.1087	.1281	.1493	.1700	.1830	.2087	.2393
	124	.0540	.0685	.0833	.0920	.1078	.1270	.1481	.1686	.1816	.2071	.2375
	125	.0536	.0679	.0826	.0913	.1069	.1260	.1470	.1673	.1801	.2055	.2357
	126	.0531	.0673	.0820	.0905	.1060	.1250	.1458	.1660	.1788	.2039	.2339
	127	.0527	.0668	.0813	.0898	.1052	.1240	.1447	.1647	.1774	.2024	.2322
	128	.0522	.0662	.0806	.0891	.1043	.1230	.1435	.1635	.1760	.2009	.2305
	129	.0518	.0657	.0800	.0884	.1035	.1221	.1424	.1622	.1747	.1994	.2288
	130	.0514	.0652	.0794	.0877	.1027	.1211	.1413	.1610	.1734	.1979	.2272
	131+	6.405*	8.181*	10.04*	11.14*	13.15*	15.67*	18.49*	21.29*	23.10*	26.74*	31.24*
17	18-27	SEE NOTE**										
	28-54	SEE NOTE***										
	55	.1427	.1772	.2115	.2311	.2658	.3068	.3499	.3901	.4146	.4612	.5136
	56	.1399	.1737	.2075	.2268	.2609	.3012	.3437	.3835	.4077	.4539	.5059
	57	.1371	.1704	.2035	.2225	.2561	.2959	.3378	.3771	.4011	.4467	.4984
	58	.1345	.1671	.1998	.2185	.2515	.2907	.3321	.3709	.3946	.4398	.4910
	59	.1320	.1640	.1961	.2145	.2471	.2857	.3266	.3649	.3884	.4331	.4839
	60	.1295	.1611	.1926	.2107	.2428	.2809	.3212	.3591	.3823	.4266	.4770
	61	.1272	.1582	.1893	.2071	.2387	.2763	.3161	.3535	.3764	.4203	.4703
	62	.1249	.1554	.1860	.2036	.2347	.2718	.3111	.3480	.3707	.4142	.4637
	63	.1227	.1527	.1829	.2001	.2308	.2674	.3062	.3427	.3652	.4082	.4573
	64	.1206	.1501	.1798	.1968	.2271	.2632	.3015	.3376	.3598	.4024	.4511
	65	.1185	.1476	.1769	.1937	.2235	.2591	.2969	.3326	.3546	.3968	.4451
	66	.1166	.1452	.1740	.1906	.2200	.2551	.2925	.3278	.3496	.3913	.4392
	67	.1147	.1429	.1713	.1876	.2166	.2513	.2882	.3231	.3448	.3860	.4335
	68	.1128	.1406	.1686	.1847	.2133	.2475	.2840	.3185	.3398	.3808	.4279
	69	.1110	.1384	.1660	.1819	.2101	.2439	.2800	.3141	.3352	.3758	.4224
	70	.1093	.1363	.1635	.1791	.2070	.2404	.2760	.3098	.3306	.3708	.4171
	71	.1076	.1342	.1610	.1765	.2040	.2370	.2722	.3056	.3262	.3660	.4119
	72	.1060	.1322	.1587	.1739	.2011	.2337	.2685	.3015	.3219	.3614	.4068
	73	.1044	.1303	.1564	.1714	.1983	.2304	.2648	.2975	.3177	.3568	.4019
	74	.1029	.1284	.1541	.1690	.1955	.2273	.2613	.2936	.3137	.3524	.3971
	75	.1014	.1266	.1520	.1666	.1928	.2242	.2579	.2899	.3097	.3480	.3924
	76	.0999	.1248	.1499	.1644	.1902	.2213	.2545	.2862	.3058	.3438	.3878
	77	.0985	.1231	.1478	.1621	.1877	.2184	.2513	.2826	.3020	.3396	.3833
	78	.0972	.1214	.1458	.1600	.1852	.2155	.2481	.2791	.2983	.3356	.3789
	79	.0958	.1197	.1439	.1578	.1828	.2128	.2450	.2757	.2947	.3317	.3746
	80	.0945	.1181	.1420	.1558	.1804	.2101	.2420	.2723	.2912	.3278	.3704
	81	.0933	.1166	.1402	.1538	.1782	.2075	.2390	.2691	.2878	.3241	.3662
	82	.0921	.1151	.1384	.1518	.1759	.2049	.2361	.2659	.2844	.3204	.3622
	83	.0909	.1136	.1366	.1499	.1737	.2024	.2333	.2628	.2811	.3168	.3583
	84	.0897	.1122	.1349	.1481	.1716	.2000	.2306	.2598	.2779	.3133	.3544
	85	.0886	.1108	.1333	.1463	.1696	.1976	.2279	.2568	.2748	.3098	.3507
	86	.0875	.1094	.1316	.1445	.1675	.1953	.2253	.2539	.2718	.3065	.3470
	87	.0864	.1081	.1300	.1428	.1656	.1931	.2227	.2511	.2688	.3032	.3433
	88	.0853	.1068	.1285	.1411	.1636	.1909	.2202	.2483	.2658	.2999	.3398
	89	.0843	.1055	.1270	.1394	.1618	.1887	.2178	.2456	.2630	.2968	.3363
	90	.0833	.1043	.1255	.1378	.1599	.1866	.2154	.2430	.2602	.2937	.3329
	91	.0823	.1031	.1241	.1363	.1581	.1845	.2130	.2404	.2574	.2907	.3296
	92	.0814	.1019	.1227	.1347	.1564	.1825	.2107	.2378	.2547	.2877	.3263
	93	.0804	.1007	.1213	.1332	.1546	.1805	.2085	.2353	.2521	.2848	.3231
	94	.0795	.0996	.1200	.1318	.1530	.1786	.2063	.2329	.2495	.2819	.3200
	95	.0786	.0985	.1186	.1303	.1513	.1767	.2041	.2305	.2470	.2791	.3169
	96	.0778	.0974	.1173	.1289	.1497	.1748	.2020	.2282	.2445	.2764	.3139
	97	.0769	.0963	.1161	.1275	.1481	.1730	.2000	.2259	.2421	.2737	.3109
	98	.0761	.0953	.1149	.1262	.1466	.1712	.1980	.2236	.2397	.2711	.3080
	99	.0753	.0943	.1137	.1249	.1451	.1695	.1960	.2214	.2374	.2685	.3051
	100	.0745	.0933	.1125	.1236	.1436	.1678	.1940	.2193	.2351	.2659	.3023
	101	.0737	.0923	.1113	.1223	.1421	.1661	.1921	.2172	.2328	.2635	.2995
	102	.0729	.0914	.1102	.1211	.1407	.1645	.1903	.2151	.2306	.2610	.2968
	103	.0722	.0905	.1091	.1199	.1393	.1629	.1884	.2130	.2284	.2586	.2942
	104	.0714	.0895	.1080	.1187	.1379	.1613	.1866	.2110	.2263	.2563	.2916
	105	.0707	.0887	.1069	.1175	.1366	.1598	.1849	.2091	.2242	.2539	.2890
	106	.0700	.0878	.1059	.1164	.1353	.1582	.1831	.2072	.2222	.2517	.2865

*** To approximate p_k, compute $m = B/C$ and $s = \sqrt{m(1-m)/(C+1)}$, find u_k in Table T4 on page 715 below, and compute $p_k \doteq m + u_k s$.

B	C	.001	.01	.05	.1	.25	.5	.75	.9	.95	.99	.999
17	107	.0693	.0869	.1048	.1153	.1340	.1567	.1815	.2053	.2202	.2494	.2840
	108	.0686	.0861	.1038	.1142	.1327	.1553	.1798	.2034	.2182	.2473	.2816
	109	.0680	.0853	.1028	.1131	.1315	.1539	.1781	.2016	.2163	.2451	.2792
	110	.0673	.0844	.1019	.1120	.1303	.1524	.1765	.1998	.2144	.2430	.2768
	111	.0667	.0836	.1009	.1110	.1291	.1511	.1750	.1980	.2125	.2409	.2745
	112	.0661	.0829	.1000	.1100	.1279	.1497	.1734	.1963	.2107	.2389	.2722
	113	.0654	.0821	.0991	.1090	.1268	.1484	.1719	.1946	.2089	.2368	.2700
	114	.0648	.0813	.0982	.1080	.1256	.1471	.1704	.1929	.2071	.2349	.2678
	115	.0642	.0806	.0973	.1070	.1245	.1458	.1689	.1913	.2053	.2329	.2656
	116	.0637	.0799	.0964	.1061	.1234	.1445	.1675	.1897	.2036	.2310	.2635
	117	.0631	.0792	.0956	.1051	.1223	.1433	.1661	.1881	.2019	.2291	.2614
	118	.0625	.0785	.0947	.1042	.1213	.1421	.1647	.1865	.2003	.2273	.2593
	119	.0620	.0778	.0939	.1033	.1203	.1409	.1633	.1850	.1986	.2254	.2573
	120	.0614	.0771	.0931	.1024	.1192	.1397	.1619	.1835	.1970	.2237	.2553
	121	.0609	.0764	.0923	.1016	.1182	.1385	.1606	.1820	.1954	.2219	.2533
	122	.0604	.0758	.0915	.1007	.1172	.1374	.1593	.1805	.1939	.2202	.2513
	123	.0599	.0752	.0908	.0999	.1163	.1362	.1580	.1791	.1924	.2184	.2494
	124	.0594	.0745	.0900	.0990	.1153	.1351	.1568	.1777	.1908	.2168	.2475
	125	.0589	.0739	.0893	.0982	.1144	.1341	.1555	.1763	.1894	.2151	.2457
	126	.0584	.0733	.0885	.0974	.1135	.1330	.1543	.1749	.1879	.2135	.2439
	127	.0579	.0727	.0878	.0966	.1126	.1319	.1531	.1736	.1865	.2119	.2421
	128	.0574	.0721	.0871	.0959	.1117	.1309	.1519	.1722	.1850	.2103	.2403
	129	.0570	.0715	.0864	.0951	.1108	.1299	.1507	.1709	.1836	.2087	.2385
	130	.0565	.0710	.0857	.0944	.1099	.1289	.1496	.1696	.1823	.2072	.2368
	131	.0560	.0704	.0851	.0936	.1091	.1279	.1484	.1684	.1809	.2057	.2351
	132	.0556	.0698	.0844	.0929	.1082	.1269	.1473	.1671	.1796	.2042	.2334
	133	.0552	.0693	.0837	.0922	.1074	.1260	.1462	.1659	.1783	.2027	.2318
	134	.0547	.0688	.0831	.0915	.1066	.1250	.1451	.1647	.1770	.2012	.2301
	135	.0543	.0682	.0825	.0908	.1058	.1241	.1441	.1635	.1757	.1998	.2285
	136	.0539	.0677	.0818	.0901	.1050	.1232	.1430	.1623	.1744	.1984	.2270
	137	.0535	.0672	.0812	.0894	.1042	.1223	.1420	.1611	.1732	.1970	.2254
	138+	7.028*	8.895*	10.83*	11.98*	14.07*	16.67*	19.57*	22.45*	24.30*	28.03*	32.62*
18	19–28	SEE NOTE**										
	29–60	SEE NOTE***										
	61	.1392	.1715	.2037	.2221	.2545	.2928	.3332	.3710	.3942	.4382	.4881
	62	.1367	.1685	.2002	.2183	.2502	.2881	.3280	.3653	.3882	.4318	.4813
	63	.1343	.1656	.1968	.2146	.2461	.2834	.3229	.3598	.3824	.4257	.4748
	64	.1319	.1628	.1935	.2111	.2421	.2790	.3179	.3544	.3768	.4196	.4683
	65	.1297	.1601	.1903	.2076	.2383	.2746	.3131	.3492	.3714	.4138	.4621
	66	.1275	.1574	.1873	.2043	.2345	.2704	.3084	.3441	.3661	.4081	.4560
	67	.1254	.1549	.1843	.2011	.2309	.2663	.3039	.3392	.3609	.4026	.4501
	68	.1234	.1524	.1814	.1980	.2274	.2624	.2995	.3344	.3559	.3972	.4443
	69	.1214	.1500	.1786	.1950	.2240	.2585	.2952	.3298	.3511	.3919	.4387
	70	.1195	.1477	.1759	.1920	.2207	.2548	.2911	.3253	.3463	.3868	.4332
	71	.1177	.1455	.1733	.1892	.2175	.2512	.2870	.3209	.3417	.3818	.4278
	72	.1159	.1433	.1707	.1864	.2144	.2477	.2831	.3166	.3372	.3769	.4226
	73	.1142	.1412	.1682	.1838	.2114	.2443	.2793	.3124	.3329	.3722	.4175
	74	.1125	.1391	.1658	.1812	.2084	.2409	.2756	.3083	.3286	.3676	.4125
	75	.1109	.1371	.1635	.1786	.2055	.2377	.2719	.3044	.3244	.3631	.4076
	76	.1093	.1352	.1612	.1762	.2028	.2345	.2684	.3005	.3204	.3587	.4028
	77	.1077	.1333	.1590	.1738	.2001	.2315	.2650	.2968	.3164	.3544	.3982
	78	.1062	.1315	.1569	.1715	.1974	.2285	.2616	.2931	.3126	.3502	.3936
	79	.1048	.1297	.1548	.1692	.1948	.2255	.2584	.2895	.3088	.3461	.3892
	80	.1034	.1280	.1527	.1670	.1923	.2227	.2552	.2860	.3051	.3421	.3848
	81	.1020	.1263	.1508	.1648	.1899	.2199	.2521	.2826	.3015	.3381	.3806
	82	.1006	.1247	.1488	.1627	.1875	.2172	.2490	.2793	.2980	.3343	.3764
	83	.0993	.1231	.1469	.1607	.1852	.2146	.2461	.2760	.2946	.3306	.3723
	84	.0981	.1215	.1451	.1587	.1829	.2120	.2432	.2728	.2912	.3269	.3683
	85	.0968	.1200	.1433	.1568	.1807	.2095	.2403	.2697	.2880	.3233	.3643
	86	.0956	.1185	.1416	.1549	.1786	.2070	.2376	.2667	.2848	.3198	.3606
	87	.0944	.1171	.1399	.1530	.1765	.2046	.2349	.2637	.2816	.3164	.3569
	88	.0933	.1157	.1382	.1512	.1744	.2023	.2322	.2608	.2786	.3130	.3532
	89	.0921	.1143	.1366	.1494	.1724	.2000	.2297	.2580	.2756	.3097	.3496
	90	.0910	.1129	.1350	.1477	.1704	.1978	.2271	.2552	.2726	.3065	.3461
	91	.0900	.1116	.1334	.1460	.1685	.1956	.2247	.2525	.2698	.3034	.3426
	92	.0889	.1103	.1319	.1444	.1666	.1934	.2223	.2498	.2669	.3003	.3392
	93	.0879	.1091	.1304	.1428	.1648	.1913	.2199	.2472	.2642	.2972	.3359
	94	.0869	.1079	.1290	.1412	.1630	.1893	.2176	.2446	.2615	.2943	.3326
	95	.0859	.1067	.1276	.1397	.1613	.1873	.2153	.2421	.2588	.2914	.3294
	96	.0850	.1055	.1262	.1382	.1595	.1853	.2131	.2397	.2562	.2885	.3263
	97	.0840	.1043	.1248	.1367	.1579	.1834	.2109	.2373	.2537	.2857	.3232

* To approximate p_k, divide the starred entry under k by $(C-1)$.

** Compute $B^* = C - B$, find p^*_{1-k} for B^* and C, and compute $p_k = 1 - p^*_{1-k}$.

B	C	.001	.01	.05	.1	.25	.5	.75	.9	.95	.99	.999
18	98	.0831	.1032	.1235	.1352	.1562	.1815	.2088	.2349	.2512	.2830	.3202
	99	.0822	.1021	.1222	.1338	.1546	.1797	.2067	.2326	.2488	.2803	.3172
	100	.0814	.1010	.1209	.1324	.1530	.1779	.2047	.2303	.2464	.2776	.3143
	101	.0805	.1000	.1197	.1311	.1515	.1761	.2027	.2281	.2440	.2750	.3115
	102	.0797	.0990	.1185	.1298	.1500	.1744	.2007	.2259	.2417	.2725	.3087
	103	.0788	.0980	.1173	.1285	.1485	.1726	.1988	.2238	.2394	.2700	.3059
	104	.0780	.0970	.1161	.1272	.1470	.1710	.1969	.2217	.2372	.2675	.3059
	105	.0773	.0960	.1150	.1259	.1456	.1693	.1950	.2196	.2350	.2651	.3005
	106	.0765	.0950	.1138	.1247	.1442	.1677	.1932	.2176	.2329	.2628	.2979
	107	.0757	.0941	.1127	.1235	.1428	.1662	.1914	.2156	.2308	.2604	.2953
	108	.0750	.0932	.1116	.1223	.1415	.1646	.1896	.2137	.2287	.2582	.2928
	109	.0743	.0923	.1106	.1212	.1401	.1631	.1879	.2118	.2267	.2559	.2903
	110	.0735	.0914	.1095	.1200	.1388	.1616	.1862	.2099	.2247	.2537	.2879
	111	.0728	.0906	.1085	.1189	.1376	.1601	.1846	.2081	.2228	.2515	.2855
	112	.0722	.0897	.1075	.1178	.1363	.1587	.1829	.2062	.2208	.2494	.2831
	113	.0715	.0889	.1065	.1167	.1351	.1573	.1813	.2045	.2189	.2473	.2808
	114	.0708	.0881	.1056	.1157	.1339	.1559	.1797	.2027	.2171	.2452	.2785
	115	.0702	.0873	.1046	.1147	.1327	.1545	.1782	.2010	.2152	.2432	.2762
	116	.0695	.0865	.1037	.1136	.1315	.1532	.1767	.1993	.2134	.2412	.2740
	117	.0689	.0857	.1028	.1126	.1304	.1519	.1752	.1976	.2117	.2393	.2718
	118	.0683	.0850	.1019	.1117	.1293	.1506	.1737	.1960	.2099	.2373	.2697
	119	.0677	.0842	.1010	.1107	.1282	.1493	.1723	.1944	.2082	.2354	.2676
	120	.0671	.0835	.1001	.1097	.1271	.1481	.1708	.1928	.2065	.2336	.2655
	121	.0665	.0828	.0992	.1088	.1260	.1468	.1694	.1912	.2049	.2317	.2635
	122	.0659	.0821	.0984	.1079	.1249	.1456	.1680	.1897	.2033	.2299	.2614
	123	.0654	.0814	.0976	.1070	.1239	.1444	.1667	.1882	.2017	.2281	.2595
	124	.0648	.0807	.0968	.1061	.1229	.1433	.1654	.1867	.2001	.2264	.2575
	125	.0643	.0800	.0960	.1052	.1219	.1421	.1640	.1852	.1985	.2246	.2556
	126	.0637	.0793	.0952	.1044	.1209	.1410	.1628	.1838	.1970	.2229	.2537
	127	.0632	.0787	.0944	.1035	.1199	.1398	.1615	.1824	.1955	.2212	.2518
	128	.0627	.0781	.0937	.1027	.1190	.1388	.1602	.1810	.1940	.2196	.2500
	129	.0622	.0774	.0929	.1019	.1181	.1377	.1590	.1796	.1925	.2180	.2481
	130	.0617	.0768	.0922	.1011	.1171	.1366	.1578	.1782	.1911	.2164	.2464
	131	.0612	.0762	.0914	.1003	.1162	.1356	.1566	.1769	.1897	.2148	.2446
	132	.0607	.0756	.0907	.0995	.1153	.1345	.1554	.1756	.1883	.2132	.2428
	133	.0602	.0750	.0900	.0988	.1144	.1335	.1542	.1743	.1869	.2117	.2411
	134	.0598	.0744	.0893	.0980	.1136	.1325	.1531	.1730	.1855	.2102	.2394
	135	.0593	.0739	.0887	.0973	.1127	.1315	.1520	.1718	.1842	.2087	.2378
	136	.0588	.0733	.0880	.0965	.1119	.1305	.1509	.1705	.1829	.2072	.2361
	137	.0584	.0727	.0873	.0958	.1111	.1296	.1498	.1693	.1816	.2058	.2345
	138	.0579	.0722	.0867	.0951	.1102	.1286	.1487	.1681	.1803	.2043	.2329
	139	.0575	.0717	.0860	.0944	.1094	.1277	.1476	.1669	.1790	.2029	.2313
	140	.0571	.0711	.0854	.0937	.1086	.1268	.1466	.1657	.1778	.2015	.2298
	141	.0567	.0706	.0848	.0930	.1079	.1259	.1456	.1646	.1766	.2001	.2282
	142	.0562	.0701	.0842	.0923	.1071	.1250	.1445	.1634	.1753	.1988	.2267
	143	.0558	.0696	.0836	.0917	.1063	.1241	.1435	.1623	.1742	.1975	.2252
	144+	7.662*	9.616*	11.63*	12.82*	14.99*	17.67*	20.65*	23.61*	25.50*	29.31*	33.99*
19	20-30	SEE NOTE**										
	31-65	SEE NOTE***										
	66	.1387	.1698	.2006	.2182	.2491	.2857	.3243	.3604	.3825	.4247	.4726
	67	.1364	.1671	.1974	.2147	.2453	.2814	.3195	.3552	.3771	.4189	.4665
	68	.1342	.1644	.1943	.2114	.2416	.2772	.3149	.3502	.3719	.4133	.4605
	69	.1321	.1618	.1913	.2082	.2379	.2732	.3104	.3454	.3668	.4079	.4547
	70	.1300	.1593	.1884	.2051	.2344	.2692	.3061	.3407	.3618	.4026	.4491
	71	.1280	.1569	.1856	.2020	.2310	.2654	.3018	.3361	.3571	.3974	.4435
	72	.1260	.1545	.1829	.1991	.2277	.2617	.2977	.3316	.3524	.3924	.4381
	73	.1241	.1523	.1802	.1962	.2245	.2581	.2937	.3272	.3478	.3875	.4328
	74	.1223	.1500	.1776	.1934	.2214	.2546	.2898	.3230	.3434	.3827	.4277
	75	.1205	.1479	.1751	.1907	.2183	.2511	.2860	.3188	.3391	.3780	.4226
	76	.1188	.1458	.1727	.1881	.2154	.2478	.2823	.3148	.3348	.3734	.4177
	77	.1171	.1438	.1703	.1855	.2125	.2446	.2787	.3108	.3307	.3689	.4129
	78	.1155	.1418	.1680	.1830	.2097	.2414	.2751	.3070	.3267	.3646	.4082
	79	.1139	.1399	.1658	.1806	.2069	.2383	.2717	.3033	.3228	.3603	.4036
	80	.1123	.1380	.1636	.1783	.2043	.2353	.2683	.2996	.3189	.3562	.3991
	81	.1108	.1362	.1615	.1760	.2017	.2324	.2651	.2960	.3152	.3521	.3947
	82	.1094	.1344	.1594	.1737	.1992	.2295	.2619	.2926	.3115	.3481	.3904
	83	.1079	.1327	.1574	.1715	.1967	.2267	.2588	.2891	.3079	.3442	.3862
	84	.1066	.1310	.1554	.1694	.1943	.2240	.2557	.2858	.3044	.3404	.3821
	85	.1052	.1293	.1535	.1673	.1919	.2214	.2528	.2826	.3010	.3367	.3780
	86	.1039	.1277	.1516	.1653	.1897	.2188	.2499	.2794	.2977	.3331	.3741
	87	.1026	.1262	.1498	.1633	.1874	.2162	.2470	.2763	.2944	.3295	.3702

*** To approximate p_k, compute $m = B/C$ and $s = \sqrt{m(1 - m)/(C + 1)}$, find u_k in Table T4 on page 715 below, and compute $p_k \doteq m + u_k s$.

B	C	.001	.01	.05	.1	.25	.5	.75	.9	.95	.99	.999
19	88	.1013	.1247	.1480	.1614	.1852	.2138	.2443	.2732	.2912	.3260	.3664
	89	.1001	.1232	.1462	.1595	.1831	.2113	.2415	.2703	.2881	.3226	.3627
	90	.0989	.1217	.1445	.1577	.1810	.2090	.2389	.2674	.2850	.3192	.3590
	91	.0978	.1203	.1429	.1559	.1790	.2067	.2363	.2645	.2820	.3160	.3555
	92	.0966	.1189	.1413	.1541	.1770	.2044	.2338	.2617	.2791	.3128	.3520
	93	.0955	.1176	.1397	.1524	.1750	.2022	.2313	.2590	.2762	.3096	.3485
	94	.0944	.1162	.1381	.1507	.1731	.2000	.2288	.2563	.2734	.3065	.3452
	95	.0934	.1149	.1366	.1491	.1713	.1979	.2265	.2537	.2706	.3035	.3418
	96	.0923	.1137	.1351	.1474	.1694	.1958	.2241	.2511	.2679	.3005	.3386
	97	.0913	.1124	.1337	.1459	.1676	.1938	.2218	.2486	.2653	.2976	.3354
	98	.0903	.1112	.1322	.1443	.1659	.1918	.2196	.2461	.2627	.2948	.3323
	99	.0893	.1100	.1308	.1428	.1642	.1898	.2174	.2437	.2601	.2920	.3292
	100	.0884	.1089	.1295	.1413	.1625	.1879	.2153	.2414	.2576	.2892	.3262
	101	.0874	.1077	.1281	.1399	.1609	.1861	.2131	.2390	.2551	.2865	.3232
	102	.0865	.1066	.1268	.1385	.1592	.1842	.2111	.2367	.2527	.2839	.3203
	103	.0856	.1055	.1256	.1371	.1577	.1824	.2090	.2345	.2504	.2813	.3175
	104	.0848	.1045	.1243	.1357	.1561	.1807	.2071	.2323	.2481	.2787	.3147
	105	.0839	.1034	.1231	.1344	.1546	.1789	.2051	.2302	.2458	.2762	.3119
	106	.0831	.1024	.1219	.1331	.1531	.1772	.2032	.2280	.2435	.2738	.3092
	107	.0822	.1014	.1207	.1318	.1517	.1756	.2013	.2260	.2413	.2713	.3065
	108	.0814	.1004	.1195	.1305	.1502	.1739	.1995	.2239	.2392	.2690	.3039
	109	.0806	.0994	.1184	.1293	.1488	.1723	.1976	.2219	.2371	.2666	.3014
	110	.0799	.0985	.1173	.1281	.1474	.1707	.1959	.2200	.2350	.2643	.2988
	111	.0791	.0976	.1162	.1269	.1461	.1692	.1941	.2180	.2329	.2621	.2963
	112	.0784	.0967	.1151	.1257	.1447	.1677	.1924	.2161	.2309	.2599	.2939
	113	.0776	.0958	.1140	.1246	.1434	.1662	.1907	.2143	.2290	.2577	.2915
	114	.0769	.0949	.1130	.1235	.1422	.1647	.1891	.2124	.2270	.2555	.2891
	115	.0762	.0940	.1120	.1223	.1409	.1633	.1874	.2106	.2251	.2534	.2868
	116	.0755	.0932	.1110	.1213	.1397	.1619	.1858	.2088	.2232	.2513	.2845
	117	.0748	.0923	.1100	.1202	.1384	.1605	.1843	.2071	.2214	.2493	.2822
	118	.0742	.0915	.1090	.1191	.1373	.1591	.1827	.2054	.2196	.2473	.2800
	119	.0735	.0907	.1081	.1181	.1361	.1578	.1812	.2037	.2178	.2453	.2778
	120	.0728	.0899	.1072	.1171	.1349	.1564	.1797	.2020	.2160	.2434	.2757
	121	.0722	.0892	.1062	.1161	.1338	.1551	.1782	.2004	.2143	.2415	.2735
	122	.0716	.0884	.1053	.1151	.1327	.1539	.1768	.1988	.2126	.2396	.2714
	123	.0710	.0876	.1044	.1142	.1316	.1526	.1753	.1972	.2109	.2377	.2694
	124	.0704	.0869	.1036	.1132	.1305	.1514	.1739	.1957	.2092	.2359	.2674
	125	.0698	.0862	.1027	.1123	.1294	.1501	.1726	.1941	.2076	.2341	.2654
	126	.0692	.0855	.1019	.1114	.1284	.1489	.1712	.1926	.2060	.2323	.2634
	127	.0686	.0848	.1011	.1105	.1274	.1478	.1699	.1911	.2044	.2306	.2615
	128	.0681	.0841	.1002	.1096	.1263	.1466	.1685	.1897	.2029	.2288	.2595
	129	.0675	.0834	.0994	.1087	.1253	.1455	.1672	.1882	.2014	.2272	.2577
	130	.0670	.0827	.0986	.1079	.1244	.1443	.1660	.1868	.1999	.2255	.2558
	131	.0664	.0821	.0979	.1070	.1234	.1432	.1647	.1854	.1984	.2238	.2540
	132	.0659	.0814	.0971	.1062	.1225	.1421	.1635	.1840	.1969	.2222	.2522
	133	.0654	.0808	.0964	.1054	.1215	.1411	.1623	.1827	.1955	.2206	.2504
	134	.0649	.0802	.0956	.1046	.1206	.1400	.1611	.1813	.1941	.2190	.2486
	135	.0644	.0795	.0949	.1038	.1197	.1390	.1599	.1800	.1927	.2175	.2469
	136	.0639	.0789	.0942	.1030	.1188	.1379	.1587	.1787	.1913	.2160	.2452
	137	.0634	.0783	.0935	.1022	.1179	.1369	.1576	.1774	.1899	.2144	.2435
	138	.0629	.0777	.0928	.1015	.1170	.1359	.1564	.1762	.1886	.2130	.2419
	139	.0624	.0772	.0921	.1007	.1162	.1349	.1553	.1749	.1873	.2115	.2402
	140	.0620	.0766	.0914	.1000	.1153	.1340	.1542	.1737	.1860	.2100	.2386
	141	.0615	.0760	.0907	.0992	.1145	.1330	.1531	.1725	.1847	.2086	.2370
	142	.0611	.0755	.0901	.0985	.1137	.1321	.1520	.1713	.1834	.2072	.2354
	143	.0606	.0749	.0894	.0978	.1129	.1312	.1510	.1701	.1822	.2058	.2339
	144	.0602	.0744	.0888	.0971	.1121	.1302	.1499	.1690	.1809	.2044	.2324
	145	.0597	.0739	.0882	.0964	.1113	.1293	.1489	.1678	.1797	.2031	.2308
	146	.0593	.0733	.0875	.0958	.1105	.1284	.1479	.1667	.1785	.2017	.2294
	147	.0589	.0728	.0869	.0951	.1098	.1276	.1469	.1656	.1773	.2004	.2279
	148	.0585	.0723	.0863	.0944	.1090	.1267	.1459	.1645	.1762	.1991	.2264
	149	.0581	.0718	.0857	.0938	.1083	.1258	.1449	.1634	.1750	.1978	.2250
	150	.0577	.0713	.0851	.0932	.1075	.1250	.1440	.1623	.1739	.1966	.2236
	151+	8.306*	10.35*	12.44*	13.67*	15.91*	18.67*	21.73*	24.76*	26.69*	30.58*	35.35*
20	21-31	SEE NOTE**										
	32-71	SEE NOTE***										
	72	.1363	.1659	.1951	.2118	.2411	.2757	.3122	.3465	.3675	.4076	.4534
	73	.1343	.1635	.1923	.2087	.2377	.2719	.3080	.3419	.3627	.4025	.4480
	74	.1323	.1611	.1895	.2058	.2344	.2682	.3039	.3375	.3581	.3976	.4427
	75	.1304	.1588	.1869	.2029	.2311	.2646	.3000	.3332	.3536	.3927	.4375

* To approximate p_k, divide the starred entry under k by $(C-1)$.

** Compute $B^* = C - B$, find p^*_{1-k} for B^* and C, and compute $p_k = 1 - p^*_{1-k}$.

B	C	.001	.01	.05	.1	.25	.5	.75	.9	.95	.99	.999
20	76	.1285	.1565	.1843	.2001	.2280	.2611	.2961	.3290	.3492	.3880	.4324
	77	.1267	.1543	.1817	.1973	.2249	.2577	.2923	.3249	.3449	.3834	.4275
	78	.1249	.1522	.1793	.1947	.2220	.2543	.2886	.3209	.3407	.3789	.4226
	79	.1232	.1501	.1769	.1921	.2191	.2511	.2850	.3169	.3366	.3744	.4179
	80	.1215	.1481	.1745	.1896	.2163	.2479	.2815	.3131	.3326	.3701	.4132
	81	.1199	.1462	.1723	.1872	.2135	.2448	.2781	.3094	.3287	.3659	.4087
	82	.1183	.1442	.1700	.1848	.2108	.2418	.2747	.3058	.3249	.3618	.4043
	83	.1167	.1424	.1679	.1824	.2082	.2389	.2714	.3022	.3212	.3578	.3999
	84	.1152	.1406	.1658	.1802	.2057	.2360	.2683	.2987	.3175	.3538	.3957
	85	.1138	.1388	.1637	.1780	.2032	.2332	.2651	.2953	.3140	.3500	.3915
	86	.1123	.1371	.1617	.1758	.2008	.2305	.2621	.2920	.3105	.3462	.3874
	87	.1109	.1354	.1598	.1737	.1984	.2278	.2591	.2888	.3071	.3425	.3834
	88	.1096	.1338	.1579	.1716	.1961	.2252	.2562	.2856	.3038	.3389	.3795
	89	.1082	.1322	.1560	.1696	.1938	.2227	.2534	.2825	.3005	.3353	.3756
	90	.1069	.1306	.1542	.1677	.1916	.2202	.2506	.2795	.2973	.3319	.3719
	91	.1057	.1291	.1524	.1658	.1895	.2177	.2479	.2765	.2942	.3285	.3682
	92	.1044	.1276	.1507	.1639	.1873	.2153	.2452	.2736	.2911	.3251	.3646
	93	.1032	.1261	.1490	.1621	.1853	.2130	.2426	.2707	.2881	.3219	.3610
	94	.1021	.1247	.1473	.1603	.1833	.2107	.2401	.2679	.2852	.3187	.3575
	95	.1009	.1233	.1457	.1585	.1813	.2085	.2376	.2652	.2823	.3155	.3541
	96	.0998	.1220	.1441	.1568	.1793	.2063	.2351	.2625	.2795	.3124	.3508
	97	.0987	.1206	.1425	.1551	.1775	.2042	.2327	.2599	.2767	.3094	.3475
	98	.0976	.1193	.1410	.1535	.1756	.2021	.2304	.2573	.2740	.3065	.3442
	99	.0965	.1181	.1395	.1519	.1738	.2000	.2281	.2548	.2714	.3036	.3411
	100	.0955	.1168	.1381	.1503	.1720	.1980	.2258	.2523	.2688	.3007	.3380
	101	.0945	.1156	.1367	.1488	.1703	.1960	.2236	.2499	.2662	.2979	.3349
	102	.0935	.1144	.1353	.1472	.1686	.1941	.2214	.2475	.2637	.2952	.3319
	103	.0925	.1132	.1339	.1458	.1669	.1922	.2193	.2452	.2612	.2925	.3289
	104	.0916	.1121	.1326	.1443	.1652	.1903	.2172	.2429	.2588	.2898	.3260
	105	.0907	.1110	.1312	.1429	.1636	.1885	.2152	.2406	.2564	.2872	.3232
	106	.0898	.1099	.1300	.1415	.1621	.1867	.2132	.2384	.2541	.2847	.3204
	107	.0889	.1088	.1287	.1401	.1605	.1850	.2112	.2362	.2518	.2822	.3176
	108	.0880	.1077	.1274	.1388	.1590	.1832	.2093	.2341	.2496	.2797	.3149
	109	.0871	.1067	.1262	.1375	.1575	.1815	.2074	.2320	.2474	.2773	.3123
	110	.0863	.1057	.1250	.1362	.1560	.1799	.2055	.2300	.2452	.2749	.3097
	111	.0855	.1047	.1239	.1349	.1546	.1783	.2037	.2279	.2431	.2725	.3071
	112	.0847	.1037	.1227	.1337	.1532	.1767	.2019	.2260	.2410	.2702	.3046
	113	.0839	.1027	.1216	.1325	.1518	.1751	.2001	.2240	.2389	.2680	.3021
	114	.0831	.1018	.1205	.1313	.1505	.1735	.1984	.2221	.2369	.2657	.2996
	115	.0823	.1008	.1194	.1301	.1491	.1720	.1966	.2202	.2349	.2636	.2972
	116	.0816	.0999	.1183	.1289	.1478	.1705	.1950	.2183	.2329	.2614	.2948
	117	.0808	.0990	.1173	.1278	.1465	.1691	.1933	.2165	.2310	.2593	.2925
	118	.0801	.0982	.1163	.1267	.1453	.1676	.1917	.2147	.2291	.2572	.2902
	119	.0794	.0973	.1152	.1256	.1440	.1662	.1901	.2130	.2273	.2551	.2879
	120	.0787	.0964	.1143	.1245	.1428	.1648	.1885	.2112	.2254	.2531	.2857
	121	.0780	.0956	.1133	.1234	.1416	.1634	.1870	.2095	.2236	.2511	.2835
	122	.0773	.0948	.1123	.1224	.1404	.1621	.1855	.2079	.2218	.2492	.2813
	123	.0767	.0940	.1114	.1214	.1393	.1608	.1840	.2062	.2201	.2472	.2792
	124	.0760	.0932	.1104	.1204	.1381	.1595	.1825	.2046	.2184	.2453	.2771
	125	.0754	.0924	.1095	.1194	.1370	.1582	.1810	.2030	.2167	.2435	.2751
	126	.0748	.0917	.1086	.1184	.1359	.1569	.1796	.2014	.2150	.2416	.2730
	127	.0741	.0909	.1077	.1174	.1348	.1557	.1782	.1998	.2134	.2398	.2710
	128	.0735	.0902	.1069	.1165	.1337	.1545	.1768	.1983	.2117	.2380	.2690
	129	.0729	.0894	.1060	.1156	.1327	.1533	.1755	.1968	.2102	.2363	.2671
	130	.0723	.0887	.1052	.1147	.1316	.1521	.1741	.1953	.2086	.2345	.2652
	131	.0718	.0880	.1043	.1138	.1306	.1509	.1728	.1939	.2070	.2328	.2633
	132	.0712	.0873	.1035	.1129	.1296	.1498	.1715	.1924	.2055	.2311	.2614
	133	.0706	.0866	.1027	.1120	.1286	.1486	.1702	.1910	.2040	.2295	.2596
	134	.0701	.0860	.1019	.1112	.1276	.1475	.1690	.1896	.2025	.2278	.2577
	135	.0695	.0853	.1012	.1103	.1267	.1464	.1677	.1882	.2011	.2262	.2560
	136	.0690	.0846	.1004	.1095	.1257	.1453	.1665	.1869	.1996	.2246	.2542
	137	.0685	.0840	.0996	.1087	.1248	.1443	.1653	.1855	.1982	.2231	.2525
	138	.0679	.0834	.0989	.1079	.1239	.1432	.1641	.1842	.1968	.2215	.2507
	139	.0674	.0827	.0982	.1071	.1230	.1422	.1629	.1829	.1954	.2200	.2490
	140	.0669	.0821	.0974	.1063	.1221	.1412	.1618	.1816	.1941	.2185	.2474
	141	.0664	.0815	.0967	.1055	.1212	.1401	.1607	.1804	.1927	.2170	.2457
	142	.0659	.0809	.0960	.1047	.1203	.1392	.1595	.1791	.1914	.2155	.2441
	143	.0655	.0803	.0953	.1040	.1195	.1382	.1584	.1779	.1901	.2141	.2425
	144	.0650	.0798	.0947	.1032	.1186	.1372	.1573	.1767	.1888	.2127	.2409
	145	.0645	.0792	.0940	.1025	.1178	.1363	.1563	.1755	.1876	.2113	.2393
	146	.0641	.0786	.0933	.1018	.1170	.1353	.1552	.1743	.1863	.2099	.2378
	147	.0636	.0781	.0927	.1011	.1162	.1344	.1541	.1732	.1851	.2085	.2363

*** To approximate p_k, compute $m = B/C$ and $s = \sqrt{m(1 - m)/(C + 1)}$, find u_k in Table T4 on page 715 below, and compute $p_k \doteq m + u_k s$.

B	C	.001	.01	.05	.1	.25	.5	.75	.9	.95	.99	.999
20	148	.0632	.0775	.0920	.1004	.1154	.1335	.1531	.1720	.1839	.2071	.2348
	149	.0627	.0770	.0914	.0997	.1146	.1326	.1521	.1709	.1827	.2058	.2333
	150	.0623	.0765	.0908	.0990	.1138	.1317	.1511	.1698	.1815	.2045	.2318
	151	.0618	.0759	.0901	.0984	.1131	.1308	.1501	.1687	.1803	.2032	.2304
	152	.0614	.0754	.0895	.0977	.1123	.1300	.1491	.1676	.1791	.2019	.2289
	153	.0610	.0749	.0889	.0970	.1116	.1291	.1481	.1665	.1780	.2006	.2275
	154	.0606	.0744	.0883	.0964	.1108	.1283	.1472	.1654	.1769	.1994	.2261
	155	.0602	.0739	.0878	.0958	.1101	.1274	.1462	.1644	.1758	.1981	.2247
	156	.0598	.0734	.0872	.0951	.1094	.1266	.1453	.1633	.1747	.1969	.2234
	157+	8.958*	11.08*	13.25*	14.53*	16.83*	19.67*	22.81*	25.90*	27.88*	31.85*	36.70*
21	22-33	SEE NOTE**										
	34-77	SEE NOTE***										
	78	.1345	.1627	.1906	.2064	.2343	.2673	.3020	.3346	.3546	.3930	.4369
	79	.1326	.1605	.1880	.2037	.2313	.2638	.2982	.3305	.3504	.3884	.4320
	80	.1308	.1584	.1856	.2010	.2283	.2605	.2946	.3266	.3462	.3840	.4272
	81	.1290	.1563	.1831	.1984	.2254	.2573	.2910	.3227	.3422	.3796	.4225
	82	.1273	.1542	.1808	.1959	.2225	.2541	.2875	.3189	.3382	.3753	.4180
	83	.1257	.1522	.1785	.1934	.2198	.2510	.2841	.3152	.3344	.3712	.4135
	84	.1240	.1503	.1762	.1910	.2171	.2480	.2807	.3116	.3306	.3671	.4091
	85	.1224	.1484	.1740	.1887	.2145	.2451	.2775	.3080	.3269	.3631	.4048
	86	.1209	.1465	.1719	.1864	.2119	.2422	.2743	.3046	.3233	.3592	.4006
	87	.1194	.1447	.1698	.1841	.2094	.2394	.2712	.3012	.3197	.3554	.3965
	88	.1179	.1430	.1678	.1820	.2070	.2366	.2682	.2979	.3163	.3516	.3924
	89	.1165	.1413	.1658	.1798	.2046	.2340	.2652	.2947	.3129	.3480	.3885
	90	.1151	.1396	.1639	.1777	.2022	.2314	.2623	.2915	.3095	.3444	.3846
	91	.1137	.1380	.1620	.1757	.2000	.2288	.2594	.2884	.3063	.3408	.3808
	92	.1124	.1364	.1601	.1737	.1977	.2263	.2567	.2854	.3031	.3374	.3770
	93	.1111	.1348	.1583	.1718	.1956	.2238	.2539	.2824	.3000	.3340	.3734
	94	.1098	.1333	.1566	.1699	.1934	.2214	.2513	.2795	.2970	.3307	.3698
	95	.1086	.1318	.1549	.1680	.1913	.2191	.2486	.2766	.2940	.3274	.3663
	96	.1074	.1304	.1532	.1662	.1893	.2168	.2461	.2738	.2910	.3243	.3628
	97	.1062	.1289	.1515	.1644	.1873	.2145	.2436	.2711	.2882	.3211	.3594
	98	.1050	.1275	.1499	.1627	.1853	.2123	.2411	.2684	.2853	.3181	.3561
	99	.1039	.1262	.1483	.1610	.1834	.2102	.2387	.2658	.2826	.3151	.3528
	100	.1028	.1248	.1468	.1593	.1815	.2081	.2364	.2632	.2799	.3121	.3496
	101	.1017	.1235	.1452	.1577	.1797	.2060	.2340	.2607	.2772	.3092	.3464
	102	.1006	.1222	.1438	.1561	.1779	.2040	.2318	.2582	.2746	.3064	.3433
	103	.0996	.1210	.1423	.1545	.1761	.2020	.2296	.2558	.2720	.3036	.3403
	104	.0985	.1198	.1409	.1530	.1744	.2000	.2274	.2534	.2695	.3008	.3373
	105	.0975	.1186	.1395	.1515	.1727	.1981	.2252	.2510	.2670	.2981	.3344
	106	.0966	.1174	.1381	.1500	.1710	.1962	.2231	.2487	.2646	.2955	.3315
	107	.0956	.1162	.1368	.1485	.1694	.1944	.2211	.2465	.2622	.2929	.3286
	108	.0947	.1151	.1354	.1471	.1678	.1926	.2190	.2442	.2599	.2903	.3258
	109	.0937	.1140	.1342	.1457	.1662	.1908	.2170	.2421	.2576	.2878	.3231
	110	.0928	.1129	.1329	.1443	.1647	.1890	.2151	.2399	.2553	.2853	.3204
	111	.0919	.1118	.1316	.1430	.1632	.1873	.2132	.2378	.2531	.2829	.3177
	112	.0911	.1108	.1304	.1417	.1617	.1856	.2113	.2357	.2510	.2805	.3151
	113	.0902	.1097	.1292	.1404	.1602	.1840	.2094	.2337	.2488	.2782	.3126
	114	.0894	.1087	.1280	.1391	.1588	.1824	.2076	.2317	.2467	.2759	.3100
	115	.0886	.1077	.1269	.1379	.1574	.1808	.2058	.2297	.2446	.2736	.3075
	116	.0877	.1068	.1257	.1366	.1560	.1792	.2041	.2278	.2426	.2714	.3051
	117	.0869	.1058	.1246	.1354	.1546	.1777	.2023	.2259	.2406	.2692	.3027
	118	.0862	.1049	.1235	.1342	.1533	.1761	.2007	.2240	.2386	.2670	.3003
	119	.0854	.1039	.1225	.1331	.1520	.1747	.1990	.2222	.2367	.2649	.2980
	120	.0846	.1030	.1214	.1319	.1507	.1732	.1973	.2204	.2348	.2628	.2957
	121	.0839	.1021	.1204	.1308	.1494	.1718	.1957	.2186	.2329	.2607	.2934
	122	.0832	.1013	.1193	.1297	.1482	.1703	.1941	.2169	.2311	.2587	.2912
	123	.0825	.1004	.1183	.1286	.1470	.1689	.1926	.2152	.2292	.2567	.2890
	124	.0818	.0996	.1173	.1276	.1458	.1676	.1910	.2135	.2274	.2547	.2868
	125	.0811	.0987	.1164	.1265	.1446	.1662	.1895	.2118	.2257	.2528	.2847
	126	.0804	.0979	.1154	.1255	.1434	.1649	.1880	.2101	.2239	.2509	.2826
	127	.0797	.0971	.1145	.1245	.1422	.1636	.1866	.2085	.2222	.2490	.2805
	128	.0791	.0963	.1136	.1235	.1411	.1623	.1851	.2069	.2206	.2471	.2784
	129	.0784	.0955	.1126	.1225	.1400	.1610	.1837	.2054	.2189	.2453	.2764
	130	.0778	.0948	.1118	.1215	.1389	.1598	.1823	.2038	.2173	.2435	.2744
	131	.0772	.0940	.1109	.1206	.1378	.1586	.1809	.2023	.2157	.2418	.2725
	132	.0766	.0933	.1100	.1196	.1368	.1574	.1795	.2008	.2141	.2400	.2706
	133	.0759	.0925	.1091	.1187	.1357	.1562	.1782	.1993	.2125	.2383	.2687
	134	.0754	.0918	.1083	.1178	.1347	.1550	.1769	.1979	.2110	.2366	.2668
	135	.0748	.0911	.1075	.1169	.1337	.1539	.1756	.1964	.2094	.2349	.2649

* To approximate p_k, divide the starred entry under k by $(C - 1)$.

** Compute $B^* = C - B$, find p^*_{1-k} for B^* and C, and compute $p_k = 1 - p^*_{1-k}$.

B	C	.001	.01	.05	.1	.25	.5	.75	.9	.95	.99	.999
21	136	.0742	.0904	.1067	.1160	.1327	.1527	.1743	.1950	.2080	.2333	.2631
	137	.0736	.0897	.1059	.1151	.1317	.1516	.1730	.1936	.2065	.2316	.2613
	138	.0731	.0891	.1051	.1143	.1307	.1505	.1718	.1922	.2050	.2300	.2595
	139	.0725	.0884	.1043	.1134	.1298	.1494	.1706	.1909	.2036	.2284	.2578
	140	.0720	.0877	.1035	.1126	.1288	.1483	.1694	.1896	.2022	.2269	.2561
	141	.0714	.0871	.1028	.1118	.1279	.1473	.1682	.1882	.2008	.2253	.2544
	142	.0709	.0864	.1020	.1110	.1270	.1462	.1670	.1869	.1994	.2238	.2527
	143	.0704	.0858	.1013	.1102	.1261	.1452	.1658	.1857	.1980	.2223	.2510
	144	.0699	.0852	.1006	.1094	.1252	.1442	.1647	.1844	.1967	.2208	.2494
	145	.0694	.0846	.0998	.1086	.1243	.1432	.1636	.1831	.1954	.2194	.2478
	146	.0689	.0840	.0991	.1079	.1234	.1422	.1625	.1819	.1941	.2179	.2462
	147	.0684	.0834	.0984	.1071	.1226	.1412	.1614	.1807	.1928	.2165	.2446
	148	.0679	.0828	.0978	.1064	.1218	.1403	.1603	.1795	.1915	.2151	.2430
	149	.0674	.0822	.0971	.1056	.1209	.1393	.1592	.1783	.1903	.2137	.2415
	150	.0670	.0817	.0964	.1049	.1201	.1384	.1582	.1772	.1890	.2124	.2400
	151	.0665	.0811	.0958	.1042	.1193	.1375	.1571	.1760	.1878	.2110	.2385
	152	.0660	.0806	.0951	.1035	.1185	.1366	.1561	.1749	.1866	.2097	.2370
	153	.0656	.0800	.0945	.1028	.1177	.1357	.1551	.1737	.1854	.2084	.2355
	154	.0651	.0795	.0939	.1021	.1169	.1348	.1541	.1726	.1843	.2071	.2341
	155	.0647	.0789	.0932	.1015	.1162	.1339	.1531	.1715	.1831	.2058	.2327
	156	.0643	.0784	.0926	.1008	.1154	.1331	.1521	.1705	.1820	.2045	.2312
	157	.0638	.0779	.0920	.1001	.1147	.1322	.1512	.1694	.1808	.2033	.2299
	158	.0634	.0774	.0914	.0995	.1139	.1314	.1502	.1683	.1797	.2020	.2285
	159	.0630	.0769	.0908	.0989	.1132	.1305	.1493	.1673	.1786	.2008	.2271
	160	.0626	.0764	.0902	.0982	.1125	.1297	.1483	.1663	.1775	.1996	.2258
	161	.0622	.0759	.0897	.0976	.1118	.1289	.1474	.1653	.1764	.1984	.2244
	162	.0618	.0754	.0891	.0970	.1111	.1281	.1465	.1643	.1754	.1972	.2231
	163	.0614	.0749	.0885	.0964	.1104	.1273	.1456	.1633	.1743	.1960	.2218
	164+	9.619*	11.83*	14.07*	15.38*	17.75*	20.67*	23.88*	27.05*	29.06*	33.10*	38.04*
22	23–34	SEE NOTE**										
	35–84	SEE NOTE***										
	85	.1313	.1581	.1845	.1994	.2258	.2569	.2898	.3207	.3397	.3761	.4180
	86	.1296	.1561	.1822	.1970	.2231	.2539	.2865	.3171	.3359	.3721	.4136
	87	.1280	.1542	.1800	.1946	.2205	.2510	.2832	.3136	.3323	.3681	.4094
	88	.1264	.1523	.1778	.1923	.2179	.2481	.2801	.3101	.3287	.3643	.4052
	89	.1249	.1505	.1757	.1901	.2154	.2453	.2770	.3068	.3252	.3605	.4012
	90	.1234	.1487	.1737	.1879	.2129	.2425	.2739	.3035	.3217	.3568	.3972
	91	.1219	.1470	.1717	.1857	.2105	.2399	.2710	.3003	.3183	.3531	.3932
	92	.1205	.1453	.1697	.1836	.2082	.2372	.2681	.2971	.3150	.3496	.3894
	93	.1191	.1436	.1678	.1816	.2059	.2347	.2652	.2940	.3118	.3461	.3856
	94	.1177	.1420	.1659	.1795	.2036	.2322	.2624	.2910	.3086	.3426	.3819
	95	.1164	.1404	.1641	.1776	.2014	.2297	.2597	.2880	.3055	.3393	.3783
	96	.1151	.1388	.1623	.1757	.1993	.2273	.2570	.2851	.3025	.3360	.3747
	97	.1138	.1373	.1605	.1738	.1972	.2249	.2544	.2823	.2995	.3328	.3712
	98	.1126	.1358	.1588	.1719	.1951	.2226	.2518	.2795	.2966	.3296	.3678
	99	.1113	.1344	.1571	.1701	.1931	.2203	.2493	.2768	.2937	.3265	.3644
	100	.1101	.1329	.1555	.1684	.1911	.2181	.2469	.2741	.2909	.3234	.3611
	101	.1090	.1315	.1539	.1666	.1892	.2160	.2445	.2714	.2881	.3204	.3579
	102	.1078	.1302	.1523	.1649	.1873	.2138	.2421	.2689	.2854	.3175	.3547
	103	.1067	.1288	.1508	.1633	.1854	.2117	.2398	.2663	.2828	.3146	.3515
	104	.1056	.1275	.1493	.1616	.1836	.2097	.2375	.2638	.2802	.3117	.3485
	105	.1045	.1263	.1478	.1601	.1818	.2077	.2352	.2614	.2776	.3090	.3454
	106	.1035	.1250	.1463	.1585	.1800	.2057	.2331	.2590	.2751	.3062	.3425
	107	.1024	.1238	.1449	.1570	.1783	.2038	.2309	.2566	.2726	.3035	.3395
	108	.1014	.1226	.1435	.1555	.1766	.2019	.2288	.2543	.2702	.3009	.3366
	109	.1004	.1214	.1421	.1540	.1750	.2000	.2267	.2521	.2678	.2983	.3338
	110	.0995	.1202	.1408	.1525	.1734	.1982	.2247	.2498	.2654	.2957	.3310
	111	.0985	.1191	.1395	.1511	.1718	.1964	.2227	.2476	.2631	.2932	.3283
	112	.0976	.1179	.1382	.1497	.1702	.1946	.2207	.2455	.2609	.2908	.3256
	113	.0967	.1168	.1369	.1483	.1687	.1929	.2188	.2434	.2587	.2883	.3229
	114	.0958	.1158	.1356	.1470	.1671	.1912	.2169	.2413	.2565	.2859	.3203
	115	.0949	.1147	.1344	.1457	.1657	.1895	.2150	.2393	.2543	.2836	.3178
	116	.0940	.1137	.1332	.1444	.1642	.1879	.2132	.2372	.2522	.2813	.3152
	117	.0931	.1127	.1320	.1431	.1628	.1863	.2114	.2353	.2501	.2790	.3128
	118	.0923	.1117	.1309	.1419	.1614	.1847	.2096	.2333	.2481	.2768	.3103
	119	.0915	.1107	.1297	.1406	.1600	.1831	.2078	.2314	.2461	.2746	.3079
	120	.0907	.1097	.1286	.1394	.1586	.1816	.2061	.2295	.2441	.2724	.3055
	121	.0899	.1088	.1275	.1382	.1573	.1801	.2044	.2277	.2421	.2703	.3032
	122	.0891	.1078	.1264	.1371	.1560	.1786	.2028	.2259	.2402	.2682	.3009
	123	.0883	.1069	.1254	.1359	.1547	.1771	.2012	.2241	.2383	.2661	.2986
	124	.0876	.1060	.1243	.1348	.1534	.1757	.1995	.2223	.2365	.2641	.2964

*** To approximate p_k, compute $m = B/C$ and $s = \sqrt{m(1 - m)/(C + 1)}$, find u_k in Table T4 on page 715 below, and compute $p_k \doteq m + u_k s$.

B	C	.001	.01	.05	.1	.25	.5	.75	.9	.95	.99	.999
22	125	.0868	.1051	.1233	.1337	.1522	.1743	.1980	.2206	.2346	.2620	.2942
	126	.0861	.1042	.1223	.1326	.1509	.1729	.1964	.2189	.2328	.2601	.2920
	127	.0854	.1034	.1213	.1315	.1497	.1715	.1949	.2172	.2311	.2581	.2899
	128	.0847	.1025	.1203	.1305	.1485	.1702	.1934	.2155	.2293	.2562	.2878
	129	.0840	.1017	.1193	.1294	.1474	.1688	.1919	.2139	.2276	.2543	.2857
	130	.0833	.1009	.1184	.1284	.1462	.1675	.1904	.2123	.2259	.2525	.2836
	131	.0827	.1001	.1174	.1274	.1451	.1662	.1890	.2107	.2242	.2506	.2816
	132	.0820	.0993	.1165	.1264	.1439	.1650	.1876	.2091	.2226	.2488	.2796
	133	.0813	.0985	.1156	.1254	.1428	.1637	.1862	.2076	.2210	.2470	.2777
	134	.0807	.0977	.1147	.1245	.1418	.1625	.1848	.2061	.2194	.2453	.2757
	135	.0801	.0970	.1138	.1235	.1407	.1613	.1834	.2046	.2178	.2435	.2738
	136	.0795	.0962	.1130	.1226	.1396	.1601	.1821	.2031	.2162	.2418	.2719
	137	.0788	.0955	.1121	.1217	.1386	.1589	.1808	.2017	.2147	.2401	.2701
	138	.0782	.0948	.1113	.1207	.1376	.1578	.1795	.2002	.2132	.2385	.2683
	139	.0777	.0941	.1105	.1199	.1366	.1566	.1782	.1988	.2117	.2368	.2665
	140	.0771	.0934	.1096	.1190	.1356	.1555	.1769	.1974	.2102	.2352	.2647
	141	.0765	.0927	.1088	.1181	.1346	.1544	.1757	.1961	.2088	.2336	.2629
	142	.0759	.0920	.1081	.1173	.1336	.1533	.1745	.1947	.2073	.2321	.2612
	143	.0754	.0913	.1073	.1164	.1327	.1522	.1732	.1934	.2059	.2305	.2595
	144	.0748	.0907	.1065	.1156	.1318	.1512	.1721	.1921	.2045	.2290	.2578
	145	.0743	.0900	.1058	.1148	.1308	.1501	.1709	.1908	.2032	.2275	.2561
	146	.0738	.0894	.1050	.1140	.1299	.1491	.1697	.1895	.2018	.2260	.2545
	147	.0732	.0888	.1043	.1132	.1290	.1481	.1686	.1882	.2005	.2245	.2528
	148	.0727	.0881	.1035	.1124	.1281	.1471	.1674	.1870	.1992	.2230	.2512
	149	.0722	.0875	.1028	.1116	.1273	.1461	.1663	.1857	.1979	.2216	.2496
	150	.0717	.0869	.1021	.1109	.1264	.1451	.1652	.1845	.1966	.2202	.2481
	151	.0712	.0863	.1014	.1101	.1256	.1441	.1641	.1833	.1953	.2188	.2465
	152	.0707	.0857	.1007	.1094	.1247	.1432	.1631	.1821	.1941	.2174	.2450
	153	.0702	.0852	.1001	.1086	.1239	.1422	.1620	.1810	.1928	.2160	.2435
	154	.0697	.0846	.0994	.1079	.1231	.1413	.1610	.1798	.1916	.2147	.2420
	155	.0693	.0840	.0987	.1072	.1223	.1404	.1599	.1787	.1904	.2134	.2405
	156	.0688	.0835	.0981	.1065	.1215	.1395	.1589	.1775	.1892	.2121	.2391
	157	.0684	.0829	.0974	.1058	.1207	.1386	.1579	.1764	.1880	.2108	.2376
	158	.0679	.0824	.0968	.1051	.1199	.1377	.1569	.1753	.1869	.2095	.2362
	159	.0675	.0818	.0962	.1044	.1191	.1368	.1559	.1743	.1857	.2082	.2348
	160	.0670	.0813	.0956	.1038	.1184	.1360	.1550	.1732	.1846	.2070	.2334
	161	.0666	.0808	.0950	.1031	.1176	.1351	.1540	.1721	.1835	.2057	.2320
	162	.0662	.0803	.0944	.1025	.1169	.1343	.1531	.1711	.1824	.2045	.2307
	163	.0657	.0797	.0938	.1018	.1162	.1335	.1521	.1701	.1813	.2033	.2293
	164	.0653	.0792	.0932	.1012	.1155	.1327	.1512	.1690	.1802	.2021	.2280
	165	.0649	.0787	.0926	.1006	.1148	.1319	.1503	.1680	.1791	.2009	.2267
	166	.0645	.0783	.0920	.0999	.1141	.1311	.1494	.1670	.1781	.1997	.2254
	167	.0641	.0778	.0915	.0993	.1134	.1303	.1485	.1661	.1770	.1986	.2241
	168	.0637	.0773	.0909	.0987	.1127	.1295	.1476	.1651	.1760	.1975	.2229
	169	.0633	.0768	.0903	.0981	.1120	.1287	.1468	.1641	.1750	.1963	.2216
	170+	10.29*	12.57*	14.89*	16.24*	18.68*	21.67*	24.96*	28.18*	30.24*	34.35*	39.37*
23	24-35	SEE NOTE**										
	36-91	SEE NOTE***										
	92	.1287	.1542	.1793	.1936	.2186	.2482	.2794	.3088	.3269	.3616	.4016
	93	.1272	.1525	.1773	.1914	.2162	.2455	.2765	.3056	.3235	.3580	.3977
	94	.1257	.1507	.1753	.1893	.2138	.2429	.2736	.3025	.3203	.3545	.3939
	95	.1243	.1490	.1734	.1872	.2115	.2403	.2707	.2994	.3170	.3510	.3902
	96	.1229	.1474	.1715	.1852	.2093	.2378	.2679	.2964	.3139	.3476	.3865
	97	.1215	.1458	.1696	.1832	.2070	.2353	.2652	.2934	.3108	.3443	.3830
	98	.1202	.1442	.1678	.1812	.2049	.2329	.2625	.2905	.3078	.3410	.3794
	99	.1189	.1426	.1660	.1793	.2028	.2305	.2599	.2877	.3048	.3378	.3760
	100	.1176	.1411	.1643	.1775	.2007	.2282	.2574	.2849	.3019	.3346	.3725
	101	.1164	.1396	.1626	.1756	.1987	.2259	.2548	.2822	.2990	.3316	.3692
	102	.1151	.1382	.1609	.1738	.1967	.2237	.2524	.2795	.2962	.3285	.3659
	103	.1139	.1368	.1593	.1721	.1947	.2215	.2500	.2768	.2934	.3255	.3627
	104	.1128	.1354	.1577	.1704	.1928	.2194	.2476	.2743	.2907	.3226	.3595
	105	.1116	.1340	.1561	.1687	.1909	.2173	.2453	.2717	.2881	.3197	.3564
	106	.1105	.1327	.1546	.1670	.1891	.2152	.2430	.2692	.2855	.3169	.3533
	107	.1094	.1314	.1531	.1654	.1873	.2132	.2407	.2668	.2829	.3141	.3503
	108	.1083	.1301	.1516	.1638	.1855	.2112	.2385	.2644	.2804	.3114	.3474
	109	.1072	.1288	.1501	.1623	.1837	.2092	.2364	.2620	.2779	.3087	.3444
	110	.1062	.1276	.1487	.1608	.1820	.2073	.2342	.2597	.2755	.3061	.3416
	111	.1052	.1264	.1473	.1593	.1804	.2054	.2321	.2574	.2731	.3035	.3388
	112	.1042	.1252	.1460	.1578	.1787	.2036	.2301	.2552	.2708	.3009	.3360
	113	.1032	.1240	.1446	.1563	.1771	.2018	.2281	.2530	.2685	.2984	.3332
	114	.1022	.1229	.1433	.1549	.1755	.2000	.2261	.2508	.2662	.2959	.3306

* To approximate p_k, divide the starred entry under k by $(C - 1)$.

** Compute $B^* = C - B$, find p^*_{1-k} for B^* and C, and compute $p_k = 1 - p^*_{1-k}$.

B	C	.001	.01	.05	.1	.25	.5	.75	.9	.95	.99	.999
23	115	.1013	.1217	.1420	.1535	.1740	.1983	.2242	.2487	.2640	.2935	.3279
	116	.1003	.1206	.1407	.1522	.1724	.1965	.2222	.2466	.2618	.2911	.3253
	117	.0994	.1196	.1395	.1508	.1709	.1948	.2204	.2446	.2596	.2888	.3228
	118	.0985	.1185	.1382	.1495	.1694	.1932	.2185	.2426	.2575	.2864	.3202
	119	.0977	.1175	.1370	.1482	.1680	.1916	.2167	.2406	.2554	.2842	.3178
	120	.0968	.1164	.1358	.1469	.1666	.1900	.2149	.2386	.2533	.2819	.3153
	121	.0959	.1154	.1347	.1457	.1652	.1884	.2132	.2367	.2513	.2797	.3129
	122	.0951	.1144	.1335	.1444	.1638	.1868	.2114	.2348	.2493	.2776	.3105
	123	.0943	.1134	.1324	.1432	.1624	.1853	.2097	.2329	.2474	.2754	.3082
	124	.0935	.1125	.1313	.1420	.1611	.1838	.2080	.2311	.2454	.2733	.3059
	125	.0927	.1115	.1302	.1409	.1598	.1823	.2064	.2293	.2436	.2712	.3036
	126	.0919	.1106	.1291	.1397	.1585	.1809	.2048	.2275	.2417	.2692	.3014
	127	.0911	.1097	.1281	.1386	.1572	.1794	.2032	.2258	.2398	.2672	.2992
	128	.0904	.1088	.1271	.1375	.1560	.1780	.2016	.2241	.2380	.2652	.2970
	129	.0897	.1079	.1260	.1364	.1547	.1766	.2001	.2224	.2362	.2632	.2949
	130	.0889	.1071	.1250	.1353	.1535	.1753	.1985	.2207	.2345	.2613	.2928
	131	.0882	.1062	.1240	.1342	.1523	.1739	.1970	.2191	.2328	.2594	.2907
	132	.0875	.1054	.1231	.1332	.1511	.1726	.1955	.2174	.2310	.2576	.2886
	133	.0868	.1045	.1221	.1322	.1500	.1713	.1941	.2158	.2294	.2557	.2866
	134	.0861	.1037	.1212	.1311	.1489	.1700	.1927	.2143	.2277	.2539	.2846
	135	.0855	.1029	.1202	.1301	.1477	.1687	.1912	.2127	.2261	.2521	.2827
	136	.0848	.1021	.1193	.1292	.1466	.1675	.1898	.2112	.2245	.2503	.2807
	137	.0841	.1014	.1184	.1282	.1455	.1663	.1885	.2097	.2229	.2486	.2788
	138	.0835	.1006	.1175	.1272	.1445	.1651	.1871	.2082	.2213	.2469	.2769
	139	.0829	.0998	.1167	.1263	.1434	.1639	.1858	.2067	.2198	.2452	.2751
	140	.0822	.0991	.1158	.1254	.1424	.1627	.1845	.2053	.2182	.2435	.2732
	141	.0816	.0984	.1150	.1245	.1413	.1615	.1832	.2038	.2167	.2419	.2714
	142	.0810	.0976	.1141	.1236	.1403	.1604	.1819	.2024	.2152	.2402	.2696
	143	.0804	.0969	.1133	.1227	.1393	.1593	.1806	.2011	.2138	.2386	.2678
	144	.0798	.0962	.1125	.1218	.1383	.1581	.1794	.1997	.2123	.2370	.2661
	145	.0793	.0955	.1117	.1209	.1374	.1570	.1782	.1983	.2109	.2355	.2644
	146	.0787	.0949	.1109	.1201	.1364	.1560	.1769	.1970	.2095	.2339	.2627
	147	.0781	.0942	.1101	.1193	.1355	.1549	.1758	.1957	.2081	.2324	.2610
	148	.0776	.0935	.1094	.1184	.1345	.1539	.1746	.1944	.2068	.2309	.2594
	149	.0770	.0929	.1086	.1176	.1336	.1528	.1734	.1931	.2054	.2294	.2577
	150	.0765	.0922	.1079	.1168	.1327	.1518	.1723	.1919	.2041	.2280	.2561
	151	.0760	.0916	.1071	.1160	.1318	.1508	.1711	.1906	.2028	.2265	.2545
	152	.0754	.0910	.1064	.1152	.1310	.1498	.1700	.1894	.2015	.2251	.2529
	153	.0749	.0903	.1057	.1145	.1301	.1488	.1689	.1882	.2002	.2237	.2514
	154	.0744	.0897	.1050	.1137	.1292	.1478	.1678	.1870	.1989	.2223	.2498
	155	.0739	.0891	.1043	.1130	.1284	.1469	.1668	.1858	.1977	.2209	.2483
	156	.0734	.0885	.1036	.1122	.1275	.1459	.1657	.1846	.1964	.2195	.2468
	157	.0729	.0880	.1029	.1115	.1267	.1450	.1646	.1835	.1952	.2182	.2453
	158	.0725	.0874	.1022	.1108	.1259	.1441	.1636	.1823	.1940	.2169	.2439
	159	.0720	.0868	.1016	.1100	.1251	.1432	.1626	.1812	.1928	.2156	.2424
	160	.0715	.0863	.1009	.1093	.1243	.1423	.1616	.1801	.1916	.2143	.2410
	161	.0710	.0857	.1003	.1086	.1235	.1414	.1606	.1790	.1905	.2130	.2396
	162	.0706	.0851	.0996	.1080	.1228	.1405	.1596	.1779	.1893	.2117	.2382
	163	.0701	.0846	.0990	.1073	.1220	.1396	.1586	.1768	.1882	.2105	.2368
	164	.0697	.0841	.0984	.1066	.1212	.1388	.1577	.1758	.1871	.2092	.2354
	165	.0692	.0835	.0978	.1060	.1205	.1379	.1567	.1747	.1860	.2080	.2341
	166	.0688	.0830	.0972	.1053	.1198	.1371	.1558	.1737	.1849	.2068	.2328
	167	.0684	.0825	.0966	.1047	.1190	.1363	.1549	.1727	.1838	.2056	.2314
	168	.0680	.0820	.0960	.1040	.1183	.1355	.1539	.1717	.1827	.2045	.2301
	169	.0675	.0815	.0954	.1034	.1176	.1347	.1530	.1707	.1817	.2033	.2288
	170	.0671	.0810	.0948	.1028	.1169	.1339	.1521	.1697	.1806	.2021	.2276
	171	.0667	.0805	.0943	.1022	.1162	.1331	.1513	.1687	.1796	.2010	.2263
	172	.0663	.0800	.0937	.1015	.1155	.1323	.1504	.1677	.1786	.1999	.2251
	173	.0659	.0796	.0931	.1009	.1148	.1315	.1495	.1668	.1776	.1988	.2238
	174	.0655	.0791	.0926	.1004	.1142	.1308	.1487	.1658	.1766	.1977	.2226
	175	.0651	.0786	.0921	.0998	.1135	.1300	.1478	.1649	.1756	.1966	.2214
	176	.0647	.0782	.0915	.0992	.1129	.1293	.1470	.1640	.1746	.1955	.2202
	177+	10.96*	13.33*	15.72*	17.11*	19.61*	22.67*	26.03*	29.32*	31.41*	35.60*	40.70*
24	25-37	SEE NOTE**										
	38-99	SEE NOTE***										
	100	.1252	.1494	.1731	.1866	.2103	.2383	.2678	.2957	.3128	.3458	.3839
	101	.1238	.1478	.1713	.1847	.2082	.2359	.2652	.2928	.3098	.3426	.3804
	102	.1225	.1463	.1696	.1828	.2061	.2336	.2626	.2900	.3069	.3395	.3771
	103	.1213	.1448	.1679	.1810	.2040	.2313	.2601	.2873	.3041	.3364	.3737
	104	.1200	.1433	.1662	.1792	.2020	.2290	.2577	.2846	.3013	.3334	.3705

*** To approximate p_k, compute $m = B/C$ and $s = \sqrt{m(1 - m)/(C + 1)}$, find u_k in Table T4 on page 715 below, and compute $p_k \doteq m + u_k s$.

B	C	.001	.01	.05	.1	.25	.5	.75	.9	.95	.99	.999
24	105	.1188	.1419	.1645	.1774	.2000	.2268	.2552	.2820	.2985	.3304	.3673
	106	.1176	.1404	.1629	.1756	.1981	.2247	.2529	.2794	.2958	.3275	.3641
	107	.1164	.1390	.1613	.1739	.1962	.2226	.2505	.2769	.2932	.3246	.3610
	108	.1152	.1377	.1597	.1723	.1944	.2205	.2482	.2744	.2906	.3218	.3580
	109	.1141	.1363	.1582	.1706	.1925	.2185	.2460	.2720	.2880	.3190	.3550
	110	.1130	.1350	.1567	.1690	.1907	.2165	.2438	.2696	.2855	.3163	.3520
	111	.1119	.1338	.1552	.1675	.1890	.2145	.2416	.2672	.2830	.3136	.3491
	112	.1108	.1325	.1538	.1659	.1873	.2126	.2395	.2649	.2806	.3110	.3463
	113	.1098	.1313	.1524	.1644	.1856	.2107	.2374	.2626	.2782	.3084	.3435
	114	.1088	.1300	.1510	.1629	.1839	.2088	.2353	.2604	.2759	.3059	.3407
	115	.1078	.1289	.1496	.1614	.1823	.2070	.2333	.2582	.2736	.3034	.3380
	116	.1068	.1277	.1483	.1600	.1807	.2052	.2313	.2560	.2713	.3009	.3353
	117	.1058	.1265	.1470	.1586	.1791	.2034	.2293	.2539	.2691	.2985	.3327
	118	.1048	.1254	.1457	.1572	.1775	.2017	.2274	.2518	.2669	.2961	.3301
	119	.1039	.1243	.1444	.1558	.1760	.2000	.2255	.2497	.2647	.2937	.3275
	120	.1030	.1232	.1431	.1545	.1745	.1983	.2237	.2477	.2626	.2914	.3250
	121	.1021	.1221	.1419	.1532	.1731	.1967	.2218	.2457	.2605	.2891	.3225
	122	.1012	.1211	.1407	.1519	.1716	.1951	.2200	.2437	.2584	.2869	.3201
	123	.1003	.1201	.1395	.1506	.1702	.1935	.2183	.2418	.2564	.2847	.3177
	124	.0995	.1190	.1383	.1493	.1688	.1919	.2165	.2399	.2544	.2825	.3153
	125	.0986	.1180	.1372	.1481	.1674	.1904	.2148	.2380	.2524	.2804	.3130
	126	.0978	.1171	.1361	.1469	.1661	.1888	.2131	.2362	.2505	.2783	.3107
	127	.0970	.1161	.1350	.1457	.1647	.1873	.2115	.2344	.2486	.2762	.3084
	128	.0962	.1151	.1339	.1445	.1634	.1859	.2098	.2326	.2467	.2741	.3062
	129	.0954	.1142	.1328	.1434	.1621	.1844	.2082	.2308	.2449	.2721	.3040
	130	.0946	.1133	.1317	.1422	.1608	.1830	.2066	.2291	.2430	.2701	.3018
	131	.0938	.1124	.1307	.1411	.1596	.1816	.2051	.2274	.2412	.2682	.2997
	132	.0931	.1115	.1297	.1400	.1584	.1802	.2035	.2257	.2395	.2662	.2976
	133	.0923	.1106	.1287	.1389	.1572	.1788	.2020	.2240	.2377	.2643	.2955
	134	.0916	.1097	.1277	.1379	.1560	.1775	.2005	.2224	.2360	.2625	.2934
	135	.0909	.1089	.1267	.1368	.1548	.1762	.1990	.2208	.2343	.2606	.2914
	136	.0902	.1081	.1257	.1358	.1536	.1749	.1976	.2192	.2326	.2588	.2894
	137	.0895	.1072	.1248	.1348	.1525	.1736	.1962	.2176	.2310	.2570	.2875
	138	.0888	.1064	.1238	.1338	.1514	.1723	.1948	.2161	.2294	.2552	.2855
	139	.0881	.1056	.1229	.1328	.1503	.1711	.1934	.2146	.2278	.2535	.2836
	140	.0875	.1048	.1220	.1318	.1492	.1699	.1920	.2131	.2262	.2517	.2817
	141	.0868	.1041	.1211	.1308	.1481	.1687	.1906	.2116	.2246	.2500	.2798
	142	.0862	.1033	.1202	.1299	.1470	.1675	.1893	.2101	.2231	.2484	.2780
	143	.0856	.1025	.1194	.1290	.1460	.1663	.1880	.2087	.2216	.2467	.2762
	144	.0849	.1018	.1185	.1280	.1449	.1651	.1867	.2073	.2201	.2451	.2744
	145	.0843	.1011	.1177	.1271	.1439	.1640	.1854	.2059	.2186	.2435	.2726
	146	.0837	.1004	.1168	.1262	.1429	.1628	.1842	.2045	.2172	.2419	.2709
	147	.0831	.0996	.1160	.1254	.1419	.1617	.1829	.2031	.2157	.2403	.2691
	148	.0825	.0989	.1152	.1245	.1410	.1606	.1817	.2018	.2143	.2387	.2674
	149	.0819	.0983	.1144	.1236	.1400	.1596	.1805	.2005	.2129	.2372	.2657
	150	.0814	.0976	.1136	.1228	.1391	.1585	.1793	.1992	.2115	.2357	.2641
	151	.0808	.0969	.1128	.1220	.1381	.1574	.1781	.1979	.2102	.2342	.2624
	152	.0802	.0962	.1121	.1211	.1372	.1564	.1770	.1966	.2088	.2327	.2608
	153	.0797	.0956	.1113	.1203	.1363	.1554	.1758	.1953	.2075	.2313	.2592
	154	.0792	.0949	.1106	.1195	.1354	.1544	.1747	.1941	.2062	.2298	.2576
	155	.0786	.0943	.1098	.1187	.1345	.1534	.1736	.1929	.2049	.2284	.2561
	156	.0781	.0937	.1091	.1180	.1336	.1524	.1725	.1917	.2036	.2270	.2545
	157	.0776	.0931	.1084	.1172	.1328	.1514	.1714	.1905	.2024	.2256	.2530
	158	.0771	.0924	.1077	.1164	.1319	.1504	.1703	.1893	.2011	.2242	.2515
	159	.0765	.0918	.1070	.1157	.1311	.1495	.1692	.1881	.1999	.2229	.2500
	160	.0760	.0912	.1063	.1149	.1302	.1485	.1682	.1870	.1987	.2216	.2485
	161	.0756	.0907	.1056	.1142	.1294	.1476	.1671	.1858	.1975	.2202	.2471
	162	.0751	.0901	.1050	.1135	.1286	.1467	.1661	.1847	.1963	.2189	.2456
	163	.0746	.0895	.1043	.1128	.1278	.1458	.1651	.1836	.1951	.2176	.2442
	164	.0741	.0889	.1037	.1121	.1270	.1449	.1641	.1825	.1939	.2164	.2428
	165	.0736	.0884	.1030	.1114	.1262	.1440	.1631	.1814	.1928	.2151	.2414
	166	.0732	.0878	.1024	.1107	.1255	.1431	.1621	.1803	.1917	.2139	.2400
	167	.0727	.0873	.1017	.1100	.1247	.1423	.1612	.1793	.1905	.2126	.2387
	168	.0723	.0867	.1011	.1093	.1239	.1414	.1602	.1782	.1894	.2114	.2373
	169	.0718	.0862	.1005	.1087	.1232	.1406	.1593	.1772	.1883	.2102	.2360
	170	.0714	.0857	.0999	.1080	.1225	.1398	.1584	.1762	.1873	.2090	.2347
	171	.0709	.0852	.0993	.1074	.1217	.1389	.1574	.1751	.1862	.2078	.2334
	172	.0705	.0847	.0987	.1067	.1210	.1381	.1565	.1741	.1851	.2067	.2321
	173	.0701	.0842	.0981	.1061	.1203	.1373	.1556	.1732	.1841	.2055	.2308
	174	.0697	.0837	.0975	.1055	.1196	.1365	.1547	.1722	.1831	.2044	.2296
	175	.0693	.0832	.0970	.1049	.1189	.1358	.1539	.1712	.1820	.2033	.2283

* To approximate p_k, divide the starred entry under k by $(C - 1)$.

** Compute $B^* = C - B$, find p_{1-k}^* for B^* and C, and compute $p_k = 1 - p_{1-k}^*$.

B	C	.001	.01	.05	.1	.25	.5	.75	.9	.95	.99	.999
24	176	.0688	.0827	.0964	.1043	.1182	.1350	.1530	.1702	.1810	.2021	.2271
	177	.0684	.0822	.0958	.1037	.1176	.1342	.1521	.1693	.1800	.2010	.2259
	178	.0680	.0817	.0953	.1031	.1169	.1335	.1513	.1684	.1790	.2000	.2247
	179	.0676	.0812	.0947	.1025	.1162	.1327	.1504	.1674	.1781	.1989	.2235
	180	.0673	.0808	.0942	.1019	.1156	.1320	.1496	.1665	.1771	.1978	.2223
	181	.0669	.0803	.0937	.1013	.1149	.1312	.1488	.1656	.1761	.1968	.2211
	182	.0665	.0799	.0931	.1008	.1143	.1305	.1480	.1647	.1752	.1957	.2200
	183+	11.65*	14.09*	16.55*	17.97*	20.54*	23.67*	27.10*	30.45*	32.59*	36.84*	42.02*
25	26-38	SEE NOTE**										
	39-107	SEE NOTE***										
	108	.1223	.1454	.1679	.1807	.2032	.2298	.2579	.2844	.3007	.3321	.3685
	109	.1211	.1439	.1663	.1790	.2013	.2277	.2556	.2818	.2980	.3293	.3654
	110	.1199	.1426	.1648	.1773	.1995	.2256	.2533	.2794	.2955	.3265	.3624
	111	.1187	.1412	.1632	.1757	.1976	.2236	.2510	.2769	.2929	.3237	.3594
	112	.1176	.1399	.1617	.1741	.1958	.2216	.2488	.2745	.2904	.3210	.3565
	113	.1165	.1386	.1602	.1725	.1941	.2196	.2466	.2722	.2879	.3183	.3536
	114	.1154	.1373	.1587	.1709	.1923	.2177	.2445	.2698	.2855	.3157	.3508
	115	.1143	.1360	.1573	.1694	.1906	.2157	.2424	.2676	.2831	.3131	.3480
	116	.1133	.1348	.1559	.1678	.1889	.2139	.2403	.2653	.2808	.3106	.3452
	117	.1122	.1336	.1545	.1664	.1873	.2120	.2383	.2631	.2784	.3081	.3425
	118	.1112	.1324	.1531	.1649	.1857	.2102	.2363	.2609	.2762	.3056	.3399
	119	.1102	.1312	.1518	.1635	.1841	.2085	.2343	.2588	.2739	.3032	.3372
	120	.1092	.1300	.1505	.1621	.1825	.2067	.2324	.2567	.2717	.3008	.3346
	121	.1083	.1289	.1492	.1607	.1810	.2050	.2305	.2546	.2696	.2985	.3321
	122	.1073	.1278	.1479	.1593	.1794	.2033	.2286	.2526	.2675	.2962	.3296
	123	.1064	.1267	.1467	.1580	.1780	.2016	.2268	.2506	.2654	.2939	.3271
	124	.1055	.1256	.1454	.1567	.1765	.2000	.2250	.2486	.2633	.2917	.3247
	125	.1046	.1246	.1442	.1554	.1751	.1984	.2232	.2467	.2613	.2895	.3223
	126	.1037	.1235	.1430	.1541	.1736	.1968	.2215	.2448	.2593	.2873	.3199
	127	.1029	.1225	.1419	.1528	.1722	.1953	.2197	.2429	.2573	.2851	.3176
	128	.1020	.1215	.1407	.1516	.1709	.1937	.2180	.2411	.2553	.2830	.3153
	129	.1012	.1205	.1396	.1504	.1695	.1922	.2164	.2392	.2534	.2810	.3130
	130	.1003	.1196	.1385	.1492	.1682	.1907	.2147	.2375	.2516	.2789	.3108
	131	.0995	.1186	.1374	.1480	.1669	.1893	.2131	.2357	.2497	.2769	.3086
	132	.0987	.1177	.1363	.1469	.1656	.1878	.2115	.2339	.2479	.2749	.3064
	133	.0979	.1167	.1352	.1457	.1643	.1864	.2099	.2322	.2461	.2729	.3043
	134	.0972	.1158	.1342	.1446	.1631	.1850	.2084	.2305	.2443	.2710	.3022
	135	.0964	.1149	.1332	.1435	.1618	.1836	.2068	.2289	.2425	.2691	.3001
	136	.0957	.1140	.1321	.1424	.1606	.1823	.2053	.2272	.2408	.2672	.2981
	137	.0949	.1132	.1311	.1414	.1594	.1809	.2038	.2256	.2391	.2653	.2960
	138	.0942	.1123	.1302	.1403	.1583	.1796	.2024	.2240	.2374	.2635	.2940
	139	.0935	.1115	.1292	.1393	.1571	.1783	.2009	.2224	.2358	.2617	.2921
	140	.0928	.1106	.1282	.1383	.1560	.1770	.1995	.2209	.2341	.2599	.2901
	141	.0921	.1098	.1273	.1372	.1548	.1758	.1981	.2193	.2325	.2582	.2882
	142	.0914	.1090	.1264	.1363	.1537	.1745	.1967	.2178	.2309	.2564	.2863
	143	.0907	.1082	.1255	.1353	.1526	.1733	.1954	.2163	.2294	.2547	.2844
	144	.0901	.1074	.1246	.1343	.1516	.1721	.1940	.2149	.2278	.2530	.2826
	145	.0894	.1067	.1237	.1334	.1505	.1709	.1927	.2134	.2263	.2514	.2808
	146	.0888	.1059	.1228	.1324	.1494	.1697	.1914	.2120	.2248	.2497	.2790
	147	.0881	.1051	.1219	.1315	.1484	.1686	.1901	.2106	.2233	.2481	.2772
	148	.0875	.1044	.1211	.1306	.1474	.1674	.1888	.2092	.2219	.2465	.2754
	149	.0869	.1037	.1202	.1297	.1464	.1663	.1876	.2078	.2204	.2449	.2737
	150	.0863	.1030	.1194	.1288	.1454	.1652	.1863	.2065	.2190	.2434	.2720
	151	.0857	.1023	.1186	.1279	.1444	.1641	.1851	.2051	.2176	.2418	.2703
	152	.0851	.1016	.1178	.1271	.1435	.1630	.1839	.2038	.2162	.2403	.2686
	153	.0845	.1009	.1170	.1262	.1425	.1619	.1827	.2025	.2148	.2388	.2670
	154	.0839	.1002	.1162	.1254	.1416	.1609	.1815	.2012	.2135	.2373	.2654
	155	.0834	.0995	.1154	.1245	.1406	.1598	.1804	.1999	.2121	.2359	.2638
	156	.0828	.0988	.1147	.1237	.1397	.1588	.1792	.1987	.2108	.2344	.2622
	157	.0823	.0982	.1139	.1229	.1388	.1578	.1781	.1974	.2095	.2330	.2606
	158	.0817	.0975	.1132	.1221	.1379	.1568	.1770	.1962	.2082	.2316	.2590
	159	.0812	.0969	.1125	.1213	.1370	.1558	.1759	.1950	.2069	.2302	.2575
	160	.0806	.0963	.1117	.1206	.1362	.1548	.1748	.1938	.2057	.2288	.2560
	161	.0801	.0957	.1110	.1198	.1353	.1539	.1737	.1926	.2044	.2274	.2545
	162	.0796	.0950	.1103	.1190	.1345	.1529	.1726	.1915	.2032	.2261	.2530
	163	.0791	.0944	.1096	.1183	.1336	.1520	.1716	.1903	.2020	.2248	.2516
	164	.0786	.0938	.1089	.1175	.1328	.1510	.1705	.1892	.2008	.2234	.2501
	165	.0781	.0933	.1083	.1168	.1320	.1501	.1695	.1880	.1996	.2221	.2487
	166	.0776	.0927	.1076	.1161	.1312	.1492	.1685	.1869	.1984	.2209	.2473
	167	.0771	.0921	.1069	.1154	.1304	.1483	.1675	.1858	.1973	.2196	.2459
	168	.0766	.0915	.1063	.1147	.1296	.1474	.1665	.1847	.1961	.2183	.2445

*** To approximate p_k, compute $m = B/C$ and $s = \sqrt{m(1-m)/(C+1)}$, find u_k in Table T4 on page 715 below, and compute $p_k \doteq m + u_k s$.

B	C	.001	.01	.05	.1	.25	.5	.75	.9	.95	.99	.999
25	169	.0762	.0910	.1056	.1140	.1288	.1465	.1655	.1837	.1950	.2171	.2431
	170	.0757	.0904	.1050	.1133	.1280	.1457	.1646	.1826	.1939	.2159	.2418
	171	.0752	.0899	.1043	.1126	.1273	.1448	.1636	.1816	.1928	.2146	.2404
	172	.0748	.0893	.1037	.1120	.1265	.1440	.1627	.1805	.1917	.2134	.2391
	173	.0743	.0888	.1031	.1113	.1258	.1431	.1617	.1795	.1906	.2123	.2378
	174	.0739	.0883	.1025	.1106	.1251	.1423	.1608	.1785	.1895	.2111	.2365
	175	.0734	.0877	.1019	.1100	.1243	.1415	.1599	.1775	.1885	.2099	.2352
	176	.0730	.0872	.1013	.1094	.1236	.1407	.1590	.1765	.1874	.2088	.2340
	177	.0726	.0867	.1007	.1087	.1229	.1399	.1581	.1755	.1864	.2076	.2327
	178	.0721	.0862	.1001	.1081	.1222	.1391	.1572	.1745	.1854	.2065	.2315
	179	.0717	.0857	.0996	.1075	.1215	.1383	.1563	.1736	.1844	.2054	.2302
	180	.0713	.0852	.0990	.1069	.1208	.1376	.1555	.1726	.1834	.2043	.2290
	181	.0709	.0847	.0984	.1063	.1202	.1368	.1546	.1717	.1824	.2032	.2278
	182	.0705	.0843	.0979	.1057	.1195	.1360	.1538	.1708	.1814	.2021	.2266
	183	.0701	.0838	.0973	.1051	.1188	.1353	.1530	.1699	.1804	.2011	.2255
	184	.0697	.0833	.0968	.1045	.1182	.1345	.1521	.1689	.1795	.2000	.2243
	185	.0693	.0828	.0963	.1039	.1175	.1338	.1513	.1681	.1785	.1990	.2232
	186	.0689	.0824	.0957	.1034	.1169	.1331	.1505	.1672	.1776	.1979	.2220
	187	.0685	.0819	.0952	.1028	.1163	.1324	.1497	.1663	.1766	.1969	.2209
	188	.0682	.0815	.0947	.1022	.1156	.1317	.1489	.1654	.1757	.1959	.2198
	189	.0678	.0810	.0942	.1017	.1150	.1310	.1481	.1646	.1748	.1949	.2187
	190+	12.34*	14.85*	17.38*	18.84*	21.47*	24.67*	28.17*	31.58*	33.75*	38.08*	43.33*
26	27-39 SEE NOTE**											
	40-115 SEE NOTE***											
	116	.1198	.1419	.1635	.1757	.1972	.2225	.2494	.2746	.2902	.3203	.3551
	117	.1187	.1406	.1621	.1742	.1955	.2206	.2472	.2723	.2878	.3177	.3523
	118	.1177	.1394	.1606	.1726	.1938	.2188	.2452	.2701	.2855	.3152	.3496
	119	.1166	.1382	.1592	.1711	.1921	.2169	.2431	.2679	.2832	.3127	.3469
	120	.1156	.1369	.1578	.1697	.1905	.2151	.2411	.2657	.2809	.3102	.3442
	121	.1146	.1357	.1565	.1682	.1889	.2133	.2392	.2636	.2787	.3078	.3416
	122	.1136	.1346	.1551	.1668	.1873	.2115	.2372	.2615	.2765	.3054	.3390
	123	.1126	.1334	.1538	.1654	.1857	.2098	.2353	.2594	.2743	.3031	.3365
	124	.1116	.1323	.1525	.1640	.1842	.2081	.2334	.2574	.2722	.3008	.3340
	125	.1107	.1312	.1513	.1627	.1827	.2064	.2316	.2554	.2701	.2985	.3315
	126	.1097	.1301	.1500	.1613	.1812	.2048	.2298	.2534	.2680	.2962	.3291
	127	.1088	.1290	.1488	.1600	.1798	.2032	.2280	.2514	.2660	.2940	.3267
	128	.1079	.1280	.1476	.1587	.1783	.2016	.2262	.2495	.2639	.2919	.3243
	129	.1070	.1269	.1464	.1575	.1769	.2000	.2245	.2476	.2620	.2897	.3220
	130	.1061	.1259	.1452	.1562	.1756	.1985	.2228	.2458	.2600	.2876	.3197
	131	.1053	.1249	.1441	.1550	.1742	.1969	.2211	.2440	.2581	.2855	.3175
	132	.1044	.1239	.1430	.1538	.1728	.1954	.2194	.2422	.2562	.2835	.3152
	133	.1036	.1229	.1418	.1526	.1715	.1940	.2178	.2404	.2544	.2815	.3130
	134	.1028	.1219	.1407	.1514	.1702	.1925	.2162	.2386	.2525	.2795	.3109
	135	.1020	.1210	.1397	.1503	.1689	.1911	.2146	.2369	.2507	.2775	.3087
	136	.1012	.1201	.1386	.1491	.1677	.1897	.2130	.2352	.2489	.2756	.3066
	137	.1004	.1192	.1375	.1480	.1664	.1883	.2115	.2335	.2472	.2737	.3046
	138	.0996	.1182	.1365	.1469	.1652	.1869	.2100	.2319	.2454	.2718	.3025
	139	.0989	.1174	.1355	.1458	.1640	.1855	.2085	.2302	.2437	.2699	.3005
	140	.0981	.1165	.1345	.1447	.1628	.1842	.2070	.2286	.2420	.2681	.2985
	141	.0974	.1156	.1335	.1437	.1616	.1829	.2056	.2271	.2404	.2663	.2965
	142	.0967	.1148	.1325	.1426	.1605	.1816	.2041	.2255	.2387	.2645	.2946
	143	.0960	.1139	.1316	.1416	.1593	.1803	.2027	.2240	.2371	.2627	.2926
	144	.0953	.1131	.1306	.1406	.1582	.1791	.2013	.2224	.2355	.2610	.2908
	145	.0946	.1123	.1297	.1396	.1571	.1778	.1999	.2209	.2340	.2593	.2889
	146	.0939	.1115	.1288	.1386	.1560	.1766	.1986	.2195	.2324	.2576	.2870
	147	.0932	.1107	.1279	.1377	.1549	.1754	.1972	.2180	.2309	.2559	.2852
	148	.0926	.1099	.1270	.1367	.1538	.1742	.1959	.2165	.2294	.2543	.2834
	149	.0919	.1091	.1261	.1358	.1528	.1730	.1946	.2151	.2279	.2526	.2816
	150	.0913	.1084	.1252	.1348	.1518	.1719	.1933	.2137	.2264	.2510	.2799
	151	.0906	.1076	.1244	.1339	.1507	.1707	.1921	.2123	.2249	.2494	.2781
	152	.0900	.1069	.1235	.1330	.1497	.1696	.1908	.2110	.2235	.2479	.2764
	153	.0894	.1062	.1227	.1321	.1487	.1685	.1896	.2096	.2221	.2463	.2747
	154	.0888	.1055	.1219	.1312	.1477	.1674	.1884	.2083	.2207	.2448	.2731
	155	.0882	.1048	.1211	.1304	.1468	.1663	.1871	.2070	.2193	.2433	.2714
	156	.0876	.1041	.1203	.1295	.1458	.1652	.1860	.2057	.2179	.2418	.2698
	157	.0870	.1034	.1195	.1287	.1449	.1642	.1848	.2044	.2166	.2403	.2682
	158	.0864	.1027	.1187	.1278	.1440	.1631	.1836	.2031	.2152	.2389	.2666
	159	.0858	.1020	.1179	.1270	.1430	.1621	.1825	.2019	.2139	.2374	.2650
	160	.0853	.1014	.1172	.1262	.1421	.1611	.1813	.2006	.2126	.2360	.2634
	161	.0847	.1007	.1164	.1254	.1412	.1601	.1802	.1994	.2113	.2346	.2619
	162	.0842	.1001	.1157	.1246	.1403	.1591	.1791	.1982	.2101	.2332	.2604

* To approximate p_k, divide the starred entry under k by $(C - 1)$.
** Compute $B^* = C - B$, find p^*_{1-k} for B^* and C, and compute $p_k = 1 - p^*_{1-k}$.

B	C	.001	.01	.05	.1	.25	.5	.75	.9	.95	.99	.999
26	163	.0836	.0994	.1150	.1238	.1395	.1581	.1780	.1970	.2088	.2318	.2589
	164	.0831	.0988	.1142	.1230	.1386	.1571	.1770	.1958	.2076	.2305	.2574
	165	.0826	.0982	.1135	.1223	.1378	.1562	.1759	.1947	.2064	.2291	.2559
	166	.0821	.0975	.1128	.1215	.1369	.1552	.1748	.1935	.2051	.2278	.2545
	167	.0815	.0969	.1121	.1208	.1361	.1543	.1738	.1924	.2039	.2265	.2530
	168	.0810	.0963	.1114	.1200	.1353	.1534	.1728	.1913	.2028	.2252	.2516
	169	.0805	.0958	.1108	.1193	.1344	.1525	.1718	.1901	.2016	.2239	.2502
	170	.0800	.0952	.1101	.1186	.1336	.1516	.1708	.1891	.2004	.2227	.2488
	171	.0795	.0946	.1094	.1179	.1328	.1507	.1698	.1880	.1993	.2214	.2474
	172	.0791	.0940	.1088	.1172	.1321	.1498	.1688	.1869	.1982	.2202	.2461
	173	.0786	.0935	.1081	.1165	.1313	.1489	.1678	.1858	.1971	.2190	.2447
	174	.0781	.0929	.1075	.1158	.1305	.1481	.1669	.1848	.1959	.2177	.2434
	175	.0776	.0924	.1069	.1151	.1298	.1472	.1659	.1837	.1949	.2165	.2421
	176	.0772	.0918	.1062	.1145	.1290	.1464	.1650	.1827	.1938	.2154	.2408
	177	.0767	.0913	.1056	.1138	.1283	.1456	.1641	.1817	.1927	.2142	.2395
	178	.0763	.0907	.1050	.1131	.1276	.1447	.1631	.1807	.1917	.2130	.2382
	179	.0758	.0902	.1044	.1125	.1268	.1439	.1622	.1797	.1906	.2119	.2370
	180	.0754	.0897	.1038	.1119	.1261	.1431	.1613	.1787	.1896	.2108	.2357
	181	.0750	.0892	.1032	.1112	.1254	.1423	.1605	.1778	.1886	.2096	.2345
	182	.0745	.0887	.1026	.1106	.1247	.1415	.1596	.1768	.1875	.2085	.2333
	183	.0741	.0882	.1021	.1100	.1240	.1408	.1587	.1759	.1865	.2074	.2320
	184	.0737	.0877	.1015	.1094	.1233	.1400	.1579	.1749	.1856	.2063	.2309
	185	.0733	.0872	.1009	.1088	.1227	.1392	.1570	.1740	.1846	.2053	.2297
	186	.0729	.0867	.1004	.1082	.1220	.1385	.1562	.1731	.1836	.2042	.2285
	187	.0725	.0862	.0998	.1076	.1213	.1377	.1553	.1722	.1826	.2031	.2273
	188	.0721	.0858	.0993	.1070	.1207	.1370	.1545	.1713	.1817	.2021	.2262
	189	.0717	.0853	.0987	.1064	.1200	.1363	.1537	.1704	.1808	.2011	.2250
	190	.0713	.0848	.0982	.1059	.1194	.1356	.1529	.1695	.1798	.2000	.2239
	191	.0709	.0844	.0977	.1053	.1188	.1349	.1521	.1686	.1789	.1990	.2228
	192	.0705	.0839	.0972	.1047	.1181	.1341	.1513	.1677	.1780	.1980	.2217
	193	.0701	.0835	.0966	.1042	.1175	.1335	.1505	.1669	.1771	.1970	.2206
	194	.0697	.0830	.0961	.1036	.1169	.1328	.1498	.1660	.1762	.1961	.2195
	195	.0694	.0826	.0956	.1031	.1163	.1321	.1490	.1652	.1753	.1951	.2185
	196+	13.03*	15.62*	18.22*	19.72*	22.40*	25.67*	29.23*	32.71*	34.92*	39.31*	44.64*
27	28-41	SEE NOTE**										
	42-124	SEE NOTE***										
	125	.1168	.1378	.1584	.1700	.1904	.2145	.2400	.2640	.2788	.3075	.3407
	126	.1158	.1367	.1571	.1686	.1889	.2128	.2381	.2619	.2767	.3052	.3382
	127	.1148	.1355	.1558	.1672	.1873	.2111	.2362	.2599	.2746	.3029	.3357
	128	.1139	.1344	.1545	.1659	.1858	.2094	.2344	.2580	.2725	.3007	.3333
	129	.1129	.1333	.1533	.1645	.1844	.2078	.2326	.2560	.2705	.2985	.3309
	130	.1120	.1323	.1520	.1632	.1829	.2062	.2308	.2541	.2685	.2963	.3286
	131	.1111	.1312	.1508	.1619	.1815	.2046	.2291	.2522	.2665	.2941	.3263
	132	.1102	.1302	.1496	.1607	.1801	.2031	.2274	.2503	.2645	.2920	.3240
	133	.1093	.1291	.1485	.1594	.1787	.2015	.2257	.2485	.2626	.2900	.3217
	134	.1085	.1281	.1473	.1582	.1774	.2000	.2240	.2467	.2607	.2879	.3195
	135	.1076	.1271	.1462	.1570	.1760	.1985	.2224	.2449	.2589	.2859	.3173
	136	.1068	.1261	.1451	.1558	.1747	.1970	.2207	.2432	.2570	.2839	.3152
	137	.1059	.1252	.1440	.1546	.1734	.1956	.2192	.2414	.2552	.2819	.3130
	138	.1051	.1242	.1429	.1535	.1721	.1942	.2176	.2397	.2534	.2800	.3109
	139	.1043	.1233	.1418	.1524	.1709	.1928	.2160	.2380	.2517	.2781	.3088
	140	.1035	.1224	.1408	.1512	.1696	.1914	.2145	.2364	.2499	.2762	.3068
	141	.1028	.1215	.1398	.1501	.1684	.1900	.2130	.2347	.2482	.2743	.3048
	142	.1020	.1206	.1387	.1490	.1672	.1887	.2115	.2331	.2465	.2725	.3028
	143	.1013	.1197	.1377	.1480	.1660	.1874	.2100	.2315	.2448	.2707	.3008
	144	.1005	.1188	.1367	.1469	.1648	.1861	.2086	.2300	.2432	.2689	.2989
	145	.0998	.1180	.1358	.1459	.1637	.1848	.2072	.2284	.2416	.2671	.2969
	146	.0991	.1171	.1348	.1448	.1625	.1835	.2058	.2269	.2400	.2654	.2950
	147	.0983	.1163	.1339	.1438	.1614	.1822	.2044	.2254	.2384	.2637	.2932
	148	.0976	.1155	.1329	.1428	.1603	.1810	.2030	.2239	.2368	.2620	.2913
	149	.0970	.1147	.1320	.1418	.1592	.1798	.2017	.2224	.2353	.2603	.2895
	150	.0963	.1139	.1311	.1409	.1581	.1786	.2003	.2210	.2338	.2586	.2877
	151	.0956	.1131	.1302	.1399	.1571	.1774	.1990	.2195	.2323	.2570	.2859
	152	.0949	.1123	.1293	.1390	.1560	.1762	.1977	.2181	.2308	.2554	.2841
	153	.0943	.1115	.1284	.1380	.1550	.1751	.1964	.2167	.2293	.2538	.2824
	154	.0936	.1108	.1276	.1371	.1539	.1739	.1952	.2154	.2279	.2522	.2807
	155	.0930	.1100	.1267	.1362	.1529	.1728	.1939	.2140	.2264	.2507	.2790
	156	.0924	.1093	.1259	.1353	.1519	.1717	.1927	.2126	.2250	.2491	.2773
	157	.0918	.1086	.1251	.1344	.1510	.1706	.1915	.2113	.2236	.2476	.2757
	158	.0912	.1079	.1243	.1336	.1500	.1695	.1903	.2100	.2223	.2461	.2740

*** To approximate p_k, compute $m = B/C$ and $s = \sqrt{m(1 - m)/(C + 1)}$, find u_k in Table T4 on page 715 below, and compute $p_k \doteq m + u_k s$.

B	C	.001	.01	.05	.1	.25	.5	.75	.9	.95	.99	.999
27	159	.0906	.1072	.1234	.1327	.1490	.1684	.1891	.2087	.2209	.2446	.2724
	160	.0900	.1065	.1226	.1318	.1481	.1674	.1879	.2074	.2196	.2432	.2708
	161	.0894	.1058	.1219	.1310	.1471	.1663	.1868	.2062	.2182	.2417	.2692
	162	.0888	.1051	.1211	.1302	.1462	.1653	.1856	.2049	.2169	.2403	.2677
	163	.0882	.1044	.1203	.1294	.1453	.1643	.1845	.2037	.2156	.2389	.2661
	164	.0877	.1038	.1196	.1286	.1444	.1633	.1834	.2025	.2144	.2375	.2646
	165	.0871	.1031	.1188	.1278	.1435	.1623	.1823	.2013	.2131	.2361	.2631
	166	.0866	.1025	.1181	.1270	.1427	.1613	.1812	.2001	.2118	.2347	.2616
	167	.0860	.1018	.1174	.1262	.1418	.1603	.1801	.1989	.2106	.2334	.2601
	168	.0855	.1012	.1166	.1254	.1409	.1594	.1790	.1978	.2094	.2321	.2587
	169	.0849	.1006	.1159	.1247	.1401	.1584	.1780	.1966	.2082	.2307	.2572
	170	.0844	.1000	.1152	.1239	.1392	.1575	.1769	.1955	.2070	.2294	.2558
	171	.0839	.0994	.1145	.1232	.1384	.1566	.1759	.1944	.2058	.2281	.2544
	172	.0834	.0988	.1138	.1224	.1376	.1556	.1749	.1932	.2046	.2269	.2530
	173	.0829	.0982	.1132	.1217	.1368	.1547	.1739	.1921	.2035	.2256	.2516
	174	.0824	.0976	.1125	.1210	.1360	.1538	.1729	.1911	.2024	.2244	.2502
	175	.0819	.0970	.1118	.1203	.1352	.1530	.1719	.1900	.2012	.2231	.2489
	176	.0814	.0964	.1112	.1196	.1344	.1521	.1710	.1889	.2001	.2219	.2476
	177	.0809	.0959	.1105	.1189	.1337	.1512	.1700	.1879	.1990	.2207	.2462
	178	.0805	.0953	.1099	.1182	.1329	.1504	.1691	.1868	.1979	.2195	.2449
	179	.0800	.0948	.1093	.1175	.1321	.1495	.1681	.1858	.1968	.2183	.2436
	180	.0795	.0942	.1087	.1169	.1314	.1487	.1672	.1848	.1958	.2172	.2423
	181	.0791	.0937	.1080	.1162	.1307	.1479	.1663	.1838	.1947	.2160	.2411
	182	.0786	.0931	.1074	.1156	.1299	.1471	.1654	.1828	.1937	.2149	.2398
	183	.0782	.0926	.1068	.1149	.1292	.1463	.1645	.1818	.1926	.2137	.2386
	184	.0777	.0921	.1062	.1143	.1285	.1455	.1636	.1809	.1916	.2126	.2374
	185	.0773	.0916	.1056	.1136	.1278	.1447	.1627	.1799	.1906	.2115	.2361
	186	.0769	.0911	.1051	.1130	.1271	.1439	.1618	.1789	.1896	.2104	.2349
	187	.0764	.0906	.1045	.1124	.1264	.1431	.1610	.1780	.1886	.2093	.2337
	188	.0760	.0901	.1039	.1118	.1257	.1424	.1601	.1771	.1876	.2083	.2326
	189	.0756	.0896	.1033	.1112	.1251	.1416	.1593	.1762	.1867	.2072	.2314
	190	.0752	.0891	.1028	.1106	.1244	.1408	.1585	.1752	.1857	.2062	.2302
	191	.0748	.0886	.1022	.1100	.1237	.1401	.1576	.1743	.1848	.2051	.2291
	192	.0744	.0881	.1017	.1094	.1231	.1394	.1568	.1735	.1838	.2041	.2280
	193	.0740	.0877	.1012	.1088	.1224	.1387	.1560	.1726	.1829	.2031	.2268
	194	.0736	.0872	.1006	.1083	.1218	.1379	.1552	.1717	.1820	.2020	.2257
	195	.0732	.0867	.1001	.1077	.1212	.1372	.1544	.1708	.1811	.2010	.2246
	196	.0728	.0863	.0996	.1071	.1205	.1365	.1536	.1700	.1802	.2001	.2235
	197	.0724	.0858	.0990	.1066	.1199	.1358	.1529	.1691	.1793	.1991	.2225
	198	.0720	.0854	.0985	.1060	.1193	.1351	.1521	.1683	.1784	.1981	.2214
	199	.0716	.0849	.0980	.1055	.1187	.1345	.1513	.1674	.1775	.1971	.2203
	200	.0713	.0845	.0975	.1050	.1181	.1338	.1506	.1666	.1766	.1962	.2193
	201	.0709	.0841	.0970	.1044	.1175	.1331	.1498	.1658	.1758	.1952	.2182
	202	.0705	.0836	.0965	.1039	.1169	.1325	.1491	.1650	.1749	.1943	.2172
	203+	13.73*	16.40*	19.06*	20.59*	23.34*	26.67*	30.30*	33.84*	36.08*	40.53*	45.94*
28	29-42	SEE NOTE**										
	43-134	SEE NOTE***										
	135	.1133	.1333	.1528	.1638	.1831	.2060	.2301	.2529	.2670	.2942	.3258
	136	.1124	.1323	.1516	.1625	.1818	.2044	.2284	.2511	.2651	.2922	.3236
	137	.1115	.1312	.1505	.1613	.1804	.2029	.2268	.2493	.2632	.2901	.3214
	138	.1107	.1302	.1493	.1601	.1791	.2015	.2252	.2475	.2614	.2882	.3193
	139	.1098	.1293	.1482	.1589	.1778	.2000	.2236	.2458	.2596	.2862	.3171
	140	.1090	.1283	.1471	.1578	.1765	.1986	.2220	.2441	.2578	.2842	.3150
	141	.1082	.1273	.1460	.1566	.1752	.1972	.2204	.2424	.2560	.2823	.3130
	142	.1074	.1264	.1450	.1555	.1739	.1958	.2189	.2407	.2543	.2804	.3109
	143	.1066	.1255	.1439	.1543	.1727	.1944	.2174	.2391	.2525	.2786	.3089
	144	.1058	.1246	.1429	.1532	.1715	.1930	.2159	.2375	.2508	.2767	.3069
	145	.1050	.1237	.1419	.1522	.1703	.1917	.2144	.2359	.2492	.2749	.3049
	146	.1043	.1228	.1409	.1511	.1691	.1904	.2129	.2343	.2475	.2731	.3030
	147	.1035	.1219	.1399	.1500	.1679	.1891	.2115	.2327	.2459	.2714	.3011
	148	.1028	.1210	.1389	.1490	.1668	.1878	.2101	.2312	.2443	.2696	.2992
	149	.1021	.1202	.1379	.1480	.1656	.1865	.2087	.2297	.2427	.2679	.2973
	150	.1013	.1194	.1370	.1469	.1645	.1853	.2073	.2282	.2411	.2662	.2955
	151	.1006	.1185	.1360	.1459	.1634	.1840	.2060	.2267	.2396	.2645	.2936
	152	.0999	.1177	.1351	.1450	.1623	.1828	.2046	.2253	.2380	.2629	.2918
	153	.0993	.1169	.1342	.1440	.1612	.1816	.2033	.2238	.2365	.2612	.2900
	154	.0986	.1161	.1333	.1430	.1602	.1804	.2020	.2224	.2350	.2596	.2883
	155	.0979	.1154	.1324	.1421	.1591	.1793	.2007	.2210	.2336	.2580	.2865
	156	.0972	.1146	.1315	.1411	.1581	.1781	.1994	.2196	.2321	.2564	.2848
	157	.0966	.1138	.1307	.1402	.1570	.1770	.1982	.2182	.2307	.2549	.2831

* To approximate p_k, divide the starred entry under k by $(C - 1)$.

** Compute $B^* = C - B$, find p_{1-k}^* for B^* and C, and compute $p_k = 1 - p_{1-k}^*$.

B	C	.001	.01	.05	.1	.25	.5	.75	.9	.95	.99	.999
28	158	.0960	.1131	.1298	.1393	.1560	.1759	.1969	.2169	.2293	.2533	.2814
	159	.0953	.1123	.1290	.1384	.1550	.1747	.1957	.2155	.2279	.2518	.2798
	160	.0947	.1116	.1281	.1375	.1541	.1736	.1945	.2142	.2265	.2503	.2781
	161	.0941	.1109	.1273	.1366	.1531	.1726	.1933	.2129	.2251	.2488	.2765
	162	.0935	.1102	.1265	.1358	.1521	.1715	.1921	.2116	.2238	.2473	.2749
	163	.0929	.1095	.1257	.1349	.1512	.1704	.1909	.2104	.2224	.2459	.2733
	164	.0923	.1088	.1249	.1341	.1502	.1694	.1898	.2091	.2211	.2445	.2718
	165	.0917	.1081	.1241	.1333	.1493	.1684	.1886	.2079	.2198	.2430	.2702
	166	.0911	.1074	.1234	.1324	.1484	.1673	.1875	.2066	.2185	.2416	.2687
	167	.0905	.1067	.1226	.1316	.1475	.1663	.1864	.2054	.2173	.2402	.2672
	168	.0900	.1061	.1219	.1308	.1466	.1653	.1853	.2042	.2160	.2389	.2657
	169	.0894	.1054	.1211	.1300	.1457	.1644	.1842	.2030	.2148	.2375	.2642
	170	.0889	.1048	.1204	.1292	.1449	.1634	.1831	.2019	.2135	.2362	.2627
	171	.0883	.1041	.1197	.1285	.1440	.1624	.1821	.2007	.2123	.2349	.2613
	172	.0878	.1035	.1189	.1277	.1431	.1615	.1810	.1996	.2111	.2335	.2599
	173	.0872	.1029	.1182	.1269	.1423	.1605	.1800	.1984	.2099	.2322	.2584
	174	.0867	.1023	.1175	.1262	.1415	.1596	.1790	.1973	.2087	.2310	.2570
	175	.0862	.1017	.1168	.1255	.1407	.1587	.1779	.1962	.2076	.2297	.2557
	176	.0857	.1011	.1162	.1247	.1398	.1578	.1769	.1951	.2064	.2284	.2543
	177	.0852	.1005	.1155	.1240	.1390	.1569	.1759	.1940	.2053	.2272	.2529
	178	.0847	.0999	.1148	.1233	.1383	.1560	.1750	.1930	.2042	.2260	.2516
	179	.0842	.0993	.1142	.1226	.1375	.1551	.1740	.1919	.2031	.2248	.2503
	180	.0837	.0987	.1135	.1219	.1367	.1543	.1730	.1909	.2020	.2236	.2489
	181	.0832	.0982	.1129	.1212	.1359	.1534	.1721	.1898	.2009	.2224	.2476
	182	.0827	.0976	.1122	.1205	.1352	.1526	.1711	.1888	.1998	.2212	.2464
	183	.0823	.0971	.1116	.1199	.1344	.1517	.1702	.1878	.1987	.2200	.2451
	184	.0818	.0965	.1110	.1192	.1337	.1509	.1693	.1868	.1977	.2189	.2438
	185	.0813	.0960	.1104	.1185	.1329	.1501	.1684	.1858	.1966	.2178	.2426
	186	.0809	.0955	.1098	.1179	.1322	.1493	.1675	.1848	.1956	.2166	.2413
	187	.0804	.0949	.1092	.1172	.1315	.1485	.1666	.1838	.1946	.2155	.2401
	188	.0800	.0944	.1086	.1166	.1308	.1477	.1657	.1829	.1936	.2144	.2389
	189	.0795	.0939	.1080	.1160	.1301	.1469	.1648	.1819	.1926	.2133	.2377
	190	.0791	.0934	.1074	.1153	.1294	.1461	.1640	.1810	.1916	.2122	.2365
	191	.0787	.0929	.1068	.1147	.1287	.1454	.1631	.1801	.1906	.2112	.2353
	192	.0783	.0924	.1062	.1141	.1280	.1446	.1623	.1791	.1896	.2101	.2342
	193	.0778	.0919	.1057	.1135	.1274	.1439	.1615	.1782	.1887	.2090	.2330
	194	.0774	.0914	.1051	.1129	.1267	.1431	.1606	.1773	.1877	.2080	.2319
	195	.0770	.0909	.1046	.1123	.1260	.1424	.1598	.1764	.1868	.2070	.2308
	196	.0766	.0904	.1040	.1117	.1254	.1416	.1590	.1755	.1859	.2060	.2296
	197	.0762	.0899	.1035	.1112	.1247	.1409	.1582	.1747	.1849	.2050	.2285
	198	.0758	.0895	.1029	.1106	.1241	.1402	.1574	.1738	.1840	.2040	.2274
	199	.0754	.0890	.1024	.1100	.1235	.1395	.1566	.1729	.1831	.2030	.2264
	200	.0750	.0886	.1019	.1095	.1229	.1388	.1558	.1721	.1822	.2020	.2253
	201	.0746	.0881	.1014	.1089	.1222	.1381	.1551	.1713	.1813	.2010	.2242
	202	.0742	.0877	.1008	.1084	.1216	.1374	.1543	.1704	.1805	.2001	.2232
	203	.0738	.0872	.1003	.1078	.1210	.1367	.1536	.1696	.1796	.1991	.2221
	204	.0735	.0868	.0998	.1073	.1204	.1361	.1528	.1688	.1787	.1982	.2211
	205	.0731	.0863	.0993	.1067	.1198	.1354	.1521	.1680	.1779	.1972	.2200
	206	.0727	.0859	.0988	.1062	.1192	.1347	.1513	.1672	.1770	.1963	.2190
	207	.0724	.0855	.0984	.1057	.1186	.1341	.1506	.1664	.1762	.1954	.2180
	208	.0720	.0850	.0979	.1052	.1181	.1334	.1499	.1656	.1754	.1945	.2170
	209+	14.44*	17.17*	19.90*	21.47*	24.27*	27.67*	31.36*	34.96*	37.23*	41.76*	47.23*
29	30-43	SEE NOTE**										
	44-145	SEE NOTE***										
	146	.1095	.1285	.1469	.1574	.1757	.1973	.2201	.2417	.2550	.2809	.3109
	147	.1088	.1276	.1459	.1563	.1744	.1959	.2186	.2401	.2534	.2790	.3089
	148	.1080	.1267	.1449	.1552	.1732	.1946	.2172	.2385	.2517	.2772	.3070
	149	.1072	.1258	.1439	.1541	.1721	.1933	.2157	.2369	.2501	.2755	.3051
	150	.1065	.1249	.1429	.1530	.1709	.1920	.2143	.2354	.2484	.2737	.3032
	151	.1057	.1240	.1419	.1520	.1697	.1907	.2129	.2339	.2469	.2720	.3013
	152	.1050	.1232	.1409	.1510	.1686	.1894	.2115	.2324	.2453	.2703	.2995
	153	.1043	.1223	.1400	.1500	.1675	.1882	.2101	.2309	.2437	.2686	.2976
	154	.1035	.1215	.1390	.1490	.1664	.1870	.2088	.2294	.2422	.2670	.2958
	155	.1028	.1207	.1381	.1480	.1653	.1857	.2074	.2280	.2407	.2653	.2940
	156	.1021	.1199	.1372	.1470	.1642	.1846	.2061	.2265	.2392	.2637	.2923
	157	.1015	.1191	.1363	.1460	.1631	.1834	.2048	.2251	.2377	.2621	.2905
	158	.1008	.1183	.1354	.1451	.1621	.1822	.2035	.2237	.2362	.2605	.2888
	159	.1001	.1175	.1345	.1441	.1611	.1811	.2023	.2224	.2348	.2589	.2871
	160	.0995	.1168	.1337	.1432	.1600	.1799	.2010	.2210	.2334	.2574	.2854
	161	.0988	.1160	.1328	.1423	.1590	.1788	.1998	.2197	.2320	.2559	.2838
	162	.0982	.1153	.1320	.1414	.1580	.1777	.1986	.2183	.2306	.2544	.2821

*** To approximate p_k, compute $m = B/C$ and $s = \sqrt{m(1-m)/(C+1)}$, find u_k in Table T4 on page 715 below, and compute $p_k \doteq m + u_k s$.

B	C	.001	.01	.05	.1	.25	.5	.75	.9	.95	.99	.999
29	163	.0975	.1145	.1311	.1405	.1570	.1766	.1974	.2170	.2292	.2529	.2805
	164	.0969	.1138	.1303	.1396	.1561	.1755	.1962	.2157	.2278	.2514	.2789
	165	.0963	.1131	.1295	.1388	.1551	.1744	.1950	.2144	.2265	.2499	.2773
	166	.0957	.1124	.1287	.1379	.1542	.1734	.1938	.2132	.2252	.2485	.2758
	167	.0951	.1117	.1279	.1371	.1532	.1723	.1927	.2119	.2239	.2471	.2742
	168	.0945	.1110	.1271	.1362	.1523	.1713	.1915	.2107	.2226	.2457	.2727
	169	.0939	.1103	.1263	.1354	.1514	.1703	.1904	.2095	.2213	.2443	.2711
	170	.0933	.1096	.1256	.1346	.1505	.1693	.1893	.2083	.2200	.2429	.2696
	171	.0928	.1090	.1248	.1338	.1496	.1683	.1882	.2071	.2188	.2415	.2682
	172	.0922	.1083	.1241	.1330	.1487	.1673	.1871	.2059	.2175	.2402	.2667
	173	.0916	.1077	.1233	.1322	.1478	.1663	.1860	.2047	.2163	.2389	.2652
	174	.0911	.1070	.1226	.1314	.1470	.1654	.1850	.2036	.2151	.2375	.2638
	175	.0905	.1064	.1219	.1307	.1461	.1644	.1839	.2024	.2139	.2362	.2624
	176	.0900	.1058	.1212	.1299	.1453	.1635	.1829	.2013	.2127	.2349	.2610
	177	.0895	.1051	.1205	.1291	.1444	.1626	.1819	.2002	.2116	.2337	.2596
	178	.0889	.1045	.1198	.1284	.1436	.1617	.1809	.1991	.2104	.2324	.2582
	179	.0884	.1039	.1191	.1277	.1428	.1608	.1799	.1980	.2093	.2312	.2569
	180	.0879	.1033	.1184	.1269	.1420	.1599	.1789	.1969	.2081	.2299	.2555
	181	.0874	.1027	.1177	.1262	.1412	.1590	.1779	.1958	.2070	.2287	.2542
	182	.0869	.1021	.1171	.1255	.1404	.1581	.1769	.1948	.2059	.2275	.2529
	183	.0864	.1016	.1164	.1248	.1396	.1572	.1760	.1937	.2048	.2263	.2515
	184	.0859	.1010	.1157	.1241	.1389	.1564	.1750	.1927	.2037	.2251	.2503
	185	.0854	.1004	.1151	.1234	.1381	.1555	.1741	.1917	.2026	.2240	.2490
	186	.0849	.0999	.1145	.1228	.1374	.1547	.1731	.1907	.2016	.2228	.2477
	187	.0845	.0993	.1138	.1221	.1366	.1538	.1722	.1897	.2005	.2216	.2465
	188	.0840	.0988	.1132	.1214	.1359	.1530	.1713	.1887	.1995	.2205	.2452
	189	.0835	.0982	.1126	.1208	.1351	.1522	.1704	.1877	.1985	.2194	.2440
	190	.0831	.0977	.1120	.1201	.1344	.1514	.1695	.1867	.1974	.2183	.2428
	191	.0826	.0972	.1114	.1195	.1337	.1506	.1686	.1858	.1964	.2172	.2416
	192	.0822	.0966	.1108	.1188	.1330	.1498	.1678	.1848	.1954	.2161	.2404
	193	.0817	.0961	.1102	.1182	.1323	.1490	.1669	.1839	.1944	.2150	.2392
	194	.0813	.0956	.1096	.1176	.1316	.1483	.1660	.1829	.1935	.2139	.2380
	195	.0809	.0951	.1090	.1170	.1309	.1475	.1652	.1820	.1925	.2129	.2369
	196	.0804	.0946	.1085	.1164	.1303	.1468	.1644	.1811	.1915	.2118	.2357
	197	.0800	.0941	.1079	.1158	.1296	.1460	.1635	.1802	.1906	.2108	.2346
	198	.0796	.0936	.1074	.1152	.1289	.1453	.1627	.1793	.1896	.2098	.2335
	199	.0792	.0931	.1068	.1146	.1283	.1445	.1619	.1784	.1887	.2088	.2323
	200	.0788	.0926	.1063	.1140	.1276	.1438	.1611	.1776	.1878	.2077	.2312
	201	.0783	.0922	.1057	.1134	.1270	.1431	.1603	.1767	.1869	.2068	.2301
	202	.0779	.0917	.1052	.1128	.1263	.1424	.1595	.1758	.1860	.2058	.2291
	203	.0775	.0912	.1046	.1123	.1257	.1417	.1587	.1750	.1851	.2048	.2280
	204	.0772	.0908	.1041	.1117	.1251	.1410	.1580	.1741	.1842	.2038	.2269
	205	.0768	.0903	.1036	.1111	.1245	.1403	.1572	.1733	.1833	.2029	.2259
	206	.0764	.0899	.1031	.1106	.1239	.1396	.1564	.1725	.1824	.2019	.2248
	207	.0760	.0894	.1026	.1100	.1232	.1389	.1557	.1716	.1816	.2010	.2238
	208	.0756	.0890	.1021	.1095	.1226	.1383	.1549	.1708	.1807	.2000	.2228
	209	.0752	.0885	.1016	.1090	.1221	.1376	.1542	.1700	.1799	.1991	.2218
	210	.0749	.0881	.1011	.1084	.1215	.1369	.1535	.1692	.1790	.1982	.2207
	211	.0745	.0877	.1006	.1079	.1209	.1363	.1528	.1684	.1782	.1973	.2197
	212	.0741	.0872	.1001	.1074	.1203	.1356	.1520	.1677	.1774	.1964	.2188
	213	.0738	.0868	.0996	.1069	.1197	.1350	.1513	.1669	.1766	.1955	.2178
	214	.0734	.0864	.0991	.1064	.1192	.1344	.1506	.1661	.1758	.1946	.2168
	215+	15.15*	17.96*	20.75*	22.35*	25.21*	28.67*	32.43*	36.08*	38.39*	42.98*	48.52*
30	31–44	SEE NOTE**										
	45–156	SEE NOTE***										
	157	.1064	.1244	.1420	.1519	.1692	.1898	.2115	.2320	.2447	.2693	.2979
	158	.1057	.1236	.1410	.1509	.1682	.1886	.2102	.2306	.2432	.2677	.2962
	159	.1050	.1228	.1401	.1499	.1671	.1874	.2089	.2292	.2417	.2660	.2944
	160	.1043	.1220	.1392	.1489	.1660	.1862	.2076	.2278	.2402	.2645	.2927
	161	.1036	.1212	.1383	.1480	.1650	.1850	.2063	.2264	.2388	.2629	.2910
	162	.1029	.1204	.1374	.1470	.1639	.1839	.2050	.2250	.2374	.2613	.2893
	163	.1023	.1196	.1366	.1461	.1629	.1828	.2038	.2237	.2360	.2598	.2876
	164	.1016	.1189	.1357	.1452	.1619	.1816	.2025	.2223	.2346	.2583	.2860
	165	.1010	.1181	.1349	.1443	.1609	.1805	.2013	.2210	.2332	.2568	.2844
	166	.1003	.1174	.1340	.1434	.1599	.1794	.2001	.2197	.2318	.2553	.2828
	167	.0997	.1167	.1332	.1425	.1590	.1784	.1989	.2184	.2305	.2539	.2812
	168	.0991	.1159	.1324	.1417	.1580	.1773	.1978	.2171	.2291	.2524	.2796
	169	.0984	.1152	.1316	.1408	.1570	.1762	.1966	.2159	.2278	.2510	.2781
	170	.0978	.1145	.1308	.1400	.1561	.1752	.1955	.2146	.2265	.2496	.2765
	171	.0972	.1138	.1300	.1391	.1552	.1742	.1943	.2134	.2252	.2482	.2750
	172	.0966	.1131	.1292	.1383	.1543	.1732	.1932	.2122	.2240	.2468	.2735

* To approximate p_k, divide the starred entry under k by $(C - 1)$.

** Compute $B^* = C - B$, find p_{1-k}^* for B^* and C, and compute $p_k = 1 - p_{1-k}^*$.

B	C	.001	.01	.05	.1	.25	.5	.75	.9	.95	.99	.999
30	173	.0961	.1124	.1284	.1375	.1534	.1722	.1921	.2110	.2227	.2454	.2720
	174	.0955	.1118	.1277	.1367	.1525	.1712	.1910	.2098	.2214	.2441	.2705
	175	.0949	.1111	.1269	.1359	.1516	.1702	.1899	.2086	.2202	.2427	.2691
	176	.0943	.1105	.1262	.1351	.1507	.1692	.1888	.2075	.2190	.2414	.2676
	177	.0938	.1098	.1254	.1343	.1498	.1682	.1878	.2063	.2178	.2401	.2662
	178	.0932	.1092	.1247	.1335	.1490	.1673	.1867	.2052	.2166	.2388	.2648
	179	.0927	.1085	.1240	.1327	.1481	.1664	.1857	.2041	.2154	.2375	.2634
	180	.0921	.1079	.1233	.1320	.1473	.1654	.1847	.2029	.2143	.2363	.2620
	181	.0916	.1073	.1226	.1312	.1465	.1645	.1837	.2018	.2131	.2350	.2607
	182	.0911	.1067	.1219	.1305	.1457	.1636	.1827	.2008	.2120	.2338	.2593
	183	.0906	.1061	.1212	.1298	.1449	.1627	.1817	.1997	.2108	.2325	.2580
	184	.0901	.1055	.1205	.1291	.1441	.1618	.1807	.1986	.2097	.2313	.2567
	185	.0895	.1049	.1199	.1283	.1433	.1609	.1797	.1976	.2086	.2301	.2553
	186	.0890	.1043	.1192	.1276	.1425	.1601	.1788	.1965	.2075	.2289	.2540
	187	.0885	.1037	.1185	.1269	.1417	.1592	.1778	.1955	.2064	.2278	.2528
	188	.0881	.1032	.1179	.1263	.1410	.1584	.1769	.1945	.2054	.2266	.2515
	189	.0876	.1026	.1173	.1256	.1402	.1575	.1760	.1935	.2043	.2254	.2502
	190	.0871	.1020	.1166	.1249	.1394	.1567	.1750	.1925	.2033	.2243	.2490
	191	.0866	.1015	.1160	.1242	.1387	.1559	.1741	.1915	.2022	.2232	.2477
	192	.0861	.1009	.1154	.1236	.1380	.1551	.1732	.1905	.2012	.2221	.2465
	193	.0857	.1004	.1148	.1229	.1373	.1542	.1723	.1895	.2002	.2209	.2453
	194	.0852	.0999	.1142	.1223	.1365	.1535	.1715	.1886	.1992	.2199	.2441
	195	.0848	.0993	.1136	.1216	.1358	.1527	.1706	.1876	.1982	.2188	.2429
	196	.0843	.0988	.1130	.1210	.1351	.1519	.1697	.1867	.1972	.2177	.2418
	197	.0839	.0983	.1124	.1204	.1344	.1511	.1689	.1857	.1962	.2166	.2406
	198	.0834	.0978	.1118	.1197	.1337	.1503	.1680	.1848	.1952	.2156	.2394
	199	.0830	.0973	.1112	.1191	.1331	.1496	.1672	.1839	.1943	.2145	.2383
	200	.0825	.0968	.1106	.1185	.1324	.1488	.1663	.1830	.1933	.2135	.2372
	201	.0821	.0963	.1101	.1179	.1317	.1481	.1655	.1821	.1924	.2125	.2360
	202	.0817	.0958	.1095	.1173	.1311	.1474	.1647	.1812	.1915	.2115	.2349
	203	.0813	.0953	.1090	.1167	.1304	.1466	.1639	.1803	.1905	.2104	.2338
	204	.0809	.0948	.1084	.1161	.1298	.1459	.1631	.1795	.1896	.2095	.2327
	205	.0805	.0943	.1079	.1156	.1291	.1452	.1623	.1786	.1887	.2085	.2317
	206	.0800	.0938	.1073	.1150	.1285	.1445	.1615	.1778	.1878	.2075	.2306
	207	.0796	.0934	.1068	.1144	.1279	.1438	.1608	.1769	.1869	.2065	.2295
	208	.0792	.0929	.1063	.1139	.1272	.1431	.1600	.1761	.1861	.2056	.2285
	209	.0789	.0925	.1058	.1133	.1266	.1424	.1592	.1752	.1852	.2046	.2274
	210	.0785	.0920	.1052	.1128	.1260	.1417	.1585	.1744	.1843	.2037	.2264
	211	.0781	.0916	.1047	.1122	.1254	.1410	.1577	.1736	.1835	.2027	.2254
	212	.0777	.0911	.1042	.1117	.1248	.1404	.1570	.1728	.1826	.2018	.2244
	213	.0773	.0907	.1037	.1111	.1242	.1397	.1563	.1720	.1818	.2009	.2234
	214	.0769	.0902	.1032	.1106	.1236	.1391	.1555	.1712	.1810	.2000	.2224
	215	.0766	.0898	.1027	.1101	.1230	.1384	.1548	.1704	.1801	.1991	.2214
	216	.0762	.0894	.1023	.1096	.1225	.1378	.1541	.1697	.1793	.1982	.2204
	217	.0758	.0889	.1018	.1091	.1219	.1371	.1534	.1689	.1785	.1973	.2195
	218	.0755	.0885	.1013	.1085	.1213	.1365	.1527	.1681	.1777	.1964	.2185
	219	.0751	.0881	.1008	.1080	.1208	.1359	.1520	.1674	.1769	.1956	.2175
	220	.0748	.0877	.1004	.1075	.1202	.1353	.1513	.1666	.1761	.1947	.2166
	221	.0744	.0873	.0999	.1070	.1197	.1346	.1506	.1659	.1754	.1939	.2157
	222+	15.87*	18.74*	21.59*	23.23*	26.15*	29.67*	33.49*	37.20*	39.54*	44.19*	49.80*
31	32-46	SEE NOTE**										
	47-169	SEE NOTE***										
	170	.1024	.1194	.1360	.1453	.1617	.1811	.2016	.2210	.2330	.2562	.2834
	171	.1018	.1187	.1352	.1445	.1608	.1800	.2004	.2197	.2317	.2548	.2818
	172	.1011	.1180	.1344	.1436	.1598	.1790	.1993	.2185	.2303	.2534	.2803
	173	.1005	.1173	.1336	.1427	.1589	.1780	.1981	.2172	.2291	.2520	.2787
	174	.0999	.1166	.1328	.1419	.1580	.1769	.1970	.2160	.2278	.2506	.2772
	175	.0993	.1159	.1320	.1411	.1571	.1759	.1959	.2148	.2265	.2492	.2757
	176	.0987	.1152	.1312	.1403	.1561	.1749	.1948	.2136	.2253	.2479	.2743
	177	.0981	.1145	.1304	.1394	.1552	.1739	.1937	.2124	.2240	.2465	.2728
	178	.0976	.1138	.1297	.1386	.1544	.1729	.1926	.2113	.2228	.2452	.2714
	179	.0970	.1132	.1289	.1378	.1535	.1720	.1916	.2101	.2216	.2439	.2699
	180	.0964	.1125	.1282	.1371	.1526	.1710	.1905	.2090	.2204	.2426	.2685
	181	.0959	.1119	.1275	.1363	.1518	.1701	.1895	.2078	.2192	.2413	.2671
	182	.0953	.1112	.1268	.1355	.1509	.1691	.1884	.2067	.2180	.2400	.2657
	183	.0948	.1106	.1260	.1348	.1501	.1682	.1874	.2056	.2169	.2388	.2644
	184	.0942	.1100	.1253	.1340	.1493	.1673	.1864	.2045	.2157	.2375	.2630
	185	.0937	.1094	.1246	.1333	.1484	.1664	.1854	.2034	.2146	.2363	.2617
	186	.0932	.1088	.1240	.1325	.1476	.1655	.1844	.2023	.2135	.2351	.2603
	187	.0926	.1082	.1233	.1318	.1468	.1646	.1834	.2013	.2123	.2339	.2590

*** To approximate p_k, compute $m = B/C$ and $s = \sqrt{m(1 - m)/(C + 1)}$, find u_k in Table T4 on page 715 below, and compute $p_k \doteq m + u_k s$.

B	C	.001	.01	.05	.1	.25	.5	.75	.9	.95	.99	.999
31	188	.0921	.1076	.1226	.1311	.1460	.1637	.1825	.2002	.2112	.2327	.2577
	189	.0916	.1070	.1219	.1304	.1453	.1628	.1815	.1992	.2102	.2315	.2564
	190	.0911	.1064	.1213	.1297	.1445	.1620	.1806	.1982	.2091	.2303	.2552
	191	.0906	.1058	.1206	.1290	.1437	.1611	.1796	.1971	.2080	.2291	.2539
	192	.0901	.1052	.1200	.1283	.1430	.1603	.1787	.1961	.2070	.2280	.2527
	193	.0896	.1047	.1193	.1276	.1422	.1594	.1778	.1951	.2059	.2269	.2514
	194	.0892	.1041	.1187	.1270	.1415	.1586	.1769	.1941	.2049	.2257	.2502
	195	.0887	.1036	.1181	.1263	.1407	.1578	.1760	.1932	.2039	.2246	.2490
	196	.0882	.1030	.1175	.1256	.1400	.1570	.1751	.1922	.2028	.2235	.2478
	197	.0877	.1025	.1169	.1250	.1393	.1562	.1742	.1912	.2018	.2224	.2466
	198	.0873	.1019	.1162	.1243	.1386	.1554	.1733	.1903	.2008	.2213	.2454
	199	.0868	.1014	.1156	.1237	.1379	.1546	.1724	.1894	.1999	.2203	.2442
	200	.0864	.1009	.1151	.1231	.1372	.1538	.1716	.1884	.1989	.2192	.2431
	201	.0859	.1004	.1145	.1224	.1365	.1531	.1707	.1875	.1979	.2182	.2419
	202	.0855	.0999	.1139	.1218	.1358	.1523	.1699	.1866	.1970	.2171	.2408
	203	.0850	.0994	.1133	.1212	.1351	.1516	.1691	.1857	.1960	.2161	.2397
	204	.0846	.0988	.1127	.1206	.1344	.1508	.1682	.1848	.1951	.2151	.2385
	205	.0842	.0984	.1122	.1200	.1338	.1501	.1674	.1839	.1941	.2141	.2374
	206	.0837	.0979	.1116	.1194	.1331	.1494	.1666	.1830	.1932	.2131	.2363
	207	.0833	.0974	.1111	.1188	.1325	.1486	.1658	.1822	.1923	.2121	.2353
	208	.0829	.0969	.1105	.1182	.1318	.1479	.1650	.1813	.1914	.2111	.2342
	209	.0825	.0964	.1100	.1177	.1312	.1472	.1643	.1804	.1905	.2101	.2331
	210	.0821	.0959	.1094	.1171	.1305	.1465	.1635	.1796	.1896	.2091	.2321
	211	.0817	.0955	.1089	.1165	.1299	.1458	.1627	.1788	.1887	.2082	.2310
	212	.0813	.0950	.1084	.1160	.1293	.1451	.1619	.1779	.1879	.2072	.2300
	213	.0809	.0945	.1079	.1154	.1287	.1444	.1612	.1771	.1870	.2063	.2290
	214	.0805	.0941	.1073	.1149	.1281	.1438	.1604	.1763	.1862	.2054	.2279
	215	.0801	.0936	.1068	.1143	.1275	.1431	.1597	.1755	.1853	.2044	.2269
	216	.0797	.0932	.1063	.1138	.1269	.1424	.1590	.1747	.1845	.2035	.2259
	217	.0793	.0927	.1058	.1132	.1263	.1418	.1582	.1739	.1836	.2026	.2249
	218	.0790	.0923	.1053	.1127	.1257	.1411	.1575	.1731	.1828	.2017	.2239
	219	.0786	.0919	.1048	.1122	.1251	.1405	.1568	.1723	.1820	.2008	.2230
	220	.0782	.0914	.1043	.1117	.1245	.1398	.1561	.1716	.1812	.1999	.2220
	221	.0778	.0910	.1039	.1111	.1240	.1392	.1554	.1708	.1804	.1991	.2210
	222	.0775	.0906	.1034	.1106	.1234	.1386	.1547	.1700	.1796	.1982	.2201
	223	.0771	.0902	.1029	.1101	.1228	.1379	.1540	.1693	.1788	.1973	.2192
	224	.0768	.0898	.1024	.1096	.1223	.1373	.1533	.1685	.1780	.1965	.2182
	225	.0764	.0893	.1020	.1091	.1217	.1367	.1526	.1678	.1772	.1956	.2173
	226	.0761	.0889	.1015	.1086	.1212	.1361	.1520	.1671	.1765	.1948	.2164
	227	.0757	.0885	.1011	.1082	.1207	.1355	.1513	.1664	.1757	.1940	.2155
	228+	16.59*	19.53*	22.44*	24.11*	27.09*	30.67*	34.55*	38.32*	40.69*	45.40*	51.08*
32	33-47	SEE NOTE**										
	48-182	SEE NOTE***										
	183	.0990	.1152	.1309	.1398	.1553	.1737	.1931	.2115	.2229	.2450	.2707
	184	.0984	.1145	.1302	.1390	.1545	.1727	.1921	.2104	.2217	.2437	.2694
	185	.0979	.1139	.1294	.1382	.1536	.1718	.1910	.2093	.2205	.2424	.2680
	186	.0973	.1133	.1287	.1375	.1528	.1709	.1900	.2082	.2194	.2412	.2666
	187	.0968	.1126	.1280	.1367	.1520	.1699	.1890	.2071	.2182	.2399	.2653
	188	.0962	.1120	.1273	.1360	.1511	.1690	.1880	.2060	.2171	.2387	.2639
	189	.0957	.1114	.1266	.1352	.1503	.1681	.1870	.2049	.2160	.2375	.2626
	190	.0952	.1108	.1259	.1345	.1495	.1673	.1861	.2039	.2149	.2363	.2613
	191	.0947	.1102	.1253	.1338	.1487	.1664	.1851	.2028	.2138	.2351	.2600
	192	.0941	.1096	.1246	.1331	.1479	.1655	.1841	.2018	.2127	.2339	.2587
	193	.0936	.1090	.1239	.1324	.1472	.1646	.1832	.2007	.2116	.2328	.2575
	194	.0931	.1084	.1233	.1317	.1464	.1638	.1823	.1997	.2106	.2316	.2562
	195	.0926	.1078	.1226	.1310	.1456	.1630	.1813	.1987	.2095	.2305	.2550
	196	.0921	.1073	.1220	.1303	.1449	.1621	.1804	.1977	.2085	.2293	.2537
	197	.0917	.1067	.1213	.1296	.1441	.1613	.1795	.1967	.2074	.2282	.2525
	198	.0912	.1061	.1207	.1289	.1434	.1605	.1786	.1958	.2064	.2271	.2513
	199	.0907	.1056	.1201	.1283	.1427	.1597	.1777	.1948	.2054	.2260	.2501
	200	.0902	.1050	.1195	.1276	.1419	.1589	.1768	.1938	.2044	.2249	.2489
	201	.0897	.1045	.1189	.1270	.1412	.1581	.1760	.1929	.2034	.2238	.2478
	202	.0893	.1040	.1183	.1263	.1405	.1573	.1751	.1920	.2024	.2228	.2466
	203	.0888	.1034	.1177	.1257	.1398	.1565	.1742	.1910	.2014	.2217	.2455
	204	.0884	.1029	.1171	.1251	.1391	.1557	.1734	.1901	.2005	.2207	.2443
	205	.0879	.1024	.1165	.1244	.1384	.1550	.1725	.1892	.1995	.2196	.2432
	206	.0875	.1019	.1159	.1238	.1378	.1542	.1717	.1883	.1986	.2186	.2421
	207	.0870	.1014	.1153	.1232	.1371	.1535	.1709	.1874	.1976	.2176	.2409
	208	.0866	.1009	.1148	.1226	.1364	.1527	.1701	.1865	.1967	.2166	.2398
	209	.0862	.1004	.1142	.1220	.1358	.1520	.1693	.1856	.1958	.2156	.2388
	210	.0857	.0999	.1136	.1214	.1351	.1513	.1685	.1848	.1949	.2146	.2377

* To approximate p_k, divide the starred entry under k by $(C - 1)$.

** Compute $B^* = C - B$, find p^*_{1-k} for B^* and C, and compute $p_k = 1 - p^*_{1-k}$.

B	C	.001	.01	.05	.1	.25	.5	.75	.9	.95	.99	.999
32	211	.0853	.0994	.1131	.1208	.1344	.1506	.1677	.1839	.1940	.2136	.2366
	212	.0849	.0989	.1125	.1203	.1338	.1498	.1669	.1831	.1931	.2126	.2355
	213	.0845	.0984	.1120	.1197	.1332	.1491	.1661	.1822	.1922	.2117	.2345
	214	.0841	.0980	.1115	.1191	.1325	.1484	.1653	.1814	.1913	.2107	.2335
	215	.0837	.0975	.1109	.1185	.1319	.1477	.1646	.1805	.1905	.2098	.2324
	216	.0833	.0970	.1104	.1180	.1313	.1471	.1638	.1797	.1896	.2088	.2314
	217	.0829	.0966	.1099	.1174	.1307	.1464	.1631	.1789	.1887	.2079	.2304
	218	.0825	.0961	.1094	.1169	.1301	.1457	.1623	.1781	.1879	.2070	.2294
	219	.0821	.0956	.1089	.1163	.1295	.1450	.1616	.1773	.1871	.2061	.2284
	220	.0817	.0952	.1084	.1158	.1289	.1444	.1609	.1765	.1862	.2052	.2274
	221	.0813	.0948	.1079	.1153	.1283	.1437	.1601	.1757	.1854	.2043	.2264
	222	.0809	.0943	.1074	.1147	.1277	.1431	.1594	.1749	.1846	.2034	.2254
	223	.0806	.0939	.1069	.1142	.1271	.1424	.1587	.1742	.1838	.2025	.2245
	224	.0802	.0934	.1064	.1137	.1266	.1418	.1580	.1734	.1830	.2016	.2235
	225	.0798	.0930	.1059	.1132	.1260	.1412	.1573	.1726	.1822	.2007	.2226
	226	.0794	.0926	.1054	.1127	.1254	.1405	.1566	.1719	.1814	.1999	.2216
	227	.0791	.0922	.1049	.1122	.1249	.1399	.1559	.1711	.1806	.1990	.2207
	228	.0787	.0918	.1045	.1117	.1243	.1393	.1553	.1704	.1798	.1982	.2198
	229	.0784	.0913	.1040	.1112	.1238	.1387	.1546	.1697	.1791	.1973	.2189
	230	.0780	.0909	.1035	.1107	.1232	.1381	.1539	.1689	.1783	.1965	.2179
	231	.0777	.0905	.1031	.1102	.1227	.1375	.1532	.1682	.1775	.1957	.2170
	232	.0773	.0901	.1026	.1097	.1221	.1369	.1526	.1675	.1768	.1949	.2162
	233	.0770	.0897	.1022	.1092	.1216	.1363	.1519	.1668	.1761	.1941	.2153
	234+	17.32*	20.32*	23.30*	25.00*	28.03*	31.67*	35.61*	39.43*	41.84*	46.61*	52.36*
33	34-48	SEE NOTE**										
	49-196	SEE NOTE***										
	197	.0956	.1109	.1259	.1343	.1490	.1664	.1848	.2022	.2130	.2340	.2585
	198	.0951	.1104	.1252	.1336	.1482	.1655	.1839	.2012	.2120	.2328	.2572
	199	.0946	.1098	.1246	.1329	.1475	.1647	.1830	.2002	.2109	.2317	.2560
	200	.0941	.1092	.1239	.1322	.1467	.1639	.1821	.1992	.2099	.2306	.2548
	201	.0936	.1087	.1233	.1315	.1460	.1631	.1812	.1983	.2089	.2295	.2536
	202	.0931	.1081	.1227	.1309	.1453	.1623	.1803	.1973	.2079	.2284	.2524
	203	.0926	.1076	.1220	.1302	.1445	.1615	.1794	.1964	.2069	.2273	.2512
	204	.0922	.1070	.1214	.1295	.1438	.1607	.1785	.1954	.2059	.2262	.2501
	205	.0917	.1065	.1208	.1289	.1431	.1599	.1776	.1945	.2049	.2252	.2489
	206	.0912	.1059	.1202	.1283	.1424	.1591	.1768	.1935	.2039	.2241	.2477
	207	.0908	.1054	.1196	.1276	.1417	.1583	.1759	.1926	.2030	.2231	.2466
	208	.0903	.1049	.1190	.1270	.1410	.1576	.1751	.1917	.2020	.2220	.2455
	209	.0899	.1044	.1184	.1264	.1403	.1568	.1743	.1908	.2011	.2210	.2444
	210	.0894	.1038	.1179	.1258	.1397	.1561	.1734	.1899	.2001	.2200	.2433
	211	.0890	.1033	.1173	.1252	.1390	.1553	.1726	.1890	.1992	.2190	.2422
	212	.0885	.1028	.1167	.1246	.1383	.1546	.1718	.1882	.1983	.2180	.2411
	213	.0881	.1023	.1162	.1240	.1377	.1538	.1710	.1873	.1974	.2170	.2400
	214	.0877	.1018	.1156	.1234	.1370	.1531	.1702	.1864	.1965	.2160	.2389
	215	.0873	.1014	.1151	.1228	.1364	.1524	.1694	.1856	.1956	.2151	.2379
	216	.0868	.1009	.1145	.1222	.1357	.1517	.1687	.1847	.1947	.2141	.2368
	217	.0864	.1004	.1140	.1216	.1351	.1510	.1679	.1839	.1938	.2132	.2358
	218	.0860	.0999	.1134	.1211	.1345	.1503	.1671	.1831	.1930	.2122	.2348
	219	.0856	.0994	.1129	.1205	.1338	.1496	.1664	.1822	.1921	.2113	.2338
	220	.0852	.0990	.1124	.1199	.1332	.1489	.1656	.1814	.1913	.2103	.2327
	221	.0848	.0985	.1119	.1194	.1326	.1483	.1649	.1806	.1904	.2094	.2317
	222	.0844	.0981	.1113	.1188	.1320	.1476	.1641	.1798	.1896	.2085	.2307
	223	.0840	.0976	.1108	.1183	.1314	.1469	.1634	.1790	.1887	.2076	.2298
	224	.0836	.0972	.1103	.1178	.1308	.1463	.1627	.1782	.1879	.2067	.2288
	225	.0832	.0967	.1098	.1172	.1302	.1456	.1620	.1775	.1871	.2058	.2278
	226	.0828	.0963	.1093	.1167	.1296	.1450	.1613	.1767	.1863	.2049	.2269
	227	.0825	.0958	.1088	.1162	.1291	.1443	.1605	.1759	.1855	.2041	.2259
	228	.0821	.0954	.1083	.1156	.1285	.1437	.1598	.1752	.1847	.2032	.2250
	229	.0817	.0950	.1079	.1151	.1279	.1431	.1592	.1744	.1839	.2023	.2240
	230	.0814	.0945	.1074	.1146	.1274	.1424	.1585	.1737	.1831	.2015	.2231
	231	.0810	.0941	.1069	.1141	.1268	.1418	.1578	.1729	.1823	.2007	.2222
	232	.0806	.0937	.1064	.1136	.1263	.1412	.1571	.1722	.1816	.1998	.2213
	233	.0803	.0933	.1060	.1131	.1257	.1406	.1564	.1715	.1808	.1990	.2203
	234	.0799	.0929	.1055	.1126	.1252	.1400	.1558	.1707	.1800	.1982	.2194
	235	.0796	.0925	.1050	.1121	.1246	.1394	.1551	.1700	.1793	.1973	.2186
	236	.0792	.0921	.1046	.1117	.1241	.1388	.1545	.1693	.1786	.1965	.2177
	237	.0789	.0917	.1041	.1112	.1236	.1382	.1538	.1686	.1778	.1957	.2168
	238	.0785	.0913	.1037	.1107	.1230	.1376	.1532	.1679	.1771	.1949	.2159
	239	.0782	.0909	.1032	.1102	.1225	.1371	.1525	.1672	.1764	.1941	.2151
	240+	18.05*	21.12*	24.15*	25.89*	28.97*	32.67*	36.67*	40.54*	42.98*	47.81*	53.63*

*** To approximate p_k, compute $m = B/C$ and $s = \sqrt{m(1-m)/(C+1)}$, find u_k in Table T4 on page 715 below, and compute $p_k \doteq m + u_k s$.

B	C	.001	.01	.05	.1	.25	.5	.75	.9	.95	.99	.999
34	35-50 SEE NOTE**											
	51-212 SEE NOTE***											
	213	.0918	.1063	.1203	.1283	.1422	.1586	.1759	.1924	.2026	.2223	.2455
	214	.0913	.1058	.1198	.1276	.1415	.1578	.1751	.1915	.2016	.2213	.2444
	215	.0909	.1052	.1192	.1270	.1408	.1571	.1743	.1906	.2007	.2204	.2433
	216	.0904	.1047	.1186	.1264	.1402	.1563	.1735	.1897	.1998	.2194	.2423
	217	.0900	.1042	.1181	.1258	.1395	.1556	.1727	.1889	.1989	.2184	.2412
	218	.0896	.1037	.1175	.1253	.1389	.1549	.1719	.1880	.1980	.2174	.2402
	219	.0891	.1033	.1169	.1247	.1382	.1542	.1711	.1872	.1971	.2165	.2391
	220	.0887	.1028	.1164	.1241	.1376	.1535	.1704	.1864	.1963	.2155	.2381
	221	.0883	.1023	.1159	.1235	.1369	.1528	.1696	.1855	.1954	.2146	.2371
	222	.0879	.1018	.1153	.1229	.1363	.1521	.1688	.1847	.1945	.2136	.2360
	223	.0875	.1013	.1148	.1224	.1357	.1514	.1681	.1839	.1937	.2127	.2350
	224	.0871	.1009	.1143	.1218	.1351	.1507	.1674	.1831	.1928	.2118	.2340
	225	.0867	.1004	.1138	.1213	.1345	.1501	.1666	.1823	.1920	.2109	.2330
	226	.0863	.1000	.1132	.1207	.1339	.1494	.1659	.1815	.1912	.2100	.2321
	227	.0859	.0995	.1127	.1202	.1333	.1488	.1652	.1807	.1903	.2091	.2311
	228	.0855	.0991	.1122	.1197	.1327	.1481	.1644	.1799	.1895	.2082	.2301
	229	.0851	.0986	.1117	.1191	.1321	.1474	.1637	.1791	.1887	.2073	.2292
	230	.0847	.0982	.1112	.1186	.1315	.1468	.1630	.1784	.1879	.2065	.2282
	231	.0843	.0977	.1107	.1181	.1309	.1462	.1623	.1776	.1871	.2056	.2273
	232	.0840	.0973	.1102	.1175	.1304	.1455	.1616	.1769	.1863	.2047	.2263
	233	.0836	.0969	.1098	.1170	.1298	.1449	.1609	.1761	.1855	.2039	.2254
	234	.0832	.0964	.1093	.1165	.1293	.1443	.1602	.1754	.1848	.2030	.2245
	235	.0828	.0960	.1088	.1160	.1287	.1437	.1596	.1746	.1840	.2022	.2236
	236	.0825	.0956	.1083	.1155	.1281	.1431	.1589	.1739	.1832	.2014	.2227
	237	.0821	.0952	.1079	.1150	.1276	.1425	.1582	.1732	.1825	.2006	.2218
	238	.0818	.0948	.1074	.1145	.1271	.1419	.1576	.1725	.1817	.1997	.2209
	239	.0814	.0944	.1069	.1140	.1265	.1413	.1569	.1718	.1810	.1989	.2200
	240	.0811	.0940	.1065	.1136	.1260	.1407	.1563	.1711	.1802	.1981	.2191
	241	.0807	.0936	.1060	.1131	.1255	.1401	.1556	.1704	.1795	.1973	.2183
	242	.0804	.0932	.1056	.1126	.1249	.1395	.1550	.1697	.1788	.1965	.2174
	243	.0800	.0928	.1051	.1121	.1244	.1389	.1544	.1690	.1781	.1958	.2165
	244	.0797	.0924	.1047	.1117	.1239	.1384	.1537	.1683	.1774	.1950	.2157
	245	.0793	.0920	.1043	.1112	.1234	.1378	.1531	.1676	.1766	.1942	.2148
	246	.0790	.0916	.1038	.1107	.1229	.1372	.1525	.1670	.1759	.1934	.2140
	247+	18.78*	21.92*	25.01*	26.77*	29.91*	33.67*	37.73*	41.65*	44.12*	49.01*	54.90*
35	36-51 SEE NOTE**											
	52-230 SEE NOTE***											
	231	.0877	.1014	.1146	.1220	.1351	.1505	.1668	.1823	.1919	.2105	.2323
	232	.0873	.1009	.1141	.1215	.1345	.1499	.1661	.1815	.1911	.2096	.2314
	233	.0869	.1005	.1136	.1210	.1339	.1492	.1654	.1808	.1903	.2088	.2304
	234	.0865	.1000	.1131	.1204	.1333	.1486	.1647	.1800	.1895	.2079	.2295
	235	.0862	.0996	.1126	.1199	.1328	.1479	.1640	.1792	.1887	.2071	.2286
	236	.0858	.0991	.1121	.1194	.1322	.1473	.1633	.1785	.1879	.2062	.2277
	237	.0854	.0987	.1116	.1189	.1316	.1467	.1626	.1778	.1871	.2054	.2267
	238	.0850	.0983	.1111	.1184	.1311	.1461	.1620	.1770	.1864	.2045	.2258
	239	.0847	.0979	.1107	.1179	.1305	.1455	.1613	.1763	.1856	.2037	.2249
	240	.0843	.0974	.1102	.1174	.1300	.1448	.1606	.1756	.1848	.2029	.2240
	241	.0839	.0970	.1097	.1169	.1294	.1442	.1600	.1749	.1841	.2021	.2231
	242	.0836	.0966	.1093	.1164	.1289	.1436	.1593	.1741	.1833	.2013	.2223
	243	.0832	.0962	.1088	.1159	.1283	.1431	.1587	.1734	.1826	.2005	.2214
	244	.0829	.0958	.1083	.1154	.1278	.1425	.1580	.1727	.1819	.1997	.2205
	245	.0825	.0954	.1079	.1149	.1273	.1419	.1574	.1720	.1812	.1989	.2197
	246	.0822	.0950	.1074	.1145	.1268	.1413	.1567	.1714	.1804	.1981	.2188
	247	.0818	.0946	.1070	.1140	.1262	.1407	.1561	.1707	.1797	.1973	.2180
	248	.0815	.0942	.1065	.1135	.1257	.1402	.1555	.1700	.1790	.1965	.2171
	249	.0811	.0938	.1061	.1130	.1252	.1396	.1549	.1693	.1783	.1958	.2163
	250	.0808	.0934	.1057	.1126	.1247	.1390	.1542	.1687	.1776	.1950	.2155
	251	.0805	.0930	.1052	.1121	.1242	.1385	.1536	.1680	.1769	.1943	.2146
	252	.0801	.0927	.1048	.1117	.1237	.1379	.1530	.1673	.1762	.1935	.2138
	253+	19.52*	22.72*	25.87*	27.66*	30.85*	34.67*	38.79*	42.76*	45.27*	50.21*	56.16*
36	37-52 SEE NOTE**											
	53-249 SEE NOTE***											
	250	.0839	.0968	.1092	.1162	.1285	.1431	.1584	.1730	.1820	.1996	.2202
	251	.0836	.0964	.1088	.1158	.1280	.1425	.1578	.1723	.1813	.1988	.2193
	252	.0832	.0960	.1083	.1153	.1275	.1419	.1572	.1716	.1806	.1980	.2185
	253	.0829	.0956	.1079	.1148	.1270	.1413	.1566	.1710	.1799	.1973	.2177
	254	.0826	.0952	.1075	.1144	.1265	.1408	.1559	.1703	.1792	.1965	.2168
	255	.0822	.0948	.1070	.1139	.1260	.1402	.1553	.1696	.1785	.1958	.2160

* To approximate p_k, divide the starred entry under k by $(C - 1)$.

** Compute $B^* = C - B$, find p^*_{1-k} for B^* and C, and compute $p_k = 1 - p^*_{1-k}$.

B	C	.001	.01	.05	.1	.25	.5	.75	.9	.95	.99	.999
36	256	.0819	.0944	.1066	.1135	.1255	.1397	.1547	.1690	.1778	.1950	.2152
	257	.0816	.0941	.1062	.1130	.1250	.1391	.1541	.1683	.1772	.1943	.2144
	258	.0812	.0937	.1058	.1126	.1245	.1386	.1535	.1677	.1765	.1936	.2136
	259+	20.26*	23.53*	26.73*	28.56*	31.79*	35.67*	39.85*	43.87*	46.40*	51.41*	57.42*
37	38-53	SEE NOTE**										
	54-264	SEE NOTE***										
	265+	21.00*	24.33*	27.59*	29.45*	32.74*	36.67*	40.90*	44.98*	47.54*	52.60*	58.67*
38	39-55	SEE NOTE**										
	56-271	SEE NOTE***										
	272+	21.75*	25.14*	28.46*	30.34*	33.68*	37.67*	41.96*	46.08*	48.68*	53.79*	59.93*
39	40-56	SEE NOTE**										
	57-277	SEE NOTE***										
	278+	22.51*	25.96*	29.33*	31.24*	34.63*	38.67*	43.01*	47.19*	49.81*	54.98*	61.17*
40	41-57	SEE NOTE**										
	58-283	SEE NOTE***										
	284+	23.26*	26.77*	30.20*	32.14*	35.57*	39.67*	44.07*	48.29*	50.94*	56.16*	62.42*
41	42-58	SEE NOTE**										
	59-289	SEE NOTE***										
	290+	24.02*	27.59*	31.07*	33.04*	36.52*	40.67*	45.12*	49.39*	52.07*	57.35*	63.66*
42	43-59	SEE NOTE**										
	60-295	SEE NOTE***										
	296+	24.78*	28.41*	31.94*	33.94*	37.47*	41.67*	46.17*	50.49*	53.20*	58.53*	64.90*
43	44-61	SEE NOTE**										
	62-302	SEE NOTE***										
	303+	25.54*	29.23*	32.81*	34.84*	38.41*	42.67*	47.22*	51.59*	54.32*	59.71*	66.14*
44	45-62	SEE NOTE**										
	63-308	SEE NOTE***										
	309+	26.31*	30.05*	33.69*	35.74*	39.36*	43.67*	48.27*	52.69*	55.45*	60.88*	67.37*
45	46-63	SEE NOTE**										
	64-314	SEE NOTE***										
	315+	27.08*	30.88*	34.56*	36.65*	40.31*	44.67*	49.32*	53.78*	56.57*	62.06*	68.60*
46	47-64	SEE NOTE**										
	65-320	SEE NOTE***										
	321+	27.85*	31.70*	35.44*	37.55*	41.26*	45.67*	50.38*	54.88*	57.69*	63.23*	69.83*
47	48-66	SEE NOTE**										
	67-326	SEE NOTE***										
	327+	28.62*	32.53*	36.32*	38.46*	42.21*	46.67*	51.42*	55.97*	58.82*	64.40*	71.06*
48	49-67	SEE NOTE**										
	68-332	SEE NOTE***										
	333+	29.40*	33.36*	37.20*	39.36*	43.16*	47.67*	52.47*	57.07*	59.94*	65.57*	72.28*
49	50-68	SEE NOTE**										
	69-338	SEE NOTE***										
	339+	30.18*	34.20*	38.08*	40.27*	44.11*	48.67*	53.52*	58.16*	61.05*	66.74*	73.51*
50	51-69	SEE NOTE**										
	70-345	SEE NOTE***										
	346+	30.96*	35.03*	38.96*	41.18*	45.07*	49.67*	54.57*	59.25*	62.17*	67.90*	74.72*
51	52-70	SEE NOTE**										
	71-351	SEE NOTE***										
	352+	31.74*	35.87*	39.85*	42.09*	46.02*	50.67*	55.62*	60.34*	63.29*	69.07*	75.94*
52	53-72	SEE NOTE**										
	73-357	SEE NOTE***										
	358+	32.53*	36.71*	40.73*	43.00*	46.97*	51.67*	56.67*	61.43*	64.40*	70.23*	77.16*
53	54-73	SEE NOTE**										
	74-363	SEE NOTE***										
	364+	33.31*	37.55*	41.62*	43.91*	47.93*	52.67*	57.71*	62.52*	65.52*	71.39*	78.37*
54	55-74	SEE NOTE**										
	75-369	SEE NOTE***										
	370+	34.10*	38.39*	42.51*	44.82*	48.88*	53.67*	58.76*	63.61*	66.63*	72.55*	79.58*
55	56-75	SEE NOTE**										
	76-375	SEE NOTE***										
	376+	34.89*	39.23*	43.40*	45.74*	49.83*	54.67*	59.80*	64.69*	67.74*	73.71*	80.79*
56	57-76	SEE NOTE**										
	77-381	SEE NOTE***										
	382+	35.69*	40.07*	44.29*	46.65*	50.79*	55.67*	60.85*	65.78*	68.85*	74.86*	82.00*

*** To approximate p_k, compute $m = B/C$ and $s = \sqrt{m(1-m)/(C+1)}$, find u_k in Table T4 on page 715 below, and compute $p_k \doteq m + u_k s$.

B	C	.001	.01	.05	.1	.25	.5	.75	.9	.95	.99	.999
57	58–78 SEE NOTE**											
	79–387 SEE NOTE***											
	388+	36.48*	40.92*	45.18*	47.56*	51.74*	56.67*	61.89*	66.86*	69.96*	76.02*	83.20*
58	59–79 SEE NOTE**											
	80–393 SEE NOTE***											
	394+	37.28*	41.76*	46.07*	48.48*	52.70*	57.67*	62.94*	67.95*	71.07*	77.17*	84.41*
59	60–80 SEE NOTE**											
	81–399 SEE NOTE***											
	400+	38.08*	42.61*	46.96*	49.40*	53.65*	58.67*	63.98*	69.03*	72.18*	78.32*	85.61*
60	61–81 SEE NOTE**											
	82–405 SEE NOTE***											
	406+	38.88*	43.46*	47.85*	50.31*	54.61*	59.67*	65.03*	70.12*	73.28*	79.48*	86.81*
61	62–82 SEE NOTE**											
	83–411 SEE NOTE***											
	412+	39.68*	44.31*	48.75*	51.23*	55.57*	60.67*	66.07*	71.20*	74.39*	80.62*	88.01*
62	63–83 SEE NOTE**											
	84–417 SEE NOTE***											
	418+	40.48*	45.16*	49.64*	52.15*	56.52*	61.67*	67.11*	72.28*	75.49*	81.77*	89.20*
63	64–85 SEE NOTE**											
	86–423 SEE NOTE***											
	424+	41.29*	46.02*	50.54*	53.07*	57.48*	62.67*	68.16*	73.36*	76.60*	82.92*	90.40*
64	65–86 SEE NOTE**											
	87–429 SEE NOTE***											
	430+	42.09*	46.87*	51.43*	53.99*	58.44*	63.67*	69.20*	74.44*	77.70*	84.07*	91.59*
65	66–87 SEE NOTE**											
	88–435 SEE NOTE***											
	436+	42.90*	47.73*	52.33*	54.91*	59.40*	64.67*	70.24*	75.52*	78.80*	85.21*	92.79*
66	67–88 SEE NOTE**											
	89–442 SEE NOTE***											
	443+	43.71*	48.58*	53.23*	55.83*	60.35*	65.67*	71.28*	76.60*	79.91*	86.36*	93.98*
67	68–89 SEE NOTE**											
	90–447 SEE NOTE***											
	448+	44.52*	49.44*	54.13*	56.75*	61.31*	66.67*	72.32*	77.68*	81.01*	87.50*	95.17*
68	69–90 SEE NOTE**											
	91–454 SEE NOTE***											
	455+	45.33*	50.30*	55.03*	57.67*	62.27*	67.67*	73.37*	78.76*	82.11*	88.64*	96.35*
69	70–92 SEE NOTE**											
	93–460 SEE NOTE***											
	461+	46.15*	51.16*	55.93*	58.59*	63.23*	68.67*	74.41*	79.84*	83.21*	89.78*	97.54*
70	71–93 SEE NOTE**											
	94–466 SEE NOTE***											
	467+	46.96*	52.02*	56.83*	59.51*	64.19*	69.67*	75.45*	80.91*	84.31*	90.92*	98.73*
71	72–94 SEE NOTE**											
	95–472 SEE NOTE***											
	473+	47.78*	52.88*	57.73*	60.44*	65.15*	70.67*	76.49*	81.99*	85.40*	92.06*	99.91*
72	73–95 SEE NOTE**											
	96–478 SEE NOTE***											
	479+	48.60*	53.74*	58.63*	61.36*	66.11*	71.67*	77.53*	83.07*	86.50*	93.20*	101.1*
73	74–96 SEE NOTE**											
	97–484 SEE NOTE***											
	485+	49.42*	54.60*	59.54*	62.29*	67.07*	72.67*	78.57*	84.14*	87.60*	94.33*	102.3*
74	75–97 SEE NOTE**											
	98–490 SEE NOTE***											
	491+	50.24*	55.47*	60.44*	63.21*	68.03*	73.67*	79.61*	85.22*	88.70*	95.47*	103.5*
75	76–98 SEE NOTE**											
	99–496 SEE NOTE***											
	497+	51.06*	56.33*	61.35*	64.14*	68.99*	74.67*	80.65*	86.29*	89.79*	96.60*	104.6*
76	77–100 SEE NOTE**											
	101–502 SEE NOTE***											
	503+	51.88*	57.20*	62.25*	65.06*	69.95*	75.67*	81.68*	87.36*	90.89*	97.74*	105.8*
77	78–101 SEE NOTE**											
	102–508 SEE NOTE***											
	509+	52.70*	58.07*	63.16*	65.79*	70.91*	76.67*	82.72*	88.44*	91.98*	98.87*	107.0*

* To approximate p_k, divide the starred entry under k by $(C - 1)$.

** Compute $B^* = C - B$, find p^*_{1-k} for B^* and C, and compute $p_k = 1 - p^*_{1-k}$.

B	C	.001	.01	.05	.1	.25	.5	.75	.9	.95	.99	.999
78	79-102 SEE NOTE**											
	103-513 SEE NOTE***											
	514+	53.53*	58.93*	64.06*	66.92*	71.88*	77.67*	83.76*	89.51*	93.07*	100.0*	108.2*
79	80-103 SEE NOTE**											
	104-519 SEE NOTE***											
	520+	54.35*	59.80*	64.97*	67.84*	72.84*	78.67*	84.80*	90.58*	94.17*	101.1*	109.3*
80	81-104 SEE NOTE**											
	105-525 SEE NOTE***											
	526+	55.18*	60.67*	65.88*	68.77*	73.80*	79.67*	85.84*	91.66*	95.26*	102.3*	110.5*
81	82-105 SEE NOTE**											
	106-531 SEE NOTE***											
	532+	56.01*	61.54*	66.79*	69.70*	74.76*	80.67*	86.88*	92.73*	96.35*	103.4*	111.7*
82	83-106 SEE NOTE**											
	107-537 SEE NOTE***											
	538+	56.84*	62.41*	67.69*	70.63*	75.72*	81.67*	87.91*	93.80*	97.44*	104.5*	112.9*
83	84-108 SEE NOTE**											
	109-543 SEE NOTE***											
	544+	57.67*	63.29*	68.60*	71.56*	76.69*	82.67*	88.95*	94.87*	98.53*	105.7*	114.0*
84	85-109 SEE NOTE**											
	110-549 SEE NOTE***											
	550+	58.50*	64.16*	69.51*	72.49*	77.65*	83.67*	89.99*	95.94*	99.62*	106.8*	115.2*
85	86-110 SEE NOTE**											
	111-555 SEE NOTE***											
	556+	59.33*	65.03*	70.42*	73.42*	78.61*	84.67*	91.02*	97.01*	100.7*	107.9*	116.4*
86	87-111 SEE NOTE**											
	112-561 SEE NOTE***											
	562+	60.16*	65.91*	71.34*	74.35*	79.58*	85.67*	92.06*	98.08*	101.8*	109.0*	117.5*
87	88-112 SEE NOTE**											
	113-567 SEE NOTE***											
	568+	61.00*	66.78*	72.25*	75.28*	80.54*	86.67*	93.10*	99.15*	102.9*	110.2*	118.7*
88	89-113 SEE NOTE**											
	114-573 SEE NOTE***											
	574+	61.83*	67.66*	73.16*	76.21*	81.50*	87.67*	94.13*	100.2*	104.0*	111.3*	119.9*
89	90-114 SEE NOTE**											
	115-579 SEE NOTE***											
	580+	62.67*	68.53*	74.07*	77.14*	82.47*	88.67*	95.17*	101.3*	105.1*	112.4*	121.0*
90	91-116 SEE NOTE**											
	117-585 SEE NOTE***											
	586+	63.51*	69.41*	74.98*	78.08*	83.43*	89.67*	96.20*	102.4*	106.2*	113.5*	122.2*
91	92-117 SEE NOTE**											
	118-591 SEE NOTE***											
	592+	64.34*	70.29*	75.90*	79.01*	84.40*	90.67*	97.24*	103.4*	107.2*	114.7*	123.3*
92	93-118 SEE NOTE**											
	119-597 SEE NOTE***											
	598+	65.18*	71.17*	76.81*	79.94*	85.36*	91.67*	98.28*	104.5*	108.3*	115.8*	124.5*
93	94-119 SEE NOTE**											
	120-603 SEE NOTE***											
	604+	66.02*	72.05*	77.73*	80.88*	86.33*	92.67*	99.31*	105.6*	109.4*	116.9*	125.7*
94	95-120 SEE NOTE**											
	121-609 SEE NOTE***											
	610+	66.86*	72.92*	78.64*	81.81*	87.29*	93.67*	100.3*	106.6*	110.5*	118.0*	126.8*
95	96-121 SEE NOTE**											
	122-615 SEE NOTE***											
	616+	67.70*	73.81*	79.56*	82.74*	88.26*	94.67*	101.4*	107.7*	111.6*	119.1*	128.0*
96	97-122 SEE NOTE**											
	123-620 SEE NOTE***											
	621+	68.55*	74.69*	80.47*	83.68*	89.22*	95.67*	102.4*	108.8*	112.7*	120.3*	129.1*
97	98-123 SEE NOTE**											
	124-626 SEE NOTE***											
	627+	69.39*	75.57*	81.39*	84.61*	90.19*	96.67*	103.4*	109.8*	113.7*	121.4*	130.3*
98	99-125 SEE NOTE**											
	126-632 SEE NOTE***											
	633+	70.23*	76.45*	82.30*	85.55*	91.15*	97.67*	104.5*	110.9*	114.8*	122.5*	131.5*

*** To approximate p_k, compute $m = B/C$ and $s = \sqrt{m(1-m)/(C+1)}$, find u_k in Table T4 on page 715 below, and compute $p_k \doteq m + u_k s$.

B	C	.001	.01	.05	.1	.25	.5	.75	.9	.95	.99	.999
99	100-126	SEE NOTE**										
	127-638	SEE NOTE***										
	639+	71.08*	77.33*	83.22*	86.48*	92.12*	98.67*	105.5*	111.9*	115.9*	123.6*	132.6*
100	101-127	SEE NOTE**										
	128-644	SEE NOTE***										
	645+	71.92*	78.22*	84.14*	87.42*	93.09*	99.67*	106.6*	113.0*	117.0*	124.7*	133.8*

$101 \leq B \leq 357$

   $B/C < 1.28$ See note **.

   $C/B \geq 1.28$ See note ***.

$B > 357$

   $C - B < 100$ See note **.

   $C - B \geq 100$ See note ***.

* To approximate p_k, divide the starred entry under k by $(C - 1)$.
** Compute $B^* = C - B$, find p^*_{1-k} for B^* and C, and compute $p_k = 1 - p^*_{1-k}$.

TABLE T4
GAUSSIAN CUMULATIVE FUNCTION

The following table gives the argument u_k corresponding to each of a number of values k of the Gaussian cumulative function defined by

$$k(u) = \int_{-\infty}^{u} (2\pi)^{-1/2} \, e^{-t^2/2} \, dt.$$

k	u_k
.001	-3.090
.01	-2.326
.05	-1.645
.10	-1.282
.15	-1.036
.20	$-\ .842$
.25	$-\ .674$
.30	$-\ .524$
.35	$-\ .385$
.40	$-\ .253$
.45	$-\ .126$
.50	.000
.55	$+\ .126$
.60	$+\ .253$
.65	$+\ .385$
.70	$+\ .524$
.75	$+\ .674$
.80	$+\ .842$
.85	$+1.036$
.90	$+1.282$
.95	$+1.645$
.99	$+2.326$
.999	$+3.090$

TABLE T5
SQUARE ROOTS[4]

n	0	1	2	3	4	5	6	7	8	9	10	Tenths of the tabular difference				
												1	2	3	4	5
.1	.316	.332	.346	.361	.374	.387						1	3	4	6	7
						.387	.400	.412	.424	.436	.447	1	2	4	5	6
.2	.447	.458	.469	.480	.490	.500	.510	.520	.529	.539	.548	1	2	3	4	5
.3	.548	.557	.566	.574	.583	.592	.600	.608	.616	.624	.632	1	2	3	3	4
.4	.632	.640	.648	.656	.663	.671	.678	.686	.693	.700	.707	1	1	2	3	4
.5	.707	.714	.721	.728	.735	.742	.748	.755	.762	.768	.775	1	1	2	3	3
.6	.775	.781	.787	.794	.800	.806	.812	.819	.825	.831	.837	1	1	2	2	3
.7	.837	.843	.849	.854	.860	.866	.872	.877	.883	.889	.894	1	1	2	2	3
.8	.894	.900	.906	.911	.917	.922	.927	.933	.938	.943	.949	1	1	2	2	3
.9	.949	.954	.959	.964	.970	.975	.980	.985	.990	.995	1.000	1	1	2	2	3
1.0	1.000	1.005	1.010	1.015	1.020	1.025	1.030	1.034	1.039	1.044	1.049	0	1	1	2	2
1.1	1.049	1.054	1.058	1.063	1.068	1.072	1.077	1.082	1.086	1.091	1.095	0	1	1	2	2
1.2	1.095	1.100	1.105	1.109	1.114	1.118	1.122	1.127	1.131	1.136	1.140	0	1	1	2	2
1.3	1.140	1.145	1.149	1.153	1.158	1.162	1.166	1.170	1.175	1.179	1.183	0	1	1	2	2
1.4	1.183	1.187	1.192	1.196	1.200	1.204	1.208	1.212	1.217	1.221	1.225	0	1	1	2	2
1.5	1.225	1.229	1.233	1.237	1.241	1.245	1.249	1.253	1.257	1.261	1.265	0	1	1	2	2
1.6	1.265	1.269	1.273	1.277	1.281	1.285	1.288	1.292	1.296	1.300	1.304	0	1	1	2	2
1.7	1.304	1.308	1.311	1.315	1.319	1.323	1.327	1.330	1.334	1.338	1.342	0	1	1	2	2
1.8	1.342	1.345	1.349	1.353	1.356	1.360	1.364	1.367	1.371	1.375	1.378	0	1	1	1	2
1.9	1.378	1.382	1.386	1.389	1.393	1.396	1.400	1.404	1.407	1.411	1.414	0	1	1	1	2
2.0	1.414	1.418	1.421	1.425	1.428	1.432	1.435	1.439	1.442	1.446	1.449	0	1	1	1	2
2.1	1.449	1.453	1.456	1.459	1.463	1.466	1.470	1.473	1.476	1.480	1.483	0	1	1	1	2
2.2	1.483	1.487	1.490	1.493	1.497	1.500	1.503	1.507	1.510	1.513	1.517	0	1	1	1	2
2.3	1.517	1.520	1.523	1.526	1.530	1.533	1.536	1.539	1.543	1.546	1.549	0	1	1	1	2
2.4	1.549	1.552	1.556	1.559	1.562	1.565	1.568	1.572	1.575	1.578	1.581	0	1	1	1	2
2.5	1.581	1.584	1.587	1.591	1.594	1.597	1.600	1.603	1.606	1.609	1.612	0	1	1	1	2
2.6	1.612	1.616	1.619	1.622	1.625	1.628	1.631	1.634	1.637	1.640	1.643	0	1	1	1	2
2.7	1.643	1.646	1.649	1.652	1.655	1.658	1.661	1.664	1.667	1.670	1.673	0	1	1	1	2
2.8	1.673	1.676	1.679	1.682	1.685	1.688	1.691	1.694	1.697	1.700	1.703	0	1	1	1	1
2.9	1.703	1.706	1.709	1.712	1.715	1.718	1.720	1.723	1.726	1.729	1.732	0	1	1	1	1
3.0	1.732	1.735	1.738	1.741	1.744	1.746	1.749	1.752	1.755	1.758	1.761	0	1	1	1	1
3.1	1.761	1.764	1.766	1.769	1.772	1.775	1.778	1.780	1.783	1.786	1.789	0	1	1	1	1
3.2	1.789	1.792	1.794	1.797	1.800	1.803	1.806	1.808	1.811	1.814	1.817	0	1	1	1	1
3.3	1.817	1.819	1.822	1.825	1.828	1.830	1.833	1.836	1.838	1.841	1.844	0	1	1	1	1
3.4	1.844	1.847	1.849	1.852	1.855	1.857	1.860	1.863	1.865	1.868	1.871	0	1	1	1	1
3.5	1.871	1.873	1.876	1.879	1.881	1.884	1.887	1.889	1.892	1.895	1.897	0	1	1	1	1
3.6	1.897	1.900	1.903	1.905	1.908	1.910	1.913	1.916	1.918	1.921	1.924	0	1	1	1	1
3.7	1.924	1.926	1.929	1.931	1.934	1.936	1.939	1.942	1.944	1.947	1.949	0	1	1	1	1
3.8	1.949	1.952	1.954	1.957	1.960	1.962	1.965	1.967	1.970	1.972	1.975	0	1	1	1	1
3.9	1.975	1.977	1.980	1.982	1.985	1.987	1.990	1.992	1.995	1.997	2.000	0	1	1	1	1
4.0	2.000	2.002	2.005	2.007	2.010	2.012	2.015	2.017	2.020	2.022	2.025	0	0	1	1	1
4.1	2.025	2.027	2.030	2.032	2.035	2.037	2.040	2.042	2.045	2.047	2.049	0	0	1	1	1
4.2	2.049	2.052	2.054	2.057	2.059	2.062	2.064	2.066	2.069	2.071	2.074	0	0	1	1	1
4.3	2.074	2.076	2.078	2.081	2.083	2.086	2.088	2.090	2.093	2.095	2.098	0	0	1	1	1
4.4	2.098	2.100	2.102	2.105	2.107	2.110	2.112	2.114	2.117	2.119	2.121	0	0	1	1	1
4.5	2.121	2.124	2.126	2.128	2.131	2.133	2.135	2.138	2.140	2.142	2.145	0	0	1	1	1
4.6	2.145	2.147	2.149	2.152	2.154	2.156	2.159	2.161	2.163	2.166	2.168	0	0	1	1	1
4.7	2.168	2.170	2.173	2.175	2.177	2.179	2.182	2.184	2.186	2.189	2.191	0	0	1	1	1
4.8	2.191	2.193	2.195	2.198	2.200	2.202	2.205	2.207	2.209	2.211	2.214	0	0	1	1	1
4.9	2.214	2.216	2.218	2.220	2.223	2.225	2.227	2.229	2.232	2.234	2.236	0	0	1	1	1
5.	2.236	2.258	2.280	2.302	2.324	2.345	2.366	2.387	2.408	2.429	2.449	2	4	6	9	11
6.	2.449	2.470	2.490	2.510	2.530	2.550	2.569	2.588	2.608	2.627	2.646	2	4	6	8	10
7.	2.646	2.665	2.683	2.702	2.720	2.739	2.757	2.775	2.793	2.811	2.828	2	4	5	7	9
8.	2.828	2.846	2.864	2.881	2.898	2.915	2.933	2.950	2.966	2.983	3.000	2	3	5	7	9
9.	3.000	3.017	3.033	3.050	3.066	3.082	3.098	3.114	3.130	3.146	3.162	2	3	5	6	8

[4] Reproduced by permission from E. V. Huntington, *Four-place Tables*, Houghton Mifflin Company, Boston, 1931.

TABLE T6
RANDOM DIGITS[5]

64249	63664	39652	40646	97306	31741	07294	84149	46797	82487	59391	58030
26538	44249	04050	48174	65570	44072	40192	51153	11397	58212	99567	76364
05845	00512	78630	55328	18116	69296	91705	86224	29503	57071	10363	97518
74897	68373	67359	51014	33510	83048	17056	72506	82949	54600	86859	19558
20872	54570	35017	88132	25730	22626	86723	91691	13191	77212	11258	24591
31432	96156	89177	75541	81355	24480	77243	76690	42507	84362	95068	88628
66890	61505	01240	00660	05873	13568	76082	79172	57913	93448	54463	47237
48194	57790	79970	33106	86904	48119	52503	24130	72824	21627	16874	62677
11303	87118	81471	52936	08555	28420	49416	44448	04269	27029	92494	63157
54374	57325	16947	45356	78371	10563	97191	53798	12693	27928	15669	56689
64852	34421	61046	90849	13966	39810	42699	21753	76192	10508	99116	75486
16309	20384	09491	91588	97720	89846	30376	76970	23063	35894	15696	10703
42587	37065	24526	72602	57589	98131	37292	05967	26002	51945	97720	15369
40177	98590	97161	41682	84533	67588	62036	49967	01990	72308	11666	13841
82309	76128	93965	26743	24141	04838	40254	26065	07938	76236	71628	73130
79788	68243	59732	04257	27084	14743	17520	95401	55811	76099	40501	51089
40538	79000	89559	25026	42274	23489	34502	75508	06059	86682	22518	55576
64016	73598	18609	73150	62463	33102	45205	87440	96767	67042	75112	30485
49767	12691	17903	93871	99721	79109	09425	26904	07419	76013	80327	02671
76974	55108	29795	08404	82684	00497	51126	79935	57450	55671	60251	45548
23854	08480	85983	96025	50117	64610	99425	62291	86943	21541	57430	82270
68973	70551	25098	78033	98573	79848	31778	29555	61446	23037	73528	39559
36444	93600	65350	14971	25325	00427	52073	64280	18847	24768	25991	65959
03003	87800	07391	11594	21196	00781	32550	57158	58887	73041	78388	16638
17540	26188	36647	78386	04558	61463	57842	90382	77019	24210	12477	09965
38916	55809	47982	41968	69760	79422	80154	91486	19180	15100	83266	32883
64288	19843	69122	42502	48508	28820	59933	72998	99942	10515	76970	80876
86809	51564	38040	39418	49915	19000	58050	16899	79952	57849	37074	65198
99800	99566	14742	05028	30033	94889	53381	23656	75787	59223	83712	06514
92345	31890	95712	08279	91794	94068	49337	88674	35355	12267	20287	56862
90363	65162	32245	82279	79256	80834	06088	99462	56705	06118	74261	32592
64437	32242	48431	04835	39070	59702	31508	60935	22390	52246	64081	49863
91714	53662	28373	34333	55791	74758	51144	18827	10704	76803	05617	75818
20902	17646	31391	31459	33315	03444	55743	74701	58851	27427	26793	74951
12217	86007	70371	52281	14510	76094	96579	54853	78339	20839	65988	72850
45177	02863	42307	53571	22532	74921	17735	42201	80540	54721	27366	42271
28325	90814	08804	52746	47913	54577	47525	77705	95330	21866	56760	10909
29019	28776	56116	54791	64604	08815	46049	71186	34650	14994	72880	43338
84979	81353	56219	67062	26146	82567	33122	14124	46240	92973	77888	38100
50371	26347	48513	63915	11158	25563	91915	18431	92978	11591	28440	07819
53422	06825	69711	67950	64716	18003	49581	45378	99878	61130	63525	94441
67453	35651	89316	41620	32048	70225	47597	33137	31443	51445	47606	93410
07294	85353	74819	23445	68237	07202	99515	62282	53809	26685	52669	45030
79544	00302	45338	16015	66613	88968	14595	63836	77716	79596	16738	60159
64144	85442	82060	46471	24162	39500	87351	36637	42833	71875	59348	11695
90919	11883	58318	00042	52402	28210	34075	33272	00840	73268	12900	71775
06670	57353	86275	92276	77591	46924	60839	55437	03183	13191	75086	23537
36634	93976	52062	83678	41256	60948	18685	48992	19462	96062	99495	51434
75101	72891	85745	67106	26010	62107	60885	37503	55461	71213	26075	31671
05112	71222	72654	51583	05228	62056	57390	42746	39272	96659	13636	93596

[5] Reproduced by permission from George W. Snedecor, *Statistical Methods*, Iowa State College Press, Ames, Iowa, 1946.

TABLE T7
COMMON LOGARITHMS

	0	1	2	3	4	5	6	7	8	9	10					
1.0	0000	0043	0086	0128	0170	0212						4	8	13	17	21
						0212	0253	0294	0334	0374	0414	4	8	12	16	20
1.1	0414	0453	0492	0531	0569	0607						4	8	12	15	19
						0607	0645	0682	0719	0755	0792	4	7	11	15	18
1.2	0792	0828	0864	0899	0934	0969						4	7	11	14	18
						0969	1004	1038	1072	1106	1139	3	7	10	14	17
1.3	1139	1173	1206	1239	1271	1303						3	7	10	13	16
						1303	1335	1367	1399	1430	1461	3	6	9	13	16
1.4	1461	1492	1523	1553	1584	1614						3	6	9	12	15
						1614	1644	1673	1703	1732	1761	3	6	9	12	15
1.5	1761	1790	1818	1847	1875	1903	1931	1959	1987	2014	2041	3	6	8	11	14
1.6	2041	2068	2095	2122	2148	2175	2201	2227	2253	2279	2304	3	5	8	11	13
1.7	2304	2330	2355	2380	2405	2430	2455	2480	2504	2529	2553	2	5	7	10	12
1.8	2553	2577	2601	2625	2648	2672	2695	2718	2742	2765	2788	2	5	7	9	12
1.9	2788	2810	2833	2856	2878	2900	2923	2945	2967	2989	3010	2	4	7	9	11
2.0	3010	3032	3054	3075	3096	3118	3139	3160	3181	3201	3222	2	4	6	8	11
2.1	3222	3243	3263	3284	3304	3324	3345	3365	3385	3404	3424	2	4	6	8	10
2.2	3424	3444	3464	3483	3502	3522	3541	3560	3579	3598	3617	2	4	6	8	10
2.3	3617	3636	3655	3674	3692	3711	3729	3747	3766	3784	3802	2	4	6	7	9
2.4	3802	3820	3838	3856	3874	3892	3909	3927	3945	3962	3979	2	4	5	7	9
2.5	3979	3997	4014	4031	4048	4065	4082	4099	4116	4133	4150	2	3	5	7	9
2.6	4150	4166	4183	4200	4216	4232	4249	4265	4281	4298	4314	2	3	5	7	8
2.7	4314	4330	4346	4362	4378	4393	4409	4425	4440	4456	4472	2	3	5	6	8
2.8	4472	4487	4502	4518	4533	4548	4564	4579	4594	4609	4624	2	3	5	6	8
2.9	4624	4639	4654	4669	4683	4698	4713	4728	4742	4757	4771	1	3	4	6	7
3.0	4771	4786	4800	4814	4829	4843	4857	4871	4886	4900	4914	1	3	4	6	7
3.1	4914	4928	4942	4955	4969	4983	4997	5011	5024	5038	5051	1	3	4	6	7
3.2	5051	5065	5079	5092	5105	5119	5132	5145	5159	5172	5185	1	3	4	5	7
3.3	5185	5198	5211	5224	5237	5250	5263	5276	5289	5302	5315	1	3	4	5	6
3.4	5315	5328	5340	5353	5366	5378	5391	5403	5416	5428	5441	1	3	4	5	6
3.5	5441	5453	5465	5478	5490	5502	5515	5527	5539	5551	5563	1	2	4	5	6
3.6	5563	5575	5587	5599	5611	5623	5635	5647	5658	5670	5682	1	2	4	5	6
3.7	5682	5694	5705	5717	5729	5740	5752	5763	5775	5786	5798	1	2	3	5	6
3.8	5798	5809	5821	5832	5843	5855	5866	5877	5888	5899	5911	1	2	3	5	6
3.9	5911	5922	5933	5944	5955	5966	5977	5988	5999	6010	6021	1	2	3	4	5
4.0	6021	6031	6042	6053	6064	6075	6085	6096	6107	6117	6128	1	2	3	4	5
4.1	6128	6138	6149	6160	6170	6180	6191	6201	6212	6222	6232	1	2	3	4	5
4.2	6232	6243	6253	6263	6274	6284	6294	6304	6314	6325	6335	1	2	3	4	5
4.3	6335	6345	6355	6365	6375	6385	6395	6405	6415	6425	6435	1	2	3	4	5
4.4	6435	6444	6454	6464	6474	6484	6493	6503	6513	6522	6532	1	2	3	4	5
4.5	6532	6542	6551	6561	6571	6580	6590	6599	6609	6618	6628	1	2	3	4	5
4.6	6628	6637	6646	6656	6665	6675	6684	6693	6702	6712	6721	1	2	3	4	5
4.7	6721	6730	6739	6749	6758	6767	6776	6785	6794	6803	6812	1	2	3	4	5
4.8	6812	6821	6830	6839	6848	6857	6866	6875	6884	6893	6902	1	2	3	4	4
4.9	6902	6911	6920	6928	6937	6946	6955	6964	6972	6981	6990	1	2	3	4	4

	0	1	2	3	4	5	6	7	8	9	10					
5.0	6990	6998	7007	7016	7024	7033	7042	7050	7059	7067	7076	1	2	3	3	4
5.1	7076	7084	7093	7101	7110	7118	7126	7135	7143	7152	7160	1	2	3	3	4
5.2	7160	7168	7177	7185	7193	7202	7210	7218	7226	7235	7243	1	2	2	3	4
5.3	7243	7251	7259	7267	7275	7284	7292	7300	7308	7316	7324	1	2	2	3	4
5.4	7324	7332	7340	7348	7356	7364	7372	7380	7388	7396	7404	1	2	2	3	4
5.5	7404	7412	7419	7427	7435	7443	7451	7459	7466	7474	7482	1	2	2	3	4
5.6	7482	7490	7497	7505	7513	7520	7528	7536	7543	7551	7559	1	2	2	3	4
5.7	7559	7566	7574	7582	7589	7597	7604	7612	7619	7627	7634	1	2	2	3	4
5.8	7634	7642	7649	7657	7664	7672	7679	7686	7694	7701	7709	1	1	2	3	4
5.9	7709	7716	7723	7731	7738	7745	7752	7760	7767	7774	7782	1	1	2	3	4
6.0	7782	7789	7796	7803	7810	7818	7825	7832	7839	7846	7853	1	1	2	3	4
6.1	7853	7860	7868	7875	7882	7889	7896	7903	7910	7917	7924	1	1	2	3	4
6.2	7924	7931	7938	7945	7952	7959	7966	7973	7980	7987	7993	1	1	2	3	3
6.3	7993	8000	8007	8014	8021	8028	8035	8041	8048	8055	8062	1	1	2	3	3
6.4	8062	8069	8075	8082	8089	8096	8102	8109	8116	8122	8129	1	1	2	3	3
6.5	8129	8136	8142	8149	8156	8162	8169	8176	8182	8189	8195	1	1	2	3	3
6.6	8195	8202	8209	8215	8222	8228	8235	8241	8248	8254	8261	1	1	2	3	3
6.7	8261	8267	8274	8280	8287	8293	8299	8306	8312	8319	8325	1	1	2	3	3
6.8	8325	8331	8338	8344	8351	8357	8363	8370	8376	8382	8388	1	1	2	3	3
6.9	8388	8395	8401	8407	8414	8420	8426	8432	8439	8445	8451	1	1	2	2	3
7.0	8451	8457	8463	8470	8476	8482	8488	8494	8500	8506	8513	1	1	2	2	3
7.1	8513	8519	8525	8531	8537	8543	8549	8555	8561	8567	8573	1	1	2	2	3
7.2	8573	8579	8585	8591	8597	8603	8609	8615	8621	8627	8633	1	1	2	2	3
7.3	8633	8639	8645	8651	8657	8663	8669	8675	8681	8686	8692	1	1	2	2	3
7.4	8692	8698	8704	8710	8716	8722	8727	8733	8739	8745	8751	1	1	2	2	3
7.5	8751	8756	8762	8768	8774	8779	8785	8791	8797	8802	8808	1	1	2	2	3
7.6	8808	8814	8820	8825	8831	8837	8842	8848	8854	8859	8865	1	1	2	2	3
7.7	8865	8871	8876	8882	8887	8893	8899	8904	8910	8915	8921	1	1	2	2	3
7.8	8921	8927	8932	8938	8943	8949	8954	8960	8965	8971	8976	1	1	2	2	3
7.9	8976	8982	8987	8993	8998	9004	9009	9015	9020	9025	9031	1	1	2	2	3
8.0	9031	9036	9042	9047	9053	9058	9063	9069	9074	9079	9085	1	1	2	2	3
8.1	9085	9090	9096	9101	9106	9112	9117	9122	9128	9133	9138	1	1	2	2	3
8.2	9138	9143	9149	9154	9159	9165	9170	9175	9180	9186	9191	1	1	2	2	3
8.3	9191	9196	9201	9206	9212	9217	9222	9227	9232	9238	9243	1	1	2	2	3
8.4	9243	9248	9253	9258	9263	9269	9274	9279	9284	9289	9294	1	1	2	2	3
8.5	9294	9299	9304	9309	9315	9320	9325	9330	9335	9340	9345	1	1	2	2	3
8.6	9345	9350	9355	9360	9365	9370	9375	9380	9385	9390	9395	1	1	2	2	3
8.7	9395	9400	9405	9410	9415	9420	9425	9430	9435	9440	9445	0	1	1	2	2
8.8	9445	9450	9455	9460	9465	9469	9474	9479	9484	9489	9494	0	1	1	2	2
8.9	9494	9499	9504	9509	9513	9518	9523	9528	9533	9538	9542	0	1	1	2	2
9.0	9542	9547	9552	9557	9562	9566	9571	9576	9581	9586	9590	0	1	1	2	2
9.1	9590	9595	9600	9605	9609	9614	9619	9624	9628	9633	9638	0	1	1	2	2
9.2	9638	9643	9647	9652	9657	9661	9666	9671	9675	9680	9685	0	1	1	2	2
9.3	9685	9689	9694	9699	9703	9708	9713	9717	9722	9727	9731	0	1	1	2	2
9.4	9731	9736	9741	9745	9750	9754	9759	9763	9768	9773	9777	0	1	1	2	2
9.5	9777	9782	9786	9791	9795	9800	9805	9809	9814	9818	9823	0	1	1	2	2
9.6	9823	9827	9832	9836	9841	9845	9850	9854	9859	9863	9868	0	1	1	2	2
9.7	9868	9872	9877	9881	9886	9890	9894	9899	9903	9908	9912	0	1	1	2	2
9.8	9912	9917	9921	9926	9930	9934	9939	9943	9948	9952	9956	0	1	1	2	2
9.9	9956	9961	9965	9969	9974	9978	9983	9987	9991	9996	10000	0	1	1	2	2

TABLE T8
COMMON ANTILOGARITHMS

	0	1	2	3	4	5	6	7	8	9	10					
.00	1.000	1.002	1.005	1.007	1.009	1.012	1.014	1.016	1.019	1.021	1.023	0	0	1	1	1
.01	1.023	1.026	1.028	1.030	1.033	1.035	1.038	1.040	1.042	1.045	1.047	0	0	1	1	1
.02	1.047	1.050	1.052	1.054	1.057	1.059	1.062	1.064	1.067	1.069	1.072	0	0	1	1	1
.03	1.072	1.074	1.076	1.079	1.081	1.084	1.086	1.089	1.091	1.094	1.096	0	0	1	1	1
.04	1.096	1.099	1.102	1.104	1.107	1.109	1.112	1.114	1.117	1.119	1.122	0	1	1	1	1
.05	1.122	1.125	1.127	1.130	1.132	1.135	1.138	1.140	1.143	1.146	1.148	0	1	1	1	1
.06	1.148	1.151	1.153	1.156	1.159	1.161	1.164	1.167	1.169	1.172	1.175	0	1	1	1	1
.07	1.175	1.178	1.180	1.183	1.186	1.189	1.191	1.194	1.197	1.199	1.202	0	1	1	1	1
.08	1.202	1.205	1.208	1.211	1.213	1.216	1.219	1.222	1.225	1.227	1.230	0	1	1	1	1
.09	1.230	1.233	1.236	1.239	1.242	1.245	1.247	1.250	1.253	1.256	1.259	0	1	1	1	1
.10	1.259	1.262	1.265	1.268	1.271	1.274	1.276	1.279	1.282	1.285	1.288	0	1	1	1	1
.11	1.288	1.291	1.294	1.297	1.300	1.303	1.306	1.309	1.312	1.315	1.318	0	1	1	1	2
.12	1.318	1.321	1.324	1.327	1.330	1.334	1.337	1.340	1.343	1.346	1.349	0	1	1	1	2
.13	1.349	1.352	1.355	1.358	1.361	1.365	1.368	1.371	1.374	1.377	1.380	0	1	1	1	2
.14	1.380	1.384	1.387	1.390	1.393	1.396	1.400	1.403	1.406	1.409	1.413	0	1	1	1	2
.15	1.413	1.416	1.419	1.422	1.426	1.429	1.432	1.435	1.439	1.442	1.445	0	1	1	1	2
.16	1.445	1.449	1.452	1.455	1.459	1.462	1.466	1.469	1.472	1.476	1.479	0	1	1	1	2
.17	1.479	1.483	1.486	1.489	1.493	1.496	1.500	1.503	1.507	1.510	1.514	0	1	1	1	2
.18	1.514	1.517	1.521	1.524	1.528	1.531	1.535	1.538	1.542	1.545	1.549	0	1	1	1	2
.19	1.549	1.552	1.556	1.560	1.563	1.567	1.570	1.574	1.578	1.581	1.585	0	1	1	1	2
.20	1.585	1.589	1.592	1.596	1.600	1.603	1.607	1.611	1.614	1.618	1.622	0	1	1	2	2
.21	1.622	1.626	1.629	1.633	1.637	1.641	1.644	1.648	1.652	1.656	1.660	0	1	1	2	2
.22	1.660	1.663	1.667	1.671	1.675	1.679	1.683	1.687	1.690	1.694	1.698	0	1	1	2	2
.23	1.698	1.702	1.706	1.710	1.714	1.718	1.722	1.726	1.730	1.734	1.738	0	1	1	2	2
.24	1.738	1.742	1.746	1.750	1.754	1.758	1.762	1.766	1.770	1.774	1.778	0	1	1	2	2
.25	1.778	1.782	1.786	1.791	1.795	1.799	1.803	1.807	1.811	1.816	1.820	0	1	1	2	2
.26	1.820	1.824	1.828	1.832	1.837	1.841	1.845	1.849	1.854	1.858	1.862	0	1	1	2	2
.27	1.862	1.866	1.871	1.875	1.879	1.884	1.888	1.892	1.897	1.901	1.905	0	1	1	2	2
.28	1.905	1.910	1.914	1.919	1.923	1.928	1.932	1.936	1.941	1.945	1.950	0	1	1	2	2
.29	1.950	1.954	1.959	1.963	1.968	1.972	1.977	1.982	1.986	1.991	1.995	0	1	1	2	2
.30	1.995	2.000	2.004	2.009	2.014	2.018	2.023	2.028	2.032	2.037	2.042	0	1	1	2	2
.31	2.042	2.046	2.051	2.056	2.061	2.065	2.070	2.075	2.080	2.084	2.089	0	1	1	2	2
.32	2.089	2.094	2.099	2.104	2.109	2.113	2.118	2.123	2.128	2.133	2.138	0	1	1	2	2
.33	2.138	2.143	2.148	2.153	2.158	2.163	2.168	2.173	2.178	2.183	2.188	0	1	1	2	2
.34	2.188	2.193	2.198	2.203	2.208	2.213	2.218	2.223	2.228	2.234	2.239	1	1	2	2	3
.35	2.239	2.244	2.249	2.254	2.259	2.265	2.270	2.275	2.280	2.286	2.291	1	1	2	2	3
.36	2.291	2.296	2.301	2.307	2.312	2.317	2.323	2.328	2.333	2.339	2.344	1	1	2	2	3
.37	2.344	2.350	2.355	2.360	2.366	2.371	2.377	2.382	2.388	2.393	2.399	1	1	2	2	3
.38	2.399	2.404	2.410	2.415	2.421	2.427	2.432	2.438	2.443	2.449	2.455	1	1	2	2	3
.39	2.455	2.460	2.466	2.472	2.477	2.483	2.489	2.495	2.500	2.506	2.512	1	1	2	2	3
.40	2.512	2.518	2.523	2.529	2.535	2.541	2.547	2.553	2.559	2.564	2.570	1	1	2	2	3
.41	2.570	2.576	2.582	2.588	2.594	2.600	2.606	2.612	2.618	2.624	2.630	1	1	2	2	3
.42	2.630	2.636	2.642	2.649	2.655	2.661	2.667	2.673	2.679	2.685	2.692	1	1	2	2	3
.43	2.692	2.698	2.704	2.710	2.716	2.723	2.729	2.735	2.742	2.748	2.754	1	1	2	3	3
.44	2.754	2.761	2.767	2.773	2.780	2.786	2.793	2.799	2.805	2.812	2.818	1	1	2	3	3
.45	2.818	2.825	2.831	2.838	2.844	2.851	2.858	2.864	2.871	2.877	2.884	1	1	2	3	3
.46	2.884	2.891	2.897	2.904	2.911	2.917	2.924	2.931	2.938	2.944	2.951	1	1	2	3	3
.47	2.951	2.958	2.965	2.972	2.979	2.985	2.992	2.999	3.006	3.013	3.020	1	1	2	3	3
.48	3.020	3.027	3.034	3.041	3.048	3.055	3.062	3.069	3.076	3.083	3.090	1	1	2	3	4
.49	3.090	3.097	3.105	3.112	3.119	3.126	3.133	3.141	3.148	3.155	3.162	1	1	2	3	4

	0	1	2	3	4	5	6	7	8	9	10					
.50	3.162	3.170	3.177	3.184	3.192	3.199	3.206	3.214	3.221	3.228	3.236	1	1	2	3	4
.51	3.236	3.243	3.251	3.258	3.266	3.273	3.281	3.289	3.296	3.304	3.311	1	2	2	3	4
.52	3.311	3.319	3.327	3.334	3.342	3.350	3.357	3.365	3.373	3.381	3.388	1	2	2	3	4
.53	3.388	3.396	3.404	3.412	3.420	3.428	3.436	3.443	3.451	3.459	3.467	1	2	2	3	4
.54	3.467	3.475	3.483	3.491	3.499	3.508	3.516	3.524	3.532	3.540	3.548	1	2	2	3	4
.55	3.548	3.556	3.565	3.573	3.581	3.589	3.597	3.606	3.614	3.622	3.631	1	2	2	3	4
.56	3.631	3.639	3.648	3.656	3.664	3.673	3.681	3.690	3.698	3.707	3.715	1	2	3	3	4
.57	3.715	3.724	3.733	3.741	3.750	3.758	3.767	3.776	3.784	3.793	3.802	1	2	3	3	4
.58	3.802	3.811	3.819	3.828	3.837	3.846	3.855	3.864	3.873	3.882	3.890	1	2	3	4	4
.59	3.890	3.899	3.908	3.917	3.926	3.936	3.945	3.954	3.963	3.972	3.981	1	2	3	4	5
.60	3.981	3.990	3.999	4.009	4.018	4.027	4.036	4.046	4.055	4.064	4.074	1	2	3	4	5
.61	4.074	4.083	4.093	4.102	4.111	4.121	4.130	4.140	4.150	4.159	4.169	1	2	3	4	5
.62	4.169	4.178	4.188	4.198	4.207	4.217	4.227	4.236	4.246	4.256	4.266	1	2	3	4	5
.63	4.266	4.276	4.285	4.295	4.305	4.315	4.325	4.335	4.345	4.355	4.365	1	2	3	4	5
.64	4.365	4.375	4.385	4.395	4.406	4.416	4.426	4.436	4.446	4.457	4.467	1	2	3	4	5
.65	4.467	4.477	4.487	4.498	4.508	4.519	4.529	4.539	4.550	4.560	4.571	1	2	3	4	5
.66	4.571	4.581	4.592	4.603	4.613	4.624	4.634	4.645	4.656	4.667	4.677	1	2	3	4	5
.67	4.677	4.688	4.699	4.710	4.721	4.732	4.742	4.753	4.764	4.775	4.786	1	2	3	4	5
.68	4.786	4.797	4.808	4.819	4.831	4.842	4.853	4.864	4.875	4.887	4.898	1	2	3	4	6
.69	4.898	4.909	4.920	4.932	4.943	4.955	4.966	4.977	4.989	5.000	5.012	1	2	3	5	6
.70	5.012	5.023	5.035	5.047	5.058	5.070	5.082	5.093	5.105	5.117	5.129	1	2	4	5	6
.71	5.129	5.140	5.152	5.164	5.176	5.188	5.200	5.212	5.224	5.236	5.248	1	2	4	5	6
.72	5.248	5.260	5.272	5.284	5.297	5.309	5.321	5.333	5.346	5.358	5.370	1	2	4	5	6
.73	5.370	5.383	5.395	5.408	5.420	5.433	5.445	5.458	5.470	5.483	5.495	1	3	4	5	6
.74	5.495	5.508	5.521	5.534	5.546	5.559	5.572	5.585	5.598	5.610	5.623	1	3	4	5	6
.75	5.623	5.636	5.649	5.662	5.675	5.689	5.702	5.715	5.728	5.741	5.754	1	3	4	5	7
.76	5.754	5.768	5.781	5.794	5.808	5.821	5.834	5.848	5.861	5.875	5.888	1	3	4	5	7
.77	5.888	5.902	5.916	5.929	5.943	5.957	5.970	5.984	5.998	6.012	6.026	1	3	4	5	7
.78	6.026	6.039	6.053	6.067	6.081	6.095	6.109	6.124	6.138	6.152	6.166	1	3	4	6	7
.79	6.166	6.180	6.194	6.209	6.223	6.237	6.252	6.266	6.281	6.295	6.310	1	3	4	6	7
.80	6.310	6.324	6.339	6.353	6.368	6.383	6.397	6.412	6.427	6.442	6.457	1	3	4	6	7
.81	6.457	6.471	6.486	6.501	6.516	6.531	6.546	6.561	6.577	6.592	6.607	2	3	5	6	8
.82	6.607	6.622	6.637	6.653	6.668	6.683	6.699	6.714	6.730	6.745	6.761	2	3	5	6	8
.83	6.761	6.776	6.792	6.808	6.823	6.839	6.855	6.871	6.887	6.902	6.918	2	3	5	6	8
.84	6.918	6.934	6.950	6.966	6.982	6.998	7.015	7.031	7.047	7.063	7.079	2	3	5	6	8
.85	7.079	7.096	7.112	7.129	7.145	7.161	7.178	7.194	7.211	7.228	7.244	2	3	5	7	8
.86	7.244	7.261	7.278	7.295	7.311	7.328	7.345	7.362	7.379	7.396	7.413	2	3	5	7	8
.87	7.413	7.430	7.447	7.464	7.482	7.499	7.516	7.534	7.551	7.568	7.586	2	3	5	7	9
.88	7.586	7.603	7.621	7.638	7.656	7.674	7.691	7.709	7.727	7.745	7.762	2	4	5	7	9
.89	7.762	7.780	7.798	7.816	7.834	7.852	7.870	7.889	7.907	7.925	7.943	2	4	5	7	9
.90	7.943	7.962	7.980	7.998	8.017	8.035	8.054	8.072	8.091	8.110	8.128	2	4	6	7	9
.91	8.128	8.147	8.166	8.185	8.204	8.222	8.241	8.260	8.279	8.299	8.318	2	4	6	8	9
.92	8.318	8.337	8.356	8.375	8.395	8.414	8.433	8.453	8.472	8.492	8.511	2	4	6	8	10
.93	8.511	8.531	8.551	8.570	8.590	8.610	8.630	8.650	8.670	8.690	8.710	2	4	6	8	10
.94	8.710	8.730	8.750	8.770	8.790	8.810	8.831	8.851	8.872	8.892	8.913	2	4	6	8	10
.95	8.913	8.933	8.954	8.974	8.995	9.016	9.036	9.057	9.078	9.099	9.120	2	4	6	8	10
.96	9.120	9.141	9.162	9.183	9.204	9.226	9.247	9.268	9.290	9.311	9.333	2	4	6	8	11
.97	9.333	9.354	9.376	9.397	9.419	9.441	9.462	9.484	9.506	9.528	9.550	2	4	7	9	11
.98	9.550	9.572	9.594	9.616	9.638	9.661	9.683	9.705	9.727	9.750	9.772	2	4	7	9	11
.99	9.772	9.795	9.817	9.840	9.863	9.886	9.908	9.931	9.954	9.977	10.000	2	5	7	9	11

INDEX